700

MONDAY 451 TO 462

PROB ① 646 (also b

② Repeat with inverse of ...

ELECTRICAL ENGINEERING TEXTS

HARRY E. CLIFFORD, Consulting Editor (deceased)

Berg
HEAVISIDE'S OPERATIONAL CALCULUS

Chaffee
THEORY OF THERMIONIC VACUUM TUBES

Dawes
COURSES IN ELECTRICAL ENGINEERING
Vol. I.—Direct Currents
Vol. II.—Alternating Currents
INDUSTRIAL ELECTRICITY—PART I
INDUSTRIAL ELECTRICITY—PART II

Glasgow
PRINCIPLES OF RADIO ENGINEERING

Langsdorf
PRINCIPLES OF DIRECT-CURRENT MACHINES
THEORY OF ALTERNATING-CURRENT MACHINERY

Lawrence and Richards
PRINCIPLES OF ALTERNATING-CURRENT MACHINERY

Laws
ELECTRICAL MEASUREMENTS

Lyon
APPLICATIONS OF THE METHOD OF SYMMETRICAL COMPONENTS

Moon
THE SCIENTIFIC BASIS OF ILLUMINATING ENGINEERS

Skilling
TRANSIENT ELECTRIC CURRENTS

Stephens
THE ELEMENTARY THEORY OF OPERATIONAL MATHEMATICS

Terman
RADIO ENGINEERING

700

MONDAY 451 to 462

PROB ① 646 (also b

② Repeat with inverse of ...

ELECTRICAL ENGINEERING TEXTS

A Course in

ELECTRICAL ENGINEERING

Volume I

DIRECT CURRENTS

ELECTRICAL ENGINEERING TEXTS

HARRY E. CLIFFORD, Consulting Editor (deceased)

Berg
HEAVISIDE'S OPERATIONAL CALCULUS

Chaffee
THEORY OF THERMIONIC VACUUM TUBES

Dawes
COURSES IN ELECTRICAL ENGINEERING
Vol. I.—Direct Currents
Vol. II.—Alternating Currents
INDUSTRIAL ELECTRICITY—PART I
INDUSTRIAL ELECTRICITY—PART II

Glasgow
PRINCIPLES OF RADIO ENGINEERING

Langsdorf
PRINCIPLES OF DIRECT-CURRENT MACHINES
THEORY OF ALTERNATING-CURRENT MACHINERY

Lawrence and Richards
PRINCIPLES OF ALTERNATING-CURRENT MACHINERY

Laws
ELECTRICAL MEASUREMENTS

Lyon
APPLICATIONS OF THE METHOD OF SYMMETRICAL COMPONENTS

Moon
THE SCIENTIFIC BASIS OF ILLUMINATING ENGINEERS

Skilling
TRANSIENT ELECTRIC CURRENTS

Stephens
THE ELEMENTARY THEORY OF OPERATIONAL MATHEMATICS

Terman
RADIO ENGINEERING

ELECTRICAL ENGINEERING TEXTS

A Course in
ELECTRICAL ENGINEERING

Volume I
DIRECT CURRENTS

CHESTER L. DAWES, S.B., A.M., Dr. Eng.
Associate Professor of Electrical Engineering
Graduate Department of Engineering
Harvard University

FOURTH EDITION

McGRAW-HILL BOOK COMPANY, INC.
New York *Toronto* *London*
1952

A COURSE IN ELECTRICAL ENGINEERING, VOLUME I

Library of Congress Catalog Card Number: 51-12827

IV

THE MAPLE PRESS COMPANY, YORK, PA.

PREFACE TO THE FOURTH EDITION

In developing the present revision of Volume I, Direct Currents, the author has kept in mind the significant and extended advance which has taken place in the field of electrical engineering during these last years. The advance has been not only in electrical theory, but in design, the wide development of control mechanisms, transmission of power, selection of units, and in various techniques and operations. There has resulted consequently and naturally a raising of the standards of engineering education and the necessity of a broader and clearer understanding of fundamental laws and relationships.

Although the scope of this text permits the inclusion only to a limited extent of the newer techniques, attempt has been made to present more completely the fundamental laws of electricity and magnetism which can then serve as the basis for the more complete developments into special fields.

The author has given long and careful consideration to the systems of electrical units which should be included. Although the mks system was adopted by the International Electrotechnical Commission in 1935, there actually are two such systems, the unrationalized and the rationalized, and as yet (1951) neither has become standard. Moreover, from the beginning, the development of electrical and magnetic theory has been based on the two cgs systems; a large number of textbooks and handbooks still use these systems and they are still widely used in current technical publications. Furthermore, the design of electrical machinery is still based on the cgs magnetic units and this will continue. Accordingly, the student is certain to encounter the two cgs systems and the two mks systems in his work, not only as student, but in the practice of his profession. Since this is ordinarily the first text in electrical engineering for most students, it seemed desirable that they should know the basis of each of the systems, the relations among their units as well as their applications. Accordingly, all four systems of units are presented, but they are so segregated that teacher and student can select and develop any or all of the systems as he sees fit. In order to clarify the relations of the units of the systems to one another, each illustrative example in the text is solved in each of the systems to which its units are adapted.

In addition, in Appendixes B and C, the magnitudes of the units of the several systems are compared and an illustrative problem is given. Also, comparison is made of corresponding quantities and formulas as they occur in the electric and magnetic circuits and in the cgs and mks systems.

Throughout the text the standards of the American Institute of Electrical Engineers and of the American Standards Association are used for letter and graphical symbols, definitions of electrical terms, standards for insulation temperatures, and rotating machinery.

Semiconductors, which include varistors and thermistors, are relatively new developments in circuit elements and are becoming widely used for such applications as temperature measurements and for conditions in which nonlinearity in a circuit is desired. These are described with typical resistance-temperature characteristics in Chapter I.

As power and communications systems expand, the circuits become more complicated and it is correspondingly difficult to determine the voltage and current relations. The solution of such circuits is greatly facilitated by such network theorems as Maxwell's mesh equations, superposition theorem, Thévenin's theorem, reciprocity theorem, and π, T, and L types of networks, all of which are now presented in Chapter IV.

In the chapter on batteries, electrolytic terms have been specifically defined in accordance with ASA standards; the newer developments in lead-lead-acid and iron-nickel-alkali batteries, and such new types as the Ruben cell, the silver-chloride-magnesium water-activated battery, and the nickel-cadmium-alkali (Nicad) storage battery have been added.

The development of Alnico-alloy permanent magnets has resulted in new designs of direct-current instruments such as the concentric-magnet and concentric-scale types. The photocell has become a common and most useful device, particularly for such applications as light meters and control apparatus, and ohmmeters are now widely used for electrical testing. Descriptions of these newer types of instruments are now given in Chapter V, as well as considerably more detail in the testing of cables for shorts, crosses, and grounds.

The treatment of magnetism has been expanded to include the theory based on the Bohr atom and the spinning-electron theory of magnetic moments resulting in the crystal and domain structure of magnetic materials and their effects on magnetic properties, such as the Barkhausen effect, the Curie point, permeability, saturation, hysteresis, and permanent magnetism. Magnetic theory now includes the relations among unit poles, field intensity, flux density, permeability of magnetic materials and of evacuated space, the several systems of units being used. Alnico alloys have attained great importance and accordingly there has been added a discussion of their composition, properties, the design and the performance of Alnico permanent magnets, and their uses in magnetic chucks. To electromagnetism has been added the Biot-Savart law in mks, as well as in cgs units; the detailed development of magnetic fields produced by straight wires, circular turns, and solenoids; magnetic circuits; hysteresis loss by integration over the entire hysteresis loop; formulas for eddy-current loss in laminations; separation of core losses into their hysteresis and eddy-current components; and obtaining the hysteresis loop by means of the cathode-ray-oscilloscope.

The electric field is analyzed in much more detail than formerly, and now includes Faraday's tubes of force, Gauss' theorem, the relationship of field intensity, flux density (or displacement), capacitivity of the dielectric material and of evacuated space, energy per unit volume, and the capacitances of parallel cylinders and of overhead transmission lines.

The chapters on electrical machinery have been revised to include illustrations of modern practice in machine construction; the calculation of distributed mmfs and their effect on armature reaction; demagnetizing effect of the cross-magnetizing armature ampere-turns; the amplidyne and rototrol power-amplifying machines; analysis of total losses in electric machinery in accordance with American Standards, with examples based on experimental combination of non-copper losses into "stray power." The industrial applications of the different types of motor have been summarized in a table; the tables of performance data and efficiencies have been revised to apply to the most modern types of machines, and the temperature characteristics of the insulation are revised in accordance with the ASA standards. There is a detailed description of the West Point type of vibrationless prony brake.

In the chapter on the transmission and distribution of electric power, there is a new wiring diagram of a typical power system beginning with the a-c generators in the power station and ending with the d-c distribution system; there is new material on d-c distribution networks with feeding centers and junction boxes; the relation of weight of transmission conductor to the transmission distance as well as to the voltage, and applications of storage batteries for standby service, regulating duty, and emergency light and power.

There are 792 new problems related closely to the material of the text, and many of these problems are adapted to solutions by the different systems of electrical and magnetic units.

The author is indebted to many teachers and other users of the book for suggestions which have been most valuable in the revision. Among those who have been particularly helpful are Colonel B. W. Bartlett, Professor and Head of the Department of Electricity at the United States Military Academy at West Point, and Lieutenant Colonel Rex I. Heinlein, Jr., Associate Professor in the same department. A considerable part of the new material was submitted by them and came from their teaching experience at the Military Academy.

Considerable assistance was received from Raymond T. Gibbs of the Graduate Department of Engineering at Harvard University, and from

A. L. Russell of the Franklin Technical Institute of Boston, who has contributed to the preparation and solution of the problems and prepared the Table of Contents and the Index.

The author is deeply indebted to the late H. W. Beedle, formerly Engineer and Manager of the Boston Office of the Electric Storage Battery Company, who advised in the revision of the chapter on batteries. Also, assistance was received from M. W. Dickover, Chief Engineer of Gould-National Batteries, Inc.; W. B. Manson, Chief Application Engineer, Thomas A. Edison, Inc., and from Dr. A. Fleischer, Research Director, Nickel-Cadmium Battery Corporation.

Valuable suggestions have been received from Professor Harry Baum (retired) of the College of the City of New York; Professor A. S. Brown of the University of Kansas; Professor Segismundo Gerszonowicz of the University of Montevideo; Professor J. Hugo Johnson of the University of Idaho; Dean J. H. Lampe of the North Carolina State College of Agriculture and Engineering, and Professor F. N. Tompkins of Brown University.

Also the assistance of the several manufacturers who contributed data and illustrations is gratefully acknowledged.

The author is very greatly indebted to Professor H. E. Clifford, Consulting Editor and formerly Dean of the Graduate School of Engineering, Harvard University, for his close collaboration and valuable suggestions in the preparation of the manuscript and for his careful editing of the printed proofs.

CHESTER L. DAWES

CAMBRIDGE, MASS.
November, 1951

PREFACE TO THE FIRST EDITION

For some time past the editors of the McGraw-Hill Electrical Engineering Texts have experienced a demand for a comprehensive text covering in a simple manner the general field of Electrical Engineering. Accordingly, these two volumes were written at their request, after the scope and general character of the two volumes had been carefully considered.

As the title implies, the books begin with the most elementary conceptions of magnetism and current-flow and gradually advance to a more or less thorough discussion of the many types of direct and alternating-current machinery, transmission devices, etc., which are met in practice. These two books are intended for Electrical Engineering students as a stepping stone to the more advanced Electrical Engineering texts which are already a part of the series.

These two volumes should be useful also to students not planning to specialize in the electrical engineering field, who are taking courses in Electrical Engineering as a part of their general training. Such men often find difficulty in obtaining detailed and straightforward discussions of the subject in any one text and the brevity of their course does not give them time to assimilate fragmentary information obtainable only by consulting a number of references. Men taking foremen's and industrial courses in Electrical Engineering, which as a rule are carried on only in the evening, require textbooks sufficiently comprehensive, but at the same time not involving much mathematical analysis. Ordinarily, this type of student does not have ready access to reference libraries and is usually out of contact with his instructors except during the short time available for classroom work. In preparing this work the needs of the foregoing types of students have been carefully kept in mind and as a result, a liberal use of figures and illustrative problems has been made. Also frequent discussions of the methods of making measurements and laboratory tests are included.

In any course in Electrical Engineering, even though it be intended for nonelectrical engineers, the author feels that the student gains little from a hurried and superficial treatment of the subject, as such treatment tends only to develop the memorizing of certain formulae which are soon forgotten. Accordingly the attempt has been made in this text to develop and explain each phenomenon from a few fundamental and well-understood laws rather than to give mere statements of facts. Such treatment will develop the student's reasoning powers and give him training that will be useful in the solution of the more involved engineering problems that may arise later in his career.

Throughout the text, especially in the treatment of the more abstract portions, an attempt has been made to show the ultimate bearing upon general engineering practice. The student takes more interest in the theory when he sees that it can be applied to the solving of practical problems. Because this work is not intended for advanced students in Electrical Engineering, little or no calculus is used and the mathematics is limited to simple equations.

The author is indebted to several of the manufacturing companies who have cooperated in the matter of supplying photographs, cuts, and material for the text; and particularly to Professor H. E. Clifford of The Harvard Engineering School, for his many suggestions and for the care and pains which he has taken in the matter of editing the manuscripts.

CHESTER L. DAWES

CAMBRIDGE, MASS.
January, 1920

CONTENTS

CHAPTER V
ELECTRICAL INSTRUMENTS AND ELECTRICAL MEASUREMENTS

CHAPTER VII
ELECTROMAGNETISM

CHAPTER VIII
THE MAGNETIC CIRCUIT

CHAPTER IX
SELF- AND MUTUAL INDUCTANCE

CHAPTER X
ELECTROSTATICS: CAPACITANCE

CHAPTER XI
THE GENERATOR

CHAPTER XII
GENERATOR CHARACTERISTICS

CHAPTER XIII
THE MOTOR

CHAPTER XIV
LOSSES; EFFICIENCY; OPERATION

CHAPTER XV
TRANSMISSION AND DISTRIBUTION OF POWER

APPENDIX A

APPENDIX B

APPENDIX C

APPENDIX D

APPENDIX E

APPENDIX F

APPENDIX G

APPENDIX H

APPENDIX I

APPENDIX J

APPENDIX K

QUESTIONS AND PROBLEMS

A COURSE IN

ELECTRICAL ENGINEERING

VOLUME I

DIRECT CURRENTS

CHAPTER I

RESISTANCE

Introduction. The importance which electricity has in the life of both the community and the individual is so evident that it hardly needs be emphasized. No city, even of moderate size, could exist today without electrical energy for light, transportation, water supply, elevators, communication, power, etc. Even automobiles become inoperative without electrical energy for ignition, starting, and lights. There are several factors which make electricity so useful and so important. Electrical energy can be readily and efficiently converted into any form of energy, such as heat, light, mechanical, and chemical energy. It may be generated at the most favorable locations, such as at a waterpower site where hydraulic energy is available, near a coal mine where fuel is readily obtainable, or at the shore of navigable water to which fuel can be economically shipped and where ample cooling water is available.

Electrical energy may be efficiently transmitted for great distances to regions where it can be used effectively, as at centers of population, for electric railways, in mills, and at industrial centers.

Electrical energy is convenient in that it can be easily applied for numerous and varied purposes such, for example, as electric traction, to operate elevators, to drive machine tools, to operate electric appliances and electric furnaces, and for lighting. It is readily concentrated to give extremely high temperatures, as in spark plugs and in arc lights, in welding and in electric furnaces. It is readily and quickly controlled.

Moreover, in connection with magnets, electrical energy can be used for operating relays, telephones, bells, and tractive magnets (p. 239).

Electrical energy is free from the products of combustion such as smoke, ashes, and fumes.

The numerous uses and applications of electricity can be accomplished only through a thorough understanding of the laws which govern its flow in circuits, its relations with magnetism, as well as its generation, its electromechanical and electrochemical effects.

1. Nature of the Flow of Electricity. According to modern theory, which has been substantiated by the experimental results of many investigators, the atoms of all matter consist of a positively charged nucleus, around which infinitesimal negative charges rotate with high angular velocity. The individual negative charges, which are called *electrons*, are indivisible and are found to be identical for all matter. In conductors, some of these electrons are free to pass from atom to atom when a difference of potential is impressed across the ends of the conductor. The movement of these electrons constitutes the electric current. Hence, the electric current may be considered as electricity in motion and is called *dynamic electricity*.

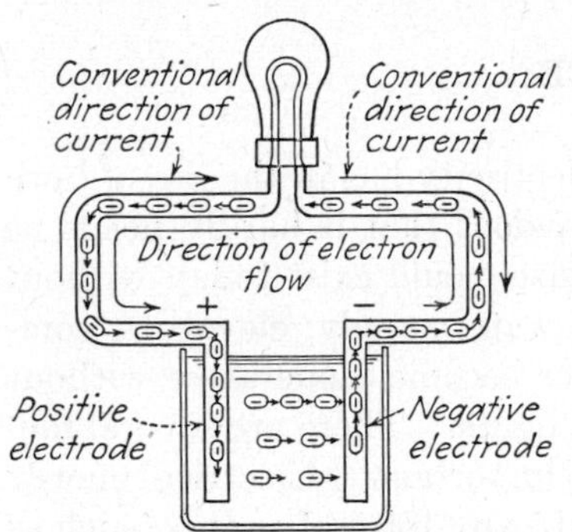

FIG. 1. Electron movement and conventional direction of current.

Since electrons are *negative* charges, the direction of their motion is opposite to the conventional direction of current. This is illustrated in Fig. 1, which shows an electrolytic cell, or battery, supplying current to an incandescent lamp. The conventional direction of current is from the positive electrode of the battery through the external circuit, which includes the lamp, to the negative electrode of the battery, and then within the battery, from the negative to the positive electrode, where the conduction is by ions (p. 133). On the other hand, the direction of flow of the electrons is opposite that of the current. In the external circuit the electrons, being negative charges, are attracted by the positive electrode and repelled by the negative electrode and have the direction shown. Within the battery, negative *ions* go from the positive to the negative electrode.

In nonconductors of electricity, or insulators,[1] the electrons are very closely bound to the nucleus, and it is difficult to remove an electron from the atom. Hence, as compared with conductors, a relatively high potential difference is required to remove only a few electrons from the atom, and the corresponding current is extremely small.

2. Electrical Resistance. The current in an electric circuit depends not only on the electromotive force impressed on the circuit but on the circuit properties as well. For example, if a copper wire be connected

[1] No substance is a perfect insulator, but the current which the usual insulator will conduct with a given potential difference is extremely small as compared with that for conductors of electricity under similar conditions.

across the terminals of a battery, a current will flow[1] through this wire. If a poor contact be made at one of the battery terminals or at some other point in the circuit, the current will decrease, even with the emf remaining constant. Also, heat will be dissipated at the point of poor contact. Likewise, if the copper wire be cut and a small incandescent lamp be inserted in the circuit, the lamp filament will be heated and may become incandescent. At the same time the current in the circuit will decrease in magnitude. In both cases heat is noticed particularly at the points in the circuit where the poorer conducting medium is inserted. Also in each case a decrease in current accompanies the insertion of the poorer conducting medium, even with a constant emf.

This property of an electric circuit tending to prevent the flow of current and at the same time causing electric energy to be converted into heat energy is called *resistance*.

Resistance may be accounted for by the electron theory of current flow discussed in Sec. 1. The electrons in moving through the conductor must pass *through* the molecules or the atoms. In doing so they collide with other electrons and with the atoms. The collision results in the evolution of heat (called joulean heating) and accounts for the heat which accompanies current in a resistance. The number of electronic collisions in a given time varies as the *square* of the current, so that the joulean heating varies as the square of the current. Also, because of the electronic and atomic collisions, the velocity of the electrons is reduced and a higher resulting potential difference is necessary in order to maintain a given current.

Resistance in the electric circuit may be likened in its effect to friction in mechanics. For example, if a streetcar is running at a uniform speed on a straight, level track, friction tends to prevent the moving of the car. The power which is used in moving the car is converted by friction into heat. Friction tends to impede the flow of water in a pipe or in a flume, some of the energy of the water being expended in overcoming this friction. The loss of energy is represented by a loss of head. This energy loss is largely absorbed by the water, and careful measurements would show a slight increase in its temperature.

As will be shown in the next chapter, the energy loss which occurs when an electric current flows in a resistance is directly proportional to the amount of resistance and to the square of the current. Also the current is equal to the applied emf divided by the resistance (Ohm's law). That is, the current $I = E/R$ (see p. 37).

[1] Actually *current* does not flow, but rather the electric charges or *quantity*. Current is *the rate of flow of quantity* (p. 31). However, in order to obtain simplicity in expression, it has become general practice to refer to "current flow." In these texts "current flow" is used only when it appears unavoidable.

3. Conductors and Insulators. It is stated in Sec. 1 that, with some substances, electrons are able to pass readily from atom to atom, and such substances are conductors. On the other hand, with other substances, electrons can be removed from the atom only with difficulty, and such substances are insulators. However, all substances[1] offer some resistance to current and are therefore not perfect conductors; moreover, all insulating substances are conducting to some extent. For the most part there is a marked distinction between conductors and insulators.

Conductors may be divided into three general classes, *metallic*, *electrolytic*, and *gaseous*. With metallic conductors, conduction is due to the interatomic movement of the electrons within the conductor (Sec. 1) and is not accompanied by any movement of material through the conductor, or by chemical action. With electrolytic conductors,[2] conduction is accompanied by a movement of material through the conductor and usually by chemical action (Sec. 109, p. 133). With gaseous conductors, conduction is due to the movement of free positive ions and free negative ions, or electrons, into which the atoms of the gas become divided when it becomes ionized (Sec. 257, p. 360, and also Chaps. XIV, XV, Vol. II).

The best conductors are the metallic ones which include such metals as copper, silver, and alloys; carbon and graphite are also metallic conductors. The electrolytic conductors include solutions of acids, bases and salts, fused salts and vitreous substances. Most organic and vitreous substances are insulators, such, for example, as rubber, oils, glass, and quartz. (At very high temperatures, vitreous substances become conductors in an *electrolytic* sense. The Nernst lamp was based on the principle that porcelain becomes conducting at the temperature of incandescence.) Electrolytes have varying degrees of conductivity, but in the electrolytic sense only.

Of the usual metals, silver is the best conductor, and copper is second best (see Appendix H, p. 592). The other metals and their alloys have varying degrees of conductivity. Oils, glass, silk, paper, cotton, ebonite, fiber, paraffin, rubber, plastic substances, etc., may be considered as nonconductors or good insulators. Wood, either dry or impregnated with oil, is a good insulator, but wood containing moisture is a partial conductor.

The marked differences between conductors and insulators are illustrated as follows:

[1] Professor Kamerlingh-Onnes of Leyden, in 1914, was able to produce a circuit in which an electric current showed no diminution in strength 5 hr after the emf had been removed. The current was induced magnetically in a short circuited coil of lead wire at −270°C produced by liquid helium, and the inducing source was then removed. Liquid helium has the lowest temperature known, being in the neighborhood of absolute zero (−273°C). This experiment indicates that the resistance of the lead was practically zero at this extremely low temperature.

[2] Electrolytic conduction is discussed in Chap. IV, p. 95.

The resistance between opposite faces of a centimeter cube of copper at 20°C is $1.7241 \cdot 10^{-6}$ ohm; the resistance between opposite faces of a centimeter cube of hard rubber is approximately 10^{16} ohms, giving for the ratio of the resistivity of hard rubber to that of copper the value $6 \cdot 10^{21}$, approximately. Likewise, the resistance between opposite faces of a centimeter cube of glass is of the order of 10^{14} ohms, making its ratio to that of copper also very high.

4. Unit of Resistance. The ohm[1] is the practical unit of resistance and is defined as that resistance which will allow 1 ampere to flow if 1 volt is impressed across its terminals (also see p. 31 for more complete definition).

An ohm has such a value that 1 ampere going through it for 1 second produces as heat 1 joule of energy.

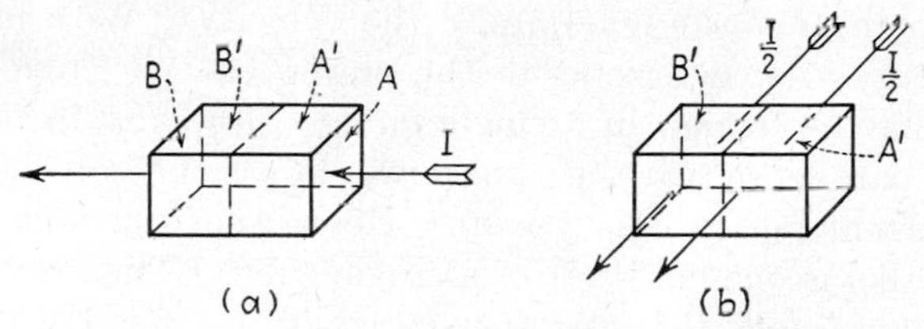

FIG. 2. Resistance and direction of current.

The resistance of insulating substances is ordinarily of the magnitude of millions of ohms, so that it is awkward to express this resistance in terms of a unit as small as the ohm. The *megohm*, equal to 1,000,000 (10^6) ohms, is the unit ordinarily used under these conditions. (The prefix "mega" means million.)

On the other hand, the resistance of bus bars and short pieces of metals may be so low that the ohm is too large a unit for conveniently expressing it. Under these conditions either the *milliohm*, equal to 1/1,000 or 10^{-3} ohm, or the *microhm*, equal to 1/1,000,000 or 10^{-6} ohm, may be used as the unit. (The prefix "milli" means one-thousandth, and the prefix "micro" means one-millionth.)

5. Resistance and Geometry of Conductors. The resistance of a body of a given material depends both on its geometry and on the direction of the current. For example, consider the rectangular prism shown in Fig. 2(a), composed of two equal cubes A' and B' 1 cm on edge and of the same conducting material. If the direction of the current I is from side A to side B, which is the side opposite A, the current must go successively through the two cubes. It is pointed out in Sec. 2 that electrical resistance is due to the collisions of the moving electrons, constituting

[1] The unit is named for Georg Simon Ohm (1787–1854), of Germany, the mathematician who about 1827 evolved the principle now known as *Ohm's law*. He also had a prominent part in the development of other basic laws of electricity.

the current, with the electrons and atoms associated with the conducting material. Hence, with the current going from side A to side B, there will be twice the number of electronic collisions as would occur with a single cube. Therefore the resistance between sides A and B is twice that of a single cube.

Hence, it follows that, with *constant cross section,* resistance varies *directly as the length* of the conductor.

Next consider Fig. 2(b), in which the direction of the current in the prism is at right angles to that shown in (a). The cross section of the current path has been doubled so that the current through each of the cubes A and B is now $I/2$ amp, or one-half that in (a). Therefore, for a given number of moving electrons, the electron velocity must now be one-half that for I amp in a single cube. The energy of electron collision is $\frac{1}{2}Mv^2$, where M is the mass and v the velocity. With half the current, the energy loss per second, or the power loss, per cube is therefore one-fourth that for I amp in a single cube. However, in (b) there are two cubes in parallel so that the total power loss is one-half that occurring when the current per cube is I amp. Hence the resistance of the two cubes in parallel is one-half that of a single cube. Thus, with a current path of *constant length,* the resistance *varies inversely* as the cross section of conductor path.

Also, the resistance in Fig. 2(b) is but *one-fourth* that between surfaces A and B in (a). This illustrates the fact that the resistance of a conducting body depends not only on its geometry but also on the *direction* of the current. In the usual electric circuit the length of the path is so great as compared with its cross section that the direction of the current is obvious. However, there are instances, such for example as current in insulation (p. 9), in which it is easily possible to choose the incorrect direction of the current.

Conductance is the reciprocal of resistance (p. 9) and, for a given voltage, determines the rate at which electric energy is converted into heat or radiant energy. Let the energy converted per second in a single cube, Fig. 2(b), be w units. The energy converted per second in the two cubes in parallel is accordingly $2w$ units. Hence the conductance of the two cubes in parallel must be twice that of a single cube. Hence, it follows that *conductances in parallel must add.*

6. Resistivity, or Specific Resistance. In Sec. 5 it is shown that, with constant cross section, the resistance of a conducting body varies as the length, and with constant length the resistance varies inversely as the cross section. Hence it follows that *the resistance of a homogeneous body of uniform cross section varies directly as its length and inversely as its cross section,* the length being taken in the direction of the current and the cross section perpendicular to the direction of the current.

That is,

$$R = \rho \frac{L^*}{A} \tag{1}$$

where R is the resistance in ohms, L is the length in the direction of the current, A is the area at right angles to the direction of the current, and ρ is a constant of the material known as its *resistivity* or *specific resistance.*

If L is 1 cm and A is 1 cm square, the substance in question must have the form of a cube, 1 cm on an edge, and

$$R = \rho \frac{1}{1 \cdot 1}$$

or

$$R = \rho.$$

ρ is called the *resistivity* or the *specific resistance* of the substance, in this case per centimeter. ρ may also be expressed in terms of an inch, *i.e.*, the resistance of an inch cube, or in other units, as will be shown later. The resistivity of copper is 1.7241 microhm-cm, or 1/580,000 ohm-cm at 20°C. The resistivities of various substances are given in Appendix H (p. 592). Knowing the resistivity in terms of the ohm-centimeter[1] or other units, the resistance of a wire, bar, etc., may be readily computed from Eq. (1).

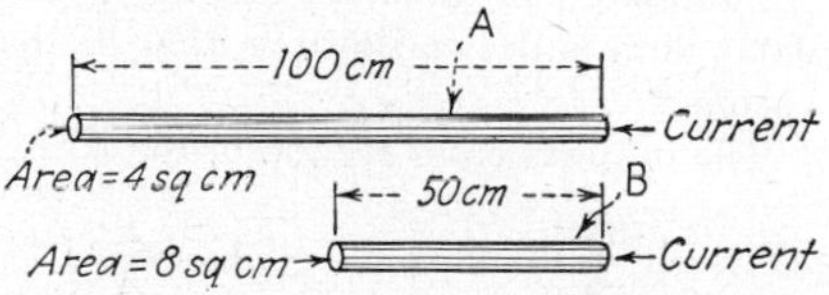

Fig. 3. Brass rods having equal volumes but unequal resistances.

Example. Determine the resistance of the two brass rods A and B, Fig. 3, the resistivity of the brass being 11.4 microhm-cm. Rod A is 100 cm long and has a circular cross section of 4 sq cm; rod B is 50 cm long and has a circular cross section of 8 sq cm.

Rod A. $R = 11.4 \frac{100}{4} = 285$ microhms. *Ans.*
Rod B. $R = 11.4 \frac{50}{8} = 71.25$ microhms. *Ans.*

Although both rods have the same volume, rod A has four times the resistance of rod B, because its length in the direction of the current is twice that of B and its cross section, perpendicular to the direction of the current, is one-half that of B.

* Equation (1) assumes that the current is uniformly distributed over the cross section of the conductor, which is usually true with direct current. However, with conductors in which the cross section is not uniform or the length for a given cross section is not constant (see Sec. 9), the current is not uniformly distributed over the cross section of the conductor. Also with alternating current, the current density is greatest in the outside layer of the conductor and decreases as the center is approached. This is called "skin effect."

[1] The term ohm-centimeter comes from Eq. (1), which may be written $\rho = R(A/L)$. Since R is in ohms, A in square centimeters, and L in centimeters, the right-hand term becomes RL, or ohm-centimeters.

Example. Determine the resistance of 3,000 ft of annealed 0000 copper wire having a diameter of 0.460 in., the resistivity of copper being taken as 1.724 microhm (= 0.000001724 ohm) cm at 20°C (see Sec. 15).

$$3{,}000 \text{ ft} = 3{,}000 \cdot 12 \cdot 2.54 = 91{,}400 \text{ cm.}$$

$$\text{Cross section} = \frac{\pi}{4}(0.460 \cdot 2.54)^2 = 1.071 \text{ sq. cm.}$$

$$R = \rho \frac{L}{A} = (0.000001724) \cdot \left(\frac{91{,}400}{1.071}\right) = 0.1471 \text{ ohm.} \quad \textit{Ans.}$$

7. Volume Resistivity. Since the volume of a body is

$$V = LA$$

where L is its length and A its uniform cross section, Eq. (1) may be written

$$R = \rho \frac{L}{A} = \rho \frac{L^2}{V} = \rho \frac{V}{A^2}. \tag{2}$$

That is:

The resistance of a conductor varies directly as the square of its length when the volume is fixed.

The resistance of a conductor varies inversely as the square of its cross section when the volume is fixed.

Example. A kilometer of wire having a diameter of 11.7 mm and a resistance of 0.031 ohm is drawn down so that its diameter is 5.0 mm. What does its resistance become?

The original cross section of the wire

$$A_1 = \frac{\pi}{4} 11.7^2 = 107.5 \text{ sq mm.}$$

The final cross section

$$A_2 = \frac{\pi}{4} 5.0^2 = 19.64 \text{ sq mm.}$$

Applying Eq. (2),

$$R_1 = \rho \frac{V}{(107.5)^2} = 0.031 \text{ ohm,}$$

$$R_2 = \rho \frac{V}{(19.64)^2} \quad \text{ohm.}$$

Since the volume of the wire does not change during the drawing process and the resistivity constant ρ remains the same,

$$\frac{R_2}{R_1} = \frac{R_2}{0.031} = \frac{\rho \dfrac{V}{(19.64)^2}}{\rho \dfrac{V}{(107.5)^2}}.$$

$$R_2 = 0.031 \frac{(107.5)^2}{(19.64)^2} = 0.031 \frac{11{,}560}{386} = 0.928 \text{ ohm.} \quad \textit{Ans.}$$

Also see the example, Sec. 6, p. 7, Fig. 3. The volume and resistivity of the two brass rods are the same. Their resistances are proportional to the square of their lengths. Likewise their resistances are inversely proportional to the square of their cross sections.

8. Conductance. Conductance is the reciprocal of resistance and may be defined as being that property of a circuit or of a material which tends to permit the flow of electricity. The unit of conductance is the reciprocal ohm, or *mho*. Conductance is usually expressed by g or G.

$$g = \frac{1}{R}, \tag{3}$$

and also

$$g = \gamma \frac{A}{L} \tag{4}$$

where γ is the *conductivity* or the *specific conductance* of a substance, A the uniform cross section, and L the length.

The conductivity of copper at 20°C is 580,000 mho-cm^{-1}.

Example. Determine the conductance at 20°C of an aluminum bus bar 0.5 in. thick, 4 in. wide, and 20 ft long.

The conductivity of aluminum is 61 per cent that of copper, and copper has a conductivity of 580,000 mho-cm^{-1} at 20°C.

The conductivity of aluminum is

$$\gamma = 0.61 \cdot 580{,}000 = 354{,}000 \text{ mho-cm}^{-1}.$$

The cross section of the bus bar

$$A = 0.5 \cdot 4 \cdot 2.54 \cdot 2.54 = 12.9 \text{ sq cm}.$$

The length

$$L = 20 \cdot 12 \cdot 2.54 = 610 \text{ cm}.$$

The conductance

$$g = 354{,}000 \cdot \frac{12.9}{610} = 7{,}490 \text{ mhos.} \quad \textit{Ans.}$$

9. Resistance Paths of Variable Cross Section. Occasionally the cross section of a resistance path is not uniform but changes with its length. An excellent example is the path of the leakage current in the insulation between the conductor and the outer wall of a cylindrical cable. For example, in Fig. 4 is shown the cross section of a cylindrical cable in which R_1 is the radius of the conductor, R_2 is the radius to the outer surface of the insulation, ρ is the resistivity of the insulating material, and l is the length of the cable in centimeters. The actual resistance to the leakage current from the conductor to the outer wall is found readily by integration. (Electrical contact with the outer wall is usually made by means of a lead sheath or by immersion of the cable in water.) An annulus at a distance r cm from the center of the cable and having an infinitesimal thickness of dr cm is first considered.

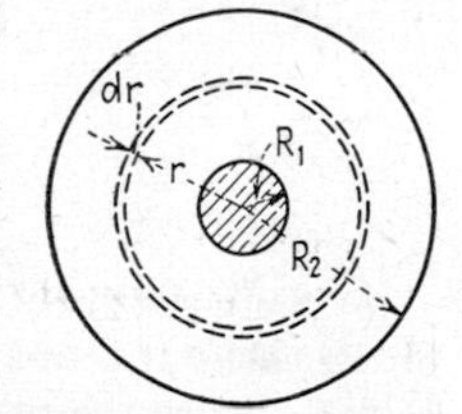

FIG. 4. Resistance path in cable insulation.

The length of this annulus in the direction of the current is dr cm, and its cross section perpendicular to the direction of the current is $2\pi rl$ cm. Hence, from Eq. (1), the resistance of the annulus is

$$dR = \rho \frac{dr}{2\pi rl} \qquad \text{ohms.}$$

The total resistance is

$$R = \frac{\rho}{2\pi l} \int_{R_1}^{R_2} \frac{dr}{r} = \frac{\rho}{2\pi l} \Big[\log_e r \Big]_{R_1}^{R_2}$$

$$= \frac{\rho}{2\pi l} \log_e \frac{R_2}{R_1} \qquad \text{ohms.} \tag{5}$$

Since R_2 and R_1 appear in Eq. (5) as a ratio, the unit in which they are expressed is immaterial so long as both are expressed in the same unit. It will be noted that in Eq. (5) l, the length of the cable, occurs in the denominator. This is due to the fact that the direction of the current in the insulation is perpendicular to the length of the cable.

Example. In a cylindrical rubber-insulated cable, the conductor is No. 6 solid AWG, the diameter of which is 0.162 in., and the thickness of the wall of insulation is ¼ in. The resistivity of the rubber is 10^{14} ohm-cm. Determine: (*a*) insulation resistance of a 1,000-ft length of the cable in megohms; (*b*) insulation resistance of a 2,100-ft length. [1 megohm = 1,000,000 ohms (see p. 5).]

(*a*) The length of the cable is $1{,}000 \cdot 12 = 12{,}000$ in.

$$R_1 = \frac{0.162}{2} \text{ or } 0.081 \text{ in.}$$

$$R_2 = 0.081 + 0.250 = 0.331 \text{ in.}$$

$$\rho = 10^{14} \frac{2.54}{(2.54)^2} = 3.94 \cdot 10^{13} \text{ ohm-in.}$$

Hence, from Eq. (5),

$$R = \frac{3.94 \cdot 10^{13}}{2\pi \cdot 12{,}000} 2.303 \log_{10} \frac{0.331}{0.081}$$

$$= 1.204 \cdot 10^9 \log_{10} 4.09$$

$$= 1.204 \cdot 10^9 \cdot 0.6117 = 7.36 \cdot 10^8 \text{ ohms}$$

$$= 7.36 \cdot 10^2, \text{ or } 736 \text{ megohms.} \quad \textit{Ans.}$$

(*b*) Since the direction of the current in the insulation is at right angles to the length of the cable, the area of the current path must be proportional to the length of the cable. Hence the resistance of the insulation must be *inversely* as the length of the cable. Therefore the resistance of a 2,100-ft length

$$R = 736 \frac{1{,}000}{2{,}100} = 350.5 \text{ megohms.} \quad \textit{Ans.}$$

10. Resistors in Series. A series circuit is one in which the resistors or other electrical devices are connected end to end as shown in Fig. 5. In such a system, there is the same current in each part of the circuit, but the total line voltage divides among the different elements of the circuit. If a number of resistors having resistances R_1, R_2, R_3, etc., Fig. 5, are connected in series, that is, consecutively end to end, the total resistance of the combination is

$$R = R_1 + R_2 + R_3 + \cdots. \quad (6)$$

That is,

In a series circuit the total resistance is the sum of the individual resistances.

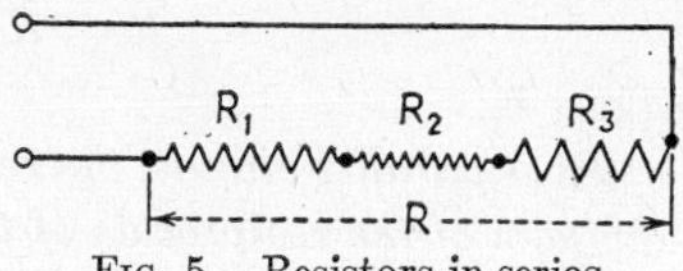

Fig. 5. Resistors in series.

Example. Four resistors having resistances R_1, R_2, R_3, R_4 are connected in series. The values of the resistances are $R_1 = 24.2$ ohms; $R_2 = 36.4$ ohms; $R_3 = 18.5$ ohms; $R_4 = 42.9$ ohms. Determine the value of a single resistance R, which is equivalent to these four in series. From Eq. (6),

$$R = 24.2 + 36.4 + 18.5 + 42.9 = 122.0 \text{ ohms.} \quad \textit{Ans.}$$

11. Resistors in Parallel. A parallel circuit is one in which one terminal of each element is connected to a common point to form one terminal of the system, and the other terminal of each element is connected to a second common point to form the other terminal of the system. Under these conditions, each element of the parallel system is across the same voltage, but the total current divides among the elements of the circuit. A parallel circuit of three resistors is shown in Fig. 6(*a*).

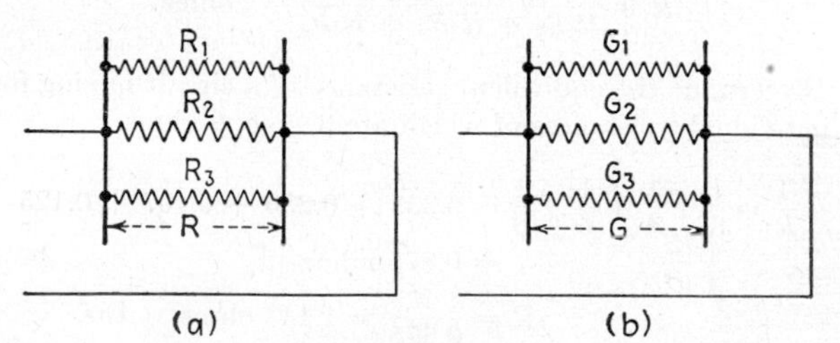

Fig. 6. (*a*) Resistors in parallel. (*b*) Conductors in parallel.

With resistors in parallel, the equivalent resistance must always be less than that of any one of the single resistors, since the adding of a resistor in parallel with another resistor increases the cross section of the current path and hence decreases the resistance.

The equivalent resistance of resistors in parallel may be determined directly if they are first considered as conductors. Thus, in Fig. 6(*a*) are shown three resistors in parallel having resistances R_1, R_2, R_3 ohms. Their conductances are G_1, G_2, G_3 mhos, where $G_1 = 1/R_1$, $G_2 = 1/R_2$, $G_3 = 1/R_3$, Fig. 6(*b*). It is shown in Sec. 5 (p. 6) that conductances in parallel are additive. Hence, in Fig. 6(*b*) the equivalent conductance in mhos is

$$G = G_1 + G_2 + G_3 \quad \text{mhos.} \quad (7)$$

If R is the equivalent resistance, $G = 1/R$ and (7) may be written

$$\frac{1}{R} = \frac{1}{R_1} + \frac{1}{R_2} + \frac{1}{R_3} \quad \text{mhos.} \tag{8}$$

That is:

In a parallel circuit, the reciprocal of the equivalent resistance is equal to the sum of the reciprocals of the individual resistances.

For a circuit with two resistors R_1 and R_2 in parallel, the equivalent resistance R is found as follows:

$$\frac{1}{R} = \frac{1}{R_1} + \frac{1}{R_2} = \frac{R_2 + R_1}{R_1 R_2} \quad \text{mhos.} \tag{I}$$

Taking the reciprocal of (I) gives

$$R = \frac{R_1 R_2}{R_1 + R_2} \quad \text{ohms.} \tag{9}$$

With three resistors R_1, R_2, R_3 in parallel, the equivalent resistance R is found as follows:

$$\frac{1}{R} = \frac{1}{R_1} + \frac{1}{R_2} + \frac{1}{R_3} = \frac{R_2 R_3 + R_3 R_1 + R_1 R_2}{R_1 R_2 R_3} \quad \text{mhos.} \tag{II}$$

Taking the reciprocal of Eq. (II),

$$R = \frac{R_1 R_2 R_3}{R_1 R_2 + R_2 R_3 + R_3 R_1} \quad \text{ohms.} \tag{10}$$

Example. Determine the equivalent resistance of a circuit having four resistors in parallel, the individual resistances of which are 3, 4, 6, 8 ohms.

$$\frac{1}{R} = \frac{1}{3} + \frac{1}{4} + \frac{1}{6} + \frac{1}{8} = 0.333 + 0.250 + 0.167 + 0.125$$

$$= 0.875 \text{ mho.}$$

$$R = \frac{1}{0.875} = 1.143 \text{ ohms.} \quad \textit{Ans.}$$

12. Circular Mil. In the English and American wire tables the circular mil is the standard unit of wire cross section.

The term *milli* means one-thousandth; for example, a millivolt = 1/1,000 volt. A *mil* is *one-thousandth of an inch.* A square mil is the area of a square, each side of which is 1 mil (0.001 in.), as shown in Fig. 7(*a*). The area of a square mil is $0.001 \cdot 0.001 = 0.000001$ sq in.

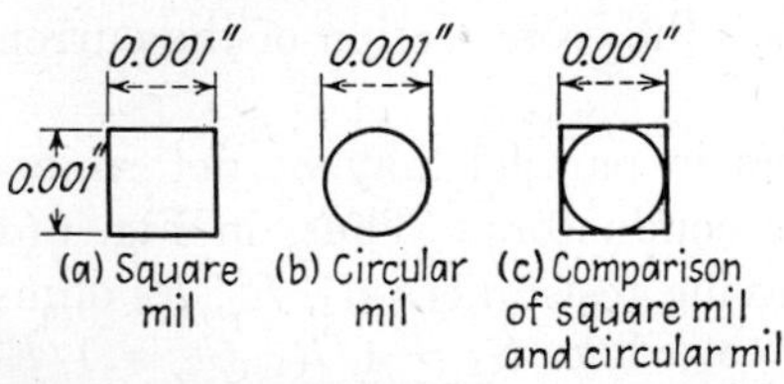

FIG. 7. Square mil and circular mil.

A *circular mil* is the area of a circle whose *diameter* is 1 *mil* (0.001 in), Fig. 7(*b*); it is usually abbreviated cir mil. As will be seen from Fig. 7(*c*), a circular mil is a smaller area than a square mil. The area in square inches of a circular mil = $(\pi/4)(0.001)^2 = 0.0000007854 = 0.7854 \cdot 10^{-6}$ sq in.

The circular mil is the unit in which the cross section of wires and cables is measured, just as the square foot is the unit in which larger areas such as floors, land, etc., are measured. The advantage of the circular mil as a unit is that circular areas measured in terms of this unit bear a very simple relation to the diameters. Also, with the circular mil as the unit, the factor π does not enter computations of cross sections.

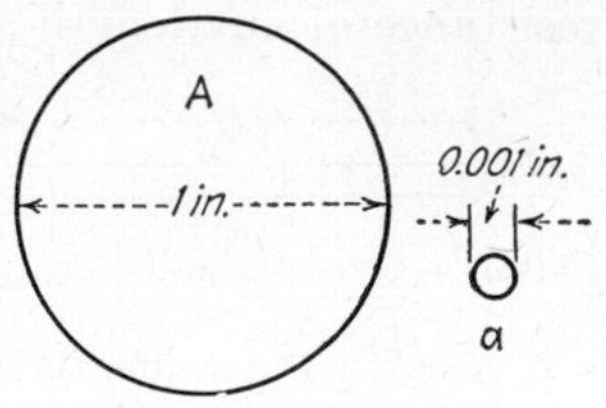

FIG. 8. Cross section expressed in circular mils.

In Fig. 8, A represents the cross section of a wire having a diameter of 1 in. Required: to determine its area in circular mils.

The area $A = (\pi/4)(1)^2$ sq in.

The area a of a circular mil $= (\pi/4)(0.001)^2$ sq in.

The ratio A/a gives the number of circular mils in A.

Therefore,

$$\frac{A}{a} = \frac{(\pi/4)(1)^2}{(\pi/4)0.000001} = 1{,}000{,}000 \text{ cir mils.}$$

The general relation may be written

$$\text{Circular mils} = \frac{D_1^2}{(0.001)^2} = 1{,}000{,}000(D_1)^2 = D^2 \qquad (11)$$

where D_1 = diameter of the wire, in.

D = diameter of the wire, mils.

The matter may be summed up in two rules:

To obtain the number of circular mils in a solid cylindrical wire of given diameter, express the diameter in mils, and then square it.

To obtain the diameter of a solid cylindrical wire having a given number of circular mils, take the square root of the circular mils, and the result will be the diameter of the wire in mils.

Example. Number 00 wire (AWG) has a diameter of 0.3648 in. Determine its circular mils.

0.3648 in. = 364.8 mils.

$(364.8)^2$ = 133,100 cir mils. *Ans.*

Example. A certain wire has a cross section of 52,640 cir mils. Determine its diameter.

$\sqrt{52{,}640}$ = 229.4 mils = 0.2294 in. *Ans.*

13. Circular-mil-foot. Another convenient unit of resistivity used in the English system is the resistance of a circular-mil-foot. This unit is the resistance of a wire having a cross section of 1 cir mil and a length of

1 ft, as shown in Fig. 9. The resistance of a circular-mil-foot of standard copper at 20°C is 10.37 ohms. (In practical work this resistance may frequently be taken as 10 ohms.) Knowing this resistivity, the resistance of any length and size of wire may be determined by Eq. (1), where ρ is the resistance of a circular-mil-foot of copper (= 10.37 ohms for standard copper at 20°C), L is in *feet*, and A is in *circular mils.*

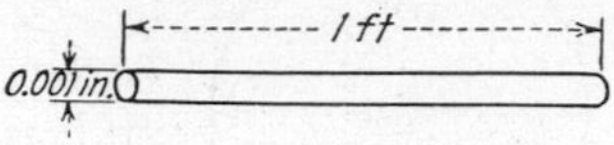

0.001 in. 1 ft

FIG. 9. Circular-mil-foot.

Example. Determine the resistance of 750,000-cir-mil copper cable, 2,500 ft long.

If the cable had a cross section of 1 cir mil, it would have a resistance of 2,500 · 10.37 = 25,900 ohms. However, the cross section is actually 750,000 cir mils; therefore,

$$R = \frac{25{,}900}{750{,}000} = 0.0346 \text{ ohm.} \quad \textit{Ans.}$$

or Eq. (1) (p. 7) may be used directly:

$$R = 10.37 \frac{2{,}500}{750{,}000} = 0.0346 \text{ ohm.}$$

14. Circular-mil-inch. The circular-mil-inch is also a very convenient unit of resistivity, particularly in connection with coils and windings. Such windings usually operate at a temperature which gives a resistivity of approximately 12 ohms per cir-mil-ft or 1 ohm per cir-mil-in. (A temperature of 60°C gives this resistivity.) It follows that the resistance of a copper conductor

$$R = 1 \frac{l}{\text{cir mils}}$$

where under these particular conditions l is in inches.

That is, *the resistance is equal to the length in inches divided by the cross section in circular mils.*

Example. A certain circular magnet coil having an inner diameter of 6 in., an outer diameter of 9 in., and a length of 3.5 in. is wound with 1,000 turns of No. 14 single-cotton-enamel magnet wire, which has a cross section of 4,110 cir mils. Assuming that the resistance of 1 cir-mil-in. of the wire is 1 ohm, determine the resistance of the coil.

The mean length of turn is $\pi \frac{9 + 6}{2} = \pi 7.5 = 23.6$ in.

The total length of copper 1,000 · 23.6 = 23,600 in.

The resistance $R = \frac{23{,}600}{4{,}110} = 5.74$ ohms. *Ans.*

15. Resistivities of Copper. Formerly, the standard for the conductivity of copper was based on results obtained in 1862 by Matthiessen, who made careful measurements of the resistance of supposedly pure copper. He found the resistivity to be 1.594 microhm-cm at 0°C. In view of the uncertainty of the quality of his copper, the Bureau of Standards[1] made a large number of measurements upon commercial copper. Its recommendation that the standard of resistivity be 0.15328 ohm per m-g at 20°C was accepted by the International Electrotechnical Commission at a meeting in Berlin, Sept. 1–6, 1913. This became known as the *International Annealed Copper Standard* and is the internationally accepted resistivity for annealed copper. The meter-gram standard is a *mass* resistivity and is equal to the resistance of a uniform annealed copper wire 1 m long and weighing 1 g. The International Standard for the density of copper is 8.89 g per cu cm at 20°C and corresponds to 0.3212 lb per cu in. The resistivity at 20°C of the International Annealed Copper Standard expressed in several units is as follows:

0.15328	ohm (meter-gram)
875.20	ohms (mile-pound)
1.7241	microhm-centimeters
0.67879	microhm-inch
10.371	ohms (circular-mil-foot)
0.017241	ohm (square millimeter-meter)

The conductivity of commercial annealed copper is about 98 per cent that of the International Standard, and the conductivity of hard-drawn copper is from 96 to 97 per cent that of the International Standard.

16. Resistivities of Aluminum. Aluminum is next to copper in importance as a commercial conductor (see Sec. 25, p. 25). It is found in clay, feldspar, and other silicates, but the chief source is the ore bauxite, a hydrated oxide of aluminum. The most common method of refining is, basically, the electrolysis of the fused ore. The metal is silver-white in color, is ductile, and can be readily worked by rolling, drawing, forging, and extruding. The density is 2.703 g per cu cm at 20°C (0.0975 lb per cu in.) as compared with 8.89 for copper, and it melts at 660°C (1220°F).

The volume resistivity of electrolytically refined annealed wire has been determined by the Bureau of Standards (*Circular* 346) as 2.674 microhm-cm at 20°C. The American Standard for hard-drawn aluminum conductor is 2.828 microhm-cm, or a volume conductivity 60.97 per cent (61 per cent, nearly) that of the International Annealed Copper Standard. Since its density is 2.703/8.89 (practically one-third) that of copper, its mass conductivity is 200.1 per cent that of copper. That is, for equal masses, the conductance of a uniform aluminum wire is practically twice that of a uniform copper wire of the same length and for the

[1] See "Copper Wire Tables," *Circ.* 31, U.S. Bureau of Standards, 1914.

same temperature. Below is given the resistivity at 20°C of aluminum expressed in several units.[1]

0.0764 ohm (meter-gram)
436 ohms (mile-pound)
2.828 microhm-centimeters
1.113 microhm-inches
17.01 ohms (circular-mil-foot)

17. Resistivity Specifications. Formerly, the conductivity of commercial copper was specified and expressed as a percentage of the conductivity of the International Annealed Copper Standard given in Sec. 15 (p. 15). The conductivity of commercial copper was about 98 per cent. More recently resistivity (and conductivity) specifications for copper wire have been based on the ohms (mile-pound) basis in accordance with ASA[2] and ASTM[3] standard specifications, which are given below. In order to meet specifications the resistivity of copper wire must not exceed the values given in the standards.

Soft or Annealed Copper Wire

Resistivity shall not exceed 875.20 ohms (mile-pound) at 20°C (68°F).

RESISTIVITY
[Ohms (mile-pound), 20°C (68°F)]

Nominal diam., in.	Medium hard-drawn ASA H4.3-1941 ASTM B2-40	Hard-drawn ASA H4.2-1941 ASTM B1-40
0.460–0.325	896.15	900.77
0.324–0.0403	905.44	910.15

Other units of resistivity at 20°C corresponding to the foregoing are as follows:

	Soft	Medium-hard-drawn	Hard-drawn
Conductivity at 20°C (68°F), %	100.00	97.16	96.16
Ohms (mile-lb)	875.20	900.77	910.15
Ohms (m-g)	0.15328	0.15775	0.15940
Ohms (cir-mil-ft)	10.371	10.674	10.785
Ohms (m-sq mm)	0.017241	0.017745	0.017930
Microhm-in	0.67879	0.69863	0.70590
Microhm-cm	1.7241	1.7745	1.7930

[1] See "Copper Wire Tables," *Circ.* 31, U.S. Bureau of Standards, 1914.
[2] American Standards Association.
[3] American Society for Testing Materials.

Note that the column corresponding to 100 per cent conductivity corresponds to the International Annealed Copper Standard (Sec. 15, p. 15).

Example. The resistance of a 000 AWG medium-hard-drawn copper wire, the diameter of which is 0.410 in., is measured at 20°C between points 112.6 cm apart and is found to be 0.0002312 ohm. Determine: (*a*) resistivity in ohms (mile-pound); (*b*) whether or not sample meets foregoing resistivity specifications; (*c*) resistivity, ohm-centimeters; (*d*) ohms (circular-mil-foot). Copper weighs 0.3212 lb per cu in.

(*a*) $\text{Length} = \frac{112.6}{2.54} = 44.33 \text{ in.}; \quad \frac{44.33}{12} = 3.694 \text{ ft.}$

$\text{Volume} = \frac{\pi}{4}(0.410)^2\, 44.33 = 5.851 \text{ cu in.}$

$\text{Weight} = 0.3212 \cdot 5.851 = 1.879 \text{ lb.}$

Since the weight of the sample and that of the mile-pound are proportional to their volumes, Eq. (2) (p. 8) may be used. The resistance of a mile-pound is R.

$$\frac{R}{0.0002312} = \frac{(5{,}280)^2/1}{(3.694)^2/1.879}.$$

$$R = \frac{0.0002312 \cdot (5{,}280)^2 \cdot 1.879}{(3.694)^2} = 887.0 \text{ ohms } [= \text{ohms (mile-lb)}]. \quad \textit{Ans.}$$

Some work could have been saved had the weight, 508 lb per 1,000 ft of 000 wire, taken from the wire tables, been used.

(*b*) The value of R in (*a*) is less than the value of 896.15 given in the specifications.

(*c*) $0.0002312 = \rho \frac{112.6}{(\pi/4)(0.410 \cdot 2.54)^2}.$

$$\rho = 0.0002312 \frac{0.8514}{112.6} = 1.748 \cdot 10^{-6} \text{ ohm-cm.} \quad \textit{Ans.}$$

(*d*) $0.0002312 = \rho \frac{112.6/30.5}{(410)^2}$

$$\rho = 0.0002312 \frac{168{,}100}{3.694} = 10.52 \text{ ohms (cir-mil-ft).} \quad \textit{Ans.}$$

Values in both (*c*) and (*d*) fall within the specifications given on page 16.

18. Resistor Materials and Alloys. Resistor materials are used where it is desired to introduce resistance in a circuit. They are used for rheostats, heater units, current limiters, instrument circuits, and shunts and for innumerable industrial purposes. There are several categories of resistor materials, nearly all of which are alloys. The nickel-chromium alloys have high electrical resistivity, low temperature coefficient of resistance, and great resistance to oxidation and to change at high temperature. They are used for heater elements operating primarily at high temperature, such as electric furnaces, for domestic appliances such as electric ranges, toasters, flatirons, and room heaters, and for space heaters. Chromium-nickel-steel alloys—one, for example, containing 17 to 20 per cent of chromium, 7 to 10 per cent of nickel, and small amounts of carbon and manganese—are used where exceptional heat and corrosion resistance are required. Ferronickel alloys have lower resistivity and lower resistance to oxidation and operate at lower temperatures but are much lower in cost than the nickel-chromium alloys. They are used for rheostats and resistors operating at moderately high temperatures. Copper-nickel alloys have heat-resisting properties that are inferior to those of the nickel-chromium alloys, but at ordinary temperatures their temperature coefficient of resistance is practically negligible. Hence, they are used extensively for precision instruments.

The nickel-chromium and chromium-nickel-steel alloys have resistivities from 60 to 70 times that of copper; the ferronickel alloys, 40 to 50 times; and the copper-nickel alloys, 18 to 30 times.

Manganin is a copper-manganese alloy of about 65 per cent copper, 30 per cent ferromanganese, 5 per cent nickel. It has a very low temperature coefficient and hence is used extensively with instruments for multipliers and shunts.

Iron wire and cast iron are also used as resistors, cast-iron grids being commonly used for starting and controller resistors. The metal tungsten, because of its high melting point and high resistivity at high temperatures, is the material used universally for lamp filaments.

The table in Appendix H (p. 592) gives the electrical properties of the more common metals and resistor materials.

19. Temperature Coefficient of Resistance. The resistance of copper and other nonalloyed metals increases appreciably with temperature. Since the temperature at which electrical conductors operate varies with the current and depends on the surrounding, or ambient, temperature as well, it is important to know the relation between temperature and resistance. For example, the temperature of electrical machinery when in operation must necessarily be higher than that of the surrounding medium, and, as will be shown later, the temperature of the windings of the machinery may be found by resistance measurements. Also, the temperature of various electrical devices such as wires and cables, the filaments of incandescent lamps, and the wire in resistor units increases during operation.

Over a limited range of temperature the resistance of the metallic conductors is a linear function of the temperature, as is shown by the graph, Fig. 10(*a*). Let R_2 and R_1 be the resistances at temperatures t_2 and t_1. Then from similar triangles *abc* and *a'b'c'*,

$$\frac{\Delta R}{\Delta t} = \frac{R_2 - R_1}{t_2 - t_1}. \quad \text{(I)}$$

Equation (I) can be used to calculate, for example, the resistance R_2 at temperature t_2 in terms of R_1 at a known temperature t_1, provided that $\Delta R/\Delta t$ is known. However, $\Delta R/\Delta t$ is a function of the resistance R of a particular conducting material and hence depends on its resistivity and geometry. For any given material, the equation becomes more general if $\Delta R/\Delta t$ is a proportion of an initial value of resistance R_1, that is, $(\Delta R/\Delta t)/R_1$, R_1 being the resistance at temperature t_1. The quantity $(\Delta R/\Delta t)/R_1$ is called the *temperature coefficient of resistance* (α_1) at tem-

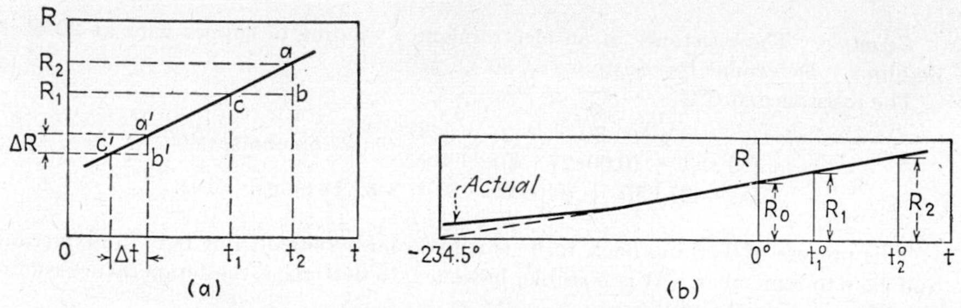

FIG. 10. Variation of resistance with temperature.

perature t_1 and is defined as the change in resistance per ohm per degree centigrade from temperature t_1, if centigrade is used.

Dividing (I) by R_1,

$$\frac{\Delta R}{\Delta t(R_1)} = \frac{R_2 - R_1}{(t_2 - t_1)R_1} = \alpha_1$$

$$R_2 - R_1 = \alpha_1 R_1(t_2 - t_1) \quad \text{ohms.}$$

$$R_2 = R_1[1 + \alpha_1(t_2 - t_1)] \quad \text{ohms.} \tag{12}$$

At 0°C, (12) becomes

$$R_2 = R_0[1 + \alpha_0(t_2 - t_0)]$$
$$= R_0(1 + \alpha_0 t_2) \quad \text{ohms} \tag{12a}$$

where R_0 is the resistance and α_0 the temperature coefficient of resistance, at 0°C, t_0.

For copper, α_0 is 0.00427 and for most of the unalloyed metals is sensibly of this value.[1] This means that with copper the resistance increases 0.427 of 1 per cent for each degree centigrade increase of temperature above 0°. For example, assume that a coil has a resistance of 100 ohms at 0°C. For every degree increase of temperature the coil resistance will increase

$$100 \cdot 0.00427 \text{ ohm, or } 0.427 \text{ ohm.}$$

At 40°C the increase of resistance will be $40 \cdot 0.427 = 17.08$ ohms, and the resistance at 40° will be $100 + 17.08 = 117.08$ ohms.

If the resistance at some definite temperature other than 0°C is known, the resistance at 0°C may first be determined and (12a) then applied. To

[1] For example, the value of α_0 for aluminum is 0.00439.

determine the resistance at 0°C, (12a) may be put in the form

$$R_0 = \frac{R_2}{1 + \alpha_0 t_2}. \tag{13}$$

Example. The resistance of an electromagnet winding of copper wire at 20°C is 30 ohms. Determine its resistance at 80°C.

The resistance at 0°C

$$R_0 = \frac{30}{1 + (0.00427 \cdot 20)} = \frac{30}{1.085} = 27.65 \text{ ohms},$$
$$R_{80} = 27.65[1 + (0.00427 \cdot 80)] = 37.11 \text{ ohms.} \quad \textit{Ans.}$$

This process of working back to 0° is a little inconvenient, but it is fundamental and easy to remember. It is possible, however, to determine the temperature coefficient for *any* initial temperature.

Let R_1 and R_2 be the resistances at temperatures t_1 and t_2, respectively. Then

$$R_1 = R_0(1 + \alpha_0 t_1), \tag{I}$$
$$R_2 = R_0(1 + \alpha_0 t_2). \tag{II}$$

Dividing (II) by (I) and solving for R_2,

$$R_2 = R_1 \frac{(1 + \alpha_0 t_2)}{(1 + \alpha_0 t_1)}. \tag{III}$$

Let R_2 be equal to $R_1[1 + \alpha_1(t_2 - t_1)]$. Then,

$$R_1 \frac{(1 + \alpha_0 t_2)}{(1 + \alpha_0 t_1)} = R_1[1 + \alpha_1(t_2 - t_1)] \tag{IV}$$

where α_1 is the temperature coefficient at an initial temperature t_1. Solving (IV) for α_1,

$$\frac{1 + \alpha_0 t_2}{1 + \alpha_0 t_1} - 1 = \alpha_1(t_2 - t_1).$$

$$\alpha_1 = \frac{1 + \alpha_0 t_2 - 1 - \alpha_0 t_1}{(1 + \alpha_0 t_1)(t_2 - t_1)} = \frac{\alpha_0(t_2 - t_1)}{(1 + \alpha_0 t_1)(t_2 - t_1)} = \frac{\alpha_0}{1 + \alpha_0 t_1}. \tag{V}$$

Dividing the right-hand member of (V) by α_0 gives

$$\alpha_1 = \frac{1}{(1/\alpha_0) + t_1}. \tag{14}$$

α_0 (for copper) equals 0.00427, and $1/\alpha_0 = 234.5$.

Then $\alpha_1 = \dfrac{1}{234.5 + t_1}$, which is easy to remember.

For example, $\alpha_{40} = 1/274.5 = 0.00364$ (see Sec. 20).

Hence, *the temperature coefficient of resistance at a given temperature is the change in resistance per ohm per degree centigrade change in temperature from the given temperature.*

Section 20 gives the temperature coefficients of copper for various initial temperatures. By using this table, temperature-coefficient problems are simplified, as shown by solving the example of Sec. 19 (p. 20).

Example. The temperature coefficient of copper at 20°C initial temperature from Sec. 20 is 0.00393. The rise in temperature = 80° − 20° = 60°.
Then the resistance at 80°C

$$R_{80} = 30(1 + 0.00393 \cdot 60) = 37.07 \text{ ohms.} \quad \textit{Ans.}$$

The American Standard temperature coefficient of hard-drawn aluminum wire from and at 20°C is 0.00403, giving 0.00439 as the temperature coefficient at 0°C.

20. Temperature Coefficients of Copper at Various Initial Temperatures.
[From formula $1/(234.5 + t)$, see Eq. (14)]

Initial Temperature	Increase in Resistance per 1°C
0	0.00427
5	0.00418
10	0.00409
15	0.00401
20	0.00393
25	0.00385
30	0.00378
35	0.00371
40	0.00364
45	0.00358
50	0.00352

21. Inferred Zero Resistance. If the resistance of copper at ordinary temperatures be plotted as ordinates and temperature as abscissas, the graph is practically a straight line, Fig. 10(*b*). If this line be extended, it will intersect the zero-resistance line at −234.5°C (an easy number to remember), as shown in Fig. 10(*b*). Hence, between ordinary limits of temperature, copper behaves as if it had zero resistance at −234.5°C. [Actually the curve departs from a straight line at extremely low temperatures, as shown by the solid line in Fig. 10(*b*).] This gives a convenient method for determining temperature-resistance relations.

By the law of similar triangles, Fig. 10,

$$\frac{R_0}{234.5°} = \frac{R_1}{234.5° + t_1}, \tag{15}$$

$$\frac{R_1}{234.5° + t_1} = \frac{R_2}{234.5° + t_2}. \tag{16}$$

Applying (16) to the example of Sec. 19 (p. 20),

$$\frac{30}{234.5° + 20°} = \frac{R_{80}}{234.5° + 80°}.$$

$$R_{80} = 30\,\frac{234.5° + 80°}{234.5° + 20°} = 30\,\frac{314.5°}{254.5°} = 37.07 \text{ ohms.} \quad \textit{Ans.}$$

22. Semiconductors; Varistors; Thermistors.[1] A semiconductor may be defined as a substance whose electrical conductivity at, or near, room temperature is much less than that of typical metals, but much greater than that of typical insulators. Although no sharp boundaries exist among conductors, semiconductors, and insulators, semiconductors may be considered as having resistivities at room temperature of between 0.1 and 10^9 ohm-cm. Semiconductors usually have high negative temperature coefficients of resistance. As the temperature is increased from 0 to 300°C, the resistivity may decrease in the ratio of 1,000 to 1, whereas

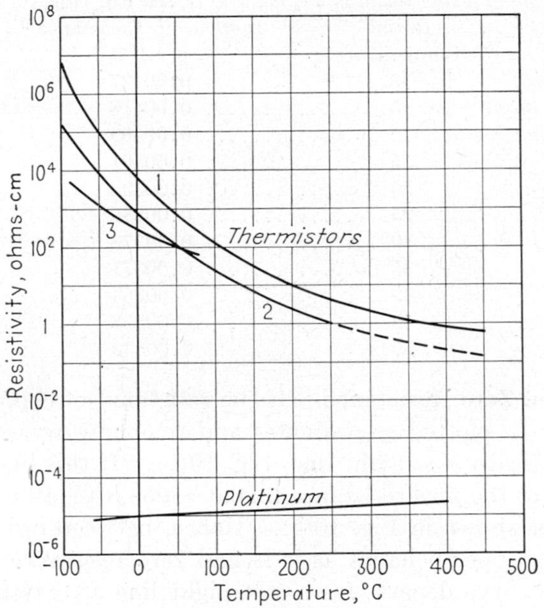

FIG. 11. Resistivities of thermistors.

over the same temperature range the resistivity of copper would increase in the ratio of only 1.28 to 1 and that of platinum in the ratio of only 2 to 1.

Substances whose resistivities vary over such wide ranges are called *varistors*. A varistor is defined as "a resistor which consists of solid material whose current-voltage characteristic is not linear." If the change in resistivity of a varistor as a function of temperature is high, it is called a *thermistor*. A thermistor is defined as "a symmetrical[2] varistor which has an unusually high temperature coefficient of resistance."

[1] BECKER, J. A., C. B. GREEN, and G. L. PEARSON, "Properties and Uses of Thermistors—Thermally Sensitive Resistors," *Trans. AIEE*, Vol. 65, p. 711, 1946.

[2] Symmetrical means that the resistivity at any one temperature is the same for increasing and for decreasing values of current.

Semiconductors of the thermistor type are made of compounds and mixtures of chlorides such as NaCl, sulfides, oxides such as Mn_2O_3, Fe_2O_3, and NiO, carbides, and elements such as boron, silicon, germanium, and tellurium. Thermistors are made in the form of beads, rods, disks, washers, and flakes. In Fig. 11, the resistances of three different thermistors are plotted to logarithmic scale as functions of temperature. For comparison, the resistance-temperature characteristic of platinum is also given.

Because of its wide variation of resistance with temperature, the thermistor is a thermally sensitive circuit element, whose resistance changes about 4 per cent per degree centigrade. Because of its high thermal sensitivity, the thermistor is finding wide application such, for example, as for sensitive thermometers, temperature control elements, temperature compensators, voltage regulators, ultra-high-frequency power meters, automatic gain controls, speech volume regulators, and many other applications.

23. American Wire Gage (AWG). The AWG (formerly Brown & Sharpe gage) is based on a constant ratio between diameters of successive gage numbers; that is, the diameters taken in order form a geometrical progression. The diameter of No. 0000 is defined as 0.4600 in. (1.168 cm) and the diameter of No. 36 as 0.0050 in. (0.0127 cm). Between No. 0000 and No. 36 are 38 gage numbers. Hence the ratio of any diameter to the diameter of the next greater gage number must be

$$\sqrt[39]{\frac{0.4600}{0.0050}} = \sqrt[39]{92} = 1.123.$$

The square $(1.123)^2$ of this ratio is 1.2610. Since the cross section varies as the square of the diameter, the ratio of any cross section to the cross section of the next greater gage number is 1.261. The sixth power of 1.123 is 2.0050. Hence the ratio of any diameter to the diameter of a gage number which is 6 greater is 2, practically. It follows that the cross section either doubles or halves for every three gage numbers. Since $(1.261)^2$ is 1.590, the ratio of any cross section to the cross section of a gage number greater by 2 is 1.60, practically. The ratio of any cross section to one of a gage number differing by 10 is $(92^{10/39})^2 = 10$ (practically), or the reciprocal, $1/10$, practically.

A working table for annealed solid copper wire, AWG, is given in Appendix E (p. 589), and a similar table for stranded cable is given in Appendix F (p. 590).

Approximations with the AWG. The diameter of No. 10 wire is 0.102 in. (0.259 cm), and the wire has a cross section of 10,400 cir mils. As an approximation, the diameter may be considered as being 0.1 in. (0.254 cm) and the cross section as 10,000 cir mils.

From the foregoing and the fact that the weight of 1,000 ft of No. 10 wire is 31.4 (10π) lb, the following approximate rules may be given:

(1) No. 10 wire has a diameter of 0.1 in. and a resistance of 1 ohm per 1,000 ft. (2) The resistance of the wire doubles with every increase of three gage numbers, and halves with every decrease of three gage numbers. (3) Therefore the resistance increases $\sqrt[3]{2} = 1.26$ ($1\frac{1}{4}$) times for each successive larger gage number and $(1.26)^2 = 1.6$ times for every two larger numbers. (4) The resistance is multiplied or divided by 10 for every difference of 10 gage numbers. (5) The weight of 1,000 ft of No. 10 wire is 31.4 lb, and the weight of 1,000 ft of No. 2 wire is 200 lb. These rules make it a comparatively simple matter to determine without reference to the table the weight or resistance for any gage number.

Example. Determine the resistance and weight of 1,000 ft of No. 0000 wire.

The resistances will decrease as follows:

Gage No.	10	7	4	1	000
Resistance	1	0.5	0.25	0.125	0.0625 (rules 1 and 2)

Resistance of 0000 = 0.0625/1.25 = 0.050 ohm (rule 3). *Ans.*
Weight of 1,000 ft No. 2 = 200 lb.
Weight of 1,000 ft 00 = 400 lb.
Weight of 1,000 ft 0000 = 400 · 1.6 = 640 lb (rules 5, 2,* and 3*). *Ans.*
The example might have been worked more quickly by rule 4.
Resistance of 1,000 ft of No. 10 = 1 ohm.
Resistance of 1,000 ft of 0 = 0.1 ohm (rule 4).
Resistance of 1,000 ft of 0000 = 0.050 ohm (rule 2). *Ans.*

Example. Determine the resistance and weight of 1,800 ft of No. 34 wire.
Resistance of 1,000 ft of No. 10 = 1 ohm (rule 1).
Resistance of 1,000 ft of 20 = 10 ohms (rule 4).
Resistance of 1,000 ft of 30 = 100 ohms (rule 4).
Resistance of 1,000 ft of 33 = 200 ohms (rule 2).
Resistance of 1,000 ft of 34 = 250 ohms (rule 3).
1.8 · 250 = 450 ohms. *Ans.*
Weight of 1,000 ft of No. 10 = 31.4 lb (rule 5).
Weight of 1,000 ft of 20 = 3.14 lb (rule 4*).
Weight of 1,000 ft of 30 = 0.314 lb (rule 4*).
Weight of 1,000 ft of 33 = 0.157 lb (rule 2*).
Weight of 1,000 ft of 34 = 0.157/1.25, or 0.126 lb (rule 3*).
1.8 · 0.126 = 0.227 lb. *Ans.*

24. Stranded Cables. Solid copper wire of greater cross section than 0000 gage is practically never used since, because of its rigidity, it cannot be readily bent. Wires of greater cross section therefore are stranded to give flexibility. Also, for certain uses, wires of comparatively small cross section are frequently stranded to obtain greater flexibility. (Lamp cord and cords for portable devices are excellent examples.)

Stranding is accomplished geometrically as follows:

Six wires will just fit about a center wire. In each successive layer

* The weight is inversely as the resistance.

6 additional wires will just fill up that layer. Thus, the first layer contains 6 wires; the second, 12 wires; the third, 18 wires, and so on, as is shown in Fig. 12. Hence the numbers of strands which standard cable will contain are 1,7,19,37,61,91,127, ... Sometimes, in order to obtain even greater flexibility, the unit strands themselves are also stranded.

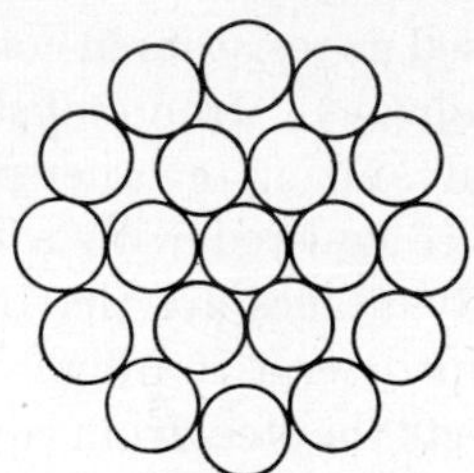
Fig. 12. Nineteen-strand cable.

Wires greater than 0000 gage are designated by their circular mils rather than by a gage number. The standard sizes differ successively by 50,000 cir mils, beginning with 250,000 cir mils. Appendix F (p. 590) gives the properties of stranded annealed copper cables. Obviously the diameter over the outside strands is greater than the diameter of a solid cylindrical conductor of equal cross section.

25. Conductors. Although silver is a better conductor than copper, its use as a conductor is very limited because of its cost. In a few instances it is used where a delicate and highly conducting material is necessary, such as in the brushes and occasionally in the commutator of watthour meters. Silver buttons and silver-plated contactors are widely used with current-interrupting devices since, because of the low vapor pressure of silver, arcs do not readily form when the circuit is opened. Copper, because of its high conductivity and moderate cost, is used more extensively as a conductor than any other material. It has many good qualities, such as ductility and high tensile strength, is not easily abraded, is not corroded by the atmosphere, and is readily soldered.

Aluminum has only 61 per cent of the conductivity of copper, but for the same length and weight it has about twice the conductance of copper. It is softer than copper, its tensile strength is much less, and it cannot be easily soldered. It is not affected by exposure to the atmosphere. Underground cables with aluminum conductors are now in common use even though the aluminum, for a given conductance, requires more insulation than copper, because of its greater cross section. However, the greater amount of insulation is more than offset by the lower cost of the aluminum and its greater availability, especially during and following the Second World War. Also, for a given conductance, the carrying capacity of aluminum is greater than that of copper because of the greater heat-dissipating surface.

Aluminum is used extensively as a conductor for high-voltage transmission lines, where its lightness and large diameter (because of corona) are an advantage (see p. 360 and Vol. II, 4th edition, p. 479). It is also used to some extent for low-voltage bus bars as it offers much greater heat-dissipating surface than copper of the same conductance.

Iron and steel have about nine times the resistance of copper for the same cross section and length. The large cross section for a given conductance prohibits their use where an insulating covering is necessary, and the increased weight prevents their use in most cases where the conductors must be placed on poles. Iron and steel are most commonly used as resistors in connection with rheostats and for third rails of electric railways. Iron and steel ordinarily must be protected from oxidation by galvanizing or other protective covering. Copperweld consists of a steel wire covered with a layer of copper fused or welded to the steel. Its advantages are that it possesses the high tensile strength of steel, combined with the high conductivity of copper. Further, the copper protects the steel from corrosion. It is frequently used as a transmission-line conductor, where long spans make high tensile strength necessary, and also it is used as an overhead ground wire.

CHAPTER II

OHM'S LAW AND THE ELECTRIC CIRCUIT

26. CGS Systems of Electrical Units. There are four basic, or fundamental, systems of electrical units, the *cgs* (centimeter-gram-second) *electrostatic* system, the *cgs electromagnetic* system, the *mks* (meter-kilogram-second) *unrationalized* system, and the *mks rationalized* system.

The units in the *cgs electrostatic* system are based on Coulomb's experimental law (see p. 325), which states that the force acting between two electrostatic point charges Q_1 and Q_2, placed r cm apart, is $Q_1Q_2/\epsilon_r\epsilon_v r^2$ dynes, where ϵ_r is the relative capacitivity (p. 334) of the medium and ϵ_v is the capacitivity of evacuated space. In the cgs system, ϵ_v is assumed to be unity. Other electrical units, such as those of current and potential, may be derived from this simple relation. The electrostatic system is used to calculate the capacitance of capacitors from their geometry [see, for example, Eq. (275), p. 344] and is also used to a large extent in the calculation of electron phenomena, since electrons themselves are minute electric charges. The units of the electrostatic system ordinarily have the prefix *stat*, for example, statvolt, statfarad, etc.

The units in the cgs *electromagnetic* system are based fundamentally on the law which states that the force acting between magnetic poles of strength mm' unit poles and concentrated at points, is $mm'/\mu_r\mu_v r^2$ dynes, where μ_r is the relative permeability of the medium (see p. 212) and μ_v is the permeability of evacuated space. In the cgs system μ_v is assumed to be unity. The unit of current is derived by means of the Biot-Savart law (pp. 230 and 233), which gives the relation existing between the current in a conductor and the force which the current exerts on a unit magnetic pole. It follows from Eq. (141) (p. 233) that if a conductor carrying a current of I' absolute amperes be bent into an arc of a circle 1 cm in length and of 1 cm radius, Fig. 13(a), and the unit pole be placed at the center of the *circle*, the force acting on the unit pole is

$$\mathbf{F} = I' \qquad \text{dynes.} \tag{17}$$

(Note that the leading-in connections to the arc, Fig. 13, are radial so that the current in them exerts no force on the unit pole.) However, particularly if measurements are to be made, it is more practical to employ a complete circular turn, Fig. 13(b), rather than a centimeter arc, Fig. 13(a). Under these conditions when the current is I' abamp, the force at the center of the circle of 1 cm radius,

$$\mathbf{F} = 2\pi I' \quad \text{dynes.} \tag{18}$$

If the coil has N turns and the radius is r cm, the force

$$\mathbf{F} = \frac{2\pi N I'}{r} \quad \text{dynes.} \tag{19}$$

(17), (18), (19) assume that the current or the turns are concentrated in a line of essentially zero diameter. If in Fig. 13(a) the current is adjusted until the force on the unit pole is 1 *dyne*, the value of the current, from (17), is 1 cgs or 1 *absolute ampere* (*abampere*). Similarly in Fig. 13(b) if the current is adjusted until the force on the unit pole is

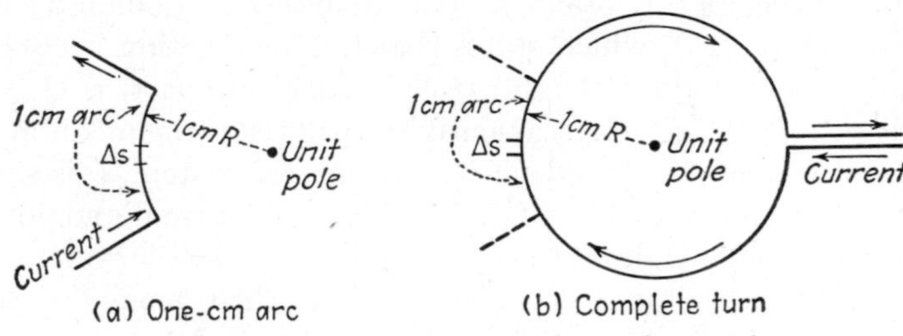

FIG. 13. Absolute determination of current.

2π dynes, from (18) the current is 1 abamp. If (19) is used, the current is 1 abamp when the force on the unit pole is $2\pi N/r$ dynes.

After having determined the current in the foregoing manner, all other units in the system may be defined. For example, the quantity Q in abcoulombs is equal to the product of current in abamperes and time in seconds. Potential difference V in abvolts between two points is measured by the work W (in ergs) performed in carrying a unit charge from one point to the other. If Q unit charges are carried, $V = W/Q$ abvolts. Q must be expressed in abcoulombs.

The units of this cgs electromagnetic system are commonly used in magnetic calculations (see Chap. VIII). They can serve also as the basis for the units of the practical system (Sec. 27). Absolute units ordinarily have the prefix *ab*, for example, abvolt, abampere, etc.

27. Practical System of Electrical Units. Most of the units of the cgs electromagnetic system are many times smaller than the quantities used in practice. For example, the absolute volt, or abvolt, has 1/100,000,000, or 10^{-8}, the magnitude of the practical volt. In the practical system, which can be derived from the cgs system, the units are of the order of magnitude of the quantities which are met ordinarily in practice. These units of the practical system differ from the units of the cgs system only by definite numerical ratios. For example, the practical ampere has one-tenth (10^{-1}) the magnitude of the abampere (Sec. 29), the practical ohm has one billion (10^9) times the magnitude of the abohm, the henry has 1,000,000,000 (10^9) times the magnitude of the abhenry, etc. (see Appendix B).

The practical system is derived from the cgs electromagnetic system by substituting a length of 10^9 cm and a mass of 10^{-11} g for the centimeter and the gram in the cgs system.

28. Meter-Kilogram-Second (MKS) System. The cgs electrostatic and electromagnetic systems are based on the dimensional units of the centimeter, the gram, and the second. Many attempts have been made to base the practical system also on suitable dimensional units. However, the magnitudes of dimensional units necessary to give the units of the practical system are so far removed from those in general use as to be impracticable. For example, to combine with the second as the unit of time, it is necessary to use a unit of length of 10^9 cm, an earth quadrant, and a unit of mass of 10^{-11} g (Sec. 27). The unit of length is far too large and the unit of mass far too small to be of practical value.

In 1901, G. Giorgi, of Italy, pointed out that the meter, kilogram, and second could be used as the dimensional units of the practical system if the permeability of free space were taken as 10^{-7} ($=\mu_v$) rather than unity. The Giorgi system gradually gained favor until in June, 1935, at its plenary session at Scheveningen-Brussels, the International Electrotechnical Commission (IEC) unanimously adopted the mks system.

So far as the electrical units of the practical system—such as the volt, ampere, coulomb, farad—are concerned, no change need be made when the mks system is used, since these quantities already are given in mks units. However, as will appear in Chaps. VI, VII, VIII, IX, X there are radical differences between mks magnetic and electrostatic units and corresponding units of the two cgs systems.

Moreover, some confusion still exists with respect to the mks system, for there are two systems, neither of which has as yet (1951) become standardized, the *unrationalized* system, in which the mmf is equal to $4\pi NI$ amp-turns, and the *rationalized* system, in which the mmf is equal to NI amp-turns.

The relations among the units in the different systems are given in Appendix B (p. 581).

29. Practical (also MKS) Electrical Units. The practical electrical units are defined as follows:

Quantity. The unit of quantity is the *coulomb*[1] (q, Q).

[1] After Charles A. Coulomb, (1736–1806), a French philosopher who began his career as a military engineer but later became interested in science. He is distinguished for his investigations in both mechanics and electricity. His noteworthy

An international coulomb is the quantity of electricity which passes any section of an electric circuit in one second, when the current in the circuit is one international ampere (05.35.175).[1]

One international coulomb equals 0.999835 absolute coulomb.

A coulomb is equal to $3 \cdot 10^9$ statcoulombs and 10^{-1} abcoulomb.

The coulomb is analogous to the unit quantity of water in hydraulics, such as the cubic foot and the gallon.

Current. The unit of current is the *ampere*[2] (i, I).

An ampere is equal to one coulomb per second.

The international ampere is defined as the current which under definite conditions will deposit silver at the rate of 0.001118 gram per second (05.35.170).[1]

An international ampere equals 0.999835 absolute ampere. An absolute ampere is $\frac{1}{10}$ cgs ampere or abampere.

The international ampere as defined above was validated by an act of Congress in 1894. The silver was deposited from a solution of nitrate of silver in a cell of standard specifications. With the recent development of high-precision techniques in measurements, it has been found that the international units, including the ampere, differ by small amounts from values derived from the cgs units. In 1933 an Advisory Committee on Electricity, established in 1927 on an international basis, recommended that absolute units replace the international ones. Precise measurements were conducted by the U.S. Bureau of Standards and similar laboratories in other countries to establish the value of the absolute units. By an act of Congress in 1947 these absolute units went into effect Jan. 1, 1948, and Public Law 617, which became effective July 21, 1950, made these units the only legal ones in the United States. It is to be noted that the differences between the absolute and international units are so small that they have no appreciable effect on measurements, except those of the very highest precision.

---

contributions were the construction of a refined torsion balance and the determination experimentally as well as mathematically of the laws governing the attraction and repulsion of magnetic poles and of electric charges.

[1] From ASA C42 Definitions of Electrical Terms, 1941 edition.

[2] After André Marie Ampère (1775–1836), a French physicist who from his early days showed unusual aptitude for mathematics and the sciences. In 1801 he was appointed professor of physics and chemistry at Bourg, in 1804 was appointed professor of physics and chemistry at the Lycée of Lyons, in 1809 was appointed professor of mathematics at the École Polytechnique at Paris, and later at the Collège de France. His important contributions were the establishment of the relations existing between electricity and magnetism, in which he gave a far more complete exposition than Oersted. He developed mathematical theory which not only explained the relations which had been observed between current and magnetic field but predicted many new ones.

It should be kept in mind that the ampere is the *rate* of flow of *electricity* or *quantity*. It corresponds in hydraulics to the rate of flow of water, which is expressed as cubic feet per second, gallons per minute, etc.

Resistance. The unit of resistance is the *ohm* (r, R).

The *international ohm* is defined as the resistance at zero degrees centigrade of a column of mercury of uniform cross section, having a length of 106.300 centimeters and a mass of 14.4521 grams (05.35.180).[1]

One international ohm equals 1.00049 *absolute* ohms.

One absolute ampere in a resistance of one absolute ohm will produce a potential difference of one absolute volt.

Potential Difference. The unit of potential difference is the *volt*[2] (v, V). (e, E are symbols for electromotive force.)

The international volt is the voltage that will produce a current of one international ampere through a resistance of one international ohm (05.35.185).[3]

The *international volt* is specifically defined as 1/1.01830 of the voltage of a normal Weston cell (see Sec. 83, p. 106).

One international volt equals 1.00034 absolute volts.

Potential difference in volts between two points is measured by the work in joules in carrying one coulomb between the two points.

The mechanical analogue of potential difference is pressure. The difference in hydraulic pressure between the ends of a pipe causes or tends to cause the flow of water. The pressure of water behind the dam tends to cause water to flow through the penstock or through any leaks. The pressure in a boiler tends to cause steam to flow through the pipes, valves, etc. Likewise electric pressure or difference of potential tends to cause electricity to flow, thus producing current.

[1] From ASA C42 Definitions of Electrical Terms, 1941 edition.

[2] After Alessandro Volta, (1745–1827), an Italian physicist and a pioneer in electrical science. In 1774 he was appointed professor of physics in the Gymnasium at Como, and in 1779 he was appointed to a similar chair at Pavia.

His first notable contribution to the science of electricity was the invention of the electrophorus (1775) with which electrical energy is evolved by the mechanical separation of a conducting disk from a layer of insulating material. About the same time he invented the electroscope, the first practical means for measuring electric potential. By means of this instrument he was able to prove the presence of electricity in various materials. By the application of a condenser (or capacitor) to the terminal of the electroscope (1782), he increased the sensitivity many times. His greatest contribution, however, was the galvanic pile (1799), which showed that an electrical potential exists between two dissimilar metals which are in joint contact with an electrolyte. This is the basis of all electric batteries. He also was the first to discriminate between metallic and electrolytic conduction.

He received numerous medals and other honors for his work.

[3] From ASA C42 Definitions of Electrical Terms, 1941 edition.

Power. The unit of electrical power is the *watt*[1] (*W*). (*P*, *p* are symbols for power.)

The international watt is the power expended when one international ampere flows between two points having a potential difference of one international volt (05.35.205).[2]

One international watt equals 1.00018 absolute watts.

Energy. The unit of electrical energy is the *joule*[3] (*j*). (*W* is the symbol for work or energy.)

The international joule is the energy required to transfer one international coulomb between two points having a potential difference of one international volt (05.35.200).[2]

One international joule equals 1.000185 absolute joules.

One joule equals 10^7 ergs.

With a steady voltage of E volts and current of I amp the joules are given by $W = EIt = I^2rt$, known as Joule's law, where t is the time in seconds and r the resistance in ohms. It follows that one joule equals one watt-second.

[1] After James Watt (1736–1819), a Scotch engineer and the inventor of the modern condensing steam engine. His father was an unsuccessful small merchant, so that at an early age James was thrown on his own resources. He first became a mathematical-instrument maker, finally obtaining employment at Glasgow College. This gave him an opportunity to repair Newcomen's engine in which the steam was condensed in the working cylinder. Seeing the advantages of a condenser external to the cylinder, in 1765 he invented and made the first engine operating on this principle. He also invented many improvements which are still used, such as the condenser air pump, the steam-jacketed cylinder, the double-acting cylinder, the early cutoff of steam to the cylinder, and the throttle valve and centrifugal governor. He also invented the engine indicator, which has been of extreme importance in the evolution of the engine, and the sun-and-planet gear. His inventions were very successful commercially.

[2] From ASA C42 Definitions of Electrical Terms, 1941 edition.

[3] After James Prescott Joule (1818–1889), an English physicist, who is best known for his pioneer researches on the mechanical equivalent of heat. Owing to spinal trouble, Joule, whose interest was primarily in forms of energy or work was, ironically, an invalid all his life. He was instructed at home, his instructor being the famous chemist Dalton. Joule's interest and brilliant work were displayed at the early age of nineteen, when he published the description of an electromagnetic motor which he had invented. He was the first to evaluate an electric current quantitatively, the value being determined by the weight of water which a given current decomposed in an hour. In 1841 he proved by experiment that heat produced in a wire by the passage of electricity varies directly with the resistance of the wire and with the square of the current, now known as Joule's law.

He proved experimentally, and in 1843 enunciated, the law that, whenever mechanical energy is converted into heat energy, an exact equivalent of heat energy is always obtained. It was he who first determined the absolute value of the Btu, and also its value in terms of electrical energy. He also was one of the first to propound the law of the conservation of energy.

One joule is equal to 0.2389 gram-calorie; 1 gram-calorie is equal to 4.186 joules.

Energy is also given in kilowatthours (abbreviated kwhr).

(See Conversion Table, Appendix A, p. 579.)

30. Absolute Potential. The absolute potential of a body in cgs units is defined as measured by the work in ergs necessary to bring a cgs unit of charge up to the body from infinity. It is practically impossible to determine the absolute potential of a body. For example, the absolute potential of the earth is not even approximately known, but for convenience the earth is assumed to be at zero potential and the potentials of bodies are usually given with reference to earth potential.

It is only occasionally that absolute potential is of interest. Usually it is desired to know *difference of potential.* The difference of potential (in cgs units) between any two points is defined fundamentally as measured by the work in ergs necessary to move a cgs unit of charge from one point to the other. In the practical system the difference in potential would be given by the work in joules (10^7 ergs) necessary to move 1 coulomb from one point to the other (p. 32). Practically, difference of potential is measured by means of some measuring device such as a voltmeter (see p. 150).

31. Nature of the Flow of Electricity. The flow of electricity through a circuit resembles in many ways the flow of water through a closed sys-

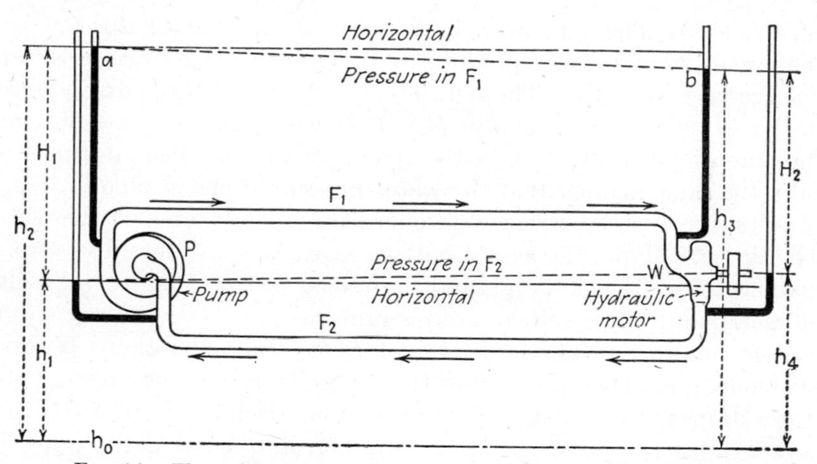

FIG. 14. Flow of water through a hydraulic motor and pipe system.

tem of pipes. For example, in Fig. 14 water enters the mechanically driven centrifugal pump P at a pressure h_1 (represented by the length of a column of mercury) above the point of zero pressure shown by the line h_0. In virtue of the action of the pump blades, the pressure of the water through the pump is increased from h_1 to h_2, representing a net increase of pressure H_1. The water then flows out along pipe F_1 to the hydraulic motor W. Because of the friction loss in the pipe F_1, the pressure h_3 at the motor terminals is slightly less than h_2. In other words, a pressure of $h_2 - h_3$ is required to overcome the frictional resistance of the pipe F_1. The line ab gives the pressure at each point along the pipe F_1. The pressure decreases uniformly in F_1, as shown by line ab.

In Fig. 15 the mechanically driven electrical generator G raises the potential of the current entering its negative terminal from v_1 to v_2 where v_1 and v_2 are measured from the earth whose potential is ordinarily assumed as zero. (The various voltages are measured with voltmeters

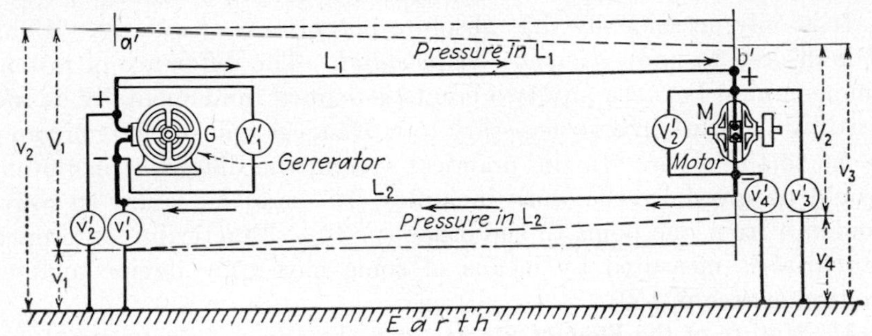

FIG. 15. Flow of an electric current through an electric motor and the connecting feeder system.

v_1', v_2', etc.) The generator, in raising the potential of this portion of the circuit from v_1 to v_2, produces a net increase in electric pressure or voltage $v_2 - v_1 = V_1$. The current now flows out through the wire L_1 to the + terminal of the motor M. Because of the resistance of wire L_1, the potential drops from v_2 at the generator to v_3 at the motor in practically the same manner that the water pressure drops in pipe F_1, Fig. 14. A voltage $v_2 - v_3$ is necessary to overcome the resistance of the wire L_1. The line $a'b'$ shows the actual voltage at each point along the wire, the distance of $a'b'$ from the ground line being proportional to the voltage at each point. The voltage drop is uniform.

Referring to Fig. 14, the water enters the hydraulic motor W, and in overcoming the back pressure of the revolving blades the pressure of the water drops from h_3 to h_4, representing a net drop in pressure H_2. Pressure h_4 must necessarily be greater than h_1 in order that the water may flow back through the pipe F_2. The pressure $h_4 - h_1$ is necessary to overcome the friction loss in the pipe F_2. It is to be noted that H_2, the net pressure at the motor terminals, is less than the pressure H_1 at the pump, by the sum of the pressures necessary to overcome the friction in the two pipes F_1 and F_2.

In a similar manner, the pressure or voltage of the electric current in going through the motor M, Fig. 15, drops from v_3 to v_4, representing a net drop in pressure V_2. A large percentage of this voltage V_2 is necessary to overcome the counter emf of the motor. v_4 is necessarily greater than v_1, or the current could not flow along L_2 back to the negative terminal of the generator. It is to be noted that, as in Fig. 14, the net potential difference V_2 at the motor M is less than the potential difference V_1 at the generator, by the drop in potential due to the resistance of both the *outgoing* and *return* wires.

Difference of potential is therefore the equivalent of pressure and *tends* to send current through a circuit; current is quantity of electricity per second. Potential difference may exist with no current, in the same manner that a boiler may have a very high steam pressure with no steam flow, owing to all the valves being closed. Likewise a generator, Fig. 16, may have a very high potential difference at its terminals; yet, because the switch S is open, there is no current.

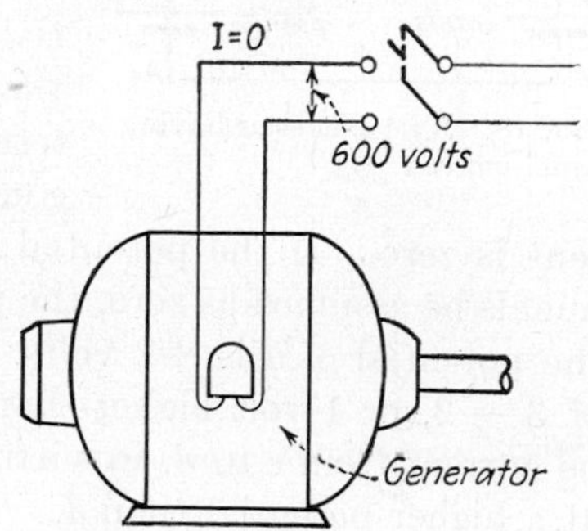

FIG. 16. Potential difference without current.

32. Difference of Potential. In order that there may be current between two points, there must be a *difference of potential* between the two points, as shown in Fig. 15. This is further illustrated in Fig. 17. A large reservoir and a small tank are connected by a pipe P. The water level in the tank and in the reservoir is the same. There is pressure in each, but there is no *difference in pressure* between them. Under these conditions when the valve V is opened, no water flows from the reservoir to the tank. However, if the valve V is opened, allowing the water level in the tank to fall, a difference of pressure results and water flows from the reservoir to the tank.

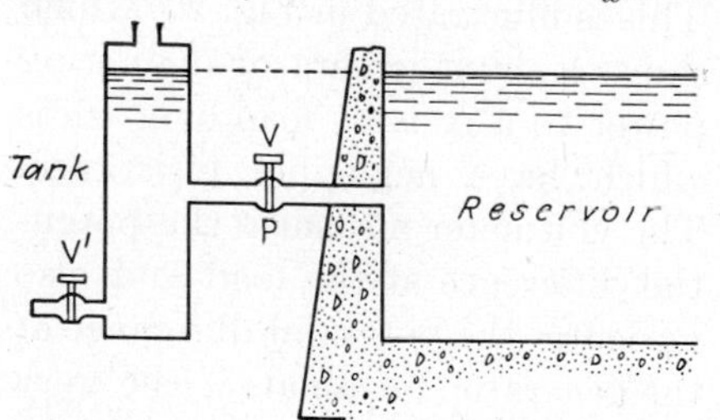

FIG. 17. Tank and reservoir at the same pressure.

Figure 18 shows two batteries A_1 and A_2 each having an emf of 2 volts. The positive terminal a of A_1 has a potential of +2 volts above its negative terminal; likewise the positive terminal b of A_2 has a potential of +2 volts above its negative terminal. The negative terminals of both batteries are at the same potential because they are connected by a copper wire in which there is no current, and consequently there can be no potential difference between the ends of the copper wire. Therefore points a and b must each be at the same potential of +2 volts. If now the switch S be closed, there will be *no* current between a and b, because there is no *difference of potential* between a and b. This is analogous to the conditions in Fig. 17 when the water level in the tank is the same as that in the reservoir.

In Fig. 19 the emf of battery B_1 is 3 volts, and therefore the potential of its positive terminal c is 3 volts above that of its negative terminal. The emf of battery B_2 is 2 volts, and therefore the potential of its positive terminal d is 2 volts above that of its negative terminal. The negative terminals are at the same potential, being connected by a conductor in which the current is zero. If the potential of this conductor and the negative terminals be assumed as zero, the point c is at a potential of +3 volts and the potential of d is +2 volts. Therefore, the point c is at a potential of 3 − 2, or 1 volt higher than d. When switch S is closed, there will be current from c to d, in virtue of c being at a higher potential than d. This is analogous to the conditions in Fig. 17 when the water level in the tank is lower than that in the reservoir.

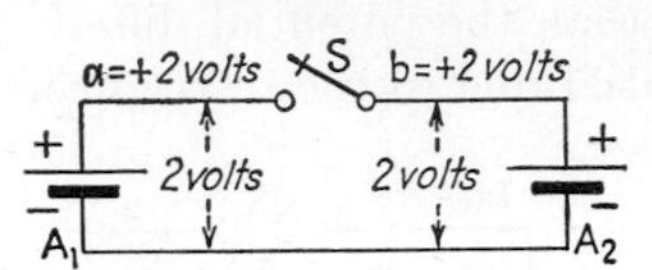

FIG. 18. Two batteries having equal emfs.

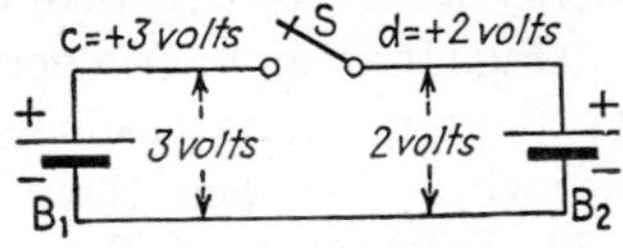

FIG. 19. Two batteries having unequal emfs.

33. Measurement of Voltage and Current. Voltage or potential difference is ordinarily measured with a voltmeter. It is rarely that *absolute potential* is of interest. Ordinarily, *difference of potential* is desired. The voltmeter, therefore, should be connected *across* or *between* the wires whose difference of potential is to be measured. This is illustrated in Fig. 20, which shows a shunt generator delivering power to a resistor load over wires which have negligible resistance. The voltmeter measures the potential difference at the load and also measures the potential difference at the generator terminals if the very small drop in the ammeter be neglected.

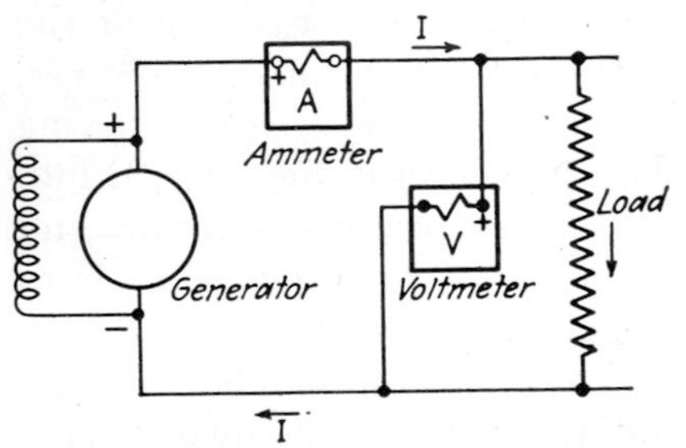

FIG. 20. Correct method of connecting voltmeter and ammeter.

Current is ordinarily measured with an ammeter. As current is the *quantity of electricity* per second passing in the wire, the ammeter must be connected so that only the current to be measured, or a known fraction of it, goes through it. This is accomplished by opening one of the wires of the circuit and inserting the ammeter, just as a water meter is inserted in a pipe when it is desired to measure the flow of water in the pipe.

When the ammeter is so connected, the current in the wire is measured by the ammeter. This is illustrated in Fig. 20, in which the ammeter in series with the generator measures the current which the generator delivers. The ammeter also measures the combined current to the load and voltmeter, but the voltmeter current is usually so small that the ammeter measures essentially the current to the load.

An ammeter should never be connected across the line.

The resistance of an ammeter is very low. Even if connected across a low voltage, it will ordinarily take a current several times its rating, which results in a bent pointer and may result in the instrument's burning out. For example, the resistance of a 10-amp instrument is approximately 0.005 ohm, and if connected across a voltage as low as 10 volts, it will take 10/0.005, or 2,000, amp (Ohm's law, Sec. 34). Such a large current would ruin the ammeter.

34. Ohm's Law.[1] Ohm's law states that, for a steady current, the current in a circuit is *directly* proportional to the *total* emf acting in the circuit and is *inversely* proportional to the total resistance of the circuit.

The law may be expressed by the following equation if the current I is in *amperes*, the emf E is in *volts*, and the resistance R is in *ohms:*

$$I = \frac{E}{R} \quad \text{amp.} \tag{20}$$

That is, the current in amperes in a circuit is equal to the total emf of the circuit in volts divided by the total resistance of the circuit in ohms. Potential difference may be represented by either the letter V or E, V usually signifying terminal voltage and E emf or induced voltage.

Example. The resistance of the field winding of a shunt motor is 30 ohms. Determine current in the winding when it is connected across 115 volts supply.

$$I = \frac{E}{R} = \frac{115}{30} = 3.83 \text{ amp.} \quad \textit{Ans.}$$

Example. Figure 21 shows a simple series circuit in which are two batteries, whose emfs are 6 volts and 10 volts, and two resistors, of 2 ohms and 6 ohms. Neglecting the resistance of the batteries, determine current in circuit.

[1] Ohm's law is defined in the ASA C42 Definitions of Electrical Terms (1941 edition) as follows:

"Ohm's law states that the current in an electric circuit is directly proportional to the electromotive force in the circuit.

"Ohm's law does not apply to all circuits. It is applicable to all metallic circuits and to many circuits containing an electrolytic resistance.

"Ohm's law was first enunciated for a circuit in which there is a constant electromotive force and an unvarying current. It is applicable to varying currents if account is taken of the induced electromotive force resulting from the self-inductance of the circuit and of the distribution of current in the cross-section of the circuit (05.40.025)."

It is clear from Fig. 21 that the 6-volt battery tends to send current in a clockwise direction, and the 10-volt battery tends to send current in a counterclockwise direction. Hence they are in *opposition*, and the net emf is 10 − 6, or 4, volts acting in the counterclockwise direction. The total resistance is 2 + 6, or 8, ohms. Hence, by Ohm's law,

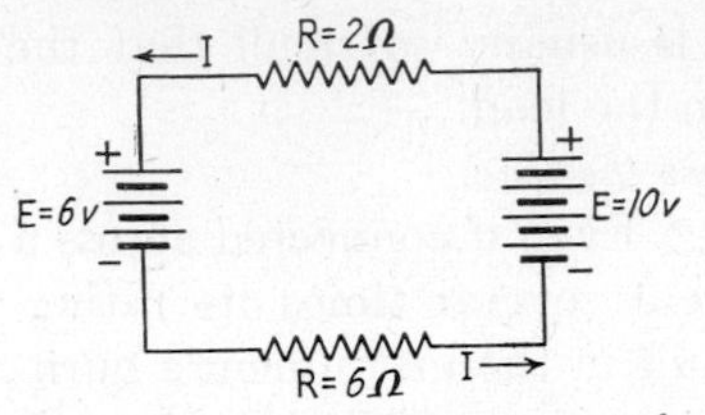

FIG. 21. Current with two emfs and two resistors.*

$$I = \frac{10 - 6}{2 + 6} = \frac{4}{8} = 0.5 \text{ amp in the counterclockwise direction.} \quad \textit{Ans.}$$

By transformation, Eq. (20) becomes

$$E = IR \quad \text{volts.} \qquad (21)$$

That is, the voltage across any part of a circuit is equal to the product of the current in amperes and the resistance in ohms, *provided that the current is steady and that there are no sources of emf within this part of the circuit.*

Example. The resistance of the field winding of a shunt generator is 48 ohms, and the resistance of its rheostat is 22 ohms, Fig. 22. If the field current is 3.2 amp, determine voltage across field-winding terminals, voltage across rheostat, and voltage across generator terminals.

$$E_1 = IR_1 = 3.2 \cdot 22 = 70.4 \text{ volts across rheostat.}$$
$$E_2 = IR_2 = 3.2 \cdot 48 = 153.6 \text{ volts across field winding.}$$
$$\text{Total } \overline{224.0} \text{ volts at generator terminals.}$$

Also,

$$E = I(R_1 + R_2) = 3.2(22 + 48) = 224.0 \text{ volts.} \quad \textit{Ans. (check).}$$

Again, if Eq. (20) be solved for the resistance, the result is

$$R = \frac{E}{I} \quad \text{ohms.} \qquad (22)$$

That is, the resistance of a circuit, or any part of a circuit, is equal to the voltage divided by the current, provided that the current is steady and that there are no sources of emf within the part of the circuit considered. This formula is very useful in making resistance measurements (see Sec. 123, p. 155).

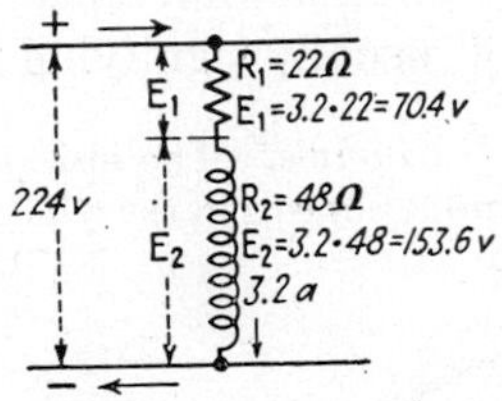

FIG. 22. Voltage drops across generator field and its rheostat.

Example. The voltage across the terminals of a generator field is 220 volts, and the field current is 4 amp. Determine the resistance of the field circuit.

$$R = \frac{E}{I} = \frac{220}{4} = 55 \text{ ohms.} \quad \textit{Ans.}$$

35. Series Circuit. As is stated in Sec. 10 (p. 10), if several resistors are connected in series, the total resistance is the sum of their individual

* The Greek letter Ω (capital omega) is used in electrical engineering as the symbol for ohms (see Appendix K, p. 595).

resistances. This may be proved as follows: In Fig. 23, the total voltage

$$E = E_1 + E_2 + E_3$$
$$= IR_1 + IR_2 + IR_3.$$

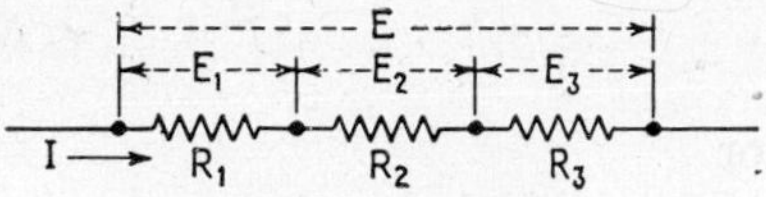

FIG. 23. Resistors in series.

But

$$E = IR$$

where R is the equivalent of the three resistors in series.

Hence

$$IR = IR_1 + IR_2 + IR_3,$$

and

$$R = R_1 + R_2 + R_3. \tag{23}$$

The current

$$I = \frac{E}{R} = \frac{E}{R_1 + R_2 + R_3}. \tag{24}$$

Example. A 50-ohm relay is connected in series with a resistor tube of 30 ohms resistance and with a small pilot lamp having a resistance of 5 ohms. The operating voltage is 115 volts. Determine the current in this relay circuit.

$$I = \frac{115}{50 + 30 + 5} = \frac{115}{85} = 1.35 \text{ amp.} \quad \textit{Ans.}$$

36. Parallel Circuit. In Sec. 11 (p. 11), the relation of total resistance to the component resistances in a parallel circuit is proved by transforming conductances into resistances. This relation may be proved by Ohm's law as follows: Consider the circuit of Fig. 24, consisting of resistors of R_1, R_2, R_3 ohms in parallel across the voltage E. Let I_1 = the current in resistor R_1, I_2 = the current in R_2, and I_3 = the current in R_3.

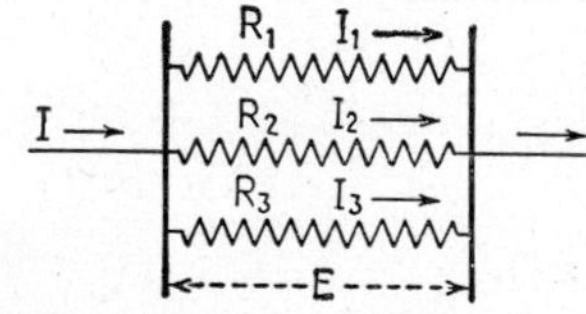

FIG. 24. Parallel circuit.

Then, from (20),

$$I_1 = \frac{E}{R_1}; \qquad I_2 = \frac{E}{R_2}; \qquad I_3 = \frac{E}{R_3}.$$

Adding,

$$I_1 + I_2 + I_3 = \frac{E}{R_1} + \frac{E}{R_2} + \frac{E}{R_3} = E\left(\frac{1}{R_1} + \frac{1}{R_2} + \frac{1}{R_3}\right).$$

The total current is $I = I_1 + I_2 + I_3$.

Let the equivalent resistance be R, so that

$$I = \frac{E}{R}.$$

Substituting I for $I_1 + I_2 + I_3$,

$$I = \frac{E}{R} = E\left(\frac{1}{R_1} + \frac{1}{R_2} + \frac{1}{R_3}\right),$$

or

$$\frac{1}{R} = \frac{1}{R_1} + \frac{1}{R_2} + \frac{1}{R_3}. \qquad (25)$$

That is, *the reciprocal of the equivalent resistance of a parallel circuit is the sum of the reciprocals of the individual resistances.*

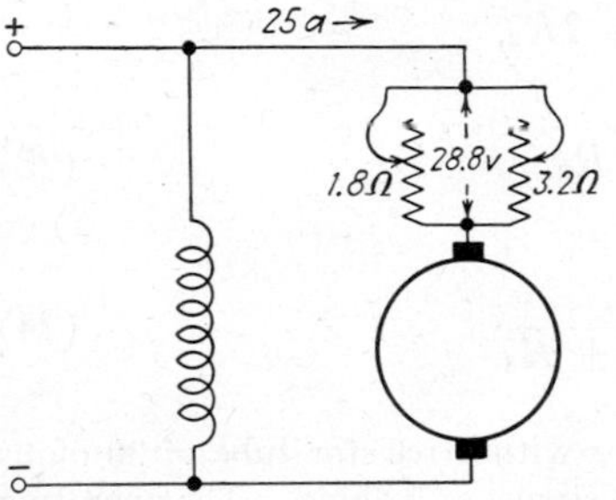

If but two resistances are involved,

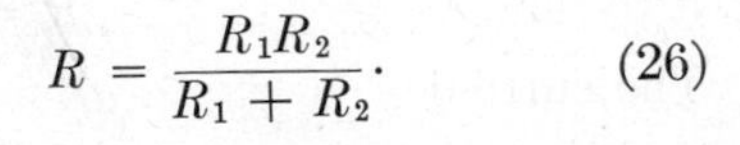

$$R = \frac{R_1R_2}{R_1 + R_2}. \qquad (26)$$

(See p. 12.)

FIG. 25. Parallel-connected rheostats in series with motor armature.

Example. Two rheostats, connected in parallel, are in series with the armature of an electric motor, Fig. 25. One rheostat is adjusted until its resistance is 3.2 ohms and the other until its resistance is 1.8 ohms. Determine: (*a*) resistance in series with armature; (*b*) voltage drop across two rheostats when armature current is 25 amp.

(*a*) Using (25),

$$\frac{1}{R} = \frac{1}{3.2} + \frac{1}{1.8} = 0.312 + 0.556 = 0.868 \text{ mho}.$$

$$R = \frac{1}{0.868} = 1.152 \text{ ohms. } \textit{Ans.}$$

Using (26),

$$R = \frac{3.2 \cdot 1.8}{3.2 + 1.8} = 1.152 \text{ ohms } (\textit{check}).$$

(*b*)

$$E = 25 \cdot 1.152 = 28.8 \text{ volts. } \textit{Ans.}$$

(The voltage drop must be the same in each rheostat, since they are in parallel.)

Example. Determine the total current in a circuit consisting of four resistors of 4, 6, 8, 10 ohms, connected in parallel across a 10-volt source.

$$\frac{1}{R} = \frac{1}{4} + \frac{1}{6} + \frac{1}{8} + \frac{1}{10} = 0.25 + 0.167 + 0.125 + 0.10 = 0.642 \text{ mho}.$$

$$R = \frac{1}{0.642} = 1.56 \text{ ohms}.$$

$$I = \frac{10}{1.56} = 6.42 \text{ amp. } \textit{Ans.}$$

The example may also be solved as follows [see Eq. (10), p. 12)]:

$$R = \frac{4 \cdot 6 \cdot 8 \cdot 10}{(4 \cdot 6 \cdot 8) + (6 \cdot 8 \cdot 10) + (8 \cdot 10 \cdot 4) + (10 \cdot 4 \cdot 6)} = 1.56 \text{ ohms } (\textit{check})$$

37. Division of Current in Parallel Circuit. In Fig. 26, two resistors R_1 and R_2 are connected in parallel across the voltage E. Then,

$$I_1 = \frac{E}{R_1} \quad \text{amp},$$

$$I_2 = \frac{E}{R_2} \quad \text{amp},$$

$$\frac{I_1}{I_2} = \frac{E/R_1}{E/R_2} = \frac{R_2}{R_1}. \qquad (27)$$

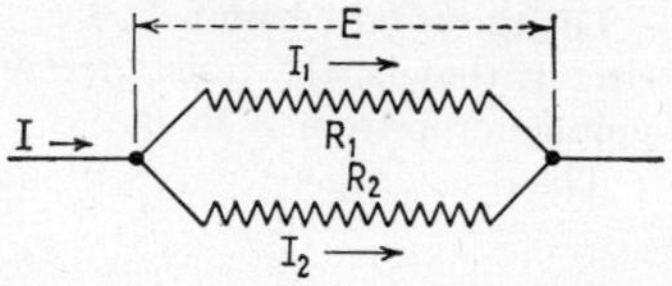

FIG. 26. Division of current in a 2-branch parallel circuit.

That is, *in a parallel circuit of two branches, the currents are inversely as the resistances.* (This relation does not hold when there is a source of emf in either branch. For example, *it does not give the division of current through the field and armature of a shunt motor when the motor is running, since the motor armature generates an emf.*)

Example. A current of 16 amp divides between two branches in parallel, one branch having a resistance of 8 ohms, the other branch having a resistance of 12 ohms. Determine current in each branch.

If I_1 be the current in the 8-ohm branch and I_2 the current in the 12-ohm branch,

$$\frac{I_1}{I_2} = \frac{12}{8} \quad [(27)]. \qquad \text{(I)}$$

Also

$$I_1 + I_2 = 16, \qquad \text{(II)}$$

$$I_1 = I_2\, {}^{12}\!/_{8} = I_2\, {}^{3}\!/_{2} \quad [\text{from (I)}].$$

Substituting in (II),

$$I_2\, {}^{3}\!/_{2} + I_2 = 16,$$

$$\frac{5I_2}{2} = 16; \quad I_2 = 6.4 \text{ amp.} \quad \textit{Ans.}$$

$$I_1 = 6.4\, {}^{3}\!/_{2} = 9.6 \text{ amp.} \quad \textit{Ans.}$$

The voltage drops

$$9.6 \cdot 8 = 76.8 \text{ volts.}$$

$$6.4 \cdot 12 = 76.8 \text{ volts } (\textit{check}).$$

From (27) the total current

$$I = I_1 + I_2 = \frac{E}{R_1} + \frac{E}{R_2}; \qquad E = I_1R_1.$$

$$I = \frac{I_1R_1}{R_1} + \frac{I_1R_1}{R_2} = I_1R_1\left(\frac{1}{R_1} + \frac{1}{R_2}\right) = I_1R_1\frac{R_1 + R_2}{R_1R_2}.$$

$$I_1 = I\frac{R_2}{R_1 + R_2}. \qquad (28)$$

Similarly,

$$I_2 = I\frac{R_1}{R_1 + R_2}. \qquad (29)$$

Applying (28) and (29) to the foregoing example,

$$I_1 = 16\frac{12}{12 + 8} = 9.6 \text{ amp.} \quad \textit{Ans.}$$

$$I_2 = 16\frac{8}{8 + 12} = 6.4 \text{ amp.} \quad \textit{Ans.}$$

If the circuit consists of three branches in parallel, Fig. 27, with resistors of R_1, R_2, R_3 ohms, the currents may be found as follows:

Let the total current $I = I_1 + I_2 + I_3$; let R be the equivalent resistance of the circuit, that is, the resistance measured between points A and B, and let E be the voltage drop from A to B.

Then

$$E = IR;$$

and also

$$E = I_1R_1.$$

Hence,

$$IR = I_1R_1,$$

and

$$\frac{I}{I_1} = \frac{R_1}{R}. \tag{I}$$

Similarly,

$$\frac{I}{I_2} = \frac{R_2}{R}, \tag{II}$$

and

$$\frac{I}{I_3} = \frac{R_3}{R}. \tag{III}$$

Combining (I) with (10) (p. 12) gives (30). Likewise combining (II) and (III) with (10) gives (31) and (32).

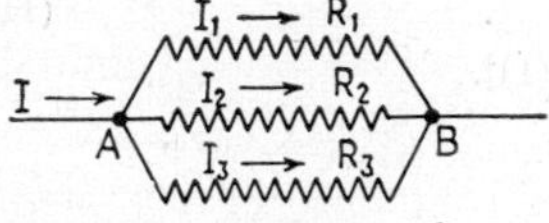

FIG. 27. Division of current in a 3-branch parallel circuit.

$$I_1 = I\left(\frac{R_2R_3}{R_1R_2 + R_2R_3 + R_3R_1}\right), \tag{30}$$

$$I_2 = I\left(\frac{R_3R_1}{R_1R_2 + R_2R_3 + R_3R_1}\right), \tag{31}$$

$$I_3 = I\left(\frac{R_1R_2}{R_1R_2 + R_2R_3 + R_3R_1}\right). \tag{32}$$

(Note the cyclic order of the subscripts.)

Example. A current of 25 amp is supplied to a circuit consisting of three resistors 2.5, 4.0, 6.0 ohms, in parallel. Determine the division of current among the resistors.

Let R be the equivalent resistance of the combination. From Eq. (25) (p. 40)

$$\frac{1}{R} = \frac{1}{2.5} + \frac{1}{4.0} + \frac{1}{6.0} = 0.817 \text{ mho.}$$
$$R = 1.225 \text{ ohms.}$$

From (I),

$$\frac{I}{I_1} = \frac{R_1}{R}, \qquad \frac{25}{I_1} = \frac{2.5}{1.225};$$

$$I_1 = 12.25 \text{ amp.} \quad \textit{Ans.}$$

Similarly,

$$I_2 = \frac{25 \cdot 1.225}{4.0} = 7.65 \text{ amp.} \quad \textit{Ans.}$$

and

$$I_3 = \frac{25 \cdot 1.225}{6.0} = \underline{5.10} \text{ amp.} \quad \textit{Ans.}$$

$$\text{Total current} = 25.00 \text{ amp } (\textit{check}).$$

The example may be solved also by means of (30), (31), and (32):

$$I_1 = 25 \frac{4.0 \cdot 6.0}{(2.5 \cdot 4.0) + (4.0 \cdot 6.0) + (6.0 \cdot 2.5)}$$

$$= 25 \frac{24}{10 + 24 + 15} = 12.25 \text{ amp.}$$

$$I_2 = 25 \frac{6.0 \cdot 2.5}{49} = 7.65 \text{ amp.}$$

$$I_3 = 25 \frac{2.5 \cdot 4.0}{49} = 5.10 \text{ amp.}$$

$$\text{Total} = 25.00 \text{ amp } (check).$$

38. Series-parallel Circuit. A circuit may consist of groups of parallel resistors in series with other resistors as shown in Fig. 28. When such is the case, each group of parallel resistors is first replaced by its equivalent single resistor and the entire circuit is then treated as a series circuit.

Example. In the series-parallel circuit shown in Fig. 28 determine: (*a*) equivalent resistance of each parallel group of resistors; (*b*) total resistance; (*c*) current; (*d*) voltages E_1, E_2, E_3; (*e*) current in each resistor.

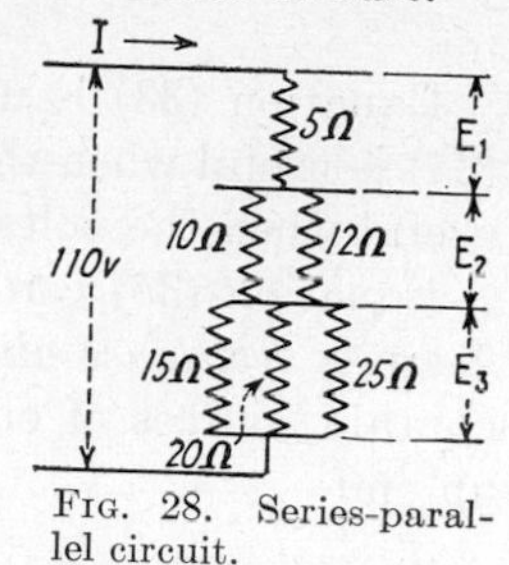

FIG. 28. Series-parallel circuit.

(*a*) Replace the 10- and 12-ohm resistors by a resistor of R_1 ohms. Then

$$\frac{1}{R_1} = \frac{1}{10} + \frac{1}{12} = 0.10 + 0.0833 = 0.1833 \text{ mho.}$$

$$R_1 = 5.45 \text{ ohms. } Ans.$$

Replace the group of three resistors by a resistor of R_2 ohms. Then

$$\frac{1}{R_2} = \frac{1}{15} + \frac{1}{20} + \frac{1}{25} = 0.0667 + 0.050 + 0.040 = 0.1567 \text{ mho,}$$

$$R_2 = \frac{1}{0.1567} = 6.38 \text{ ohms. } Ans.$$

(*b*) $R = 5 + 5.45 + 6.38 = 16.83$ ohms. *Ans.*

(*c*) $I = \frac{110}{16.83} = 6.54$ amp. *Ans.*

(*d*)
$$E_1 = 6.54 \cdot 5.0 = 32.7 \text{ volts.}$$
$$E_2 = 6.54 \cdot 5.45 = 35.6 \text{ volts.}$$
$$E_3 = 6.54 \cdot 6.38 = 41.7 \text{ volts. } Ans.$$
$$\text{Total} = 110.0 \text{ volts } (check).$$

(*e*) Current in 10 ohms $= \frac{35.6}{10} = 3.56$ amp.

Current in 12 ohms $= \frac{35.6}{12} = 2.97$ amp.

Total = 6.53 amp (*check*).

Current in 15 ohms $= \frac{41.7}{15} = 2.78$ amp.

Current in 20 ohms $= \frac{41.7}{20} = 2.09$ amp.

Current in 25 ohms $= \frac{41.7}{25} = 1.67$ amp. *Ans.*

Total = 6.54 amp (*check*).

39. Electrical Power. The practical or mks unit of electrical power, the watt, is defined in Sec. 29 (p. 32). Since one watt is defined as the power expended when one ampere flows between two points having a potential difference of one volt, the power must be given by

$$P = EI \quad \text{watts.} \tag{33}$$

Since by Eq. (21) (p. 38) $E = IR$ in a circuit containing resistance only, (33) may be written

$$P = (IR)I = I^2R. \tag{34}$$

Substituting for I its value $I = E/R$ in (33),

$$P = \frac{E^2}{R}. \tag{35}$$

Equation (33) is useful when the volts and the amperes are known; (34) is useful when the current and the resistance are known; and (35) is useful when the voltage and the resistance are known.

Equation (35) can be used for only those parts of a circuit in which there is *resistance alone.* It cannot be used for parts of circuits which contain sources of emf, such as batteries, or armatures which generate an emf.

Example. The resistance of a 150-scale voltmeter is 12,000 ohms. Determine the power consumed by this voltmeter when it is connected across a 125-volt circuit.

Since the voltage and the resistance are known (35) is most convenient.

$$P = \frac{(125)^2}{12{,}000} = 1.30 \text{ watts.} \quad \textit{Ans.}$$

This may be checked by (33).

$$I = \frac{125}{12{,}000} = 0.0104 \text{ amp.}$$

$$P = 125 \cdot 0.0104 = 1.30 \text{ watts } (\textit{check}).$$

Example. A field rheostat is adjusted until the field current is 4.7 amp. The resistance of the rheostat is found to be 12.8 ohms. Determine the power lost as heat in the rheostat.

Since the current and the resistance are given, (34) is most convenient.

$$P = (4.7)^2 \cdot 12.8 = 283 \text{ watts.} \quad \textit{Ans.}$$

Since conductance $G = 1/R$, it follows from (35) that power

$$P = \frac{E^2}{R} = E^2G. \tag{36}$$

The watt is frequently too small a unit, particularly when large amounts of power are being considered, so that the *kilowatt* (equal to 1,000 watts) is then used. The amount of power on some large systems has become so great that the *megawatt* (1,000,000 watts) is often found to be a convenient unit.

It is often necessary to transform from mechanical horsepower to electrical power and conversely, and a knowledge of the relation of the two is therefore useful.

$$746 \text{ watts} = 1 \text{ hp}, \tag{37}$$
$$0.746 \text{ kw} = 1 \text{ hp}, \tag{38}$$

and

$$1 \text{ hp} = \tfrac{3}{4} \text{ kw very nearly}, \tag{39}$$
$$1 \text{ kw} = \tfrac{4}{3} \text{ hp very nearly}. \tag{40}$$

(Also see Appendix A, p. 579.)

Example. An electric motor takes 28 amp at 550 volts and has an efficiency of 89 per cent. Determine the horsepower which it delivers.

$$\text{Input} = 28 \cdot 550 = 15{,}400 \text{ watts.}$$
$$\text{Output} = 15{,}400 \cdot 0.89 = 13{,}700 \text{ watts.}$$
$$\frac{13{,}700}{746} = 18.37 \text{ hp at the pulley.} \quad \textit{Ans.}$$

40. Maximum Power. Figure 29 shows a fixed resistor of R' ohms in series with a variable resistor of R ohms, connected across a constant voltage E. It is required to determine the value of R for which the power P in R will be a maximum. It is clear that the power in R is zero when R is zero and also when R is infinite. Hence there must be at least one finite value of R for which the power P is a maximum. This may be determined as follows:

$$I = \frac{E}{R + R'}.$$

$$P = I^2R = \frac{E^2}{(R + R')^2} R = E^2 \frac{R}{(R + R')^2}.$$

$$\frac{dP}{dR} = E^2 \frac{(R + R')^2 - R \cdot 2(R + R')}{(R + R')^4} = 0.$$

$$R^2 + 2RR' + R'^2 - 2R^2 - 2RR' = 0.$$
$$R = R'.$$

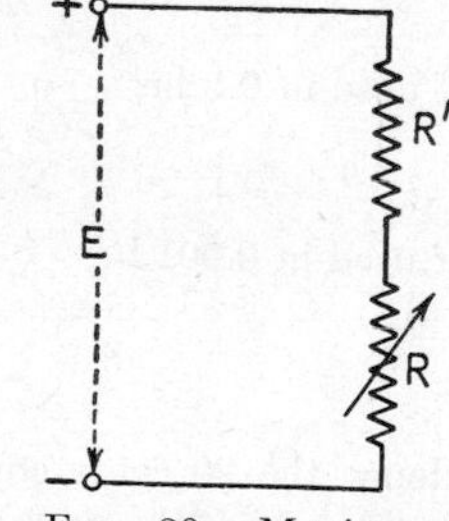

FIG. 29. Maximum power in resistor.

That is, for maximum power in the variable resistor R, its resistance must be equal to that of the fixed resistor R'.

41. Electrical Energy. Power is the *rate of doing work*, or the *rate of expenditure of energy*. Therefore electrical energy is equal to the product of electrical power (Sec. 39) and time. The practical or mks unit of energy, the *joule*, is defined in Sec. 29 (p. 32) and is equal to one watt-second. The joule is also equal to 10^7 (10,000,000) ergs where the erg is the cgs unit of energy. The erg is equal to a *dyne-centimeter*, which is the work done when a force of 1 dyne is exerted through a distance of 1 cm in the direction of the force.

From Sec. 29,

$$W = EIt \quad \text{wsec or joules,} \tag{41}$$

where t is in seconds, E is in volts, and I is in amperes.

Even the watt-second is ordinarily too small a unit for commercial purposes; hence the larger unit, the *kilowatthour* (kwhr), is commonly used. 1 kwhr = 1,000 · 60 · 60 = 3,600,000 joules or wsec.

The distinction between power and energy (or work) should be kept clearly in mind. Power is *rate* of doing work, just as velocity is rate of motion. On the other hand, energy is the total work done and is equal to the power multiplied by the time during which the power acts, just as distance covered is the velocity or rate of motion multiplied by the time. To speak of a train traveling at a rate of 40 mph gives no information as to the total distance which the train travels. Likewise, to speak of 50 kw does not state the amount of energy that is involved. The statement "electricity is sold for so many cents per kilowatt" is incorrect. The correct expression is "electrical *energy* is sold for so many cents per kilowatt*hour*." To illustrate:

Example. If energy is sold for 5 cents per kwhr, how many kilowatts may be purchased for 20 cents? This question as it stands cannot be answered, since the *time* is not given. If, however, it is assumed that the power is to be used for 1 hr,

$$\frac{20 \text{ cents}}{5 \text{ cents/kwhr}} = 4 \text{ kwhr available.}$$

$$\frac{4 \text{ kwhr}}{1 \text{ hr}} = 4 \text{ kw is available.} \quad \textit{Ans.}$$

If used in 0.5 hr,

$$\frac{4 \text{ kwhr}}{0.5 \text{ hr}} = 8 \text{ kw.} \quad \textit{Ans.}$$

If used in 0.001 hr,

$$\frac{4 \text{ kwhr}}{0.001 \text{ hr}} = 4{,}000 \text{ kw.} \quad \textit{Ans.}$$

Hence the 20 cents could purchase *any number of kilowatts*, depending on the time during which the power is supplied.

In a similar way, horsepower is *rate of doing work* and is equivalent to 33,000 ft-lb *per min* and *not* to 33,000 ft-lb. A motor developing ⅛ hp could do 33,000 ft-lb of work if allowed 8 min in which to do it. In speaking of *work* in connection with horsepower, the *horsepower-hour* (hp-hr) is the unit ordinarily used.

Example. An electric motor develops 2 hp for 5 hr. Determine output in (*a*) watt-seconds; (*b*) kilowatthours.

(*a*)

$$2 \cdot 5 = 10 \text{ hp-hr.}$$

$$10 \text{ hp-hr} \cdot 746 = 7{,}460 \text{ whr.}$$

$$7{,}460 \cdot 3{,}600 = 2.69 \cdot 10^7 \text{ wsec.} \quad \textit{Ans.}$$

(b) Since 1 kw is equal to 1,000 watts, from (a),

$$\text{Kwhr} = \frac{7,460}{1,000} = 7.46. \quad \textit{Ans.}$$

42. Heat and Energy. It is well known that heat energy may be converted into mechanical and into electrical energy and, conversely, that electrical and mechanical energy may be converted into heat energy. The complete cycle of energy transformations is well illustrated by a steam power plant. The energy is brought to the plant in the coal as *chemical energy*. The constituents of the coal combine with the oxygen of the air, thus converting the chemical energy into *heat energy*. A certain percentage of this heat energy is transferred to the boiler and produces steam. The expansion of the steam in the engine cylinders, or through the buckets and blades of the turbine, converts the heat energy of the steam into *mechanical energy*. This mechanical energy drives the electrical generator which converts a large proportion of the mechanical energy into *electrical energy*. A portion of this electrical energy is transformed into heat in the wires, bus bars, transformers, and the transmission system. Finally, the remainder is used to operate motors, supply lamps, propel electric cars, and some may be used for chemical processes. Ultimately all the energy appears again as heat energy or is converted into other forms of energy.

The accompanying table shows approximately what becomes of each 100 heat units existing initially in the coal in the most efficient modern

EFFICIENCY OF ENERGY CONVERSION

	Form of energy	Efficiency, per cent	Heat units converted
Coal	Chemical	....	100.0
Boiler	Heat	85	85.0
Turbine	Mechanical	34	28.9
Generator	Electrical	98	28.3
Transmission system (to point of utilization)	Electrical	85	24.1
Substation transformers	Electrical	99	23.8
Large motors (average)	Mechanical	88	21.0
Small motors (average)	Mechanical	70	16.7
Lamps	Light	3.5	0.67

steam power plants, using superheaters, condensers, and large units, and operating under the best conditions.

Figure 30 illustrates the flow of energy (expressed in terms of power) in a typical modern electrical system, from the chemical energy in the coal as it is fed to the stokers beneath the boilers to the point of utilization, which in this case is represented by motors.

Energy is delivered to the stokers in the form of coal at a rate of 94,860 Btu per sec, corresponding to 100,000 kw. The power loss and the power transferred are indicated by the flow lines at the top of the diagram.

This system is a typical high-efficiency system, and the efficiencies given are those obtained under very favorable operating conditions. For simplicity many details in the system, such as switches, step-up transformers, bus bars, have been omitted (also see Fig. 431, p. 552, and Vol. II, Fig. 374, p. 458).

It is to be noted that in the most modern steam plants operating under the most favorable conditions the steam turbine is wasteful, con-

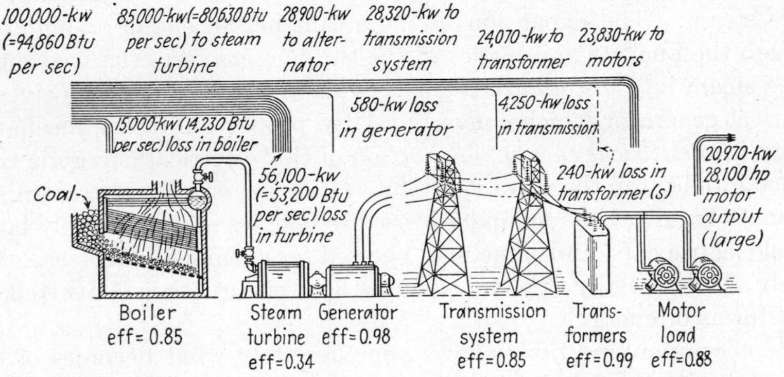

FIG. 30. Energy flow—chemical, thermal, mechanical, and electrical—in typical power system.

verting only 34 per cent of the received thermal energy into mechanical energy. The over-all efficiency of such modern systems is not high, being from coal to motors only 21.0/100, or 21.0 per cent. The efficiencies of the motors, lights, and other devices reduce the total over-all efficiency to a still lower value.

43. Thermal Units. The unit of heat energy in the English system is the Btu (British thermal unit) and is equal to the amount of heat required to raise the temperature of 1 lb of water 1°F. It is equal to 778 ft-lb (called the *mechanical equivalent of heat*).

In the cgs system, the heat unit is the gram-calorie and is equal to the amount of heat required to raise the temperature of 1 g of water 1°C.[1]

A gram-calorie is equal to 4.2 wsec or joules.

By Joule's law the heat developed in a circuit is

$$W = \frac{1}{4.2} I^2Rt = 0.24\, I^2Rt \qquad \text{cal} \tag{42}$$

where t is in seconds, I in amperes, and R in ohms.

[1] See Appendix A, p. 579.

Example. Ten horsepower is delivered by a pump in circulating 400 gal of water per minute through a certain cooling system. How many degrees Fahrenheit is the temperature of the water raised by the action of the pump?

$$10 \text{ hp} = 10 \cdot 33{,}000 = 330{,}000 \text{ ft-lb per min.}$$

$$\frac{330{,}000}{778} = 424 \text{ Btu per min.}$$

$$400 \text{ gal} = 400 \cdot 8.34 = 3{,}336 \text{ lb.}$$

$$\frac{424}{3{,}336} = 0.127°\text{F.} \quad \textit{Ans.}$$

Example. An incandescent lamp taking 0.5 amp from 110-volt mains is immersed in a small tank, containing 2,000 cu cm of water. Neglecting any loss, by how many degrees per minute is the temperature of the water raised?

$$W = 0.24 \cdot 0.5 \cdot 110 \cdot 60 = 792 \text{ g-cal per min.}$$

$$\frac{792}{2{,}000} = 0.396°\text{C.} \quad \textit{Ans.}$$

44. Potential Drop in a Feeder Supplying One Concentrated Load. Figure 31 shows a feeder (consisting of a positive and a negative wire)

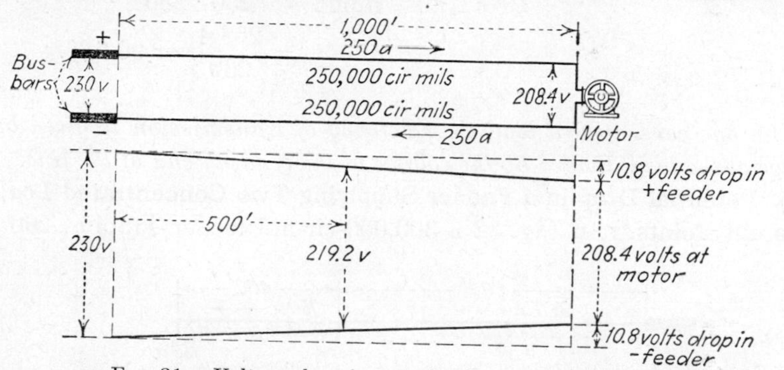

FIG. 31. Voltage drop in a feeder due to a single load.

supplying a motor load. The feeder is connected to bus bars having a constant potential difference of 230 volts. The feeder is 1,000 ft long and consists of two 250,000-cir-mil conductors. The maximum load on the feeder is 250 amp. It is required to determine the voltage at the motor terminals and the efficiency of transmission.

As is stated in Sec. 31 (p. 33), the voltage at the motor must be less than that at the bus bars because of the voltage lost in supplying the resistance drop in the feeder.

From Appendix F (p. 590), the resistance of 1,000 ft of 250,000-cir-mil cable is 0.0431 ohm. As is shown in Sec. 31, the net voltage at the receiving end of the line is less than the voltage at the sending end by the voltage loss in both the *outgoing* and the *return* wire. Therefore the drop in 2,000 ft of cable must be taken, the total resistance being 0.0862 ohm. The current is 250 amp.

By Eq. (21) (p. 38) the voltage drop in the line is

$$E' = 250 \cdot 0.0862 = 21.55 \text{ volts.}$$

Therefore, the voltage at the motor terminals is

$$230 - 21.6 = 208.4 \text{ volts.} \quad \textit{Ans.}$$

In Fig. 31 the voltage along the line is shown graphically. The voltage at the sending end of the line is 230 volts, and there is a uniform drop in each wire, this drop increasing uniformly to 10.8 volts, making a total voltage loss of 21.6 volts. The potential difference between the two wires 500 ft from the sending end will be 230 − 10.8 = 219.2 volts as shown.

$$\text{The power delivered to the motor} = 208.4 \cdot 250 \text{ watts.}$$

$$\text{The power delivered to the line} = 230 \cdot 250 \text{ watts.}$$

$$\text{The efficiency of the line} = \frac{\text{output}}{\text{input}} = \frac{208.4 \cdot 250}{230 \cdot 250}$$

$$= \frac{208.4}{230}, \text{ or } 90.6\%.$$

With one concentrated load the efficiency of transmission is given by the voltage at the load divided by the voltage at the sending end of the line.

45. Potential Drop in a Feeder Supplying Two Concentrated Loads at Different Points. In Fig. 32 a 300,000-cir-mil feeder supplies 200 amp

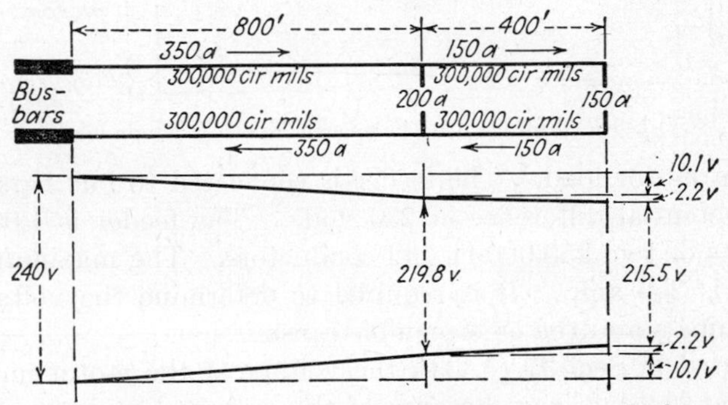

Fig. 32. Voltage drops in a feeder supplying two loads.

to a load 800 ft from the bus bars and 150 amp to a load 400 ft farther on. If the bus-bar voltage is maintained constant at 240 volts, determine the voltage at each load, the total line loss, and the efficiency of transmission.

From Appendix F (p. 590), the resistance of 1,000 ft of 300,000-cir-mil cable is 0.0360 ohm. The resistance of 800 ft = 800/1,000 · 0.0360 = 0.0288 ohm.

Voltage drop to the 200-amp load

$$E' = 350(2 \cdot 0.0288) = 20.16 \text{ volts.}$$

Voltage at 200-amp load

$$E_1 = 240 - 20.2 = 219.8 \text{ volts.} \quad \textit{Ans.}$$

Resistance of one conductor from the 200-amp load to the 150-amp load = 400/1,000 · 0.0360 = 0.0144 ohm.

Voltage drop from 200-amp load to 150-amp load

$$E'' = 150(2 \cdot 0.0144) = 4.32 \text{ volts.}$$

Voltage at 150-amp load

$$E_2 = 219.8 - 4.3 = 215.5 \text{ volts.} \quad \textit{Ans.}$$

The voltage distribution along the line is shown graphically in Fig. 32.

To determine the efficiency:

Line loss to 200-amp load

$$P_1 = (350)^2(2 \cdot 0.0288) = 7{,}060 \text{ watts} \qquad \text{[Eq. (34), p. 44].}$$

Line loss from 200-amp load to 150-amp load

$$P_2 = (150)^2(2 \cdot 0.0144) = 648 \text{ watts} \qquad \text{[Eq. (34)].}$$

Total line loss

$$P_1 + P_2 = 7{,}060 + 648 = 7{,}708 \text{ watts, or } 7.708 \text{ kw.}$$

$$\text{Eff} = \frac{\text{input} - \text{losses}}{\text{input}} = \frac{(240 \cdot 350) - 7{,}708}{240 \cdot 350} = \frac{76{,}290}{84{,}000}, \text{ or } 90.8\%.$$

46. Estimation of Feeders. It is stated in Sec. 13 (p. 13) that a circular-mil-foot of copper has a resistance of 10.37 ohms. In many cases it is sufficiently exact to assume this value as 10 ohms. Assume the current density in a feeder to be 1 amp per 1,000 cir mils, or 0.001 amp per cir mil. Call this the *normal* current density. (Bus bars and large feeders operate at a density very nearly equal to this.)

The voltage drop through a circular-mil-foot carrying 0.001 amp is

$$E = IR = 0.001 \cdot 10 = 0.01 \text{ volt.}$$

Another circular-mil-foot, carrying 0.001 amp, will also have a drop of 0.01 volt between its ends. If these be placed side by side, the drop across the two will still be 0.01 volt. With any number of wires, each having 1 cir mil cross section, a length of 1 ft, and a current of 0.001 amp, the drop between the ends of each wire will be 0.01 volt. The wires may be separated, or they may be made into a cable.

In Fig. 33(*a*) are shown four separate conductors, each of 1 cir-mil-ft and each carrying 0.001 amp. The voltage across each must be 0.01 volt. In Fig. 33(*b*) these same four conductors are grouped together, and as each carries 0.001 amp, the total current must be 0.004 amp. The voltage drop across the group is still 0.01 volt. If any number of circular-mil-foot conductors each carrying 0.001 amp are added in parallel to the group of Fig. 33(*b*), the drop remains 0.01 volt.

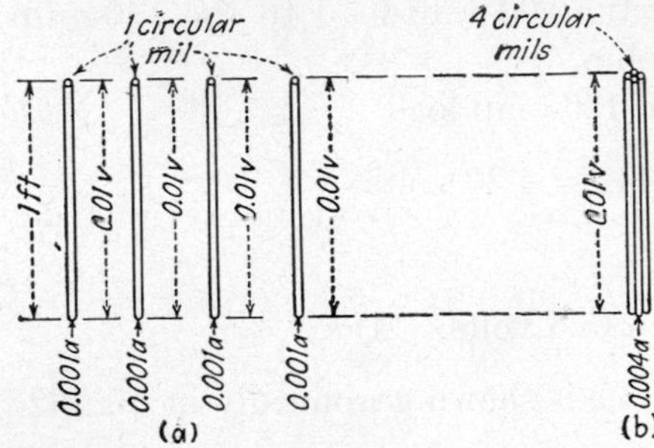

FIG. 33. Voltage drop in a circular-mil-foot.

From the foregoing the following rule may be deduced:

The voltage drop per foot of copper conductor whose resistivity is 10 *ohms (cir-mil-ft) is* 0.01 *volt if the current density is* 0.001 *amp per cir mil. Further, if the current density is other than* 0.001 *amp per cir mil, the voltage drop will be in direct proportion to the current density.* This last follows from Eq. (21) (p. 38).

Example. A motor 800 ft from the powerhouse is to take 500 amp from 230-volt bus bars. What size cable is necessary in order that the voltage drop shall not exceed 20 volts?

A cable to operate at the *normal* density must have

$$500 \cdot 1{,}000 = 500{,}000 \text{ cir mils.}$$

The total voltage drop then becomes

$$0.01 \cdot 800 \cdot 2 = 16 \text{ volts.}$$

The allowable drop is 20 volts, and so a smaller cable may be used.

$$500{,}000 \cdot \frac{16}{20} = 400{,}000 \text{ cir mils.} \quad \textit{Ans.}$$

This makes the actual current density

$$\frac{500}{400} = 1.25 \text{ amp per } 1{,}000 \text{ cir mils.}$$

The foregoing relation may also be treated from the following point of view:

The voltage drop per unit length of conductor is known as the *voltage gradient* in the conductor and is the slope of the voltage graph in Fig. 31 (p. 49). The relation between voltage gradient and current density is shown by combining Eq. (21) (p. 38) with Eq. (1) (p. 7). That is, $E = IR = I\rho L/A$, from which

$$\frac{E}{L} = \rho\left(\frac{I}{A}\right). \tag{I}$$

Hence, the voltage gradient is equal to the product of the current density and the resistivity. As has just been shown for copper conductor, the resistivity of which is 10 ohms (cir-mil-ft), the voltage drop per foot is 10 times the current density in amperes per circular mil.

The example may also be solved from the voltage-gradient point of view. The voltage gradient in the cable is 20/(2 · 800) volts per ft.

From (I),

$$\frac{20}{2 \cdot 800} = 10 \frac{500}{A}$$

where $\rho = 10$ and $I = 500$.
Hence,

$$A = 400{,}000 \text{ cir mils}$$

giving an actual current density of 500/400,000, or 0.00125, amp per cir mil.

This density is somewhat in excess of the normal density but not unduly so.

47. Power Loss in a Feeder. The method of Sec. 46 may be used to determine the power loss in a copper conductor. At the normal density,

$$P' = I^2R = (0.001)^2 10 = 0.00001 \text{ (or } 10^{-5}\text{) watt per cir-mil-foot.} \quad \text{(I)}$$

The total power loss at the *normal density* is

$$P_0 = 0.00001 \cdot \text{C.M.} \cdot l \quad \text{(II)}$$

where C.M. is the conductor cross section in circular mils and l the length in feet.

The *actual* power loss is proportional to the *square* of the ratio of the actual to the normal current density.

That is,

$$P = P_0 D^2 \quad \text{(III)}$$

where P is the actual power loss, P_0 the power loss at the normal current density, and D the actual current density in amperes per 1,000 cir mils.

Example. Determine the power loss in the example of Sec. 46.

$$P_0 = 0.00001 \cdot 400{,}000 \cdot 800 \cdot 2 = 6{,}400 \text{ watts at the normal density.}$$

The actual power loss

$$P = 6{,}400 \cdot (1.25)^2 = 10{,}000 \text{ watts} = 10 \text{ kw.} \quad \textit{Ans.}$$

Also if the voltage drop and the current are known, the power loss is readily determined. For example, in the foregoing example the voltage drop is 20 volts, and the current is 500 amp. Hence the power loss

$$P = 20 \cdot 500 = 10{,}000 \text{ watts} = 10 \text{ kw } (\textit{check}).$$

The foregoing gives an easy and rapid method of solution for many problems. It is sufficiently exact under most practical conditions.

The foregoing relations may be developed also in the following manner: From Eq. (34) (p. 44) and Eq. (2) (p. 8), the power loss in a conductor,

$$P = I^2R = I^2\rho \frac{V}{A^2} = \left(\frac{I}{A}\right)^2 \rho V \quad \text{(IV)}$$

where V is the volume.

Also from Eq. (35) (p. 44) and Eq. (2) (p. 8),

$$P = \frac{E^2}{R} = \frac{E^2}{\rho L^2/\text{V}} = \left(\frac{E}{L}\right)^2 \frac{\text{V}}{\rho}. \tag{V}$$

From (IV) and (V), the power loss per unit volume,

$$\frac{P}{\text{V}} = \rho \left(\frac{I}{A}\right)^2 = \frac{1}{\rho}\left(\frac{E}{L}\right)^2. \tag{VI}$$

If with the circular-mil-foot of copper, $\rho = 10$ and $I/A = 0.001$ (the *normal* current density), $P/\text{V} = 10 \cdot (0.001)^2 = 10^{-5}$ watt per cir-mil-ft at the normal current density, which agrees with (I).

Likewise at the normal current density the voltage drop per foot is $E/L = 0.01$ volt, $P/\text{V} = 10^{-5}$ watt (VI).

The *total* power loss is given by (IV) and (V).

Example. Repeat the foregoing example, using (IV).

$$P = \left(\frac{500}{400{,}000}\right)^2 10(1{,}600 \cdot 400{,}000) \text{ or } 10 \text{ kw.} \quad \textit{Ans.}$$

In this example the actual power loss per unit volume using (VI), for both the current and the voltage relation,

$$\frac{P}{\text{V}} = 10\left(\frac{500}{400{,}000}\right)^2 = \frac{1}{10}\left(\frac{20}{1{,}600}\right)^2 = 1.563 \cdot 10^{-5} \text{ watt per cir-mil-ft.}$$

(which is not excessive).

NOTE. Power transmission is further considered in Chap. XV, Transmission and Distribution of Power.

CHAPTER III

BATTERY ELECTROMOTIVE FORCES—KIRCHHOFF'S LAWS

48. Battery Electromotive Force and Resistance. If a voltmeter be connected across the terminals of a battery, Fig. 34, the switch S being open, the instrument will indicate an emf E. If the switch S be closed, allowing the current I to flow, the instrument will indicate a voltage V which is less than E.

The voltage E, measured when the battery delivers no current, is the *internal voltage* or the *emf* of the battery; the voltage V, measured when a current I flows, is known as the *terminal voltage* of the battery for that particular current value.

The difference between the open-circuit emf E and the voltage V, measured when current is being taken from the battery, is the *voltage drop* in the battery due to the passage of current through the battery resistance. Every cell has resistance, lying for the most part in the electrolyte, but partly in the plates and terminals. When the external circuit is closed so that current flows, voltage is required to send this current through the battery resistance, just as voltage is required to send current through an external resistance.

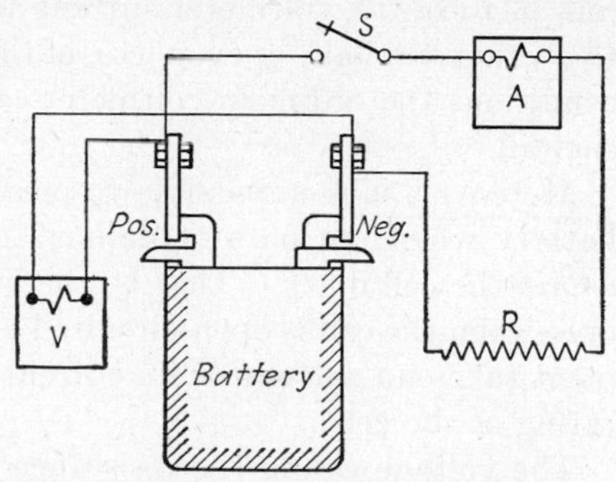

FIG. 34. Connections for measuring battery resistance.

If the voltage E, measured at the battery terminals when the circuit is open, drops to V when the circuit is closed, the voltage $V_b = E - V$ is the voltage drop through the cell due to the passage of the current I. Let the cell resistance be r. Then, by Ohm's law,

$$E - V = V_b = Ir \qquad \text{[by Eq. (21), p. 38]}$$

or

$$r = \frac{V_b}{I} = \frac{E - V}{I} \qquad \text{[by Eq. (22), p. 38].} \qquad (43)$$

That is, *the internal resistance of the battery is equal to the difference of the open-circuit and closed-circuit terminal voltages divided by the current.*

$$E = V + Ir. \qquad (44)$$

That is, *the emf of the battery is equal to the closed-circuit terminal voltage plus the resistance drop in the battery.*

$$I = \frac{E - V}{r}. \tag{45}$$

That is, *the current in any cell is equal to the voltage drop in the cell divided by the resistance of the cell.*

Example. The open-circuit voltage of a storage cell is 2.20 volts. The terminal voltage, measured when the current is 12 amp, is found to be 1.98 volts. What is the internal resistance of the cell?

The voltage drop through the cell

$$E - V = 2.20 - 1.98 = 0.22 \text{ volt.}$$

Then

$$r = \frac{0.22}{12} = 0.0183 \text{ ohm.} \quad \textit{Ans.}$$

In making a measurement of this character, it must be remembered that even under open-circuit conditions the ordinary voltmeter takes some current. If the cell capacity is small (as in the case of a Weston cell, p. 106), the voltmeter current alone may reduce the terminal voltage to a value one-half, or even less, of the open-circuit voltage. Under these conditions the ordinary voltmeter cannot be used to measure the emf of the cell.

Moreover, it is impossible to measure directly the internal emf of the battery when the battery delivers current, for the voltage drop occurs *within* the cell itself. That is, the internal emf can be measured directly only when the cell is open-circuited and when either the measuring instrument takes no current or its current is negligible in comparison with the rating of the cell.

The voltage E and the resistance r are seldom constants but are more or less dependent on the current. They are also affected by temperature, change in specific gravity of the electrolyte, polarization, etc. (see p. 99).

49. Battery Resistance and Current. As is shown in Sec. 48, the resistance within the battery tends to reduce the current. If, in Fig. 34, the switch S be closed, the cell emf E will be acting on a circuit consisting of the internal resistance of the cell r and the resistance of the external circuit R in series, and the total resistance in the circuit is their sum. Then by Ohm's law (p. 38), the current

$$I = \frac{E}{r + R}. \tag{46}$$

The power lost in the battery is

$$P = I^2 r. \tag{47}$$

If the cell is short-circuited, R becomes zero and $I = E/r$. Under these conditions all the electrical energy developed by the cell is converted into heat within the cell itself.

Example. A battery having an emf of 2.2 volts and an internal resistance of 0.03 ohm is connected to an external resistance of 0.10 ohm. Determine current and efficiency of battery under this condition of operation.

$$I = \frac{2.2}{0.03 + 0.10} = \frac{2.2}{0.13} = 16.92 \text{ amp.} \quad \textit{Ans.}$$

Power lost in battery

$$P = (16.92)^2 \cdot 0.03 = 8.59 \text{ watts.}$$

The useful power

$$P' = (16.92)^2 \cdot 0.10 = 28.63 \text{ watts.}$$

P' is equal to the total power P_0 developed by the battery minus the battery loss.

$$P_0 = 2.2 \cdot 16.92 = 37.22 \text{ watts.}$$
$$P' = 37.22 - 8.59 = 28.63 \text{ watts.}$$
$$\text{Eff} = \frac{28.63}{28.63 + 8.59}, \text{ or } 76.9\%. \quad \textit{Ans.}$$

The foregoing is a further illustration of Ohm's law, namely: *The current in a circuit is equal to the total emf acting in the circuit divided by the total resistance of the circuit* (see Sec. 34, p. 37).

50. Maximum Power Delivered by a Battery. Assume that the emf E and the internal resistance r of the battery, Fig. 34, are constant and that the external resistance R may be varied. If the battery delivers a current i, the power p, delivered to the external circuit, is $vi = i^2R$, where v is the terminal voltage of the battery. Since the terminal voltage $v = E - ir$, v will decrease as the current i increases, as was shown in Sec. 49. Hence the power p, delivered to the external circuit, is the product of two variables, one of which, v, decreases as the other, i, increases. The external power will be a maximum when the product vi is a maximum. The conditions under which this occurs may be determined as follows:

$$p = vi = (E - ir)i = Ei - i^2r. \tag{I}$$

Differentiating (I) with respect to the variable i and equating to zero,

$$\frac{dp}{di} = E - 2ir = 0; \qquad i = \frac{E}{2r} = \frac{E}{r + r}.$$

From Eq. (46) it follows that

$$R = r.$$

That is: *Maximum power is obtained when the external resistance is made equal to the internal resistance of the battery.*

Since

$$E = v + ir \qquad \text{and} \qquad v = iR = ir, \tag{48}$$

$$E = 2v; \qquad v = \frac{E}{2}. \tag{49}$$

That is: *When a battery is delivering the maximum power, the terminal voltage is equal to one-half the internal emf of the battery.*

The *total* power which the battery is developing equals the product of its internal emf E and the current I. That is, this total power

$$P_0 = EI. \tag{50}$$

The power lost within the battery is I^2r, and the power given to the external circuit is I^2R. Since $r = R$, it follows that $I^2r = I^2R$.

That is, *when a battery is delivering its maximum power, half the total power is lost within the battery itself.* Therefore the efficiency of the battery under these conditions is 50 *per cent.*

It has been shown that the *maximum current* occurs when the external resistance R is zero. Under these conditions, the terminal voltage v is zero, and the power delivered to the external circuit is zero. The total power EI, developed by the battery, is lost in heating the battery itself.

Usually, it is not economical to operate a battery so that it delivers maximum power, because of the low efficiency and the fact that the battery heats unduly. Occasionally, however, batteries are so operated for short periods. For example, automobile-starting batteries during the cranking period frequently operate at such a current that the terminal voltage approaches one-half the emf, and therefore the power that the battery delivers is nearly the maximum value.

Example. A battery has an emf of 1.2 volts and an internal resistance of 0.8 ohm. Determine: (*a*) value of current for which power delivered by cell is a maximum; (*b*) power delivered under conditions of (*a*); (*c*) external resistance; (*d*) current and power when external resistance is 1 ohm; (*e*) current and power when external resistance is 0.6 ohm; (*f*) maximum current which cell can deliver; (*g*) external power in (*f*).

(*a*) Power is a maximum when the terminal voltage $V = \frac{E}{2} = 0.60$ volt. Current $I = \frac{1.2 - 0.60}{0.8} = \frac{0.6}{0.8} = 0.75$ amp. *Ans.*

(*b*) $P = 0.60 \cdot 0.75 = 0.45$ watt. *Ans.*

(*c*) External resistance $R = \frac{V}{I} = \frac{0.60}{0.75} = 0.8$ ohm (= internal resistance). *Ans.*

(*d*) $I = \frac{1.2}{0.8 + 1.0} = \frac{1.2}{1.8} = 0.6667$ amp. *Ans.*

$V = 1.2 - 0.6667 \cdot 0.8 = 1.2 - 0.5333 = 0.6667$ volt.

$P = VI = 0.6667 \cdot 0.6667 = 0.4445$ watt. *Ans.*

(*e*) $I = \frac{1.2}{0.8 + 0.6} = \frac{1.2}{1.4} = 0.857$ amp. *Ans.*

$V = 1.2 - 0.857 \cdot 0.8 = 1.2 - 0.686 = 0.514$ volt.

$P = VI = 0.514 \cdot 0.857 = 0.440$ watt. *Ans.*

(*f*) $I = \frac{1.2}{0.8} = 1.5$ amp. *Ans.*

(*g*) Since $V = 0$,

$p = 0 \cdot 1.5 = 0$. *Ans.*

Note that the product VI is a maximum when $V = E/2$. In (*d*), V is greater than in (*a*), but I is so much less that the product VI is less. In (*e*) I is greater than in (*a*), but V is so much less that the product VI is less. (*d*) and (*e*) may be solved more readily by using $p = I^2R$, but this equation does not so clearly illustrate the fact of the product VI being a maximum.

51. Batteries Receiving Energy. If a resistance load be connected across a battery, the direction of the current is from the positive terminal of the battery through the external circuit to the battery at the negative terminal. As has been pointed out, the battery terminal voltage will be less than its open-circuit value, due to current flowing through the internal resistance of the battery. Under these conditions the battery is a source of energy and acts like a generator, in that it *delivers* energy.

If current is forced to *enter* at the positive terminal of the battery, the battery will no longer be supplying energy but will be receiving energy. This energy must be supplied from some external source, as from another

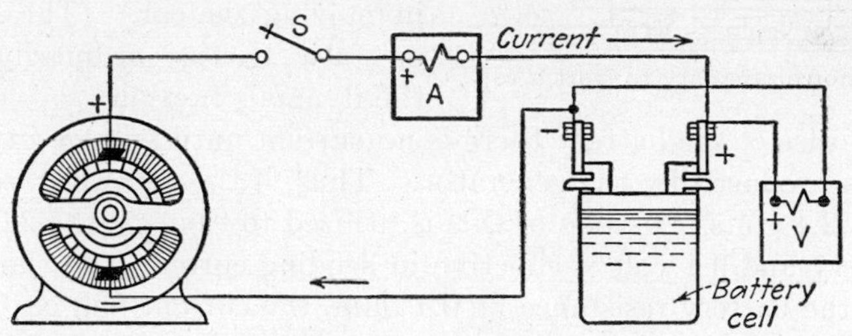

FIG. 35. Generator charging a battery.

battery or, as is more common, from an electric generator. The battery shown in Fig. 35 has an emf of 2 volts, and a voltmeter V, connected across its terminals, indicates 2 volts when there is no current, that is, when switch S is open. Another source of electrical energy, such as a d-c generator, is adjusted so that its terminal voltage is exactly 2 volts. The negative ($-$) terminal of the generator is connected to the negative ($-$) terminal of the battery. The positive ($+$) terminal of the generator is connected to the switch S, which at first is open. However, when the switch S is closed, connecting the positive ($+$) terminal of the battery to the positive ($+$) terminal of the generator as shown in the figure, no current flows. The voltmeter V still reads 2 volts, and the ammeter A still reads zero. That is, the battery neither delivers nor receives energy, and no effects are noted other than those observed when the battery is open-circuited. Under these conditions the battery is said to be "floating."

If, however, the voltage of the generator be raised slightly, the ammeter A will indicate a current whose direction is from the positive terminal of the generator *to* the positive terminal of the battery, a direction just opposite to that which the current has when the battery *supplies* energy.

The voltmeter will no longer read 2 volts but will indicate a potential difference somewhat in excess of 2 volts.

The relation in the generator-battery combination may be illustrated by a mechanical analogy. Figure 36 shows a car standing on the track. A force of 400 lb is necessary to overcome the standing friction of the car on the track. At one end of the car a force F is applied. Before the force F can move the car, its value must equal at least 400 lb. When F is exactly 400 lb, the car will not move, just as there is no current to the battery when the generator voltage is exactly equal to that of the battery. When the force F exceeds 400 lb, however, the car will move, the force effective in producing this motion being the amount by which F exceeds 400 lb. Thus, if $F = 450$ lb, 400 lb of this is utilized in overcoming the 400-lb opposing force due to friction and the 50 lb is effective in moving the car. (The standing, or static, friction ordinarily exceeds the dynamic friction.)

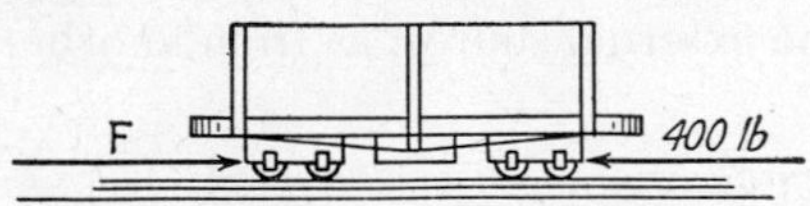

FIG. 36. Force necessary to start a car.

In the case of the battery there is no current until voltage in excess of 2 volts is produced by the generator. Thus, if the generator voltage be raised to 2.4 volts, 2.0 volts of this is utilized to "buck" the 2.0 volts of the battery and 0.4 volt is effective in sending current into the battery. Thus, if the battery resistance be 0.1 ohm, the current will be

$$I = \frac{0.4}{0.1} = 4.0 \text{ amp.}$$

This assumes that the resistance of the leads is negligible.

Therefore, if E is the emf of a battery, r its resistance, and V the terminal voltage when current *enters* its positive terminal,

$$I = \frac{V - E}{r} \tag{51}$$

and

$$E = V - Ir. \tag{52}$$

That is, the emf of the battery is *less than the terminal voltage* by the amount of the resistance drop in the battery itself. These equations should be compared with Eqs. (44) and (45) (pp. 55 and 56).

Under the foregoing conditions, the battery is *receiving* electric energy, as when a storage battery is being charged.

Example. The emf of a 3-cell storage battery is 5.80 volts, and the internal resistance is 0.072 ohm. The battery is being charged, the current being 12 amp. Determine: (*a*) terminal voltage of battery; (*b*) power loss in internal heating of battery; (*c*) energy stored per second.

(a) The terminal voltage must at least equal the counter emf before current can flow and in addition must supply the internal-resistance drop. Hence,

$$V = 5.80 + 12 \cdot 0.072 = 5.80 + 0.864 = 6.664 \text{ volts. } \textit{Ans.}$$

(b) $P = (12)^2 \cdot 0.072 = 10.37$ watts. *Ans.*

(c) The storage of energy must be represented by the direction of the current being *against* the counter emf of the battery. Hence, the energy stored per second

$$w = 5.80 \cdot 12 = 69.6 \text{ wsec or joules. } \textit{Ans.}$$

52. Battery Cells in Series. Strictly speaking, a battery consists of more than one unit or cell. However, the term battery has come also to mean a single cell, when this cell is not acting in conjunction with others.

When cells are connected in series, their emfs are added to obtain the total emf of the battery and their resistances are added to obtain the total resistance of the battery.

Thus, if several cells, having emfs E_1, E_2, E_3, E_4, etc., and resistances r_1, r_2, r_3, r_4, etc., are connected in series, the total emf of the combination is

$$E = E_1 + E_2 + E_3 + E_4 + \cdots \tag{53}$$

and the total resistance is

$$r = r_1 + r_2 + r_3 + r_4 + \cdots . \tag{54}$$

Equation (53) assumes that the cells are connected with positive to negative terminals so that their emfs are additive. If any cell be connected so that its emf opposes the others, its voltage in (53) must be preceded by a minus sign.

If an external resistance R is connected across the two terminals of these cells in series, by Ohm's law (p. 37), and also from Eq. (46), the current is

$$I = \frac{E}{r + R} = \frac{E_1 + E_2 + E_3 + E_4 + \cdots}{r_1 + r_2 + r_3 + r_4 + \cdots + R}. \tag{55}$$

Example. Four dry cells having emfs of 1.30, 1.30, 1.35, 1.40 volts and resistances of 0.3, 0.4, 0.2, 0.1 ohm, are connected in series to operate a relay having a resistance of 10 ohms. Determine current to relay.

$$I = \frac{1.30 + 1.30 + 1.35 + 1.40}{0.3 + 0.4 + 0.2 + 0.1 + 10} = \frac{5.35}{11.0} = 0.486 \text{ amp. } \textit{Ans.}$$

A battery consisting of n equal cells in series has an emf n times that of one cell but has the current capacity of one cell only.

53. Equal Batteries in Parallel. To operate satisfactorily in parallel, all the batteries should have the same emf. The operation of batteries having unequal emfs is given in Sec. 56. (Also see Sec. 57, and Sec. 67, p. 84.)

Figure 37 shows a battery of six cells in parallel, each having an emf of 2.0 volts and a resistance of 0.2 ohm. It is clear that the emf of the entire battery is no greater than the emf of any one cell. There are, however, six current paths. Therefore, for a fixed external current, the voltage drop in each cell is one-sixth that occurring if all the current were through one cell. If the internal resistance of one cell is 0.2 ohm, the resistance of the battery as a whole must be 0.2/6 = 0.033 ohm.

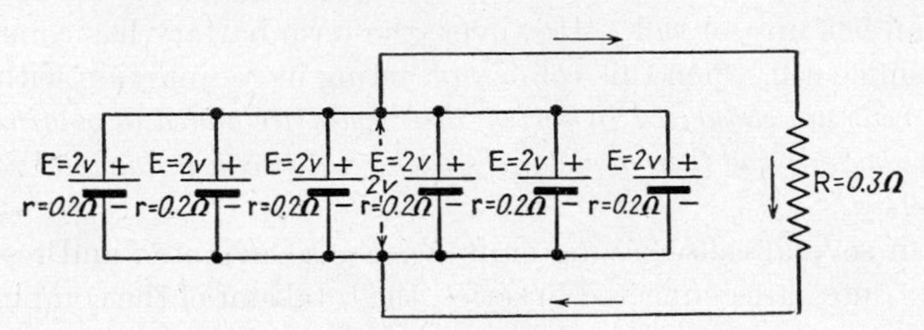

FIG. 37. Parallel connection of equal cells.

Example. In Fig. 37 the external resistance connected across the terminals of the battery is 0.3 ohm. Determine the current.

Resistance of battery = 0.2/6 = 0.033 ohm.

$$I = \frac{2.0}{0.033 + 0.3} = \frac{2.0}{0.333} = 6 \text{ amp} \qquad \text{[Eq. (46)]}. \quad \textit{Ans.}$$

If the emfs. are equal but the resistances of the cells are not equal, being r_1, r_2, r_3, r_4, etc., the battery resistance r is found by considering these resistances as in parallel [Eq. (8), p. 12].

$$\frac{1}{r} = \frac{1}{r_1} + \frac{1}{r_2} + \frac{1}{r_3} + \frac{1}{r_4} + \cdots \qquad (56)$$

Example. A battery consists of four cells connected in parallel, each having an emf of 2.0 volts and resistances of 0.30, 0.25, 0.22, 0.20 ohm. A resistance of 0.50 ohm is connected across the terminals of the battery. Determine: (*a*) current; (*b*) terminal voltage; (*c*) current in each cell.

(*a*) $\frac{1}{r} = \frac{1}{0.30} + \frac{1}{0.25} + \frac{1}{0.22} + \frac{1}{0.20} = 16.87$ mhos.

$$r = \frac{1}{16.87} = 0.0593 \text{ ohm.}$$

$$I = \frac{2.0}{0.0593 + 0.50} = \frac{2.0}{0.5593} = 3.576 \text{ amp.} \quad \textit{Ans.}$$

(*b*) Terminal voltage

$$V = IR = 3.576 \cdot 0.5 = 1.788 \text{ volts}$$
$$= 2.0 - 3.576 \cdot 0.0593 \text{ volts.} \quad \textit{Ans.}$$

(*c*) The current in each cell may be found by means of Eq. (45) (p. 56).

Solving,

$$I_1 = \frac{2.0 - 1.788}{0.30} = \frac{0.212}{0.30} = 0.707 \text{ amp.}$$

$$I_2 = \frac{2.0 - 1.788}{0.25} = \frac{0.212}{0.25} = 0.848 \text{ amp.}$$

$$I_3 = \frac{2.0 - 1.788}{0.22} = \frac{0.212}{0.22} = 0.964 \text{ amp.}$$

$$I_4 = \frac{2.0 - 1.788}{0.20} = \frac{0.212}{0.20} = 1.060 \text{ amp.}$$

$$\text{Total current} = \overline{3.579} \text{ amp} \quad \textit{Ans. (check).}$$

Since the terminal voltages and the emfs of all the cells are equal, it follows that the product of current and resistance is the same for each cell. That is,

$$0.707 \cdot 0.30 = 0.848 \cdot 0.25 = 0.964 \cdot 0.22 = 1.060 \cdot 0.20 = 0.212.$$

Cells connected in parallel *must have the same terminal voltage* since all the positive terminals are connected together and all the negative terminals are connected together. If the emfs of the cells are all equal, the total battery emf is equal to the emf of but one cell. The total battery resistance may be found by the equation for resistances in parallel. *If the emfs are all equal*, the current in each cell is inversely proportional to the resistance of the cell. The current capacity of the battery is the sum of the current capacities of the individual cells.

54. Series-parallel Grouping of Cells. Rows of series-connected cells may be connected so that the rows themselves are grouped in parallel. Figure 38 shows a row of four cells in series, and five of these rows in parallel.

If there are m equal cells in series in each row, the emf of each row must be

$$E = mE' \quad \text{volts} \quad \text{[by Eq. (53)]} \quad (57)$$

where E' is the emf of one cell.

The resistance of each row must be

$$r_1 = mr' \quad \text{ohms} \quad \text{[by Eq. (54)]} \quad (58)$$

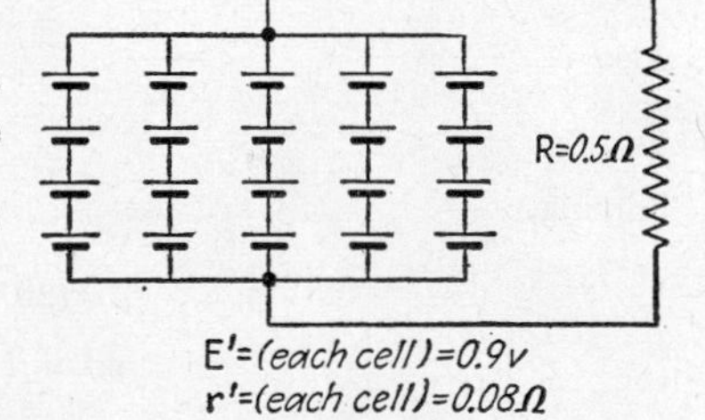

Fig. 38. Series-parallel grouping of cells.

where r' is the resistance of one cell.

Since there are n rows in parallel, the resistance of the entire system must be

$$r = \frac{r_1}{n} = \frac{m}{n} r' \quad \text{ohms.} \quad (59)$$

If an external resistance R is connected to the battery, from Eq. (46) (p. 56), the current is

$$I = \frac{mE'}{(m/n)r' + R} \quad \text{amp.} \quad (60)$$

Example. Let each of the cells of Fig. 38 have an emf of 0.9 volt and an internal resistance of 0.08 ohm. The external resistance R is 0.5 ohm. Determine the current.

$$I = \frac{4 \cdot 0.9}{4/5(0.08) + 0.5} = \frac{3.6}{0.564} = 6.38 \text{ amp.} \quad \textit{Ans.}$$

55. Grouping of Cells. A primary consideration in the grouping of cells is the required voltage. The cells must be so arranged as to give this voltage, regardless of other considerations. However, if no definite terminal voltage is required, the following considerations may govern the manner of grouping.

a. To obtain the best economy, group the cells so that the battery resistance is as low as possible. This requires the connecting in parallel of as many cells as seems justified economically.

b. To obtain the maximum current with fixed external resistance make the internal resistance $(m/n)r'$ of the battery equal to the external resistance. This is not economical, since only one half of the energy developed by the battery is available in the external circuit; the other half is lost in the cells themselves. Under these conditions the battery delivers maximum power (see Sec. 50, p. 57).

Example. In the example of Sec. 54, how should the cells be arranged to obtain the maximum current?

The total battery resistance $(m/n)0.08$ must be equal to the external resistance. That is,

$$\frac{m}{n} 0.08 = 0.5.$$

Also

$$mn = 20; \qquad n = \frac{20}{m}.$$

Solving,

$$\frac{m}{(20/m)} 0.08 = 0.5.$$

$$m^2 = \left(\frac{20}{0.08}\right) 0.5 = 125.$$

$$m = 11+. \quad \textit{Ans.}$$

The best arrangement is 10 cells in series and two rows in parallel. (Eleven cells in series would not operate satisfactorily if connected in parallel with the remaining nine cells in series.)

c. To obtain quick action for intermittent operation, as of relays or bells, group the cells in series if possible. Since such devices are highly inductive, the current is delayed in reaching the necessary operating value (see Fig. 230, p. 306). With a higher impressed emf to overcome the emf of self-induction, the rate of rise of current increases, resulting in quicker operation.

56. Batteries with Unequal Electromotive Forces and Resistances. Two batteries in parallel having unequal emfs and unequal resistances may be replaced by a single or equivalent battery having an emf equal to the common terminal voltage of the two batteries in parallel and with no external load. The internal resistance of the equivalent battery is the joint resistance of the two batteries in parallel. These relations may be proved as follows:

First consider Fig. 39(a), which shows two batteries A and B in parallel with no external load and having emfs of E_1 and E_2 volts and internal resistances of r_1 and r_2 ohms. Assume that E_1 is greater than E_2.

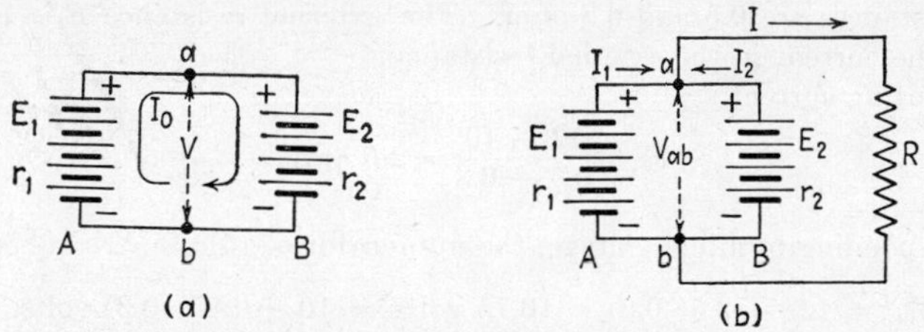

FIG. 39. Equivalent of unequal batteries in parallel.

The circulating current through the batteries is

$$I_0 = \frac{E_1 - E_2}{r_1 + r_2} \quad \text{amp.}$$

The common terminal voltage is

$$V = E_1 - I_0 r_1 = E_1 - \frac{E_1 - E_2}{r_1 + r_2} r_1 \quad \text{volts}$$

$$= E_1 \frac{r_2}{r_1 + r_2} + E_2 \frac{r_1}{r_1 + r_2} \quad \text{volts.} \qquad \text{(I)}$$

Next consider Fig. 39(b), which shows the batteries of Fig. 39(a) connected in parallel and with an external resistance R across their terminals. Let the current in battery A be I_1, that in battery B be I_2; and let the current in the resistance R be I.

The common terminal voltage

$$V_{ab} = E_1 - I_1 r_1 = E_2 - I_2 r_2 \quad \text{volts}$$

from which

$$I_1 = \frac{E_1 - E_2 + I_2 r_2}{r_1} \quad \text{amp.} \qquad \text{(II)}$$

The load current

$$I = \frac{V_{ab}}{R} = \frac{E_1 - I_1 r_1}{R} \quad \text{amp.} \qquad \text{(III)}$$

Also,

$$I = I_1 + I_2. \qquad \text{(IV)}$$

Solving (II), (III), and (IV) simultaneously gives

$$I = \frac{E_1 \dfrac{r_2}{r_1 + r_2} + E_2 \dfrac{r_1}{r_1 + r_2}}{\dfrac{r_1 r_2}{r_1 + r_2} + R} \quad \text{amp.} \qquad \text{(61)}$$

The numerator of (61) is (I), which gives the common terminal voltage of the two batteries when they are in parallel without external load. The denominator of (61) is the sum of the external resistance R and the equivalent resistance of the batteries in parallel [see Eq. (56), p. 62].

Example. In Fig. 39(*b*), the emfs of batteries A and B are 12 and 10 volts, and their internal resistances are 0.5 and 0.3 ohm. The external resistance R is 1.156 ohms. Determine the current in the external resistance.

The circulating current

$$I_0 = \frac{12 - 10}{0.5 + 0.3} = 2.5 \text{ amp.}$$

The corresponding terminal voltage, the numerator of (61),

$$V_{ab} = 12 - (2.5 \cdot 0.5) = 10.75 \text{ volts} = 10 + (2.5 \cdot 0.3) \text{ volts.}$$

The equivalent parallel resistance of the two batteries,

$$r = \frac{0.5 \cdot 0.3}{0.5 + 0.3} = 0.1875 \text{ ohm.}$$

The external current

$$I = \frac{10.75}{1.156 + 0.1875} = 8.00 \text{ amp.} \quad \textit{Ans.}$$

The same result is obtained if (61) is used directly.

57. Division of Current among Unequal Batteries in Parallel. In the method for determining the current delivered by two batteries having unequal emfs and unequal resistances (Sec. 56) the resistance of the

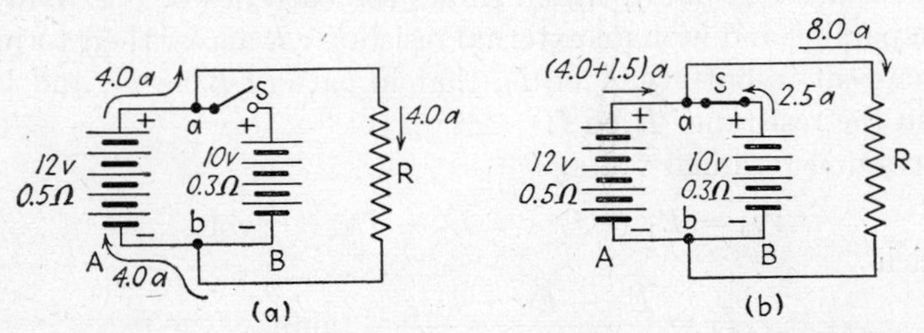

Fig. 40. Unequal batteries in parallel—floating-battery method.

external load is given. Below are given two methods by which the division of current between two such batteries may be determined when the current to the load is given rather than the resistance of the load. The division of current among such batteries is based on two principles.

For simplicity consider two batteries only, Figs. 40 and 41. First, an initial current is allowed to flow either in one battery or in both batteries, with the object of bringing the terminal voltages of the two batteries to equality. This current has no direct relation to the total load current. After the terminal voltages have been brought to equality, the two batteries behave like any two batteries having equal emfs but different internal resistances. Accordingly (Sec. 53, p. 61), they will divide all *additional* current inversely as their internal resistances. The total current delivered by each battery is then readily found by adding to the initial current of each battery the additional current, the division of which between the batteries is determined by their internal resistances.

There are two common methods. In the first method the battery with the greater emf delivers an initial current which is just sufficient to make its terminal voltage equal to the emf of the second battery, so that the second battery neither takes nor delivers current but "floats" (see p. 59). In the second method the load itself is first considered as being open-circuited and the resulting circulatory current through the two batteries, Fig. 41(*a*), constitutes the initial current which brings the two batteries

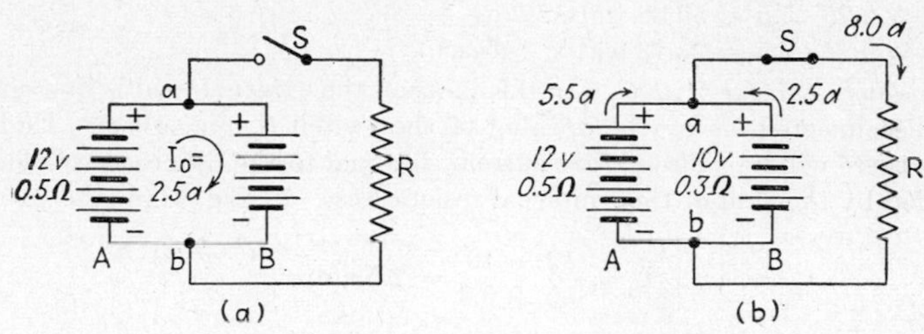

FIG. 41. Unequal batteries in parallel—circulatory-current method.

to equality of terminal voltage. (These two methods are based on the *superposition theorem* (Sec. 67, p. 84.) Such methods are very useful in the analysis and solution of more complex problems, such as determining the division of load among d-c generators, alternators, and transformers, in parallel.)

The application of the two methods to two batteries in parallel is illustrated by the following example:

Example. Two batteries A and B, Fig. 40, having emfs of 12 and 10 volts and internal resistances of 0.5 and 0.3 ohm are connected in parallel. An external resistor R connected across the batteries takes 8 amp. (This battery system is the same as that shown in Fig. 39.) Determine: (*a*) current delivered by each battery; (*b*) voltage V_{ab} across their terminals; (*c*) value of the external resistance; (*d*) total power developed by each battery; (*e*) power delivered to the load by each battery.

I. *Floating-battery Method.* (*a*) In this method the battery with the lower emf is first considered as being disconnected, as by the opening of switch S in series with the battery B, Fig. 40(*a*). In the battery A having the higher emf, a current is assumed which will just make the terminal voltage of battery A equal to the emf of B. Thus in Fig. 40(*a*) the value of this current is $(12 - 10)/0.5 = 4.0$ amp. Since the terminal voltage of battery A is now 10 volts, or is equal to the emf of battery B, switch S may be closed, Fig. 40(*b*), without causing any change in the currents of the system. For any additional current to the load, resistor R, the parallel combination behaves like two batteries of equal emfs but unequal resistances (Sec. 53, p. 61). The additional current necessary to produce a total current of 8 amp in resistance R is 4.0 amp. This current will divide inversely as the battery resistances, or the portions of the additional current delivered by batteries A and B are

$$I_A' = \frac{0.3}{0.8}4 = 1.5 \text{ amp}; \qquad I_B' = \frac{0.5}{0.8}4 = 2.5 \text{ amp.}$$

Hence the total currents of batteries A and B are

$$I_A = 4.0 + 1.5 = 5.5 \text{ amp}; \qquad I_B = 0 + 2.5 = 2.5 \text{ amp.} \quad \textit{Ans.}$$

[See Fig. 40(*b*).]

(*b*) $V_{ab} = 12 - 5.5 \cdot 0.5 = 10 - 2.5 \cdot 0.3 = 9.25$ volts. *Ans.*

(*c*) $R = \dfrac{9.25}{8} = 1.156$ ohms. *Ans.*

(Compare with example in Sec. 56, p. 64.)

(*d*) $P_A' = 12 \cdot 5.5 = 66$ watts.

$P_B' = 10 \cdot 2.5 = 25$ watts. *Ans.*

(*e*) $P_A = 9.25 \cdot 5.5 = 50.88$ watts.

$P_B = 9.25 \cdot 2.5 = 23.13$ watts. *Ans.*

II. *Circulatory-current Method.* In this method the external load is first considered as being disconnected, as by the opening of the switch S, Fig. 41(*a*). Under these conditions there will be a circulatory current I_0 equal to the difference of the battery emfs divided by the sum of their internal resistances. In Fig. 41(*a*) the current

$$I_0 = \frac{12 - 10}{0.5 + 0.3} = 2.5 \text{ amp.}$$

Since the emf of battery A is greater than that of battery B, the direction of the circulatory current will be clockwise, as shown. It is positive with respect to battery A and negative with respect to battery B. This current brings the terminal voltages of the two batteries to equality. Thus, $12 - 2.5 \cdot 0.5 = 10 + 2.5 \cdot 0.3 = 10.75$ volts.

After such equality of terminal voltages has been established, any additional current will divide inversely as the resistances of the two batteries as in method I and in Sec. 53 (p. 61). Since until now the load current has been considered as zero, the total load current must be divided between the batteries. Accordingly, switch S is closed, Fig. 41(*b*), and

$$I_A' = \frac{0.3}{0.8}8 = 3.0 \text{ amp}; \qquad I_B' = \frac{0.5}{0.8}8 = 5.0 \text{ amp.}$$

Since battery A already delivers +2.5 amp, its total current

$$I_A = 3.0 + 2.5 = 5.5 \text{ amp.} \quad \textit{Ans.}$$

The battery B already delivers −2.5 amp, so that its total current is

$$5.0 + (-2.5) = 2.5 \text{ amp.} \quad \textit{Ans.}$$

These values of current are the same as those obtained in method I(*a*).

The solutions of (*b*), (*c*), (*d*), and (*e*) are identical with those in method I.

58. Kirchhoff's[1] Laws. Kirchhoff's laws provide means for solving electrical networks that may not be solved readily by simple application of Ohm's law.

[1] Gustav Robert Kirchhoff (1824–1887). A German physicist, born and educated at Königsberg; became extraordinary professor of physics at Breslau in 1850 and in

1. *In any electrical network, the algebraic sum of the currents that meet at a point is zero.*

2. *In any closed electrical circuit the sum of all the emfs and all the resistance drops, taken with their proper signs, is zero.*

The first law may be expressed as follows: At any junction

$$\Sigma I = 0. \tag{62}$$

The second law may be similarly expressed. In any closed electrical circuit

$$\Sigma \text{emfs} + \Sigma IR\text{'s} = 0. \tag{63}$$

[Equation (63) is frequently written as Σemfs $= \Sigma IR$'s. Both equations have the same meaning.]

The first law is obvious. It states that the total current *leaving* a junction is equal to the total current *entering* the junction.

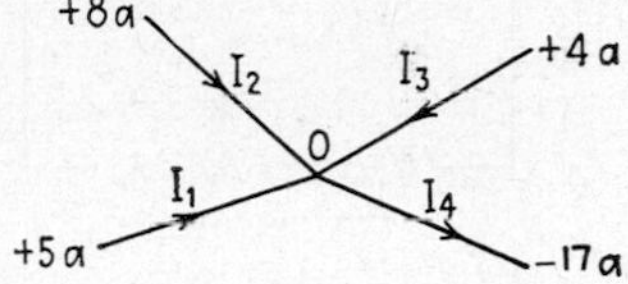

FIG. 42. Illustrating Kirchhoff's first law.

The law is illustrated by Fig. 42. Four currents, I_1, I_2, I_3, I_4, meet at the junction O. The directions of the first three currents are *toward* the junction so the currents have plus signs as they *add* to the quantity of electricity at the junction O. The direction of the current I_4 is away from the junction, hence has a minus sign, since it subtracts from the quantity at the junction O. Then,

$$I_1 + I_2 + I_3 - I_4 = O. \tag{64}$$

Assume that $I_1 = 5$ amp, $I_2 = 8$ amp, and $I_4 = 17$ amp. Then,

$$5 + 8 + I_3 - 17 = O$$

and $I_3 = +4$ amp, the plus sign indicating that the direction of the current is toward the junction.

The second law is merely another application of Ohm's law [Eq. (21), p. 38]. The basis of the law is obvious: if one starts at a certain point in a circuit, and follows continuously around the paths of the circuit until the starting point is again reached, he must be at the same potential with which he started. Therefore the sources of emf encountered in this pas-

1854 was appointed to a similar position at Heidelberg. He transferred to Berlin in 1875. His contributions to electrical science were numerous. Besides originating the laws which bear his name, he worked out the solution of many difficult problems, such as electrical conduction in thin plates and in curved sheets, the distribution of electricity in two influencing spheres, and laws of induced currents and of magnetic distribution. He also made notable contributions in radiation and in spectrum analysis.

sage must necessarily be equal to the voltage drops in the resistances, every voltage being given its proper sign.

This second law is illustrated by the following example:

Two batteries, Fig. 43, having emfs of 10 and 6 volts and internal resistances of 1 and 2 ohms, are connected in series opposing (their positive terminals connected together) and in series with an external resistor of 5 ohms. Determine the current and the voltage at each part of the circuit.

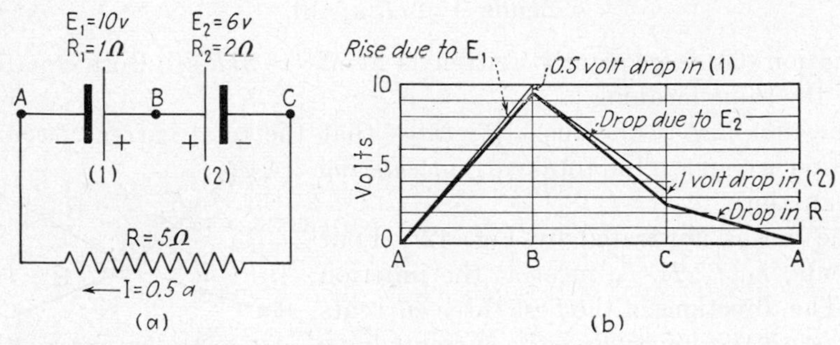

FIG. 43. Variation of potential in circuit—Kirchhoff's second law.

Since the two batteries act in opposition, the net emf of the two batteries is $10 - 6 = 4$ volts.

The current is

$$I = \frac{10 - 6}{1 + 2 + 5} = \frac{4}{8} = 0.5 \text{ amp.}$$

Consider the point A as being at zero or reference potential. In going from A to B there is a 10-volt *rise* in potential due to the emf of battery 1, but around the circuit in the direction of the current there occurs a simultaneous 0.5-volt drop of potential due to the current in the 1-ohm resistance of battery 1. Therefore the net potential at B is but 9.5 volts greater than that at A, as shown in Fig. 43(b). From B to C there is a drop of 6 volts due to going from the positive to the negative terminal of battery 2, and there is also a further drop of 1 volt due to the current of 0.5 amp in the 2-ohm resistance of battery 2. This makes the net potential at $C = 9.5 - 6 - 1 = +2.5$ volts. From C to A there is a drop in potential of 2.5 volts due to the current of 0.5 amp in the 5-ohm resistor. When point A is reached, the potential has dropped to zero.

Therefore the sum of all the emfs in the circuit, taken with their proper signs, is equal to the sum of the Ir drops. This is illustrated as follows:

Electromotive Forces		*Ir* Drops	
Battery 1 = $+10$ volts.		Battery 1 = $-0.5 \cdot 1 =$	-0.5 volt.
Battery 2 = $-\ 6$ volts.		Battery 2 = $-0.5 \cdot 2 =$	-1.0 volt.
Total = $+\ 4$ volts.		5-ohm res. = $-0.5 \cdot 5 =$	-2.5 volts.
		Total =	-4.0 volts.

$$+4 + (-4) = 0.$$

The current also may be found by applying Kirchhoff's second law directly. Starting at point A, which is assumed to be at zero or reference potential,

$$+10 - I(1) - 6 - I(2) - I(5) = 0.$$
$$8I = +4; \qquad I = +0.5 \text{ amp}.$$

Kirchhoff's second law applies whether the currents and emfs are steady or variable. However, if the currents are variable, the emfs must include any emfs of self-induction (p. 302) and any emfs that may exist across capacitors.

59. Applications of Kirchhoff's Laws. In the application of Kirchhoff's second law to specific problems, the question of algebraic signs may be troublesome and is a frequent source of error. If, however, the following rules are kept in mind, no difficulties should occur:

A rise in potential should be preceded by a + sign.

A drop in potential should be preceded by a − sign.

For example, in going *through a battery* from the − terminal to the + terminal, the potential *rises*, and so this voltage should be preceded by a + sign. On the other hand, in going from the + terminal to the − terminal, the potential *drops*, and so a − sign should precede this voltage. These voltages are all due to sources of emf. *Hence, the sign preceding them is independent of the direction of current.*

In going through a resistor in the *same* direction as the current, the voltage drops in the same manner that the level of a stream of water decreases when one goes in the direction of current flow. Hence, a voltage taken through a resistor in the direction of current, whether a battery resistance or an external resistor, should be preceded by a − sign. In going through a resistor in the direction *opposite* to the current, the voltage rises in the same manner that the level of a stream of water rises when one goes in the direction opposite to the current. Hence, a voltage taken through a resistor in a direction opposed to that of the current, whether a battery resistance or an external resistor, should be preceded by a + sign.

It should be noted that the algebraic signs preceding the voltages across resistors depend *only on the direction of current and are independent of the polarity of any sources of emf in the circuit.*

The applications of these principles are illustrated by the electric circuit shown in Fig. 44. Three batteries having emfs E_1, E_2, E_3 are connected as shown in different parts of the network of resistors R_1, R_2, R_3, R_4. The *assumed* directions for the various currents are indicated by the arrows. The battery resistances are assumed negligible as compared with the other circuit resistances.

Starting at the point a and applying Kirchhoff's second law to the path *abcda*, an equation may be written,

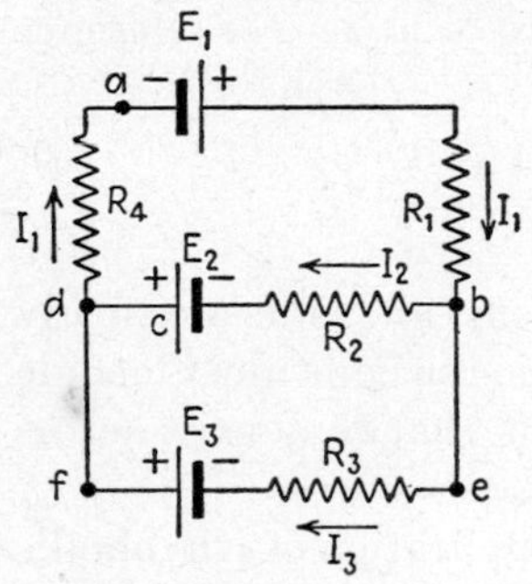

FIG. 44. Application of Kirchhoff's laws.

$$+E_1 - I_1R_1 - I_2R_2 + E_2 - I_1R_4 = 0. \quad \text{(I)}$$

Starting at f and going along the path *febcdf*,

$$-E_3 + I_3R_3 - I_2R_2 + E_2 = 0. \quad \text{(II)}$$

This gives but two equations for the determination of three unknown currents. Three equations are necessary. A third equation may be obtained by applying Kirchhoff's second law to a third path *febadf*. This equation, however, when combined with either (I) or (II) would give either (II) or (I), showing that another condition must be placed on the network so that a solution may be found. This third condition must be obtained by applying Kirchhoff's first law to some junction as b.

$$+I_1 - I_2 - I_3 = 0,$$

since the direction of I_1 is assumed *toward* the junction and I_2 and I_3 *away* from the junction.

With these three equations it is possible to determine the three currents.

In applying Kirchhoff's laws to any network, the following conditions are necessary for the solution:

Kirchhoff's first law must be applied to a sufficient number of junctions to include every unknown current at least once.

Kirchhoff's second law must be applied a sufficient number of times to include every element in the network at least once.

Example. Figure 45 shows a network identical with that shown in Fig. 44, except that numerical values are used. The battery resistances are assumed to be negligible compared with the circuit resistances.

Considering path *abcda*,

$$+4 - (I_1 0.5) - (I_2 3) + 2 - (I_1 1) = 0$$

or

$$1.5I_1 + 3I_2 = 6. \quad \text{(I)}$$

Similarly, for path *febcdf*, starting at *f*,

$$-3 + (I_3 1) - 3I_2 + 2 = 0$$

or

$$3I_2 - I_3 = -1. \qquad \text{(II)}$$

At the junction *b*,

$$+I_1 - I_2 - I_3 = 0$$

or

$$I_1 = I_2 + I_3. \qquad \text{(III)}$$

Substituting I_1 [(III)] in (I),

$$1.5(I_2 + I_3) + 3I_2 = 6,$$
$$4.5I_2 + 1.5I_3 = 6,$$

and combining with (II),

$$9I_2 - 3I_3 = -3 \qquad \text{(II)}.$$
$$9I_2 + 3I_3 = 12.$$
$$-6I_3 = -15.$$
$$I_3 = 2.5 \text{ amp.} \quad \textit{Ans.}$$

Substituting this value in (II),

$$3I_2 - 2.5 = -1.$$
$$3I_2 = 1.5.$$
$$I_2 = 0.5 \text{ amp.} \quad \textit{Ans.}$$
$$I_1 = I_2 + I_3 = 3.0 \text{ amp} \quad \text{[(III)]}. \quad \textit{Ans.}$$

As a check on the correctness of these solutions, Kirchhoff's second law may be applied to circuit *abefda*, which was not utilized in forming the network equations.

$$+4 - (3.0 \cdot 0.5) - (2.5 \cdot 1) + 3.0 - (3.0 \cdot 1) = 0 \ (\textit{check}).$$

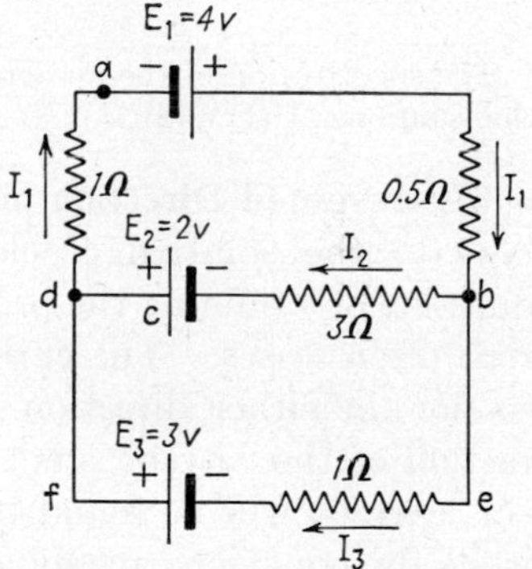

FIG. 45. Application of Kirchhoff's laws.

60. Procedure in Network Solutions. The solution of networks by means of Kirchhoff's laws is greatly facilitated, and likelihood of error is minimized, if a systematic procedure, as suggested below, is followed.

1. Make a clear diagram of the network. Letter the diagram, and mark on it every given quantity in the network.
2. Indicate the assumed direction of current in each element of the network. Then designate the currents in the different elements by I_1, I_2, I_3, etc. (The number of unknown currents may be reduced by applying Kirchhoff's first law to certain junctions, as explained in Sec. 61.)
3. The number of unknowns may be found from item 2, and the same number of *independent* equations is necessary in order to determine these unknowns. Write the equations in accordance with Kirchhoff's first and second laws. Each equation must contain some element which has not been considered in any previous equation. Verify the sign of each quantity.
4. Solve the equations algebraically for the unknowns, and verify the solutions by substituting in the equation of a circuit not already utilized.

Example. In the circuit shown in Fig. 46, determine the direction and value of the current in each of the batteries A, C, and E. The assumed directions of currents are indicated by the arrows. It will be noted that the current in battery E is the sum of I_1 and I_2 and is represented as such (see Sec. 62). Since there are two unknowns, two independent equations are necessary.

In circuit $ABCFA$, starting at A,

$$+20 - 2I_1 - 4I_1 + 8I_2 - 30 + 3I_2 - 6I_1 = 0. \qquad \text{(I)}$$

In circuit $FCBDEF$, starting at F,

$$+30 - 3I_2 - 8I_2 - 5(I_1 + I_2) + 10 - 1(I_1 + I_2) = 0. \qquad \text{(II)}$$

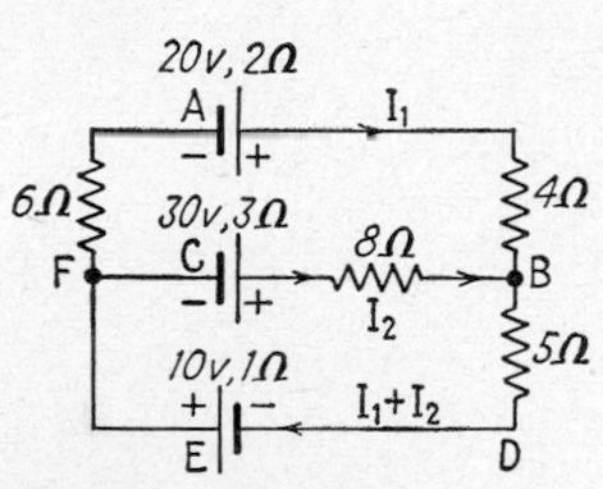

Fig. 46. Procedure in network solution.

Simplifying,

$$12I_1 - 11I_2 = -10 \qquad [(\text{I})]$$
$$6I_1 + 17I_2 = 40 \qquad [(\text{II})].$$

Solving,

$$I_1 = 1 \text{ amp} = \text{current through } A. \quad \textit{Ans.}$$
$$I_2 = 2 \text{ amp} = \text{current through } C. \quad \textit{Ans.}$$
$$I_1 + I_2 = 3 \text{ amp} = \text{current through } E. \quad \textit{Ans.}$$

The assumed directions of current are correct.

In circuit $ABDEFA$, starting at A,

$$20 - 2I_1 - 4I_1 - 5(I_1 + I_2) + 10 - 1(I_1 + I_2) - 6I_1 = 0.$$
$$18I_1 + 6I_2 = 30. \qquad \text{(III)}$$

The substitution of the numerical values of I_1 and I_2 in (III) gives 30 and verifies the solutions of (I) and (II).

61. Assumed Direction of Current. In the application of Kirchhoff's laws to the solution of electric networks, the question of assuming the proper direction of current often arises. The current may be *assumed* to flow in either direction. If the assumed direction of the current is not the actual direction, this current will be found to have a minus sign when the equations are solved. However, when a direction has been assumed for a current, that direction must remain unchanged throughout the solution of the problem.

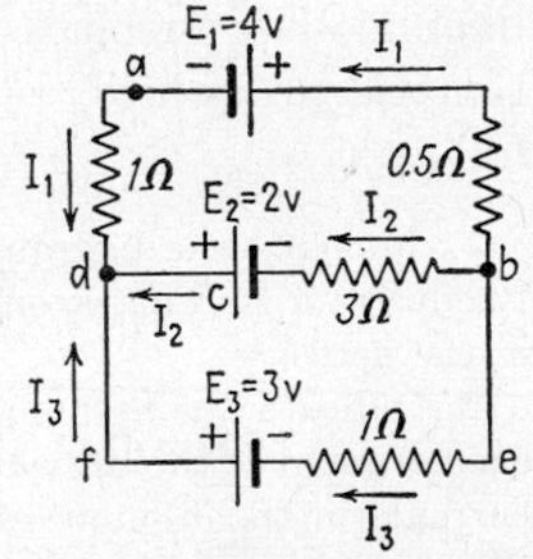

Fig. 47. Assumed direction of current.

Example. This is illustrated by assuming that the directions of the three currents of Fig. 45, Sec. 59, are toward point d as shown in Fig. 47. This condition is of course impossible.

Considering circuit $abcda$, starting at a,

$$+4 + 0.5I_1 - 3I_2 + 2 + I_1 = 0.$$
$$1.5I_1 - 3I_2 + 6 = 0.$$

Similarly with circuit *febcdf*, starting at *f*,

$$-3 + I_3 - 3I_2 + 2 = 0.$$
$$I_3 - 3I_2 - 1 = 0.$$

The directions of the three currents I_1, I_2, I_3 are toward junction *d*; therefore,

$$I_1 + I_2 + I_3 = 0.$$

Substituting and solving,

$$I_1 = -3 \text{ amp.} \quad Ans.$$
$$I_2 = 0.5 \text{ amp.} \quad Ans.$$
$$I_3 = 2.5 \text{ amp.} \quad Ans.$$

The minus sign occurring in the value of I_1 signifies that the actual direction of this current is opposite to the assumed direction, which is indicated by the arrow, Fig. 47. The positive values of I_2 and I_3 indicate that the assumed directions for these two currents are the actual directions.

62. Further Applications of Kirchhoff's Laws. It is stated in Sec. 59 (p. 72) that Kirchhoff's first law must be applied to a sufficient number of junctions to include every current at least once. Also, Kirchhoff's second law must be applied to every branch of the network at least once. By applying these two rules, the number of independent equations can be made equal to the number of unknowns. These facts are illustrated in the examples of Secs. 59 and 61.

It is possible, however, to reduce the number of unknown currents, and hence the number of equations, by combining the currents directly on the diagram, in accordance with Kirchhoff's first law. This is in part illustrated by the example in Sec. 60 but is more completely illustrated by the following example, in which the resistance of the batteries is no longer negligible:

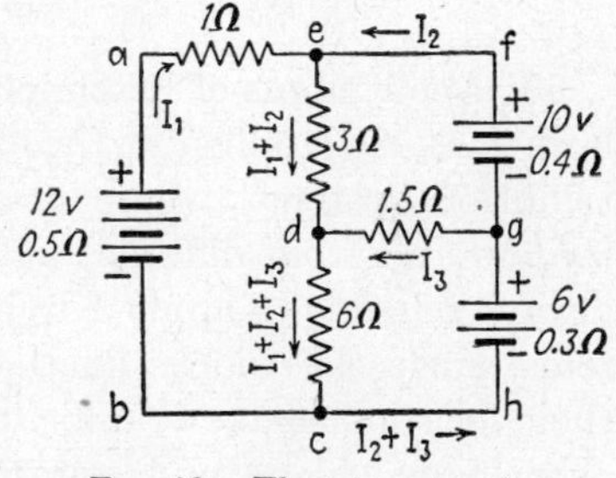

FIG. 48. Electric network.

Example. Determine all the currents in the network of Fig. 48 and also the voltages between points *ed* and *dc*. There are six unknown currents, but by combining at the junctions *e* and *d*, as shown in the diagram, the number of unknown currents is reduced to three. Applying Kirchhoff's second law to path *abcdea*,

$$-12 + 0.5I_1 + 6(I_1 + I_2 + I_3) + 3(I_1 + I_2) + (1)I_1 = 0$$

or

$$10.5I_1 + 9I_2 + 6I_3 = 12. \qquad \text{(I)}$$

Path *efgde*,

$$-10 + 0.4I_2 - 1.5I_3 + 3(I_1 + I_2) = 0$$

or

$$3I_1 + 3.4I_2 - 1.5I_3 = 10. \qquad \text{(II)}$$

Path *cdghc*,

$$+6(I_1 + I_2 + I_3) + 1.5I_3 - 6 + 0.3(I_2 + I_3) = 0$$
$$6I_1 + 6.3I_2 + 7.8I_3 = 6. \qquad \text{(III)}$$

(I), (II), and (III) give three independent equations, and since there are but three unknowns, I_1, I_2, I_3, these can be determined by the simultaneous solutions of (I), (II), and (III).

For example, if I_3 is eliminated between (I) and (II) and then between (II) and (III),

$$22.5I_1 + 22.6I_2 = 52,$$
$$32.4I_1 + 35.95I_2 = 87,$$

from which

$$I_1 = -1.242 \text{ amp.} \quad \textit{Ans.}$$
$$I_2 = +3.540 \text{ amp.} \quad \textit{Ans.}$$

By substituting these values in (II),

$$I_3 = -1.126 \text{ amp.} \quad \textit{Ans.}$$

Hence, the directions of I_1 and I_3 are actually opposite to those assumed.

The current from e to $d = I_1 + I_2 = +2.298$ amp. *Ans.*

The current from d to $c = I_1 + I_2 + I_3 = +1.172$ amp. *Ans.*

The current from c to h to $g = I_2 + I_3 = +2.414$ amp. *Ans.*

The voltage across $ed = +2.298 \cdot 3 = 6.89$ volts. *Ans.*

The voltage across $dc = +1.172 \cdot 6 = 7.03$ volts. *Ans.*

The voltage across $ce = 12 - (-1.242)(1.5) = 13.9$ volts (*check*).

As a further check on the correctness of the solutions (Sec. 60), Kirchhoff's second law may be applied to circuit *abchgfea*, which was not utilized in deriving (I), (II), and (III).

$$-12 + (-1.242)0.5 + 6 - (2.414)0.3 + 10 - (3.540)0.4 + (-1.242)1 = 0.$$
$$+16 - 16 = 0 \ (\textit{check}).$$

63. Applications of Kirchhoff's Laws to Railway Systems. Kirchhoff's laws may be applied to problems involving electric railways and distribution systems, where power is fed to the loads through different feeders and from different substations. In practice, however, it is not always possible to apply Kirchhoff's laws directly to electric railway systems, since the widely fluctuating loads, which are constantly shifting their location, make it difficult to formulate a definite problem. However, loads which simulate typical operating conditions may be assumed, and Kirchhoff's laws then can be applied. In practice, such an analysis may be supplemented by a voltage survey of the system. From data so obtained, together with the analytical results, the number and sizes of feeders can be determined quite accurately.

In the networks which have so far been used, the voltages and resistances have been given. In railway and power networks the factors which are generally known are the supply voltages, the resistances of trolleys, feeders, and rails, and the ampere loads at designated locations. However, the applications of Kirchhoff's laws are identical with those which already have been discussed.

The following example illustrates the application of these laws to a simple railway system.

Example. In Fig. 49 there is shown a simple railway system, with a ring-connected trolley and a single feeder connected to the bus bars at A and to the trolley system at C. The station bus bars at AA' are maintained at 600 volts, bus bar A being positive and A' being negative and grounded. The resistance of the bus bars is negligible. The resistance of the overhead trolley is as follows: A_1 to B, 0.30 ohm; B to C, 0.20 ohm; C to D, 0.20 ohm; D to A, 0.28 ohm. A feeder is connected from A to C, and its resistance is 0.25 ohm. The resistance of rail and ground return is as follows: A' to B', 0.40 ohm; B' to C', 0.25 ohm; C' to D', 0.25 ohm; D' to A', 0.36 ohm. A trolley car at BB' takes 70 amp, and a trolley car at DD' takes 80 amp. Determine: (*a*) current in each section of trolley and in feeder; (*b*) voltage at each car and at feeding point CC'.

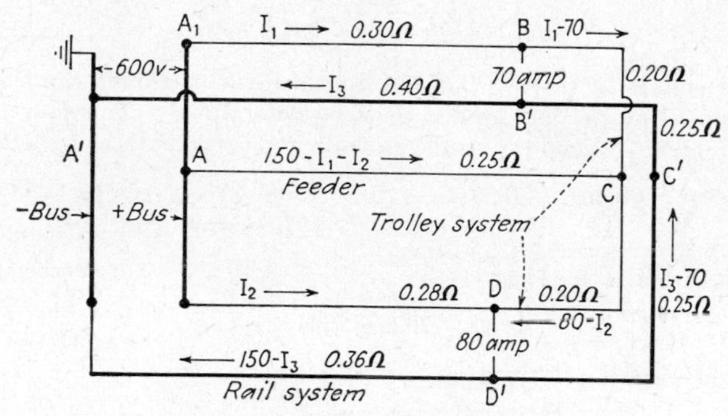

FIG. 49. Kirchhoff's laws applied to railway system.

The current from A_1 to B is designated as I_1 and that from A to D as I_2. Since the total current is 150 amp, the current in the feeder AC is equal to $150 - I_1 - I_2$. By applying the principle of Sec. 62, the currents between points B and C, and C and D, may be expressed in terms of I_1 and I_2, as shown.

Applying Kirchhoff's second law to path A_1BCA,

(*a*) $-0.30I_1 - 0.20(I_1 - 70) + 0.25(150 - I_1 - I_2) = 0.$

$$-0.75I_1 - 0.25I_2 + 51.5 = 0. \qquad \text{(I)}$$

Applying the law to path $ACDA$,

$$-0.25(150 - I_1 - I_2) - 0.20(80 - I_2) + 0.28I_2 = 0.$$
$$0.25I_1 + 0.73I_2 - 53.5 = 0. \qquad \text{(II)}$$

Multiplying (II) by 3 and adding the result to (I),

$$0.75I_1 + 2.19I_2 - 160.5 = 0.$$
$$-0.75I_1 - 0.25I_2 + 51.5 = 0.$$
$$1.94I_2 = 109.$$
$$I_2 = 56.2 \text{ amp.} \quad \textit{Ans.}$$

Substituting the value of I_2 in (II),

$$0.25I_1 + 41.0 - 53.5 = 0.$$
$$I_1 = 50.0 \text{ amp.} \quad \textit{Ans.}$$

The current from B to C is

$$50.0 - 70.0 = -20.0 \text{ amp.} \quad \textit{Ans.}$$

And in view of the – sign its actual direction is from C to B.

The current from C to D is $80 - I_2 = 23.8$ amp. *Ans.*

The current in the feeder AC is $150 - 50.0 - 56.2 = 43.8$ amp. *Ans.*
(These solutions may be verified by application of Kirchhoff's second law to path AA_1BCDA.)

(*b*) The voltage at B (above that of the station negative bus bar) is

$$600 - 50.0 \cdot 0.30 = 585 \text{ volts.}$$

Likewise; the voltage at C is

$$600 - 43.8 \cdot 0.25 = 589.1 \text{ volts,}$$

and that at D is

$$600 - 56.2 \cdot 0.28 = 584.2 \text{ volts.}$$

Before the voltage at the two cars and from point C to ground can be found, the voltage drops in the rail and ground must be determined. This may be done by applying Kirchhoff's second law to the ground circuit, the path being $A'B'C'D'A'$,

$$+0.40I_3 + 0.50(I_3 - 70) - 0.36(150 - I_3) = 0.$$
$$1.26I_3 = 89; \qquad I_3 = 70.6 \text{ amp.}$$

The current from D' to A' is

$$150 - 70.6 = 79.4 \text{ amp.}$$

The voltage drop from B' to A' is

$$70.6 \cdot 0.40 = 28.2 \text{ volts.}$$

The voltage drop from D' to A' is

$$79.4 \cdot 0.36 = 28.6 \text{ volts.}$$

The voltage drop from B' to C' and from D' to C' is $0.6 \cdot 0.25 = 0.15$ volt and may be neglected.
Hence the voltage at car BB' is

$$585 - 28.2 = 556.8 \text{ volts.} \quad \textit{Ans.}$$

And the voltage at car DD' is

$$584.2 - 28.6 = 555.6 \text{ volts.} \quad \textit{Ans.}$$

Since the current from D' to C' to B' is 0.4 amp, the voltage at C' is practically the same as that at D' and B'.

Hence, the voltage from C to ground is practically 589.1 volts. *Ans.*

It is to be noted that the division of currents in the overhead system depends only on the resistances of the overhead system and is independent of the ground system. Likewise, the division of currents in the ground system depends only on the resistances in the ground system.

64. Application of Kirchhoff's Laws to Power Systems. The following example illustrates the application of Kirchhoff's laws to a 240-volt power system. This system is in general similar to the railway system of Sec. 63, except that the outgoing and return systems are now symmetrical. This simplifies the solution, since corresponding currents in the return and outgoing systems are the same. Such a system ordinarily would be a

3-wire one with 120 volts between each outer wire and neutral (see Sec. 374, p. 557). However, 3-wire systems ordinarily are well balanced and usually are solved on that basis. Under these conditions the neutral current is zero, so that the neutral has no effect on voltage drops. Hence it is omitted in Fig. 50.

For illustration, two methods of solution are given, the second being the simpler.

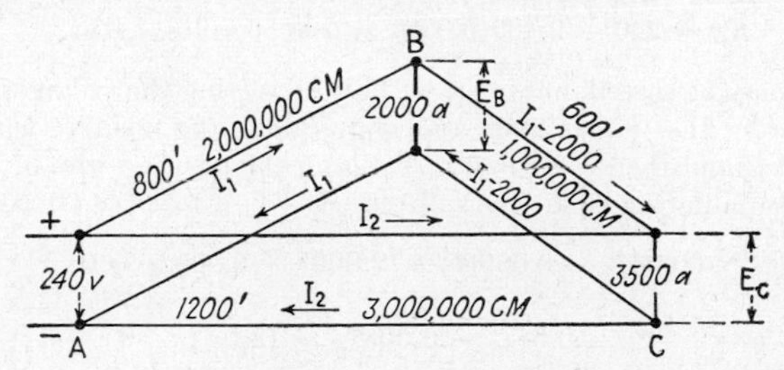

FIG. 50. Ring-feeder power system.

Example. In Fig. 50, a 240-volt substation at A supplies two distributing centers B and C, by a ring system of feeders. Between A and B, a distance of 800 ft, two 1,000,000-cir-mil feeders are paralleled; between A and C, a distance of 1,200 ft, three 1,000,000-cir-mil feeders are paralleled; between B and C, a distance of 600 ft, a 1,000,000-cir-mil tie line is connected. Determine the current in each feeder and the voltage at each distributing center, when the load at B is 2,000 amp and that at C is 3,500 amp.

Assuming 10 ohms per circular-mil-foot,

$$\text{Resistance per wire } A \text{ to } B = \frac{800 \cdot 10}{2{,}000{,}000} = 0.004 \text{ ohm.}$$

$$\text{Resistance per wire } B \text{ to } C = \frac{600 \cdot 10}{1{,}000{,}000} = 0.006 \text{ ohm.}$$

$$\text{Resistance per wire } A \text{ to } C = \frac{1{,}200 \cdot 10}{3{,}000{,}000} = 0.004 \text{ ohm.}$$

Going from A to B to C, out on the positive and back on the negative conductor,

$$240 - I_1(0.004) - (I_1 - 2{,}000)0.006 - E_C - (I_1 - 2{,}000)0.006 - I_1(0.004) = 0.$$

$$240 - I_1(0.02) + 24 = E_C. \qquad \text{(I)}$$

Likewise, going directly from A to C,

$$240 - I_2(0.004) - E_C - I_2(0.004) = 0.$$

$$240 - I_2(0.008) = E_C. \qquad \text{(II)}$$

Equating (I) and (II),

$$240 - I_1(0.02) + 24 = 240 - I_2(0.008).$$

$$0.02I_1 - 0.008I_2 = 24. \qquad \text{(III)}$$

At center C,

$$I_1 - 2{,}000 + I_2 = 3{,}500.$$

$$I_1 + I_2 = 5{,}500. \qquad \text{(IV)}$$

Substituting in (III) for $I_1 = 5{,}500 - I_2$,

$$0.02(5{,}500 - I_2) - 0.008I_2 = 24.$$
$$110 - 0.02I_2 - 0.008I_2 = 24.$$
$$0.028I_2 = 86.$$
$$I_2 = 3{,}070 \text{ amp.} \quad \textit{Ans.}$$
$$I_1 = 2{,}430 \text{ amp.} \quad \textit{Ans.}$$

From (II)

$$E_C = 240 - 3{,}070(0.008) = 215.44 \text{ volts.} \quad \textit{Ans.}$$
$$E_B = 240 - 2{,}430(0.008) = 220.56 \text{ volts.} \quad \textit{Ans.}$$

The problem may be solved, however, without involving the voltages at A, B, or C. Taking a path from the + bus at A and going along the positive wires of the two feeders to B and C and then returning to A along the positive wire of the 3,000,000-cir-mil feeder, the following equation is obtained:

$$-0.004I_1 - 0.006(I_1 - 2{,}000) + 0.004I_2 = 0$$

or

$$0.01I_1 - 0.004I_2 = 12,$$

which is equal to (III) divided by 2; and at C,

$$I_1 - 2{,}000 + I_2 = 3{,}500$$

or

$$I_1 + I_2 = 5{,}500 \text{ amp},$$

which is the same as (IV).

In this example it is to be noted that, as in the railway type of problem, currents as well as emfs and resistances are included in the given data.

65. Maxwell's Mesh Equations. So far, in the applications of Kirchhoff's laws to electric networks, the current in each individual element of the network is the unit on which the equations are based. Maxwell,[1] however, originated a method in which the *current circulating in each mesh* of the network is the unit on which the equations are based. Thus, any network may be divided into *meshes*, Fig. 51, and a separate current is assumed to circulate in each *mesh*. The current circulating about the mesh then becomes one of the units on which the solutions are based.

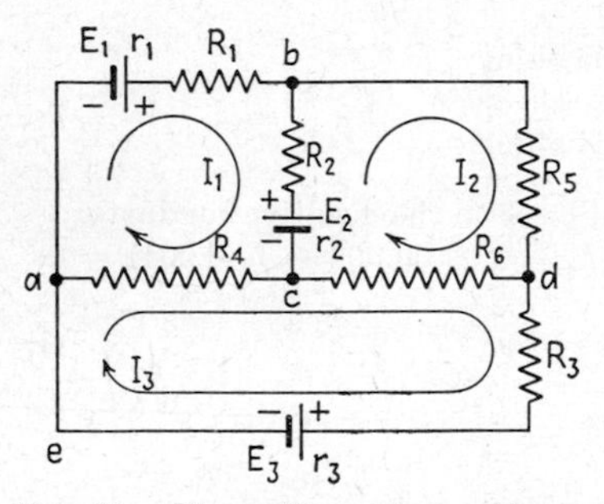

Fig. 51. Maxwell's mesh equations.

Although, so far as the correct solution is concerned, the direction of any mesh current can be taken either as clockwise or as counterclockwise, the method of solution becomes far more systematic if the directions of all currents are assumed to be the same. Because clockwise rotation seems to be the natural direction, it is the one which is usually selected, although counterclockwise rotation would serve equally well.

[1] See footnote, p. 211.

In Fig. 51, applying Kirchhoff's second law to the three meshes, the following equations are obtained:

abca

$$+E_1 - I_1r_1 - I_1R_1 - I_1R_2 - E_2 - I_1r_2 - I_1R_4 + I_2(r_2 + R_2) + I_3R_4 = 0 \quad \text{(I)}$$

or

$$+E_1 - E_2 - I_1(r_1 + R_1 + R_2 + r_2 + R_4) + I_2(r_2 + R_2) + I_3R_4 = 0. \quad \text{(II)}$$

cbdc

$$+E_2 - I_2r_2 - I_2R_2 - I_2R_5 - I_2R_6 + I_1(R_2 + r_2) + I_3R_6 = 0 \quad \text{(III)}$$

or

$$+E_2 - I_2(r_2 + R_2 + R_5 + R_6) + I_1(R_2 + r_2) + I_3R_6 = 0. \quad \text{(IV)}$$

eacde

$$-I_3R_4 - I_3R_6 - I_3R_3 - E_3 - I_3r_3 + I_1R_4 + I_2R_6 = 0 \quad \text{(V)}$$

or

$$-E_3 - I_3(R_4 + R_6 + R_3 + r_3) + I_1R_4 + I_2R_6 = 0. \quad \text{(VI)}$$

There are several features of the mesh equations which render them systematic and reduce the opportunities for error.

In (I), (III), (V), the IR drops due to the mesh currents under consideration are taken in the direction of the current, and so all are *negative.* The IR drops due to the other mesh currents in the mutual elements of the network such as R_2, r_2, R_4, R_6 are taken in opposition to the currents, and so all are *positive.* Hence, it follows that the resistances of the elements through which the mesh current under consideration goes may all be *added* within a set of parentheses and multiplied by the negative of the mesh current. All other IR drops, which are produced in the mutual elements by the other mesh currents, are positive. This is illustrated in (II), (IV), (VI).

The signs of the emfs in the energy sources are positive when going from $-$ to $+$ and are negative when going from $+$ to $-$, as in the usual application of Kirchhoff's second law.

Unlike the conventional application of Kirchhoff's laws, it is not necessary to apply directly the first law to any junction.

The number of unknown currents is the same as the number of meshes, so that the number of simultaneous equations must also be equal to the number of meshes.

As in the conventional applications of Kirchhoff's laws, if a solution of the equations gives a negative value of current, the actual direction of current is the reverse of that assumed (see I_3 below).

The current in each mutual element is the difference of the two mesh currents.

Note that when the voltage drops due to a mesh current such as I_1 are primarily under consideration, the emf E_2 of a source of emf in a mutual element such as *bc*, Fig. 51, is ignored in considering the effect of the second mesh current such as I_2. That is, under these conditions the resistances only, including those in the source of emf, such as r_2, are considered, as in (I). However, when mesh current I_2 is primarily under consideration, the emfs in the mutual elements must be taken into consideration as in (III).

As has been pointed out, the advantages of Maxwell's mesh equations are that the signs of the *IR* drops are written systematically so that there is almost no chance of their being in error. Also note that the number of simultaneous equations is reduced over those normally used. For example, in Fig. 51, there are six circuit elements requiring six current equations, whereas there are only three meshes requiring only three current equations.

A common application of the Maxwell mesh equations is in the solution of bridge circuits. This is illustrated by Prob. 198 (p. 622).

Example. In Fig. 51, let $E_1 = 15$ volts, $E_2 = 12$ volts, $E_3 = 20$ volts. In ohms, $r_1 = 0.2$; $r_2 = 0.4$; $r_3 = 0.5$; $R_1 = 4$; $R_2 = 3$; $R_3 = 7.5$; $R_4 = 2$; $R_5 = 5$; $R_6 = 6$. Determine: (*a*) I_1, I_2, I_3; (*b*) current in elements *bc*, *ca*, and *dc*; (*c*) voltages across *bc*, *ca*, and *dc*; (*d*) voltage across battery with emf E_1.

(*a*) Substituting the foregoing data in (II), (IV), (VI),

$$+15 - 12 - I_1(0.2 + 4 + 3 + 0.4 + 2) + I_2(0.4 + 3) + 2I_3 = 0 \qquad [(\text{II})].$$
$$+12 - I_2(0.4 + 3 + 5 + 6) + I_1(3 + 0.4) + 6I_3 = 0 \qquad [(\text{IV})].$$
$$-20 - I_3(2 + 6 + 7.5 + 0.5) + 2I_1 + 6I_2 = 0 \qquad [(\text{VI})].$$

These three equations reduce to

$$9.6I_1 - 3.4I_2 - 2I_3 = 3. \qquad (\text{VII})$$
$$3.4I_1 - 14.4I_2 + 6I_3 = -12. \qquad (\text{VIII})$$
$$2.0I_1 + 6.0I_2 - 16I_3 = 20. \qquad (\text{IX})$$

Combining (VII) and (VIII) gives

$$32.2I_1 - 24.6I_2 = -3. \qquad (\text{X})$$

Combining (VIII) and (IX) gives

$$33.2I_1 - 97.2I_2 = -36. \qquad (\text{XI})$$

From (X) and (XI),

$$I_1 = 0.2568 \text{ amp.} \quad \textit{Ans.}$$
$$I_2 = 0.4582 \text{ amp.} \quad \textit{Ans.}$$

From (IX),

$$I_3 = -1.047 \text{ amp.} \quad \textit{Ans.}$$

(*b*) $I_{bc} = I_1 - I_2 = 0.2568 - 0.4582 = -0.2014$ amp. *Ans.*
$I_{ca} = I_1 - I_3 = 0.2568 - (-1.047) = +1.304$ amp. *Ans.*
$I_{dc} = I_2 - I_3 = 0.4582 - (-1.047) = +1.505$ amp. *Ans.*

(*c*) $V_{bc} = -I_{bc}(R_2 + r_2) - E_2 = 0.2014(3.4) - 12 = -11.32$ volts. *Ans.*
$V_{ca} = -I_{ca}R_4 = -1.304 \cdot 2 = -2.608$ volts. *Ans.*
$V_{dc} = -I_{dc}R_6 = -1.505 \cdot 6 = -9.030$ volts. *Ans.*

(*d*) $V_1 = E_1 - I_1r_1 = 15 - 0.268 \cdot 0.2 = 14.95$ volts. *Ans.*

ELECTRIC-NETWORK THEOREMS[1]

66. Circuit Definitions. Electric-network solutions may frequently be simplified by applying certain theorems which either simplify the network itself or simplify the analytical solution. These methods are equally applicable to a-c systems, vector impedances being substituted for resistances. Circuits in accordance with their properties may be defined as follows:

A *circuit* is a conducting part or a system of conducting parts through which an electric current flows or is intended to flow (35.40.010).[2]

The various elements of a circuit are called *parameters.* In an electrical circuit the parameters are resistance, inductance, and capacitance. The parameters may be *lumped,* as in a circuit consisting of a capacitor, an inductance coil, and a resistor unit, or *distributed,* as in a transmission line where the capacitance exists between the conductors and the resistance and inductance are due to the conductors themselves.

A *linear circuit* is one in which the parameters are constant.

A *nonlinear circuit* is one in which the parameters change with the voltage or current.

A *bilateral circuit* is one which has the same characteristics in either direction. For example, the usual transmission line is bilateral because power may be supplied to either end and delivered from the opposite end. The source and load may be interchanged without effect.

A *unilateral circuit* is one whose characteristics change with the direction of operation. A vacuum-tube rectifier is a unilateral circuit because if alternating current is supplied to end A, direct current is delivered at end B; but if direct current is supplied at end B, the circuit will not deliver alternating current at end A.

An *electric network* is a combination of any number of electric elements, the impedances of which may be either lumped or distributed, or both, which are connected in any manner, conductively, inductively, or capacitively (65.20.625).[2]

NOTE. An electric network is understood to be passive unless the contrary is stated.

An *active electric network* is an electric network containing one or more sources of energy (65.20.630).[3]

A *passive electric network* is an electric network containing no source of energy (65.20.635).[3]

An *L network* is a network composed of two impedance branches in

[1] A more complete analysis is given in "Introduction to Circuit Analysis," by Abner R. Knight and Gilbert H. Fett, Harper & Brothers.

[2] ASA C42 Definitions of Electrical Terms, 1941 edition. (In 35.40.010 the words "flows or" have been added.)

[3] ASA C42 Definitions of Electrical Terms, 1941 edition.

series, the free ends being connected to one pair of terminals and the junction point and one free end being connected to another pair of terminals (65.20.645).[1]

A *T network* is a network composed of three impedance branches connected in star; that is, one end of each branch is connected to a common point, while the three remaining ends are connected to an input terminal, an output terminal, and a common input and output terminal, respectively (65.20.655).[1]

A *π network* is a network composed of three impedance branches connected in delta, that is, connected in series with each other to form a closed circuit, the three junction points forming an input terminal, an output terminal, and a common input and output terminal, respectively (65.20.665).[1]

67. Superposition Theorem. In a linear bilateral network, the current at any point, or the potential difference which exists between any two points due to the simultaneous action of a number of emfs distributed throughout the network, is the sum of the component currents and voltages in the network. A component current or voltage is that due to one emf acting alone. In other words, each emf acts independently to produce current in the network.

In applying the superposition theorem to a network, one source of emf is applied at a time, the others being removed. However, the internal resistances of the emfs which are removed must remain in the circuit. An example of the application of the theorem is given in Fig. 52.

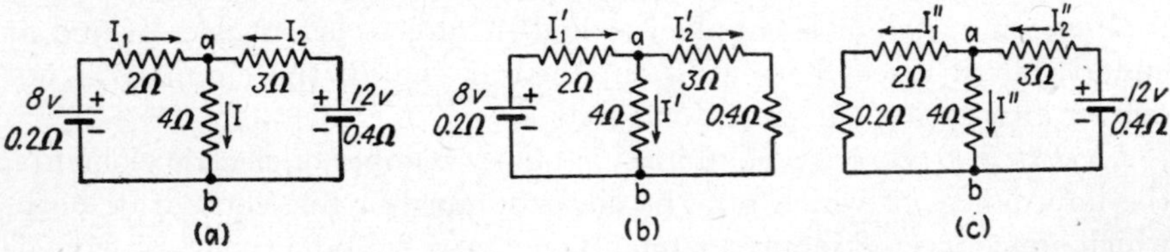

Fig. 52. Example of superposition theorem.

Example. In Fig. 52 (*a*) two batteries having emfs of 8 and 12 volts and internal resistances of 0.2 and 0.4 ohm are connected to the network as shown. Determine: (*a*) current I_1; (*b*) current I_2; (*c*) current I; (*d*) voltage across ab.

In (*b*) the 12-volt battery is removed but its internal resistance of 0.4 ohm remains. The currents I_1', I', and I_2' are found by the simple application of Ohm's law.

The external resistance

$$R' = 2 + \frac{4 \cdot 3.4}{4 + 3.4} = 2 + \frac{13.6}{7.4} = 3.839 \text{ ohms;}$$

$$I_1' = \frac{8}{0.2 + 3.839} = \frac{8}{4.039} = 1.981 \text{ amp.}$$

$$I' = \frac{3.4}{7.4} 1.981 = 0.910 \text{ amp;} \qquad I_2' = \frac{4.0}{7.4} 1.981 = 1.071 \text{ amp.}$$

[1] ASA C42 Definitions of Electrical Terms, 1941 edition.

In (c) the 8-volt battery is removed, but its resistance of 0.2 ohm remains. The currents I_2'', I'', and I_1'' are then found.

The external resistance

$$R'' = 3 + \frac{4 \cdot 2.2}{4 + 2.2} = 3 + \frac{8.8}{6.2} = 4.419 \text{ ohms};$$

$$I_2'' = \frac{12}{0.4 + 4.419} = \frac{12}{4.819} = 2.490 \text{ amp};$$

$$I'' = \frac{2.2}{6.2} 2.490 = 0.884 \text{ amp}; \qquad I_1'' = \frac{4}{6.2} 2.490 = 1.606 \text{ amp}.$$

In (a), $I_1 = I_1' + (-I_1'') = 1.981 - 1.606 = 0.375$ amp. *Ans.*

(b), $I_2 = (-I_2') + I_2'' = -1.071 + 2.490 = 1.419$ amp. *Ans.*

(c), $I = I' + I'' = 0.910 + 0.884 = 1.794$ amp. *Ans.*

The voltage across the 4-ohm resistor,

(d) $V_{ab} = 1.794 \cdot 4 = 7.18 \text{ volts} = 8 - (0.375 \cdot 2.2) = 12 - (1.419 \cdot 3.4)$ volts. *Ans.*

Further applications of the method are given by Probs. 200 to 202 (p. 623).

68. Thévenin's Theorem. If a resistor[1] of R ohms be connected between any two terminals of a linear bilateral network, the resulting steady-state current through the resistor is the ratio of the potential difference E' between the two points prior to the connection and the sum of the values of (1) the resistance R' of the network measured between the two points and (2) the connected resistance R.

The application of the theorem to a specific network is given in Fig. 53, which shows a source of emf E with internal resistance r ohms connected to an external circuit consisting of resistors of R_1 and R_2 ohms in series. So far as terminals ab across R_1 are concerned, the network acts as a source of emf of E' volts where E' is the voltage across ab before the connection of R, that is, the conditions shown in the figure. The resistance R_0 of the network as it would be measured between terminals ab (with E removed) is determined from the relation,

$$\frac{1}{R_0} = \frac{1}{R_1} + \frac{1}{r + R_2} \qquad \text{mhos.}$$

The network, so far as terminals ab are concerned, behaves as a source having an emf of E' volts and an internal resistance of R_0 ohms. For example, if the resistor of R ohms be connected across ab, the current I in R becomes

$$I = \frac{E'}{R_0 + R} \qquad \text{amp.}$$

[1] In the generalized case, which includes alternating currents, "impedor," "impedance," and Z may be substituted for "resistor," "resistance," and R.

The more complete solution of the circuit is as follows:

$$E' = \left(\frac{E}{r + R_1 + R_2}\right) R_1; \qquad R_0 = \frac{R_1(r + R_2)}{r + R_1 + R_2}.$$

$$I = \frac{E\dfrac{R_1}{r + R_1 + R_2}}{\dfrac{R_1(r + R_2)}{r + R_1 + R_2} + R} = E\frac{R_1}{R_1(r + R_2) + R(r + R_1 + R_2)}.$$

Example. In Fig. 53, let $E = 20$ volts, $r = 1$ ohm, $R_1 = 12$ ohms, $R_2 = 3$ ohms, and $R = 27$ ohms. Determine: (*a*) equivalent emf of the network with reference to terminals *ab*; (*b*) equivalent resistance of the network with reference to terminals *ab*; (*c*) current in R when connected across terminals *ab*.

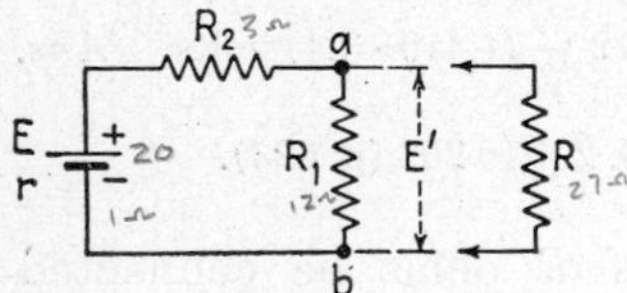

FIG. 53. Example of Thévenin's theorem.

(*a*) Current in network before R is connected,

$$I_1 = \frac{20}{1 + 12 + 3} = 1.25 \text{ amp.}$$

$$E' = 1.25 \cdot 12 = 15 \text{ volts.} \quad \textit{Ans.}$$

(*b*) $$R_0 = \frac{12(1 + 3)}{1 + 12 + 3} = \frac{48}{16} = 3.0 \text{ ohms.} \quad \textit{Ans.}$$

(*c*) $$I = \frac{15}{3.0 + 27} = 0.5 \text{ amp.} \quad \textit{Ans.}$$

If desired, the current in R_1 and the source of emf E are readily determined. For example,

Current in R_1,

$$I_1' = \frac{0.5 \cdot 27}{12} = 1.125 \text{ amp.}$$

Current in source,

$$I_1'' = 0.5 + 1.125 = 1.625 \text{ amp.}$$

Figures 39(*a*), (*b*) in Sec. 56 (p. 65) also illustrate Thévenin's theorem. In (*a*) the emf V across *ab* is given by Eq. (I, p. 65). The current I, Fig. 39(*b*), in R when it is connected across *ab* is given by Eq. (61), the numerator of which is equal to V and the denominator of which is equal to the sum of the resistance measured across *ab* in Fig. 39(*a*) and R.

(Problems 203 to 206, pp. 623 and 624, illustrate further application of Thévenin's theorem.)

69. Reciprocity Theorem. In any network composed of invariable bilateral elements it can be shown that, if any emf E is applied in any element and the current I is measured in any other element, their ratio E/I, called the *transfer impedance*, is equal in magnitude (and in phase) to the ratio obtained if the positions of E and I are interchanged. If an emf inserted at point A in such a network produces a current at point B, the same emf moved to point B would produce the same current at A.

For example, in the network shown at (*a*) in Fig. 54 if the battery E at point A in the network produces a current I in the network at point B, then in (*b*) if battery E be inserted at point B, the current in the network at point A will be I amp.

Example. In the network let $E = 16$ volts; $R_1 = 3$ ohms; $R_2 = 2$ ohms; $R_3 = 12$ ohms; $R_4 = 6$ ohms; $R_5 = 4$ ohms. Let the internal resistance of the battery and the resistance of the ammeter be negligible. Determine: (*a*) in Fig. 54(*a*), current to

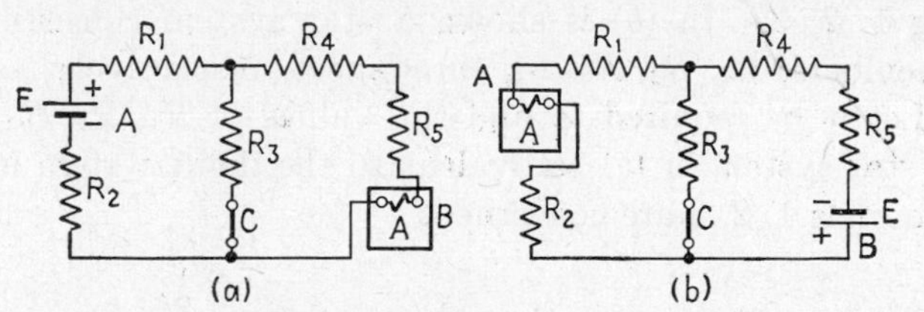

FIG. 54. Reciprocity theorem.

ammeter at B with E applied at A; (*b*) in Fig. 54(*b*), current to ammeter at A with E applied at B; (*c*) transfer resistance (impedance).

(*a*) Equivalent resistance external to battery,

$$R = R_1 + R_2 + \frac{R_3(R_4 + R_5)}{R_3 + R_4 + R_5} = 5 + \frac{12(10)}{22} = 5 + 5.45 = 10.45 \text{ ohms.}$$

$$I = \frac{16}{10.45} = 1.530 \text{ amp.}$$

Current at B,

$$I_B = \frac{12}{12 + 10} 1.530 = 0.835 \text{ amp.} \quad Ans.$$

(*b*) Equivalent resistance external to battery,

$$R = R_4 + R_5 + \frac{R_3(R_1 + R_2)}{R_1 + R_2 + R_3} = 10 + \frac{12(5)}{17} = 10 + 3.53 = 13.53 \text{ ohms.}$$

$$I = \frac{16}{13.53} = 1.182 \text{ amp.}$$

Current at A,

$$I_A = \frac{12}{12 + 5} 1.182 = 0.835 \text{ amp.} \quad Ans.$$

Thus, $I_A = I_B$.

(*c*) The transfer resistance is

$$R_t = \frac{16}{0.835} = 1.915 \text{ ohms.} \quad Ans.$$

(See also Probs. 207 to 210, p. 624.)

70. Equivalent Delta and Star (or Y) Systems. The solution, by means of Kirchhoff's laws, of electric networks having a considerable number of elements, or branches, may become much involved owing to the large number of simultaneous equations which must be solved. In many cases such networks may be reduced to very simple circuits by successively replacing delta meshes with star systems, and vice versa. So far as the respective three terminals are concerned, any delta system of passive[1] resistors (or impedors) may be replaced by an equivalent 3-terminal star, or Y, system. In a similar manner, the 3-terminal star system may be replaced by an equivalent delta system.

I. *Delta System Replaced by Star System.* In Fig. 55(*a*) is shown a delta system consisting of three resistors, R_{12}, R_{23}, R_{31}, the three terminals being 1, 2, 3. In (*b*) is shown a star system consisting of three resistor members, R_1, R_2, R_3, which connect, respectively, to terminals 1, 2, 3. Let it be required to find the values of R_1, R_2, R_3 which will make the star system in (*b*) equivalent to the delta system in (*a*) so far as the terminals 1, 2, 3 are concerned.

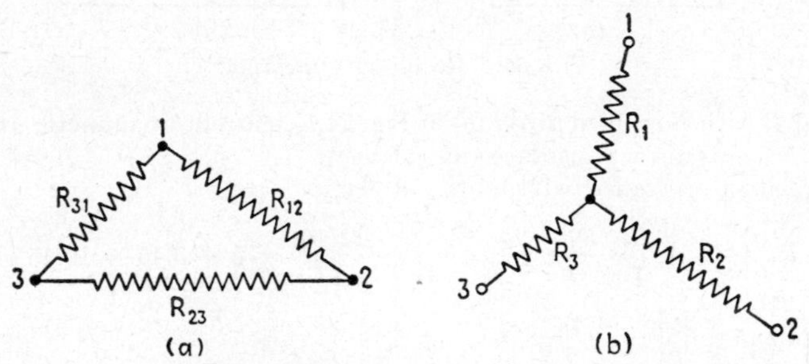

FIG. 55. Equivalent delta and star meshes.

In (*b*) the resistance between terminals 1 and 2 is $R_1 + R_2$. In (*a*) the resistance between terminals 1 and 2 consists of R_{12} in parallel with R_{31} and R_{23} in series. Hence,

$$R_1 + R_2 = \frac{R_{12}(R_{31} + R_{23})}{R_{12} + R_{23} + R_{31}} \qquad \text{[see Eq. (9), p. 12].} \tag{I}$$

In a similar manner, for terminals 2 and 3, and terminals 3 and 1,

$$R_2 + R_3 = \frac{R_{23}(R_{12} + R_{31})}{R_{12} + R_{23} + R_{31}} \tag{II}$$

and

$$R_3 + R_1 = \frac{R_{31}(R_{23} + R_{12})}{R_{12} + R_{23} + R_{31}}. \tag{III}$$

There are now three unknowns and three equations, (I), (II), and (III). Solving these equations simultaneously gives

$$R_1 = \frac{R_{12}R_{31}}{\Sigma R_n}, \tag{65}$$

$$R_2 = \frac{R_{23}R_{12}}{\Sigma R_n}, \tag{66}$$

$$R_3 = \frac{R_{31}R_{23}}{\Sigma R_n}, \tag{67}$$

[1] Sec. 66.

where

$$\Sigma R_n = R_{12} + R_{23} + R_{31}.$$

II. *Star System Replaced by Delta System.* The conversion of the star system to the delta system is quite readily made by the use of (65), (66), and (67). First let

$$\Sigma R_0 = R_1R_2 + R_2R_3 + R_3R_1. \quad \text{(IV)}$$

Multiplying (65) by (66), (66) by (67), and (67) by (65), and then adding, gives

$$R_1R_2 + R_2R_3 + R_3R_1 = \frac{R_{12}^2R_{23}R_{31} + R_{12}R_{23}^2R_{31} + R_{12}R_{23}R_{31}^2}{(R_{12} + R_{23} + R_{31})^2}. \quad \text{(V)}$$

From (IV) and (V),

$$\Sigma R_0 = \frac{R_{12}R_{23}R_{31}(R_{12} + R_{23} + R_{31})}{(R_{12} + R_{23} + R_{31})^2}.$$

$$R_{12} = \frac{\Sigma R_0(R_{12} + R_{23} + R_{31})}{R_{23}R_{31}}.$$

From (67),

$$R_{23}R_{31} = R_3(R_{12} + R_{23} + R_{31}).$$

Hence,

$$R_{12} = \frac{\Sigma R_0(R_{12} + R_{23} + R_{31})}{R_3(R_{12} + R_{23} + R_{31})} = \frac{\Sigma R_0}{R_3}. \quad (68)$$

In a similar manner,

$$R_{23} = \frac{\Sigma R_0}{R_1}, \quad (69)$$

and

$$R_{31} = \frac{\Sigma R_0}{R_2}. \quad (70)$$

Example. In Fig. 56(*a*) is shown a resistance network *AB*. The number near each element gives its resistance in ohms. Determine the equivalent resistance of the network between points *A* and *B*.

One method of solving the problem is to convert the delta meshes *AOC* and *aOB* into equivalent stars. These equivalent stars are shown in (*b*) and (*c*), (65), (66), (67) being used for the conversion.

For example in (*b*),

$$AP = \frac{8 \cdot 9}{22} = 3.27; \qquad OP = \frac{8 \cdot 5}{22} = 1.82; \qquad CP = \frac{5 \cdot 9}{22} = 2.04.$$

In (*c*),

$$Oq = \frac{4 \cdot 6}{20} = 1.20; \qquad aq = \frac{4 \cdot 10}{20} = 2.00; \qquad Bq = \frac{10 \cdot 6}{20} = 3.00.$$

Substituting the stars in (*b*) and (*c*) for the corresponding deltas gives the network structure shown at (*d*). This again may be simplified by converting the delta *AqP*

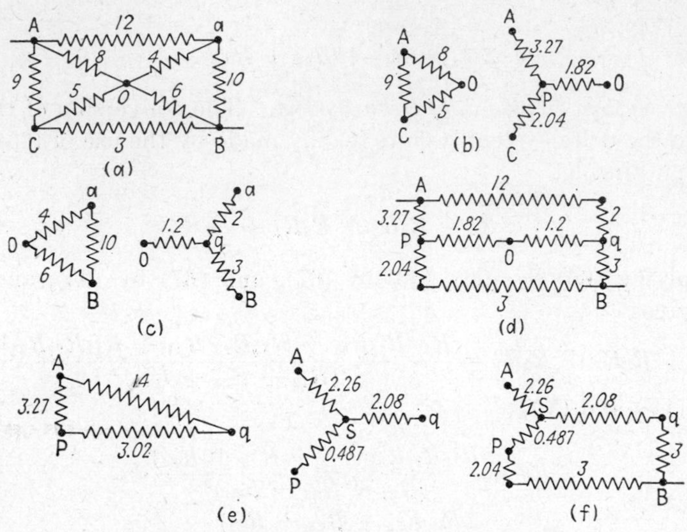

FIG. 56. Simplification of complex network.

into a star as shown in (*e*),

$$AS = \frac{3.27 \cdot 14}{20.29} = 2.26; \qquad qS = \frac{3.02 \cdot 14}{20.29} = 2.08; \qquad PS = \frac{3.27 \cdot 3.02}{20.29} = 0.487.$$

Substituting this star for its equivalent delta in (*d*) gives the structure shown in (*f*). This consists merely of a series-parallel circuit, the resistance of which is

$$R = 2.26 + \frac{(3.0 + 2.08)(0.487 + 2.04 + 3.0)}{3.0 + 2.08 + 0.487 + 2.04 + 3.0} = 2.26 + 2.65 = 4.91 \text{ ohms.} \quad \textit{Ans.}$$

71. Four-terminal Networks. A 4-terminal network is one in which the terminals are grouped in two pairs, one pair usually serving as input

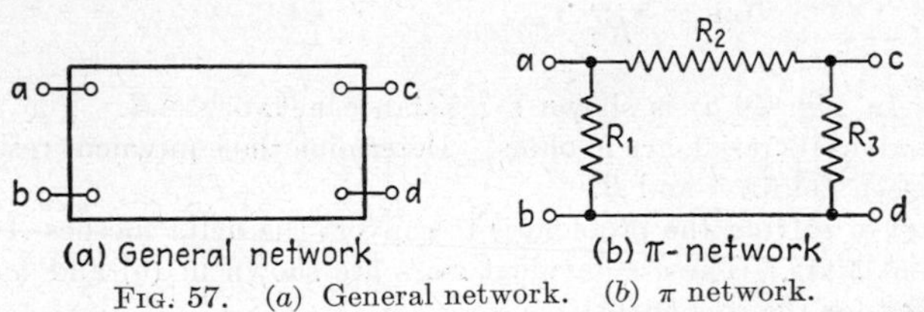

FIG. 57. (*a*) General network. (*b*) π network.

terminals and the other pair serving as output terminals. Thus, in Fig. 57(*a*), which represents a passive network, the terminals *ab* may serve as input terminals and terminals *cd* as output terminals, or vice versa. Such networks are widely used in communication circuits as artificial lines, filters, alternating networks, etc.

Any 4-terminal passive network, no matter how complicated, can be defined in terms of three quantities. For example in Fig. 57(*a*), the network can be defined in terms of three of the four following: resistance

R_{ab} measured between terminals *ab* with terminals *cd* open; resistance R_{cd} between terminals *cd* with terminals *ab* open; resistance R_{ab}' measured between terminals *ab* with terminals *cd* short-circuited; resistance R_{cd}' measured between terminals *cd* with terminals *ab* short-circuited. As three of the quantities define the network, the fourth is unnecessary.

π Networks. Since any passive network may be defined in terms of three properties, it can likewise be simulated by either a π or a T network, each of which is made up of three independent elements. For example, in Fig. 57(*b*) is shown a π network consisting of the three independent elements, R_1, R_2, R_3. It is desired that this network be made to simulate that shown in Fig. 57(*a*) so far as the terminals *ab* and *cd* are concerned. To fulfill this condition the following relations are necessary:

With terminals *cd* open-circuited,

$$\frac{1}{R_1} + \frac{1}{R_2 + R_3} = \frac{1}{R_{ab}} \quad \text{mhos,} \tag{71}$$

or

$$\frac{R_1(R_2 + R_3)}{R_1 + R_2 + R_3} = R_{ab} \quad \text{ohms.} \tag{72}$$

With terminals *ab* open-circuited,

$$\frac{1}{R_3} + \frac{1}{R_1 + R_2} = \frac{1}{R_{cd}} \quad \text{mhos,} \tag{73}$$

or

$$\frac{R_3(R_1 + R_2)}{R_1 + R_2 + R_3} = R_{cd} \quad \text{ohms.} \tag{74}$$

With terminals *cd* short-circuited,

$$\frac{1}{R_1} + \frac{1}{R_2} = \frac{1}{R_{ab}'} \quad \text{mhos,} \tag{75}$$

or

$$\frac{R_1 R_2}{R_1 + R_2} = R_{ab}' \quad \text{ohms.} \tag{76}$$

The π network could also be defined by the resistance R_{cd}' measured between terminals *cd* with *ab* short-circuited, taken together with any two of the three foregoing quantities, R_{ab}, R_{cd}, R_{ab}'.

Example. Measurements of the resistances between terminals *ab* and *cd*, Fig. 57(*a*), give the following values: with *cd* open, $R_{ab} = 37.4$ ohms; with *ab* open, $R_{cd} = 32.8$ ohms; with *cd* short-circuited, $R_{ab}' = 18.12$ ohms. Determine the resistances of R_1, R_2, R_3 of an equivalent π network, Fig. 57(*b*), that is, one which will simulate the network, Fig. 57(*a*).

From (72), (74), (76),

$$\frac{R_1(R_2 + R_3)}{R_1 + R_2 + R_3} = 37.4 \text{ ohms.} \tag{I}$$

$$\frac{R_3(R_1 + R_2)}{R_1 + R_2 + R_3} = 32.8 \text{ ohms.} \tag{II}$$

$$\frac{R_1 R_2}{R_1 + R_2} = 18.12 \text{ ohms.} \tag{III}$$

In (III)

$$R_1 = \frac{18.12 R_2}{R_2 - 18.12} \quad \text{ohms.} \tag{IV}$$

Substituting (III) in (I) and (II) gives

$$R_2^2 + R_2 R_3 - 35.1 R_3 = 0. \tag{V}$$

$$R_3(R_2^2 - 32.8 R_2 + 594) = 32.8 R_2^2. \tag{VI}$$

From (V) and (VI)

$$R_3 = \frac{-R_2^2}{R_2 - 35.1} \quad \text{ohms.} \tag{VII}$$

$$R_3 = \frac{32.8 R_2^2}{R_2^2 - 32.8 R_2 + 594} \quad \text{ohms.} \tag{VIII}$$

Equating (VII) and (VIII),

$$32.8 R_2 - 1{,}150 = -R_2^2 + 32.8 R_2 - 594.$$

$$R_2 = 23.6 \text{ ohms.} \quad \textit{Ans.}$$

Substituting R_2 in (IV),

$$R_1 = 78.0 \text{ ohms.} \quad \textit{Ans.}$$

Substituting R_2 in (VII),

$$R_3 = 48.4 \text{ ohms.} \quad \textit{Ans.}$$

Hence the π network, Fig. 57(*b*), with $R_1 = 78.0$ ohms, $R_2 = 23.6$ ohms, and $R_3 = 48.4$ ohms, can replace the network in (*a*), so far as terminals *ab* and *cd* are concerned.

T Networks. Any general passive network, Fig. 57(*a*), may also be replaced by a T network, Fig. 58, the T network also consisting of three independent elements, R_1, R_2, R_3. To be equivalent to the general network, Fig. 57(*a*), the following conditions must be fulfilled:

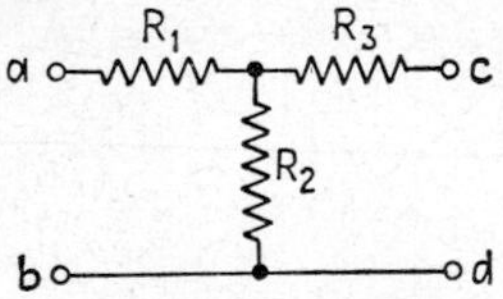

$$R_{ab} = R_1 + R_2 \quad \text{ohms.} \tag{77}$$

$$R_{cd} = R_2 + R_3 \quad \text{ohms.} \tag{78}$$

$$R_{ab}' = R_1 + \frac{R_2 R_3}{R_2 + R_3} \quad \text{ohms.} \tag{79}$$

FIG. 58. T network.

Example. Determine a T network, Fig. 58, which is equivalent to the general network, Fig. 57(*a*), for which $R_{ab} = 37.4$ ohms, $R_{cd} = 32.8$ ohms, and $R_{ab}' = 18.12$ ohms, the method being similar to that used to obtain the π network.

From (77),

$$R_2 = 37.4 - R_1 \text{ ohms.} \tag{I}$$

From (78),

$$R_2 = 32.8 - R_3 \text{ ohms.} \tag{II}$$

From (I) and (II),

$$R_3 = R_1 - 4.6 \text{ ohms.} \tag{III}$$

Substituting (I) and (III) into (79),

$$R_1 + \frac{(37.4 - R_1)(R_1 - 4.6)}{(37.4 - R_1) + (R_1 - 4.6)} = 18.12 \text{ ohms.}$$

Noting that the denominator is equal to 32.8,

$$32.8R_1 + 37.4R_1 - 172 - R_1^2 + 4.6R_1 = 32.8 \cdot 18.12.$$
$$R_1^2 - 74.8R_1 = -766.$$

Completing the square and solving,

$$R_1^2 - 74.8R_1 + (37.4)^2 = -766 + 1{,}399.$$
$$R_1 = 37.4 \pm \sqrt{633} = 37.4 \pm 25.17$$
$$= 62.57 \text{ or } 12.23 \text{ ohms.}$$

If the value 62.57 ohms be used, R_2 in (I) becomes negative, which is contrary to the conditions of a passive network.

Hence

$$R_1 = 12.23 \text{ ohms.} \quad \textit{Ans.}$$

From (I) and (III),

$$R_2 = 25.17 \text{ ohms,} \qquad R_3 = 7.63 \text{ ohms.} \quad \textit{Ans.}$$

Note that, electrically, the π network, Fig. 57(b), is identical with the delta network, Fig. 55(a); and the T network, Fig. 58, is identical with the Y network, Fig. 55(b). In fact the last example could have been solved by converting from a delta to a Y system, applying (65), (66), (67) (p. 88).

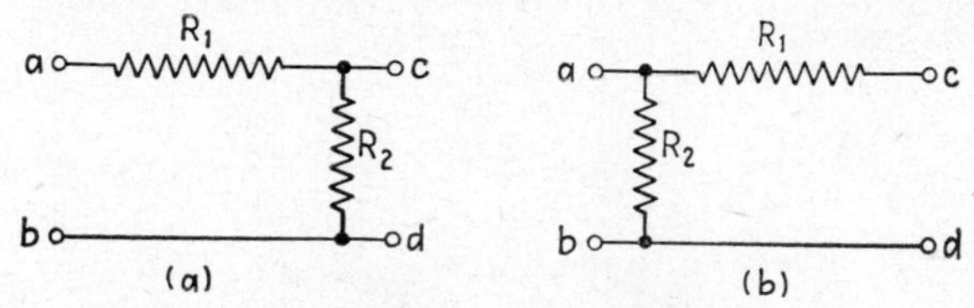

FIG. 59. L networks.

In the general case the resistors R_1 and R_3 in the π and T networks of Figs. 57(b) and 58 are unequal, and the networks are *dissymmetrical.* However, if $R_1 = R_3$, the networks are *symmetrical.*

L Networks. If, in Fig. 57(b) or in Fig. 58 either R_1 or R_3 is omitted, a 4-terminal L network results, as shown in Figs. 59(a) and (b). Each L network can be made equivalent to the general network, Fig. 57(a), so far as either terminals ab or cd alone are concerned. This condition holds true irrespective of the impedance or load connected to the other pair of terminals, for example, bc, if terminals ab are considered. However, with only two independent elements, neither L network can be made equal to a general passive network, in a bilateral sense.

Example. With $R_{ab} = 37.4$ ohms and $R_{ab}' = 18.12$ ohms, in the network of Fig. 57(a), determine the two types of L networks, Figs. 59(a) and (b), which will replace the network so far as terminals ab are concerned.

(a)
$$R_{ab} = R_1 + R_2 = 37.4 \text{ ohms.}$$
$$R_{ab}' = R_1 = 18.12 \text{ ohms.} \quad \textit{Ans.}$$
$$R_2 = 19.28 \text{ ohms.} \quad \textit{Ans.}$$

(b)
$$R_{ab} = R_2 = 37.4 \text{ ohms.} \quad \textit{Ans.}$$
$$R_{ab}' = \frac{R_1R_2}{R_1 + R_2} = 18.12 \text{ ohms.}$$
$$\frac{37.4R_1}{R_1 + 37.4} = 18.12 \text{ ohms.}$$
$$R_1 = 35.1 \text{ ohms.} \quad \textit{Ans.}$$

CHAPTER IV

PRIMARY AND SECONDARY BATTERIES

72. Principle of the Electric Battery. If two copper strips or plates be immersed in a dilute sulfuric acid solution, Fig. 60(*a*), and be connected to the terminals of a voltmeter, no appreciable deflection of the voltmeter will be observed. This shows that no appreciable difference of potential exists between the copper strips. If, however, one of the copper strips, Fig. 60(*b*), be replaced by a zinc strip, the voltmeter needle

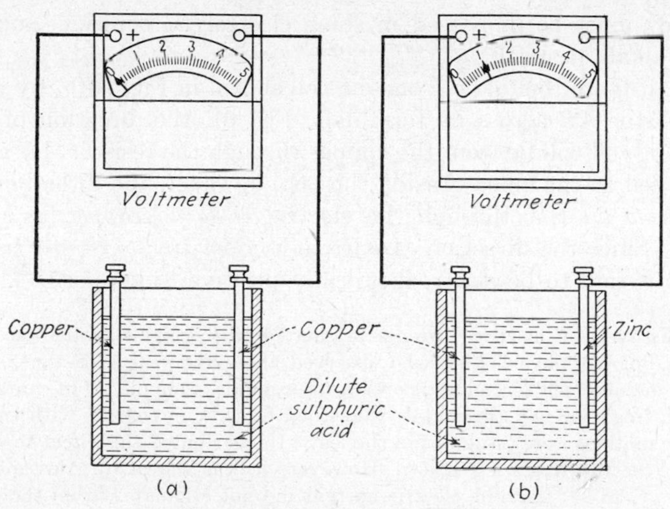

FIG. 60. Simple primary cell.

will deflect and will indicate approximately 1 volt, showing that a potential difference between strips now exists. It will be necessary to connect the copper to the positive terminal and the zinc to the negative terminal of the voltmeter for the voltmeter to read up scale. This shows that, so far as the *external* circuit is concerned, the copper is positive to the zinc.

The experiment may be repeated with various metals. For example, carbon or lead may be substituted for the copper, and a potential difference will be found to exist between each of these and the zinc, although it will not be of the same value as for the copper-zinc combination. Various metals may be substituted for the zinc, and potential differences will be found to exist between them and the copper.

Furthermore, it is not necessary that sulfuric acid be used for the solution. Other acids, such as hydrochloric acid, and chromic acid, may be substituted for the sulfuric acid; or salt solutions such as common salt (sodium chloride), sal ammoniac (ammonium chloride), copper sulfate, or zinc sulfate may be used.

Because of the early discoveries of Galvani and Volta,[1] such batteries, or cells, came to be known as *galvanic* batteries, or *voltaic* cells.

Solutions, such as are used with batteries, are called *electrolytes*, or *electrolytic conductors*, and are defined as "conducting medium(s) in which the flow of electric current is accompanied by the movement of matter."[2] An electrolyte is also defined as "a substance which when dissolved in a specified solvent (usually water) produces a conducting medium."[3]

In order to obtain a difference of potential between the two metal plates, only two conditions are necessary:

1. The plates must be of different metals.
2. They must be immersed in some electrolytic solution, such as an acid, an alkali, or a salt.

Again, if power be taken from the cell shown in Fig. 60(b) by connecting a resistor AB across its terminals, Fig. 61, the direction of current outside the cell will be from the copper through the resistor AB and then into the cell at the zinc. Inside the cell, however, the direction of current is *from the zinc* through the electrolyte *to the copper*, as shown in Fig. 61. Since the direction of current is *from zinc to copper within the cell*, zinc is said to be electrochemically positive to copper. Therefore,

[1] The discovery of electric currents originated with Luigi Galvani (see footnote, p. 138), a Bologna physiologist, who observed about the year 1768 that, when two dissimilar metals, such as iron and copper, for example, were placed in contact with a nerve in a frog's leg and the metals were then brought in contact with each other, convulsive motions were produced in the leg. He attributed this effect to electricity originating in the frog's leg itself. However, it was shown by Alessandro Volta (see footnote, p. 31) that the electric current did not originate within the muscle or nerve of the frog's leg but originated from the contact of the dissimilar metals and that the convulsive motions of the frog's leg were produced by this current. Volta had thus made the discovery that the production of electric energy by electrolytic action was due to the contact of two dissimilar metals. Then he performed a more convincing experiment. Two disks of dissimilar metals, such as zinc and copper, were placed in contact. A piece of blotting paper or flannel moistened with brine was placed on the copper disk and another pair of zinc and copper disks was added. In this manner he built up what is known as a *voltaic pile* in which the electrical effects were additive and which was capable of delivering a substantial amount of electrical energy. Because of the discoveries of the two foregoing scientists, dynamic electricity or an electric current is sometimes called *galvanic* and also *voltaic* electricity. Later, Volta devised an actual battery consisting of a number of electrolytic cells in series. The electrodes of each cell consisted of strips of copper and zinc, and the electrolyte was either brine or a dilute acid.

[2] ASA Definitions of Electrical Terms, 1941 edition, 60.05.020.

[3] 60.05.021.

in considering such an electrochemical cell, the copper is positive to the zinc when the external circuit is considered, but the zinc is electropositive to the copper when the plates and the electrolyte alone are considered.

73. Definitions of Electrolytic Quantities. The cell described in Sec. 72 is an *electrolytic* cell. Such a cell is defined as follows (italics are the author's):

"An *electrolytic cell* is a unit apparatus designed for carrying out an electrochemical reaction and includes a vessel, two or more electrodes, and one or more electrolytes."[1]

"An *electrode* is a conductor belonging to the class of metallic conductors, but not necessarily a metal, through which a current enters or leaves an electrolytic cell. . . . "[2]

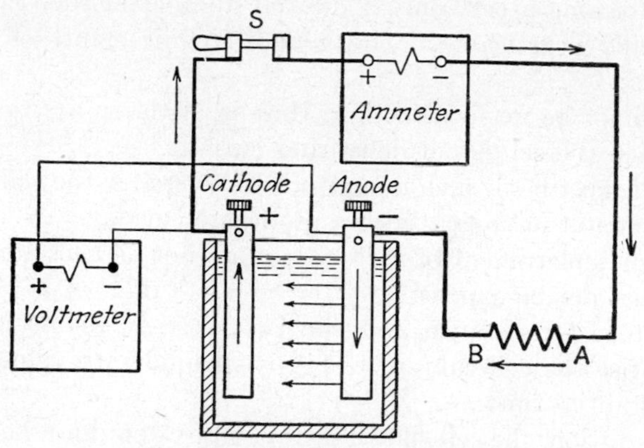

FIG. 61. Cell delivering power.

"An *anode* is an electrode through which current enters any conductor of the non-metallic class. . . . "[3]

"A *cathode* is an electrode through which current leaves any conductor of the non-metallic class. . . . "[4]

In the last two definitions the "conductor of the non-metallic class" is obviously the electrolyte. In an electrolytic cell delivering energy, Fig. 60(*b*), the anode is the negative terminal, or zinc, and the cathode is the positive terminal, or copper.

"A *primary cell* is a cell designed to produce electric current through an electrochemical reaction which is not efficiently reversible and hence the cell, when discharged, cannot be efficiently recharged by an electric current."[5]

[1] ASA Standard Definitions of Electrical Terms, 1941 edition, 60.05.050.
[2] ASA Standard Definitions of Electrical Terms, 1941 edition, 60.05.030.
[3] ASA Standard Definitions of Electrical Terms, 1941 edition, 60.05.040.
[4] ASA Standard Definitions of Electrical Terms, 1941 edition, 60.05.045.
[5] ASA Standard Definitions of Electrical Terms, 1941 edition, 60.11.005.

"A *storage cell* is an electrolytic cell for the generation of electric energy in which the cell after being discharged may be restored to a charged condition by an electric current flowing in a direction opposite to the flow of current when the cell discharges."[1] A storage cell is frequently called a *secondary cell.*

Energy stored in electrolytic cells is *chemical energy,* and electrical energy is delivered at the expense of the electrode, which either goes into solution or is converted into a lower form of chemical energy. Therefore, a primary cell or battery transforms *chemical energy* into *electrical energy.*

74. Primary Cells. Although it is stated in Sec. 72 that there are many combinations of metals and solutions capable of generating an emf and so forming a cell, only a limited number of such combinations is commercially practicable. The general requirements of a good cell are as follows:

a. There must be no local action, that is, little or no wastage of the materials when the cell is not delivering current.

b. The emf must be of such magnitude as to enable the cell to deliver a reasonable amount of energy with a moderate current.

c. Frequent replacement of materials must not be necessary, and such materials must not be expensive.

d. The internal resistance and the polarization effects must not be large; otherwise the cell cannot supply even moderate values of current for any substantial time.

As an illustration, the cell shown in Fig. 60(*b*) would not be practicable, because both copper and zinc would waste away, even were the battery delivering no current. Polarization (see Sec. 76) would be substantial, and the cell would be capable of delivering only a comparatively small current.

75. Internal Resistance. As is pointed out in Chap. III, every cell or battery has an internal resistance, which tends to reduce the magnitude of the current and also of the terminal voltage, when current is taken from the cell. Such resistance lies in the electrodes, in the contact surface between the electrodes and the electrolyte, and in the electrolyte itself. This resistance may be reduced by changing the dimensions of the cell in the same way as would be done for any electric conductor. The cross section of the path through which the current flows inside the cell should be made as large as is practicable. This means large area of electrodes in contact with the electrolyte. Also the transverse cross section of the electrodes must be large enough to carry the current to the cell terminals without excessive drop in voltage. Little difficulty is experienced in making the voltage drop negligible in the electrodes themselves. It

[1] ASA Standard Definitions of Electrical Terms, 1941 edition, 60.12.005.

will be appreciated that larger electrodes mean a larger cell, with a greater current capacity. In addition to increasing the area of the electrodes in contact with the electrolyte, the resistance of the cell may also be diminished by decreasing the distance between the electrodes. This reduces the length of the path of the current within the cell and correspondingly reduces the cell resistance.

Increasing the size of the cell does not increase its emf. The emf depends solely on the material of the two electrodes and of the electrolyte. For example, if two cells, one being very much larger than the other, have the same materials for electrodes and the same electrolyte, their emfs will be the same. That is, if they are connected with positive terminals together and with negative terminals together, there will be no circulatory current. However, increasing the size of the elements of a cell does increase its current capacity.

76. Polarization. If a test be made to determine the decrease of terminal voltage when a cell delivers current as, for example, a dry cell, by connecting voltmeter, ammeter, and external resistor as in Fig. 61, the results will be somewhat as follows:

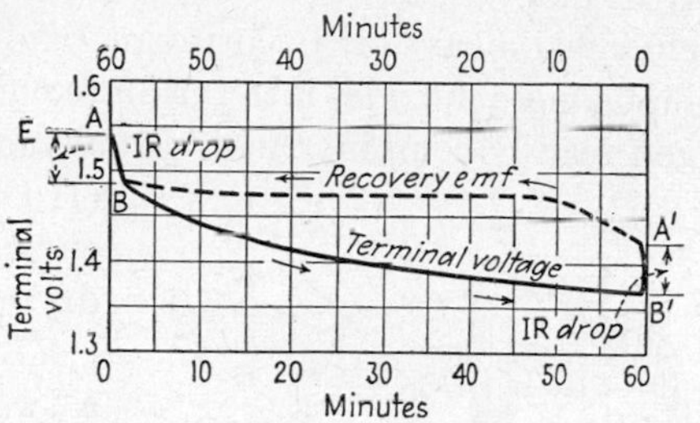

FIG. 62. Discharge and recovery characteristics of a dry cell.

When the cell is on open circuit, the voltmeter will indicate the cell emf E, Fig. 62.[1] When the switch S is closed, the cell delivers current and the terminal voltage drops immediately by the amount AB. The distance AB represents approximately the voltage drop due to the internal resistance of the cell, and this has just been considered. As time elapses, the terminal voltage will continue to drop, as shown by the portion BB' of the graph, Fig. 62, even though the external resistance be maintained constant. This further drop of voltage is due almost entirely to *polarization.*

If at the time B' the external resistance is open-circuited, the terminal voltage almost immediately rises by the amount $B'A'$, this distance representing the internal-resistance drop in the cell. With further lapse of time, now represented from right to left, as shown by the top scale, Fig. 62, the emf of the cell gradually recovers, owing to the escape of hydrogen bubbles at the cathode.

Polarization is due to the fact that, when the cell delivers current, small bubbles of hydrogen form upon the positive plate, or cathode, practically covering it, and these bubbles have two effects.

[1] See "Standard Handbook for Electrical Engineers," 8th ed., Sec. 21, p. 1969, McGraw-Hill Book Company, Inc.

1. They cause a substantial increase in the resistance at the contact surface between the cathode and the electrolyte.

2. Hydrogen acting in conjunction with the cathode, or positive electrode, sets up an *emf of polarization* which opposes that of the cell.

These two effects explain the reduction in the emf and current capacity of many types of cells after they have delivered current for some time.

Depolarization. Partial or almost complete depolarization may be accomplished either physically or chemically. Physical depolarization consists in roughening the electrode surface. It is sometimes accomplished by the electrodeposition of a loose mass of metal on the electrode surface such as platinum black on a platinum surface. Hydrogen escapes more readily from such roughened surfaces.

In practice, however, depolarization is almost always accomplished by chemical means, as by bringing oxidizing agents, such as chromic acid or manganese dioxide, into intimate contact with the cathode. The hydrogen readily combines with the oxygen of these compounds to form water (H_2O). This method is used in the bichromate cell, in the Leclanché cell, and in dry cells.

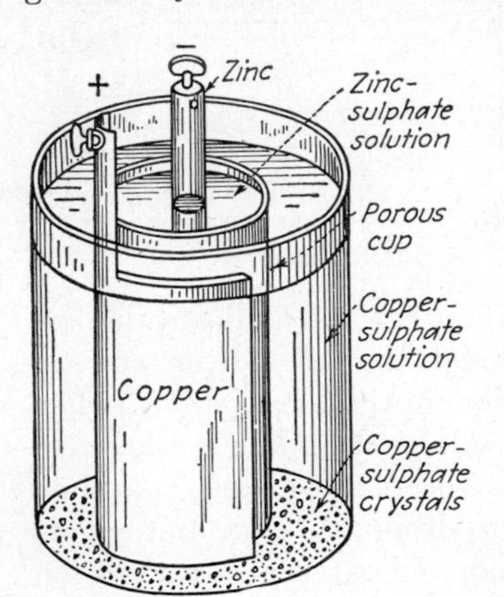

FIG. 63. Daniell cell.

77. Daniell Cell. This cell, Fig. 63, is a two-fluid cell having copper and zinc as electrodes. It consists of a glass jar, inside of which is a porous cup containing zinc sulfate solution or a solution of zinc sulfate and sulfuric acid. The anode, or negative electrode, is zinc which is immersed in this electrolyte. The porous cup is placed in a solution of copper sulfate with copper sulfate crystals in the bottom of the jar. The cathode is a copper plate which surrounds the porous cup. The porous cup keeps the two solutions separated. As the copper is in a copper sulfate solution, there is no polarization. This cell is designed for use in a circuit which is continuously closed. If left on open circuit, the electrodes waste away. When the cell is taken out of service for some time, the electrodes should be removed and the porous cup should be thoroughly washed. The emf of this cell is about 1.1 volts. So far as practical use is concerned, the Daniell cell is obsolete but it illustrates the principle of operation of the gravity cell.

78. Gravity Cell. The gravity cell is a modification of the Daniell cell, depending on gravity rather than a porous cup to keep the two electrolytes separated. This cell is shown in Fig. 64. The cathode, which is of copper, is made of thin strips riveted together and placed in the bottom of the cell together with copper sulfate crystals. A solution of copper sulfate is then poured to within a few inches of the top of the jar. The connection to the copper is usually an insulated copper wire fastened to the copper and carried out through the solution to the top of the jar. There should always be copper sulfate crystals at the bottom of the cell.

The anode is zinc, is usually rather massive, and is cast in the form of a crow's-foot and hung on the top of the jar. This is surrounded by a zinc sulfate solution. The solutions are kept separated by gravity. The copper sulfate is the heavier of the two solutions and therefore tends to remain at the bottom. The solutions should be poured in carefully, for if the copper sulfate solution comes in contact with the zinc, copper will be deposited on the zinc. This copper should be removed, if by chance it becomes deposited in any way. In the operation of the cell the zinc goes into solution as zinc sulfate, and metallic copper comes out of the copper sulfate solution and is deposited upon the copper electrode. The copper cathode will therefore gain in weight, whereas the zinc anode will lose in weight. This is the reason for having the zinc electrode massive and the copper electrode of very thin sheet copper when the cell is set up initially. The emf of the cell is practically that of the Daniell cell, being about 1.09 volts, and varies slightly with the concentration of the solutions.

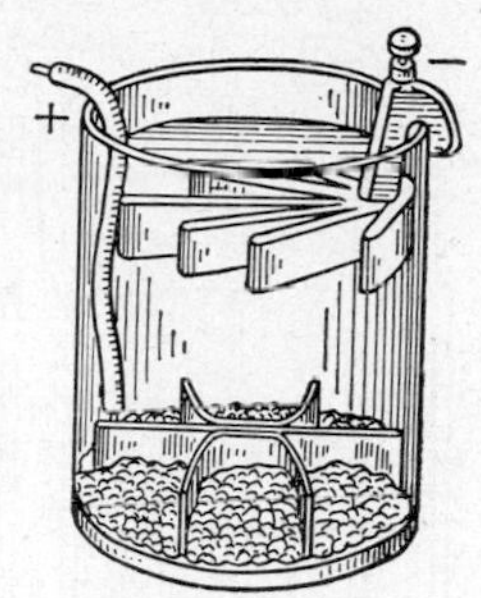

Fig. 64. Gravity cell.

To prevent creepage of the zinc sulfate, the top of the jar should be paraffined. To prevent evaporation, the upper surface of the electrolyte may be covered with oil. When the cell is replenished, metallic zinc and copper sulfate crystals are supplied and metallic copper and zinc sulfate are removed.

The gravity cell is a *closed-circuit* battery, and the circuit should be kept closed for the best results. Otherwise the copper sulfate will gradually mix with the zinc sulfate. The cell has been used for railway signals, fire-alarm systems, and telephone exchanges, all closed-circuit work. This cell has been largely replaced by the storage battery and frequently by a-c power which may be rectified.

79. Leclanché Cell. The Leclanché cell is perhaps the most familiar type of primary battery, because it forms the basis of the dry cell which has such a wide application. In fact the dry cell is merely a form of the Leclanché cell in which the electrolyte is retained by an absorbent medium. The cathode is molded carbon, and the anode is amalgamated zinc. The electrolyte is sal ammoniac (ammonium chloride). Because of the rapidity with which it polarizes, this type of cell is suited for open-circuit work only. The emf is from 1.4 to 1.5 volts, but because of the drop due to internal resistance and that due to polarization the *terminal voltage* may be considered as being 1 volt when the cell is in service. The most common method of reducing polarization is to bring manganese dioxide into intimate contact with the carbon. The manganese dioxide gives up oxygen readily, which unites with the hydrogen bubbles to form water.

In one type of Leclanché cell, a pencil zinc is suspended in the center of a hollow cylinder of carbon and manganese dioxide. An improved type, the porous-cup cell, is shown in Fig. 65. In this form a carbon cup is filled with manganese dioxide, and the zinc, bent into cylindrical form, surrounds the carbon cup, being separated from it by rubber rings.

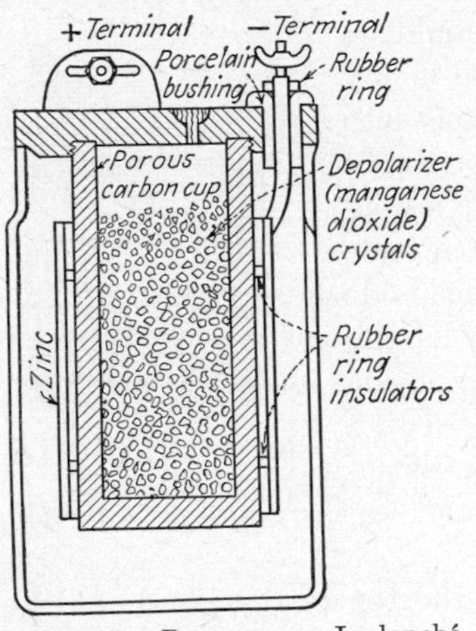

Fig. 65. Porous-cup Leclanché cell.

The solution should consist of 3 oz of sal ammoniac to 1 pt of water. A more concentrated solution produces zinc chloride crystals on the zinc and carbon. To prevent the solution "creeping," the top of the cell is dipped in paraffin and the top of the carbon is covered with wax.

Because of its simplicity and the fact that it contains no injurious acids or alkalies, this type of cell was once widely used for intermittent work, such as for doorbells, telephone work, and open-circuit telegraph work. Because of its more convenient form, the dry cell has to a large extent replaced this type of cell.

80. Dry Cell. The dry cell is in reality a Leclanché cell with the electrolyte held by an absorbent material, and the entire cell is sealed to prevent evaporation. Since this type of cell is relatively very light and is portable and convenient, it has practically replaced other types of primary cells. The name "dry cell" is really a misnomer, for no cell that is dry will deliver any appreciable current. In fact the chief cause of dry cells becoming exhausted is their actually becoming dry.

A cross section of a typical dry cell is shown in Fig. 66. The anode is sheet zinc, in the form of a cylindrical cup, and acts as the container of the cell. The binding post is soldered to the top of the zinc. The zinc is lined with some nonconducting material such as blotting paper or plaster of paris. The cathode consists of a carbon rod, with the mixture of coke, carbon, etc., which surrounds this rod. The rod itself varies in shape among manufacturers. It is located axially in the zinc container, and the binding post is secured to the top of the rod. The depolarizing agent, powdered manganese dioxide, is mixed with finely crushed coke and pressed solidly into the container between the carbon rod and the non-conducting material which lines the zinc. It fills the cell to within about an inch of the top. Sal ammoniac, with a little zinc sulfate, is added, and the cell is then sealed with wax or some tar compound. The outside of the zinc is frequently lacquered, and the cells are always set in close-fitting cardboard containers.

The emf of a dry cell when new is from 1.5 to 1.6 volts but this drops to about 1.4 volts with time, even though the cell remains idle. An emf of much less than 1.5 volts usually indicates that deterioration has begun. The internal resistance of the cell when new is about 0.1 ohm and increases to several times this value with time. The polarization effect is large as compared with the internal resistance, so that a low value of internal resistance is not important except as an indication of the condition of the cell. A method for testing the condition of a cell is to short-circuit it through an ammeter, when it should deliver an instantaneous value of 1.5/0.1, or 15, amp, if in good condition. When new, the current under these conditions may reach even 25 amp. When delivering appreciable current, the terminal voltage is very nearly 1 volt.

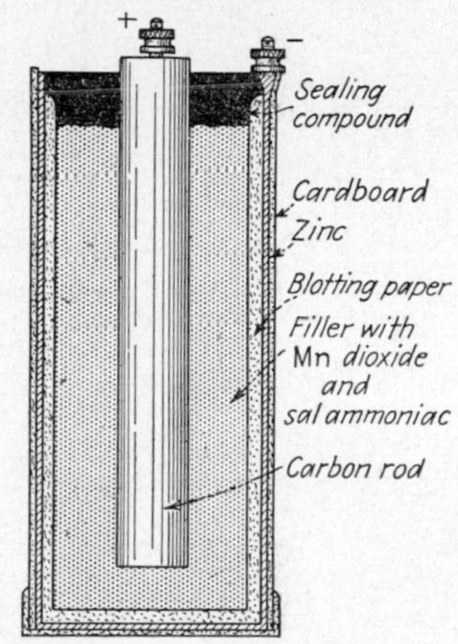

Fig. 66. Sectional view—dry cell.

One of the chief causes of a cell's becoming useless is the using up of the zinc as a result of electrochemical reactions within the cell. This allows the solution to leak out and to dry up, and the cell then becomes worthless. The life of a cell may be prolonged temporarily by introducing fresh solution, but the results are usually far from satisfactory.

The two most common types of dry cell are the No. 6, which is $2\frac{1}{4}$ in. diameter and 6 in. high, and the flashlight battery, which is $1\frac{3}{4}$ in. diameter and $2\frac{1}{4}$ in. high. The first type has a capacity of approximately 30 amp-hr and the second a capacity of approximately 3 amp-hr.

As is well known, dry cells have many applications. Their field is limited to supplying moderate currents intermittently, but they are capable of supplying continuously very small currents of the magnitude of 0.1 amp. They are used extensively for doorbells, electric bells, buzzers, telephones, telegraph instruments, gas-engine ignition, flashlights, and for many other purposes. They are also used as A, B, and C batteries in d-c radio sets.

81. Ruben Cell. The Ruben (RM) cell[1] was developed jointly by the Ruben Laboratories and P. R. Mallory and Company during the Second World War to meet the need of the armed forces for dry batteries to operate equipment such as radar and other electronic devices which require a high ratio of ampere-hour capacity to volume at higher current densities than were considered practicable for the Leclanché cell. The anode is of amalgamated zinc, and the cathode is a mercuric oxide depolarizing material intimately mixed with graphite in order to reduce

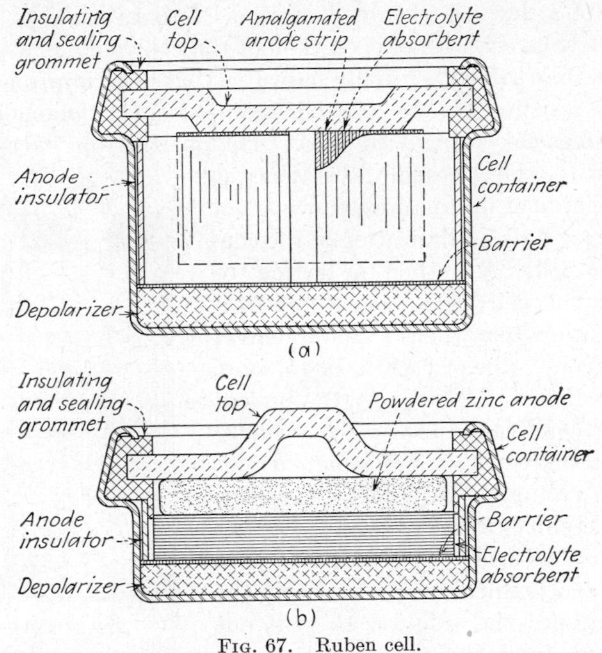

FIG. 67. Ruben cell.

its electrical resistivity. The electrolyte is a solution of potassium hydroxide (KOH) containing potassium zincate. The cell is made in two forms. In one form the anode consists of a spirally wound corrugated strip of zinc, Fig. 67(*a*), 0.002 to 0.005 in. (0.051 to 0.13 mm) thick, which is amalgamated after assembly. Two strips of alkali-resistant (electrolyte) absorbent paper are interwound with the zinc foil so that the zinc protrudes at the upper side and paper at the lower side. The anode is insulated from the steel cell container by a polystyrene anode insulator. The cathode depolarizer is separated from the anode by a barrier of alkali-resistant paper. The cell top is copper which contacts the zinc strip to form the negative terminal of the cell. The cell is sealed by an insulating grommet of neoprene. The steel container,

[1] RUBEN, SAMUEL, "Balanced Alkaline Dry Cells," *Trans. Electrochem. Soc.*, Vol. 92, 1947.

which is inert chemically to the cell ingredients, forms the positive electrode.

In the second, or "button," type of cell, Fig. 67(*b*), the anode is a pressed powdered zinc amalgam disk. The other elements of the cell are identical with those in (*a*). The button type of cell has higher volumetric efficiency than the roll type, which, together with other factors, may result in its replacing the roll type.

The no-load emf of the cell is 1.34 volts, which remains essentially constant irrespective of time and temperature. Advantages of the cell are long "shelf life," which enables it to be stored indefinitely; long service life, about four times that of the Leclanché dry cell of equivalent volume; small weight; a flat voltage characteristic which is advantageous for electronic uses in which the characteristics of tubes vary widely with voltage; adaptability to operating at high temperatures without deterioration; high resistance to shock.

As an example of the high capacity of the Ruben cell as compared with the ordinary dry cell, both types were used to operate a Walkie-Talkie radio set. The battery of dry cells weighed 9½ lb and operated continuously for 7.8 hr before replacement. The RM battery of the same voltage weighed 8 lb 10 oz and operated 38 hr before replacement.

82. Silver Chloride–Magnesium Water-activated Battery. At the beginning of the Second World War, owing to the many advances in electronic equipment for the armed forces, a serious need arose for extremely lightweight small-size high-powered batteries. The existing storage and dry batteries either were too large or did not have the necessary capacity to meet the requirements of the new lightweight small-size electronic equipment. Moreover, since the batteries were used in all parts of the world, an indefinite storage life was necessary. As a result a silver chloride–magnesium water-activated battery was developed by the C. F. Burgess Laboratories, Inc. The positive electrode consists of silver foil 0.001 to 0.003 in. thick, coated with electrolytically formed silver chloride, and the negative electrode is magnesium foil. In the type designed for moderate voltage but high current, the silver foil is coated on both sides with silver chloride, and a wire lead is welded to each electrode. The two electrodes are wound spirally with dry absorbent paper interleaved between. This forms a cylindrical cell with two wires protruding from the end. Thus formed the cell in the dry condition is entirely inert and will keep indefinitely. When the absorbent paper becomes saturated with an electrolyte, preferably fresh or salt water, the cell is capable of delivering substantial currents.

[1] Mullen, J. B., and P. L. Howard, "Characteristics of the Silver Chloride–Magnesium Water Activated Battery," *Trans. Electrochem. Soc.*, Vol. 90, p. 529, 1946. (The authors are with the Burgess Battery Company.)

To make a battery of two or more cells, it is convenient to wrap the cylindrical cell with a plastic film or varnished paper and then wrap a second cell around this. For high voltages where the current is not large the batteries are preferably made in flat form, and the silver foil is coated with silver chloride on one side only.

The cell can deliver relatively high currents at a discharge voltage of 1.3 to 1.5 volts, and the voltage is relatively constant over the discharge range. A cell with an electrode diameter of 1¾ in. and a height of 3¼ in. has 0.875 amp-hr capacity when discharged to 1 volt and weighs 74 g dry and 110 g wet. The average ampere-hours and watthours per pound are 2.9 and 19.4, which are much greater than with other commercial types of battery, being about twice as great as the value for the lead–lead acid battery. Inasmuch as water is universally available, the batteries can be shipped anywhere without electrolyte. The cell is well adapted to such applications as radio rescue buoys which are dropped from airplanes into the ocean near downed aircraft crews. As soon as the buoy hits the water, sea water enters the battery, activating it and causing it to supply power to an automatic radio-sending device which guides rescue ships or airplanes to the spot. This type of cell is expensive, but it is justified by the special services to which the cell can be applied.

83. Weston Standard Cell. It is essential in practical work to be able to reproduce accurately standards of current, voltage, and resistance. Obviously if two of these quantities are known, the third is readily obtainable by Ohm's law. It is a matter of no great difficulty to make and to reproduce resistance standards, as such standards are nothing more than metals in strips and in other forms, carefully mounted and calibrated. Such standards are practically permanent, so that their resistance remains constant indefinitely.

A standard of current or of voltage is much more difficult to reproduce and to maintain than a standard of resistance. It has been found more practicable to produce and maintain a voltage standard rather than a current standard. This voltage standard is the emf of a *standard cell*. The emf of a cell depends on its materials and their impurities, the concentration of the electrolyte, the temperature, the polarization effects, etc. It is difficult, therefore, to select such materials for a cell as will enable it to be reproduced at different times and at various places with a high degree of accuracy. The Weston cell meets the foregoing requirements and is now used universally as a standard cell.

In the Weston cell the cathode is mercury, and the anode is cadmium amalgam. The electrolyte is a solution of cadmium sulfate and mercurous sulfate.

The cell is made in two forms, the *normal cell* and the unsaturated, or *secondary, cell*. In the normal cell, cadmium sulfate crystals are left in the solution so that it is always saturated. Its emf is affected slightly by temperature, a change of about 50 microvolts per °C taking place in the zone from 25 to 40°C, but corrections can be accurately made. It is possible to reproduce such cells with emfs differing among themselves by only a few parts in 1,000,000.

The container for the cell is an *H* tube of glass, each leg of which is 25 mm, or about 1 in., in diameter. The *H* tube is glass-sealed to provide a hermetic closure. The mercury cathode is located at the bottom of one leg of the *H* tube. Above this is mercurous sulfate paste. In the bottom of the other leg of the *H* tube is the cadmium-amalgam anode. The leads from the cathode and the anode are sealed into the legs at the bottom. Rapid changes in temperature do not affect both legs equally, and an error develops until the temperature has become stabilized. To minimize this effect the cell is enclosed within a bakelite case, Fig. 68, in which the front is cut away to show the cell construction. More recently a shell of heavy copper has been added, Fig. 68, to reduce the temperature effect still further.

Fig. 68. Internal view of Weston standard cell (unsaturated).

The terminal voltage of any cell differs from its emf by the *IR* drop due to the cell resistance. As the resistance of a Weston cell is of the order of 125 ohms, it is evident that if any appreciable current be taken from the cell, its terminal voltage will be quite different from its emf. The cell must be used, therefore, in such a manner that it delivers no appreciable current. By means of the *Poggendorff method,* described in Sec. 137 (p. 179), the cell is used without delivering current. Not more than 0.0001 amp should be taken from the cell at any time. If appreciable current is taken, the emf drops, but when the circuit is again opened, the emf slowly recovers its initial value.

STORAGE BATTERIES

84. Storage Batteries. A storage, or secondary, cell (sometimes called an *accumulator*) involves the same principles as a primary cell, but the two differ from each other in the manner in which they are renewed. The materials of a primary cell which are used up in the process of delivering current are replaced by new materials, whereas, in the storage cell, the cell materials are restored to their initial condition by sending a current through the cell in a reverse direction. For this reason the electrochemical products resulting from discharge must remain within the cell. Therefore, if a cell in its operation gives off material, usually in the form of gas, so that it cannot be brought back to its original condition with a reverse current, it is not suitable for a storage cell. For example, the Leclanché cell gives off free ammonia gas and therefore cannot be used as a storage cell. The Daniell and gravity cells are both reversible and hence are theoretically capable of being used as storage cells; but as the active materials go into solution and do not all return during the reverse cycle, the life of such a cell would be short. There are three types of storage cells in common use: the *lead-lead-acid* type, the *nickel-iron-alkali* type, and the *nickel-cadmium-alkali* type. In all of these cells the active materials do not leave the electrodes.

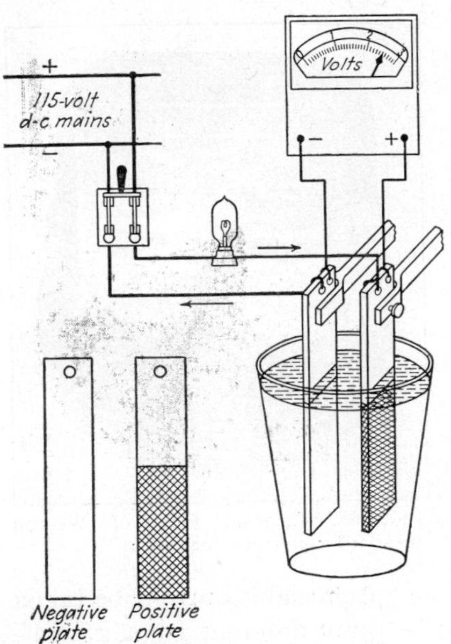

FIG. 69. Forming the plates of an elementary lead storage cell.

85. Lead-lead-acid Cell. The principle underlying the lead cell may be illustrated by the following simple experiment: Two plain lead strips, Fig. 69, are immersed in a glass of dilute sulfuric acid (sp gr = 1.200 approximately). These are connected in series with an incandescent lamp or equivalent resistance and are supplied from a 115-volt d-c source. The current causes bubbles of gas to be given off from each electrode. After a short time, one plate will have changed to a dark chocolate color, and the other apparently will not have changed its appearance. A careful examination, however, will show that the metallic lead at the surface of the latter plate has started to change from solid metallic lead to spongy lead.

When energy is supplied to the cell, the cell is being charged and the voltmeter connected across the cell indicates about 2.5 volts. If the current is interrupted, the voltmeter reading will fall to about 2.05 volts and the cell will now be found capable of delivering a small current. However, the energy that such a cell can deliver is very limited and even the small current will exhaust the cell in a very short time. As the cell discharges, the voltage drops off slowly to about 1.75 volts, after which it drops more rapidly until it becomes zero and the cell is apparently exhausted. The color of the dark-brown plate will now have become lighter and will more nearly resemble its initial lead color. After a short rest the cell will recover slightly and will again deliver current for a very brief time.

The plate which is a dark chocolate color is the positive plate, or cathode, and the one which is partially converted to spongy lead is the negative plate, or anode. The bubbles come mostly from the negative plate and are free hydrogen gas. Some bubbles, however, come from the positive plate, and these are oxygen. The current to such a cell converts the metallic lead of the positive plate into lead peroxide, whereas the negative plate is not changed chemically but is converted from solid lead into the spongy form of lead, which is softer and more porous than ordinary metallic lead. When the cell delivers energy, the peroxide of the positive plate is changed to lead sulfate and the spongy lead of the negative plate also is changed to lead sulfate so that both plates tend to become electrochemically equivalent.

The electrolytic principle of the cell is the same as that of a primary cell. When the two lead plates are the same electrochemically, that is, when both are lead sulfate, no emf exists between them. When the positive plate is converted to the peroxide and the negative plate to spongy lead by the action of the current during charge, the two plates become dissimilar and an emf now exists between them. This emf is about 2.05 volts, the difference of 0.45 volt between this and the 2.50 volts at the terminals during charge being necessary to overcome the internal-resistance and polarization effects. This simple experiment illustrates the principle underlying the operation of lead storage cells.

The chemical reactions which take place in a lead storage cell are as follows:

Battery Discharged						Battery Charged				
(+ plate)		(− plate)				(+ plate)		(− plate)		
$PbSO_4$	+	$PbSO_4$	+	$2H_2O$	$\leftrightarrows$	PbO_2	+	Pb	+	$2H_2SO_4$
Lead sulfate	+	lead sulfate	+	water	is changed to	lead peroxide	+	lead	+	sulfuric acid

When read from left to right, the equation shows the reactions which occur in the battery on charge. When read from right to left, it shows the reactions which occur on discharge.

When the battery is being charged, the only change that takes place in the electrolyte is that water is converted into sulfuric acid. This accounts for the increase of specific gravity on charge. On discharge, the sulfuric acid is dissociated and reacts with the lead peroxide to form water. Therefore, on discharge, the specific gravity of the electrolyte decreases. When charging, free hydrogen is given off at the negative plate and oxygen at the positive plate. Because of the explosive nature of hydrogen, *no flame should be allowed to come in proximity to a storage battery while the battery is charging.*

86. Planté Plates. It would not be practicable to construct storage cells of plain lead sheets as used in the foregoing experiment. The surface area exposed to electrochemical action would be so small compared with the volume of the lead that the ampere-hours capacity of the cell would be too limited to be of commercial value. Moreover, with relatively little charging the dark lead peroxide of the positive plate would fall off in flakes and drop to the bottom of the cell.

Hence it is necessary to construct the plates so that a relatively large surface is exposed to electrochemical action and at the same time the opportunities for the peroxide to flake from the positive plate are minimized. There are two methods for obtaining these results, the Planté process and the Faure process. In the Planté process the active material on the plates is formed from the metallic lead by causing current to flow through the cell, first in one direction and then in the reverse direction, which procedure works the lead on the surface of the plates into active material.

One method for obtaining a large surface is illustrated by the Gould positive plate, Fig. 70. A smooth plate of a corroding grade of lead, containing no antimony, is first subjected to a spinning, or grooving, mechanical process, Fig. 70(top), which produces thin fins with a core of solid lead, Fig. 70(bottom). The plate is then placed in an oxidizing solution and charged. This process causes active lead peroxide to form on the fins, which is shown by the dark material between them, Fig. 70 (bottom). The core, of solid lead, is more or less protected from the action of the electrolyte and remains a conducting medium. It also supplies additional lead, which forms into active material as the surface material falls off or loses contact.

Another type of Planté plate, the Exide-Manchester type, is shown in Fig. 71. A grid made of lead and antimony is perforated. The active material consists of a corrugated lead ribbon, which is coiled into spirals and pressed into the perforations of the grid. The peroxide has a greater volume than the lead from which it is derived. Therefore, when the cell is charged, these spirals expand and become more firmly embedded in the plate. The grid itself is not acted upon to any great extent but serves as a mechanical support. The advantages of this type of plate are its rigidity and mechanical strength. Since the grid acts merely as the support for the lead buttons, the plate can be used until all the lead is converted into active material, without having the plate as a whole disintegrate.

Planté positive plates should be designed to give from 1,800 to 2,400 complete cycles of charge and discharge. With Planté plates, the charg-

FIG. 70. Gould "spun plate." (*Gould National Batteries, Inc.*)

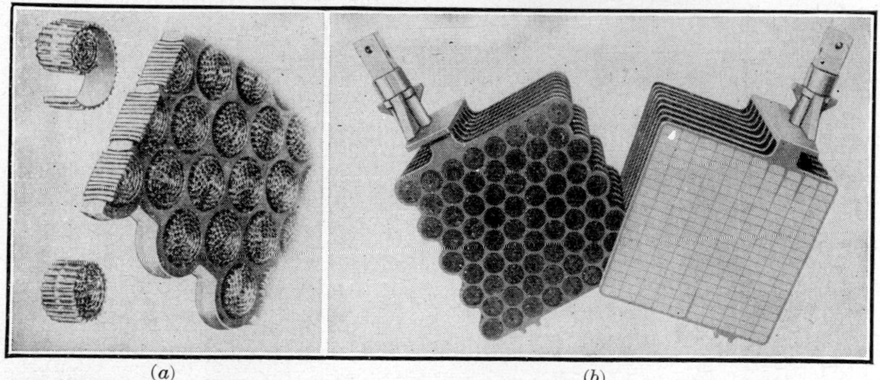

(*a*) (*b*)

FIG. 71. (*a*) Planté (Manchester) buttons and positive group. (*b*) Manchester positive group with negative pasted-plate group. (*Electric Storage Battery Company.*)

ing and discharging during the use of the battery convert more and more of the plate into active material. Hence the positive plates must gradually shed some of the active material to make room for this new active material. Therefore, there must be sufficient space between the bottom of the jar and the bottom of the plates to prevent the accumulation of lead peroxide from short-circuiting the plates.

Planté negative plates should give between 2,500 and 3,000 complete cycles of charge and discharge before their capacity falls to 80 per cent of its initial value. They fail from a loss of capacity due to the lead losing its spongy form rather than from mechanical disintegration of the plate. Only occasionally are Planté negative plates used, the Faure, or pasted, plate being almost always used, even with Planté positives.

87. Faure, or Pasted, Plate. This type of plate consists of a lead-antimony latticework, or grid, into which lead oxide is applied in the form of a paste. The battery is then charged. The paste on the positive grid is converted into peroxide and on the negative grid into spongy lead. The grid of a pasted-type positive plate is shown in Fig. 72.

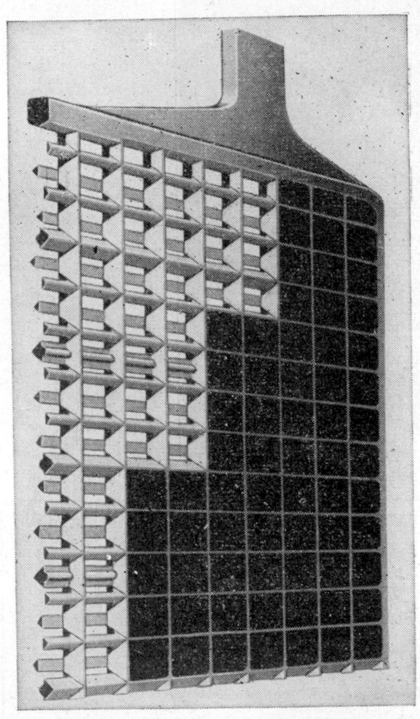

FIG. 72. Faure, or pasted, plate. Grid (positive or negative) partially filled with active material. (*Electric Storage Battery Company.*)

The chief advantage of the pasted plate is its high energy capacity, especially for short periods, together with its lesser size, cost, and weight for a given discharge rate. It is therefore very useful where lightness and compactness are necessary, such as in electric-vehicle batteries and in ignition and starting batteries for automobiles.

Flat-pasted positive plates also lose active material by shedding or by the erosive action of the bubbles. A pasted plate should give from 300 to 400 complete cycles of charge and discharge before its capacity falls to 80 per cent of its initial value.

By the use of fiberglas mats against the positive plates which act as erosion retarders, a life of the order of 750 cycles may be obtained at some sacrifice of electrical characteristics, due probably to the retarding of the flow of free electrolyte. These plates are also designed to give the utmost in electric performance at the expense of life where factors other than life are of greater importance.

Pasted positive plates gain in capacity during the early part of their life, increasing in capacity to about 120 per cent of the initial value. This extra capacity is available during the greater part of their life, since new active material is available as rapidly as it is shed. However, as soon as all the reserve active material has been utilized, further erosion results in a considerable loss in capacity. The erosion and the rate at which the plates lose capacity then become so rapid that the useful life of the plate is practically ended.

At high rates of discharge, pasted plates have a much greater ampere capacity per unit area than Planté plates. On the other hand, the Planté plate is more rugged and has a much longer life.

In all batteries there is one more negative than positive plate. This allows all the positives to be worked on *both* sides. Were any of the positives to be worked on one side only, the expansion of the active material, which occurs when it is converted to the peroxide on charge, would be unequal on the two sides of the plate and buckling would result.

Fig. 73. Cutaway of an Exide-Ironclad cell. (*Electric Storage Battery Company.*)

88. Exide-Ironclad Cell. For the propulsion of vehicles of various kinds and for many purposes where it is desirable to combine the characteristics of the pasted plate with much of the ruggedness and long life of the Planté plate, the Exide-Ironclad cell is the type of lead storage cell most generally used. Its positive plate consists of a lead-antimony frame which supports a number of slotted hard-rubber tubes. An irregular-shaped lead-antimony core passes through the center of each tube and serves as a collecting device for the current. The peroxide, or active material, is pressed into the tubes, filling the space between the irregular core and the inner wall of the tube. The perforations are so small that the peroxide does not drop out readily, and erosion of the positive plate is practically eliminated. An ordinary pasted plate, somewhat thickened, is used for the negative plate of this cell. Although slightly more expensive, this type of cell has a life well in excess of that of the usual flat pasted-plate cell. Also, this type of battery can withstand considerable rough usage. A view of an Exide-Ironclad cell, cut away to show the assembly, is given in Fig. 73.

Storage batteries are divided into two general classes, *stationary batteries* and *portable batteries.*

89. Stationary Batteries. The plates of this type of battery may be either of the Planté type or of the pasted type, depending on the nature of the service. For continuous "cycling" or regulating duty at a moderate though continuous rate of charging and discharging, the Planté plate is preferable. Where a battery is installed for emergency service, to carry an extreme overload for a very short period during a temporary shutdown of the generating apparatus, the Faure, or pasted, plate is preferable. For a given floor area, a pasted-plate battery can discharge at the 1-hr

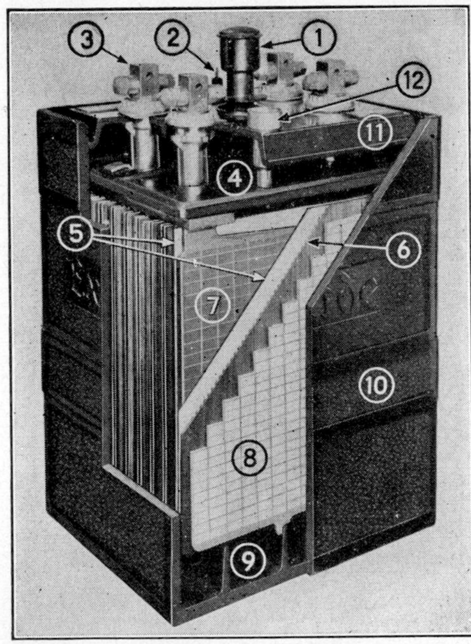

1. Gas escape vent
2. Indicator of electrolyte level
3. Heavy post with seal nut
4. Gas collector hood
5. Vitrex retainers, next to positive plates
6. Grooved wood separators
7. Heavy positive plates
8. Negative plate
9. Ribs, supporting plates
10. Thick-walled hard-rubber jars
11. Deep cover seal, sealed with compound

Fig. 74. Telephone-type stationary battery. (*Electric Storage Battery Company.*)

rate twice the current that a Planté plate can, and at higher ampere rates this ratio becomes even greater. This is an important factor in thickly settled city districts, where such batteries are usually located and where floor area is valuable.

When the battery is used for continuous cycling or regulating duty, the plates of stationary batteries may be of the Planté type, because of their long life. However, in most of the modern installations, thick pasted-type plates are used. Because of the tight fit of the cell elements within the container and the resulting pressure of the separators against the plate surfaces, shedding of active material is reduced to a minimum and long life is obtained. The pasted plate is advantageous for emergency service, since it can carry an extreme overload for a short period, as may be necessary, for example, during a shutdown of generating apparatus.

The containers are made of hard rubber and are provided with covers to prevent acid spray. (In the past, glass jars and lead-lined wooden tanks were used, but these have been superseded by rubber containers.) Figure 74 shows a cutaway view of a stationary battery cell of the type used for telephone-exchange service.

90. Separators. Except for some special assemblies where wide spacing between plates is provided, all battery cells, whether sealed or open, are assembled with some form of mechanical separation held in place between the plate surfaces. Separators have several distinct functions. They act as mechanical spacers to prevent the plates coming in contact with one another. They prevent the growth of "lead trees" formed by small particles which develop and grow on the negative plate and which otherwise would reach the positive plate and produce a short circuit. They may act as a retainer to prevent active material shedding from the plates.

Fig. 75. Assembly of a wooden separator.

All separators should permit the circulation of the electrolyte. For a number of years wood-veneer separators have proved eminently satisfactory. Natural wood, however, must be treated by soaking in a hot alkaline solution to remove acetic acid and other ingredients, as otherwise the sulfuric acid would act on the wood chemically, causing it to disintegrate. Even when the wood is treated, it is attacked by the oxygen of the positive plate so that it is necessary to groove the separators vertically or provide hard-rubber pins or dowels, Fig. 75. Also, wood is frequently used in combination with other materials, as described below. The wood, after being treated, must never be allowed to dry, as otherwise it disintegrates and becomes unserviceable.

Grooved-wood separators alone are used with low-priced, relatively short-lived automobile starting and lighting batteries.

Glass-wool (fiberglas) mats are frequently used in combination with wood, the wool pressing against the positive plate and preventing the shedding of active material. The mat separates the wood from the positive plate and thus prevents its oxidation.

Thin hard-rubber sheets, perforated either with small round holes or longitudinal slots, are also used. This type of separator is frequently used, however, in combination with grooved wood for long-life batteries (see Vitrex retainers, Fig. 74).

Separators made from rubber or latex having microscopic pores have been developed by the several storage-battery companies. They are made either in plain sheet form or in sheet form with grooves like wood separators. In grooved form they are used with long-life batteries.

91. Electrolyte. The sulfuric acid of the electrolyte should be chemically pure. From the standpoint of life, a low specific gravity is desirable since there is less local action. On the other hand, a high specific gravity increases the output of the cell and reduces the amount of electrolyte, resulting in a smaller and lighter cell. Hence, when the cell is fully charged, the specific gravity should not exceed 1.300, since at higher values the local action becomes excessive. On the other hand, it is desirable that the specific gravity at the end of discharge should be not less than 1.100, since the cell emf would then drop rapidly. Therefore it is customary in stationary batteries where a considerable quantity of electrolyte is no serious disadvantage to design for a range of 1.210 to about 1.150 during the discharge cycle. In batteries of the portable type where small volume and weight are of importance and therefore the amount of electrolyte is restricted, the range is from 1.275 to 1.125. The solution may be made from concentrated acid (oil of vitriol, sp gr 1.84) by *pouring the acid into water* in the ratios shown in the accompanying table.

Parts Water to 1 Part Acid

Specific gravity	Volume	Weight
1.200	4.3	2.4
1.210	4.0	2.2
1.240	3.4	1.9
1.280	2.75	1.5

Considerable heat is evolved when acid and water are mixed, resulting in a large amount of steam being generated if the water is added to the acid. This should be avoided as it may scatter the acid, break the container, and cause personal injury.

The specific gravity of a solution may be determined directly by the use of a hydrometer, consisting of a weighted bulb and a graduated tube which floats in the liquid. The specific gravity is read at the point where the surface of the liquid intercepts the tube. In stationary batteries of the open type such a tube may be left floating permanently in a representative cell called a *pilot cell.*

The small amount of liquid and the design of vehicle and starting batteries as well as stationary batteries of the sealed type make the use of such a hydrometer impossible in such batteries. To determine the specific gravity with such batteries, the syringe hydrometer is used. The syringe contains a small hydrometer, and when sufficient liquid is drawn into the syringe tube, the small hydrometer floats and may be read directly.

Figure 76 shows the change in specific gravity during charge and discharge at constant normal-current rate. This relation is important, as the specific gravity of the electrolyte is an accurate indication of the condition of charge of the battery.

Change in Specific Gravity. When the battery is charged, oxygen (O_2) is given to the positive plate to convert it into the peroxide and sulfate ions (SO_4) are given off at the negative plate, leaving spongy lead. The oxygen given to the positive plate is obtained from the oxygen ion of the water, leaving the hydrogen ion of the water to combine with the SO_4 ion

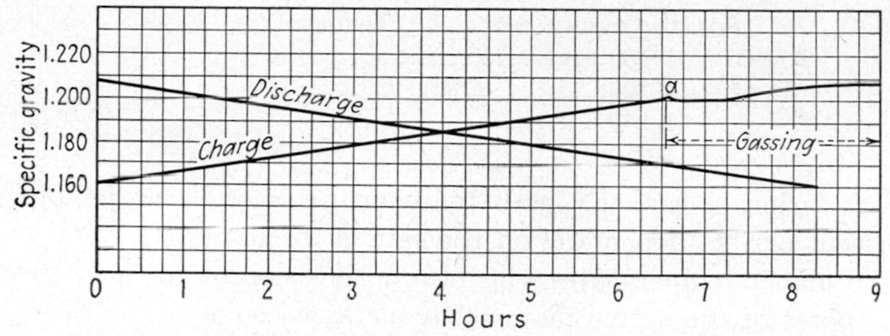

FIG. 76. Variation of specific gravity in a stationary battery.

given up by the negative plate, to form H_2SO_4, or sulfuric acid (see chemical equation, p. 109). Hence the electrolyte gives up water, and sulfuric acid is formed, which means that during charge the solution becomes more concentrated. For example, the specific gravity will rise from the complete discharge value of 1.160 to a value of 1.210 when the battery becomes fully charged, as shown in Fig. 76. Point *a* is called the gassing point because it is the point at which all the hydrogen, oxygen, or both are not absorbed in the chemical reactions and are given off rapidly as gas. At this point the specific gravity decreases slightly owing to the presence of the gas bubbles in the electrolyte. After the charging has ceased, the specific gravity continues to rise for some time. This is due to the very concentrated acid in the pores of the active material diffusing out into the solution and also to the fact that the gas bubbles are escaping from the solution. The discharge curve is also shown in Fig. 76. The specific gravity continues to decrease even after the battery has ceased to deliver current. This is due to the dilute acid in the pores of the active material diffusing into the solution. The specific gravity is such a good indicator of the state of charge of the battery that the hydrometer reading is generally used to determine how nearly charged or discharged the battery is.

As the hydrogen and oxygen which escape from the battery during the charging and discharging periods are merely dissociated water, the battery loses nothing but the equivalent of water. Ordinarily, therefore, only water need be added to replace the electrolyte. A small amount of the acid is carried away as a spray by the gas bubbles, but this loss is hardly appreciable. Acid need be added only when an actual loss of electrolyte takes place, such as occurs with a leaky tank. As a rule, distilled water is used to replace the evaporation of the electrolyte.

Temperature. The relation between the freezing point of the electrolyte and its specific gravity is given in the accompanying table. It will be noted that the freezing point is considerably lowered with increasing specific gravity, so that if a battery is well charged there is no danger of its freezing in the temperate zone.

Specific Gravity	Freezing Temperature, °F
1.180	− 6°
1.200	−16°
1.240	−51°
1.280	−90°

The variation of capacity with temperature is of the order of 0.5 to 1.0 per cent per °F, depending on the rate of discharge.

At the higher temperatures, the rate of diffusion of the acid throughout the pores of the active material is increased so that the rating of a battery increases markedly with increasing temperature.

92. Installing and Removing from Service. The sealed-type batteries are shipped complete with electrolyte in the cells and are ready for service. They should be given a freshening charge after assembling and before using. If the battery stands without being used over a long period of time, the active material becomes more or less converted into inactive lead sulfate, which is a nonconductor and so is difficult to reduce electrically. Therefore a battery if idle should be charged occasionally. If the battery is to remain idle for a long time, and it is impracticable to charge it periodically, the following procedure is necessary to prevent sulfation: Give the battery a full charge, then siphon off the electrolyte, which may be saved and used again. Fill the cells with water, and allow them to stand for 12 to 15 hr. Siphon off the water, and the cells will stand indefinitely without injury to the plates. To put back in service, replace the separators if warped or cracked, fill the battery with the electrolyte having a specific gravity of 1.210, and charge in the same manner as with the initial charge.

93. Portable Batteries. In the design of batteries for propelling vehicles and for automobile starting and lighting, it is necessary to obtain a high discharge rate with minimum weight and size. For portable batteries, and even for some stationary installations, these last two factors are important. Therefore, pasted plates are used for both positives and negatives. These are made relatively thin and are insulated from one another by thin separators. They are then packed tightly in a container which may be made of hard rubber, special compositions, or plastics. The assembly is essentially the same as that of the Ironclad cell shown in Fig. 73. The cover is sealed with an asphaltum compound to prevent the splashing of the liquid. There is a hole in the top of the jar which is closed with a cap. This permits the replenishing of water of the electrolyte. A vent in the cap allows the gases to escape. The discharge rates of this type of battery may be high as, for example, when doing starting duty. Furthermore, the ampere-hours capacity of the battery for its weight and size must be high. Hence, the volume of the electrolyte is small and the specific gravity must vary between wide limits. When the battery is fully charged, the specific gravity is as high as 1.280 and 1.300, and when it is completely discharged, the specific gravity is as low as 1.100.

The individual cells are mounted in assemblies or in multiple-unit containers in accordance with the type of duty for which they are intended. The individual cells are connected by lead straps which may be bolted to the connecting posts or "lead-burned." Automobile starting and lighting batteries are usually assembled with their units in a plastic or composition container, giving an emf of approximately 6 volts. Multiple containers are adapted to several types of duty, such as vehicle propulsion, industrial trucks, mine locomotives, and railroad lighting. The number of cells per container may be as high as eight in the smaller sizes and as low as two in the largest sizes, such as are used in railroad lighting. The containers, particularly in the larger sizes, are commonly made of steel rather than wood, permitting the assembly of batteries of considerable size.

Portable batteries are usually shipped assembled, charged and complete with the electrolyte so that they are ready for use when received. However, a freshening charge is advisable.

As the space for the electrolyte is very limited in vehicle batteries, and as considerable gassing occurs, the level of the electrolyte falls quite rapidly, so that frequent additions of water are necessary, usually once for each week of active service.

94. Rating and Batteries. Practically all batteries have a nominal rating based on the 8-hr rate of discharge. Thus, if a Planté battery can deliver a current of 40 amp continuously for 8 hr, the battery will have a rating of $40 \cdot 8 = 320$ amp-hr. The normal charging rate of such a battery would be 40 amp. Assuming the battery to be capable of delivering just 40 amp for 8 hr, it would not be able to deliver 64 amp for 5 hr (320 amp-hr), but only 88 per cent of this, or 56.3 amp for 5 hr. Fifty-six and three-tenths amperes is called *the 5-hr rate.*

The accompanying table shows the percentage capacity with various discharge rates.

	Hours				Minutes	
Discharge rate	8	5	3	1	20	6
Percentage of capacity at 8-hr rate:						
Planté type	100	88	75	55.8	37	19.5
Pasted type	100	93	83	63	41	25.5

This falling off in capacity with higher rates of discharge is due to the inability of the free solution to penetrate rapidly the pores of the active material. Consequently it is not possible to reduce all the active material during the short periods of discharge. After such a battery has stood for a short time, it will be found to have recovered to some extent and to be capable of delivering more current, even after apparently having become exhausted. This is due to the final penetration of the pores of the active material by the free solution.

Batteries are able to discharge at extreme rates for very short intervals. For example, a starting battery having an 8-hr rating of 10 amp is often called upon to supply 450 amp when doing starting duty.

95. Charging. The following rule may be observed in charging a lead battery: The charging rate in amperes may always be made equal to the number of ampere-hours that have been discharged by the battery. For example, if 200 amp-hr is out of the battery, a charging rate of 200 amp may be used. As the battery charges, the ampere-hours out of the battery decrease and the charging rate must decrease correspondingly. The rate should never be such that violent gassing occurs.

Gassing represents a waste of energy because a considerable portion of the charging energy is used in merely breaking up the water into hydrogen and oxygen. In addition, gassing causes the battery to become heated, the acid is carried out in a fine spray by the bubbles, and active material may be carried from the plates by the erosive action of the bubbles.

When a battery is fully charged, any rate will produce gassing, but the rate can be reduced to such a low value that the gassing is not excessive and is practically harmless. This rate is called the *finishing rate.*

A battery may be charged in 5 hr by beginning at a rate several times the finishing rate and tapering off to the finishing rate as the charge progresses (constant-voltage method). On the other hand, a constant current of moderate value may be used over a much longer period, even as long as 16 hr (constant-current method).

A common example of the constant-current method is the charging of low-voltage batteries from a 115-volt d-c supply. This is illustrated by Fig. 77, which shows the charging of a 6-volt starting battery. The emf of the battery is so small in comparison with the 115 volts of the d-c supply that the current is determined almost entirely by the resistance of the series resistor. Since the series resistance is practically constant, the current remains substantially constant, irrespective of the small changes in battery emf.

Where only an a-c supply is available, it is common practice to employ rectifiers for converting the alternating to direct current for battery charging. Commercial rectifiers which are available for this service are the dry-disk types, such as the copper oxide (Rectox) and the selenium rectifier, and the hot-cathode types, such as the Tungar and the Rectigon. (These are described in Volume II, Chap. XV.) These rectifier devices may be adapted to constant-current or modified constant-voltage methods of charging.

Before connecting the battery, it should be definitely determined that the mains supply *direct current,* and it is also necessary to know which main is positive. If doubt exists as to the polarity and a voltmeter is not available, dip the two ends of the wires which connect the mains to the battery into a glass of slightly acidulated water or into salt water. Bubbles form about the *negative* wire. When using the constant-current method of charging, the charging rate must be reduced as the battery approaches the fully charged condition.

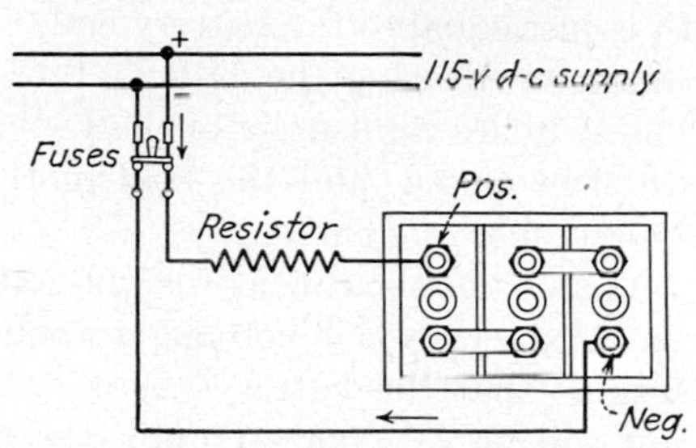

FIG. 77. Charging a starting battery from 115-volt supply.

The constant-potential method of charging is frequently to be preferred, as the charging current automatically tapers off owing to the rise in the cell emf as the cell approaches the completely charged condition, and little or no attention is required. The applied voltage should be about 2.3 volts for each cell of the battery when there is no series resistance in the circuit. The diverter-pole generator is well adapted to this method of charge (see Sec. 318, p. 468).

With 2.3 volts per cell and no series resistance, the current at the beginning of charge is usually too great, so that it is advisable to use a small series resistor. If a series resistor is used, a voltage source of 2.5 or 2.6 volts per cell is desirable, as otherwise adjustments must be made during the charging period.

Many installations, such, for example, as oil-switch control batteries in power stations, are operated as "floating" batteries connected continuously to the bus. Usually these installations consist of 60 cells, and the bus is held at an average voltage of 129 volts, or 2.15 volts per cell, at which voltage the cells are kept in a charged condition.

If a recharge of the battery is required after an extended discharge or to give a periodic equalizing charge, the bus voltage is raised somewhat, the limit being determined by the character of connected load.

When it is not feasible to raise the bus voltage for this purpose, a series booster may be used for raising the charging potential to a value sufficiently high to send current into the battery. The booster ordinarily consists of a low-voltage, separately excited shunt generator, driven by a shunt motor. Figure 78 shows the connections of a booster system. The booster generator is connected with its negative terminal to the + bus bar and raises the bus-bar voltage V_1 to a value V_2, which can be adjusted to give the desired charging current. To put the set in operation, switch S_1 is first closed and the motor started. Switches S_2 and S_3 are then closed, and the field current of the booster is adjusted until the voltage V_2 is just equal to the battery emf. This condition is determined by the voltmeter V using the D-P D-T (double-pole double-throw) switch S_4. The switches S_5, usually of the D-P S-T (double-pole single-throw) type, are then closed, and the field of the booster is readjusted to give the desired charging current.

As an example, consider a 129-volt installation with a floating battery. As the average cell voltage is about 2.15 volts, 60 cells are necessary. Assume that the battery has a 320-amp-hr rating. The charging current will be $^{320}/_{8}$, or 40, amp (the normal 8-hr rating). The voltage of each cell should be boosted to approximately 2.5 volts, on charge. Therefore the total voltage necessary will be $2.5 \cdot 60 = 150$ volts. Of this 150 volts, the bus bars can supply 129 volts. The booster supplies the remaining 21 volts, and its rating will be

$$\frac{21 \cdot 40}{1{,}000} = 0.84 \text{ kw.}$$

The *total* power utilized in charging the battery is, however,

$$\frac{150 \cdot 40}{1{,}000} = 6.0 \text{ kw.}$$

(Also see p. 59.)

The terminal voltage of a cell rises on being charged, as is shown in Fig. 79. The terminal voltage is about 2.18 volts at the beginning of charge at the normal, or 8-hr, rate and rises slowly to about 2.4 volts, after which it rises rapidly to 2.6 volts. This last rise occurs in the gassing period. This final rise of voltage also indicates that the cell is nearing the completion of charge. It is this rise of voltage which automatically cuts down the charging rate when the constant-potential method is used. The voltage does not rise so rapidly when the charging rate is reduced toward the end of charge, because of the lesser *IR* drop in the cell itself.

In Fig. 79 the charge characteristic holds for a temperature of approximately 70°F (21°C). The final voltage ranges from 2.75 to 2.45 volts with

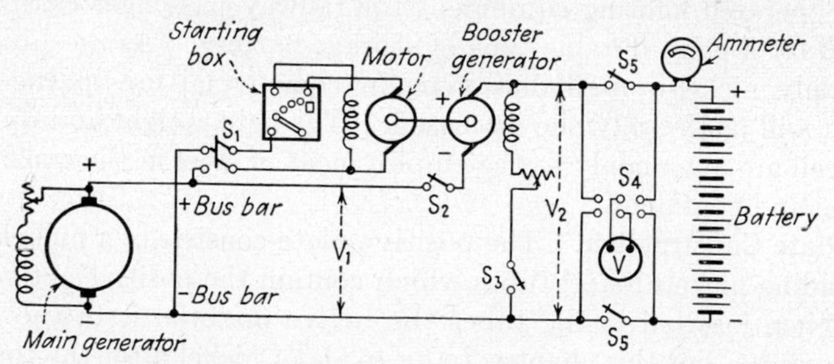

FIG. 78. Booster method of charging a storage battery.

variations of temperature ranging from 30°F (−1°C) to 110°F (43°C). Hence the final cell voltage cannot be used as a criterion of charge unless the temperature of the electrolyte is taken into consideration.[1]

The *drop* of voltage at various rates of discharge is also shown in Fig. 79. It will be noted that the battery voltage at the 8-hr discharge rate is

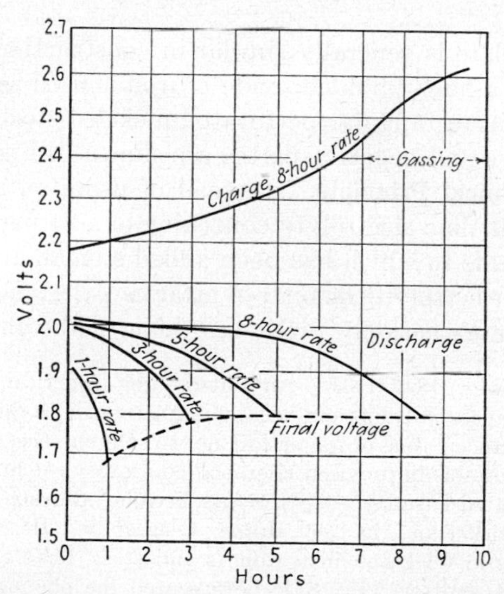

FIG. 79. Voltage curves on charge and discharge for lead cell.

practically constant up to 5 hr, and at even greater values of time the change in voltage is not great. This is a distinct advantage if the battery is used to supply incandescent lamps.

[1] For an excellent discussion of lead-storage-battery characteristics, see J. LESTER WOODBRIDGE, "Storage Battery Charging," *Trans. AIEE*, Vol. 54, p. 516, 1935.

EDISON[1] NICKEL-IRON-ALKALINE CELL

History. This type of cell was invented by Edison in 1901 when the use of battery-propelled trucks, tractors, and locomotives, as well as electrically operated lighting equipment for railway passenger cars, created the need for a light, durable type of storage battery. As the Edison cell is the only nickel-iron-alkaline type in commercial use in the United States it will be the only one discussed. The light weight and durability of this cell are due mainly to the employment of steel in the construction of plates and container.

96. Plate Construction. The positive plate consists of a nickeled-steel grid, holding nickeled-steel tubes which contain the positive active material. When inserted in the tubes the active material is in the form of nickel hydrate, but this changes to an oxide of nickel after the formation treatment. In order to give the electrolyte free access to the active material, the tubes are perforated. To obtain improved electrical conductance, the active material is alternated with layers of pure metallic nickel flake at the time it is tamped into the tubes. The tubes are ¼ in. (0.635 cm) inside diameter and about 4 in. (10.16 cm) long and are reinforced by eight encircling seamless steel rings spaced equidistantly over the tube length.

The negative plate is generally similar in construction to the positive plate except that a finely divided oxide of iron is used as active material and is contained in rectangular perforated nickeled-steel pockets instead of tubes. Positive and negative plates are shown in Fig. 80.

97. Electrochemical Principle. Instead of using an acid, the Edison cell employs an alkaline electrolyte consisting of a 21 per cent solution of potassium hydroxide to which has been added a small amount of lithium hydroxide. The electrolyte, instead of attacking the steel tubes, pockets, grids, container, etc., actually preserves them. The chemical reactions

[1] Thomas A. Edison, 1847–1931. An outstanding American inventor. In his youth he sold newspapers on trains and became acquainted with the telegraph through using it to send advance notice of important news. On one occasion he was ejected from the train because his improvised chemical laboratory set fire to a railroad car. He studied and repeated Faraday's experiments, became interested in telegraphy, and invented the stock ticker and, in 1869, duplex telegraphy. He started a shop, made many improvements in telegraph instruments and stock tickers, and invented the carbon telephone transmitter. In 1877, he invented the phonograph. In 1879 he invented the incandescent lamp, his most important invention. He improved dynamos and invented methods for the distribution of electrical energy, including the 3-wire system which bears his name. In 1889 he invented motion pictures. He also invented the primary battery and the storage battery which bear his name. He was a tireless worker and extremely resourceful. He took out more than a thousand patents. His laboratories and factories were located at Menlo Park, West Orange, N.J.

which take place within the cell are complex, but their nature is indicated by the equations on p. 126.

In any condition of the electrolyte it does not cause disintegration or solution of the active materials, and since only a relatively small quantity of the potassium and lithium hydroxide is absorbed by the higher nickel oxide electrode, the composition of the electrolyte does not vary appreciably throughout the cycle of charge and discharge. The conductivity and specific gravity of the electrolyte are therefore practically constant.

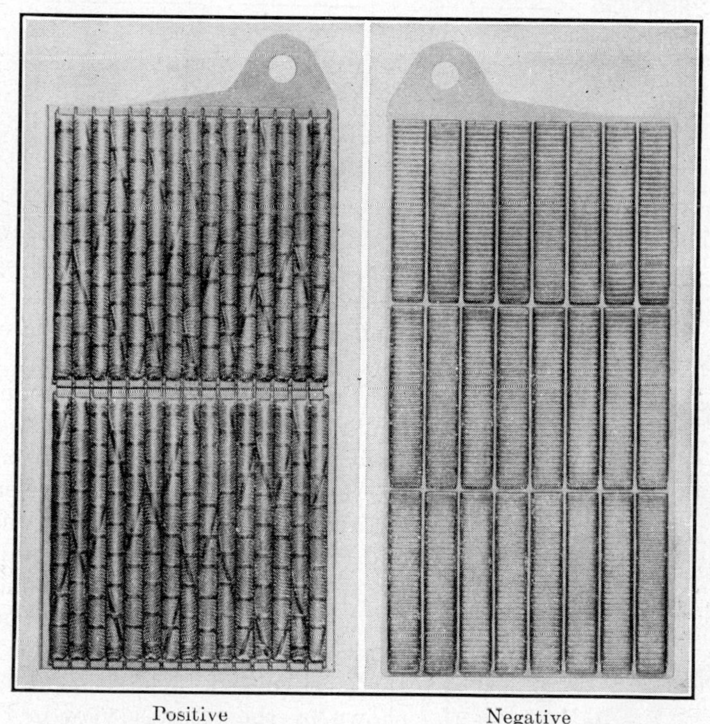

Positive Negative

FIG. 80. Positive and negative plates of an Edison storage cell.

This is also shown by the reaction diagram. On charge, the active material of the negative plate, iron oxide (FeO), is reduced to iron (Fe). The active material of the positive plate, nickel oxide (NiO), is oxidized to nickel dioxide (NiO_2). On discharge, the reverse process occurs, the negative plate being oxidized to iron oxide and the positive plate being reduced to nickel oxide. It will be noted that throughout charge and discharge the solution consisting of $2KOH + H_2O$ remains unchanged, both chemically and in concentration. Hence, unless evaporation is allowed to take place, the specific gravity of the electrolyte does not change with charge and discharge as it does in the lead-acid cell.

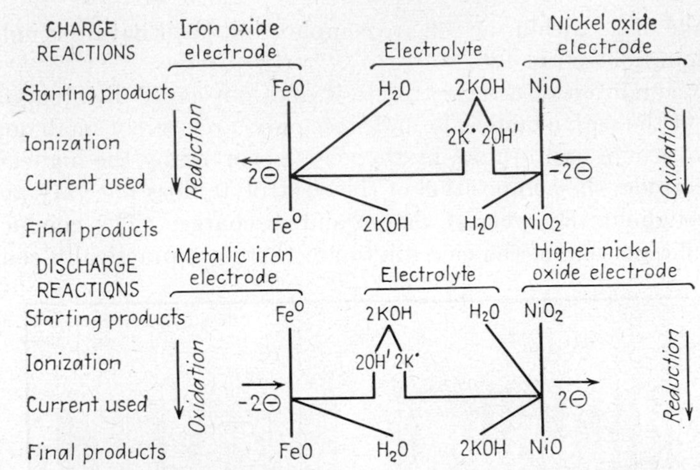

98. Assembly. By passing a steel connecting rod through holes at the top of the grids, the positive and negative plates are assembled into positive and negative groups. Steel spacing washers between adjacent plates on the connecting rod ensure proper plate spacing. A lock washer and nut are drawn tight at each end of the connecting rod, binding the plate group firmly together. Positive and negative plate groups are intermeshed to form complete elements, separation between alternate positive and negative plates being accomplished by vertical hard-rubber grids and pins.

FIG. 81. Cutaway of Edison storage cell showing plate assembly. (*Thomas A. Edison, Inc.*)

The assembled elements are placed in a nickeled-steel container, after which the steel cover is welded in position, as shown by the cutaway view in Fig. 81. The poles are insulated from the cover by a series of hard-rubber and soft-rubber washers which also provide a gastight and liquid-tight packing. Projecting from the cell cover is the filling aperture, on which is mounted a hinged filler cap. The filler cap is held either positively open or positively closed by a steel clip spring. Suspended from the filler cap is a hard-rubber valve which seats by gravity when the cap is closed, thus excluding external air and reducing evaporation, yet permitting the escape of gas.

The tops of the pole pieces are threaded. Immediately below they are tapered to fit the lugs of the intercell and intertray connectors. The connector lugs are steel forgings bored to fit the taper of the pole pieces and are swedged upon heavy copper connecting links. All lugs, links, and

FIG. 82. Assembly of Edison 30 storage cells in metal tray for industrial truck service. (*Thomas A. Edison, Inc.*)

nuts are nickel-plated. Individual cells are mounted in metal trays to form a battery, Fig. 82.

99. Discharge and Charge Characteristics. The rated capacity of the Edison cell is based on a normal 5-hr discharge until the voltage becomes 1 volt per cell for *A*, *B*, *C*, *D*, *F*, and *N* types. Figure 83 shows normal

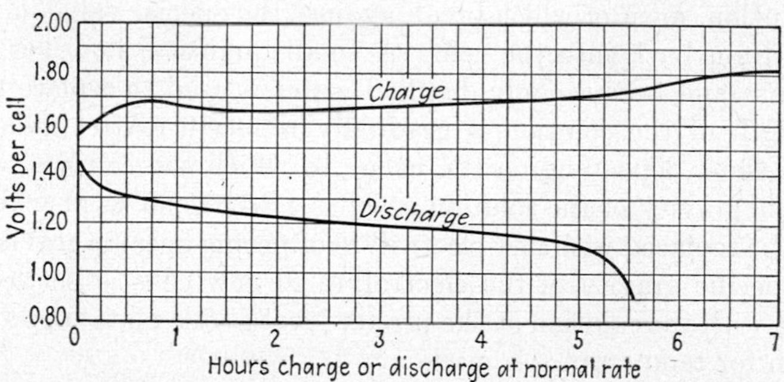

FIG. 83. Voltage changes during the charge and discharge of an Edison cell.

charge and discharge curves for the Edison *A*-type cell. It will be noted that the average discharge voltage at these rates is about 1.2 volts per cell. At discharge rates other than normal, voltage values will vary above or below this average figure, Fig. 84. These discharge characteristics are based on a preceding normal-rate charge for a period of 7 hr for *A*-, *B*-, *C*-, *D*-, *F*-, and *N*-type cells. The specific gravity of the electrolyte changes but slightly between charge and discharge and cannot be used to determine the state of charge. The completion of full charge is indicated when the voltage ceases to rise over a period of ½ hr during charge with constant current flowing. The state of charge can be approximated at any time by use of an ampere-hour meter or by a charge-test fork which indicates from a pilot cell the voltage delivered at a given rate of discharge.

100. Electrolyte. As with other cells, the solution level gradually drops during service due to the electrolysis of water into hydrogen and

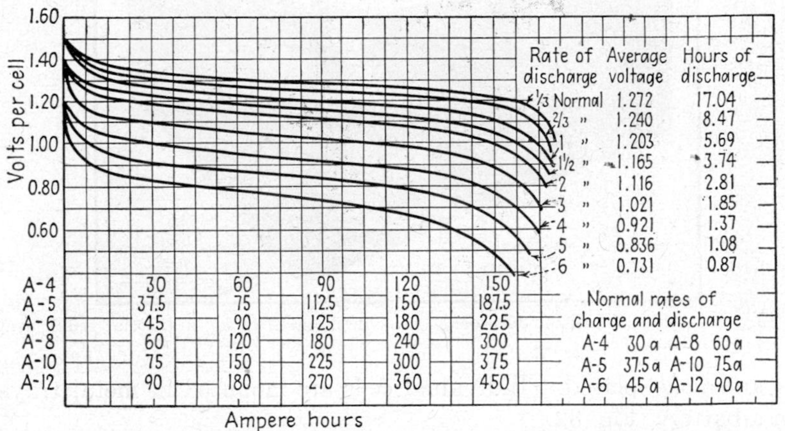

FIG. 84. Discharge characteristics of type *A* Edison cells at various rates subsequent to normal charges.*

oxygen gas on charge. Bubbles of gas carry with them small particles of the solution, most of which break against the special valve in the filler cap and drain back into the cell. A small quantity, however, escapes into the air, and because only distilled water is used to replace this loss, the strength of the solution is gradually reduced. After an extended period of time, depending on the usage to which the cell has been put, the specific gravity of the solution reaches 1.160 at 60°F, at which point it should be replaced with new electrolyte of proper specific gravity. The normal specific gravity of the electrolyte in new cells is between 1.195 and 1.215 with the solution at the proper level above plate tops and when correction for temperature is made.

101. Advantages. The nickel-iron-alkaline cell possesses important advantages which make it well suited to the various services to which it is applied. These advantages result from the nature of the materials used, the method of construction, and the fundamental electrochemical

* See also curve 1.

principle involved. The extensive use of steel permits precision manufacturing and results in a cell capable of withstanding the vibration and shock incidental to commercial service. Moreover, the use of steel for tubes, pockets, grids, etc., makes possible a plate construction which securely retains the active materials and which eliminates buckling and warping.

Aside from its rugged construction, additional advantages of the Edison cell are its light weight per watt-hour of capacity and its ability to withstand electrical abuse. It may be overcharged, overdischarged, accidentally short-circuited, charged in the reverse direction, or left standing idle in a discharged condition indefinitely without injury. It is free from corrosive acid fumes and is not subject to ordinary storage-battery diseases such as sulfation, sedimentation, or terminal corrosion. Its tray assembly and cell connections are simple, it requires no replacement of separators throughout its life, and it is not damaged by freezing. Operation is dependable over a long period of time.

102. Application. Edison cells find their greatest usefulness in storage-battery-propelled street trucks, industrial trucks, tractors, mine and industrial locomotives; for railway passenger-car lighting and air conditioning; for multiple-unit car control; for all types of railway signaling, as in track circuits, target lighting, highway crossing signals, and interlocking plants; for marine power and lighting, miners' electric safety-cap lamps, emergency lighting, isolated electric light plants; for time clocks, fire-alarm systems, and other services. The various types manufactured at present are not adapted to low-voltage automobile-starting service and are not sold for this purpose. Below are tabulated the types and sizes of Edison cells, together with their capacities and weights.

103. Data on Edison Cells.

Cell type	Normal ratings*			Wt,† lb per cell, standard type
	Amp-hr capacity	Amp	Whr	
*D*4	300	60	360	33.4
*D*5	375	75	450	40.0
*D*6	450	90	540	45.6
*D*7	525	105	630	53.4
*D*8	600	120	720	60.0
*D*10	750	150	900	77.3
*D*12	900	180	1,080	91.6
*N*1	5⅝	1⅛	6¾	1.74
*N*2	11¼	2¼	13½	1.94
*F*2*B*	10	2	12	1.31

* Ratings are on basis of 5-hr rate for *A*-, *B*-, *C*-, *D*-, and *N*-type cells with average of 1.2 volts per cell and final of 1.0 volt per cell.

† Weights are for completely assembled cells, including trays, connectors, etc.

NICKEL-CADMIUM-ALKALI (NICAD) CELL

History. Work to produce a storage battery having an alkaline electrolyte was begun by Jungner and Berg jointly in Sweden in 1893, and the patent covering the modern pocket design was applied for by Berg in 1903. The work of these inventors coincided in time with that of Edison, and the two types of alkaline battery were developed almost concurrently. Both used potassium hydroxide (KOH), or caustic potash, for the electrolyte. At first, the Swedish inventors used nickelous (green) hydroxide for the positive electrode, as did Edison, but added graphite to render it conductive. Ultimately the Swedish inventors used nickelic (black) hydroxide for the positive electrode, retaining the graphite as a conductor. This material does not swell with charge and discharge as does the nickelous hydroxide and can be contained in flat pockets. In 1905, the decision was made to use as the negative electrode cadmium oxide in a finely divided state with a small admixture of ferric trioxide acting as a disperser. Although this type of cell had become common in Europe, it was not introduced for wide commercial use in the United States until recent years.

104. Mechanical Construction. Both positive and negative plates consist of thin, finely perforated flat steel pockets in which the active materials are securely contained, Fig. 85. The active material of the positive plate consists of nickel hydroxide and specially treated graphite and that of the negative plate consists of a mixture of oxides of cadmium and iron. The separators are thin strips of polystyrene, which permit close spacing of the plates. This combined with the high conductivity of the active materials makes the cell resistance low. The complete plate group consists of a number of alternate positive and negative plates assembled on bolts and connected to terminal posts common to plates of the same polarity. The entire plate assembly is placed within a sealed steel container, polystyrene being used for insulation. The cells are assembled in wooden trays to form batteries for specific services.

105. Electrolyte. The electrolyte is potassium hydroxide (KOH), or caustic potash. When the batteries are shipped from the factory fully charged, they are filled with electrolyte having a specific gravity of 1.210 at 72°F (22°C). On charge, the positive active material is oxidized, and the negative active material is reduced. On discharge, the opposite reaction occurs. The electrolyte functions virtually only as an electrical conductor and does not enter into any permanent chemical reaction with the active plate materials. Hence, its specific gravity remains the same during charge and discharge. On charge, the cell does not gas until the voltage per cell has risen to 1.47 to 1.48 volts. The gas consists of hydrogen and oxygen and represents a slight loss of water, although the vent, Fig. 85, prevents most of the gas escaping. The level of the electrolyte should always be such as to cover the plates.

106. Charge and Discharge. The charging may be by either the constant-current or the constant-voltage method, constant current being

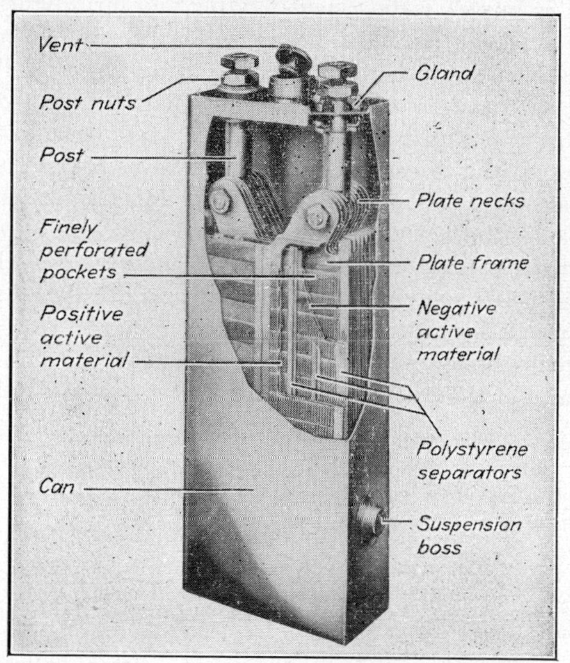

Fig. 85. Construction of a nickel-cadmium-alkali storage cell.

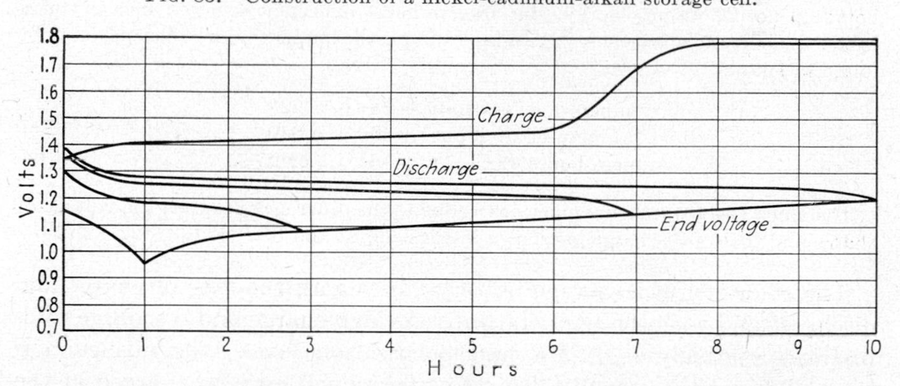

Fig. 86. Charge and discharge characteristics of nickel-cadmium-alkali cell.

recommended. Normally the battery may be charged at the 7-hr rate, although higher rates may be employed. The voltage is essentially constant at approximately 1.4 to 1.5 volts, Fig. 86, until near the end of charge, when it rises rapidly to approximately 1.8 volts. The battery may be trickle-charged. On discharge the voltage is constant at approximately 1.2 volts until it drops to 1.0 to 1.1 end volts, depending on the discharge rate, Fig. 86.

107. Applications and Advantages. Nicad batteries are used for many services such as busses, radio, yacht lighting and farm lighting, railroad-car lighting, air conditioning, railroad signals, portable lamps and lanterns, internal-combustion-engine starting, including diesel engines. A special form of Nicad battery, the Alcad battery, is designed for high discharge rates and thus is particularly adapted to diesel-engine starting.

Advantages of the Nicad (and Alcad) type of battery are that it is strong mechanically, it is not damaged by overcharge or when idle even for long periods, the active material cannot flake off, it performs well over wide ranges of temperature, there is no gassing on discharge and no corrosion, and it has low internal resistance and nearly constant voltage over a wide range of ampere-hours discharge.

108. Efficiency of Storage Batteries. The efficiency of a storage battery is the ratio of the watthours output to the watthours input.

Example. A fully charged cell is discharged at a uniform rate of 38 amp for 6 hr at an average voltage of 1.95 volts. The cell is now charged at a uniform rate of 40 amp for 6 hr, the average voltage being 2.3 volts. The cell is then in its original condition of charge. Determine the efficiency of the cell.

$$\text{Watthours output} = 38 \cdot 1.95 \cdot 6 = 445.$$
$$\text{Watthours input} = 40 \cdot 2.3 \cdot 6 = 552.$$
$$\text{Efficiency} = 445/552, \text{ or } 80.6\%.$$

One often hears of the ampere-hours efficiency of a storage battery. As ampere-hours do not represent energy, the ampere-hours efficiency is not a measure of a battery's ability to store energy. In the example the ampere-hours efficiency may be found as follows:

$$\text{Ampere-hours output} = 38 \cdot 6 = 228.$$
$$\text{Ampere-hours input} = 40 \cdot 6 = 240.$$
$$\text{Ampere-hours efficiency} = 228/240, \text{ or } 95\%.$$

The much lower watthours efficiency is due to the difference between the voltage of charge and that of discharge, as shown in Figs. 79, 83 and 86 (pp. 123, 127, and 131).

The efficiency of a storage battery varies with the rate of charge and discharge and with the temperature. As high charge and discharge rates produce relatively high I^2R and polarization losses, the efficiency is lowered under these conditions. Further, a cell may be charged at the 8-hr rate and discharged at the 3-hr rate and have an apparent efficiency of 60 per cent. This does not represent the true efficiency, as the cell actually will not be completely discharged, even if it appears to be. Owing to the inability of the free acid in the lead cell to permeate the active material, much of the active material has not been reduced, and after a short time the cell will be found to have recuperated to a considerable extent and will be able to deliver more energy.

The ampere-hours efficiency of a storage battery is of the order of magnitude of 95 per cent. For a complete cycle the watthour efficiency of a stationary battery of moderate size is about 75 per cent at the 8-hr charge and discharge rates. The watthour efficiency of a large stationary battery is about 85 per cent under the same conditions. Where a battery merely "floats" and the cycle of charge and discharge is a matter of minutes or perhaps of seconds even, the watthours efficiency may be as high as 95 or 96 per cent.

In selecting a battery, the efficiency is only one of the factors to be considered. The initial cost and the maintenance of batteries form a substantial proportion of the total cost and hence are important considerations. Also, such factors as weight, ruggedness, voltage regulation, and overload capacity must be considered for each individual installation.

The uses of storage batteries in the generation and distribution of power are considered in Chap. XV.

109. Electrolysis. Pure water is a poor conductor of electricity. In fact, it may be considered as practically an insulator. If, however, even a very small amount of acid, alkali, or salt be added to water, the solution becomes a good conductor. Moreover, if an electric current flows through such a solution, it dissociates the molecules of the substance in solution, or the molecules of the water itself, into simpler substances which appear at the anode and at the cathode. The phenomenon of the electric current in causing such dissociation under these conditions is called *electrolysis*. The solution which becomes conducting under these conditions is called an *electrolyte*.

If current flows in slightly acidulated water, using an inert material such as platinum for the electrodes, hydrogen is released at the cathode and oxygen is released at the anode. Moreover, the volume of hydrogen released is twice that of oxygen. Hence, the water molecule (H_2O) is broken up or dissociated into its two constituent elements.

The theory of electrolysis is based on electrolytic dissociation. In solution, the molecules of acids, alkalies, and salts dissociate into positive and negative ions. Thus hydrochloric acid (HCl) dissociates into a positive (+) H ion and a negative (−) Cl ion. Likewise, the copper sulfate molecule ($CuSO_4$) becomes dissociated into the +Cu ion and the $-SO_4$ ion. According to the electron theory, the negative ion has an excess of electrons, and the positive ion has a deficiency of electrons (see p. 323 and also Vol. II, Chap. XIV). When no potential difference is applied between electrodes, the ions drift about in the solution. However, when a potential difference is applied to the electrodes in the solution, the positive ions migrate to the negative electrode, or cathode, and accordingly are called *cations*. The negative ions go to the anode, or positive electrode, and accordingly are called *anions*.

The positive ions give up their charge to the cathode and the negative ions give up their charge to the anode, thus constituting the current. Hence, the conduction of current through an electrolyte is a convection effect, the charges being carried to the electrodes by the ions. Thus, electrolytic conduction differs from the ordinary metallic conduction in that it involves a transfer of matter and is accompanied by chemical change.

In Fig. 87 are indicated the effects which occur when two copper plates are immersed in copper sulfate solution and current is caused to flow from one plate to the other. The positive copper (Cu) ions move to the cathode and deposit metallic copper. The negative sulfate (SO_4) ions move to the anode and combine with the hydrogen ion of the water to form sulfuric acid, an oxygen molecule being given off at the anode. The reaction is as follows:

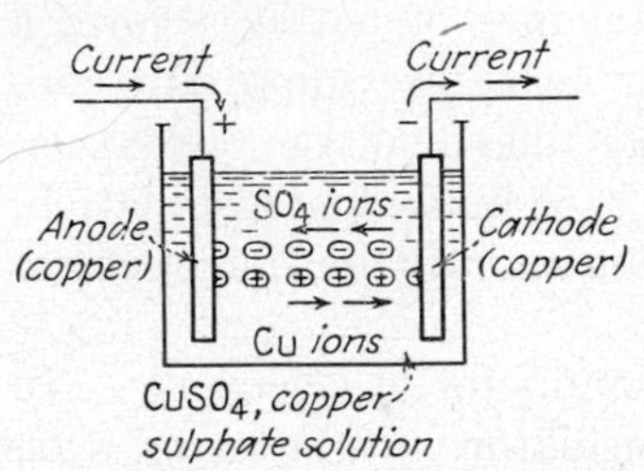

FIG. 87. Electrolysis of copper in copper-sulfate solution.

$$SO_4 + H_2O = H_2SO_4 + O.$$

This reaction occurs in the electrolytic refining of copper. The copper ingot to be refined is used as anode, and a thin plate of copper is used as cathode. Copper goes into solution from the anode and deposits as pure copper on the cathode. Impurities are precipitated as *anode mud* in the bottom of the cell. However, considerable value in metals, such as silver and gold, may be recovered from the "mud," or sludge.

Electrolysis is not confined to substances in water solution, but fused salts may also be subjected to electrolysis. For example, the electrolysis of fused table salt (NaCl) produces sodium (Na) at the cathode and chlorine (Cl) at the anode. Aluminum is produced by the electrolysis of the fused salt, aluminum oxide (Al_2O_3), at a temperature of from 900 to 1000°C.

110. Faraday's Laws of Electrolysis. As a result of his experiments, Faraday discovered two fundamental laws of electrolysis. The first law states that *the weight of the products of electrolysis is proportional to the quantity of electricity which has passed through the electrolyte.* That is, the weight

$$w = \epsilon q = \epsilon i t \tag{80}$$

where ϵ is a constant called the *electrochemical equivalent* of the substance, q is the quantity of electricity in coulombs, i is the current in amperes, and t is the time in seconds.

The second law states that *for a given quantity of electricity the weight of the products of electrolysis is proportionate to their electrochemical equivalents.* For example, the atomic weight of hydrogen is 1.008 and 1 coulomb will cause 0.0104 mg to be released. The value 0.0104 is the electrochemical equivalent of hydrogen. Below are given the electrochemical equivalents of a few of the elements.

ELECTROCHEMICAL EQUIVALENTS, MILLIGRAMS PER COULOMB

Element	mg per coulomb	Element	mg per coulomb
Aluminum	0.09316	Nickel	0.3041
Chlorine	0.3674	Oxygen	0.08291
Chromium	^{3}0.1797	Potassium	0.40516
	^{6}0.0898		
Cobalt	0.3054	Silver	1.118
Copper	^{1}0.6588	Sodium	0.2382
	^{2}0.3294		
Gold	^{1}2.0436	Tin	0.3075
	^{3}0.6812		
Lead	1.0737	Tungsten	0.3180

The small superior numbers give the valency.

Example. A current of 25 amp flows for 8 hr through an electrolytic cell with copper electrodes and copper sulfate solution similar to that shown in Fig. 87. Determine the kilograms of copper deposited on the cathode. With copper sulfate, the valence of copper is 2. Eight hours equals $8 \cdot 3{,}600 = 28{,}800$ sec. Hence, using (80) and the electrochemical equivalent of copper in the table, the weight of copper

$$w = 0.3294 \cdot 10^{-6} \cdot 25 \cdot 28{,}800 = 0.237 \text{ kg.} \quad \textit{Ans.}$$

111. Electroplating.[1] Electroplating is merely an application of the principles of electrolysis given in Secs. 109 and 110, by which thin coatings of metal are deposited on other metal. Because of the desirability of plating the baser metals with protective coverings, such as copper, nickel, chromium, and silver, electroplating is an important industry.

As a simple illustration, assume that it is desired to copper-plate a carbon brush. The portions of the brush to be plated are immersed in a solution of copper sulfate, Fig. 88. A copper strip is also immersed in the solution and is connected to the positive terminal of a dynamo or some other source of d-c supply. The brush is connected to the negative terminal of this supply. Under these conditions the current will carry copper from the solution and deposit it on the carbon brush. This copper which leaves the solution is replaced by copper which is carried from the copper strip (the anode) into the solution so that there is no change in the solution itself. The current should be such that the density is about 0.02 amp per sq in. of the surface to be plated.

It is not necessary that the anode be of the metal which it is desired to deposit. Other metals may be used. Under these conditions, however,

[1] See "Standard Handbook for Electrical Engineers," 8th ed., Sec. 20, Par. 49 to 80, for a more complete discussion.

the solution in time becomes contaminated by the going into solution of the anode. If an inert substance such as carbon is used as anode, acid is formed in the solution. If the anode is of the same material as is being deposited on the cathode the *only opposing* emf in the bath just described is the IR drop in the solution. This may be reduced by bringing the electrodes close together, but if the electrodes are too close together, the deposit will not be uniform. On the other hand if the anode material is other than that being deposited on the cathode, such as a platinum anode in copper sulfate solution, then in addition to the voltage necessary to overcome the IR drop in the solution there is a voltage of decomposition of the solution which must be supplied. This latter voltage is of the order of a few volts. The amount of metal deposited per second is proportional to the current. Because of the

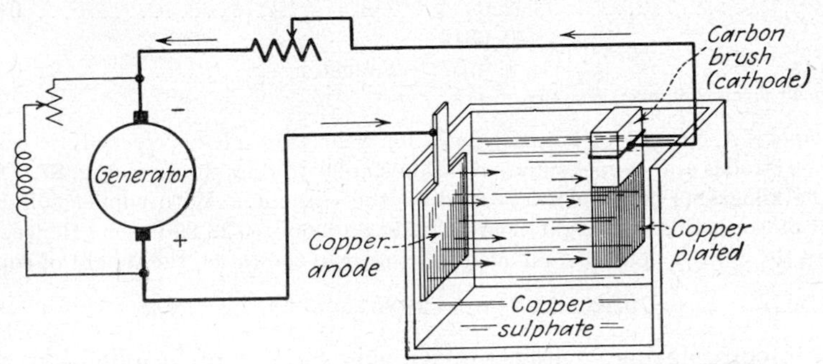

FIG. 88. Copper-plating bath.

nature of electroplating baths, they are naturally low-voltage devices. When practicable, several are connected in series. A low-voltage and high-current generator is generally used for plating purposes. In practice there are many refinements to be observed.

Acid is added to the solution to prevent impurities from depositing. A cyanide solution of copper is found to give better results than the sulfate. Nickel, tin, zinc, silver, gold, etc., may be deposited by the use of suitable baths and electrodes.

A gravity cell is an example of electroplating in which the source of current is derived from the cell itself. The current flows from the zinc to the copper within the solution, zinc is carried into the solution as sulfate, and copper is deposited or plated from its sulfate on the positive electrode.

Electrotyping is another common example of electroplating. An impression is made in wax with the type or object to be reproduced. The surface of the wax is made conducting by applying a thin coating of graphite. Copper is then plated on this surface. It is later backed by type metal to give it the necessary mechanical strength.

CHAPTER V

ELECTRICAL INSTRUMENTS AND ELECTRICAL MEASUREMENTS[1]

112. Principle of Direct-current Instruments. Most d-c instruments operate on the principle that a coil may be so placed in a magnetic field that the coil will tend to turn when there is a current in it. This turning action is the underlying principle of the electric motor and is discussed more in detail in Chap. XIII. It may be explained briefly as follows:

It is a fundamental law that a conductor carrying a current and lying in a magnetic field tends to move at right angles to both the direction of the field and the direction of the current (p. 479). For example, in Fig. 89 is shown the top view of a coil *C* placed in a magnetic field between two pole pieces *N* and *S*. The direction of the current in the conductors *a* at the left-hand side of the coil is outward and in the conductors *b* at the right-hand side is inward. As a result, conductors *a* develop a force f_1 and tend to move upward, and conductors *b* develop an equal force f_2 and tend to move downward, thus producing a couple tending to turn the coil in a clockwise direction.

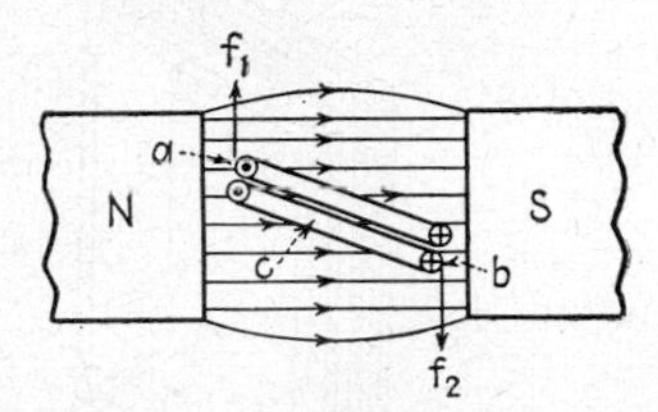

FIG. 89. Turning forces on a coil carrying current.

This turning moment may be explained also on the basis of attraction and repulsion between magnetic poles (Chaps. VI and VII). The current in the turns of the coil produces a magnetic field through the coil with *N* and *S* poles distributed on opposite faces of the coil, Fig. 90.

If the coil be placed in a magnetic field, the coil will tend to turn in such a direction that the ampere-turns of the coil will increase the strength of the magnetic field and the total flux of the system will be a maximum (see Sec. 160, p. 216).

The *N* pole face of the coil will be attracted toward the south pole of

[1] "I often say that when you can measure what you are speaking about and can express it in numbers, you know something about it; but when you cannot measure it, when you cannot express it in numbers, your knowledge is of a meager and unsatisfactory kind; it may be the beginning of knowledge but you have scarcely in your thoughts advanced to the stage of science whatever the matter may be." Lord Kelvin, 1883.

the magnetic field, and the S pole face of the coil will be attracted toward the north pole of the magnetic field.

This tendency of the coil to turn is shown in Fig. 91(a), where the coil tends to turn in the direction indicated by the arrows, at n and s. If the coil is pivoted and free to turn, it will reach the position shown in Fig. 91(b). Under these conditions the coil has placed itself in such a position that its flux is in the same direction as that of the main field. Also, the n pole face of the coil has been attracted toward and is facing the S pole of the magnet. Similarly, the s pole face of the coil has been attracted toward and is facing the N pole of the magnet.

This behavior of a coil carrying a current and placed in a magnetic field should be thoroughly understood, for it is the underlying principle of most current-measuring instruments and is in addition the principle on which electric motors operate.

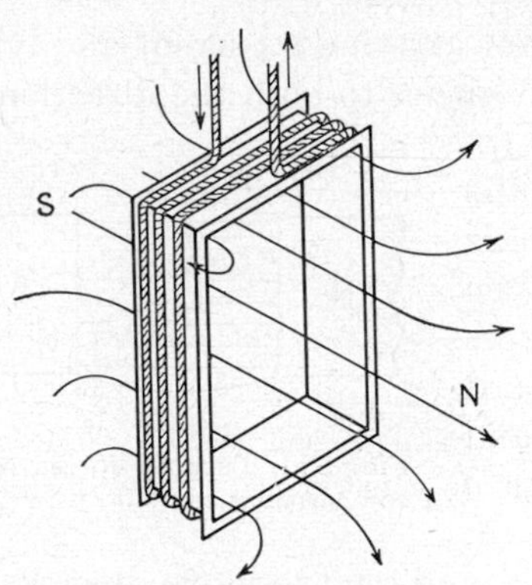

FIG. 90. Magnetic field produced by an instrument coil.

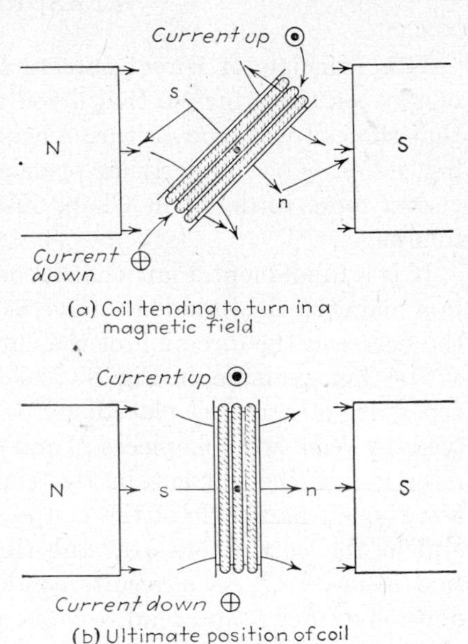

FIG. 91. Turning moment of an instrument coil.

113. D'Arsonval Galvanometer.[1] A galvanometer is a sensitive instrument used for detecting and measuring small electric currents. The

[1] Galvanometer is derived from *galvano*, a prefix derived from the surname of Luigi Galvani, codiscoverer of electric current, and *meter*, meaning to measure. Luigi Galvani, a physiologist, was born in Bologna, Italy, Sept. 9, 1737, and was appointed lecturer on anatomy at the university there in 1762. He gained reputation as a comparative anatomist from his researches on the hearing organs of birds. From his experiments on the effect of electricity on the muscles of frogs (see footnote, p. 96), he enunciated a theory of animal electricity, a treatise which was published in 1791. The adjective *galvanic*, which when applied to electricity came to mean electricity in motion, or *dynamic* electricity, is derived from his name. Also, *galvanism* is sometimes used to designate dynamic electricity. Galvani died in Bologna on Dec. 4, 1798

D'Arsonval galvanometer, which is based on the principle of a coil turning in a magnetic field, is the most common type of galvanometer. Due to its simplicity, it has superseded practically all other types. In addition it is comparatively rugged and is not appreciably affected by stray magnetic fields. Figure 92 shows the principle of its construction. A coil of very fine wire is suspended between the poles of a permanent magnet by means of a filament, usually a flat strip of phosphor bronze. The coil may be wound with or without a bobbin. The bobbin is usually either of fiber or of aluminum. The advantage of an aluminum bobbin will be considered later. The poles of the magnet are usually cylindrical in shape, and a cylindrical soft-iron core is placed between the poles and coaxial with them, Fig. 93. The cylindrical form of pole faces and core is advantageous for two reasons. The length of the air path is reduced so that the amount of flux linking the coil is increased, thus making the galvanometer more sensitive; the flux between the pole faces and the core is practically radial. In such a radial field the deflections of the coil are directly proportional to the current in the coil, so that a uniform scale is obtained.

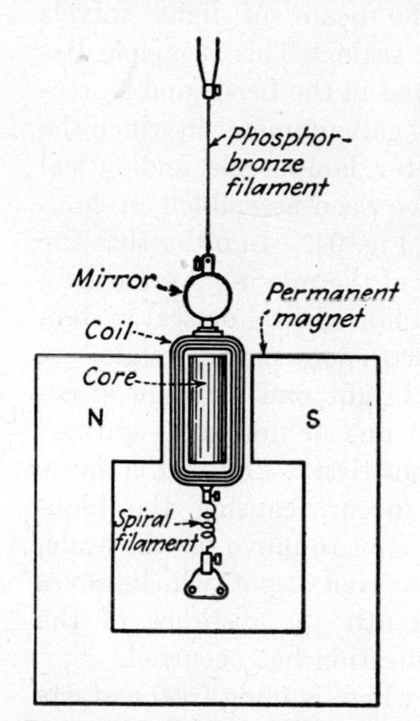

FIG. 92. Principle of the D'Arsonval galvanometer.

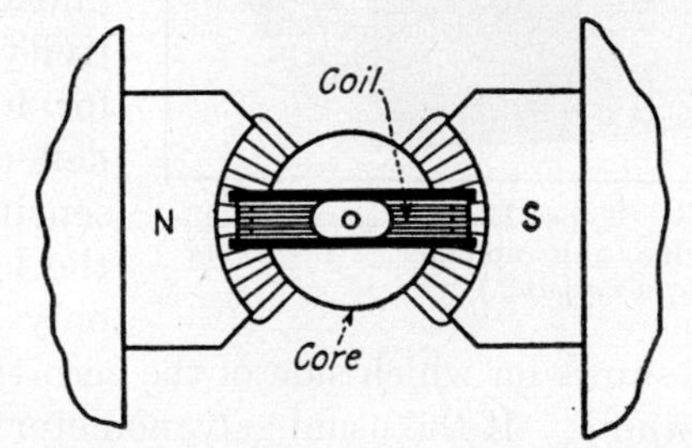

FIG. 93. Radial field produced by cylindrical core and pole faces.

In Fig. 92 the coil is shown suspended by the phosphor-bronze filament. Any turning of the coil produces torsion in the filament which opposes the turning of the coil and is called the *restoring force*. When the moment of the restoring force and the turning moment due to the current are equal, the galvanometer assumes a steady deflection. For all practical purposes the galvanometer deflection is proportional to the current. The phosphor-bronze filament usually serves as one of the leading-in wires which conduct current to the coil. The other leading-in wire consists of a flexible spiral filament fastened to the bottom of the coil, Fig. 92.

There are two common methods of reading the deflection of a galvanometer. A plane mirror is mounted on the coil system, and a scale and telescope are mounted about 0.5 m from the galvanometer. The reflection of the scale in the mirror can be seen with the telescope. When the mirror turns, the reflection of the scale in the mirror deflects. The value of this deflection is determined by means of a crosshair in the telescope.

Another method is to use a concave mirror on the galvanometer moving system. A lamp filament is placed some distance from the mirror, and its image is focused on a ground glass to which a scale graduated in centimeters is fastened. As the mirror deflects, the beam of light travels across the scale. This principle has been adopted in the Leeds and Northrup type E galvanometer in which the galvanometer, lamp, scale, and optical system have been assembled in compact form, Fig. 94. In order that the deflections of the moving system may be easily followed, the optical system projects two spots on the scale: an unusually bright one for high sensitivity, and one of normal brightness for low sensitivity. Should a large deflection occur, causing the high-sensitivity spot to move off the scale, the low-sensitivity spot, which moves only one-tenth the distance of the other, shows on which side of the zero the deflection has occurred.

FIG. 94. Type E short-period high-sensitivity galvanometer. (*Leeds and Northrup Company.*)

Damping. If the usual galvanometer coil, which is hung freely, starts to swing, it will continue swinging for a long time unless special means are provided for damping or retarding it. Electrodynamic damping is the simplest and most effective method of damping instruments of the D'Arsonval type. If the coil be wound on an aluminum bobbin, the motion of the bobbin through the magnetic field will induce currents in the bobbin and these will be in such a direction as to put an electric load on the moving coil as in an electric generator. This opposes the motion of the coil. The same result may be obtained by binding short-circuited copper coils on the main coil, by shunting the galvanometer externally with resistance (see Ayrton Shunt, Sec. 114), or even by short-circuiting it. However, an excessive damping or overdamping makes the motion of the coil so slow that the time to attain the steady deflection may be too long, sometimes as long as with the coil swinging freely. The damping increases when the resistance of the circuit of the coil decreases; the value of the external resistance for which the steady deflection is reached as rapidly as possible is called the *external critical resistance*, and the corresponding damping is called *critical damping*.

114. Galvanometer Shunts. When galvanometers are used to detect small currents, as in null methods (see Wheatstone Bridge, p. 163), the conditions may be such that there is a comparatively large current in the galvanometer. This causes a violent deflection of the coil and may result in injury to the galvanometer. In certain other measurements, the current that it is desired to measure with the galvanometer may be so large that the deflection is well beyond the scale.

In either case the sensitivity of the galvanometer may be reduced by the use of a shunt, that is, a resistor which diverts a known proportion of the current from the galvanometer. There are two common types of shunt. One type is shown in Fig. 95 and consists of three or four separate resistors which are plugged across the galvanometer one at a time. These are so adjusted in value that, with a given external current to be measured, each two successive galvanometer currents are in the ratio of 10 to 1. For example, if the galvanometer is to measure one-tenth the external current, the resistance of the top resistor, Fig. 95, is of such a value that, when the latter is plugged across the galvanometer, it shunts nine-tenths of the current away from the galvanometer.

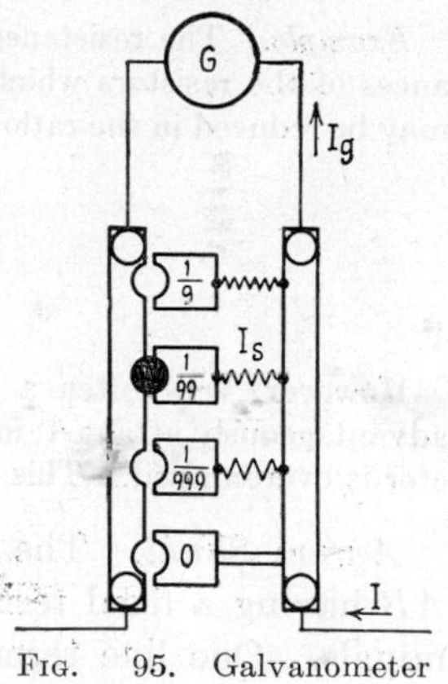

Fig. 95. Galvanometer shunt.

The resistances of these resistors are determined as follows:

Let R_g = galvanometer resistance.
I_g = galvanometer current.
I = circuit current.
I_s = shunt current.
R_s = shunt resistance.

To reduce the galvanometer current to one-tenth the value which it would have with the entire current I through the galvanometer, I_g must be one-tenth of I. That is,

$$\frac{I_g}{I} = \frac{1}{10}. \qquad \text{(I)}$$

The shunt current

$$I_s = I - I_g. \qquad \text{(II)}$$

But the shunt current and the galvanometer current are inversely as the respective resistances. Hence,

$$\frac{R_g}{R_s} = \frac{I_s}{I_g} = \frac{I - I_g}{I_g}. \qquad \text{(III)}$$

If

$$I_g = \frac{I}{10} \quad [(I)],$$

$$\frac{R_g}{R_s} = \frac{I - I/10}{I/10} = 9,$$

$$R_s = \tfrac{1}{9}R_g \quad \text{ohms.} \tag{81}$$

For a reduction of 100 to 1,

$$\frac{R_g}{R_s} = \frac{I - I/100}{I/100} = 99$$

and

$$R_s = \tfrac{1}{99}R_g. \tag{82}$$

Example. The resistance of a galvanometer is 600 ohms. Determine the resistances of the resistors which should be used to shunt it in order that its deflections may be reduced in the ratio of 10 to 1 and 100 to 1.

$$R_1 = \frac{600}{9} = 66.7 \text{ ohms.} \quad \textit{Ans.}$$

$$R_2 = \frac{600}{99} = 6.06 \text{ ohms.} \quad \textit{Ans.}$$

However, very often a large reduction in the galvanometer current cannot be advantageously attained; for if the resistance of the shunt is too small, the galvanometer is overdamped. This difficulty is overcome by the Ayrton shunt.

Ayrton Shunt. The *Ayrton shunt* is shown in Fig. 96(a). A resistor AB having a fixed resistance is connected across the galvanometer terminals. One line terminal A is permanently connected to one end of

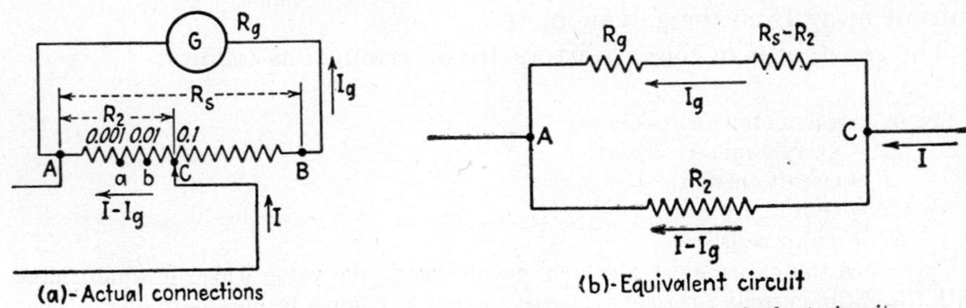

FIG. 96. Ayrton shunt. (a) Actual connections. (b) Equivalent circuit.

this resistor, and the other line terminal is connected to a contactor C which can be connected to various contacts along AB. With a fixed line current, the maximum deflection is obtained when C is at B. If contactor C be moved to a, where resistance Aa is 1/1,000 of the total resistance of AB, the galvanometer deflection will be 1/1,000 its maximum value. If C be moved to b, where Ab is $\tfrac{1}{100}$ the resistance of AB, the galvanometer deflection will be $\tfrac{1}{100}$ its maximum value, etc. This may be proved as follows:

Let I be the line current, I_g the galvanometer current, R_g the resistance of the galvanometer, R_s the total resistance of the Ayrton shunt, and R_2 the resistance of that portion of the shunt between the point A and the movable contactor C.

The equivalent parallel circuit for Fig. 96(*a*) is shown in Fig. 96(*b*). The line current I will divide at contact point C inversely as the resistances of the two parallel branches.

$$\frac{I_g}{I - I_g} = \frac{R_2}{R_g + R_s - R_2}.$$

Solving for the galvanometer current,

$$I_g = I \frac{R_2}{R_g + R_s} \tag{I}$$

or

$$I_g = I \frac{R_2}{R_g + R_s} \cdot \frac{R_s}{R_s} = I \frac{R_s}{R_g + R_s} \cdot \frac{R_2}{R_s}.$$

Since for any particular galvanometer-shunt combination R_s and R_g remain constant, the above equation may be written.

$$I_g = IK \frac{R_2}{R_s}. \tag{II}$$

Equation (II) shows that the galvanometer current (and hence the galvanometer deflection) is proportional to the setting of the shunt for a particular value of line current.

Equation (II) may be rewritten

$$I = I_g K' \frac{R_s}{R_2}$$

where $K' = 1/K = (R_g + R_s)/R_s$
or

$$I = I_g K' M \tag{83}$$

where M ($= R_s/R_2$) is the *multiplying ratio*, or multiplying factor, of the shunt and equals 1,000, 100, 10, or 1 depending on where the contact point C is set.

Galvanometers are used only occasionally to measure current directly but more often are employed for comparing two or more currents. Since the galvanometer deflection is proportional to the galvanometer current, (83) may be written

$$I = K''DM \tag{84}$$

where D is the galvanometer deflection.

Writing the equations for two values of line current I_1 and I_2 and then comparing them,

$$I_1 = K''D_1M_1 \quad \text{and} \quad I_2 = K''D_2M_2. \tag{III}$$

$$\frac{I_1}{I_2} = \frac{D_1M_1}{D_2M_2}. \tag{85}$$

It will be noted that (85) is independent of the galvanometer resistance and involves only the galvanometer deflections and the fractional settings of the Ayrton shunt since K'', which includes the galvanometer resistance, cancels in (85). This shows the universal nature of the Ayrton shunt since the current ratio does not depend on the galvanometer resistance. Hence the shunt can be used with *any* galvanometer, provided, of course, that both deflections are taken with the same galvanometer and that the same shunt is used with it.

If no shunt were used, the entire line current would flow through the galvanometer. If the contact C be moved to B, the galvanometer current is reduced from what it would be if there were no shunt. The shunt then produces a reduction in the sensitivity of the galvanometer. The galvanometer sensitivity may be defined as the ratio of the galvanometer current with the shunt contact set at B to the galvanometer current when no shunt is used.

When C is at B, $R_2 = R_s$ and

$$I_g = I\frac{R_s}{R_g + R_s} \quad \text{from (I).}$$

The sensitivity is therefore

$$\frac{I\dfrac{R_s}{R_g + R_s}}{I} = \frac{R_s}{R_g + R_s}. \tag{86}$$

Actually the shunt gives best results when the total resistance of the shunt is about 10 times the resistance of the galvanometer.

The advantages of the Ayrton shunt are: (1) Within the limits of the required sensitivity and of damping, the shunt with its fixed multiplying ratios is applicable to any galvanometer, regardless of the galvanometer resistance. (2) A fixed resistance is shunted across the galvanometer, which gives a constant value of damping in open-circuit ballistic measurements (see Sec. 114, p. 142).

Example. The resistance of a galvanometer is 800 ohms, and a 10,000-ohm Ayrton shunt is employed in conjunction with it. The shunt is marked in decimal proportions from 0.0001 to 1. The sensitivity of the galvanometer is such that a galvanometer current of $8 \cdot 10^{-8}$ amp produces full scale deflection of 50 cm. Determine: (*a*) sensitivity of galvanometer when used with this shunt; (*b*) line current with the shunt contact set at 0.01 and the galvanometer deflection 20 cm; (c) line current with the shunt contact set at 0.001 and the galvanometer deflection 40 cm.

(a) Sensitivity from (86),

$$\frac{R_s}{R_g + R_s} = \frac{10,000}{800 + 10,000} = 0.926. \quad Ans.$$

(b) If I_{g1} is current with 50-cm deflection, current with 20-cm deflection,

$$I_{g2} = I_{g1}{}^{20}/_{50} = (8 \cdot 10^{-8})^{20}/_{50} = 3.2 \cdot 10^{-8} \text{ amp.}$$

From (I), the line current

$$I = I_{g2}\frac{R_g + R_s}{R_2} = (3.2 \cdot 10^{-8})\frac{10,800}{0.01 \cdot 10,000}$$
$$= 3.456 \cdot 10^{-6} \text{ amp.} \quad Ans.$$

(c) From (85),

$$\frac{I_1}{I} = \frac{D_1M_1}{DM},$$

$$I_1 = I\frac{40 \cdot 1,000}{20 \cdot 100} = 3.456 \cdot 10^{-6}\frac{40}{2} = 6.912 \cdot 10^{-5} \text{ amp.} \quad Ans.$$

115. Weston-type Instrument. In general, the measurement of current and voltage requires instruments that are rugged as well as portable, and at the same time their precision should be high. The suspension-type galvanometer obviously is not adapted to such measurements. For the measurement of direct current and voltage, the Weston-type instrument is in universal use. The instrument is based on the principle of the D'Arsonval galvanometer but is so constructed that it is portable and is provided with a pointer and scale for indicating the deflections of the moving coil. In fact, the permanent-magnet–moving-coil element is often called the "D'Arsonval movement." The same movement may be used as either ammeter or voltmeter. For use as ammeter, except for extremely small currents, it is provided with a shunt through which the greater portion of the current flows; for use as voltmeter, a resistor is connected in series with the moving coil so that the instrument can be connected across the line without taking excessive current.

The essential parts of the instrument are shown in Fig. 97. As in the D'Arsonval galvanometer, a permanent magnet is necessary, being made in horseshoe form. Magnets of this form are made usually of chrome or tungsten steel (see p. 224). Two soft-iron pole pieces are fitted to the magnet poles, and a cylindrical core is held between these pole pieces by a strip of brass. This gives uniform air gaps and a radial field. The length of the air gap is very much shorter than is usual with D'Arsonval galvanometers. The moving coil consists of very fine silk-covered copper wire, and sometimes aluminum wire, usually wound on an aluminum bobbin. The aluminum bobbin, besides supporting the coil mechanically, makes the instrument highly damped. This damping is due to the currents induced in the aluminum because of its cutting the magnetic field. Some damping is due also to the current induced in the coil itself, the circuit being closed external to the coil.

Instead of suspending the coil by a filament, it is supported at the top and bottom by hardened-steel pivots turning in cup-shaped jewels, usually sapphire. This method of supporting the moving coil is almost frictionless and makes the instrument portable, whereas the D'Arsonval galvanometer is not portable. The current is led in and out of the coil

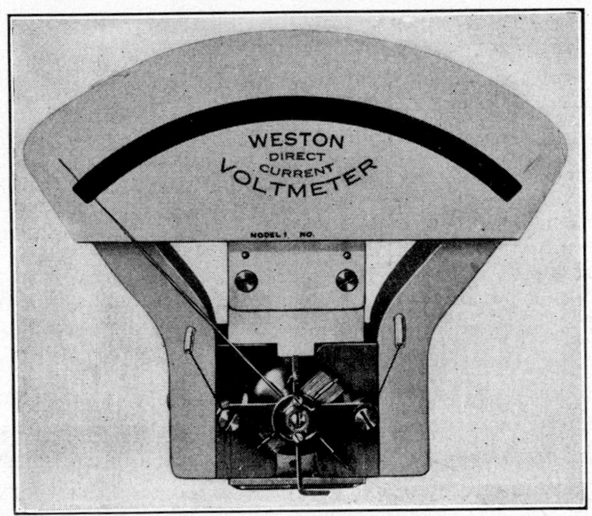

FIG. 97. Movement of Weston instrument. (*Weston Electrical Instrument Company.*)

by two flat spiral springs, one at the top of the coil and the other at the bottom. These springs also serve as the controlling device for the coil, any tendency of the coil to turn being opposed by these two springs. The top and bottom springs are coiled in opposite directions so that the effect of change of temperature, which causes a spiral spring to coil or uncoil, will not cause the needle to change its zero position. A light and delicate aluminum pointer is attached to the moving element to indicate the deflection of the coil. The pointer is carefully balanced by small counter-weights so that the whole moving element holds its zero position very closely, even if the instrument is not level. The pointer moves over a graduated scale, which may be marked in volts or in amperes as the case may be. Because of the radial field, the deflection of the moving coil in this type of instrument is practically proportional to the current in the moving coil, so that the scale of the instrument has substantially uniform graduations, which is desirable.

The internal connections of a Weston-type instrument, for use as a milliammeter, are shown in Fig. 98. Inasmuch as the copper of the coil has a substantial temperature coefficient of resistance, an increase in temperature would cause a lesser proportion of the current to go through the coil, thus causing the instrument to read low. To avoid such temperature errors, a swamping resistor of substantially zero temperature coefficient of resistance and having four or five times the resistance of the coil is connected in series. Thus a change in the coil resistance has little effect on the resistance of the coil circuit, and changes in temperature produce negligible errors.

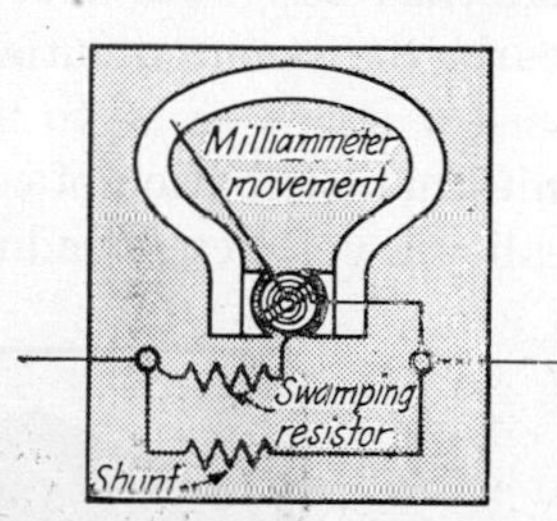

FIG. 98. Milliammeter shunted to permit current measurement in amperes. (*General Electric Company.*)

Instruments of this construction having very weak springs are often used for portable galvanometers. Although lacking the extreme sensitivity of the suspended type, they can be made sufficiently sensitive for certain classes of work, and their ruggedness and portability make them very useful. An instrument of the type shown in Fig. 113, p. 160, can be readily adapted to operate as a portable galvanometer.

116. Ammeters. In accordance with present practice, coils of Weston-type portable instruments are wound so that currents of 20 microamp to 25 ma will give full-scale deflection. Such instruments are called *microammeters* and *milliammeters.* The coils for the smallest currents are wound with the largest number of turns using the smallest size of wire. In order to measure larger currents than the coil can carry, a *shunt* to divert a portion of the current from the coil is used. Thus, in Fig. 98, a shunt is used to increase the milliamperes range above the maximum of 25 ma which the coil can carry. An instrument with its shunt designed for a higher current rating is shown in Fig. 99. When the instrument movement is designed for use in an ammeter, the coil is wound for low resistance so that the voltage drop across the instrument is low. The ammeter then will not introduce any great resistance when connected in the circuit. Hence, the cross section of the wire in the coil should be as large as is practicable, and the number of turns will be correspondingly small. The shunt is merely a low resistor, usually made of manganin

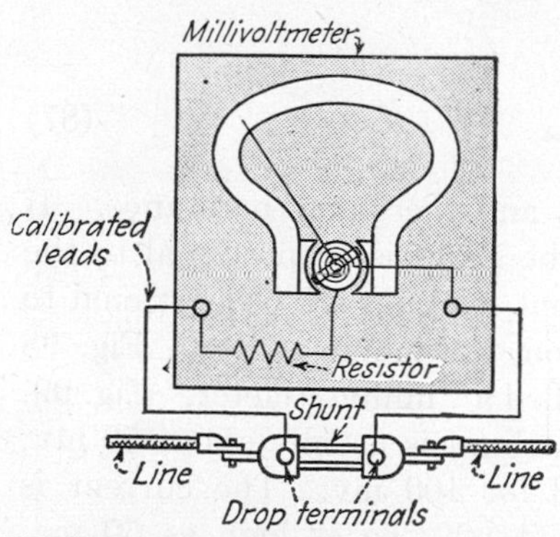

FIG. 99. Millivoltmeter with external shunt. (*General Electric Company.*)

strips brazed to comparatively heavy copper blocks, Fig. 100. The external line is connected to the "line terminals" which are designed to carry the large currents that are being measured. The lighter "drop terminals" are used for connecting the leads which go to the instrument. The heavy copper blocks serve two purposes. They are an excellent conductor of heat and so carry the heat away from the manganin strip, and their low resistance keeps all parts of each copper block at very nearly the same potential. The drop terminals are located close to the resistor strips so as to avoid errors which might result from any non-uniform distribution of current in the copper blocks. The ammeter is in reality a voltmeter reading the voltage drop across a resistor.

FIG. 100. Portable external shunt for high-current measurement. (*General Electric Company.*)

The voltage drop across the shunt is

$$V_{sh} = I_{sh}R_{sh} \tag{87}$$

where I_{sh} and R_{sh} are the shunt current and the shunt resistance. If R_{sh} is constant, the voltage drop across the shunt is proportional to the current in the shunt, so that the instrument readings are proportional to the current in the shunt. For this reason, the ammeter itself, Fig. 98 with the shunt circuit omitted, is often called a "millivoltmeter," Fig. 99. For full-scale deflection the drop across a shunt is usually about 50 mv, although some instruments are designed for 100 mv. The current is usually of the order of 25 ma although it may be as high as 50 ma. Hence, the instrument current is usually negligible as compared with the shunt current, and accordingly in most cases the line current practically equals the shunt current.

An ammeter and its shunt may be considered also as a divided circuit. In Fig. 101, let R_{sh} and I_{sh} be the shunt resistance and shunt current, and let R_m and I_m be the instrument resistance and instrument current. By the law of divided circuits,

$$\frac{I_{sh}}{I_m} = \frac{R_m}{R_{sh}}, \tag{88}$$

that is, the current divides between the instrument and the shunt inversely as their resistances.

Example. Assume that an instrument has a resistance of 4 ohms, the shunt a resistance of 0.0005 ohm, and that the line current is 90 amp. Determine the value of the instrument current.

As the current in the line differs from the shunt current by a very small amount, the two may be assumed equal. Then,

$$\frac{I_m}{90} = \frac{0.0005}{4}$$

$$I_m = 0.01125 \text{ amp.} \quad \textit{Ans.}$$

For accuracy, the current must always divide between the instrument and the shunt in a fixed ratio. This means either that the resistance of the shunt and the resistance of the instrument must not change at all or that both must change in the same ratio. As the shunt operates at a higher temperature than the instrument, it should be made of a metal such as manganin (see p. 18) whose resistance does not change appreciably with temperature. The resistance of the instrument circuit should also remain constant. The resistance of the leads connecting the shunt to the instrument should remain constant, *and the leads with which the instrument is calibrated should always be used to connect the shunt to the instrument.* The lugs and binding-post contacts should be kept clean from oxide and dirt. A low adjustable resistor (the swamping resistor, Fig. 98) is connected inside the instrument. By varying the resistance of this resistor, the instrument is adjusted to its shunt.

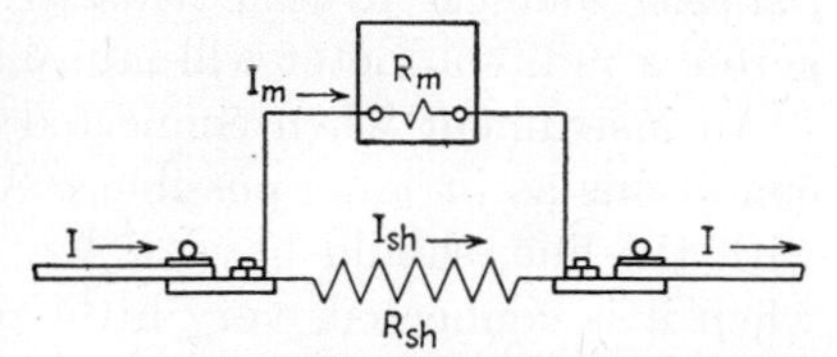

FIG. 101. Division of current between an ammeter and its shunt.

An ammeter with an external shunt may be made to have a large number of scales or ranges. Assume that an instrument gives full-scale deflection when the instrument current is 0.02 amp and that its resistance is 2.5 ohms. The resistance of the shunt is 0.0005 ohm. The voltage across the instrument terminals is $0.02 \cdot 2.5 = 0.050$ volt, or 50 mv. Dividing this voltage by the shunt resistance, the shunt current is

$$I = \frac{0.050}{0.0005} = 100 \text{ amp.}$$

The instrument then deflects full scale with 100 amp in the line.

If the foregoing shunt be replaced by one having a resistance of 0.005 ohm, the 50 mv drop across the shunt may be obtained with 10 amp ($10 \cdot 0.005 = 0.050$). Therefore, a 10-scale ammeter results. By the choice of suitable shunts, the same instrument may be made to give full-scale deflection with 1 amp and with 5,000 amp.

In the smaller sizes of instruments up to 50 amp and where only one scale is desired, the shunt is usually placed within the instrument. For ranges between 50 and 100 amp, the use of an internal or an external shunt is optional. Above 100 amp, it is usual to have the shunt external to the instrument on account of its size and its heating loss.

An ammeter can usually be distinguished from a voltmeter by the fact that the ammeter's binding posts are heavy and are of bare metal, except in the case of an instrument having an external shunt. The binding posts of millivoltmeters and voltmeters are of much lighter construction, and the metal posts are covered with hard rubber, mostly for insulation purposes. Since the binding posts of millivoltmeters and voltmeters are usually identical, *care should be taken not to mistake a millivoltmeter for a voltmeter and use it as a voltmeter.* Even a comparatively low voltage across a millivoltmeter will injure it seriously.

An instrument when connected in a circuit should disturb the circuit conditions as little as possible. An ammeter shunt, as it goes in series with the line, should have as low a resistance as is practicable, so that when it is connected, very little additional resistance is introduced into the circuit. To protect ammeters from heavy currents, provision may be made for *short-circuiting* them when readings are not being taken.

117. Voltmeters. The construction of a voltmeter does not differ materially from that of an ammeter in so far as the movement is concerned, Fig. 97. The moving coil of the voltmeter is usually wound with more turns and of finer wire than that of the ammeter and so has a higher resistance. The principal difference, however, lies in the manner of connecting the instrument to the circuit. As a voltmeter is connected directly across the line to measure the voltage, it is desirable that the voltmeter take as little current as is practicable. Because of its comparatively low resistance, the moving coil of the voltmeter cannot be connected directly across the line, as it would ordinarily take an excessive current and be burnt out. Therefore it is necessary to connect a resistor of high resistance in series with the moving coil, Fig. 102. By Ohm's law the current through the instrument is proportional to the voltage at its terminals, so that the instrument scale can be graduated in volts. The value of resistance required is easily determined. Assume that an instrument gives full-scale deflection with 0.01 amp in the moving coil and that the coil resistance is 20 ohms. If it is desired that the instrument indicate 150 volts, full scale, the total resistance of the instrument circuit must be

$$R = \frac{V}{I} = \frac{150}{0.01} = 15{,}000 \text{ ohms.}$$

As the instrument has a resistance of 20 ohms, 14,980 ohms additional is necessary, Fig. 102(*a*). If it be desired that this same instrument also have full-scale deflection with 15 volts, the resistance of 14,980 ohms may be tapped so that the resistance between *O* and *B*, Fig. 102(*a*), = 15/0.01 = 1,500 ohms, and this tap can be brought to a binding post. Another method of securing the same result is shown in Fig. 102(*b*). A separate resistor having 1,500 − 20 = 1,480 ohms is connected from the 15-volt binding post to the junction of the resistor and the moving coil. This last method is advantageous in that it permits independent adjustment of each resistor; also, injury or repair in one resistor does not affect

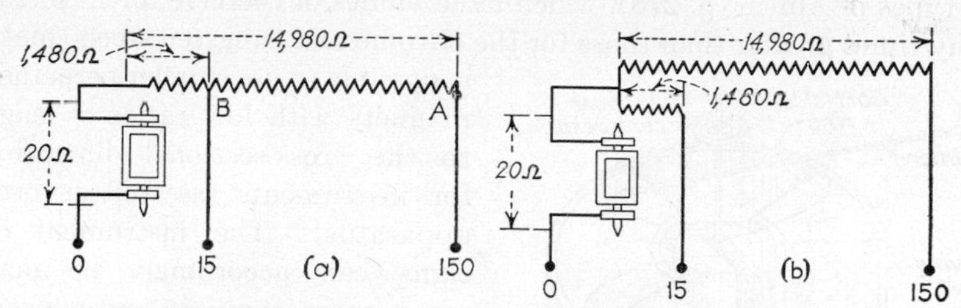

FIG. 102. Methods of connecting a voltmeter resistor.

the other. Figure 113 (p. 160) is a combination instrument with several voltage ranges.

118. Multipliers, or Extension Coils. The range of a voltmeter, having its series resistor incorporated within the instrument, may be increased by the use of an external resistor connected in series with the instrument.

Example. A 150-scale voltmeter has a resistance of 17,000 ohms. Determine resistance of an external resistor which can be connected in series with it in order that its range may be (*a*) 300 volts; (*b*) 600 volts.

(*a*) In order to obtain full-scale deflection at 300 volts, the voltmeter current must be equal to the current which produces full-scale deflection at 150 volts. Accordingly, the total resistance of the instrument for 300 volts must be twice the 150-volt value. Therefore, a total resistance of 17,000 · 2 = 34,000 ohms is necessary. As the instrument already has 17,000 ohms, the added resistance will be

$$34{,}000 - 17{,}000 = 17{,}000 \text{ ohms.} \quad \textit{Ans.}$$

(*b*) The total resistance must now be

$$\frac{600}{150} \cdot 17{,}000 = 68{,}000 \text{ ohms.}$$

As 17,000 ohms is already within the instrument, 68,000 − 17,000 = 51,000 ohms must be added external to the instrument. *Ans.*

External resistors used in this manner are called *multipliers*, or sometimes *extension coils*. They are usually placed within a perforated box and the terminals brought out to binding posts. The multiplying power of the multiplier is marked near a terminal.

The equation giving the relation of the resistance of the multiplier R_x, the resistance of the instrument R_m, and the multiplying power M is as follows:

$$M = \frac{R_x + R_m}{R_m}. \tag{89}$$

Example. In the above example (*b*), the multiplying power of the multiplier is as follows:

$$M = \frac{51{,}000 + 17{,}000}{17{,}000} = 4.$$

119. Concentric-magnet Instruments. The development of the different types of Alnico (p. 278), which have values of coercive force (p. 202) many times greater than those for the chrome and tungsten steels, makes it possible to use smaller permanent magnets with low ratios of length to the cross-sectional dimensions for instruments (as well as other apparatus). The instrument designs can accordingly be made much more compact and efficient. The General Electric Company has designed different types of instruments based on shapes of magnets which are possible only with magnets of the Alnico type.

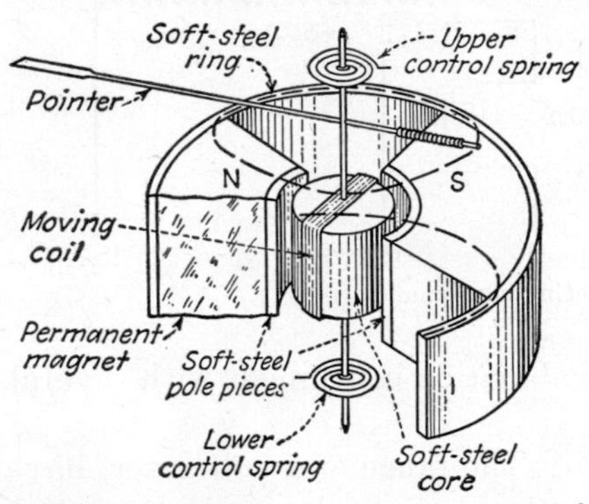

FIG. 103. Arrangement of basic parts of concentric-magnet instrument. (*General Electric Company.*)

In one type, two segmental pieces of Alnico are held by a soft iron ring, Fig. 103. The N and S poles of the Alnico magnets and the general paths of the magnetic flux are indicated. The soft-steel ring serves two purposes. It completes the magnetic circuit, and it effectively shields the movement from any stray fields. Hence there is no need for special shielding. The soft-steel pole pieces and the cylindrical soft-steel core mounted concentric with the pole pieces produce a radial field which gives a uniform scale. The coil, pointer, control springs, pivots, and jewels do not differ from those in the conventional Weston-type of instrument described in Sec. 115. Since Alnico magnets are much stronger in proportion to their size than chrome- or tungsten-steel magnets, there can be fewer ampere-turns in the coil and more torque can be produced in a given space. Instruments embodying the concentric-magnet principle are available in all the usual ratings.

120. Concentric-scale Instruments. In the conventional types of d-c instruments the length of scale and the general ease of reading are limited by the bearing load which can be imposed by excessively long pointers and by considerations of instrument size. These limitations, in a large measure, are overcome by an Alnico permanent-magnet instrument design by the General Electric Company and called the "concentric-scale" type. The concentric-scale design differs from the conventional type in that there is but a single air gap rather than two and only one side of the moving coil, rather than two, is effective in producing torque. This general design, which is shown in Fig. 104, permits 240° rotation of the coil rather than the usual 85 to 90°. With the length of pointer used, a scale 36 per cent longer than the usual is obtained with 40 per cent of the panel space. A single sector-shaped Alnico magnet produces the flux, and a laminated-steel shell serves not only to provide a return path for the flux but also to provide an excellent shield. The soft-steel pole piece which is cast integral with the magnet has a cylindrical surface and in conjunction with the soft-steel pole piece S produces a radial field which gives a uniform scale. The general paths of the flux are indicated in the figure by the dotted lines. The moving coil must necessarily be pivoted at one side. Aside from this, the moving system with the pointer, control springs, pivots, and jewels is the same as that of conventional instruments. The instrument is manufactured in a large number of ratings in accordance with circuit requirements.

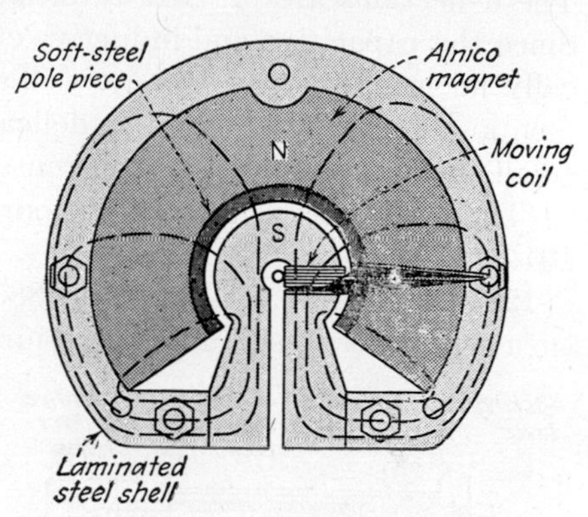

FIG. 104. Arrangement of basic parts of concentric-scale instrument. (*General Electric Company.*)

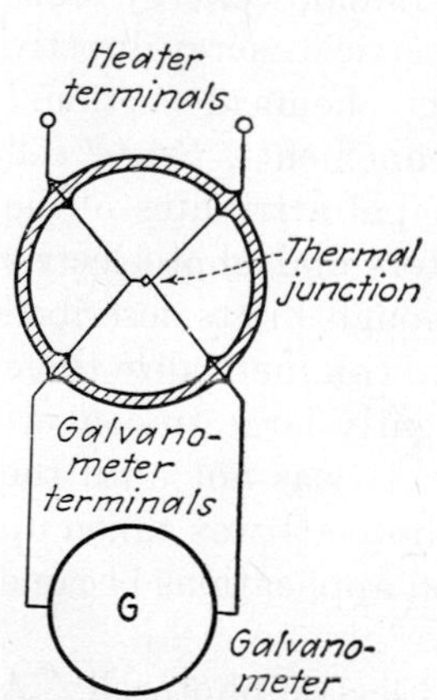

FIG. 105. Vacuum thermocouple and galvanometer.

121. Vacuum Thermocouple. The vacuum thermocouple in conjunction with an associated galvanometer or sensitive deflecting instrument is a current-measuring device based on the heating effect of the current. A very small thermal junction is in thermal contact with a small resistor or heater through which the current to be measured flows, Fig. 105. The junction and the small connecting wires are sealed within a small evacuated glass bulb, thus reducing heat dissipation from the junction. The thermal-junction terminals are connected to a galvanometer or to some other sensitive type of D'Arsonval instrument. The current in the heater circuit raises the temperature of the thermal junction, and as a result of the thermal emf the indicating instrument deflects. The deflections are practically proportional to the square of the current. Since the capacitive and inductive effects in the heater circuit are practically nil, such instruments are well adapted to radio-frequency measurements. The heater circuit is delicate, and its rating is limited to very small currents. With large currents a shunt is necessary.

(The wattmeter and the watthour meter are described on pp. 190 and 191.)

122. Photocells. As early as 1885 and even earlier it was known that such materials as sodium, potassium, selenium, and cesium were light-sensitive and that when light impinged on them they generated small emfs. In terms of modern knowledge the effect was that of photoemission, and the light impinging on these materials caused them to emit electrons. In 1885 Fritts made a dry-disk cell consisting of selenium covered with fine gold leaf in which "the current thus produced is radiant energy converted into electrical energy directly and without chemical action." Except for refinements, Fritts' cell had the principal attributes of the modern photocell, and he made candle power meters and photoelectric relays basically similar to our modern ones. Although Fritts described his cells widely in lectures and writings, he failed to commercialize them and the fact that they could not be made sufficiently large to convert large amounts of power caused a loss of interest. It was not until the 1930's that the development of the dry type of photocell was taken up in earnest and cells readily adaptable to commercial applications became available.

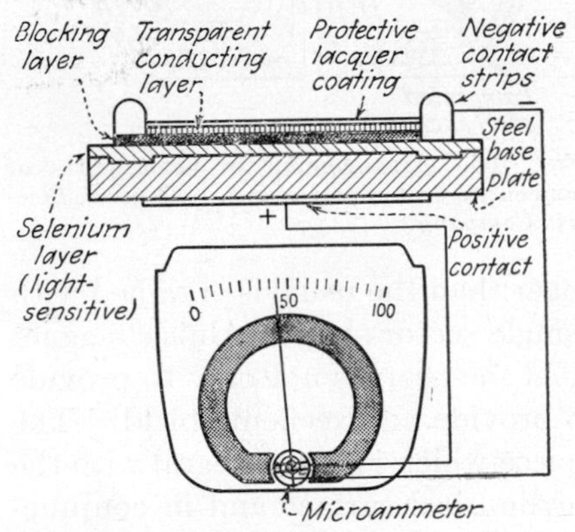

FIG. 106. Light-sensitive cell and associated microammeter of a typical indicating light meter. (*General Electric Company.*)

Figure 106 shows a cross section of the General Electric photocell. A layer of selenium is deposited on a steel base plate. Several extremely thin layers of conducting metals, or "blocking layers," are then deposited on the selenium, and the entire cell, except for the electric contacts, is covered with a transparent-lacquer coating to protect it against atmospheric effects such as moisture. Figure 107 shows the current output as a function of the illumination in foot-candles for different values of circuit resistance R. Such cells have wide applications such as for photometers, which are readily portable and are widely used for measuring local foot-candles, for light meters used in photography, for initiating, through relays, controls and other monitoring operations in industry.

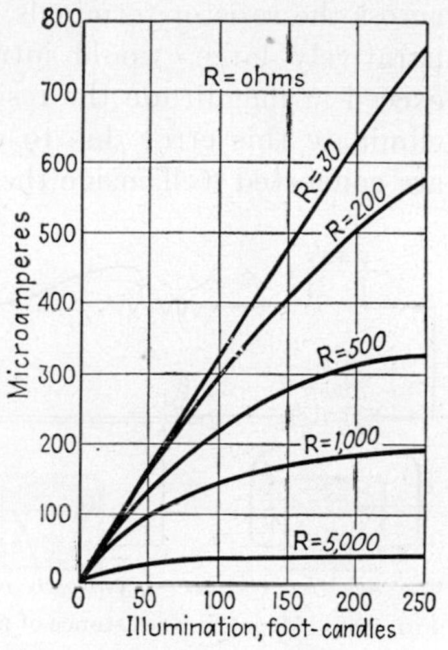

FIG. 107. Current-foot-candle characteristics of light meter.

ELECTRICAL MEASUREMENTS

MEASUREMENT OF RESISTANCE

123. Voltmeter-Ammeter Method. The resistance of any portion of an electric circuit which does not contain a source of emf is, by Ohm's law,

$$R = \frac{V}{I} \tag{90}$$

where V is the voltage across that portion of the circuit and I is the steady current flowing in that portion of the circuit. Obviously, the voltage V may be measured with a voltmeter, the current I measured with an ammeter, and the resistance R computed.

Let it be required to determine the resistance of resistor R in the circuit shown in Fig. 108. The source of power is the 110-volt supply. The resistance of R is comparatively small, and if R were connected directly across 110 volts, it would take an excessive current. Therefore, it is necessary to insert a resistor R' in series with R to limit the current. The voltmeter, however, must be connected directly across R as it is desired to know the resistance of this portion of the circuit only.

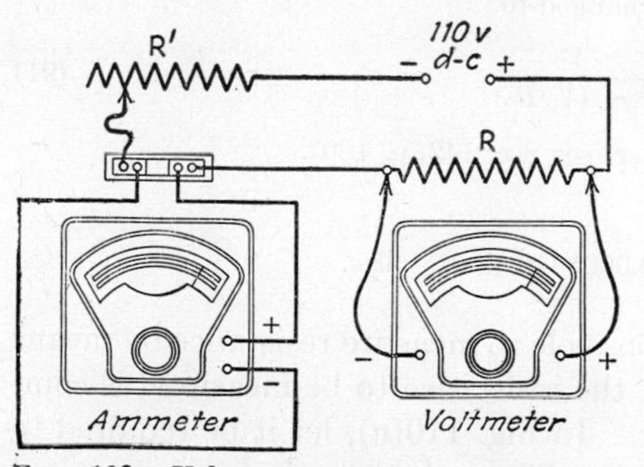

FIG. 108. Voltmeter-ammeter method of measuring resistance.

Example. The voltmeter, Fig. 108, reads 19 volts when the ammeter reads 24 amp. What is the resistance of R?

The resistance is

$$R = \frac{19}{24} = 0.792 \text{ ohm.} \quad \textit{Ans.}$$

As a matter of interest let it be required to determine the resistance of R'. The voltmeter terminals are transferred from across R to across R'. Under these conditions the voltmeter reads 91 volts, and the ammeter still reads 24 amp. Therefore,

$$R' = \frac{91}{24} = 3.79 \text{ ohms.}$$

Elimination of Contact Resistance. It is sometimes desired to measure resistances of such low value that if a voltmeter were connected directly across the resistor terminals, the contact resistance, which may be comparatively large, would introduce considerable error and might even exceed in magnitude the resistance which it is desired to measure. To eliminate this error due to contact resistance, the voltmeter terminals are connected well inside the terminals BB, Fig. 109, through which the current is led to the specimen. Since the voltmeter takes but a small current, small sharp-pointed contacts CC may be used. As the resistance of the voltmeter is comparatively high, it is necessary only that the contact resistances at CC be negligible compared with the resistance of the instrument. This condition is easily met. As these contacts are small and sharp, the points of contact on the specimen can be determined very accurately.

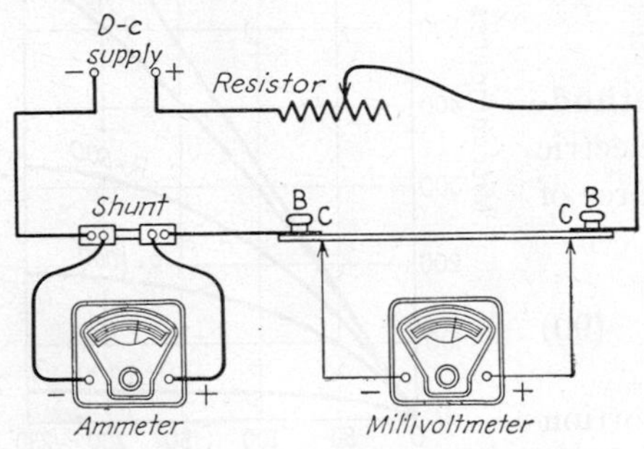

FIG. 109. Measuring resistance of metal rod.

Example. When the ammeter, Fig. 109, reads 50 amp, the millivoltmeter indicates 40 mv. The contacts CC are 23 in. apart. What is the resistance per inch length of the rod?

The resistance for 23 in. is

$$R = \frac{0.040}{50} = 0.00080 \text{ ohm.}$$

In applying (90) it is assumed that the voltmeter current is negligible compared with the current to the resistor. Under most conditions the voltmeter current is negligible, but if it is not, (90) must be changed to

$$R = \frac{V}{I - (V/R_v)} \tag{91}$$

where R_v is the resistance of the voltmeter (see Sec. 142, p. 189).

The resistance per inch is

$$R = \frac{0.00080}{23} = 0.0000348 \text{ ohm. } \textit{Ans.}$$

124. Voltmeter Method. It is possible to measure resistance by means of a voltmeter alone provided that the resistance to be measured is comparable with that of the voltmeter. In Fig. 110(a), let it be required to measure the resistance of resistor R. The voltmeter is first connected across the source of supply and a reading V_1 taken. The voltmeter is then transferred so that the resistor R is in series with it across the source of supply, and the reading is again taken. Let this reading be V_2.

As V_1 is the total circuit voltage and V_2 is the voltage across the instrument, the voltage across the resistor R is obviously $V_1 - V_2$. When the voltmeter is in series with R, the same current i must flow through each so that the voltages are as follows:

$$V_2 = iR_v, \tag{I}$$
$$V_1 - V_2 = iR, \tag{II}$$

where R_v is the resistance of the voltmeter.

Dividing (II) by (I) and solving for R,

$$R = R_v \frac{V_1 - V_2}{V_2}. \tag{92}$$

If desired, the voltage V_1 may be measured with a second voltmeter. This makes it possible to increase the voltage V_1 above the range of the voltmeter in series with R and thus increases the sensitivity of the measurement.

This method of measuring resistance is particularly useful in determining insulation resistance, such as for dynamo windings or cables. As

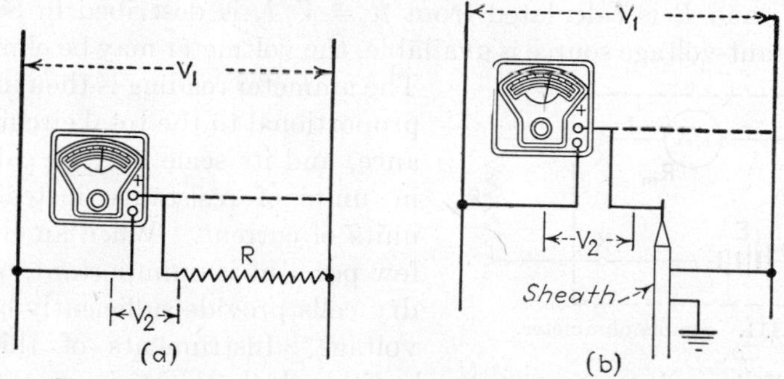

FIG. 110. Measurement of resistance by voltmeter method.

such resistances are very high, they are usually expressed in megohms (1 megohm = 1,000,000 ohms). It will be seen from (92) that the greater the value of R_v the greater the resistance that can be measured by this method. For this reason 150-scale voltmeters, having resistances of 100,000 ohms (0.1 megohm), are available. These give a sensitivity about six times as great as can be obtained with the ordinary 150-scale voltmeter. Special types of voltmeters which have sensitivities as high as 2,000, 5,000, and 10,000 ohms per volt are also available.

Figure 110(*b*) shows the application of this method to the measurement of the insulation resistance of a cable. The ground connection to the sheath represents the condition usually met in practice where the lead sheath is in actual contact with the ground and is frequently bonded to pipes and other grounded systems. Accordingly, if one side of the supply system is grounded, as is frequently the case, *that side* should be connected to the sheath. (Theoretically, under these conditions no connection from the grounded conductor to the sheath is necessary, but nevertheless such connection should be made to avoid any uncertainty.)

If any one of the conductors of the supply system is grounded, the connecting of the grounded sheath to any conductor other than the grounded one will result in a *short circuit.* If the cable is isolated, that is, if it is coiled on a reel and the sheath is insulated from ground, the ground connection shown in Fig. 110(*b*) may be removed.

Example. When a 100,000-ohm voltmeter is connected across a d-c line, it reads 120 volts. One terminal of the voltmeter is then connected to the core of a lead-covered cable, and the sheath of the cable is connected to the other side of the line as in Fig. 110(*b*). The voltmeter now reads 10 volts. What is the insulation resistance of the cable?

$$X = 0.1 \frac{120 - 10}{10} = 1.1 \text{ megohms.} \quad \textit{Ans.}$$

125. Ohmmeters. The voltmeter-ammeter method of measuring resistance, in which a voltmeter and an ammeter are used to measure V and I, and R is calculated from $R = V/I$, is described in Sec. 123. If a constant-voltage source is available, the voltmeter may be eliminated. The ammeter reading is then inversely proportional to the total circuit resistance, and its scale may be calibrated in units of resistance instead of in units of current. When an error of a few per cent is unimportant, ordinary dry cells provide sufficiently constant voltage. Instruments of this type, with built-in voltage sources and with which the resistance may be read directly, are known as *ohmmeters.* They are available in several sizes and ranges. Some have switching arrangements by which the same moving coil may be connected through appropriate multipliers or shunts as voltmeter or ammeter or ohmmeter, each instrument having a number of ranges. Such combinations for measuring voltage, current, and resistance are particularly convenient for portable test purposes. An instrument of this type is shown in Fig. 113.

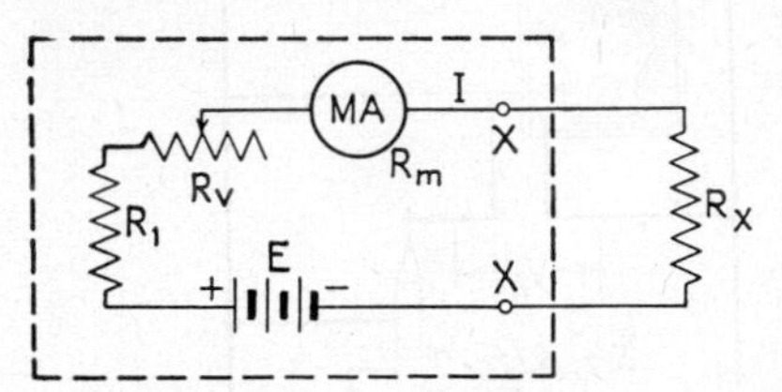

FIG. 111. Simple ohmmeter.

The principle of operation is as follows: Figure 111 shows a simple ohmmeter with terminals XX for measuring an unknown resistor R_x. The resistance of the milliammeter (MA) coil is R_m, and the battery voltage is E. Resistor R_1 is inserted to limit the maximum current to the milliammeter when R_x is small. A variable resistor R_v is used to bring the pointer to the resistance reading when $R_x = 0$. The milliammeter current

$$I = \frac{E}{R_m + R_v + R_1 + R_x}.$$

The maximum current $I_{\max}$, which occurs when $R_x = 0$, is determined by the permissible full-scale instrument current.

$$I_{\max} = \frac{E}{R_v + R_1 + R_m} \quad \text{and} \quad R_1 = \frac{E}{I_{\max}} - (R_m + R_v) \tag{93}$$

from which the proper value for R_1 may be determined. Hence the zero point of the R scale, which occurs when $R_x = 0$, corresponds to the maxi-

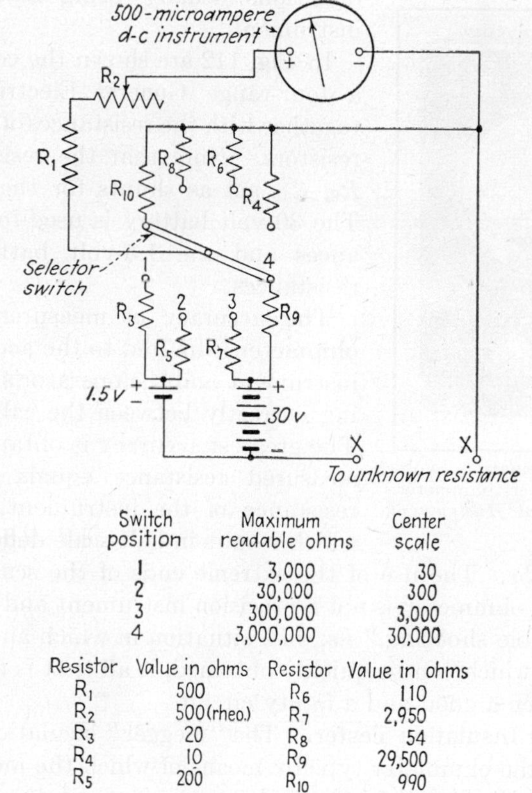

Switch position	Maximum readable ohms	Center scale
1	3,000	30
2	30,000	300
3	300,000	3,000
4	3,000,000	30,000

Resistor	Value in ohms	Resistor	Value in ohms
R_1	500	R_6	110
R_2	500 (rheo.)	R_7	2,950
R_3	20	R_8	54
R_4	10	R_9	29,500
R_5	200	R_{10}	990

FIG. 112. Circuit diagram of four-range ohmmeter. *(General Electric Company.)*

mum point of the I scale. In order to make $I = 0$, it is necessary for R_x to be infinite; therefore the zero point on the I scale becomes the infinity point on the R scale. The range of the ohmmeter scale is thus from zero to infinity, but its scale is not uniform, being progressively crowded toward the high-resistance end. For this reason there is a practical upper limit of readability for each range.

In most ohmmeters a single battery is good for resistance measurements up to several megohms. Various lower resistance ranges may be obtained from the same battery by the employment of different shunts across the instrument and sometimes voltage-divider circuits which shunt the battery. A preliminary adjustment, such as that of R_2 in Fig. 112, is usually necessary to be certain that the resistance reading is zero when the terminals are short-circuited.

The actual use and operation of ohmmeters, that is, with pin jacks to use, with switches to throw, and with scales and multiplying factors to use, depend on the make and design of the particular ohmmeter, the directions usually being marked on the instrument.

FIG. 113. Combination voltmeter, milliammeter, ohmmeter. (*Weston Electrical Instrument Company.*)

In Fig. 112 are shown the connections of a four-range General Electric ohmmeter together with the resistances of the different resistors. Note that the resistors R_4, R_6, R_8, R_{10} act as shunts for the instrument. The 30-volt battery is used for high resistances and the 1.5-volt battery for low resistances.

The accuracy of measurement by the ohmmeter is limited to the accuracy of the instrument and the operator's skill in reading correctly between the calibrated lines. The greatest accuracy is obtained when the measured resistance equals the internal resistance of the instrument, a condition which results in half-scale deflection on the instrument scale. The use of the extreme ends of the scales should be avoided. The ohmmeter is not a precision instrument and is of greatest value in "trouble shooting," *i.e.*, in a situation in which an approximate measurement, which can be quickly obtained, is all that is needed to distinguish between a good and a faulty circuit.

126. Megger Insulation Tester. The "megger" insulation tester is an instrument of the ohmmeter type by means of which the measured value of a resistance is directly indicated on a scale and the indication is independent of the voltage. The tester consists of two primary elements, a d-c generator of the magneto type, usually hand-driven, which supplies the current for making the measurement; and the instrument movement by means of which the value of the resistance under measurement is indicated.

A diagram of the tester is shown in Fig. 114(a). MM are two parallel permanent bar magnets. The generator armature D, together with its iron pole pieces, is bridged across one pair of poles of the two magnets, and the iron pole pieces and the core of the instrument movement are bridged across the other pair of poles. The armature of the generator is usually hand-driven, its speed being stepped up through gears. For ordinary insulation testing, 500 volts is most common, but in order to apply a simultaneous high-test potential, ratings as high as 2,500 volts are available.

The instrument system consists primarily of two coils A and B, mounted on the same moving system, Fig. 114(b). Coil A, called the

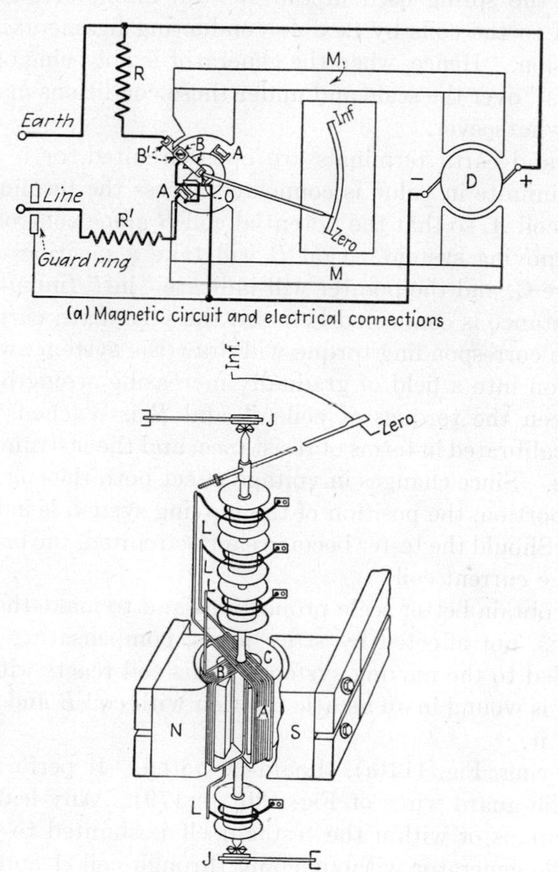

FIG. 114. Construction of megger insulation tester. (*James G. Biddle Company.*)

current coil, is identical with the moving coil of the Weston movement, Fig. 97 (p. 146); one terminal is connected to the negative brush of the generator, and the coil is in series with the resistor R' to the "line" terminal. When the resistance to be measured (not shown) is connected from the line to the "earth" terminal, the coil A, the resistor R', and the resistance being measured are all in series across the armature brushes.

Coil B, called the *potential coil*, is connected across the armature brushes in series with a suitable resistor R. Coil B is narrower than coil A and moves so that in some positions it encircles a part of the C-shaped iron core C in the manner shown in Fig. 114(b).

The moving system, Fig. 114(b), is mounted in spring-supported jewel bearings J and is free to rotate on its axis, there being no restraining force such as the spring used in the Weston ammeter and voltmeter. Current is led to the coils by flexible conducting ligaments LLL having negligible tension. Hence, when the generator is not being operated, the pointer "floats" over the scale and under these conditions may remain in any position whatsoever.

If the line and earth terminals are open-circuited, or if a resistance substantially infinite in value is connected across the terminals, there is no current in coil A, so that the potential coil B alone controls the movement of the moving system. Coil B will take a position opposite the gap in the core C, and the pointer will indicate "inf" (infinity). When, however, resistance is connected between the terminals, current flows in coil A and the corresponding torque will draw the system away from the infinity position into a field of gradually increasing strength, until equilibrium between the torques of coils A and B is reached. Hence the scale may be calibrated in terms of resistance, and the instrument becomes direct-reading. Since changes in voltage affect both the coils A and B in the same proportion, the position of the moving system is independent of the voltage. Should the tester become short-circuited, the ballast resistor R' protects the current coil.

In order to obtain better scale proportions and to make the instrument astatic, that is, not affected by stray fields, compensating coil B', Fig. 114(a), is added to the moving system. This coil reacts with one of the pole tips. It is wound in an astatic relation with coil B and is connected in series with it.

The guard ring, Fig. 114(a), should be noted. It performs the same function as the guard wires of Fig. 130 (p. 179). Any leakage current over the terminals or within the tester itself is shunted to the negative terminal of the generator without going through coil A and so does not affect the indications of the instrument. Usually a terminal is provided by means of which this guard ring may be connected to a guard wire on the insulation under measurement, see Fig. 115.

If the tester is used to measure the resistance of devices having relatively large capacitance, fluctuations of voltage affect the current in resistor R', in series with the capacitance, to a greater extent than fluctuations of voltage affect the current in the pure resistance R. For this reason, some types of the tester are provided with a clutch which slips when a certain maximum speed of the armature is reached. Therefore, so long as the driving speed exceeds this value, the speed of the armature and hence the emf remain constant and the difficulty due to capacitance is eliminated.

The resistance range is very great. For insulation measurements, it is in thousands of megohms. The tester is also designed to measure resistance of only a few ohms, such as the resistance to ground of transmission-tower footings or ground wires. The tester is widely used for measuring insulation resistance, such as the resistance between the windings and the frame of electric machinery, the insulation resistance of cables, of insulators, of bushings.

Figure 115 shows an exterior view of a "megger" insulation tester.

FIG. 115. Standard high-range megger insulation testing set. (*James G. Biddle Company.*)

127. Wheatstone Bridge.[1] In distinction to the foregoing methods of measuring resistance, the Wheatstone-bridge method is one in which a resistor of *unknown* resistance is balanced against other resistors of *known* resistances. The bridge, in its simplest form, is shown in Fig. 116. Three known resistors A, B, P and the unknown resistor X are con-

[1] The Wheatstone-bridge circuit was first described by S. Hunter Christie, an English scientist, in a paper read before the Royal Society in 1833. For 10 years it remained almost unnoticed, but in 1843 it received the endorsement of Sir Charles Wheatstone. Because of the prominence of Wheatstone and his high endorsement of the circuit, his name became associated with it, although he gave full credit to Christie.

Sir Charles Wheatstone, a famous physicist, was born in Gloucester, England, in 1802. He graduated from Kings College, Cambridge, and began a business career as a musical-instrument maker. The behavior of the strings of the instruments led him to experimentation with sound waves. In 1834 he was appointed professor of experimental philosophy at Kings College, where he made many improvements in measuring instruments. He conducted experiments to determine the velocity of electricity and devised a magnetic telegraph but did not apply for a patent and made no practical application until after Morse had his telegraph in operation. He was knighted in 1868 and died in Paris in 1875. He was the uncle of the great scientist and mathematician, Oliver Heaviside.

nected to form a diamond. The arms A and B usually consist only of decimal values of resistance such as 1, 10, 100, 1,000 ohms. The arm P is adjustable, usually so that integral values of resistance from 1 ohm to as high as 11,000 ohms and more may be obtained. A battery B is connected to the two opposite corners o and c of the diamond. Across the other two corners a and b a galvanometer is connected.

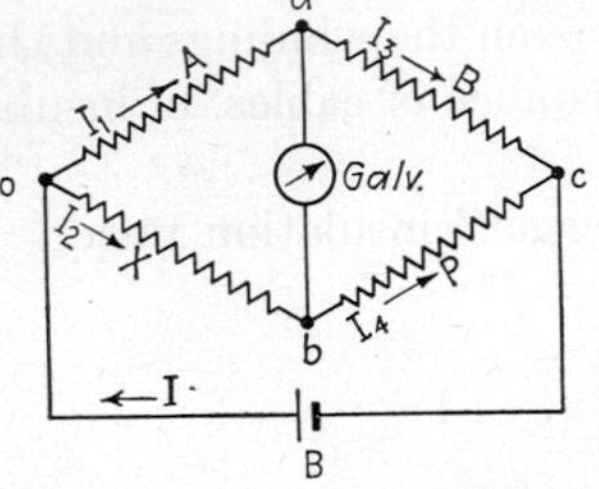

FIG. 116. Elementary Wheatstone bridge.

To make a measurement, each of the two arms A and B is set at some fixed value of resistance, usually at some decimal value, such as 1, 10, 100, 1,000 ohms. The arm P is then adjusted until the galvanometer does not deflect. If the galvanometer does not deflect, no current flows through it and therefore the two points a and b must be at the *same potential*. Since no current flows through the galvanometer, $I_1 = I_3$ and $I_2 = I_4$.

If the points a and b are at the same potential, the voltage drops E_{oa} and E_{ob} are equal and

$$I_1A = I_2X. \tag{I}$$

Also the voltage drop $E_{ac} = E_{bc}$, and

$$I_3B = I_4P.$$

Since $I_1 = I_3$ and $I_2 = I_4$,

$$I_1B = I_2P. \tag{II}$$

Dividing (I) by (II),

$$\frac{I_1A}{I_1B} = \frac{I_2X}{I_2P} \quad \text{or} \quad \frac{A}{B} = \frac{X}{P};$$

$$X = \frac{A}{B}P, \tag{94}$$

which is the equation of the Wheatstone bridge. A and B are called the *ratio arms* and P the *balance*, or *rheostat, arm*. Obviously the battery and the galvanometer may be interchanged without affecting the relation in (94).

The many types of Wheatstone bridge found in practice do not differ in principle from that shown in Fig. 116. The differences lie in the geometrical positions of the arms A, B, P on the bridge, as well as in the manner in which the coils in these arms are cut in and out of circuit.

Most of the early bridges were of the plug type, the function of the plugs being to short-circuit the resistor units when not in use. Oxide and dirt readily accumulated on the plugs, and they required frequent cleaning in order that the contact resistance should not be excessive. Moreover, the use of plugs in obtaining a balance was inconvenient and tedious.

Plug-type bridges have been superseded in large measure by the dial type employing the decade arrangement of resistors.

Equation (94) for the bridge holds irrespective of the positions of the battery and the galvanometer. However, for any given setting of the arms of the bridge, the galvanometer sensitivity is greatest when the equivalent resistance of the bridge arms between the galvanometer terminals is equal to the galvanometer resistance. Since it is impracticable except under special conditions, to realize this relation, the best sensitivity is obtained when the galvanometer is connected to those terminals between which the equivalent resistance is most nearly equal to the resistance of the galvanometer.

Example. In Fig. 116, the bridge is balanced when $A = 100$ ohms; $B = 1{,}000$ ohms; $X = 426.4$ ohms; $P = 4{,}264$ ohms. The resistance of the galvanometer is 500 ohms. Determine best position of galvanometer, that is, whether it should be connected between terminals *ab* or terminals *oc*.

$P = 4{,}264$ ohms; $X = 426.4$ ohms; the resistance measured between points *ab* is

$$\frac{526.4 \cdot 5{,}264}{526.4 + 5{,}264} = 478.6 \text{ ohms.}$$

The resistance between points *oc* is

$$\frac{1{,}100 \cdot 4{,}690.4}{1{,}100 + 4{,}690.4} = 891.0 \text{ ohms.}$$

The resistance of the galvanometer is 500 ohms, which is closer to 478.6 ohms than to 891.0 ohms, so that it is connected for the greater sensitivity.

128. Decade and Dial Bridges. The decade arrangement of the resistor units of the rheostat arm P is shown in Fig. 117. The resistors are arranged in groups of equal resistances, one group consisting of ten 1-ohm coils, the next of ten 10-ohm coils, the next of ten 100-ohm coils, etc. Each group is called a *decade*. Only one plug per decade is necessary. This arrangement has the advantage that the plugs are always in service and so are not so likely to be mislaid or to become dirty; there is less probability of error in reading; it is a simple matter to see that the few plugs used are fitting tightly, and a balance can be quickly obtained. It is obvious that nine coils per decade are sufficient for obtaining any desired resistance, although ten coils per decade are often used.

The decade principle has been extended to an even more convenient type of bridge, the dial bridge. Instead of using plugs, a dial arm similar to the type used in rheostats is employed to select the required resistors. Because of its ease of manipulation, this type has come into extensive use. Care should be taken to keep the dials and contacts free from dirt and oxides.

Figure 118 shows a dial-type portable Wheatstone bridge, together with the diagram of connections. Although the battery and galvanometer are self-contained, binding posts are provided so that external units can be used if desired. When the internal battery is used, the battery switch *BA* is set at "in"; when an external battery is used, the switch is set at "out." Note that the two ratio arms are combined into a single "ratio" dial at the upper left part of the bridge top. The values given are ratios, not ohms. The unknown resistance is connected between binding posts X_1 and X_2. Connections *Rh* and X_2 permit the four-dial rheostat to be used as a four-dial resistance standard.

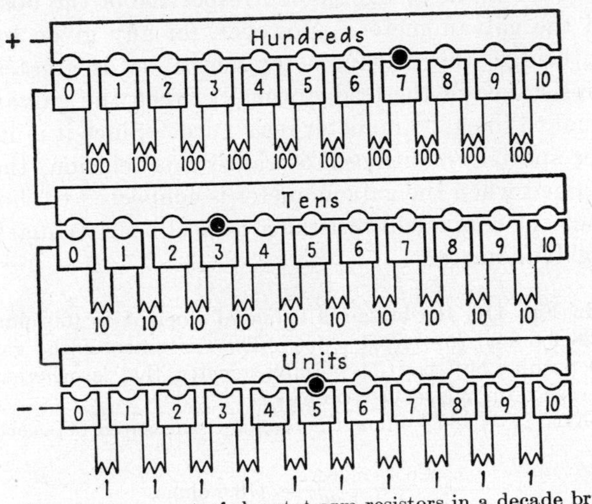

Fig. 117. Arrangement of rheostat arm resistors in a decade bridge.

129. Method of Balancing a Bridge. In using the bridge, much time may be saved if a systematic procedure is followed in obtaining a balance. Assume that it is desired to measure a certain unknown resistor. The battery and galvanometer are connected to their respective terminals *oc* and *ab*, Fig. 116, and the unknown resistor is connected at *X*. A shunt should be used with the galvanometer (Sec. 114, p. 141), to protect it from deflecting violently when the bridge is considerably out of balance. The ratio arms *A* and *B* should at first be given a one-to-one ratio, preferably 1,000 ohms each.

With the galvanometer well shunted and all the dials in *P* set to 0 ($P = 0$) (see Fig. 118(*b*)), depress first the battery key and then the galvanometer key. The galvanometer is observed to deflect to the left. Now start turning the contactor in the 1,000 dial, depressing the battery key and then the galvanometer key at each contact. At the first contact the galvanometer deflects to the right.

From these observations, three facts are determined. The unknown resistance is less than 1,000 ohms; when the galvanometer deflects to the left, the value of resistance in *P* is too small; when it deflects to the right, the value of *P* is too large. The contactor in the 1,000 dial is returned to zero, and the contactor in the 100 dial is then moved to the first contact and the galvanometer still deflects to the right, indicating that 100 ohms in *P* is too large. This procedure is repeated with 10 ohms, and then with 1 ohm, where it is found that the galvanometer deflection now reverses, that is, it deflects to the left. It does not reverse and deflect to the right again until 3 ohms is selected by the contactor. Hence, the unknown resistance is narrowed down to between 2 and 3 ohms. To obtain a more precise measurement, the ratio arms must be changed. *A* is now made 10 ohms and *B* changed to 10,000 ohms, and the dials in *P* are set at 2,000 ohms. By successive trials, all the time reducing the effect of

(a)

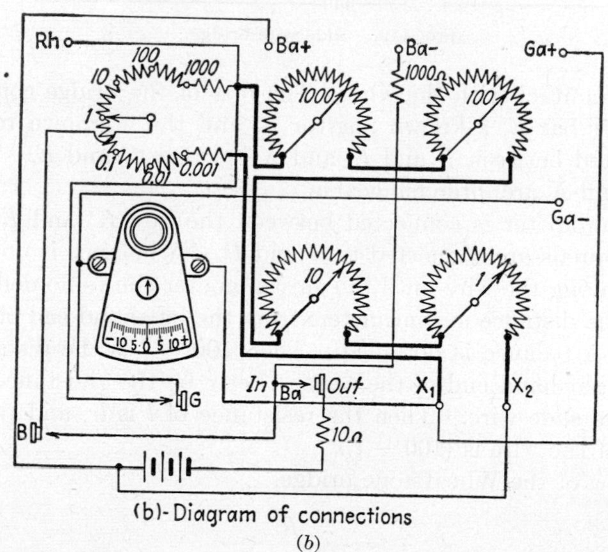

(b)-Diagram of connections

(b)

FIG. 118. Dial-type portable Wheatstone bridge. (a) Type S general-purpose bridge. (b) Diagram of connections. (*Leeds and Northrup Company.*)

the galvanometer shunt, a balance is obtained at 2,761 ohms in P. Then,

$$X = \frac{A}{B}P = \frac{10}{10,000}2,761 = 2.761 \text{ ohms.}$$

If a different balance is obtained with the battery reversed, it indicates a thermoelectric emf in the bridge and the average of the two readings should be taken.

In obtaining a balance, the battery key should always be depressed before the galvanometer key, so that the current in the bridge has time to reach a constant value. Otherwise any emf of self-induction may introduce an error.

130. Slide-wire Bridge. The slide-wire bridge is a simplified Wheatstone bridge, in which the balance is obtained by means of a slider which moves over a resistor wire of manganin, constantan, or similar material. A typical slide-wire bridge is shown in Fig. 119. The resistor wire AB, 100 cm long, is stretched tightly between two heavy copper blocks CD, 100 cm apart. A meter scale is placed along this wire. A contact key K' is movable along the scale, and when the key K' is depressed, a knife-

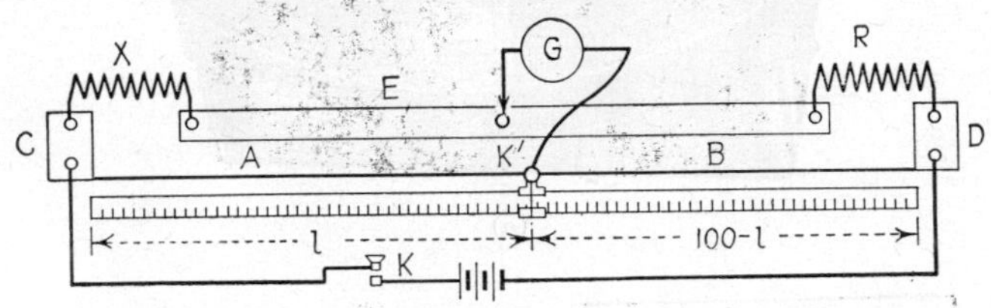

FIG. 119. Slide-wire bridge.

edge makes contact with the wire. The rest of the bridge consists of a heavy copper bar E, a known resistor R, and the unknown resistor X. R is connected between D and E, and X between C and E. The positions of R and X are interchangeable.

The galvanometer is connected between the key K' and E, and the battery terminals are connected to C and D. A balance is obtained by moving K' along the wire until the galvanometer shows no deflection.

Let l be the distance in centimeters from the left-hand end of the scale to K' when a balance is obtained. Then $100 - l$ is the distance from K' to the right-hand end of the scale. Let r be the resistance per unit length of the slide wire. Then the resistance of l is lr, and that of the remainder of the wire is $(100 - l)r$.

By the law of the Wheatstone bridge,

$$\frac{X}{lr} = \frac{R}{(100 - l)r}. \tag{95}$$

r cancels, and (95) becomes

$$X = l\frac{R}{(100 - l)}. \tag{96}$$

(95) may also be written

$$\frac{X}{R} = \frac{l}{100 - l}. \tag{97}$$

This is equivalent to stating that when a balance is obtained, the slide wire is divided into two parts which are to each other as X is to R.

The slide wire is not so accurate as the coil bridge, because the slide wire may not be uniform; the solder at the points of contact at C and D makes the length of the wire uncertain, although it is possible to correct for this error; the slide wire cannot be read so accurately as the resistor units of a bridge can be adjusted.

Example. Assume that R, Fig. 119, equals 10 ohms and that a balance is obtained at 74.6 cm from the left-hand end of the scale. Determine the unknown resistance X.

From (96),

$$X = 74.6 \frac{10}{100 - 74.6} = 74.6 \frac{10}{25.4}$$
$$= 29.37 \text{ ohms.} \quad Ans.$$

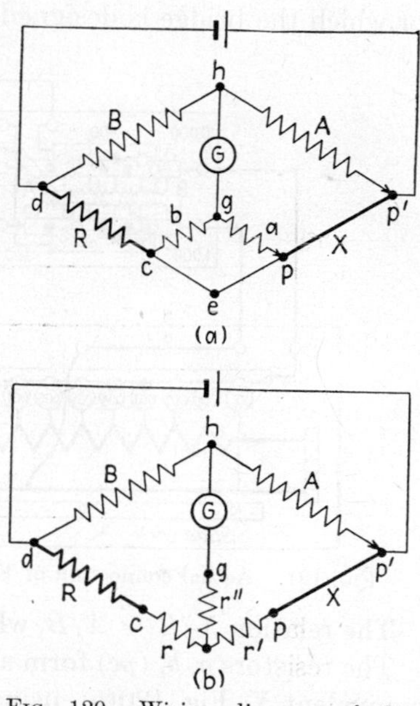

FIG. 120. Wiring diagram of the Kelvin double bridge.

131. Kelvin Bridge. In the measurement of very low resistances with the Wheatstone bridge, the contact resistances between the sample and the bridge terminals may be so large, compared with the resistance of the sample itself, that values of resistance obtained for the sample are practically worthless (also see p. 156). The effect of these contact resistances is eliminated in the Kelvin bridge, Fig. 120(a). A and B are two ratio arms, similar to those of the usual type of bridge. The values of A and B may be made so high that the contact resistances at p', h, d are negligible in comparison.

Let X be the resistance of the unknown resistor, which may be the resistance included between two knife-edge contacts $p'p$ on a copper rod, as indicated in Figs. 120 and 121. The arm R or the resistor between points c and d is the rheostat arm. The resistance of this arm must be low, and it is made adjustable, Fig. 121. The contact resistance between X and R is the resistance of the connection pec, and this resistance may be a large portion of the resistance of arms X and R and may even exceed the resistance of the arm R or of the sample X. Hence, unless this contact resistance is eliminated, it introduces so large an error that the measured value of the unknown resistance is worthless. However, this contact resistance pec may be eliminated by connecting the galvanometer to the junction of two auxiliary resistors a and b, rather than to either p or c as in the usual Wheatstone bridge. The other end of arm a is connected to contact p, and the other end of arm b is connected to point c, Fig. 120(a). If a and b are adjusted so that $a/b = A/B$, the contact resistance is eliminated and $X/R = A/B$ as in the ordinary bridge.

In order to obtain sufficient sensitivity, it is necessary that the current to the bridge be from 15 to 150 amp depending on the range of resistance for which the bridge is designed.

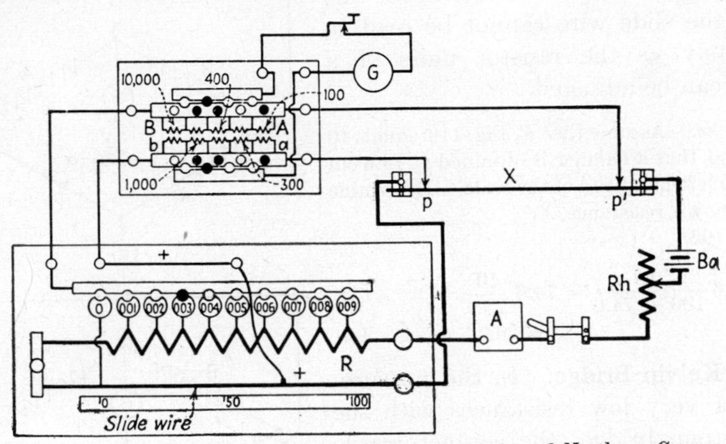

FIG. 121. Actual connection of Kelvin bridge. (*Leeds and Northrup Company.*)

The relation $X/R = A/B$, when $a/b = A/B$, may be proved as follows: The resistors a, b, (pc) form a delta. This delta may be replaced by an equivalent Y, Fig. 120(b), using Eqs. (65), (66), (67) (p. 88),

$$r = \frac{b(pc)}{a + b + (pc)}; \qquad r' = \frac{a(pc)}{a + b + (pc)}; \qquad r'' = \frac{ab}{a + b + (pc)}.$$

From Eq. (94) the condition of balance in Fig. 120(b) is

$$\frac{(R + r)}{B} = \frac{(X + r')}{A},$$

or

$$\left[R + \frac{b(pc)}{a + b + (pc)}\right] A = \left[X + \frac{a(pc)}{a + b + (pc)}\right] B. \tag{I}$$

The resistor r'' is in series with the galvanometer and has no effect when the bridge is in balance.

From (I)

$$X = \frac{A}{B} R + \frac{(pc)}{a + b + (pc)} \left(\frac{A}{B} b - a\right). \tag{II}$$

It follows that if $A/B = a/b$,

$$X = \frac{A}{B} R. \quad \text{Q.E.D.} \tag{98}$$

The actual arrangement of the bridge, as manufactured by Leeds and Northrup Company, is shown in Fig. 121. The lettering corresponds to the diagram of Fig. 120(*a*).

In Fig. 121, $A = a = 300$ ohms, and $B = b = 10{,}000$ ohms. $R = 0.003$ ohm plus the slide-wire reading.

Bridges are also manufactured where R is constant and the ratios $A/B = a/b$ are made simultaneously variable. Although, theoretically, the resistance pc has no effect on the measurement, it should be made as small as possible in order to minimize errors.

132. Opens, Grounds, Crosses. In overhead lines or underground cables for either power or communications, continuity of service is highly essential. Faults, however, occur at times. A fault may be an *open* (circuit), a *ground*, or a *cross* (sometimes called a *short*).

An open is a total disconnection such as would occur when a wire breaks inside the insulation covering and the ends are pulled far enough apart to be insulated from each other. Section 260 (p. 364) describes the test for the location of this type of fault.

A ground, or earth fault, occurs when the insulation is either impaired or destroyed to the point where a current may flow from the wire to the earth or to the cable sheath. A cross is due to the impairment of insulation between two wires so that current may flow between them. In either a ground or a cross, the current path may be either of high or of low resistance. The location of these faults can be determined readily by a resistance-bridge method.

Two commonly employed applications of this method are the Murray loop and the Varley loop tests. The superiority of the loop tests is due to the fact that the results are independent of the resistance of the fault itself.

The first step in either test is to select the conductor or conductors that are faulty and to determine the type of fault. This may be accomplished by means of a voltmeter and battery, or an ohmmeter, as illustrated in Fig. 122, which shows the test for a ground in conductor a. In a similar manner, tests for an open, such as is shown in conductor b, may be made by grounding the conductors at B and using the voltmeter or ohmmeter. The test for a cross is made by connecting the voltmeter or ohmmeter and battery to two conductors cd at their ends at A, with their ends at B disconnected.

The next step in the tests for a ground or a cross is to determine the *loop resistance* r, should it not be already known; this may be determined by the usual Wheatstone-bridge measurement. (In measuring loop resistance, or in locating a fault by either loop method, one good conductor must always be used to complete the loop.)

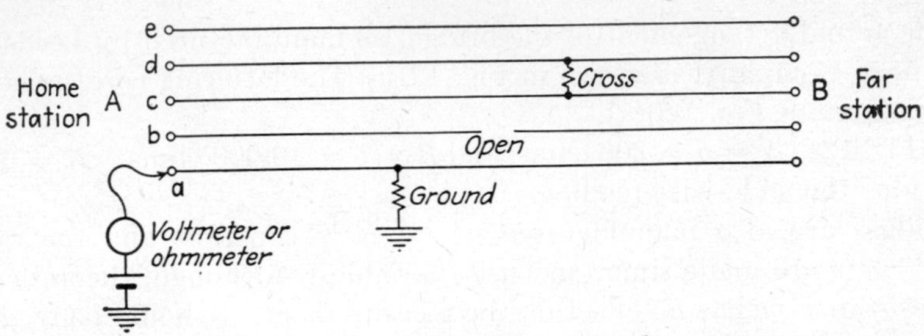

FIG. 122. Tests for type of fault.

133. Murray Loop Test. The Murray loop test is very useful for locating faults in relatively low-resistance loops, such as short sections of communication and power cables. In this test, the connections are made as shown in Fig. 123.

The relative positions of the galvanometer and battery are important; with the connections as shown, earth currents and increased resistance due to fault have no effect on the readings. The voltage of the battery may be adjusted to give the desired sensitivity. Let X be the distance to the fault and x the resistance to the fault.

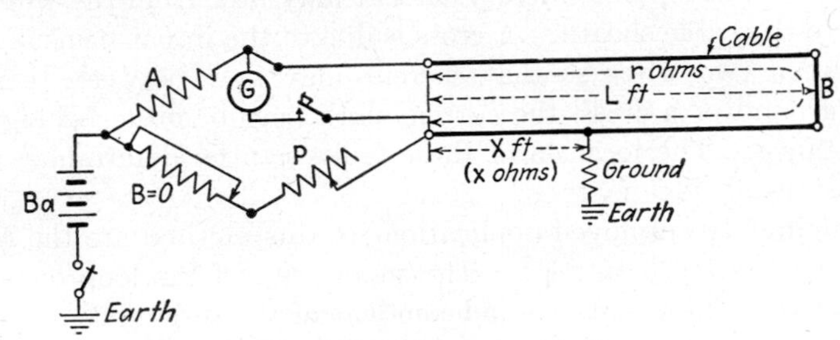

FIG. 123. Murray loop test.

When the galvanometer reads zero,

$$\frac{A}{P} = \frac{r - x}{x}, \tag{99}$$

or

$$x = \frac{P}{A + P} r. \tag{100}$$

A slide wire or a voltage divider may be used instead of arms A and P, Fig. 124, in which two cables, each of length L ft, are shown. Again let the loop resistance be r ohms.

When the galvanometer reads zero,

$$\frac{l}{l'} = \frac{r - x}{x} \tag{101}$$

and the resistance to the fault is

$$x = \frac{l'}{l + l'} r. \tag{102}$$

Let ρ be the resistance per foot of conductor and X the distance in feet to the fault. Then from (102),

$$x = X\rho \qquad \text{and} \qquad r = 2L\rho, \qquad \text{and} \qquad X = 2L\left(\frac{l'}{l + l'}\right). \tag{103}$$

If the two conductors are alike and uniform in resistance, the distance to the fault is, from (100),

$$X = 2L\left(\frac{P}{A + P}\right), \tag{104}$$

where $2L$ is the length of the loop.

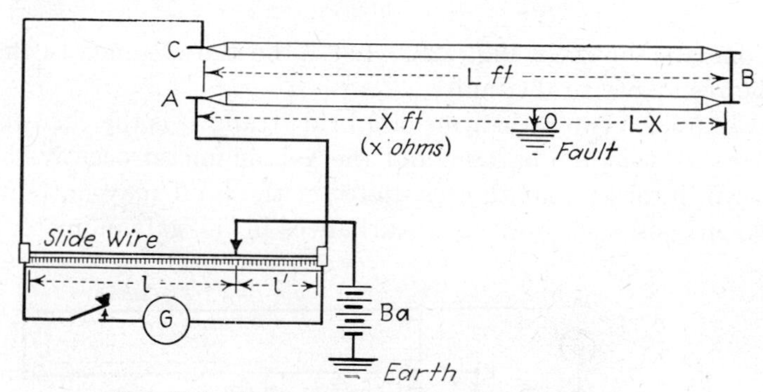

FIG. 124. Slide-wire Murray loop test for ground.

Example. A cable, 2,000 ft long, consists of two conductors. One conductor is grounded at some point between stations. A Murray loop test, with a 100-cm slide wire, is connected as in Fig. 124 to locate the fault. A balance is obtained at 85 cm. Determine the distance of the fault or ground from the home station. Using (103),

$$X = 4{,}000(15/100) = 600 \text{ ft.} \quad \textit{Ans.}$$

If a test is made for a cross, the battery is connected to one faulty conductor instead of to ground and the second faulty conductor is looped with a nonfaulty conductor, Fig. 125.

$$\frac{l}{l'} = \frac{r - x}{x}, \tag{105}$$

as in (101), and the distance to the cross,

$$X = 2L\left(\frac{l'}{l + l'}\right). \tag{106}$$

134. Varley Loop Test. The Varley loop test is best adapted to fault location in high-resistance loops, such as long communication lines. The

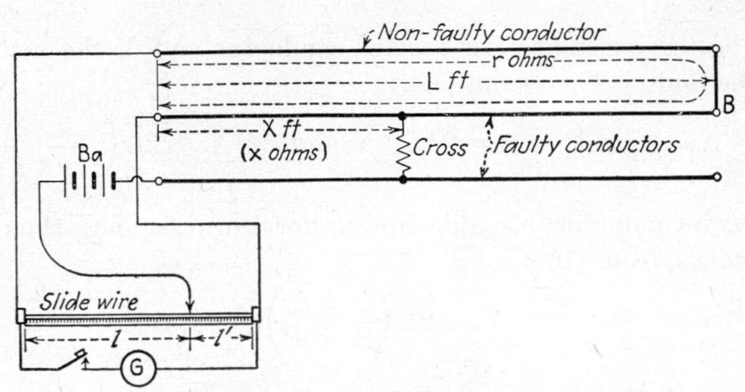

FIG. 125. Slide-wire Murray loop test for cross.

connections are shown in Fig. 126. Let X be the distance to the fault and x the resistance to the fault.

A and B are the two ratio arms of a bridge, and P is the rheostat arm. It is necessary that the battery and the galvanometer occupy the positions shown, in order that the resistance of the fault may not affect the measurement and also to avoid disturbances in the galvanometer due to

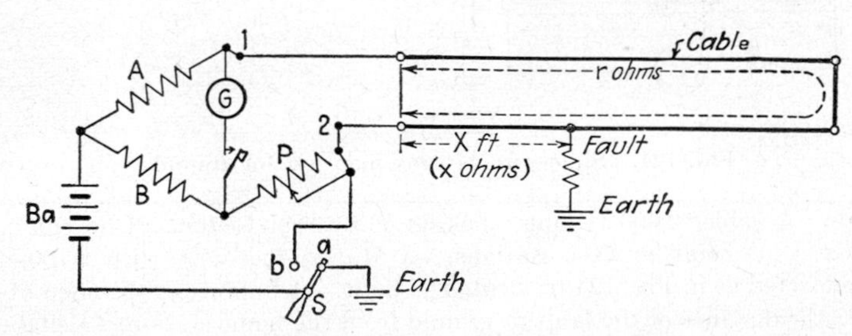

FIG. 126. Varley loop test for ground.

earth currents. The balance to locate the fault is first obtained by means of P, with the switch S at a.

Before X can be found, it is necessary to know the total loop resistance r, which may be obtained by throwing the switch S to position b. This connects both lengths of cable in series and makes them the fourth arm of a bridge. A simple bridge measurement gives the resistance r.

When the galvanometer reads zero (with the switch S at a),

$$\frac{A}{B} = \frac{r - x}{P + x} \tag{107}$$

or

$$x = \frac{Br - AP}{A + B}. \tag{108}$$

Since $x = (r/2L)X$,

$$X = \frac{2L}{r}\left(\frac{Br - AP}{A + B}\right). \tag{109}$$

Example. In locating a fault by the Varley loop test, the connections shown in Fig. 126 with the switch at a are used. Each conductor is 5 miles long. When a balance is obtained, $A = 10$, $B = 90$, and $P = 2{,}374$ ohms. With the switch at b, a regular Wheatstone-Bridge measurement gives the loop resistance as 417.2 ohms.

From (108),

$$x = \frac{90(417.2) - 10(2{,}374)}{10 + 90} = \frac{13{,}808}{100} = 138.08 \text{ ohms.}$$

From (109), the distance to the fault in feet,

$$X = \frac{2 \cdot 5 \cdot 5{,}280}{417.2}(138.08) = 17{,}500 \text{ ft.} \quad \textit{Ans.}$$

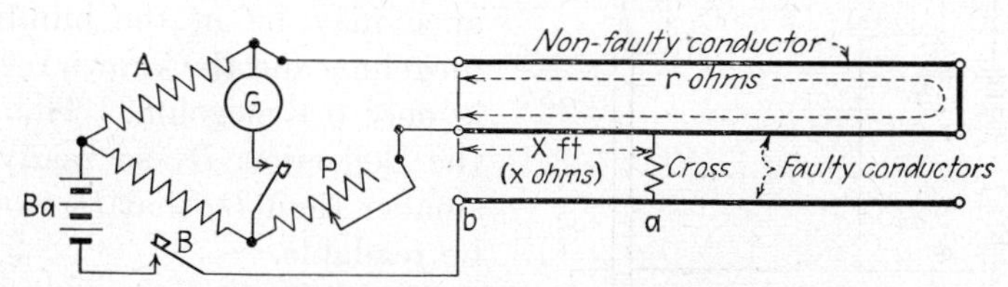

FIG. 127. Varley loop test for cross.

The connections for locating a cross are shown in Fig. 127. A study of the circuits shows that (107) applies, since the resistance of the cross and that of the length of conductor ab are in the battery circuit. Hence (107) and also (108) apply.

135. Insulation Testing. In practice it is necessary to measure the resistance of the insulation of cables, both at the factory and after the cable is installed. A low value of insulation resistance may indicate that the insulation is of an inferior grade. A low insulation resistance after installation may indicate improper handling or faulty installation. The voltmeter method described in Sec. 124 (p. 156) is applicable in many cases, but where the insulation resistance is high, even a high-resistance voltmeter is not sufficiently sensitive.

To make the measurement, a sensitive galvanometer is utilized. A source of considerable potential, from 100 to 500 volts, is usually necessary. Such potential may be secured from d-c mains, although dry cells and silver chloride cells, connected in series, are more satisfactory. A simple diagram of connections is shown in Fig. 128.

The method is one of substitution. A known resistance, usually 0.1 megohm (100,000 ohms), is first connected in the circuit and the galvanometer deflection noted. The unknown resistance X is then substituted, and the galvanometer reading again noted. As the currents in the two cases are inversely proportional to the circuit resistances, the unknown resistance can be determined, the galvanometer deflections being used rather than actual values of current. Let D_1 be the deflection with the 0.1 megohm and D_2 be the deflection with the unknown resistance.

$$\frac{X}{0.1} = \frac{D_1}{D_2}$$

$$X = 0.1 \frac{D_1}{D_2} \quad \text{megohms.} \tag{110}$$

Under ordinary circumstances it is not possible to obtain accurate results by the direct comparison of the galvanometer deflections [Eq. (110)], because the unknown resistance may be in the hundreds of megohms and the known resistance is only 0.1 megohm. This makes the deflection D_2 so many times smaller than D_1 that D_2 would not be readable.

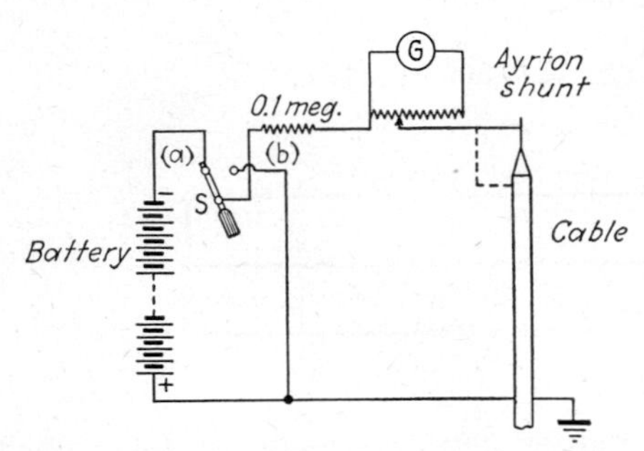

Fig. 128. Measurement of insulation resistance of cable.

This difficulty is overcome by the use of the Ayrton shunt described in Sec. 114 (p. 141). When only the 0.1 megohm is in circuit, the galvanometer sensitivity is such ordinarily that the deflection would be off the scale unless the galvanometer were shunted.

Therefore the shunt is adjusted to some low value as 0.0001. Let this reading of the shunt be S_1 and the galvanometer deflection be D_1. The multiplying power of the shunt $M_1 = 1/S_1$. The cable is now introduced into the circuit and the shunt adjusted until an on-scale deflection is obtained. Let this deflection be D_2 and the value of the shunt be S_2. Its multiplying power is now $M_2 = 1/S_2$.

The ratio of the currents in the circuit in the two cases is

$$\frac{I_1}{I_2} = \frac{M_1 D_1}{M_2 D_2}, \tag{111}$$

and the unknown resistance, from (110), is

$$X = 0.1 \frac{I_1}{I_2} = 0.1 \frac{M_1 D_1}{M_2 D_2} \quad \text{megohms.} \tag{112}$$

In practice, instead of substituting the cable for the 0.1 megohm, the cable is first short-circuited by the wire shown dotted, Fig. 128, and the constant determined. This wire is then removed, placing the cable in circuit. The 0.1 megohm is left permanently in circuit to protect the galvanometer in case of accidental short circuit of the cable. The 0.1 megohm is usually not appreciable compared with the insulation resistance of the cable, so that ordinarily no correction is necessary for it.

A switch or key S is usually provided. When in position (a), Fig. 128, the circuit is closed through the cable. When thrown over to (b),

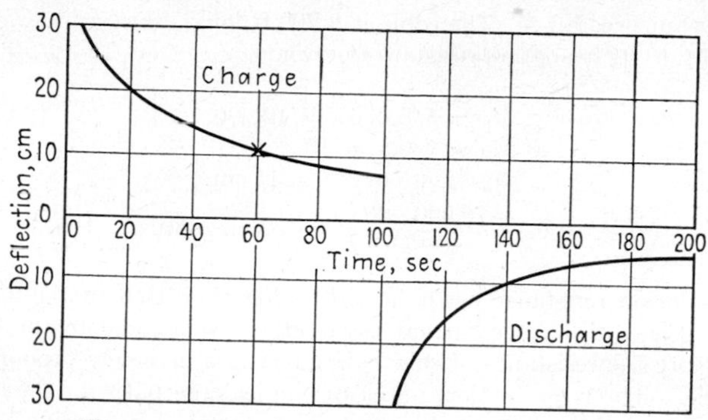

Fig. 129. Charge and discharge curves of cable.

the cable, which is charged electrostatically, discharges through the galvanometer.

When the switch S is first closed at (a), there is a rush of current which charges the cable electrostatically (see Sec. 240, Chap. X). Because of the "absorption" characteristic of the insulation, it takes time to charge the cable, and for some time this charging current flows, decreasing continuously. This is shown in Fig. 129, which gives the relation of galvanometer deflection to time. As it is often inconvenient to wait for the galvanometer to reach a steady deflection, it has been agreed to take the deflection at the end of 1 min as the arbitrary value to be used in determining insulation resistance.

When the switch S is thrown to (b), the electrostatic charge in the cable rushes out through the galvanometer in the reverse direction. Again, owing to absorption, it requires considerable time for the cable to become totally discharged. This is also shown in Fig. 129, where the cable is discharged at 100 sec.

In making insulation-resistance measurements, precautions must be taken to insulate thoroughly the apparatus itself. Hard-rubber posts should be used for supports, and, wherever possible, the leads should be carried through the air rather than be allowed to rest on the ground. As the insulation resistance varies widely with temperature, the temperature at which the measurements are made should be carefully determined and stated.

Although the method is described as being applied to the insulation of cables, it is equally applicable to other types of insulation such as that of transformers and rotating machinery.

Example. The cable whose insulation characteristics are shown in Fig. 129 was tested for its insulation resistance. The deflection with 0.1 megohm only in circuit was 20 cm, and the shunt read 0.0001. When the curve shown in Fig. 129 was obtained, the shunt read 0.1. The cable is 2,200 ft long. Determine: (*a*) its insulation resistance; (*b*) its insulation resistance per mile.

$$M_1 = 1/0.0001 = 10{,}000.$$
$$M_2 = 1/0.1 = 10.$$
$$D_2 \text{ (from curve)} = 11 \text{ cm}.$$
$$(a)\quad X = 0.1\left(\frac{10{,}000 \cdot 20}{10 \cdot 11}\right) = 182 \text{ megohms.} \quad \textit{Ans.}$$

(*b*) The insulation resistance per mile will be *less* than that of the 2,200-ft length because the amount of leakage current is directly proportional to the length of the cable. Therefore the resistance of this leakage path is inversely proportional to the length of cable. The cross-sectional area of the leakage path for the mile length is greater than it is for the 2,200-ft length. Therefore the insulation resistance per mile

$$R = \left(\frac{2{,}200}{5{,}280}\right) 182 = 75.8 \text{ megohms.} \quad \textit{Ans.}$$

136. Guard Wire. In determining the insulation resistance of cables and of other insulation, precautions against end leakage must frequently be taken. Moisture, combined sometimes with dust, provides comparatively low-resistance paths over the surface of the insulation between the core and sheath. These conducting paths are in shunt with the insulation, so that this end leakage may give values of insulation resistance which are entirely too low. To prevent such leakage, the ends of the cable are frequently dried with a torch, care being taken not to carbonize the insulation, and hot paraffin is then poured over the ends.

Where both ends of the cable are accessible, the end leakage may be shunted around the galvanometer by the use of *guard wires* and its effect, so far as the measurement is concerned, is thus eliminated. The method is shown in Fig. 130. A few turns of bare wire are wrapped tightly around the insulation at *a* and *b* between the sheath or ground and the core of the cable. These turns of wire are connected directly with the terminal C of the battery, which also connects with the galvanometer, Fig. 130. A study of Fig. 130 shows that any leakage current is conducted back to the negative terminal of the battery without going through the galvanometer. That is, when leakage current reaches a and b, it has the choice of two paths to the negative terminal of the battery, one through the low-resistance wire aC and the other over the remainder of the insulation through the galvanometer to the battery. Practically all the leakage current will pass through the wire aC and will not affect the galvanometer deflection.

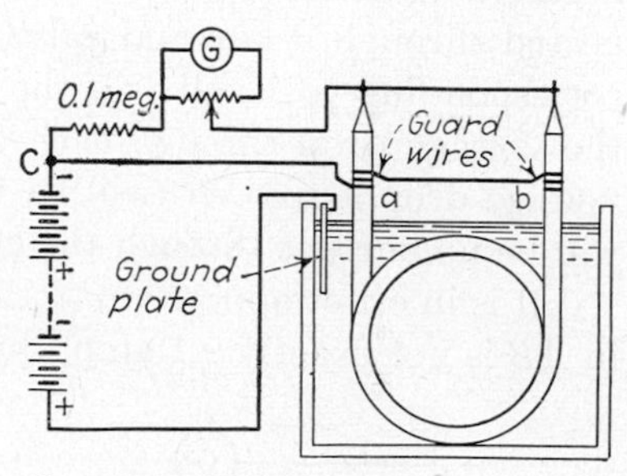

FIG. 130. Use of guard wires to by-pass surface-leakage current of cable immersed in water.

POTENTIOMETERS

137. Potentiometer. The potentiometer is an instrument for making accurate measurements of emf. For many types of precise measurement it is used rather than the usual type of voltmeter, for two reasons. First, actual emf E can be measured, since the potentiometer takes no current, whereas a voltmeter requires current for its operation and thus produces an internal resistance drop in the source of emf, so that often it measures the terminal voltage V. (The internal-resistance drop is often negligible.) Second, the most precise voltmeters are accurate only to one-tenth of 1 per cent, whereas with a potentiometer it is not difficult to make measurements which are accurate to one one-hundredth of 1 per cent. The potentiometer is essentially a means of comparing an unknown emf with the emf of a standard cell, such as the Weston type (Sec. 83, p. 106). With the potentiometer no current is taken, so that it is possible to measure accurately sources of emf which cannot supply even the small current which a voltmeter requires. The method is to oppose the unknown emf by a known emf with the negative terminals of the two emfs connected together and also the positive terminals connected together through a galvanometer, as shown in Fig. 131(a) (see Figs. 18 and 19, p. 36). If the galvanometer indicates no current, the two emfs must be equal. To use this method, however, requires an emf which can be varied to give a large number of known values. Since it is not practicable to do this with the system shown in Fig. 131(a), the unknown emf is connected in parallel with and in opposition to a voltage drop in a resistor, Fig. 131(b). It is a simple matter to vary the current in this resistor and thus obtain with very fine adjustment any desired voltage. The foregoing voltage drop may be determined very accurately by calibrating the resistor with a standard cell (Sec. 83).

In Fig. 132(*a*), assume that a standard cell *S* has an emf of exactly 1 volt. Let a storage cell *Ba* supply current to a resistor wire *AB* through a rheostat *R*. Let the wire *AB* be divided into 15 divisions, each of 1 ohm resistance, making the total resistance of *AB* 15 ohms. Obviously the resistance of the wire *AB* can have any value, but the resistance is generally made of such a value that the operating current is reasonable in magnitude. The standard cell is connected with its negative terminal to the negative terminal *A* of the storage cell, and its positive terminal is connected through a key and galvanometer to point *C* on the resistor wire corresponding to 1 volt. If the current through the wire *AB* is 0.1 amp, the voltage drop through each division of *AB* will be 0.1 volt, and the voltage drop across *AC* will be 1.0 volt. If the key be depressed, there will be no current through the galvanometer, as the standard-cell emf of 1 volt is in exact opposition to this 1-volt drop. If, however, the current in *AB* is not exactly 0.1 amp, there will be current through the standard-

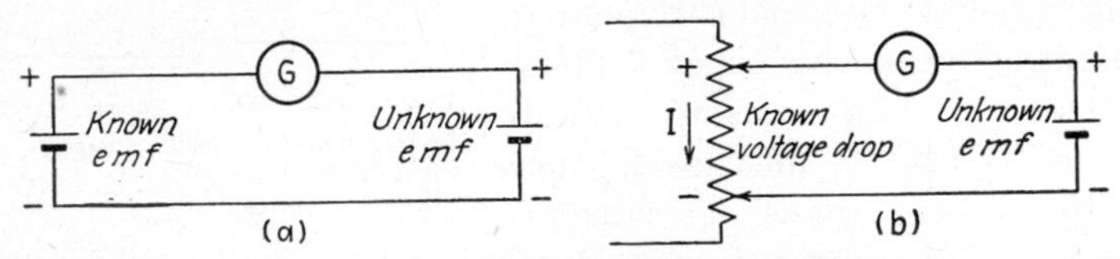

Fig. 131. Methods of balancing emfs.

cell circuit due to the voltage drop from *A* to *C* being either greater or less than 1 volt. If the current is less than 0.1 amp, the galvanometer deflects in one direction; if it is greater than 0.1 amp, the galvanometer deflects in the reverse direction. Obviously it is possible to adjust the current in *AB* to such a value that the galvanometer deflection is zero. Under these conditions the current in *AB* is exactly 0.1 amp, and the potential drop across each division in *AB* is 0.1 volt. Therefore *AB* may be marked in volts, as shown. The potentiometer is then said to be calibrated.

Let it be required to measure some unknown emf *E* whose value is known to be less than 1.5 volts. The negative terminal of *E* is connected to the end *A* of the wire *AB*, Fig. 132(*b*). The positive terminal of *E* is connected through the galvanometer and key to a movable contact *b*. It is assumed that the current in *AB* has been adjusted to exactly 0.1 amp. Contact *b* is moved along *AB* until the galvanometer deflection is zero. This means that the emf *E* is just balanced against an equal drop in the wire *AB*. As *AB* is calibrated in volts, the value of *E* may be read directly on *AB*. This method of measuring voltage is the *Poggendorff method* and is the fundamental principle of the potentiometer.

The two diagrams (*a*) and (*b*), Fig. 132, may be combined into one by the use of the single-pole double-throw (S-P D-T) switch *Sw*, Fig. 132(*c*).

When the switch is in its left-hand position, the standard cell is in circuit for calibration as in (*a*). When the switch is in its right-hand position, the unknown emf is in contact with the wire *AB* so that its value may be determined.

138. Leeds and Northrup Low-resistance Potentiometer. Figure 133 shows the wiring diagram of the Leeds and Northrup low-resistance potentiometer. The principle is the same as that of the simple potentiometer shown in Fig. 132.

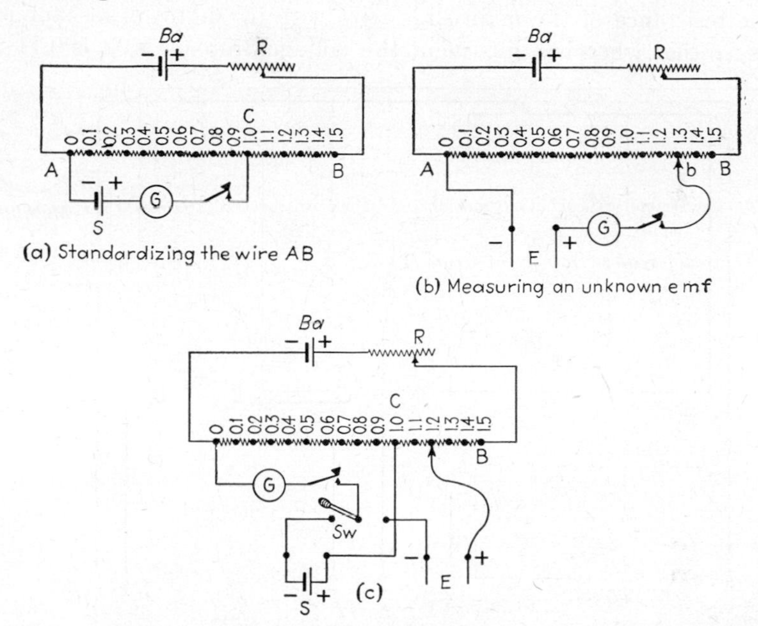

FIG. 132. Simple potentiometer.

A 2-volt battery is connected to the terminals *Ba*. The potentiometer working current is controlled by the three adjustable rheostats *P* (shown as "coarse," "medium," and "fine").

The path of the current from the *Ba*+ terminal is through the standard-cell slide wire and its shunt, through the main slide wire and its shunt *BD*, through the dial switch to range switch *C*. When the contactor of *C* is on 1, the path continues through the three rheostats *P* to *Ba*−. By turning the switch *C* to 0.1 or 0.01, the current in the main slide wire and the dial switch is reduced to 0.1 or 0.01 its normal value, and the potentiometer range is reduced accordingly. The resistor of the dial switch is divided into fifteen 5-ohm 0.1-volt divisions. Since the resistance corresponding to 0.1 volt is 5 ohms, the working current is $0.1/5 = 1/50$, or 0.02 amp. The main slide wire, shown as a single turn in Fig. 133, consists of a resistor wire, over 5 m long, wound in 11 turns in a spiral groove on a bakelite cylinder, 15 cm in diameter. The contact M' is a spring strip of phosphor-bronze with a polished hard-steel tip. The negative terminal of the standard cell is connected through the D-P D-T switch U and the galvanometer to the 0.9 contact in the dial switch when the contacts at C are at 1. The positive terminal of the standard cell is connected to the contact T on the standard-cell slide wire. This contact is set to the value of the emf of the standard cell, the range being 1.0176 to 1.0204 volts.

The resistance of the main slide wire with its shunting resistor is 5.5 ohms, so that when in adjustment the voltage drop across it is 0.11 volt.

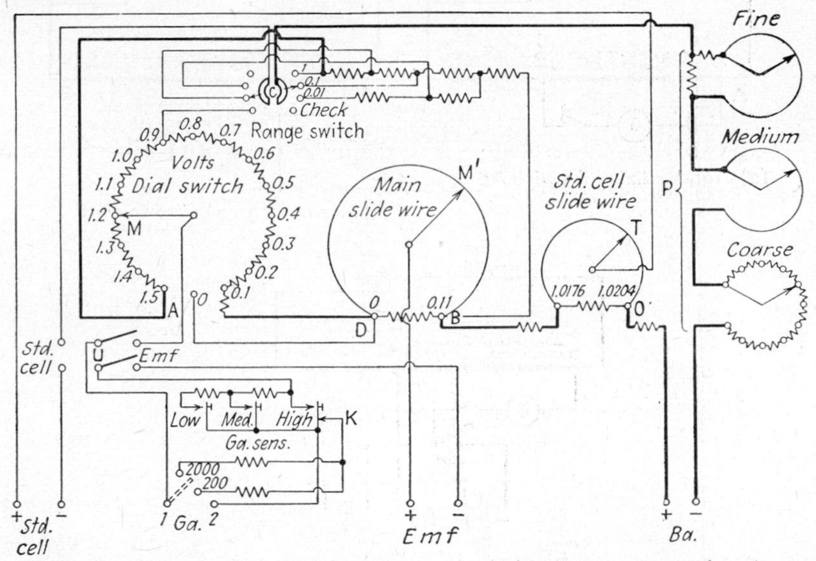

FIG. 133. Connections of Leeds and Northrup low-resistance potentiometer.

Since the slide wire consists of 11 turns of resistance wire, each turn represents 0.01 volt and the entire wire is divided into 1,100 divisions.

M and M' are movable contacts, which are adjusted to balance the unknown emf. M moves over the 15 contacts, each corresponding to 0.1 volt, and M' moves over the slide wire. A D-P D-T switch U [corresponding to Sw, Fig. 132(c)] changes the connection of the galvanometer from the standard cell to the unknown emf. There are three galvanometer keys, "high," "med.," "low." "Low" should first be depressed as it inserts high resistance in series with the galvanometer and prevents a violent deflection if there is considerable unbalance. "Med." inserts less resistance, and there is no resistance in series with "high," which is depressed when the final balance is obtained. When the "high" key is released, it connects a resistor across the galvanometer terminals, which damps the galvanometer.

The normal range of voltage is 1.61 volts, 1.5 volts in the dial switch, and 0.11 volt in the main slide wire. The "emf" can be measured in steps of 50 microvolts by actual divisions and 10 microvolts by estimation. The range can be reduced to 0.1 and 0.01 normal simply by turning the rotary range switch C. This causes current to be shunted away from the dial switch and the main slide wire so that the current in this circuit is only 0.1 or 0.01 the normal value of 0.02 amp, thus reducing the emf between contacts M and M' by corresponding ratios. At the same time, resistors are inserted in the circuit so that the total current from the battery remains unchanged; also, the network is so arranged

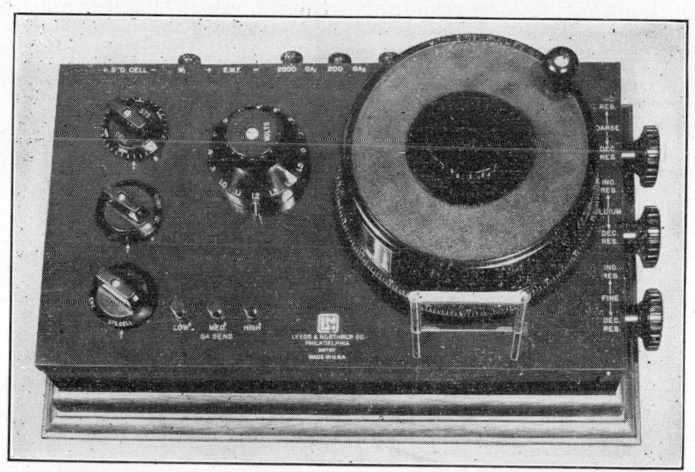

FIG. 134. Leeds and Northrup type K-2 potentiometer.

that the point of application of the standard-cell connection is shifted to permit standardization at all ratios.

When the D-P D-T switch U is turned to the position "emf," the unknown emf is measured by adjusting the range switch C and the contacts M and M'.

An external view of this potentiometer is shown in Fig. 134.

139. Other Potentiometer Methods. In the simple potentiometer, Fig. 132, and in the Leeds and Northrup potentiometer, Fig. 133, there are no contacts in series with the working current within the calibrated portion of the potentiometer circuit. This type of potentiometer is advantageous in that there can be no errors due to contact resistance. When a balance is obtained, there is no current in either the emf or standard-cell contacts, so that resistance in these contacts causes no error. However, with this type of potentiometer it is impossible to have more than two dial or slide-wire readings. For example, in the Leeds and Northrup type, the tenths of a volt are obtained on one dial with contact M, Fig. 133, and all the smaller divisions, such as hundredths, thousandths, and ten-thousandths of a volt, must be obtained on the single slide wire with the contact M'. To obtain more than two significant figures, it is necessary that the hundredths, thousandths, etc., of a volt be obtained on the slide wire. It is possible, however, to arrange a potentiometer so that the tenths, hundredths, thousandths, etc., of a volt are each read on a separate dial. In any of such types of potentiometer, it is essential to maintain a fixed resistance in the potentiometer itself, for the current must remain constant irrespective of the positions of the dials. There are two common methods of obtaining more than two significant figures by separate dials and at the same time maintaining constant potentiometer resistance, the Thomson-Varley method and the Wolff method.

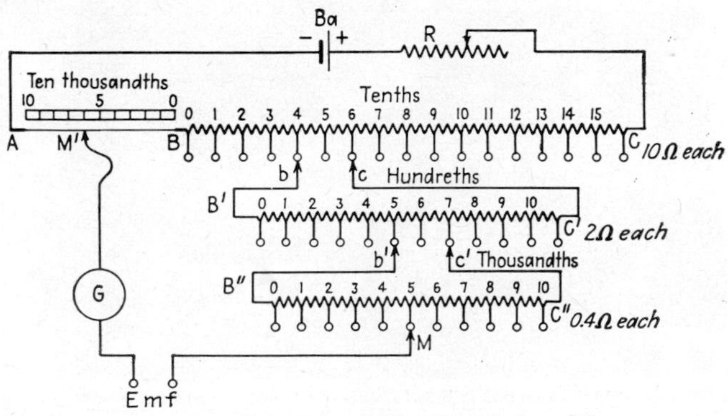

Fig. 135. Principle of Thomson-Varley slide.

The *Thomson-Varley method* is illustrated in Fig. 135. It is desired that tenths, hundredths, thousandths, and ten-thousandths of a volt be obtained on a separate resistance unit or dial divided into 10 or more equal divisions. In the potentiometer shown in Fig. 135, the tenths, hundredths, and thousandths of a volt are each obtained on a separate dial, and the ten-thousandths of a volt are obtained on a slide wire. Fundamentally, *it is necessary to maintain constant resistance in the entire potentiometer circuit AC irrespective of the position* of the *contacts on the* emf dials. Assume that the resistance corresponding to $\frac{1}{10}$ volt is 10 ohms. The resistor BC consists of sixteen 10-ohm resistors. Two contacts b and c, fastened rigidly together, always span two of the 10-ohm coils in BC. Between b and c there are connected eleven 2-ohm coils, $B'C'$. Two contacts b' and c', fastened rigidly together, always span two of the 2-ohm coils in $B'C'$. In the resistor bank $B''C''$ between b' and c' there are connected ten 0.4-ohm coils. One contact arm M operates over the contacts in the dial $B''C''$. These resistors are usually arranged in circular dials. The total resistance of $B''C''$ is 4 ohms, and it is connected across two 2-ohm resistors in $B'C'$. Hence, the equivalent resistance between the contactors $b'c'$, and therefore between any two of the contact points which contactors $b'c'$ may bridge, is 2 ohms. This is the value of the resistance of each of the resistor units in the resistor bank $B'C'$. Hence the effect of bridging resistor bank $B''C''$ across any two resistor units in resistor bank $B'C'$ is to reduce the resistance between B' and C' by 2 ohms, or by one resistor unit. However, since there are 11 resistor units of 2 ohms each in bank $B'C'$, and since the contacts $b'c'$ are always across two such units, the resistance between points $B'C'$ always remains constant at 20 ohms.

In a similar manner the resistor bank $B'C'$, the total resistance of which is 20 ohms, is always bridged across two resistor units in resistor bank BC by contactors bc, making the resistance between contactors bc equal to 10 ohms. Hence the bridging effect of contacts bc is to reduce the resistance of BC by 10 ohms, the resistance of a single unit. There are, however, 16 such units in BC so that the resistance of BC is reduced to 150 ohms, corresponding to 15 units. This resistance remains constant irrespective of the position of contactors bc. With the normal current of 0.01 amp, the total voltage across BC is 1.5 volts; the total voltage across $B'C'$ is 0.1 volt; and the total voltage across $B''C''$ is 0.01 volt. Hence the tenths of volts are read at b on dial BC; the hundredths of volts are read at b' on dial $B'C'$; and the thousandths of volts are read at M on scale $B''C''$. The ten-thousandths of volts may be read at contact M' on a slide wire AB, having a total resistance of 0.1 ohm. The reading with the dials set as in Fig. 135 is 0.4556 volt. It is obvious that the resistance between points A and C remains constant at 150.1 ohms irrespective of the position of any of the contact arms.

Since contact resistance, except at M and M', introduces error, it is desirable that potentiometers of this type have a high inherent resistance, so that the contact resistance may be neglected. This reduces the sensitivity. Another disadvantage of this type is the fact that the contacts must be kept clean from oxide and dust.

Wolff Method. The principle of the Wolff potentiometer is illustrated in Fig. 136. The potentiometer has a total resistance of 15,000 (actually 14,999.9) ohms, and the working current is 0.0001 amp, so that it is a high-resistance potentiometer. The dial E consists of fourteen 1,000-ohm coils, and the dial A consists of nine 100-ohm coils. The dials B, C, D are double, and have double dial switches, the purpose of which is to maintain constant resistance in the battery circuit. There are nine 10-ohm resistors in each half of dial D, nine 1-ohm resistors in each half of dial C, and nine 0.1-ohm resistors in each half of dial B. The path of the current, shown by arrows, is from the battery positive terminal through the entire dial A, through those portions of the lower halves of dials B, C, D which are not cut out by the lower parts of the dial switches *b*, *c*, *d*, thence through the entire dial *E* and so through those portions of the upper halves of dials *D*, *C*, *B* which are not cut out by the upper parts of the dial switches *d*, *c*, *b*, and thus to the battery negative terminal.

A study of Fig. 136 shows that the resistance of the battery circuit is constant irrespective of the positions of the dial switches, for each double dial switch always cuts out as much resistance in the upper half of the dial as it inserts in the lower half. On the other hand, the moving of any of the double dial switches changes the resistance between points a' and e' and hence causes a change in the potential difference between points *a* and *e*.

With the setting of the dials shown in Fig. 136, the potentiometer reads 0.92355 volt.

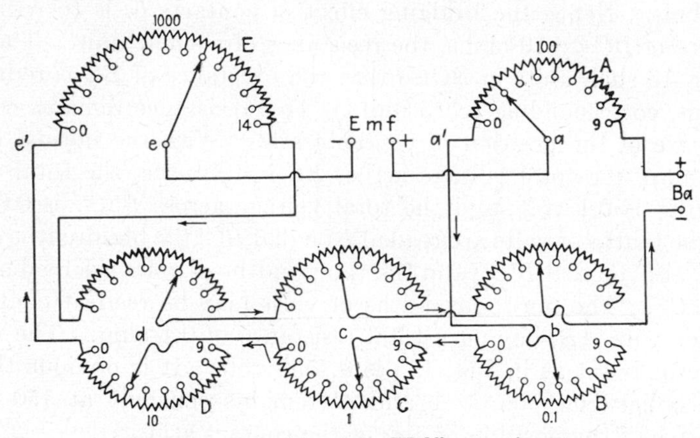

FIG. 136. Principle of the Wolff potentiometer.

140. Voltage Measurements with Potentiometer. Potentiometers themselves are designed to measure potentials up to only 1.6 volts. For the measurement of potentials in excess of this value, a *volt box* is necessary. A volt box is merely a resistor of very high resistance from which suitable taps are brought. This is illustrated by the resistor *AD* with taps *B* and *C*, Fig. 137. Assume *AD* to have a resistance of 10,000 ohms and *AB* a resistance of 100 ohms. If no current leaves the wire at *B*, the voltage drop across *AB* will be $100 \div 10{,}000$, or $1/100$ that across *AD*. If leads be carried from *AB* to the potentiometer, the potentiometer will measure one-hundredth the voltage across *AD*, since the potentiometer principle is an opposition method so that no current is taken from *B*. Therefore, if a voltmeter *V* is being calibrated, it should be connected in parallel with *AD*. If the voltmeter reads 119.0 volts and the potentiometer reads 1.184 volts, the true voltage across the voltmeter will be $1.184 \cdot 100 = 118.4$ volts. Therefore the correction to the voltmeter is -0.6 volt.

In a similar manner, voltages from 1.5 to 15 volts are connected across AC, the multiplying factor in this case being 10.

Voltage Divider. GH is a resistor wire connected directly across the line. One voltmeter terminal and one terminal of the volt box are connected to the end G of this wire. The other terminal of the voltmeter and the remaining terminal of the volt box are connected to a movable contact K. By sliding K along GH any desired voltage can be obtained. When used in this manner, GH is called a *voltage divider.* It is not necessary to the operation of the volt box but is merely a convenient means for adjusting the voltage.

141. Measurement of Current with Potentiometer. As has just been pointed out, the potentiometer is designed primarily to measure emf.

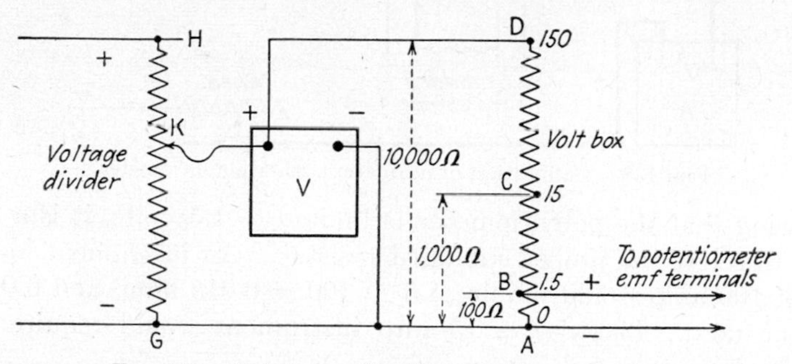

FIG. 137. Volt-box and voltage-divider connections.

By merely applying Ohm's law, the *current* in a circuit may also be determined with the potentiometer. The unknown current I is passed through a resistor of R ohms, and the voltage drop E across the resistor is measured. The current I is then determined, since for this part of the circuit both the voltage and the resistance are known. Therefore,

$$I = \frac{E}{R}. \tag{113}$$

The method of making the measurement is shown in Fig. 138. It is desired to know the exact current to the ammeter, in order to determine its errors, if any exist. The ammeter is connected in series with the standard resistor and also with a rheostat to control the current. Standard resistors are provided with four terminals as a rule, two heavy ones for current and two smaller binding posts for potential, Fig. 139 and also Fig. 100 (p. 148). The two potential binding posts are connected to the potentiometer, the proper polarity being observed. The voltage across the standard resistor is then measured by means of the potentiometer.

Standard resistors are usually adjusted to even decimal values such as 10, 1, 0.1, 0.01 ohms. Some are air-cooled, some are oil-cooled, and those designed for higher current ratings, Fig. 139, are set in a water-jacketed oil bath provided with a motor-driven stirrer. This stirrer circulating the oil assists in the cooling. Resistance standards are ordinarily rated at 2.5 and 10 watts for still-air and oil cooling, respectively. Large low-resistance standards frequently are constructed as a unit with combined oil and water cooling and have rating from 100 to 2,500 watts and higher.

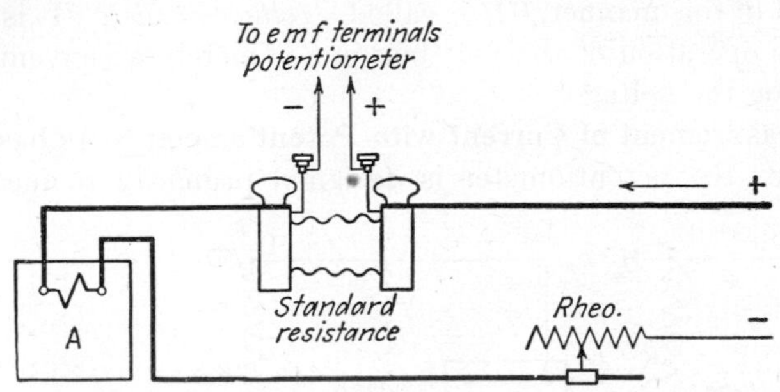

Fig. 138. Calibration of ammeter with a potentiometer.

Knowing that the potentiometer is limited to 1.5 volts, it is a simple matter to select the proper standard resistor. An instrument having a range of 100 amp would require $1.5 \div 100 = 0.015$ ohm, and 0.01 ohm would be used. Likewise, a 15-amp instrument would require $1.5 \div 15 = 0.1$ ohm.

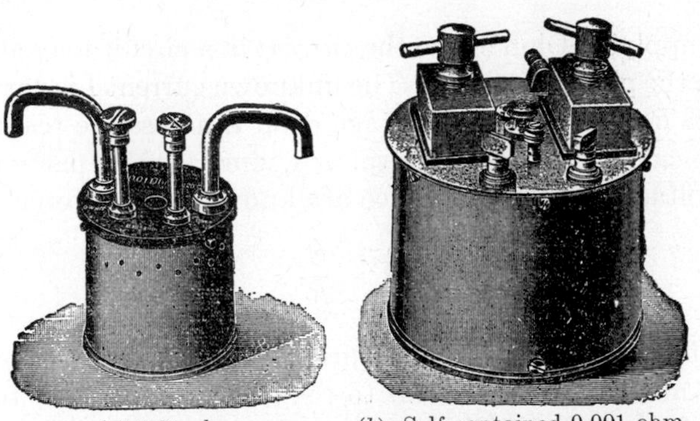

(a) 0.01 ohm. (b). Self-contained 0.001 ohm.

Fig. 139. Standard resistors.

When instruments are calibrated, they should be checked at 10 or 15 points on the scale and the corresponding correction at each point is plotted as ordinate, the instrument readings being plotted as abscissas. As an instrument scale is subject to scale errors, it is customary to connect successive points of the correction curve by straight lines, Fig. 140. For example, Fig. 140, the correct current when the instrument reads 50 amp is $50 + 0.8 = 50.8$ amp.

142. Measurement of Power. Direct-current power is usually measured by means of a voltmeter and an ammeter. Since the power is the product of the volts and the amperes ($P = EI$), it is merely necessary to multiply the volts by the amperes to obtain the power in watts. However, certain precautions may be necessary in measuring the power.

Assume that it is desired to measure the power taken by an incandescent lamp. If the voltmeter is connected as shown by the line marked "Incorrect" in Fig. 141(a), the current taken by the voltmeter is measured by the ammeter. In other words, the voltmeter is a load connected in parallel with the lamp. As the current taken by the lamp is small, this voltmeter current, although of itself small, may introduce an appreciable error into the measurement; that is, the power taken by the voltmeter

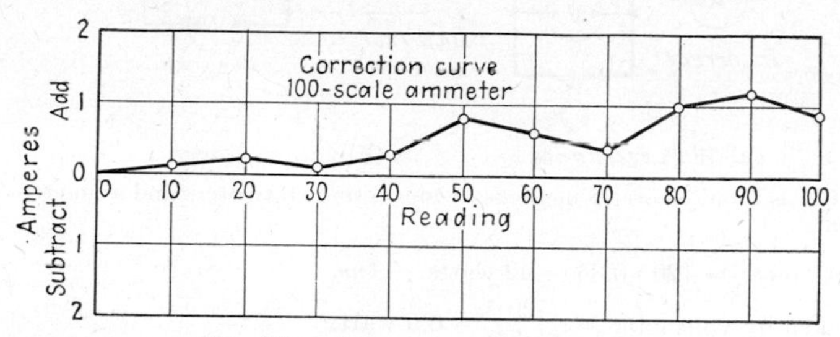

FIG. 140. Ammeter correction curve.

will be included in the measurement. There are three methods of eliminating this error. (1) The voltmeter power may be calculated, knowing the voltmeter resistance, and proper correction made. (2) The voltmeter may be open-circuited when the ammeter is being read, if it is certain that this will not alter the voltage across the lamp. (3) The voltmeter lead may be connected as shown by the solid line, Fig. 141(a), so that the voltmeter current does not go through the ammeter. Under this last condition, the voltmeter is not reading the true voltage across the lamp, but its reading is too high by the voltage drop through the ammeter. As the resistance of the lamp is high and that of the ammeter low, this last error is usually negligible.

However, if a resistor CD of low resistance is being measured, Fig. 141(b), the voltage drop across the resistor is necessarily low; and if the voltmeter is now connected outside the ammeter, an appreciable error may be introduced, as the voltmeter reading includes the voltage drop in the ammeter. The voltmeter should now be connected *inside* the ammeter. This will not introduce an appreciable error, for presumably a large current is required for the measurement of low resistance, and the very small voltmeter current is negligible in comparison with the ammeter current.

These precautions should be observed also in making resistance measurements.

Example. It is desired to measure the power taken by a 40-watt tungsten lamp. A 0.5-scale ammeter having a resistance of 0.15 ohm and a 150-scale voltmeter having a resistance of 16,000 ohms are used for the measurement. When the voltmeter is connected inside the ammeter incorrectly, Fig. 141(*a*), it reads 120 volts and the ammeter reads 0.35 amp. Determine true power taken by the lamp and the apparent power if the voltmeter loss is neglected.

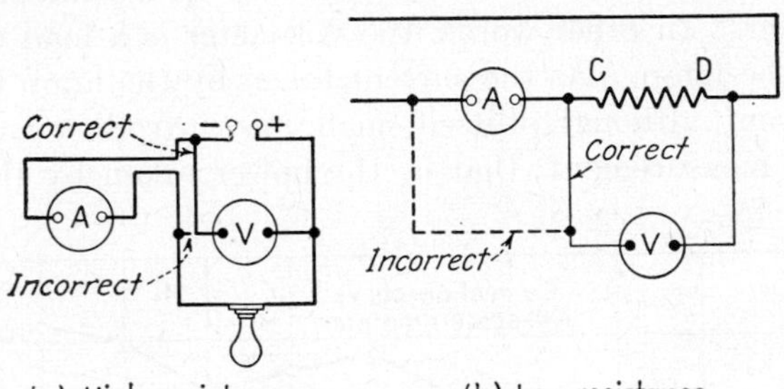

FIG. 141. Correct and incorrect methods of connecting voltmeters and ammeters in power measurements.

Apparent power $= 120 \cdot 0.35 = 42$ watts. *Ans.*

Power taken by voltmeter $= \dfrac{(120)^2}{16{,}000} = 0.9$ watt.

True power to lamp $= 41.1$ watts. *Ans.*

The voltmeter introduces a 2 per cent error in this case.

From the foregoing data, the line voltage is

$$120 + (0.35)(0.15) = 120.053 \text{ volts.}$$

If the voltmeter is connected outside the ammeter ["Correct", Fig. 141(*a*)], the voltmeter will now read the line voltage (assumed constant), the ammeter

$$0.35 - \frac{120}{16{,}000} = 0.3425 \text{ amp,}$$

and the apparent power is $120.053 \cdot 0.3425 = 41.12$ watts, an error of 0.05 per cent, which is negligible.

143. Wattmeter. The wattmeter measures power directly. It consists of fixed coils *FF* and a pivoted coil *M*, free to turn within the magnetic field produced by coils *FF*, Fig. 142. The coils *FF*, which may be connected in series or in parallel, are wound with comparatively few turns of wire and are capable of carrying the entire current of the circuit. The moving coil *M* is wound with very fine wire, and the current is led into it through two control springs in the same manner that current is led into the movable coil of a Weston instrument. The fixed coils are connected in series with the load in the same manner as an ammeter is connected. The moving coil is connected across the line in series with a high resistance *R* in the same manner as a voltmeter coil is connected ordinarily.

The field of the coils *FF* is proportional to the current, and the current in the coil *M* is proportional to the voltage. Therefore, the turning moment is proportional to both the current and the voltage and hence to the power of the circuit. It also depends on the angular position of *M* with respect to *FF*, which is taken into consideration when the scale is marked.

Owing to the high degree of accuracy obtainable by the use of voltmeter and ammeter, the wattmeter is seldom used for d-c measurements of power. As it is subject to stray fields, reversed readings should be taken, that is, both current and voltage should be reversed and the average of the two readings used. The wattmeter is used almost exclusively for the measurement of power with alternating currents. A more complete description, together with its uses, is found in Chap. IV, Vol. II.

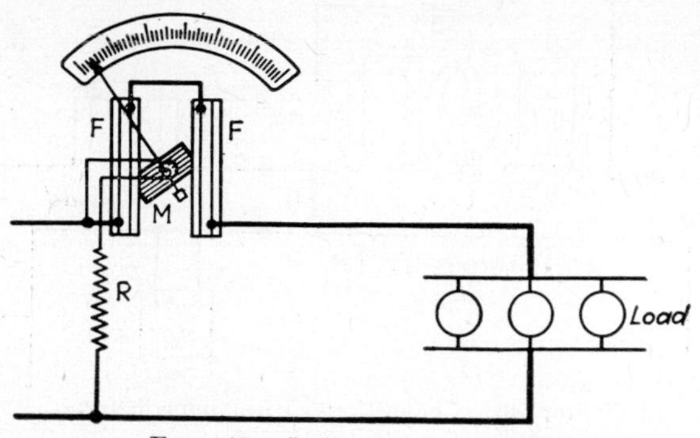

FIG. 142. Indicating wattmeter.

144. Watthour Meter. The watthour meter is a device for measuring electrical *energy* (see Sec. 41, p. 45). As energy is the product of power and time, the watthour meter must take into consideration both of these factors. As electrical power is usually sold on an energy basis, a saving of many dollars may depend on the accuracy of such a meter. Therefore, a proper understanding of its mechanism and the method of adjustment is essential.

In principle the watthour meter is a small motor whose instantaneous speed is proportional to the power and whose total revolutions in a given time are proportional to the total energy or watthours during that time.

Referring to Fig. 143, the line is connected to two terminals on the left-hand side of the meter. The upper terminal is connected to two fixed coils *FF* in series, wound with wire sufficiently large to carry the maximum current taken by the load, which should not greatly exceed the rated current of the meter. The connection through coils *FF* terminates at the upper binding post on the right-hand side of the meter. The coils *FF* are wound so that they aid each other, and they supply the field in which the armature rotates. The other line wire runs straight through the meter to the load. A shunt circuit is tapped to the upper line on the left-hand side. It runs first to the armature, through the small silver brushes *B*, which rest on the small commutator *C*. From the brushes, connection is made through coil *F′* and through a resistor *R* to the lower line wire. This resistor *R* is omitted in certain types of meters.

As the load current goes through *FF* and there is no iron in the circuit, the magnetic field produced by these coils is proportional to the *load current.* As the armature, in series with resistance, is connected directly across the line, the current in the meter armature is proportional to the

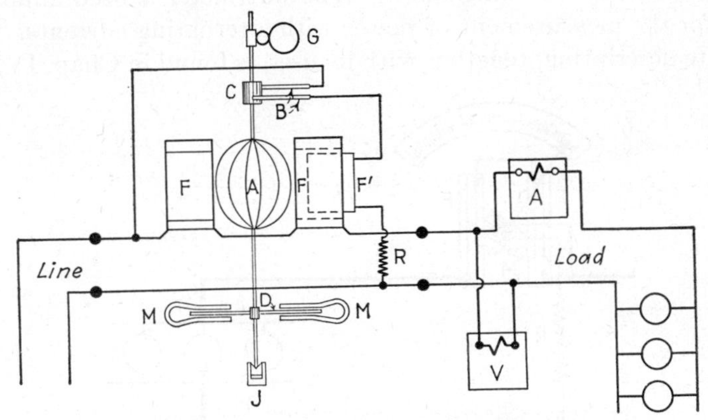

Fig. 143. Connections of watthour meter.

line voltage, the counter emf of the armature being negligible in comparison with the line voltage. Neglecting the small voltage drop in *FF*, the torque acting on the armature will be proportional to the product of the load current and the load voltage, in other words, proportional to the power through the meter to the load.

It can be proved[1] that, if the meter is to register correctly, there must be a retarding torque acting on the moving element proportional to its angular velocity. To meet this condition an aluminum disk *D* is pressed on the motor shaft. This disk rotates between the poles of two permanent magnets *MM*. In cutting the field produced by these magnets, eddy currents are induced in the disk, retarding its motion. As the value of these currents is proportional to the angular velocity of the disk, and they are acting in conjunction with a magnetic field of constant strength, their retarding effect is proportional to the angular velocity, so that the condition for correct registration is fulfilled.

Friction cannot be entirely eliminated in the rotating element, even with the most careful construction. Near the rated load of the meter

[1] See Laws, F. A., "Electrical Measurements," McGraw-Hill Book Company, Inc.

the effect of friction is practically negligible, but since the friction torque is nearly constant, it has a much greater proportionate effect at light loads. As the ordinary meter may operate at light loads during a considerable portion of the time, it is desirable that the error due to friction be eliminated. This is accomplished by means of coil F' connected in series with the armature. F' is so connected that its field acts in the same direction as that due to coils FF. Therefore it assists the armature A to rotate. Being connected in the shunt circuit and across practically constant voltage, it is acting continuously and produces nearly constant torque. The coil F' is movable, and its position can be adjusted so that the friction error is compensated.

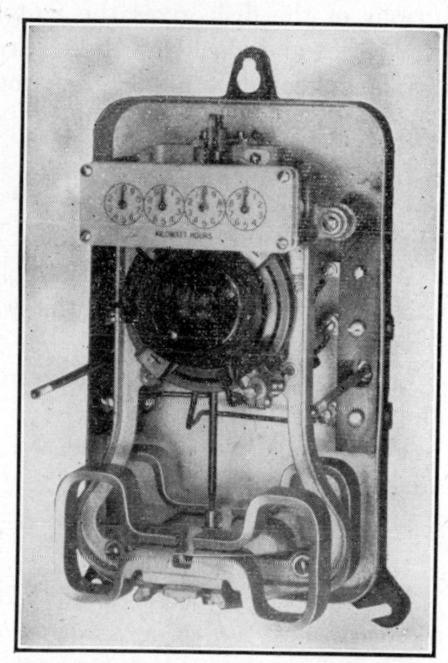

FIG. 144. Interior view of watthour meter. (*General Electric Company.*)

To reduce friction and wear, the rotating element of the meter is made as light as possible. The element is supported by a hardened steel pivot turning in a jewel bearing J, which is a sapphire in the smaller sizes and a diamond in the heavier types. The jewel is supported on a spring. In time the pivot becomes dulled and the jewel roughened, which increases friction and causes the meter to run more slowly unless F' is readjusted. The moving element turns the clockwork of the meter dials through a worm and gears G.

Figure 144 shows the interior view of a Thomson watthour meter. The friction-compensating coil is plainly shown at the front of the meter.

145. Adjustment of the Watthour Meter. Even if the initial adjustment be accurate, the registration of a watthour meter may, in time, become incorrect. This is due to many causes, such as pitting of the commutator, roughening of the jewel, wear on the pivot, or change in the strength of the retarding magnets. As the cost of energy to consumers is largely based on the registration of such meters, it is important that they be kept in adjustment, as a small error, particularly in the larger sizes, may ultimately mean a difference of many dollars to either the consumer or the power company.

To adjust the meter, it may be loaded as shown in Fig. 143. The power taken by the load is measured by a calibrated voltmeter and ammeter. The revolutions of the disk D are counted over a period of time which is measured with a stop watch. In most meters, the relation between watthours and the revolutions of the *disk* is

$$P \cdot H = K \cdot N \tag{114}$$

where P is in watts, H is in hours, K is the meter constant or watthour constant, usually marked on the disk, and is equal to the watthours registered for each revolution of the disk, and N is the revolutions of the disk.

Equation (114) shows that the meter constant multiplied by the revolutions of the disk gives the watthours registered by the meter. The gear ratios and clockwork take care of the dial registration.

When checking a meter, the time is usually measured in seconds. Equation (114) then becomes

$$\frac{P \cdot t}{3{,}600} = K \cdot N \tag{115}$$

where t is the time in seconds.

When the meter is tested, the voltmeter and ammeter are read at intervals, while the revolutions of the disk are being counted. A run of about 1 min gives good results.

Let the average watts determined from the corrected voltmeter and ammeter readings be P_1.

The average watts as indicated by the meter during the same period are, from (115),

$$P = \frac{K \cdot N \cdot 3{,}600}{t}. \tag{116}$$

The accuracy of a watthour meter is the percentage of the total energy passed through a meter which is registered by the dials.

The accuracy of the meter is

$$\frac{100P}{P_1} \quad \text{per cent.} \tag{117}$$

Example. In the test of a 10-amp watthour meter having a constant of 0.4, the disk makes 40 revolutions in 53.6 sec. The average volts and amperes during this period are 116 volts and 9.4 amp. Determine accuracy of the meter at this load.

Average standard watts $P_1 = 116 \cdot 9.4 = 1{,}090.$

Average meter watts, from (116),

$$P = \frac{0.4 \cdot 40 \cdot 3{,}600}{53.6} = 1{,}075.$$

$$\text{Accuracy} = \frac{100 \cdot 1{,}075}{1{,}090} = 98.6\,\%. \quad \textit{Ans.}$$

This means that the meter is 1.4 per cent slow and should be speeded up slightly. With calibrated indicating instruments and careful adjustment, a meter may easily be brought within 0.5 per cent of accurate registration.

There are two adjustments to be made. Near full load, the magnets are moved. If the meter is running slow, the magnets are moved nearer the center of the disk where the effect of the retarding currents is reduced, and if the meter is running fast the magnets are moved farther from the center. If the meter has been correctly adjusted near full load and is found to be in error near light load, the error is obviously due to friction. The light-load adjustment, made at from 5 to 10 per cent rated load, is effected by moving the friction-compensating coil F'. If the meter is slow, the coil F' is moved in nearer the armature, and if the meter is fast, it is pulled out farther from the armature. This adjustment of F' may affect the full-load adjustment slightly, so that the meter should be rechecked at full load and then again at light load.

146. Other Types of Watthour Meter. The 3-wire meter is designed to register energy in a 3-wire system. It does not differ materially from the meter shown in Fig. 143 except that the two coils *FF* are connected in opposite sides of the line, Fig. 145. Hence, the field in which the armature *A* rotates is produced by the joint effect of the current in the positive conductor to neutral and the current in the negative conductor to neutral. Therefore, the torque is proportional to the power to the 3-wire system irrespective of any unbalancing of the current. The armature circuit may be connected to the neutral as shown, or it may be connected across the outer wires. If this latter connection is used, the neutral connection to the meter is omitted. The meter does not register accurately unless the voltages between the two outer lines and neutral are equal. This error is usually small.

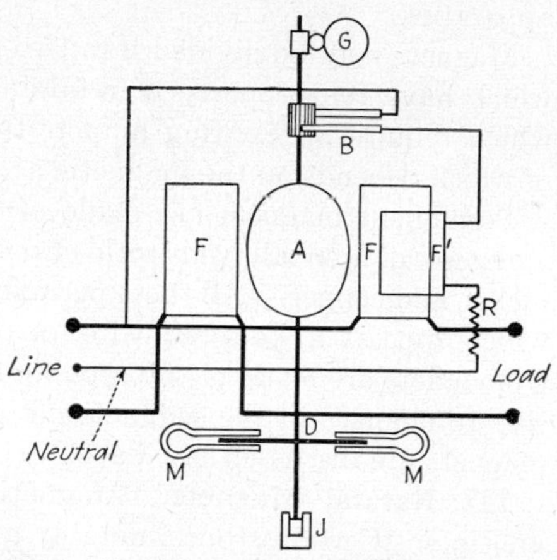

FIG. 145. Diagram of a 3-wire watthour meter.

The meters already described should not be installed near bus bars carrying heavy currents because the strength of the meter field and of the retarding magnets may be affected by the stray fields. To eliminate the effect of stray fields, an astatic type of meter is available. There are two armatures on the spindle, each of which rotates in a magnetic field produced by a few turns or a single turn in series with the load. These two magnetic fields act in opposite directions so that any stray field presumably will strengthen the field in which one armature rotates as much as it will weaken the field in which the other armature rotates, and the resulting effect will be nil. There are two sets of retarding magnets. These magnets are placed so that if a stray field increases the strength of one set, it simultaneously reduces the strength of the other. For further protection these magnets are surrounded by an iron box.

CHAPTER VI

MAGNETISM AND PERMANENT MAGNETS

Magnets and magnetism are involved in the operation of practically all electrical apparatus. Therefore an understanding of their underlying principles is essential to a clear conception of the operation of such apparatus.

Magnets may be divided into two general classes: *permanent* magnets, which have the property of retaining their magnetism indefinitely and which require no exciting ampere-turns; *electromagnets*, the magnetism of which depends on the magnetic action of electric currents (Chap. VII).

Permanent magnets are made of hardened carbon (1 per cent) steel and also of iron alloyed with chromium, tungsten, cobalt, aluminum, nickel, and copper. All these permanent-magnet materials are very hard, which appears to be a requisite for permanent-magnet materials. Electromagnets are made of soft iron and soft steel, which are highly responsive to changes in the magnetizing effect of electric currents. Electromagnets are discussed in Chaps. VII and VIII.

147. Natural Magnets. Magnetic phenomena were noted by the ancients. Certain stones, notably at Magnesia, Asia Minor, were found to have the property of attracting bits of iron, and the name "magnets" was given to these magic stones. The fact that such stones had the property of pointing north and south, if suspended freely, was not discovered until the tenth or twelfth century. The practical use of such a stone in navigation gave it the name of "lodestone," or leading stone. Natural magnets are composed of an iron ore known in metallurgy as *magnetite*, an iron oxide having the chemical composition Fe_3O_4. Iron filings, when brought in contact with lodestone, concentrate at two or more regions, showing that the lodestone possesses two or more localized magnetic regions, or poles.

148. Magnetic Materials. Of all the metals or elements only iron (or steel) possesses pronounced magnetic properties. Cobalt and nickel and some of their alloys and a few nonferrous alloys (Heusler's alloy of copper, manganese, and aluminum) possess magnetic properties to a much less degree than iron. Materials possessing pronounced magnetic properties are said to be *ferromagnetic*.[1] Other elements and metals having

[1] These quantities are defined in the ASA Definitions of Electrical Terms (1941 edition) as follows: "A ferromagnetic material is a material having a permeability that

slight magnetic properties are called *paramagnetic*. Elements and materials having magnetic properties which are less than those of a vacuum are called *diamagnetic*. The difference in the permeabilities of diamagnetic materials and a vacuum is so slight that it can be detected by highly precise measurements only.

From the earliest times when iron first came into use as a magnetic material, attempts have been made to explain why it alone of all the elements should have such pronounced magnetic properties. About a century ago, Ampère[1] suggested that the molecules of iron might behave as magnets because of the electric currents circulating in them. Later, Ewing and Weber (p. 204) explained practically all observed magnetic phenomena, such as saturation and hysteresis, on the basis of the molecules of iron being small permanent magnets. Their theory did not, however, explain why such magnetized molecules were an exclusive property of iron (nickel and cobalt to a much less extent) but not of the large number of other elements. Only recently, with the advent of more detailed knowledge of atomic structure and the properties and interactions of the associated electrons, has it become possible to offer a rational explanation. It is beyond the scope of this text to give more than a general explanation, but a most complete analysis can be found in the several excellent references given below.[2]

The Bohr atom consists of a heavy central positive nucleus and a number of electrons moving in either circular or elliptical orbits around the nucleus, Fig. 146. The number of positive charges in the nucleus is just equal to the number of orbital electrons, each constituting a negative charge. Recently there has been added the conception that each electron

---

varies with the magnetizing force and that is considerably greater than the permeability of a vacuum" (05.25.060).

"A paramagnetic material is a material having a permeability which is slightly greater than that of a vacuum and which is approximately independent of the magnetizing force" (05.25.065).

"A diamagnetic material is a material having a permeability less than that of a vacuum" (05.25.055).

[1] See footnote, p. 30.

[2] BOZORTH, R. M., "Present State of Ferromagnetic Theory," *Bell System Tech. Jour.*, January, 1936, p. 63.

BOZORTH, R. M., "The Physical Basis of Ferromagnetism," *Bell System Tech. Jour.*, January, 1940, p. 1.

BOZORTH, R. M., "Teaching of Ferromagnetism," *Am. Jour. Phys.*, 1942 (10), p. 73.

WILLIAMS, H. J., R. M. BOZORTH, and W. SHOCKLEY, "Magnetic Domain Pattern in Single Crystal of Silicon Iron," *Phys. Rev.*, Vol. 75, No. 1, p. 155, January, 1949.

WILLIAMS, H. J., and W. SHOCKLEY, "A Simple Domain Pattern in an Iron Crystal Showing a Direct Correlation with Magnetization," *Phys. Rev.*, Vol. 75, No. 1, p. 178, January, 1949.

itself is spinning about an axis through its center, this motion being known as "electron spin."

Some electrons spin in a positive direction, and others spin in the opposite, or negative, direction. Because of the motion of the electrons in their orbits and their angular rotation, there is a circulation of electricity, or of minute electrical charges, both around the nucleus and within each electron. Each electron then is a small gyroscope possessing a definite magnetic moment because of its moving electrical charge, and it has a definite angular momentum because of its rotating mass. Although the electrons moving in the orbits also possess both magnetic moments and angular momentums, it has been established that when the applied magnetizing force[1] is changed, the orbital motions remain unchanged, the entire change occurring in the direction, or the "sense," of the *spin* of certain of the electrons.

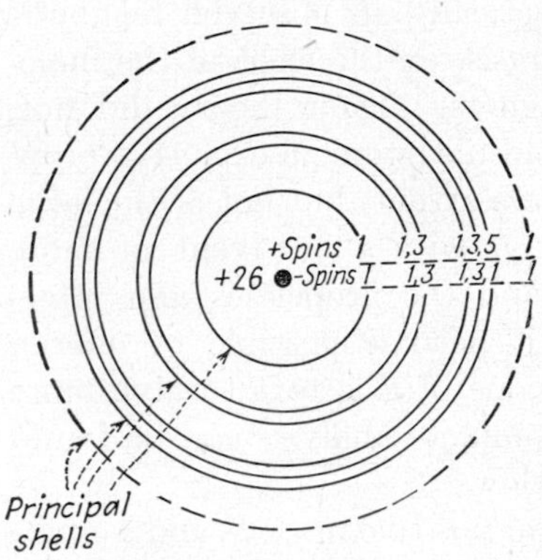

FIG. 146. Electron shells in an isolated iron atom.

The reason why iron is magnetic can now be explained by a study of Fig. 146, which shows the structure of an iron atom. The electron orbits are represented by shells. There are four principal shells, one of which is divided into two subshells and one other into three subshells. The numbers denote the number of electrons for each subshell. In order that the atom may have magnetic properties, there must be an *uncompensated* spin of electrons in an *inner* orbit. In Fig. 146, the electrons having positive (+) and negative (−) spins are designated. It will be noted that in the two inner shells there is an equal number of electrons having positive and negative spins, there being one pair of such electrons in the innermost shell and two pairs of 1 and 3 electrons each in the adjacent shell. Hence, in these two shells all the magnetic moments are compensated so that these shells develop no resultant magnetic moments. However, in the third shell there are 1, 3, 5 electrons with positive spins, and 1, 3, 1 electrons, with negative spins, so that there is an uncompensated number of positive spins. This condition is responsible for the magnetic properties of the iron atom. The two electrons in the outermost orbit, shown dotted, one with a plus spin and the other with a minus spin are the electrons that are free to pass to adjacent atoms, accounting for conduction of current p. 2).

[1] As is explained later, the magnetizing force in a magnetic field is measured by the force acting on a unit pole. Magnetizing force may be produced by the poles of a magnet or by current in a wire or a coil.

However, for one element to be ferromagnetic it is not only necessary that there be uncompensated spinning electrons in the individual atoms, but also the resultant spins in neighboring atoms must be parallel. Calculation has shown that in order that this condition be fulfilled there is a critical relation of the atomic diameter to the diameter of the uncompensated electron shell (next to outermost, Fig. 146). Since the influence of electron spins of one atom on those of a neighboring atom depends on the distances between them, this distance is known as the "exchange." This exchange force is an electrostatic one and is so powerful that at room temperature it would require a magnetizing force of 10,000,000 oersteds[1] to accomplish the same alignment of electron spins.

The explanation, then, of the rarity of ferromagnetic materials is that only the iron atom and to a lesser extent the nickel and cobalt atoms fulfill simultaneously the conditions of uncompensated electron spin in an inner orbit and the resultant spins in neighboring atoms being parallel. Furthermore, this latter condition is fulfilled only when a critical relation of atomic diameter to diameter of the shell containing the uncompensated electron spins is also met.

Although the forces of exchange are powerful, for some reason not yet known, they do not extend over the entire specimen but act only over limited areas which are practically so small as to be invisible. On the average these highly magnetized regions have the volume of a cube of somewhat less than 0.001 in. on an edge. The actual ferromagnetic material is thus composed of a great number of such small regions called *domains*. Each domain consists of an aggregate of molecules all with the axes of their spinning electrons in parallel, so that each domain is magnetized to saturation. Each domain contains about 10^{15} atoms and has a volume of about 10^{-9} cu cm.

With iron, a domain may be considered as a cube with an atom at each corner and one at the center. The direction of easy magnetization is along any one of the edges of the cube.

It is to be noted that Ampère's theory of a current circulating in the molecule is not far removed from the actual condition of the spinning-electron phenomenon just described. It seems remarkable that more than a century ago Ampère could have postulated so accurately at a time when nothing was known of the internal structure of the atom.

149. Effect of Temperature. Except at the temperature of absolute zero the atoms of all substances are in a continual state of agitation. In iron, at the lower temperatures, it is necessary for the exchange forces among the atoms to overcome the forces of agitation in order to bring the axes of spinning electrons of neighboring atoms into parallelism. However, as the temperature is increased, the atomic agitation also increases

[1] See p. 213.

and ultimately at about 750°C the forces of agitation become so great that they prevail over the exchange forces, the atoms and domains assume more or less haphazard relations among themselves, and the domains, as well as the material, lose their magnetic properties. This temperature is called the "Curie point" and is illustrated in Fig. 147, which shows the flux density in gauss as a function of temperature. Note the rapid decrease of the flux density toward zero at 750°C, the Curie point.

150. Magnetization and Hysteresis. The well-known phenomena of the magnetization curve, saturation, and hysteresis may now be explained on the basis of the reaction among the electrons, atoms, domains, and crystals of the iron. Ordinary metals are composed of a large number of crystals, or grains, which often are too small to be seen by the naked eye. Recently, however, methods for making large crystals readily visible to

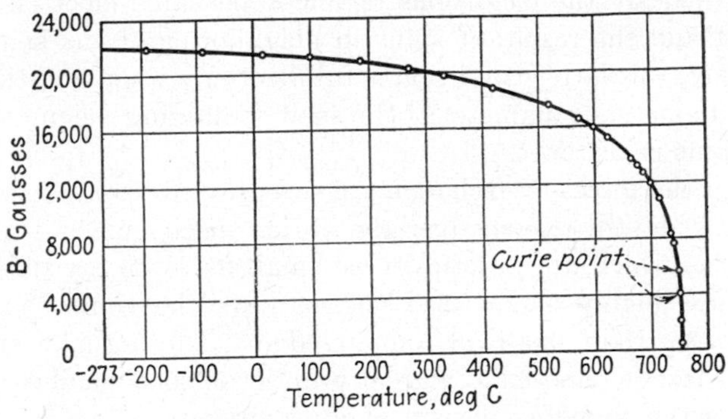

FIG. 147. Effect of temperature on magnetization.

the eye have been developed. The domains tend to group themselves into the crystals, or grains, and when no external magnetic force is applied, the domains, which are small local regions magnetized to saturation, align themselves in any one of the six equivalent directions of the crystal axes, or edges. This is illustrated in Fig. 148(a), which shows a portion of a crystal, the directions of the crystal axes being shown by the lines within the crystal boundaries.

For convenience, the domains are represented by small cubes, and the arrows represent the directions of the magnetization of the domains. A + represents the feathered end of an arrow and indicates that the direction of magnetization of the domain with which it is associated is into the paper. Similarly, a ⊙ represents the tip of an arrow and indicates that the direction of magnetization of the domain is outwards from the paper. The probability of domain orientation is the same for all six equivalent directions of the crystal axes. This is indicated in Fig. 148(a), in which practically the same number of arrows point in each of the six directions. The crystal as a whole, however, will be unmagnetized. When a weak magnetizing force is applied, the crystal begins to show weak magnetic orientation. This initial effect has recently been found to be due to a slight displacement of the boundary between two domains, as is indicated at the right in Fig. 148(*b*). The dimension of a domain oriented in the direction of the applied magnetizing force is enlarged at the expense of a domain oriented in a less favorable direction. That is, a boundary displacement is produced between adjacent domains. This effect produces the beginning of the magnetization curve shown as ① in Fig. 149, in which

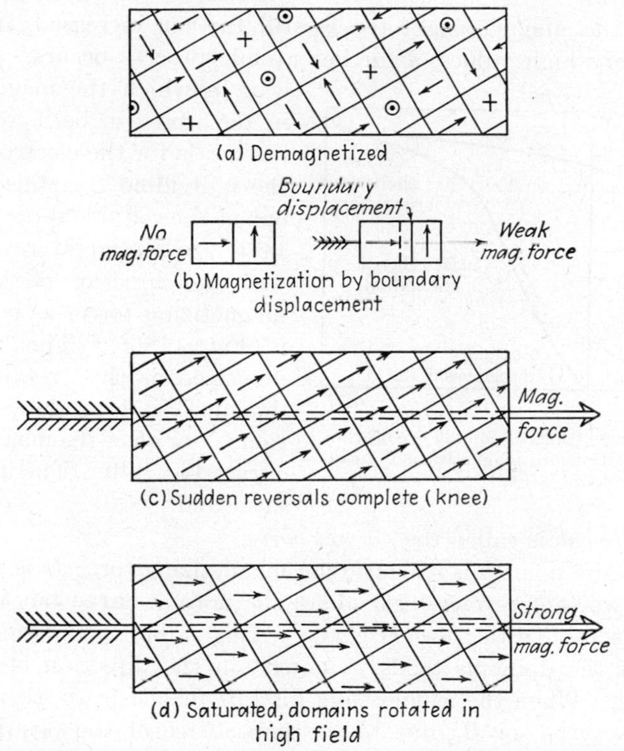

FIG. 148. Turning actions of domains in crystal by magnetic field.

the flux density, B gauss,[1] or maxwells per sq cm, is plotted as a function of the magnetizing force H. (H is equal to $0.4\pi NI$, where NI is the ampere-turns per centimeter, Sec. 182). This lowest part of the magnetization curve is slightly concave upwards.

As the magnetizing force H is further increased, the magnetization of the domains tends to change from one direction of easy magnetization to one that is more nearly in the direction of H, and the domains become progressively aligned in the direction of H, some of the domains changing

[1] See p. 214.

before the others. This alignment of the domains is more or less uniform, producing the nearly linear portion of the magnetization curve shown as ② in Fig. 149. When the magnetizing force becomes very strong, the directions of orientation of all the domains approach coincidence with the direction of the magnetizing force, as is indicated in Fig. 148(*c*). When all the domains are thus oriented in the same direction, each crystal, or grain, acts like one very large domain. This condition is represented by the "knee" of the curve at *a* in Fig. 149, and the iron is near saturation.

If then the magnetizing force is still further increased, ultimately reaching very high values, a further atomic process occurs. The only way in which the magnetization in the iron can be increased still further is for the electron spins in the individual domains to rotate out of their stable directions, Fig. 148(*c*), toward greater coincidence with the direction of the applied magnetizing force, as is indicated in Fig. 148(*d*). This process is described as the "rotation of the domain" and produces the portion ③, or *ab* of the magnetization curve, Fig. 149. The iron is now saturated.

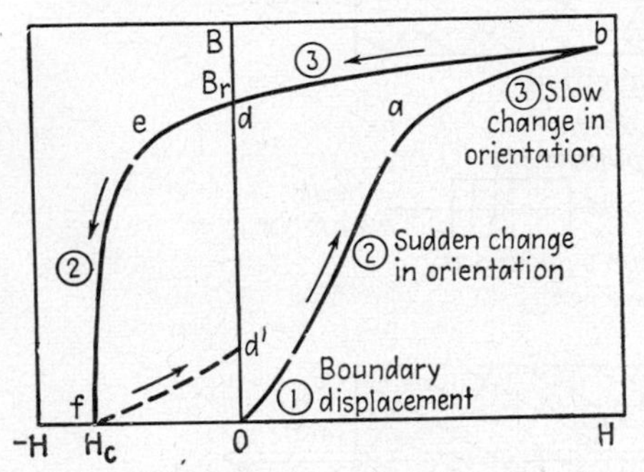

FIG. 149. Three types of domain orientation and their relation to magnetization curve and hysteresis loop.

The curve *oab* is called the *normal curve.*

If, when the point *b* is reached, the magnetizing force H is decreased, the curve will not retrace itself along the normal curve but will follow the curve *bd* above the normal curve. This is due to the fact that the position of the domains tends to persist in the direction of their last orientation. When the magnetizing force H reaches zero, there remains a flux density *od*, or B_r, due to the persistence of the position of the domains. The flux density B_r is called the *remanence.* If after the magnetizing force reaches zero, it is reversed in direction, the curve follows the path *de*. At or near point *e* the domains have reached the condition shown in Fig. 148(*c*). Further negative increase in the magnetizing force H causes a rapid drop *ef* in the flux density. This sudden drop is due to the domains in the crystals progressively becoming deoriented from the condition shown in Fig. 148(*c*), approaching that shown in (*a*). This portion of the curve is discussed more in detail in connection with permanent magnets (Sec. 201, p. 276, et seq.).

At point *f*, when the magnetizing force reaches the value *of*, or $-H_c$, the flux density has reached zero. It has required a negative magnetizing force H_c to bring the flux to this zero value. The magnetizing force H_c is called the *coercive force.*

The curve *bdef* is the decreasing part of the hysteresis loop for assumed positive values of flux density. The purpose of this analysis with reference to Fig. 149 is to relate the magnetization curve and hysteresis to the relations occurring among the electrons, atoms, domains, and crystals as the iron is subjected to increasing and decreasing values of magnetizing force. Further discussion and analyses of magnetization curves and hysteresis loops will be given later when magnetic circuits and their applications are being considered.

151. Barkhausen Effect. There are many experimental evidences of the different phases of domain and crystal orientation which have just been briefly discussed. Several of these experiments are described in the

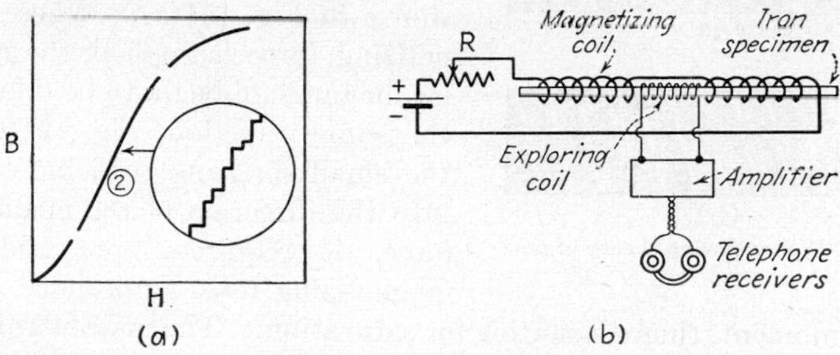

FIG. 150. Barkhausen effect.

footnote references (p. 197). There is, however, one simple but convincing experiment of domain orientation called the *Barkhausen effect.* If a small portion of that part of the curve ② (at the right), Fig. 149, were amplified a billion (10^9) times, it would be found to consist of a large number of very small steps, as is shown in the circle, Fig. 150(a). If the magnetizing force is increased gradually, the magnetization remains constant for a very short interval and then increases suddenly in a small steplike increment, as is indicated in the circle, Fig. 150(a). Then there is no further increase until the magnetizing force reaches another higher value. These sudden stepped increases in magnetization are due to the individual domains becoming progressively oriented from the pattern of Fig. 148(a) to the pattern of Fig. 148(c). No known apparatus is sufficiently sensitive to measure these small increments, but they can be detected audibly.

Thus, Fig. 150(b), an iron specimen can be gradually magnetized by a coil supplied by a battery through a rheostat R. An exploring coil, also wound about the specimen, is connected to a set of telephone receivers through an amplifier. As the magnetizing force is gradually increased, a series of "clicks," or noises, is heard in the receivers. Each click corresponds to the orientation of a domain as it turns, corresponding to one of the steps, Fig. 150(*a*), so that its magnetic axis turns to coincide with the direction of the magnetizing force. Under favorable conditions these noises, or clicks, may be heard without an amplifier.

152. Weber and Ewing Theory. Although the foregoing atom-domain explanation of magnetic action is without doubt the correct one, at the end of the last century both Weber and Ewing[1] advanced a molecular theory which departs but little from it. Weber and Ewing, of course, had no knowledge of spinning electrons and domains, so that they assumed that the molecules themselves were the unit magnets. Thus when a magnet is in a nonmagnetic condition, the molecular magnets are arranged in the haphazard manner shown in Fig. 151(*a*). When a magnetizing force is applied, the molecular magnets all begin to be oriented in the same direction, Fig. 151(*b*). As the small magnets turn more nearly into the direction of the magnetizing force, it requires more and more magnetizing force to produce a given turning moment, thus accounting for saturation. The molecular friction of the turning molecular magnets accounts for hysteresis and hysteresis loss.

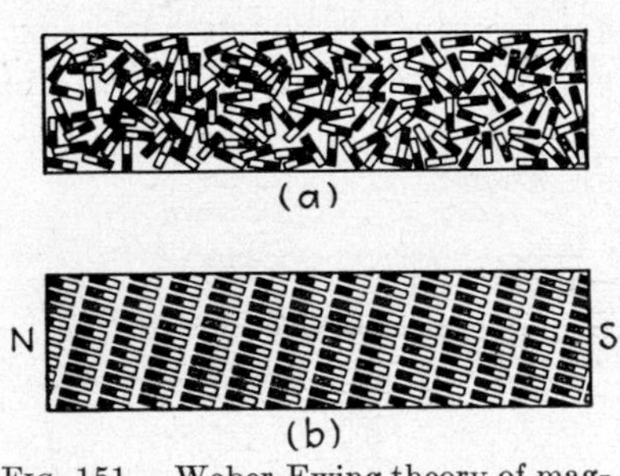

FIG. 151. Weber-Ewing theory of magnets.

Although this molecular theory has been superseded, it is remarkable how closely it approaches the true one, particularly when the limited knowledge of molecular structure which was available at the time is considered.

153. Magnets. If hardened steel or certain alloys of iron, tungsten, nickel, and aluminum are subjected to magnetic influences, or magnetizing forces, such as in coming in contact with an electromagnet or a permanent magnet or in being subjected to the magnetizing force produced by a coil of wire conducting an electric current, these materials not only will become magnetized but will retain indefinitely a considerable proportion of the magnetism imparted to them. Such magnets are called *permanent magnets*, the properties of which are discussed in considerable detail in Sec. 201 (p. 276) *et seq.* When such permanent magnets become magnetized, the domains not only become oriented with the pole axes parallel to one another but also become so closely locked in position that it requires a high demagnetizing force to unlock them and to cause them

[1] EWING, J. A. "Magnetic Induction in Iron and Other Metals," 3d ed., 1900. *Electrician*, London, 1900. Also see footnote, p. 220.

to assume the random relation to one another which results in the demagnetization of the magnet.

When iron or other magnetic material becomes magnetized, either as a permanent magnet or as an electromagnet, the magnetic influence, such as the ability to attract small pieces of iron or iron filings, becomes localized in two or more different regions on the magnet. Also, the magnetic influence emerges from the magnet at one or more such regions and returns at one or more other regions. These regions are called the *poles* of the magnet. The region at which the influence appears to emerge is called the *north*, or *N*, *pole* of the magnet; the region at which the influence appears to enter is called the *south*, or *S*, *pole* of the magnet. These poles are readily detected by sprinkling iron filings on the magnet, Fig. 155.

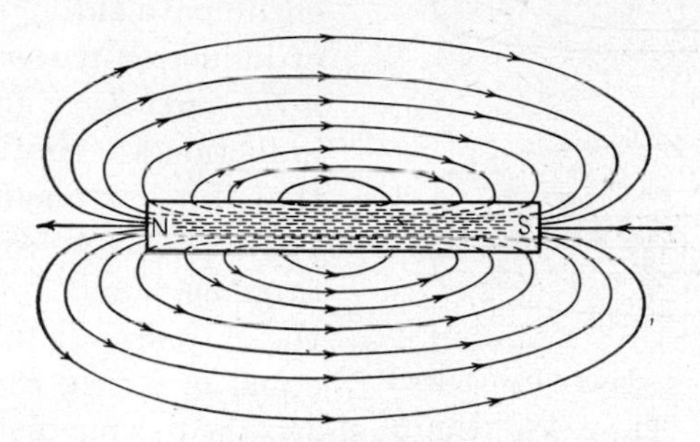

FIG 152. Magnetic field about a bar magnet.

Although magnetic influence itself is entirely invisible, its existence can be portrayed to the eye by *lines* whose directions coincide with the direction in which the magnetic influence is acting and the density of the lines can be made proportional to the intensity of the magnetic influence. Such magnetic lines are called *lines of force* and *lines of induction*. For example, in the bar magnet shown in Fig. 152 the magnetic influence is represented by lines which are shown to emerge from the left-hand end of the magnet and to enter at the right-hand end. In a magnet of the general shape shown in Fig. 152, the plane midway between the poles is the *neutral zone*, or *equator*, of the magnet. The magnetic lines are not necessarily confined to the ends of a magnet, but they may emerge or enter at any portion of the surface of the magnet, Figs. 152 and 154. Hence, a magnetic pole may be defined *as any surface from which magnetic lines are emerging or into which magnetic lines are entering*. The two poles are distinguished by the position which they seek if the magnet is suspended freely. The pole which points north is called the *north-seeking pole*, or *north pole* for short, and the other pole is the *south-seeking pole*, or *south pole*. Magnetic lines are assumed to leave the magnet at a north pole and to enter it at a south pole. As is shown in Sec. 155, the magnetic lines which are continuous, or which form closed loops, Fig. 152, are *lines of induction.* It follows that in a single magnet neither a *N* pole nor a *S* pole can exist alone. Also, all the *N* poles taken together must be equal magnetically to all the *S* poles taken together. That the *N* poles and *S* poles of a magnet are equal in strength is substantiated by the fact that when a magnet is free to move in a uniform magnetic field, like that of the earth, no tendency toward translation has ever been observed. The magnet merely tends to align itself in the direction of the field.

The influence of a magnet extends to a region well outside the magnet itself. The region in which magnetic influence exists constitutes the *magnetic field*, the presence of which is frequently represented by lines of force or lines of induction. The entire path through which the lines of induction pass is called the *magnetic circuit.* Since the lines of induction are continuous, it follows that if a bar magnet be broken, *N* poles and *S* poles appear on each fragment, and for each fragment the *N* poles all taken together are equal in strength to the *S* poles all taken together. Thus, Fig. 153(*b*) shows the bar magnet of (*a*) broken in two places. The continuity of the lines of induction causes an *S* pole to appear at the broken end of the fragment containing the original *N* pole and an *N* pole to appear at the broken end of the fragment containing the original *S* pole. The center fragment will also have an *N* and an *S* pole, as shown. However, the same number of lines of induction does not necessarily pass through each of the fragments, so that the *N* and *S* poles on one fragment are not necessarily equal to those on some other fragment.

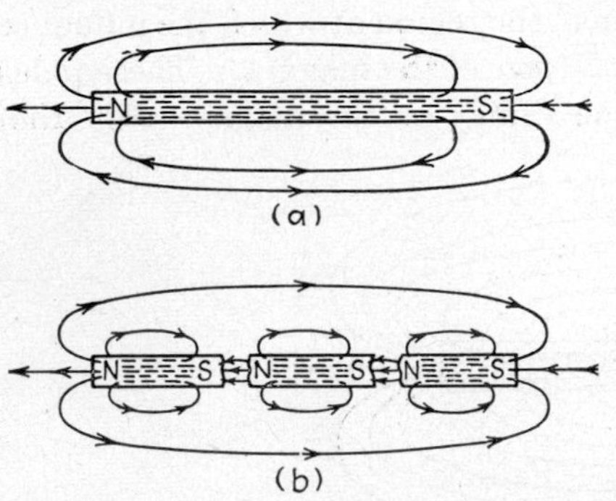

FIG. 153. Effect of breaking a bar magnet.

Consequent poles are poles which form on the sides of a magnet rather than at the ends. Such poles for a bar magnet are shown in Fig. 154. Consequent poles are occasionally found in bar magnets where different portions have been rubbed by an *N* pole or an *S* pole or when exciting coils, acting in opposition, have been placed over the bar. Consequent poles are in reality due to the fact that the bar consists of two or more magnets arranged so that two *N* or two *S* poles exist in the same portion of the magnet. Consequent poles are frequently produced on iron and steel bars due to their having come in contact with lifting magnets (see p. 244). Also, the recording of sound on steel wires and tapes is accomplished by means of consequent poles that are produced by a small tapered pole piece energized by the amplified voice currents.

Magnetic Figures. If a card be placed over a magnet and iron filings be sprinkled over the card, a magnetic figure is obtained. At each point the filings set themselves in the direction of the line of force at that point, and the resultant figure shows in detail the character of the magnetic field. Figure 155 shows the magnetic field due to two bar magnets placed side by side, with unlike poles adjacent. Note that the lines of force have the appearance of elastic bands attempting to pull the unlike poles together. It is true that *unlike poles attract each other, whereas like magnetic poles repel each other.*

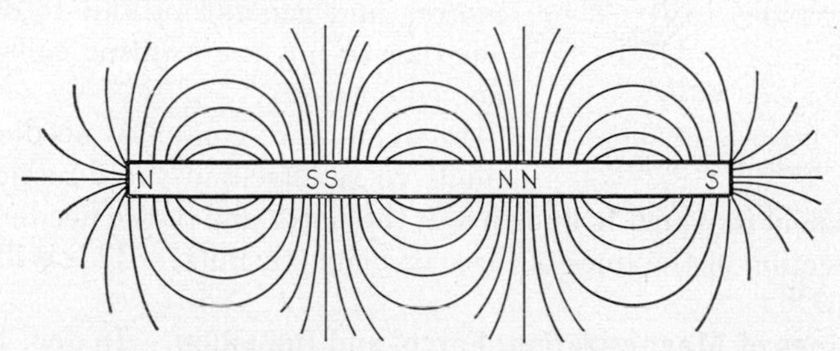

FIG. 154. Consequent poles.

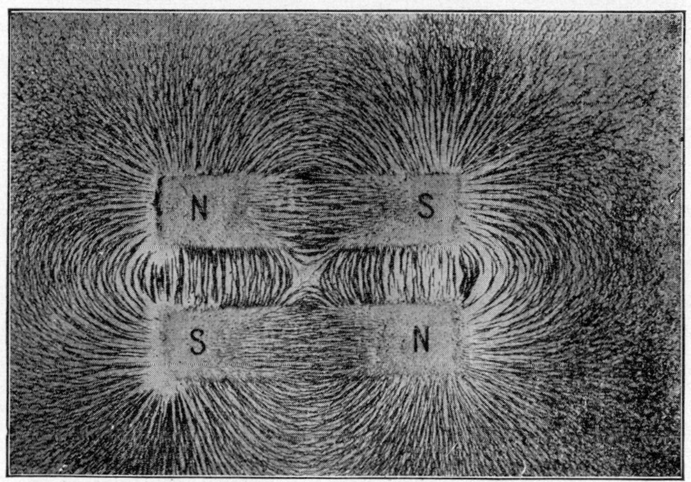

FIG. 155. Magnetic figure, unlike poles adjacent.

154. Compass Needle. The compass consists of a hardened-steel needle or small bar, permanently magnetized and accurately balanced upon a sharp pivot. The north-seeking end, or *N* pole, points north, and the south-seeking end, or *S* pole, points south. The *N* pole of the needle is frequently colored blue or is given some distinguishing mark. With the exception of a few magnet needles used for lecture purposes, the needle is enclosed in an airtight case for mechanical protection. Mariner's compasses are mounted carefully upon gimbals, so that they always remain level. Upon steel ships, heavy iron balls are placed near the compass to neutralize the magnetic effect of the ship itself.

By means of the compass needle, the polarity of a magnet is readily determined. The S pole of the compass needle points to the N pole of the magnet, Fig. 156. Likewise, the N pole of the compass needle points to the S pole of the magnet. This action of the compass needle follows immediately from the law that like poles repel and unlike poles attract each other. This is very useful in practical work, for it enables one to determine the polarity of the poles of motors and generators and to determine whether or not the exciting coils are connected correctly.

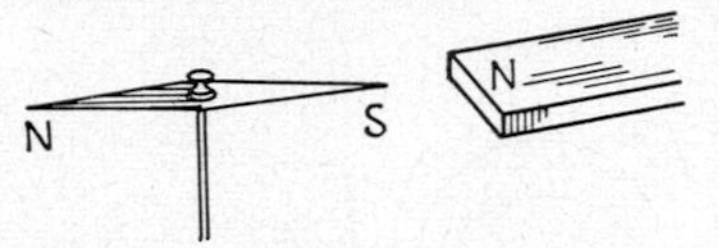

FIG. 156. Relation of direction of compass needle to N pole.

Further, the compass needle always tends to set itself in the direction of the magnetic field in which it finds itself, the north end of the needle pointing in the direction of the lines of force or magnetic lines. This is illustrated in Fig. 157.

155. Lines of Magnetization, Force, and Induction. In Sec. 153 reference is made to both "lines of force" and "lines of induction." The existence of the two types of lines, in accordance with a theory evolved by Ewing, explains many phenomena which occur with permanent mag-

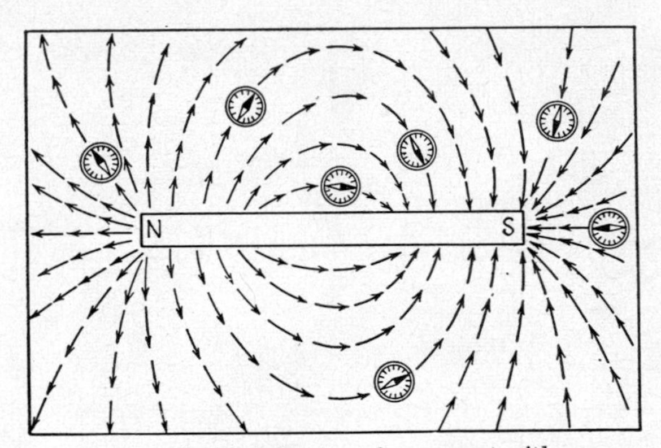

FIG. 157. Exploring field about bar magnet with compass.

nets, such as the lines of induction emerging from the sides of a bar magnet and the difficulty encountered in magnetizing bar magnets whose length is short compared with their cross-sectional dimensions. There is some disagreement with the theory, but it has long been accepted as offering simple explanations of several magnetic phenomena.

A magnet is considered as being made up of a number of very thin filaments, Fig. 158(a), and an inherent magnetizing force exists in each filament due to the domains having been brought into alignment by an external magnetizing force. Accordingly an N pole is produced at one end and a S pole at the other end of each filament. Experiments, as for example with a steel knitting needle, show that in this type of magnet the poles exist almost entirely at the ends. Owing to this inherent magnetizing force within the filament, *lines of magnetization* pass within the magnet from south to north, Fig. 158(*b*). The lines of magnetization remain entirely within the magnet, and were there no free poles at the ends, that is, were each filament closed on itself, these lines of magnetization would constitute the lines of induction also.

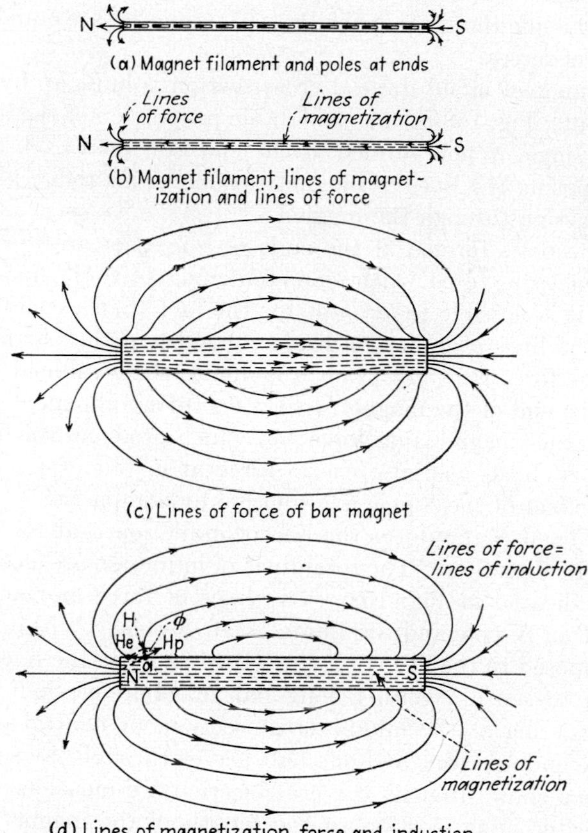

FIG. 158. Permanent magnetism in bar magnet.

However, because of the poles formed at the ends, *lines of force* leave the poles, Figs. 158(*a*) and (*b*). The cross section of the filaments is so small, however, that practically none of these lines passes back through the filament itself.

Lines of force *originate* on a *N* pole and *terminate* on a *S* pole and *are not closed lines.* This is indicated in Fig. 158(*b*), in which the solid lines are lines of force, and in Fig. 158(*c*), which shows roughly the lines of force in and about a bar magnet. The *lines of induction within the magnet* are defined as *the vector difference within the magnet of the lines of magnetization and the lines of force.* Since the lines of magnetization do not leave the magnet, it follows that in the region outside the magnet the lines of induction are equal in number to the lines of force. However, with very small filaments, Fig. 158(*b*), the number of lines of force passing back through the filament is negligible, so that within the filamentary magnet the lines of induction are essentially equal in number to the lines of magnetization; outside the magnet the lines of induction are equal in number to the lines of force.

As a bar magnet of substantial cross section is built up by combining these filaments, Fig. 158(*c*), a considerable proportion of the lines of force leaving the single N pole formed at the end now pass back through the magnet, opposing the lines of magnetization. This reduces the lines of induction passing through the magnet.

Hence, the poles formed at the ends of a magnet are the source of a countermagnetizing force which tends to demagnetize the magnet. With this theory it is possible to account for the fact that a considerable proportion of the lines of induction leave the sides of the bar magnet, Fig. 158(*d*). The force H at any point a is due to the combined effect of the N pole at the end of the magnet, which exerts a component of force H_p, and the internal magnetizing force H_e, which produces the lines of magnetization. (The S pole also exerts force at a, but at points near the N pole the effect of the S pole is negligible by comparison.) The resultant H of H_p and H_e produces the line of induction ϕ at the point a and determines its direction. The total lines of induction are closed and have the form indicated in Fig. 152. The lines of force are not closed but originate at an N pole and terminate at an S pole. Within the magnet they are opposed to the lines of magnetization, since the lines of force go from north to south. With a long bar magnet, one half the lines of induction existing at the middle cross section, or neutral plane, leaves through the end surfaces, and one half leaves through the sides.

Experience shows that as the cross-sectional dimensions of the poles become greater in proportion to the length of the magnet, permanent magnetization becomes more difficult.

It follows that the lines of magnetization, which are inherent within the magnet, originate at the S pole and pass through the magnet to the N pole; the lines of force originate at the N pole, pass through the air and the magnet, and terminate at the S pole; the lines of induction are continuous closed lines, passing outside the magnet from N pole to S pole and passing within the magnet from S pole to N pole.

The distinction of lines of magnetization, lines of force, and lines of induction should be kept clearly in mind.

The cgs unit of magnetic flux, whether in lines of force or lines of induction, is the *maxwell.*[1]

156. CGS Electromagnetic System of Units. It is obviously necessary that there be some system of units by which the magnitudes of such quantities as the strength of magnetic poles, the magnitudes of electric currents, voltages, inductances, capacitances, and other electrical quantities can be measured. Until 1935 there were three systems of electrical units in general use, the *cgs electromagnetic system,* the *cgs electrostatic system,* and the *practical system.* In 1935 the International Electrotechnical Commission adopted the mks (meter-kilogram-second) system, which so far as electrical quantities are concerned is identical with the practical system. Magnetic and electrical phenomena manifest themselves in several ways, such as the forces exerted between magnetic poles, forces acting on conductors carrying current in a magnetic field, forces between conductors carrying current, heating effects of current, and the dielectric breakdown of air between electrodes due to the applied voltage. However, it has been found most practicable to define electrical and magnetic quantities in terms of the mechanical quantities, force, work, and power. Force, work, and power are readily defined in terms of length L, mass M, and time T. The cgs electromagnetic system, based on the centimeter, gram, and second (cgs) as the units of length, mass, and time, was first proposed by the British Association for the Advancement of Science in 1873 and was adopted by the First Electrical Congress at Paris in 1881.[2]

The unit magnetic pole is based on the law of attraction and repulsion between unlike and like magnetic poles, which was first proved experimentally by Coulomb[3] in 1820. By means of a torsion balance, he found that attraction or repulsion between point magnetic poles was proportional to the pole strength and *inversely* proportional to the square of the distance between the poles. This is illustrated in Fig. 159.

In (a) two small N poles of m, m' units strength spaced a distance of

[1] After James Clerk Maxwell (1831–1879), an eminent British physicist who for more than half of his brief life held a prominent position in the very front rank of natural philosophers. Although he made admirable contributions to the subjects of mechanics and heat, his great contributions were in the field of electricity and magnetism. His work "Electricity and Magnetism," which appeared in 1873, is still considered to be one of the most outstanding scientific contributions of all time. In it he reduced all electric and magnetic phenomena to stresses in a material medium, expressing these facts by general mathematical equations. In addition he also deduced the electromagnetic theory of light and actually predicted the existence of electromagnetic (radio) waves years before their discovery by Hertz in 1888. He was also the first one to develop the theory of the *RLC* resonant a-c circuit.

[2] KENNELLY, ARTHUR E., "Magnetic Circuit Units," *Trans. AIEE,* Vol. 49, p. 486, 1930.

[3] See footnote, p. 29.

r cm repel each other with a force of **F** dynes; in (b) a small N pole of m units strength and a small S pole of m' units strength attract each other with a force of **F** dynes.

In a vacuum, the force between the poles

$$\mathbf{F} = \frac{mm'}{\mu_v r^2} \quad \text{dynes.} \tag{118}$$

where μ_v is a space constant, equal to 1 for vacuum. [(118) also applies in air with negligible error.]

In a medium of permeability μ_r, (118) becomes

$$\mathbf{F} = \frac{mm'}{\mu_v \mu_r r^2} \quad \text{dynes.} \tag{119}$$

Example. Two N poles, one having a strength of 500 units and the other a strength of 150 units, are placed a distance apart of 4 in. in air. Determine the force in grams acting between these poles and the direction in which the force is acting.

$$4 \text{ in.} = 4 \cdot 2.54 = 10.16 \text{ cm.}$$

Applying (118),

$$\mathbf{F} = \frac{500 \cdot 150}{(10.16)^2} = \frac{75{,}000}{103.2} = 726.6 \text{ dynes.}$$

$$\frac{726.6}{981} = 0.7407 \text{ g.} \quad \text{Poles repel each other.} \quad \textit{Ans.}$$

If in (118) the two poles are of equal strength, are spaced 1 cm apart, and the force is 1 dyne, $m = m' = 1$. Hence, under these conditions m and m' are *unit* cgs poles. Accordingly, the unit cgs pole is defined as follows:

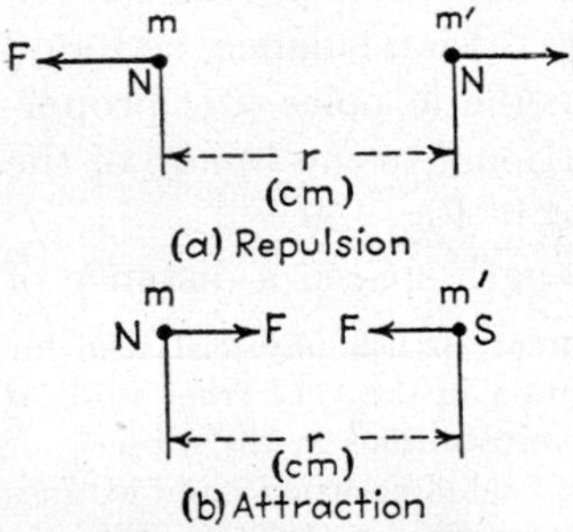

A unit cgs magnetic pole is one of such strength that if placed at a distance of one centimeter in a vacuum from a like pole of equal strength will repel it with a force of one dyne. Pole strength is measured by the number of such unit poles to which the pole is equivalent. The dimensions of pole strength in terms of length L, mass M, time T may be determined from (119). First, force $F = Ma = Mv/t = MLT^{-2}$, where a is acceleration in centimeters per second per second and v is velocity in centimeters per second. Hence, from (119), making $m' = m$, and letting $\mu = \mu_v \mu_r$, where μ_v is the permeability of evacuated space, which is taken as unity in the cgs electromagnetic system,

FIG. 159. Repulsion and attraction between magnetic poles.

$$MLT^{-2} = \frac{m^2}{\mu L^2}.$$

Pole strength, defined in terms of length, mass, and time, then becomes

$$m = \mu^{1/2}L^{3/2}M^{1/2}T^{-1} \qquad \text{maxwells.} \tag{120}$$

In the cgs electromagnetic system, L is given in centimeters, M in grams, T in seconds.

157. Field Intensity. It is stated that the force at a point acting on a magnetic pole in a magnetic field is proportional to the density of the lines of force at that point. *Unit field intensity is defined as the field strength which will act on a unit pole with a force of one dyne.* One *line of force* perpendicular to and passing through a square centimeter represents *unit field intensity.* Field intensity is given in *dynes per unit pole* and is represented by the symbol H.

In 1930, the International Electrotechnical Commission assigned the name *oersted* to the unit of field intensity in honor of Hans Christian Oersted[1] of Copenhagen, who in 1819 showed that a magnet tends to place itself at right angles to an electric current (Sec. 169, p. 228; also see p. 255).

If a pole of m units be placed in a field of intensity H, the force acting on this pole is

$$\mathbf{F} = m \cdot H \qquad \text{dynes.} \tag{121}$$

A pole placed in such a field must be of such small strength that it will have no appreciable disturbing effect on the magnetic field.

Example. When a small pole having a strength of 25 unit poles is placed in a magnetic field, it is acted on with a force of 200 dynes. Determine the field intensity at this point.

The force per unit pole

$$H = 200 \div 25 = 8 \text{ dynes per unit pole, or 8 oersteds.} \quad \textit{Ans.}$$

It also follows that the density of the lines of force, taken for an area perpendicular to the direction of these lines, is 8 lines per square centimeter, or 8 gauss (see Sec. 158).

Example. A total flux of 200,000 maxwells exists in air between two parallel pole faces, each 8 cm square. The field is uniform. Determine the force in grams acting on an N pole having a strength of 100 cgs units, when placed in this field.

Flux density $= 200{,}000/(8 \cdot 8) = 3{,}125$ maxwells per sq cm, or 3,125 gauss. Being in air this value of flux density is also equal numerically to the field intensity H.

$$\mathbf{F} = m \cdot H = 100 \cdot 3{,}125 = 312{,}500 \text{ dynes.}$$

$$312{,}500 \div 981 = 318.6 \text{ g.} \quad \textit{Ans.}$$

158. Flux Density and Pole Strength. Flux density is the number of maxwells per unit area taken perpendicular to the induction. In free

[1] Hans Christian Oersted (1777–1851), a Danish physicist who at first studied medicine but in 1806 was appointed professor of physics at the University of Copenhagen. In 1829 he became director of the Polytechnic of the same city and in 1850 privy councilor. His outstanding works were the establishment of the intimate interrelations of electricity, "galvanic" currents, and magnetism.

space, flux density and field intensity are the same numerically, but within magnetic material the two are quite different. The two should not be confused. The cgs unit of flux density (one maxwell per square centimeter) is the *gauss*.[1]

By definition, the force exerted by a unit pole upon another unit pole at centimeter distance in air is one dyne. The field intensity on a spherical surface of one centimeter radius and with a unit pole at its center must then be unity and can be represented by one line per square centimeter over the entire spherical surface, Fig. 160.

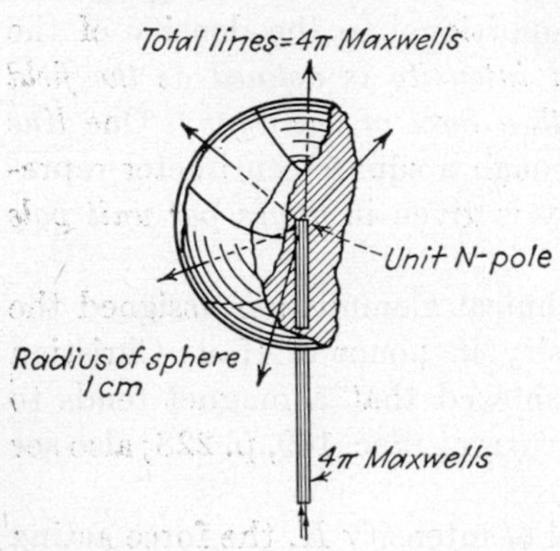

FIG. 160. Lines of force leaving unit N pole.

Since there are 4π sq cm on the surface of a sphere of 1 cm radius, each unit pole must have 4π, or 12.57, maxwells leaving it.[2] Figure 160 represents a portion of a spherical surface of 1 cm radius and shows the passage of 1 maxwell through each square centimeter of surface, each line originating in the unit N pole. This also explains the appearance of the 4π term encountered so often in magnetic formulas: $4\pi m$ lines of force leave a N pole having a strength of m units.

Consider a bar magnet with a cross section of A sq cm, Fig. 161, having magnetic poles of m units strength at each end. The *intensity of magnetization*, or the number of unit poles per unit area at each end, is

$$\sigma = \frac{m}{A} \quad \text{unit poles per sq cm.} \qquad (122)$$

[1] After Karl Friedrich Gauss (1777–1855), a German mathematician and astronomer, who was director of the Göttingen Observatory from 1807 until his death. He became much interested in the study of the earth's magnetism and in conjunction with Weber invented new apparatus for its measurement, apparatus of the same type being still in use. In 1833, with Weber's assistance, he erected a magnetic observatory at Göttingen almost entirely free from iron, where he made many valuable magnetic observations of the earth's magnetism. He wrote a large number of papers on mathematical and magnetic subjects. His work resulted in a number of important contributions to the knowledge of magnetism.

[2] Obviously the magnetic flux does not leave in individual lines but occupies the entire field, filling it uniformly if the field is uniform. The actual condition is represented by *tubes of force* (an expression originated by Faraday, p. 326), the axis of each tube coinciding with the direction of the field. With the unit pole, there would be 4π, or 12.57, tubes of force. Each tube is represented by a single line at its axis as in Fig. 160. The conception of tubes of force explains the possibility of the fractional 0.57 line. At the surface of a sphere of unit radius, the cross-sectional area of each of the 12 tubes of force is 1 sq cm, and the area of the remaining tube of force is 0.57 sq cm (4π = 12.57). In air or vacuum, tubes of induction would coincide with the tubes of force.

Since $4\pi m$ maxwells must either leave or enter the magnet at each pole, the total flux at the center zone of the magnet is $\phi_0 + 4\pi m$ maxwells, where ϕ_0 is the flux which would exist in space were no magnetic material present. Using (122), the flux density

$$B = \frac{\phi_0 + 4\pi m}{A} = B_0 + 4\pi\sigma \quad \text{gauss.} \tag{123}$$

Practically, B_0 is almost always negligible compared with $4\pi\sigma$, and (123) may be written

$$B = 4\pi\sigma \quad \text{gauss.} \tag{124}$$

Example. A cylindrical bar magnet is 20 cm long and has a diameter of 0.5 cm. The N and S poles at the ends have a strength of 40 cgs units. Determine: (*a*) intensity of magnetization; (*b*) flux density at surface of a sphere having a radius of 2 cm and its center at either pole, assuming point poles; (*c*) force on a pole of 8 units strength at surface of the sphere; (*d*) flux density at center zone of bar magnet.

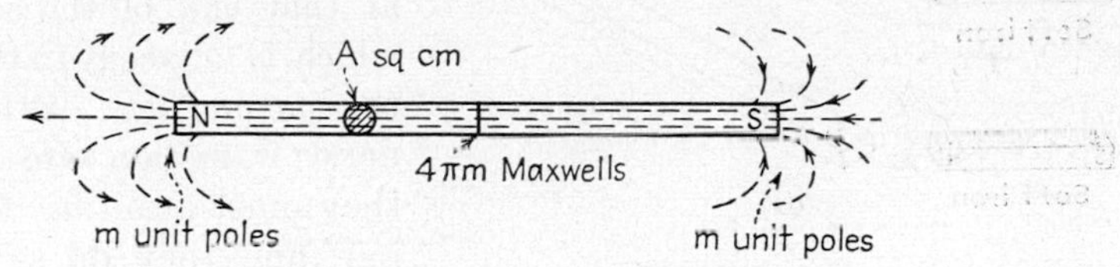

FIG. 161. Flux density and pole strength.

(*a*) Cross section of magnet is $\frac{\pi}{4}(0.5)^2 = 0.1964$ sq cm.

From (122), $\sigma = 40/0.1964 = 203.7$ unit poles per sq cm. *Ans.*

(*b*) Total maxwells leaving N pole $= 40 \cdot 4\pi = 502.7$.

Area of surface of sphere $= 4\pi(2)^2 = 50.27$ sq cm.

Flux density $= \dfrac{502.7}{50.27} = 10.0$ gauss. *Ans.*

(*c*) Field intensity is 10.0 oersteds.

From (121), force on pole of 8.0 units, $\mathbf{F} = 8.0 \cdot 10 = 80.0$ dynes. *Ans.*

(*d*) From (124), $B = 4\pi \cdot 203.7 = 2{,}561$ gauss. *Ans.*

Note that (*c*) can be solved using (118).

$$\mathbf{F} = \frac{40 \cdot 8}{(2)^2} = 80 \text{ dynes } (\textit{check}).$$

A study of Fig. 160 explains why the force between point poles varies inversely as the square of the distance, as given in (118) and (119). The area of the surfaces of spheres having their center at either magnetic pole varies as the square of their radii. Hence, the density of the lines of force intercepted by each sphere must vary inversely as its area and hence inversely as the square of its radius. Thus the field intensity produced by a point pole varies inversely as the square of the distance from the pole.

159. Induced Magnetism. If a magnet is brought near a piece of soft, nonmagnetized iron, the piece of iron becomes *magnetized by induction.* If the N pole of the magnet is brought near the soft iron, an S pole is induced in that part of the iron nearest the inducing magnet, and if the S pole of the magnet is brought near the iron, an N pole is similarly induced. This is illustrated in Fig. 162(a).

The reason why an N pole induces an S pole and an S pole induces an N pole is illustrated in Fig. 162(b). The lines of induction which leave the N pole of the bar magnet will concentrate in the soft iron, because iron permits the passage of magnetic lines far better than air does. Since the magnetic lines which leave the N pole of the bar magnet must *enter* the soft iron at the end which is adjacent to the N pole of the bar magnet, an S pole is formed at that end of the soft-iron bar which is adjacent to the N pole of the bar magnet. As lines of magnetic induction are continuous, they must also *leave* the soft-iron bar, and they do so at the end which is more remote from the magnetizing N pole. Hence an N pole is formed at the more remote end of the soft-iron bar.

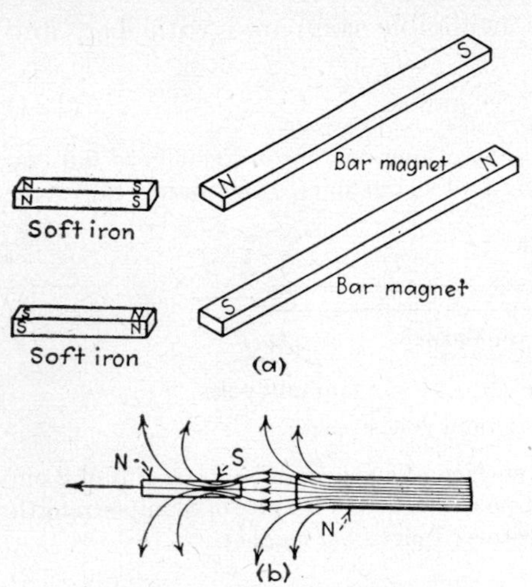

Fig. 162. Induced magnetic poles.

The inducing N pole attracts the induced S pole and repels the induced N pole on the soft iron. As the induced S pole is nearer to the inducing pole, attraction predominates.

It is sometimes noticed that if a comparatively weak N pole be brought into the vicinity of a strong N pole, attraction between the two results, rather than the repulsion which might be expected. This is no violation of the laws governing the attraction and repulsion of magnetic poles but is due to the fact that the strong N pole induces an S pole which overpowers the existing weak N pole and hence attraction results. In this way it is easy to reverse the polarity of a compass needle by holding one end close to a strong magnetic pole of the same polarity.

160. Law of Magnetic Field. *The magnetic field always tends to conform itself so that the maximum amount of flux is attained.* This offers further explanation of the attraction of iron to poles of magnets. The iron is drawn toward the magnet so that the magnetic lines may utilize the iron as a part of their path, since iron conducts these lines much better than air. This is illustrated by the action of a horseshoe magnet in attracting an armature to its poles. As the armature is drawn toward the poles the return path through the air is materially shortened, so that the number of magnetic lines is materially increased. The maximum flux exists when the armature is in contact with the poles.

161. Force Due to Distributed Pole. It is already shown that Coulomb's law, which states that the force between magnetic poles varies inversely as the square of the distance [Eqs. (118) and (119)], assumes that the poles are concentrated at points. Usually, however, magnetic poles are distributed over surfaces of considerable area and under these conditions Coulomb's inverse-squares law does not apply to the pole as a whole. To find the effect of the entire polar surface, the law of inverse squares must be applied to the poles of differential area or to the point poles, which make up the polar surface. The effect of the entire polar surface can then be obtained by integration. The field intensity at any point on a perpendicular erected at the center of a circular magnetic pole can be easily determined. Thus, Fig. 163 shows a bar magnet having a radius of R cm and an intensity of magnetization of σ unit magnetic poles per square centimeter. Since field intensity is measured by the dynes per unit pole, a unit pole is shown at P on a perpendicular erected at the center of the polar surface and h cm distant from it.

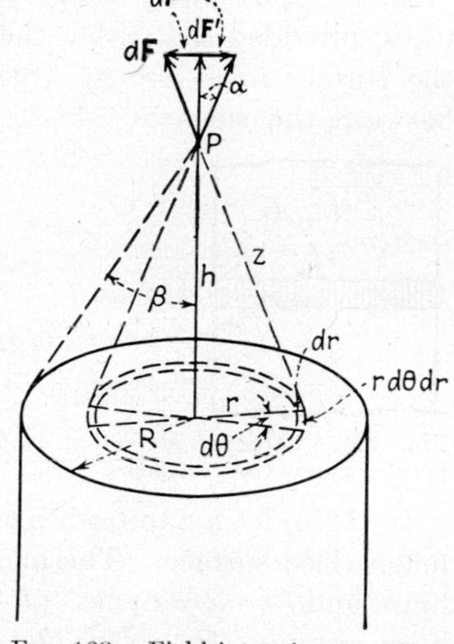

FIG. 163. Field intensity on axis of bar magnet.

An annular ring of r cm radius and dr cm radial width is drawn. Let $d\theta$ be a differential angle. Then the differential area in the ring intercepted by the angle $d\theta$ is $r\,d\theta\,dr$ sq cm, and the differential pole strength is $\sigma r\,d\theta\,dr$ unit poles. The force $d\mathbf{F}$ at P due to the differential pole is $\sigma r\,d\theta\,dr/Z^2$ dynes. The component $d\mathbf{F}'$ along the perpendicular h is $d\mathbf{F}\cos\alpha$ dynes.

The component $d\mathbf{F}''$ perpendicular to $d\mathbf{F}'$ will be balanced by an equal, but opposite component due to the differential area diametrically opposite to the one under consideration. Hence, all such components cancel one another. Noting that $Z^2 = h^2 + r^2$, and $\cos\alpha = h/\sqrt{h^2 + r^2}$, the total force due to the magnetized surface,

$$\mathbf{F} = \sigma \int_0^{2\pi} \int_0^R \frac{r\,d\theta\,dr\cos\alpha}{Z^2} = \sigma \int_0^{2\pi} \int_0^R \frac{hr\,d\theta\,dr}{(h^2 + r^2)^{3/2}}$$

$$= 2\pi\sigma h \int_0^R \frac{r\,dr}{(h^2 + r^2)^{3/2}} = 2\pi\sigma h \left[\frac{-1}{\sqrt{r^2 + h^2}}\right]_0^R$$

$$= 2\pi\sigma h \left[\frac{-1}{\sqrt{R^2 + h^2}} + \frac{1}{h}\right] = 2\pi\sigma \left(1 - \frac{h}{\sqrt{R^2 + h^2}}\right) \quad \text{dynes.} \qquad (125)$$

$$\mathbf{F} = 2\pi\sigma\,(1 - \cos\beta) \quad \text{dynes,} \qquad (126)$$

where β is the angle subtended by the radius of the circular pole.

Example. In the example, p. 215, determine the force due to the N pole at a point P outside and on the axis of the magnet, 0.5 cm from the N pole.

$$\sigma = 40 \Big/ \left[\frac{\pi}{4}(0.5)^2\right] = 203.7 \text{ unit poles per sq cm;}$$

$$\cos\beta = \frac{0.5}{\sqrt{(0.25)^2 + (0.5)^2}} = 0.8945;$$

$$\mathbf{F} = H = 2\pi \cdot 203.7\,(1 - 0.8945) = 135.0 \text{ dynes per unit pole or oersteds.} \quad \textit{Ans.}$$

162. Force between Magnetized Parallel Surfaces. By means of (125) it is possible to compute the force acting between magnetized surfaces, provided that either the distance between such surfaces is small or the surface areas are so large that a substantially uniform field exists between the surfaces. First, it should be pointed out that magnetic lines are essentially normal to magnetized surfaces such as those of iron, when they either enter or leave the air. Otherwise there would be a component of magnetic force tangential to the surface. Usually, except under highly saturated conditions, such tangential components are negligible.

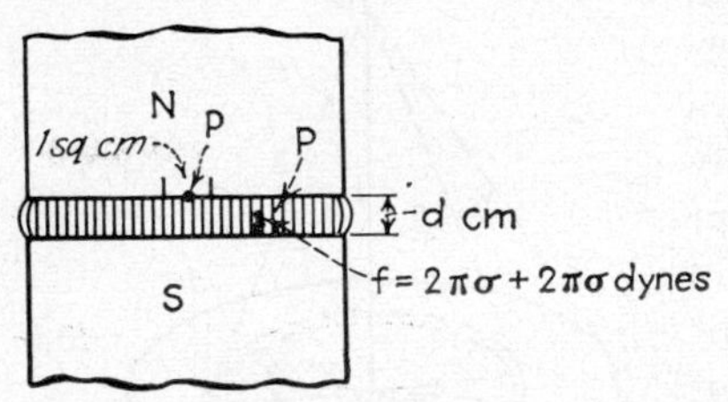

Fig. 164. Force of attraction between parallel magnetized surfaces.

In (125), let h approach zero, bringing unit N pole P very close to the magnetized surface. The angle β in (126) approaches $\pi/2$, or 90°, as a limit, and $F = 2\pi\sigma$ dynes. P is so close to the surface that the magnetic lines are normal. Next, let R approach infinity, h remaining finite. Under these conditions the fringing of the magnetic flux at the edges of the surface is so far removed that it has no effect on the region under consideration. Under these conditions the field where the point P is located must be uniform, and (125) and (126) become

$$\mathbf{F} = H = 2\pi\sigma \quad \text{oersteds.} \tag{127}$$

Now consider two magnetic poles of opposite polarity having parallel surfaces of equal area separated by a short air-gap, d cm in length, Fig. 164. The area of each pole face is A sq cm, and the magnetization is uniform over the two pole faces. Let the number of unit poles per square centimeter of each surface be σ. If the length of air-gap d is small compared with the length and breadth of the poles, the lines of force between the surfaces may be considered as straight, parallel, and uniformly distributed, except for a small number of lines at the edges of the poles.

P is a unit N pole in the field. The force acting on such a unit pole must be $2\pi\sigma$ dynes due to each pole, or each magnetized surface, so that the total force, or field intensity,

$$H = 2\pi\sigma + 2\pi\sigma = 4\pi\sigma \quad \text{oersteds.} \tag{128}$$

(128) may be verified, since from Eq. (126), $B = 4\pi\sigma$ gauss, which is equal numerically to the field intensity H. The field intensity H in (128) is independent of the position of the pole P since this field everywhere in the gap is uniform (except at the edges).

Now consider the unit pole p as placed on the surface of the N pole. The S pole will attract it with a force of $2\pi\sigma$ dynes. However, there are σ unit poles in each square centimeter of the N pole. Hence, the S pole will exert a force of $2\pi\sigma^2$ dynes on each square centimeter of the N pole. Therefore, the total force exerted by the S pole on the N pole must be

$$\mathbf{F} = 2\pi\sigma^2 A \quad \text{dynes.} \tag{129}$$

Since the flux density $B = H = 4\pi\sigma$ (numerically),

$$\mathbf{F} = 2\pi\sigma^2 A = \frac{B^2 A}{8\pi} \quad \text{dynes} \tag{130}$$

where B = maxwells per sq cm, or gauss.
Also, since 981 dynes = 1 g force, the force

$$\mathbf{F} = \frac{B^2 A}{24.64} \quad \text{kg,} \tag{131}$$

if B is expressed in kilomaxwells per square centimeter. If B is expressed in maxwells per square inch and A in square inches,

$$\mathbf{F} = \frac{B^2 A}{72{,}130{,}000} \quad \text{lb.} \tag{132}$$

Example. The iron core of a solenoid is 2 in. diameter, and a uniform flux of 200,000 lines passes from the end of the core into an iron armature of equal area. Determine the force of attraction in pounds between the core and the armature.

$$A = \frac{\pi}{4}(2)^2 = 3.142 \text{ sq in.}$$

$$B = \frac{200{,}000}{3.142} = 63{,}650 \text{ maxwells per sq in.}$$

$$\mathbf{F} = \frac{63{,}650^2 \cdot 3.142}{72{,}130{,}000} = 176.5 \text{ lb.} \quad \textit{Ans.}$$

Stored Energy. If, in (130), the surfaces are permitted to move toward each other a distance of 1 cm, the work done would be $B^2A/8\pi$ ergs. Hence, it follows that the energy stored per cubic centimeter in air is

$$W = \frac{B^2}{8\pi} \quad \text{ergs.} \tag{133}$$

MKS SYSTEMS

163. Meter-Kilogram-Second (MKS) System. In Sec. 156 (p. 211) it is pointed out that until 1935, when the mks system was adopted by the IEC, there were three systems of electrical units in general use. Inherently it is difficult to devise a system of electrical units which come within the range of practical magnitudes (such as the volt, ampere, watt) and which at the same time are based on physical units whose magnitudes adapt them to practical usage (such as the meter, kilogram, and second) [see Eq. (120), p. 213]. For example, in the cgs electromagnetic system the unit of potential difference is only $1/10^8$ the magnitude of the volt, and the unit of resistance is only $1/10^9$ the magnitude of the ohm. Maxwell pointed out that a dimensional system having the unit of length 10^9 cm and the unit of mass 10^{-11} g could be the basis of the practical system, but the magnitudes of these units obviously deviate so far from those which are in common usage that the system would be impracticable. In 1901 G. Giorgi of Italy showed that if the permeability μ_v of evacuated space be taken as 10^{-7}, a practical system of units having the meter as the unit of length, the kilogram as the unit of mass, and the second as the unit of time is possible. In 1904 Ascoli, a colleague of Giorgi, pointed out that with the unit of time the second, there are innumerable practical systems which need only follow the rule $2 \cdot l + m = 7$, where 10^l cm is the unit of length and 10^m g is the unit of mass. Then in Maxwell's system $2 \cdot 9 - 11 = 7$ and in Giorgi's system $2 \cdot 2 + 3 = 7$.

The Giorgi system is the basis of the mks system adopted by the IEC in 1935. Although basic quantities, the meter, the kilogram, and the second have magnitudes that adapt them to practical use, it is necessary that density be 1 kg per cu m, which is 1/1,000 that of water.

At present there are two mks systems, the *unrationalized* and the *rationalized*. In the unrationalized system 4π webers[1] leave or enter each unit pole, the mmf is $4\pi NI$, where NI is ampere-turns, and the permeability of evacuated space is $\mu_v = 10^{-7}$. In the rationalized system, 1 weber leaves or enters each unit pole, and the unit of mmf is the ampere-turn. In computing the force between point poles, permeability must be taken as $(4\pi)^2 10^{-7}$, as in Eq. (136). On the other hand, in computing the reluctance or permeance of a magnetic circuit a value $\mu_v' = 4\pi \cdot 10^{-7}$ must be used [see Eq. (187), p. 273]. With either system the permeability of magnetic materials, μ_r, called *relative permeability*, is a number. There is no agreement as to which system is standard. On account of the convenience in using the ampere-turn as the unit of mmf, the rationalized system appears to be more commonly used. In the text examples will be given using both the unrationalized system and the rationalized system.

[1] The weber is the mks unit of magnetic flux = 10^8 maxwells. It is named after Wilhelm Eduard Weber (1804–1891), a German physicist, who for most of his life occupied the chair of professor of physics at Göttingen. He showed, as did his colleague Gauss for magnetic quantities, that electrical quantities could be defined absolutely in terms of length, mass, and time. He also conducted researches in magnetism and invented a system of electromagnetic telegraphy.

It should be pointed out that μ_v and μ_v' are quite different physically from μ_r. μ_v and μ_v' are *space constants* and correspond to the gravitational constant; μ_r is a property of magnetic materials and is dependent on the mmfs of the spinning electrons.

The mks system also requires a new unit of force. This unit is equal to 10^5 dynes, or one joule per meter, and is called the *newton*.[1]

164. MKS Magnetic Poles. The relation of the mks unit magnetic pole (unrationalized) to the cgs unit magnetic pole is readily determined from Eq. (118) (p. 212). Consider two unit mks poles m', m', spaced 1 meter apart in free space. From definition the force acting between the two poles is 1 newton. That is,

$$\mathbf{F} = \frac{m'^2}{\mu_v(1)^2} = 1 \text{ newton.} \qquad \text{(I)}$$

Now determine the number of cgs unit poles which, with the same spacing, will be repelled with the same force of 1 newton or 10^5 dynes.

$$10^5 = \frac{m^2}{\mu(1 \cdot 10^2)^2}. \qquad \text{(II)}$$

Dividing (II) by (I), noting that $\mu_v = 10^{-7}$ and $\mu = 1$,

$$\frac{m^2}{m'^2} = 10^{16}, \qquad \text{or} \qquad m = 10^8\, m'. \qquad (134)$$

That is, it requires 10^8 cgs unit poles to produce the same force as 1 mks unrationalized unit pole, so that the mks pole must have a magnitude 10^8 that of the cgs unit pole. The factor 10^8 is also the ratio of the magnitude of the weber to the maxwell.

It follows, since 4π magnetic lines must leave or enter each unit pole, that the weber, the mks unit of flux, must have 10^8 the magnitude of the maxwell, the cgs unit of flux.

[1] After Sir Isaac Newton (1642–1727), English natural philosopher, born at Woolsthorpe. At the age of fourteen he was taken from school to assist on his widowed mother's farm, but he occupied himself with mathematics rather than farm work. Through the good offices of his uncle, he was enabled to attend Trinity College, Cambridge University, from which he graduated in 1665. He was elected a fellow in 1667 and Lucasian professor of mathematics in 1669. He discovered what is now the binomial theorem and was an originator of differential and integral calculus. He did much to promote the theory of light and color and developed lenses and eyepieces for telescopes, and also the reflecting telescope, in which there is no chromatic aberration. His proof that the planets and stars could be treated as points with their masses concentrated at their centers and his development of the laws of mechanics and their applications to the motions of celestial bodies were his other outstanding contributions. He was president of the Royal Society for a number of years, was appointed Warden of the Mint, and in 1705 was knighted by Queen Anne.

The force acting between poles of M_1, M_2 units strength is

$$\mathbf{F} = \frac{M_1 M_2}{\mu_v R^2} \quad \text{newtons.} \tag{135}$$

Example. An mks point pole has a strength of 10^{-4} mks unit poles (= 10,000 cgs unit poles). Determine force in newtons on (*a*) a point mks pole of $1.5 \cdot 10^{-4}$ unit poles at a distance of 10 cm; (*b*) on a point mks unit pole at same distance.

(*a*) Using (135),

$$\mathbf{F} = \frac{(1 \cdot 10^{-4})(1.5 \cdot 10^{-4})}{10^{-7}(10^{-1})^2} = 15 \text{ newtons.} \quad \textit{Ans.}$$

$$(b)\ \mathbf{F} = \frac{10^{-4} \cdot 1}{10^{-7}(10^{-1})^2} = 10^5 \text{ newtons.} \quad \textit{Ans.}$$

(This also gives the field intensity in ampere-turns per meter. That is, $H = B/\mu_v$.) Since $4\pi \cdot 10^{-4}$ weber must come from the pole and the area of the spherical surface with 10 cm radius is $4\pi(10^{-1})^2$ sq m, $B = (4\pi \cdot 10^{-4})/4\pi(10^{-1})^2 = 10^{-2}$ weber per sq m. Hence $H = 10^{-2}/10^{-7} = 10^5$ amp-turns per m.

Example. Determine in unrationalized mks units the force on a unit pole on the axis of a cylindrical magnet, Fig. 163, 0.5 cm from the end, as is done in Sec. 161 (p. 217).

The equation will be identical with (126) except that μ_v will appear in the denominator. The force will be in newtons. The number of unit mks poles is $40/10^8 = 4 \cdot 10^{-7}$. The intensity of magnetization,

$$\sigma = \frac{4 \cdot 10^{-7}}{(\pi/4)(0.5 \cdot 10^{-2})^2} = 2.037 \cdot 10^{-2} \text{ pole per sq m.}$$

$$\begin{aligned} \mathbf{F} &= \frac{2\pi \cdot 2.037 \cdot 10^{-2}}{10^{-7}}(1 - 0.8945) \\ &= 1.350 \cdot 10^5 \text{ newtons per unit mks pole.} \quad \textit{Ans.} \\ \mathbf{F}' &= 1.350 \cdot 10^{-3} \text{ newton per unit cgs pole} \\ &= 1.350 \cdot 10^2 \text{ dynes per unit cgs pole } (\textit{check}). \end{aligned}$$

165. Rationalized MKS System. It has long been considered advantageous that the mmf be expressed by ampere-turns, NI, rather than by $4\pi NI$ as in the unrationalized system. In order that with a given number of ampere-turns the flux may be the same, it is necessary that $4\pi\mu_v = 4\pi \cdot 10^{-7} = \mu_v'$ be used rather than μ_v, as is demonstrated in Sec. 198 (p. 273). It is shown (p. 220) that in the rationalized system only 1 weber enters or leaves a unit pole. Hence, the rationalized unit pole has only $1/4\pi$ the magnitude of the unrationalized unit pole. The equation for the force between poles in free space becomes

$$\mathbf{F} = \frac{M_1' M_2'}{4\pi \cdot 4\pi \cdot \mu_v R^2} = \frac{M_1' M_2'}{4\pi\mu_v' R^2} = 6.329 \cdot 10^4 \frac{M_1' M_2'}{R^2} \quad \text{newtons.} \tag{136}$$

Example. Solve (*a*) in the first example, Sec. 164, using rationalized mks poles. 10^{-4} unrationalized poles are equal to $4\pi \cdot 10^{-4}$ rationalized poles; $1.5 \cdot 10^{-4}$ unrationalized poles are equal to $4\pi \cdot 1.5 \cdot 10^{-4}$ rationalized poles.

Using (136),

$$\mathbf{F} = \frac{(4\pi \cdot 10^{-4})(4\pi \cdot 1.5 \cdot 10^{-4})}{(4\pi)^2 10^{-7} \cdot (10^{-1})^2} = 15 \text{ newtons.} \quad \textit{Ans.}$$

Example. Solve the second example, Sec. 164, using rationalized mks poles at the end of the magnet and a rationalized unit pole.

The number of rationalized mks poles is $\dfrac{40}{(10^8/4\pi)} = 5.027 \cdot 10^{-6}$.

$$\sigma = \frac{5.027 \cdot 10^{-6}}{(\pi/4)(0.5 \cdot 10^{-2})^2} = 0.2560 \text{ pole per sq m.}$$

Using Eq. (126) converted to the mks rationalized pole,

$$\begin{aligned} \mathbf{F} &= \frac{2\pi\sigma}{(4\pi)^2 10^{-7}} (1 - \cos\beta) = \left(\frac{2\pi \cdot 0.2560 \cdot 10^7}{(4\pi)^2}\right)(1 - 0.8945) \\ &= 1.075 \cdot 10^4 \text{ newtons.} \quad \textit{Ans.} \\ \mathbf{F}' &= \frac{1.075 \cdot 10^4}{10^8/4\pi} = 1.350 \cdot 10^{-3} \text{ newton per unit cgs pole} \\ &= 1.350 \cdot 10^2 \text{ dynes per unit cgs pole } (\textit{check}). \end{aligned}$$

166. Permanent-magnet Materials (Steel). Permanent magnets depend for their operation on the ability of steel and other magnetic alloys to retain a substantial proportion of the magnetic flux which has been produced in them by some external magnetizing force. Permanent magnets not only must retain their magnetism after the magnetizing force has been removed but also must maintain it when used in connection with air gaps, soft-iron pole pieces, and other parts of magnetic circuits to which they may be required to supply magnetic flux. The properties of magnetic materials which account for permanent magnetism are discussed in Secs. 148 and 150 (pp. 196 and 200). It is pointed out that magnetism is produced by the turning of the domains by some external magnetizing force so that their individual magnetic poles act in the same direction. The domains which are most difficult to turn are, however, most valuable in producing permanent magnets in that it is difficult to force them from their locked positions. Referring to the portion of the hysteresis loop shown in Fig. 149 (p. 202), when the magnetizing force is removed, that is, when H is reduced to zero, a large number of the domains remain locked in position, producing the *remanence* B_r given by the ordinate *od*. The magnetic flux can be brought to zero only by the application of a *coercive* force $H_c = of$. The application of the coercive force H_c, however, does not destroy all the magnetism, for if the coercive force is removed, positive magnetism will appear again as is indicated by the ordinate *od′*.

The entire performance of permanent magnets is given by the portion of the hysteresis loop lying in the second quadrant, such as *def*, Fig. 149, which often is called the *demagnetization curve*. The area of this part of the hysteresis loop to scale divided by 4π gives the magnetic energy in ergs per cubic centimeter stored in the magnet. This area, in general, is the criterion of the suitability of permanent-magnet materials, although as is shown later (p. 276 *et seq.*), some applications require higher degrees of remanence and others higher degrees of coercive force.

In the early days, carbon tool steel was used for permanent magnets. This was followed by tungsten steel, the cobalt-chromium alloys, and last by the Alnico alloys. The permanent-magnet characteristics of the Alnicos are so far superior to those of all alloys that had heretofore developed that they have almost entirely superseded these earlier alloys. Since an understanding of permanent-magnet phenomena requires a knowledge of electromagnetism, the detailed description of the materials, their properties, and the operation of the magnets is given in Chap. VIII (p. 276 *et seq.*).

167. Applications. As is already stated, the discovery and development of the Alnico alloys have extended many times the applications of permanent magnets and in many cases have revolutionized the design of apparatus. Many devices employing the older magnetic materials have been redesigned to become more compact and usually more efficient. In many applications, permanent magnets have replaced electromagnets, with the advantages of eliminating the exciting coil and the connecting leads, which frequently involve sliding contacts. Also, permanent magnets do not consume energy, and there is no heating. The use of Alnico magnets in electrical instruments is described in Chap. V (see Figs. 103 and 104, pp. 152 and 153).

The ignition magneto is an example of making the design compact and efficient. It will be remembered that with the older magnets the magnetism was supplied by several large horseshoe magnets, which formed a compound magnet. In Fig. 165 is shown a modern ignition magneto in the design of which advantage is taken of the strong magnetic fields produced by Alnico magnets. Two Alnico bar magnets are inserted in the soft-iron magnetic circuit as shown. A primary and a secondary coil are used on the yoke. When the soft-iron armature is in the position shown, the flux goes through the yoke and hence through the coils from left to right. When the armature turns 90°, tracing the path of the flux will show that it now goes through the yoke, and hence the coils, from right to left. Hence, the coils are linked by an alternating flux which, with assistance by the interrupter, induces a high-voltage emf in the secondary which is supplied to the spark plugs.

There are many advantages in using permanent magnets for magnetic chucks, such as there being no necessity for a d-c power supply, the absence of exciting coils, connecting leads, slip rings if the chuck is a rotating one, and there being no heating which may change the shape and dimensions of the workpiece. In Fig. 166 is shown one form of magnetic chuck as manufactured by the Brown and Sharpe Company. The permanent magnets A, A, are in contact with a soft-steel bottom plate Y

which acts as a yoke. Between each two permanent bar magnets *A*, *A*, there is a soft-steel conductor bar *B* which acts as a return path for the magnetic flux, as indicated. On top of each permanent magnet and each conductor bar there is a soft-steel pole piece *P* which has the same cross section as the magnet or conductor bar with which it is associated.

These pole pieces have considerable length in the direction perpendicular to the paper and so are actually bars, and they are integrated into a solid faceplate by being held together with a nonmagnetic metal. The spaces between the pole pieces are also filled with the nonmagnetic metal, so that the faceplate surface is smooth and continuous. The design in

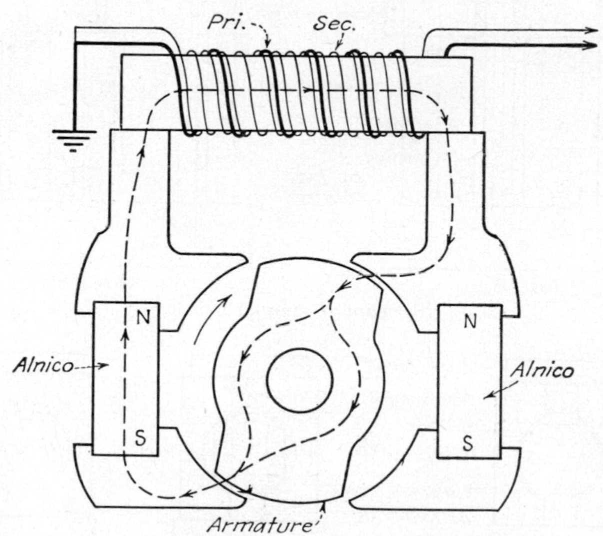

FIG. 165. Magneto with Alnico magnets. (*American Bosch Corporation.*)

which intermediate soft-steel conductor bars are used rather than another set of magnets, but with reversed polarity, has two advantages. The permanent magnets can all be magnetized in their operating positions by placing the chuck between the *N* and *S* pole pieces of a powerful electromagnet. This would not be possible if all permanent magnets were used since consecutive magnets would need to have *N*, *S*, *N* poles at the top and *S*, *N*, *S* poles at the bottom. Moreover, the permeability of the soft steel is much greater than that of the Alnico magnet material so that the cross section of the conductor bars may be made much less than that of the magnets, making the chuck much more compact. (The importance of magnetizing the magnets in operating position is better understood after reading Sec. 204, p. 281.)

Figure 166(*a*) shows the chuck in the holding position. It will be noted that the flux passes from the magnets through the pole piece and thence through the workpiece, holding it firmly. The method of releasing the work is shown in (*b*). The faceplate is slid laterally a short distance so that the soft-iron pole pieces *P* now bridge each gap between the magnets and conductor bars. The flux is now shunted, or diverted, from the workpiece, which is easily removed.

Another method, whereby the work is held and released by the rotation of the permanent magnet, is shown in Fig. 166(*c*). A permanent

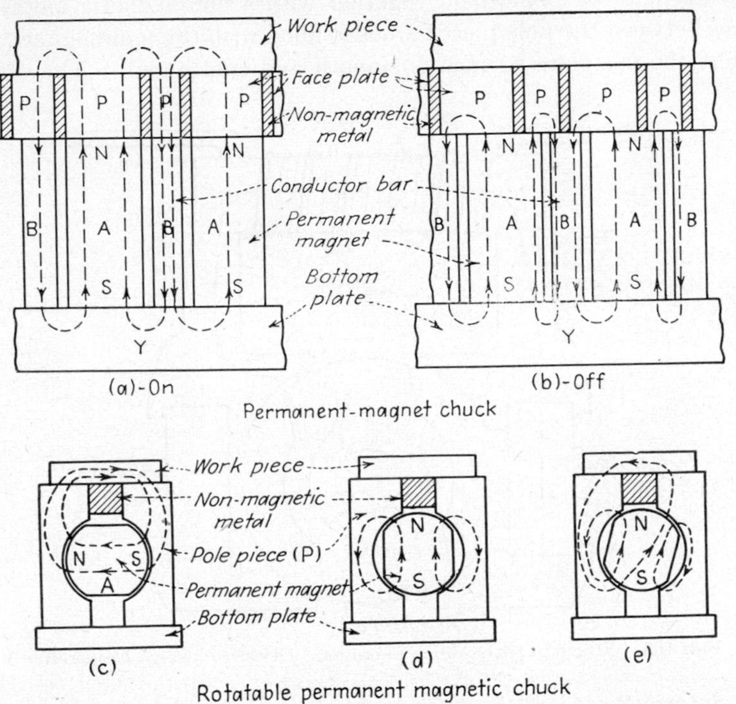

FIG. 166. Permanent-magnetic chucks. (*Brown and Sharpe Company.*)

magnet with two cylindrical surfaces *A* can be rotated between the soft-steel pole pieces *P*. Figure 166(*c*) shows the chuck in the holding position. The flux goes through the workpiece placed on top of the pole pieces, holding it firmly. In order to release the work the magnet is turned 90°, as shown in (*d*). This causes the pole pieces of the magnet to become short-circuited by the soft-iron pole pieces, diverting the flux from the workpiece and permitting its release. Should there be some residual magnetism, or remanence, which still holds the workpiece, the magnet can be turned slightly beyond 90°, as shown in (*e*), sending a small reversed flux through the workpiece, thus releasing it.

A chuck may be made by assembling a number of such units and gearing together the rotating magnets. Brown and Sharpe Company manufactures a single unit to make a magnetic block for holding gages onto iron blocks, bedplates, etc.

168. Magnetic Shielding. There is no known insulator for magnetic flux. No appreciable change in the flux or in the pull of a magnet is noticed if glass, paper, wood, copper, or other such nonmagnetic material be placed in the magnetic field. However, it is often desirable to shield galvanometers and electrical measuring instruments from the earth's field and from stray fields due to generators, conductors carrying currents, etc.

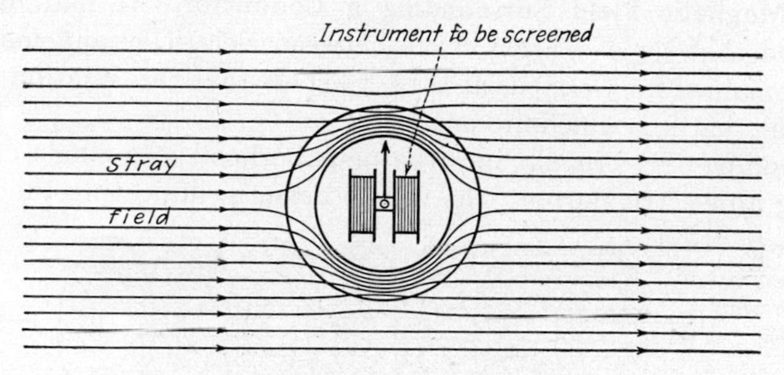

FIG. 167. Magnetic shielding.

This is done by surrounding the instrument with an iron shell, Fig. 167. This shell by-passes *practically* the entire flux and thus prevents it from affecting the sensitive portions of the instrument. The smaller the openings in the shell, the more effective the screening. Three or four shells, with air spaces between, are found to be more effective than one shell of the same total thickness. Such shells, however, are used only in screening the most sensitive galvanometers.

It should be emphasized that perfect screening by this method cannot be attained since there is always an air path in parallel with the iron path of the shell. However, it is usually possible to reduce the stray field within the shell to a negligible value.

CHAPTER VII

ELECTROMAGNETISM

169. Magnetic Field Surrounding a Conductor. It had long been suspected that some relation exists between electricity and magnetism, but it remained for Oersted, in 1819, to show that this relation not only exists but that it is a definite one.

If a compass be brought into the neighborhood of a single conductor carrying an electric current, the needle deflects, indicating the presence

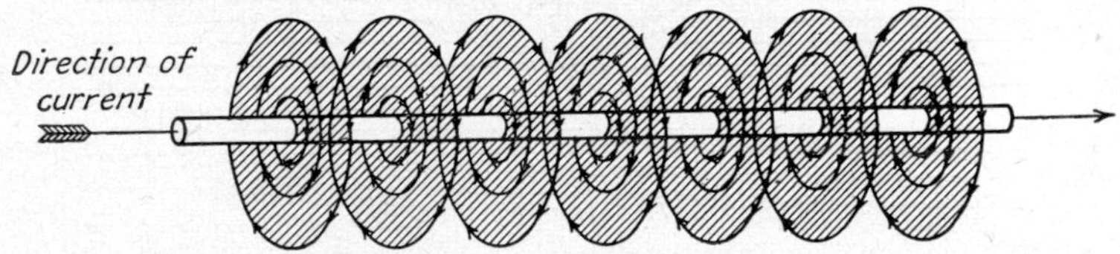

Fig. 168. Magnetic field surrounding a cylindrical conductor.

of a magnetic field. It is further observed that the needle always tends to set itself at right angles to the current. When it is held above the conductor, the needle points in a direction opposite to that which it assumes when held beneath the conductor. Further investigation shows that the magnetic flux exists in circles about the conductor (if there is no other magnetic field in the vicinity), as in Figs. 168, 169, and 170. These

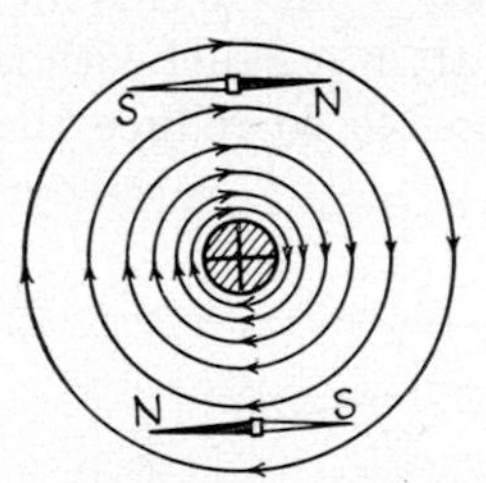

Fig. 169. Lines of flux surrounding a cylindrical conductor—current inward.

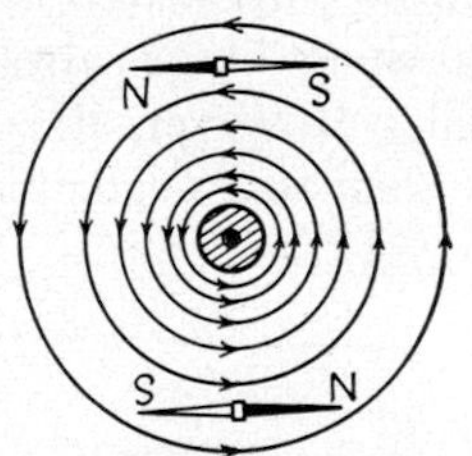

Fig. 170. Lines of flux surrounding a cylindrical conductor—current outward.

circles have their centers at the axis of the conductor, and their planes are perpendicular to the conductor. If the current in the conductor be reversed, the direction in which the compass needle is deflected will also reverse, showing that the direction of this magnetic field depends on the direction of the current. The relation between the two is shown in Fig.

168. The fact that the magnetic flux exists in circles perpendicular to the conductor explains the reversal of the direction of the compass needle when moved from a point above the conductor to a point beneath it, since the direction of the field above the conductor must be opposite to that beneath the conductor. This is illustrated in Figs. 169 and 170.[1] Also, if a cylindrical conductor carrying current is brought vertically downward through a sheet of cardboard, iron filings sprinkled on the cardboard form circles concentric with the conductor.

170. Relation between Magnetic Field and Current. A definite relation exists between the direction of the current in a conductor and the direction of the magnetic field surrounding the conductor. There are two simple rules by which this relation may be remembered.

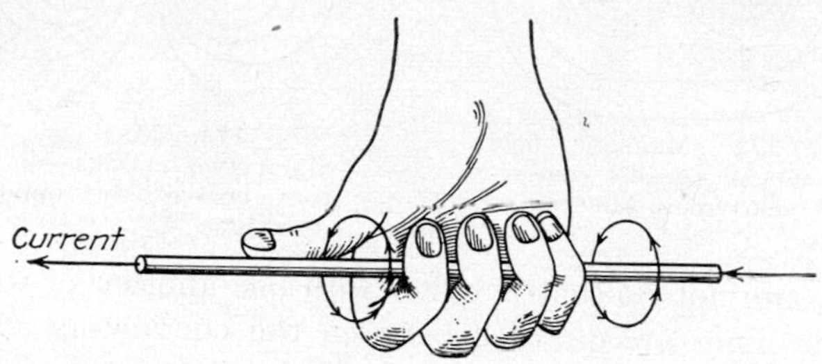

Fig. 171. Hand rule.

Hand Rule. Grasp the conductor in the *right hand* with the thumb pointing in the direction of the current. The fingers will then point in the direction of the lines of flux, Fig. 171.

Corkscrew Rule. The direction of the current and that of the resulting magnetic field are related to each other as the forward travel of a corkscrew and the direction in which it is rotated.

This last rule is probably the most common and the most easily remembered. However, it must not be inferred from this rule that the magnetic field exists in spirals about the conductor. It exists actually in planes perpendicular to the conductor.

171. Magnetic Field of Two Parallel Conductors. When two parallel conductors carry electric currents in the same direction, there is a tendency for the two conductors to be drawn together. The reason for this is obvious. In Fig. 172 the lines of force encircle each conductor in the same direction (corkscrew rule), and the resultant field is an envelope of lines acting like elastic bands tending to pull the conductors together. Further reason for this attraction is given by the rule of Sec. 160 (p. 216),

[1] A circle having a cross inside (⊕) represents the feathered end of an arrow and indicates that the direction of current is into the paper, away from the observer. A circle having a dot at the center (⊙) represents the approaching tip of an arrow and indicates that the direction of current is out of the paper, toward the observer.

stating that the magnetic field tends to conform itself so that the number of magnetic lines is a maximum. The pulling together of the conductors reduces the length of path *abcd* through which the magnetic lines must pass. The field due to each conductor separately is still circular in form, but the resultant magnetic field is no longer circular, as is shown in Fig. 172.

In Fig. 173 is shown the field which exists when two parallel conductors carry current in opposite directions. The magnetic lines are circles, but

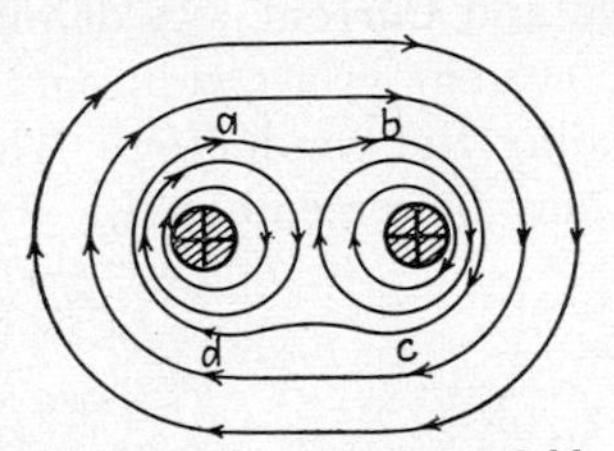

Fig. 172. Magnetic field about two parallel conductors—current in same direction.

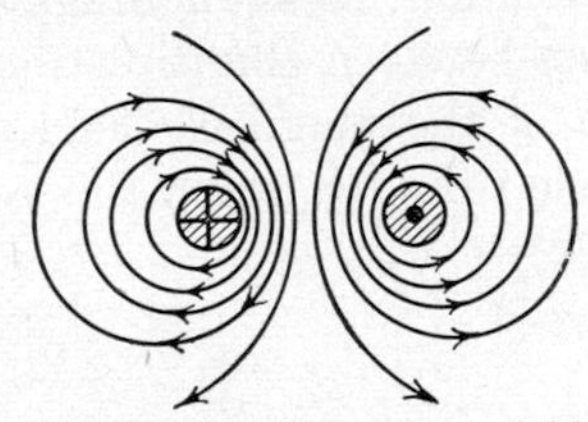

Fig. 173. Magnetic field about two parallel conductors—current in opposite directions.

these circles are not concentric either with one another or with the conductor. The lines are crowded between the conductors and therefore exert a repelling action tending to push the conductors farther apart. Again, when the conductors separate, the area through which the flux passes is increased, so that the magnetic circuit in this case also tends to conform itself so that the magnetic flux is a maximum.

From the foregoing, the following rules may be formulated:

Conductors carrying currents in the same direction tend to be drawn together; conductors carrying currents in opposite directions tend to be repelled from one another.

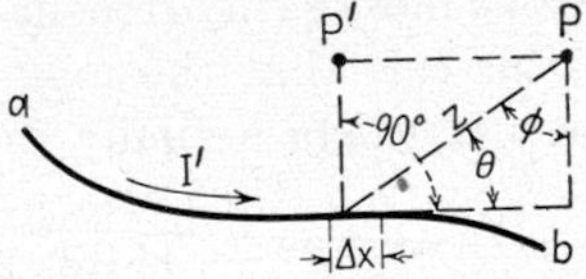

Fig. 174. Biot-Savart law.

All electric circuits tend to take such a position as will make their currents parallel and flowing in the same direction.

This effect is especially pronounced in modern large-capacity power systems. Bus bars have been wrenched from their clamps, transformer coils have been pulled out of place and transformers wrecked by the forces produced by the excessive currents arising under short-circuit conditions.

172. Biot-Savart[1] Law, and Field Intensity Due to Current. The Biot-Savart law gives a quantitative relation between an electric current and the field intensity produced by it. The law thus permits the calculation of the forces which exist between electric currents and magnetic

[1] After Jean Baptiste Biot (1774–1862), a French physicist and collaborator of Laplace, and Félix Savart (1791–1841), a French physician and physicist.

fields. In Fig. 174, let I' be a current in a wire ab expressed in absolute amperes [1 absolute ampere (abamp) = 10 practical amperes]. The current in a very short element Δx of the wire produces a field intensity at P,

$$\Delta H = \frac{I' \Delta x}{z^2} \sin \theta \qquad \text{oersteds,} \tag{137}$$

where z is the distance in centimeters from point P to Δx and θ is the angle which the element Δx makes with the line connecting P and Δx. The field intensity at P is the force in dynes on a unit pole placed at P.

The law which (137) expresses may be stated as follows:

Each element of length of a current-carrying conductor makes a contribution ΔH to the field intensity at a point P, which is proportional to the length Δx of the element, to the current I' flowing in it, to the sine of the angle θ between the direction of the current and the line z connecting Δx with P and which is inversely proportional to the square of the distance z. The direction of the magnetic field is perpendicular to the plane $abco$ determined by Δx and z, as may be seen from a study of Fig. 175, and its direction into or out of this plane is readily determined by the rule illustrated in Fig. 171.

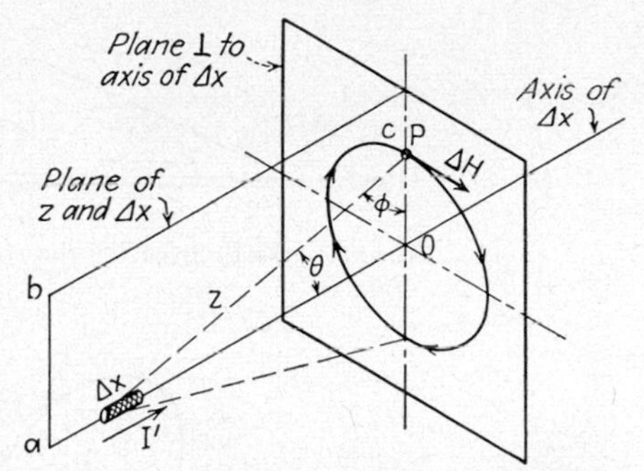

FIG. 175. Relations among Δx, z, θ, ΔH.

It will be noted that $\Delta x \sin \theta$ is the component of current element Δx which is perpendicular to z and which alone is effective in producing a field intensity at P. It follows that the field intensity at all points on the axis of the element, due to a current element, is zero since $\theta = 0$ at all such points; at a given distance from the element the field intensity is a maximum in a plane passing through the element perpendicular to its axis, since $\theta = 90°$ and $\sin \theta = 1$ at all points in such a plane (see point P', Fig. 174).

Equation (137) is not readily proved by experiment but (138), (141), (145), which are derived from (137), can be so proved.

From relation (137) it may be shown that the field intensity H at a point P located at a perpendicular distance h cm from an infinitely long straight wire carrying a current of I' abamp is

$$H = \frac{2I'}{h} \qquad \text{oersteds.} \tag{138}$$

This may be proved as follows: In Fig. 176 let the current in the wire be I' abamp. Let the origin O be taken at the point where the perpendicular h from P intersects the conductor. (Figure 177 shows Fig. 176 in perspective.) The field intensity at P due to the current I' in an element dx situated at a positive distance x from the origin is [from (137)]

$$d\mathbf{F}_P = \frac{I' \, dx}{z^2} \sin \theta. \tag{1}$$

In order to determine the force due to the entire conductor, integrate with respect to x. However, simplification will result if θ, rather than x, is chosen as the independent variable.

From inspection of Fig. 176, it is seen that $z = h \csc \theta$, $x = h \cot \theta$. Also, $dx = h \cdot d(\cot \theta) = -h \csc^2 \theta \, d\theta$. Hence,

$$d\mathrm{F}_P = -\frac{I'h \csc^2 \theta \, d\theta}{h^2 \csc^2 \theta} \sin \theta = -\frac{I'}{h} \sin \theta \, d\theta, \tag{II}$$

and

$$\mathrm{F}_P = H = -\frac{I'}{h} \int_\alpha^\beta \sin \theta \, d\theta = \frac{I'}{h} (\cos \beta - \cos \alpha) \quad \text{oersteds.} \tag{139}$$

For an infinitely long wire, $\beta = 0$ and $\alpha = \pi$, so that

$$H = \frac{2I'}{h} \quad \text{dynes per unit pole, or oersteds} \quad [(138)].$$

The difference between the effect of an infinitely long wire and one whose length is 30 to 50 times the distance h is so small as to be negligible. The direction of the field intensity at P, Fig. 176, is perpendicular to the plane of the paper.

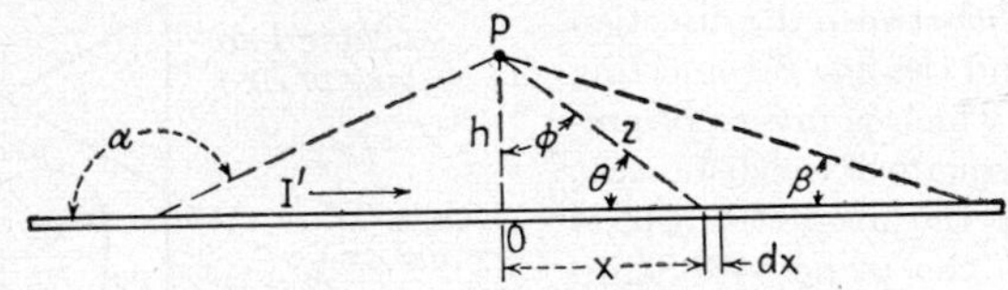

FIG. 176. Field intensity due to current in single conductor.

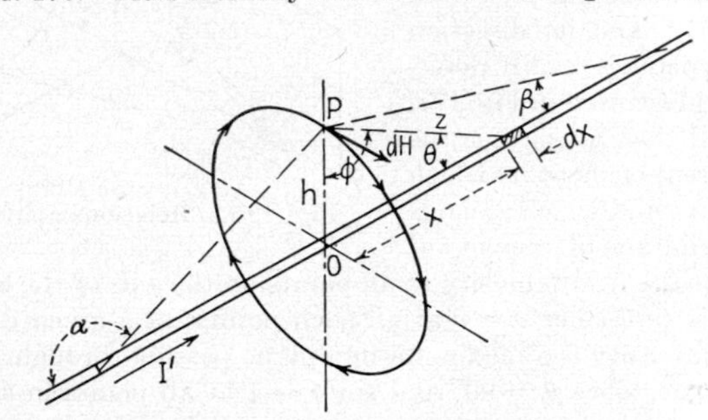

FIG. 177. Relations among x, h, αH, β, and α.

Equation (138) may also be developed by noting that $\sin \theta = \cos \phi$, $x = h \tan \phi$, $dx = h \sec^2 \phi \, d\phi$, and $z = h/\cos \phi$. Hence,

$$dH_P = \frac{I'h \sec^2 \phi \, d\phi}{h^2/\cos^2 \phi} \cos \phi, \tag{II}$$

$$dH_P = \frac{I'}{h} \cos \phi \, d\phi,$$

and

$$H = \frac{I'}{h} \int_{-\pi/2}^{\pi/2} \cos \phi \, d\phi = \frac{I'}{h} \sin \phi \Big|_{-\pi/2}^{\pi/2}, \tag{III}$$

$$H = \frac{2I'}{h} \quad \text{dynes per unit pole, or oersteds} \quad [(138)].$$

It is to be noted that if a unit pole at P be carried at constant radius h about the conductor, the work done in making one complete circuit is

$$w = \left(\frac{2I'}{h}\right) 2\pi h = 4\pi I' \quad \text{ergs.} \tag{140}$$

Hence the work is independent of the radius. By definition, w of (140) is the mmf of a single long conductor carrying a current I' abamp (p. 249).

Example. A current of 60 amp flows in a long straight wire. Determine: (*a*) field intensity at a point P, 10 cm perpendicularly from axis of wire; (*b*) work done in carrying a unit pole once around wire; (*c*) force exerted on a pole of 60 cgs unit pole strength at point P.

$$60 \text{ amp} = 6.0 \text{ abamp.}$$

(*a*) Using (138),

$$H = \frac{2 \cdot 6.0}{10} = 1.2 \text{ oersteds.} \quad \textit{Ans.}$$

(*b*) $w = 1.2 \cdot 2\pi \cdot 10 = 75.4$ ergs. *Ans.*
(*c*) $\mathbf{F} = 1.2 \cdot 60 = 72$ dynes. *Ans.*

173. Magnetic Field of a Single Turn. If a wire carrying a current be bent into a loop, a field results similar to that shown in Fig. 178.

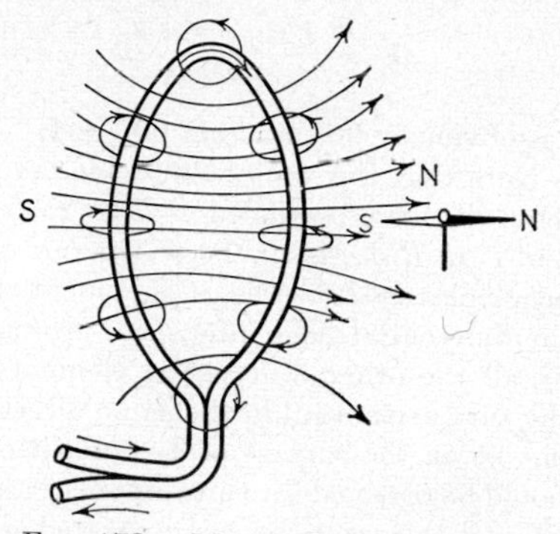

FIG. 178. Magnetic field produced by a single turn.

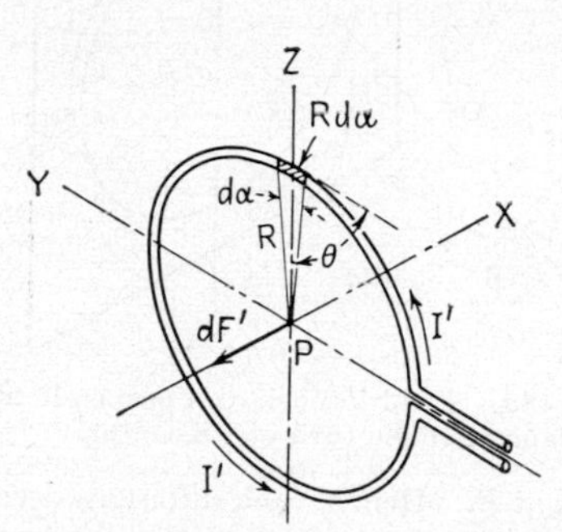

FIG. 179. Field intensity at the center of a single turn.

This magnetic field has an N pole and an S pole which possess all the properties of similar poles of a short bar magnet. A compass needle placed in this field assumes the direction shown, the N pole pointing in the direction of the magnetic lines.

The field intensity at any point on a perpendicular to the plane of a circular turn at its center is readily computed by the Biot-Savart law (Sec. 172).

In Fig. 179 is shown a single turn, of radius R cm, lying in the YZ plane and carrying a current of I' abamp. First, the field intensity at the center of the turn is to be derived. Let $R\,d\alpha$ be a differential element of the turn. In applying the Biot-Savart law, $R\,d\alpha$ corresponds to Δx in Fig. 174, R corresponds to z, and the angles θ are corresponding angles. In Fig. 179, angle θ is 90°. Since $R\,d\alpha$ and R are both perpendicular to the X axis, the differential contribution to field intensity made by $I'R\,d\alpha$ is $d\mathbf{F}'$. The field intensity produced by the complete turn will be the integral of $d\mathbf{F}'$ between 0 and 2π. Thus,

$$H_c = \int_0^{2\pi} d\mathbf{F}' = \int_0^{2\pi} \frac{I'R\,d\alpha \sin\theta}{R^2} = \frac{2\pi I'}{R} \quad \text{oersteds.} \tag{141}$$

If a coil consists of n closely grouped turns, so that the thickness of the coil is small as compared with its radius,

$$H_c = \frac{2\pi n I'}{R} \quad \text{oersteds,} \tag{142}$$

where I' is the current in abamperes.

If, in (141), $R = 1$ and the field intensity at the center of the coil is 2π dynes, the current I' is 1 *abamp*. This should be compared with the definition of the abampere (p. 28).

Next let it be required to compute the field intensity at a point on the axis of the turn but not at its center, such as P, Fig. 180. Let the length of a perpendicular OP at the center O of the coil be h cm. Let the current in the turn be I' abamp. Consider a differential element of the turn $R\,d\alpha$. A line z drawn from the element $R\,d\alpha$ to P makes an angle β with OP. The field intensity at P, due to $I'R\,d\alpha$ is

$$d\mathbf{F}' = \frac{I'R\,d\alpha \sin\theta}{z^2}. \tag{I}$$

θ is obviously 90°, and $\sin 90° = 1$.

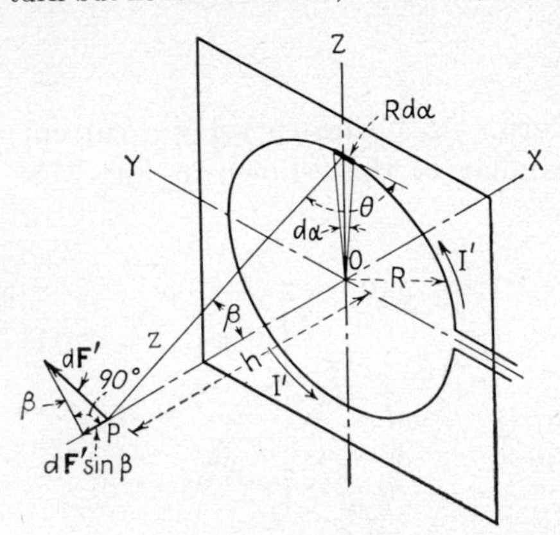

Fig. 180. Field intensity on perpendicular to plane of single turn at its center.

Note that the vector dF', which represents the force produced at P by the current I' in $R\,d\alpha$, is in the XZ plane, perpendicular to Z. Also, it is evident that the differential field intensities produced by all the other differential elements in the turn are not all in the same direction but lie on the surface of a cone with the apex at P. Hence, each differential vector should be resolved into a component along the X axis and one perpendicular to this axis, and the components integrated separately. But it is evident from symmetry that the components perpendicular to the X axis cancel for the entire turn. (This becomes evident if another element is considered diametrically opposite $R\,d\alpha$.) Thus only the components along the X axis, given by $d\mathbf{F}' \sin\beta$, contribute to the field intensity at P and must be summed. Hence,

$$H = \int d\mathbf{F}' \sin\beta = \int_0^{2\pi} \frac{I'R\,d\alpha \sin\beta}{z^2} = \frac{I'2\pi R \sin\beta}{z^2}. \tag{II}$$

But $\sin\beta = R/z$ and $z^2 = R^2 + h^2$. Hence,

$$H = \frac{2\pi R^2 I'}{(R^2 + h^2)^{3/2}} \quad \text{oersteds.} \tag{143}$$

If $h = 0$, it is evident that (143) reduces to (141).

Example. A coil of 25 turns has a radius of 12 cm, and its thickness is small compared with its radius. When the current is 20 amp, determine: (*a*) field intensity on a perpendicular to plane of coil at its center and 16 cm from plane of coil; (*b*) field intensity at center of coil.

(*a*) 20 amp = 2.0 abamp. From (143) (with n turns).

$$H = \frac{2\pi \cdot \overline{12}^2 \cdot 2.0 \cdot 25}{(\overline{12}^2 + 16^2)^{3/2}} = 5.655 \text{ oersteds.} \quad \textit{Ans.}$$

(*b*) Using (142),

$$H_c = \frac{2\pi \cdot 25 \cdot 2.0}{12} = 26.18 \text{ oersteds.} \quad \textit{Ans.}$$

174. Solenoids. An electric conductor wound about an axis in the form of a helix is called a *solenoid*. The operation of all electromagnets is based fundamentally on the properties of the solenoid, so that an understanding of these properties is important. A simple solenoid and

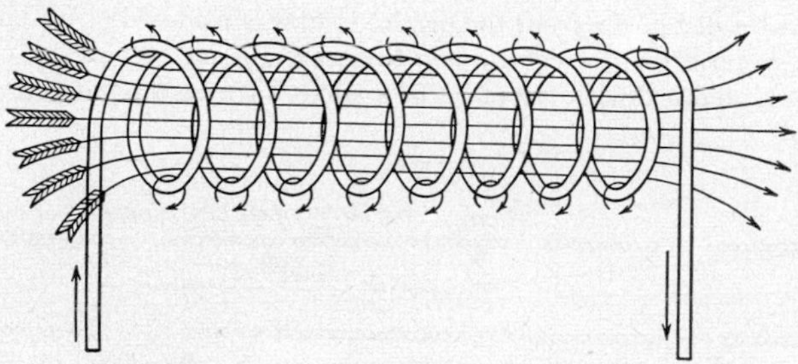

FIG. 181. Magnetic field produced by a helix or solenoid.

the magnetic field produced within it when current flows through the conductor are shown in Fig. 181. The solenoid may be considered as consisting of a large number of the turns shown in Fig. 178 (p. 233), placed together. The solenoid winding may also consist of several layers as shown in the plunger type of Fig. 185 (p. 240).

The relation of the direction of the flux within the solenoid to the direction of the current in the helix may be determined by the hand rule or by the corkscrew rule of Sec. 170 (p. 229). Another simple method is shown in Fig. 182, where the arrows at the ends of the *N* and the *S* show the direction of current in the coil. For example, when looking down on an *N* pole the current direction in the coil will be counterclockwise as shown by the *N*; when looking down on an *S* pole the direction of the current will be clockwise as shown by the *S*.

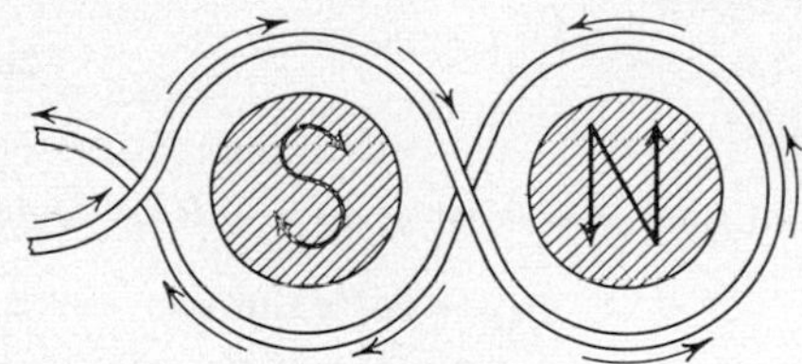

FIG. 182. Relation of magnetic poles to direction of exciting current.

175. Field Intensity within a Long Air Solenoid. Long air solenoids of uniform cross section are used as standards for magnetic flux, since the total flux across the center section may be accurately computed when the dimensions of the solenoid and the value of the current are known (see p. 288). First, the equation giving the field intensity at any point on the axis of the solenoid will be derived. Next, the equation for the field intensity on the axis of an infinitely long solenoid will be obtained, and it will be shown that under most conditions this equation can be used when the ratio of length to radius is as low as 40 to 1. Finally, the equation for the field intensity at either end of the solenoid will be obtained.

Consider the long cylindrical solenoid in Fig. 183, of helically wound wire. There are n turns per centimeter length, and the mean radius of the solenoid is R cm. The solenoid may be finite, or it may be infinite in length. The current is I' abamp. The origin is taken at P, the center of the solenoid.

The effect of the current in a very thin transverse section of the solenoid, dx in thickness and at a distance x from the origin, is first considered. Within the section dx there are $n\,dx$ turns and the cgs ampere-turns are $I'n\,dx$. The effect of this section at the point P is identical with the effect of a single turn on a point P situated on the

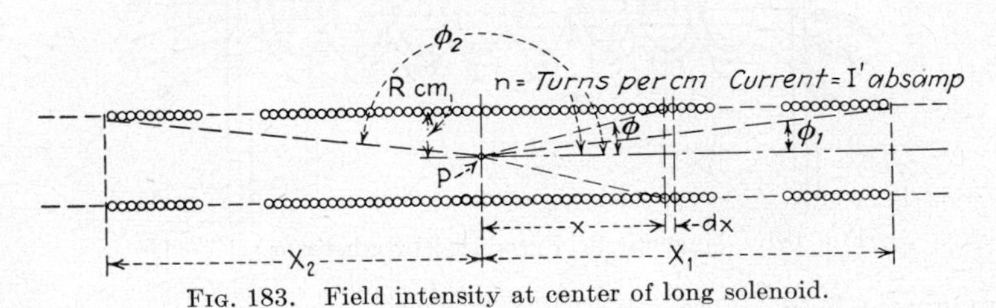

FIG. 183. Field intensity at center of long solenoid.

perpendicular at the center of the turn, Fig. 180. Hence (143) (p. 234) is used. The field intensity at P due to the section is

$$dH_P = \frac{2\pi R^2 I'n\,dx}{(R^2 + x^2)^{3/2}} \quad \text{oersteds.} \tag{I}$$

The total intensity at P may be found by integrating (I). This may be facilitated by using the angle ϕ instead of x as the independent variable. Let $z = (R^2 + x^2)^{1/2}$,

$$dH_P = \frac{2\pi R^2 I'n\,dx}{z^3} \tag{II}$$

and since $x = R \cot \phi$, $dx = -R \csc^2 \phi\, d\phi$, and $\sin \phi = R/z$,

$$dH_P = 2\pi I'n \sin^3 \phi(-\csc^2 \phi\, d\phi) = 2\pi I'n\,(-\sin \phi\, d\phi), \tag{III}$$

$$H_P = 2\pi I'n \int_{\phi_2}^{\phi_1} (-\sin \phi\, d\phi) = 2\pi I'n(\cos \phi_1 - \cos \phi_2), \tag{144}$$

where ϕ_1 and ϕ_2 are the values of ϕ which correspond to the values of X_1 and X_2 at the ends of the solenoid, Fig. 183.

(III) may also be derived as follows: Note from Figs. 183 and 184 that $-z\,d\phi = dx \sin \phi$ and $dx = -z\,d\phi/\sin \phi$. Since $R/z = R/(x^2 + R^2)^{1/2} = \sin \phi$, (I) becomes

$$dH_P = \frac{2\pi R^2 I'n(-z\,d\phi)}{(R^2 + x^2)^{3/2} \sin \phi} = -2\pi I'n \sin \phi\, d\phi$$

which is identical with (III).

When the solenoid is of infinite length, $\phi_1 = 0$ and $\phi_2 = \pi$ so that

$$H_P = 4\pi I'n \quad \text{oersteds.} \tag{145}$$

If the current is expressed in amperes,

$$H_P = 0.4\pi nI \qquad \text{oersteds.} \tag{145a}$$

Note that (145) and (145*a*) give the field intensity on the axis of an infinitely long solenoid but that (144) can be used to find the field intensity inside a solenoid of finite length. Also, (144) applies to any axial point and is not restricted to points inside the solenoid.

Assume that the solenoid is not infinite but that the ratio of length to radius is 40 to 1. Hence,

$$\cos \phi_1 = \frac{20}{\sqrt{(20)^2 + (1)^2}} = 0.9987; \qquad \cos \phi_2 = \frac{-20}{\sqrt{(20)^2 + (1)^2}} = -0.9987.$$

Hence, from (144), $H_P = 2\pi I'n(1.9974) = 3.9948\pi I'n$ oersteds. This differs from (145*a*) by only 0.13 per cent. This difference is so small that it may generally be neglected.

At an axial point at one end of a long solenoid, $\phi_1 = 0$, $\phi_2 = \pi/2$, or vice versa. Hence on the axis at either end,

$$H_P = 2\pi nI' \qquad \text{oersteds,} \tag{146}$$

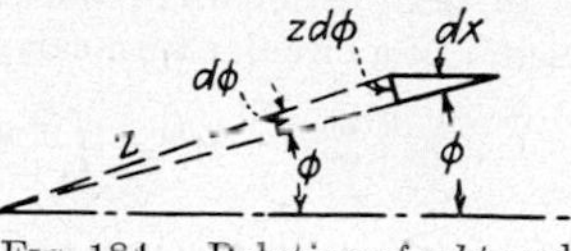

FIG. 184. Relation of $z\,d\phi$ and $dx \sin \phi$.

or the field intensity at either end is one-half its magnitude at the center. However, the field intensity, except near the ends, is very nearly constant at the value given by (145) and (145*a*), that is, $4\pi nI'$, or $0.4\pi nI$ oersteds. In consequence the lines of flux enter and leave the solenoid in relatively small regions near its ends.

MKS SYSTEMS

176. Magnetic Fields in MKS Units. In either the rationalized or the unrationalized mks system, a conductor 1 m long carrying a current of 1 amp in a field having a density of 1 weber per sq m is acted upon by a force of 1 newton. The current, the field, and the force are mutually perpendicular. Consider Fig. 174 (p. 230), illustrating the Biot-Savart law. Let there be one rationalized mks unit pole at P. The current is now in amperes, and the distances Δx and z are in meters. Since but 1 weber leaves a rationalized N pole, the flux density at Δx is $B_x = 1/4\pi z^2$. Hence the force on the element Δx is

$$\mathbf{F}_x = H_x = \frac{I\,dx \cos \phi}{4\pi z^2} = \frac{I\,dx \sin \theta}{4\pi z^2} \qquad \text{amp-turns per m.} \tag{147}$$

Hence, Eq. (139) (p. 232), now giving the field intensity h m from a long straight wire, Fig. 177 (p. 232), becomes

$$H = -\frac{I}{4\pi h}\int_\alpha^\beta \sin \theta\, d\theta = \frac{I}{4\pi h}(\cos \beta - \cos \alpha) \qquad \text{amp-turns per m.} \tag{148}$$

Equation (138) then becomes

$$H = \frac{I}{2\pi h} \qquad \text{amp-turns per m.} \tag{149}$$

Equation (140) becomes

$$W = \left(\frac{I}{2\pi h}\right) 2\pi h = I \qquad \text{joules.} \tag{150}$$

(In the rationalized system the unit of mmf is the ampere-turn.)

The example on p. 233 is then solved as follows:

(*a*) Using (149), $H = \dfrac{60}{2\pi(10^{-1})} = 95.49$ amp-turns per m. *Ans.*

(*b*) From (150), $W = 60$ joules. *Ans.*

(*c*) 60 cgs unit poles equal $60\,\dfrac{4\pi}{10^8}$ mks rationalized unit poles. *Ans.*

$$\mathbf{F} = \frac{60}{2\pi(10^{-1})} \cdot \frac{60 \cdot 4\pi}{10^8} = 7.20 \cdot 10^{-4} \text{ newtons. } \textit{Ans.}$$
$$= 72.0 \text{ dynes } (\textit{check}).$$

In mks rationalized units using (147), Eq. (141) giving the field intensity at the center of a circular turn carrying current, Fig. 179 (p. 233), becomes

$$H_c = \int_0^{2\pi} \frac{IR\,d\alpha \sin\theta}{4\pi R^2} = \frac{I}{2R} \qquad \text{amp-turns per m.} \tag{151}$$

[Note that in (141), $\theta = 90°$.]

Likewise, again using (147), Eq. (143) (p. 234) giving the field intensity at any point on the axis of a circular turn, Fig. 180 becomes

$$H = \int_0^{2\pi} \frac{IR\,d\alpha \sin\beta}{4\pi z^2} = \frac{IR\sin\beta}{2z^2},$$

$$\sin\beta = \frac{R}{z} = \frac{R}{\sqrt{R^2 + h^2}},$$

$$H = \frac{IR^2}{2(R^2 + h^2)^{3/2}} \qquad \text{amp-turns per m.} \tag{152}$$

Example. Solve the example, p. 234, using rationalized mks units.

$$R = 12 \cdot 10^{-2}\text{ m}; \qquad h = 16 \cdot 10^{-2}\text{ m}.$$

(*a*) Using (152),

$$H = \frac{(20 \cdot 25)(12 \cdot 10^{-2})^2}{2[(12 \cdot 10^{-2})^2 + (16 \cdot 10^{-2})^2]^{3/2}} = 450 \text{ amp-turns per m. } \textit{Ans.}$$

$$450 \text{ amp-turns per m} = 4.50 \text{ amp-turns per cm} = 0.4\pi \cdot 4.50$$
$$= 5.655 \text{ gilberts per cm} = H\ (\textit{check}).$$

(*b*) Using (151),

$$H_c = \frac{I(n)}{2R} = \frac{20 \cdot 25}{2 \cdot 12 \cdot 10^{-2}} = 2.083 \text{ amp-turns per m.}$$

In order to obtain the field intensity on the axis of a long solenoid, Fig. 183 (p. 236), (152) is used [see (II), p. 236].

$$dH_{P}' = \frac{IR^2 n\,dx}{2z^3} \qquad \text{amp-turns per m.} \tag{I}$$

Substituting (see Fig. 183),

$$x = R\cot\phi, \qquad dx = -R\csc^2\phi\,d\phi; \qquad \sin\phi = \frac{R}{z}.$$

$$dH_{P}' = \frac{IR^2 n(-R\csc^2\phi\,d\phi)\sin^3\phi}{2R^3}. \tag{II}$$

$$H_{P}' = \int_{\phi_2}^{\phi_1} -\frac{In\sin\phi\,d\phi}{2} = \frac{In}{2}(\cos\phi_1 - \cos\phi_2) \qquad \text{amp-turns per m.} \tag{153}$$

If the length of solenoid becomes infinite, $\phi_1 = 0$, $\phi_2 = \pi$, and (153) becomes

$$H_P' = In \qquad \text{amp-turns per m.} \tag{154}$$

Unrationalized Units. In unrationalized units the foregoing equations become as follows:

Equation (149), giving the field intensity h m from a long straight wire, Fig. 177 (p. 232), becomes

$$H = \frac{2I}{h} \qquad \text{amp-turns per m.} \tag{155}$$

Equation (150), giving the work done in carrying a unit pole one complete circuit about a long straight wire, becomes

$$W = 4\pi I \qquad \text{joules.} \tag{156}$$

Equation (151), giving the field intensity at the center of a circular turn carrying current, Fig. 179 (p. 233), becomes

$$H_c = \frac{2\pi I}{R} \qquad \text{amp-turns per m.} \tag{157}$$

Equation (152), giving the field intensity at any point on the axis of a circular turn carrying current, Fig. 180 (p. 234), becomes

$$H = \frac{2\pi I R^2}{(R^2 + h^2)^{3/2}} \qquad \text{amp-turns per m.} \tag{158}$$

Equation (153), giving the field intensity on the axis of a long solenoid, Fig. 183 (p. 236), becomes

$$H_P = 2\pi In(\cos \phi_1 - \cos \phi_2) \qquad \text{amp-turns per m.} \tag{159}$$

Equation (154), giving the field intensity on the axis of a long solenoid, Fig. 183, when the solenoid is infinite in length, becomes

$$H_P = 4\pi In \qquad \text{amp-turns per m.} \tag{160}$$

Example. Solve the example, p. 234, using unrationalized mks units.

(*a*) Using (158), with n = turns,

$$H = \frac{2\pi(20 \cdot 25)(12 \cdot 10^{-2})^2}{[(12 \cdot 10^{-2})^2 + (16 \cdot 10^{-2})^2]^{3/2}}$$
$$= 5{,}655 \text{ unrationalized units. } \textit{Ans.}$$

(*b*) Using (157),

$$H_c = \frac{2\pi(20 \cdot 25)}{12 \cdot 10^{-2}} = 26{,}180 \text{ unrationalized units. } \textit{Ans.}$$

(Note that these answers are 4π times those for the rationalized units and 1,000 times those for the cgs units.)

177. Commercial Solenoids or Electromagnets. When turns of a conductor carrying current are wound about an iron core, an electromagnet results. The electromagnetic action of the current in producing magnetic flux in the iron core is the same as that which produces the magnetic flux in the air solenoid (Fig. 183, p. 236). However, owing to the much greater permeability of iron, a given number of ampere-turns produces a very much greater flux in the iron core than in air.

Electromagnets are used in practice for tripping circuit breakers (Sec. 364, p. 547); for operating contactors in automatic motor starters (Sec. 337, p. 505); for operating voltage-regulating devices (Sec. 315, p. 464;) for arc-lamp feeds, for operating valves, and for many other purposes. In practically all cases, either a soft-iron (or soft-steel) plunger or an armature is necessary for obtaining the required tractive force.

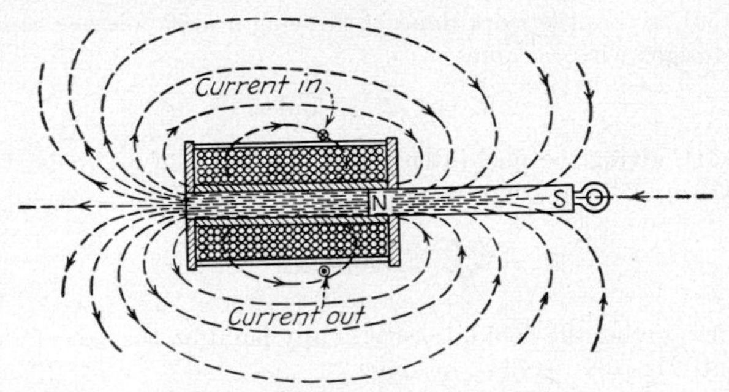

FIG. 185. Simple solenoid and plunger.

The principle of the solenoid and plunger type of electromagnet is illustrated in Fig. 185. The flux due to the solenoid produces magnetic poles on the plunger. The pole nearer the solenoid will be of such sign that it will be urged along the lines of force (see Sec. 157, p. 213), and in such a direction as to be drawn within the solenoid.

A position of equilibrium is reached when the center of the plunger is at the center of the solenoid, Fig. 185, and then all tractive effort ceases. Solenoids with plungers only are seldom used in practice except in special cases where it is desired to take advantage of their long-pull characteristic. They are frequently surrounded with an iron yoke to act as a return path for the flux, and frequently a stop is used, Fig. 186. The yoke, or "ironclad" feature, increases the range of uniform pull and produces a marked increase of pull as the plunger approaches the end of the stroke. When a stop a is used, Fig. 186, the solenoid becomes a *plunger electromagnet.* This changes the characteristics of the solenoid in that the maximum pull now occurs when the end of the plunger is near the stop. Figure 187 shows the results of solenoid tests made by C. R. Underhill.[1] Curve (a) shows the pull on the plunger

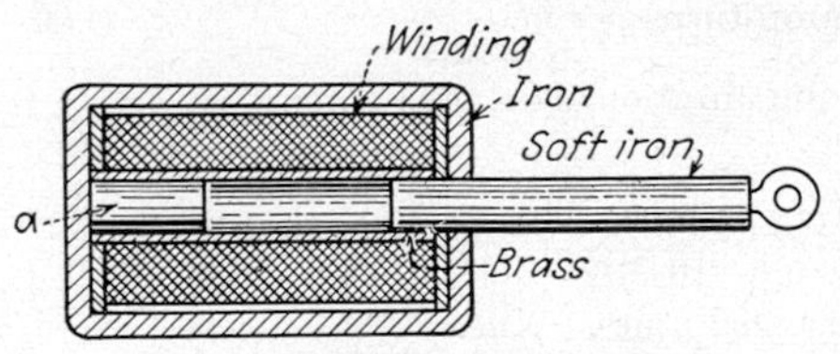

FIG. 186. "Ironclad" solenoid and plunger with stop.

[1] "Standard Handbook for Electrical Engineers," 8th ed., Sec. 5, McGraw-Hill Book Company, Inc.

of a simple solenoid like that of Fig. 185; curve (*b*) shows the pull when this solenoid is ironclad as in Fig. 186 but without a stop; curve (*c*) shows the effect of the stop on the pull. It will be noted that the ironclad feature as well as the stop causes the pull to attain very high values as the plunger approaches the end of its stroke. It will be noted, Fig. 187, that the usual ironclad feature and the usual stop have little effect on the pull except near the end of the stroke.

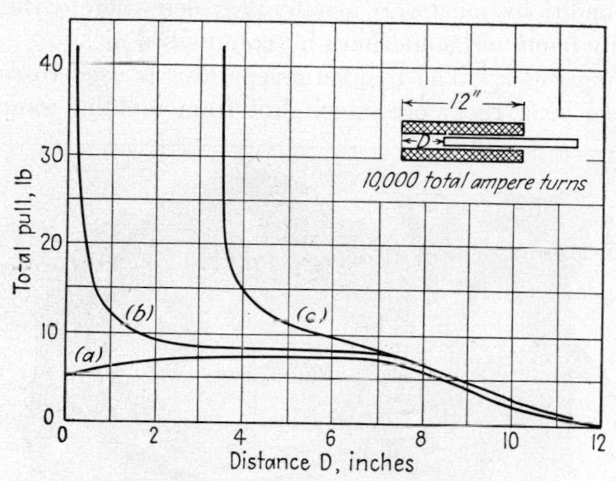

FIG. 187. Pull of solenoid on plunger.

Example. Assume in Fig. 185 that the field intensity at the center of the solenoid is 2,000 oersteds and that one end of the plunger is at the center. The cross section of the plunger is 6 sq cm, and the pole induced on the end of the plunger is 1,920 unit poles. The other end of the plunger is well outside the field.

Determine the pull on the plunger in kilograms.

Since the definition of field intensity is the force in dynes exerted on a unit pole, the field will exert a force of 2,000 dynes on each unit pole on the end of the plunger. Hence the total force

$$\mathbf{F} = \frac{2{,}000 \cdot 1{,}920}{981 \cdot 1{,}000} = 3.913 \text{ kg.} \quad \textit{Ans.}$$

Solution, MKS Rationalized System.

$$2{,}000 \text{ oersteds} = 2{,}000 \cdot \frac{10^3}{4\pi} = 159{,}000 \text{ amp-turns per m.} \qquad \text{(I)}$$

$$1{,}920 \text{ cgs unit poles} = 1{,}920 \cdot 4\pi \cdot 10^{-8} = 2.411 \cdot 10^{-4} \text{ rationalized mks poles.} \qquad \text{(II)}$$

$$159{,}000 \cdot 2.411 \cdot 10^{-4} = 38.39 \text{ newtons.} \quad \textit{Ans.}$$

$$38.39 \cdot 10^5 = 3.839 \cdot 10^6 \text{ dynes.}$$

$$\frac{38.39 \cdot 10^5}{981 \cdot 10^3} = 3.913 \text{ kg } (\textit{check}).$$

The work is simplified if (I) and (II) are multiplied directly.

$$2{,}000 \frac{10^3}{4\pi} \cdot 1{,}920 \cdot 4\pi \cdot 10^{-8} = 38.40 \text{ newtons.}$$

Magnetic Brakes. An important application of the solenoid occurs in the braking of elevators and cranes. When the power to the lifting motor is removed or fails, the brake must be applied immediately. The usual method of accomplishing this is illustrated by the brake shown in Fig. 188. Normally, the spring causes pressure of the brake shoes against the surface of the drum, thus applying the brake. The brake is released by energizing the solenoid contained in the left-hand housing. Under emergency conditions, means are usually provided whereby the brake may be released by hand and sometimes by compressed air.

Magnetic Separator. The magnetic separator is used to remove steel and iron from coal, rock, ore, steel shot from molding sand, and iron

FIG. 188. Electromagnetic brake for hoists and machinery. (*Electric Controller and Mfg. Co.*)

chips from machine-shop turnings. The method of operation of one type is shown in Fig. 189. The material is fed into the hopper, from which it is directed over the upper steel pulley. This pulley, as well as the lower one, is magnetized by induction from the exciting coil in combination with the magnetic circuit, which directs the flux to the two pulleys. The magnetic particles tend to adhere to the pulleys and are diverted to the left. The force of gravity and centrifugal force cause them ultimately to leave the pulley as indicated. The nonmagnetic particles are thrown to the right as shown. Some magnetic particles which happen to escape the first pulley are for the most part separated by the lower pulley. The position of the "splitter" which divides the falling particles is adjustable.

178. Lifting Magnets. Lifting magnets are used commercially to handle iron and steel having various forms. A great saving of time and labor is effected by their use, because chains and slings for holding the load are not necessary. They are very useful for handling steel billets in rolling mills, although the billets cannot be picked up when red-hot as they lose their magnetic properties at this temperature. Lifting magnets are especially useful in loading and unloading steel rails, for an entire layer may be picked up and laid down again without being disarranged. Lifting magnets effect a great saving of labor when small pieces of iron, such as scrap iron, are handled, for they will pick up large quantities at every lift. Without such a magnet it would be necessary to move each individual piece by hand. Figure 190 shows in cross section a typical Cutler-Hammer lifting magnet. The magnetic circuit for a lifting magnet is

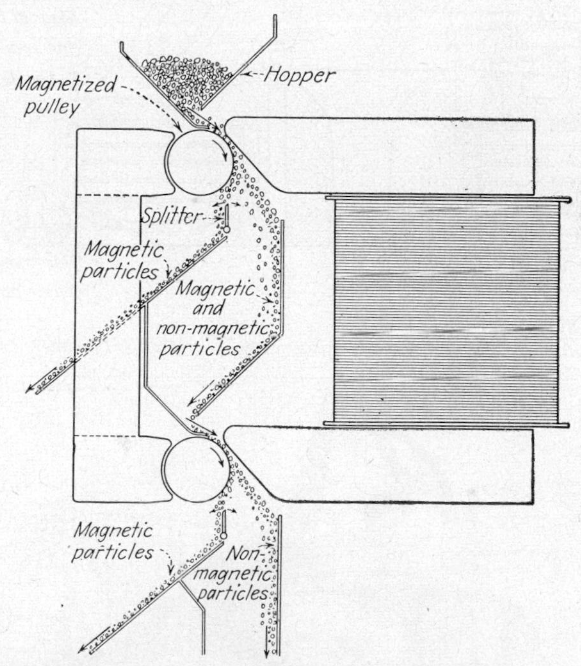

FIG. 189. Magnetic separator. (*Dings Magnetic Separator Co.*)

shown in Fig. 389*A* (p. 661). Figure 191 shows the Giant 77-in. lifting magnet, the largest in the world, lifting a load of baled scrap.

Formulas for the holding force of electromagnets are given in Sec. 162 (p. 219).

It should be understood that the magnet itself does little or no work in the lifting but merely serves as a holding device. The actual work is performed by the engine or motor which operates the ropes or chains attached to the magnet.

179. Magnetic Track Brakes. From early days the magnetic track brake has been employed to some extent on electric railway cars, particularly in regions where grades are severe. The more recent developments in high-speed high-acceleration cars have made rapid, uniform braking imperative. Such braking is not readily attainable with wheel brakes, and wheel braking produces flat wheels. A modern brake as made by the General Electric Company is shown in Fig. 192(a), (b). It is a simple electromagnet and consists of two parallel side plates with an iron core A between them, all bolted together. The brake is magnetized

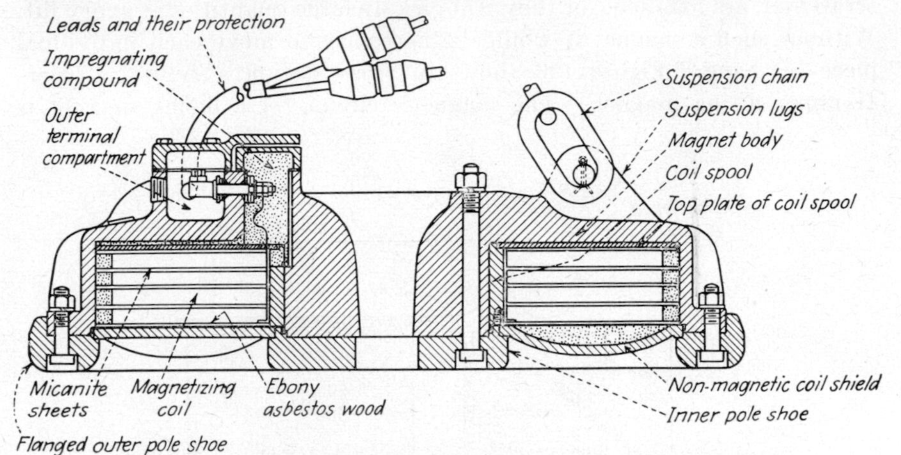

Fig. 190. Cross section of lifting magnet. (*Cutler-Hammer, Inc.*)

Fig. 191. "Giant" 77-in. lifting magnet with load of baled scrap. (*Cutler-Hammer, Inc.*)

by a long longitudinal coil which surrounds the core. The brake shoes B are of opposite polarity and are made of a hard, wear-resisting steel. They are readily removed from the side plates and can be renewed without difficulty. The path of the magnetic flux, when the shoes are on the rail, is shown in Fig. 192(a).

In the simplest method of operation, the brake is suspended on springs so that the shoes normally clear the rail by from 1/4 to 3/8 in. The brake moves in guides, which also serve to transmit the braking force to the car. When the coil is energized, the brake is magnetically attracted to the rail and the magnetism then provides the necessary adhesion for braking. The braking action is readily controlled by a rheostat in series with the magnet coil. When the exciting current is interrupted, the springs pull the brake up to its normal position clear of the rails.

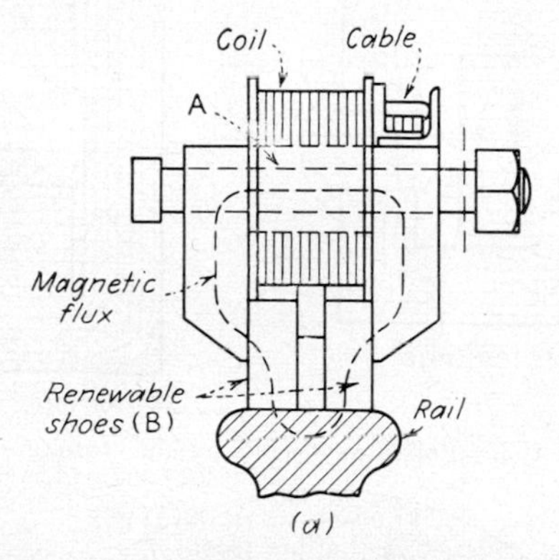

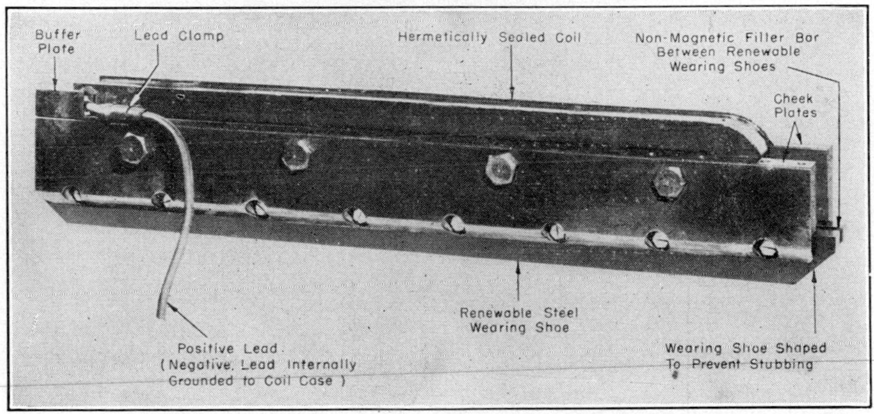

(b)

FIG. 192. Magnetic track brake. (*General Electric Company.*)

The magnetic brake provides a large braking surface and thus acts more effectively than the wheel brake, particularly with a slippery rail. Since the force between the brake and the rail is due to magnetic attraction, there is no reduction in the weight on the wheels during braking such as occurs when track brakes are applied mechanically.

180. Magnetic Circuits of Dynamos. One of the most important uses of electromagnets is in the magnetic fields of motors and generators. A basic principle of magnetic-circuit design is that the windings, or exciting coils, should be placed as closely as possible to the air-gap or to the point in the magnetic circuit where the flux is to be utilized. This minimizes the leakage flux, as is shown in Fig. 193. It will be noted that in (*a*), where the exciting coil is placed on the yoke, there is considerable leakage flux, whereas in (*b*), where there are two exciting coils, each placed adjacent to the air-gap, the leakage flux is essentially a minimum.

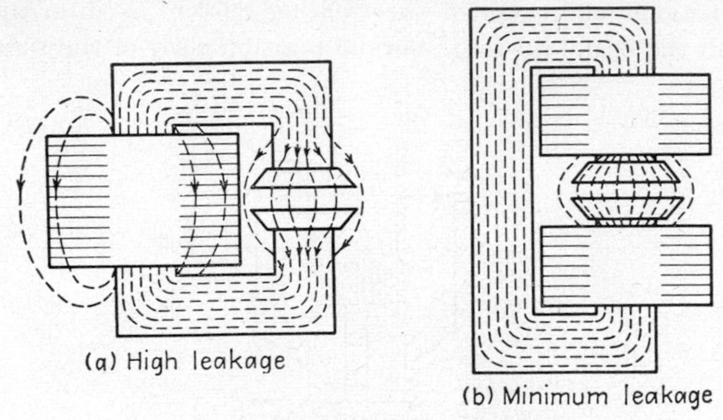

FIG. 193. Positions of coils on electromagnet.

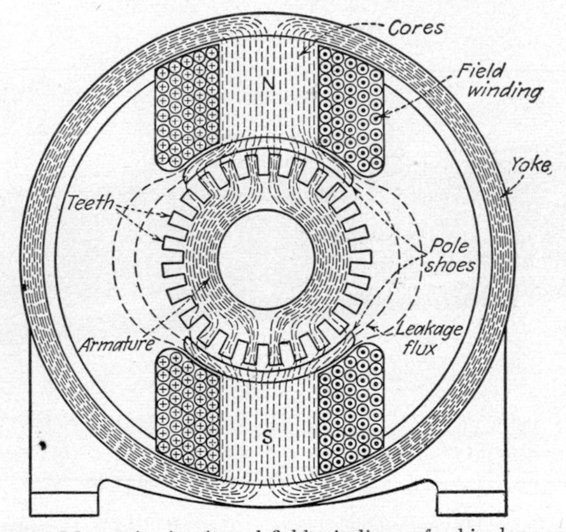

FIG. 194. Magnetic circuit and field windings of a bipolar generator.

In Fig. 194 is shown the magnetic circuit of a typical bipolar dynamo. The field windings are placed around the cores of the two poles as close to the air-gaps as possible. Note that with this design the path for the leakage flux is long, making the reluctance high, which results in low leakage. Note that the flux in the cores divides as it passes into the yoke. Ordinarily the yoke need be only one-half the cross section of the field cores. Direct-current machines of the bipolar type are used for small units and are used also for units of higher rating when the speed is high.

Figure 195 shows the more complex magnetic circuits of a multipolar generator with eight poles. It is to be noted that the poles are alternately north and south. The flux passing through the field cores divides, both on reaching the yoke and on reaching the armature path, and the cross section of the yoke need be only one-half that of the cores.

The magnetic leakage is reduced materially by placing the exciting ampere-turns as near the armature as possible.

Magnetic leakage does not lower the power efficiency of a dynamo, but it does result in increased weight and cost. A steady magnetic flux

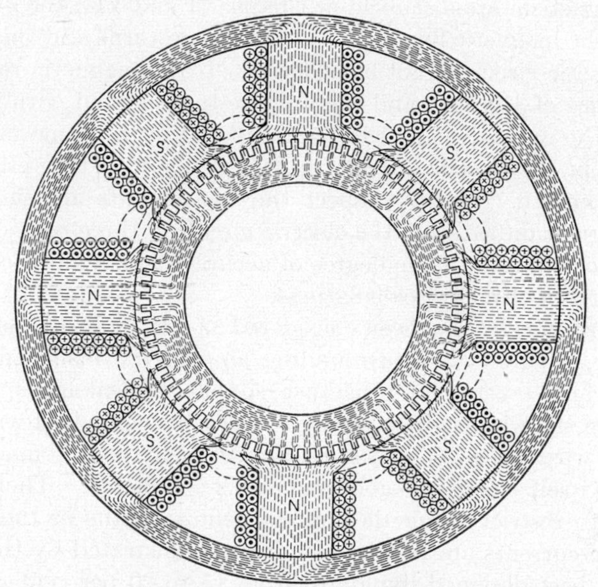

FIG. 195. Magnetic circuits of a multipolar generator.

cannot cause any power loss, since it represents merely stored energy. No power is required to maintain a steady magnetic field. After the flux has reached a steady value, the power to the exciting coils is all accounted for by the copper loss in the coils themselves (see Sec. 221, p. 310). Hence, since the leakage flux is steady, it cannot cause any power loss and therefore cannot affect the power efficiency.

However, the leakage flux must pass through the field cores and yoke, Figs. 194 and 195. Therefore, these parts of the machine must be of greater cross section than would be necessary for the useful flux alone. Moreover, the larger cross section of the field cores results in a greater amount of copper in the exciting coils if the field loss is to remain constant. Hence, the effect of leakage flux is not to lower the power efficiency of dynamos but to make them heavier and more expensive to manufacture.

CHAPTER VIII

THE MAGNETIC CIRCUIT

181. Magnetic Circuit. Although the general nature and characteristics of magnetism are discussed in Chaps. VI and VII, the quantitative relation of the magnetic flux to both the ampere-turns and the properties of the magnetic circuit is not considered. If the magnetic resistance or the reluctance of a circuit and the ampere-turns linked with this circuit be known, the magnetic flux can be calculated in the same manner that the current in the electric circuit can be calculated if the resistance and voltage be known. In this respect the two circuits are similar. The magnetic circuit differs from the electric circuit in three respects, making it difficult to attain the same degree of accuracy in magnetic calculations as is obtained in electrical calculations.

The electric current has been considered as confined to a definite path, for example, a wire. The surrounding air and the insulating supports for the wire have a very high resistance, so that any leakage current which escapes from the wire is almost always negligible compared with the current in the wire itself. There is no known insulator for magnetic flux. In fact, air itself is a fairly good magnetic conductor. Therefore, it is impossible to restrict magnetic lines to definite paths in the same way that electric currents are restricted. This is illustrated by the fact that even in the best designed dynamos, from 15 to 20 per cent of the total flux produced leaks across air paths where it cannot be utilized. The presence of this leakage flux may be detected with a compass, and its intensity is often sufficient to magnetize watches even when they are several feet distant from the dynamo.

Magnetic paths are usually short and have large cross-sectional dimensions in proportion to their length. They are often so complicated in their geometry that only approximations to their magnetic resistance can be obtained. This may cause errors of considerable magnitude in magnetic calculations. This is well illustrated by the air-gap of a dynamo. The geometry of the magnetic path between the armature teeth and slots and the pole face is very complicated, and at best only approximations to the actual distribution of the magnetic flux can be made (see Fig. 195).

Under ordinary conditions of use, the resistance of electric conductors becomes substantially constant, although temperature changes may cause variations of several per cent under differing conditions of operation. Correction for the effect of temperature changes can be accurately made. The magnetic resistance of materials, however, is not constant but varies over wide ranges. This resistance depends to a large extent on the magnetic history of the material. The magnetic resistance of iron may increase 50 times when the magnetic-flux density alters from a low to a high value.

Although the foregoing factors prevent magnetic calculations being made with the same degree of accuracy as can be obtained with electric circuits, yet if one understands magnetic relations he can, by the use of certain approximations, make computations that are sufficiently accurate for most purposes.

Systems of Magnetic Units. It is already pointed out (p. 27 *et seq.*) that three systems of magnetic units are now in use: the cgs, the unrationalized mks, and the rationalized mks systems. The cgs system will be considered first, to be followed by the two mks systems.

182. CGS Magnetic Units. The magnetic units with their definitions are as follows:

Ampere-turns (IN). The ampere-turns acting on a magnetic circuit are given by the product of the turns linked with the circuit and the amperes in these turns. For example, 10 amp in 150 turns gives 1,500 amp-turns. The same result is produced by 15 amp in 100 turns. If any ampere-turns act in opposition, they must be subtracted.

Magnetomotive Force (mmf, also $\mathfrak{F}$). Magnetomotive force tends to drive the flux through the magnetic circuit and corresponds to emf in the electric circuit. It is directly proportional to the ampere-turns of the circuit and differs from the numerical value of the ampere-turns only by the constant factor $0.4\pi = 1.257$. That is, $\mathfrak{F} = 0.4\pi IN = 1.257IN$.

In the cgs magnetic system, the mmf of a circuit is the work in ergs in carrying a unit N pole once through the entire magnetic circuit.

The unit of mmf is the *gilbert.*[1] The gilberts acting on a circuit are obtained by multiplying the ampere-turns by 0.4π or 1.257.

[1] After William Gilbert (1544–1603) (originally spelled Gilberd). A physician and experimenter and the most distinguished man of science in England during the reign of Queen Elizabeth. His early education was obtained at Colchester, England; he entered St. John's College, Cambridge, in 1568, from which he received his B.A. and M.A. degrees and his M.D. degree in 1569. He was elected president of the College of Physicians in 1600 and became the physician to Queen Elizabeth. His fame rests on the results of his experiments published in 1600 in a monumental work, "De Magnete, magneticisque corporibus, et de magno magnete, tellure, physiologia nova." He was in reality the first to investigate electric and magnetic phenomena since the early observations of frictional electricity, 2,000 years before. He devised what is now an electroscope and was the first to use the word "electric" after the Greek word "elektron" meaning amber. He was the first to demonstrate that the earth is in

Reluctance ($\mathcal{R}$). Reluctance is resistance to the passage of magnetic flux and corresponds to resistance in the electric circuit. (Reluctance is the ratio of magnetic potential difference to flux. $\mathcal{R} = \mathfrak{F}/\phi$.) The unit of reluctance is that of a centimeter cube of vacuum. As yet, no name has been standardized for the unit of reluctance.

Permeance ($\mathcal{P}$). The permeance of a circuit is the reciprocal of the reluctance ($\mathcal{P} = 1/\mathcal{R}$) and may be defined as that property of the circuit which permits the passage of the magnetic flux or of the lines of induction. (Permeance is the ratio of flux to magnetic potential difference. $\mathcal{P} = \phi/\mathfrak{F}$.) It corresponds to conductance in the electric circuit.

Relative Permeability (μ_r). The relative permeability, or permeability, of a material is the ratio of the flux or the number of lines of induction existing in the material to the flux, or number of lines of induction, which would exist in the space occupied by the material if it were replaced by vacuum, the mmf acting on the space remaining unchanged. The permeability of vacuum is taken as unity; and with the exception of iron, steel, nickel, liquid oxygen, and certain iron oxides, most materials, including air, may be considered as having a permeability of unity. The permeability of commercial iron and steel ranges from 50 and even lower to about 2,000. In special investigations, vacuum-treated iron has attained a permeability of 5,000 and even greater (also see Permalloy, p. 274).

Example. In a ring solenoid wound on an iron core similar to that of Fig. 218 (p. 286), or of the test specimens, Figs. 219 and 221 (pp. 288 and 291), the magnetic flux is 4,000 maxwells. When the iron core is removed, the flux in air is only 20 maxwells. What is the permeability of the iron?

Removing the iron core does not change the ampere-turns or the geometry of the magnetic circuit. Therefore,

$$\mu_r = \frac{4{,}000}{20} = 200. \quad \textit{Ans.}$$

Flux (ϕ). The magnetic flux is equal to the total number of lines of induction existing in the magnetic circuit and corresponds to current in the electric circuit. The cgs unit of flux is the *maxwell*.[1]

Magnetic Induction or Flux Density (B). The flux density is the number of maxwells or lines of induction per unit area, the area being taken at right angles to the direction of the flux. The unit of flux density in the cgs system is one line per square centimeter and is called the *gauss*.[2]

$$B = \frac{\phi}{A} \tag{161}$$

where A is the area and ϕ the flux through and normal to this area.

reality a large permanent magnet. He recognized the field surrounding a magnet and called the region the "orb of virtue." Galileo once wrote that Gilbert deserved the highest praise for his work.

[1] See footnote, p. 211.

[2] See footnote, p. 214.

(A comparison of the units of the electric and the magnetic circuits is given in Appendix C, p. 585.)

183. Reluctance of Magnetic Circuit. The unit reluctance is defined as that of a centimeter cube of vacuum or of air. If the portion of a magnetic circuit between pole faces a and b, Fig. 196(a)[1], consists of a path in air having a length of 3 cm and a cross section of 1 sq cm, as in the figure, this path is equivalent to three centimeter cubes placed in series. As the total flux must pass in succession through each cube, it is evident that the total reluctance is 3 units. *The reluctance is proportional to the length of the flux path.*

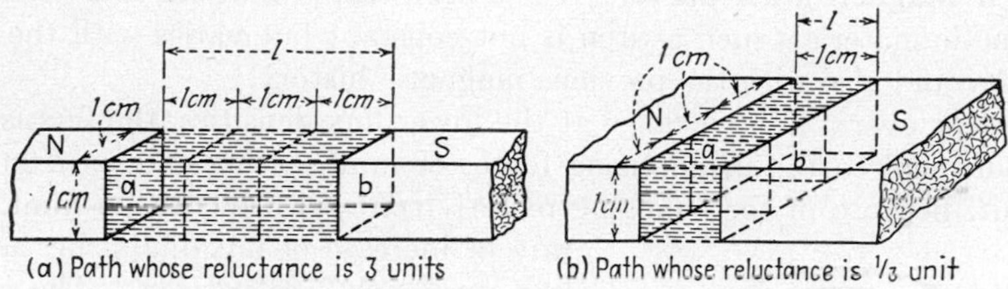

Fig. 196. Reluctance of simple magnetic paths.

On the other hand, if the path has a length of 1 cm and a cross section of 3 sq cm, as in Fig. 196(b), the reluctance of the path through which the flux passes is one-third that of one centimeter cube alone, or is ⅓ unit. *The reluctance is inversely proportional to the cross section of the path.*

Moreover, if these paths were in iron, having a relative permeability μ_r, the flux would be μ_r times its value in air, provided that the same mmf were maintained between the two pole faces. This results in lower reluctance.

It follows that *the reluctance of any portion of a magnetic circuit is proportional to its length, inversely proportional to its cross section, and inversely proportional to the permeability of the material.* The constant of proportionality is unity, since the reluctance of a path in air 1 cm long and 1 sq cm cross section is 1 unit. Hence,

$$\mathcal{R}_1 = \frac{l_1}{A_1 \mu_{r1}} \tag{162}$$

where l_1 is the length in centimeters of that part of the circuit under consideration, A_1 is the uniform cross section in square centimeters of that part of the circuit, and μ_{r1} is the relative permeability of that part of the circuit.

If a magnetic circuit consists of four parts in series as in Fig. 197, the total reluctance is

$$\mathcal{R} = \mathcal{R}_1 + \mathcal{R}_2 + \mathcal{R}_3 + \mathcal{R}_4 = \frac{l_1}{A_1 \mu_{r1}} + \frac{l_2}{A_2 \mu_{r2}} + \frac{l_3}{A_3 \mu_{r3}} + \frac{l_4}{A_4 \mu_{r4}}. \tag{163}$$

[1] The actual flux path between pole faces would not exist as shown in Fig. 196(a), (b), since the flux would "fringe" as shown in Fig. 193 (p. 246).

Permeances in parallel are added together to find the total permeance just as conductances in parallel are added together to find the total conductance.

The total permeance

$$\mathcal{P} = \mathcal{P}_1 + \mathcal{P}_2 + \mathcal{P}_3 + \mathcal{P}_4. \tag{164}$$

Reluctances in parallel combine just as resistances in parallel,

$$\frac{1}{\mathcal{R}} = \frac{1}{\mathcal{R}_1} + \frac{1}{\mathcal{R}_2} + \frac{1}{\mathcal{R}_3} + \frac{1}{\mathcal{R}_4}. \tag{165}$$

184. Magnetization Curve. It has been stated that the reluctivity of magnetic materials such as iron is not constant but varies with the flux density and also with the previous magnetic history.

Except over a limited range at the lower flux densities, the flux is not proportional to the magnetizing force, or mmf, acting on the magnetic circuit, because of the changing reluctivity. With increasing mmf, the rate of increase of flux diminishes as the iron approaches saturation. The basic reasons for these relations between magnetic flux and magnetizing force are the changes and different degrees of orientation in the domains, and these phenomena have already been discussed (p. 196 *et seq.*). Magnetization curves for different types of magnetic materials and their applications to magnetic circuits will now be considered.

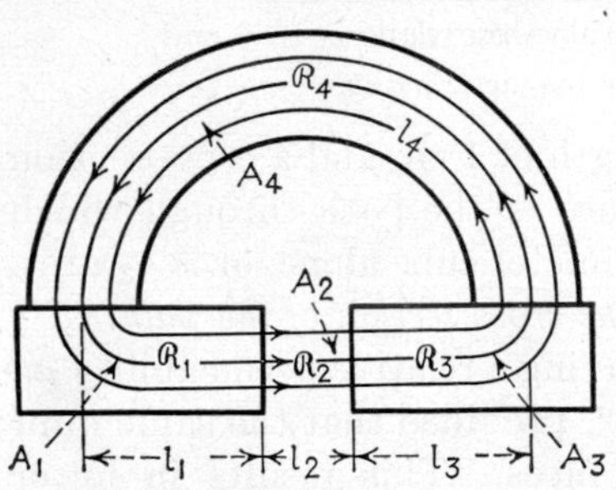

FIG. 197. Reluctances in series.

The relation of flux to mmf in ferromagnetic and similar materials can seldom be expressed by any simple equation, so that it is almost always necessary to express the relation graphically by a *magnetization curve.*

Magnetization curves almost always give magnetic properties in terms of a unit cube of the material, flux density being plotted as ordinates and mmf per unit length as abscissas. With the cgs system it is customary to plot maxwells per square centimeter, or gauss, as ordinates; and gilberts per centimeter, or oersteds (numerically), as abscissas. In the United States, the common use of the British system for the dimensions of electric machinery has made it common also to use maxwells per square inch as ordinates and ampere-turns per inch as abscissas.

A typical magnetization curve for cast steel is shown in Fig. 198. Abscissas are mmf in gilberts per centimeter (H),[1] and ordinates are the corresponding flux densities (B).

[1] H is the symbol for field intensity, but H is *numerically* equal to the mmf per centimeter (see Sec. 187, p. 255).

From 0 to A the curve concaves upward slightly.[1]

From A to B, the curve is practically a straight line. Beyond B, the flux density increases much less rapidly for a given increase in mmf, and the iron approaches saturation. The point C, where the bend in the curve is pronounced, is the *knee of the curve*. Beyond C, the flux can be increased but slightly even with a great increase in the mmf. The steel is now said to be *saturated*. The type of curve shown in Fig. 198, which starts with zero induction and is taken with increasing values of magnetizing force, is called the *normal* saturation or induction curve. Figure 202 (p. 258) shows normal induction curves for commercial grades of iron.

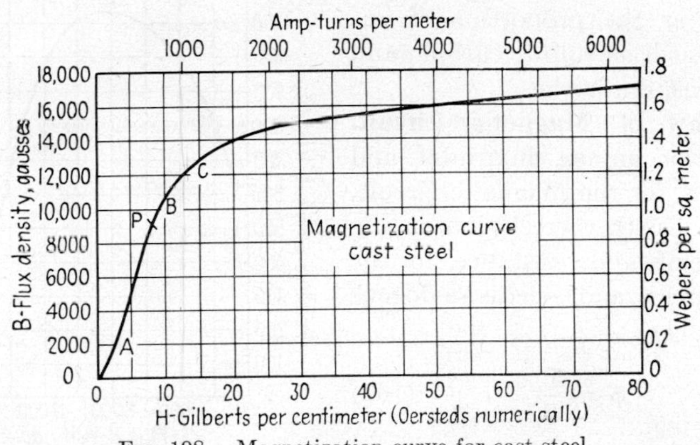

FIG. 198. Magnetization curve for cast steel.

185. Relative Permeability. Relative permeability μ_r is defined as the ratio of the flux in the magnetic substance to the flux in vacuum or air, the mmf and the geometry of the magnetic circuit being the same in both cases (Sec. 182, p. 250). The magnetization curve, Fig. 198, gives the relation of the flux in a centimeter cube of steel to the mmf acting across two opposite faces of the cube. If the steel were removed, the same mmf is acting across a centimeter cube of air. Also, since the flux now is equal numerically to the mmf acting between the two opposite faces of the cube, the reluctance being unity, the flux is also equal to H (Sec. 157, p. 213). Hence, from definition, the relative permeability, or permeability

$$\mu_r = \frac{B}{H}. \tag{166}$$

Thus the permeability is found by dividing each ordinate B of the magnetization curve, Fig. 198, by the corresponding value of H.

[1] See p. 200 *et seq.*

Figure 199 shows the permeability curve of cast steel, Figs. 198 and 202, determined by this method, plotted as a function of the flux density B.

It will be noted that the permeability varies over a wide range. It begins at a comparatively low value, corresponding to the portion $0A$ of the magnetization curve, Fig. 198, increases to a maximum at the point p, and then decreases as the degree of saturation increases, until the curve reaches about one-fifth its maximum value.

The permeability of iron or steel depends on the quality of the material, the flux density, and the previous magnetic history. Also, in general, the permeability of iron increases as the proportion of impurities, such as sulfur, carbon, and phosphorus, diminishes.

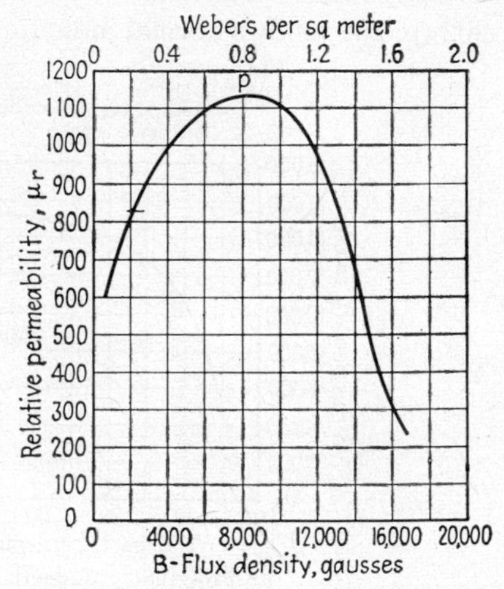

FIG. 199. Relative permeability characteristic of cast steel.

186. Law of Magnetic Circuit. The relation among flux, mmf, and reluctance, for the magnetic circuit, is identical with the relation among current, emf, and resistance, for the electric circuit, and hence is analogous to Ohm's law:

$$\phi = \frac{\mathcal{F}}{\mathcal{R}}. \tag{167}$$

The flux is directly proportional to the mmf and inversely proportional to the reluctance of the circuit.

Also, *the flux is equal to the mmf divided by the reluctance.*

Since $\mathcal{F} = 0.4\pi NI$ (Sec. 182, p. 249) and $\mathcal{R} = l/A\mu_r$ (Sec. 183, p. 251),

$$\phi = \frac{0.4\pi NI}{l/A\mu_r}. \tag{168}$$

If the magnetic circuit consists of several distinct parts in series, having reluctances $\mathcal{R}_1$, $\mathcal{R}_2$, etc., and mmfs $\mathcal{F}_1$, $\mathcal{F}_2$, etc., from (168),

$$\phi = \frac{\mathcal{F}_1 + \mathcal{F}_2 + \mathcal{F}_3 + \cdots}{\dfrac{l_1}{A_1\mu_{r1}} + \dfrac{l_2}{A_2\mu_{r2}} + \dfrac{l_3}{A_3\mu_{r3}} + \cdots}$$

$$= \frac{0.4\pi(I_1N_1 + I_2N_2 + I_3N_3 + \cdots)}{\dfrac{l_1}{A_1\mu_{r1}} + \dfrac{l_2}{A_2\mu_{r2}} + \dfrac{l_3}{A_3\mu_{r3}} + \cdots}. \tag{169}$$

Example. A ring magnet, Fig. 200, is wound with 250 turns of wire and the current is 1.5 amp. Assume the permeability of the iron to be 800. Neglecting fringing, determine flux in ring and also flux density.

$$\mathfrak{F} = 0.4\pi \cdot 1.5 \cdot 250 = 471.4 \text{ gilberts.}$$
$$l_1 = 18 \text{ in.} = 18 \cdot 2.54 = 45.72 \text{ cm.}$$
$$l_2 = 3/16 \text{ in.} = 3/16 \cdot 2.54 = 0.4763 \text{ cm.}$$
$$A_1 = A_2 = 0.2 \text{ sq in.} = 0.2 \cdot 2.54 \cdot 2.54 = 1.290 \text{ sq cm.}$$

From (169)

$$\phi = \frac{471.4}{\frac{45.72}{1.290 \cdot 800} + \frac{0.4763}{1.290 \cdot 1.0}} = \frac{471.4}{0.04430 + 0.3692} = 1{,}140 \text{ maxwells.} \quad \textit{Ans.}$$

The flux density

$$B = \frac{1{,}140}{1.290} = 883.7 \text{ maxwells per sq cm, or gauss}$$
$$= 5{,}700 \text{ maxwells per sq in.} \quad \textit{Ans.}$$

187. Magnetomotive Force per Centimeter and Field Intensity H. In air the mmf in gilberts per centimeter is equal *numerically* to the field

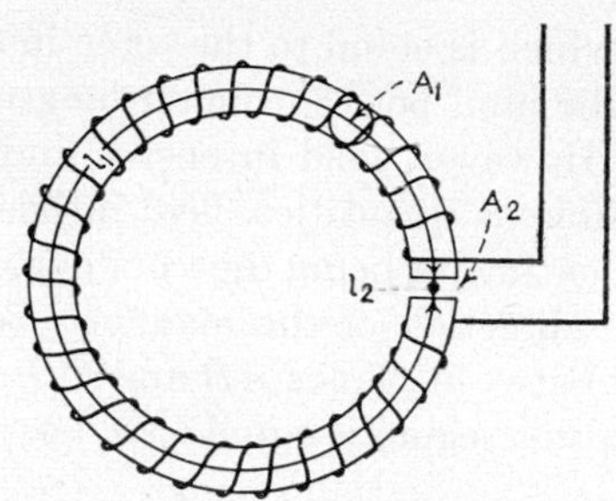

FIG. 200. Ring-type electromagnet.

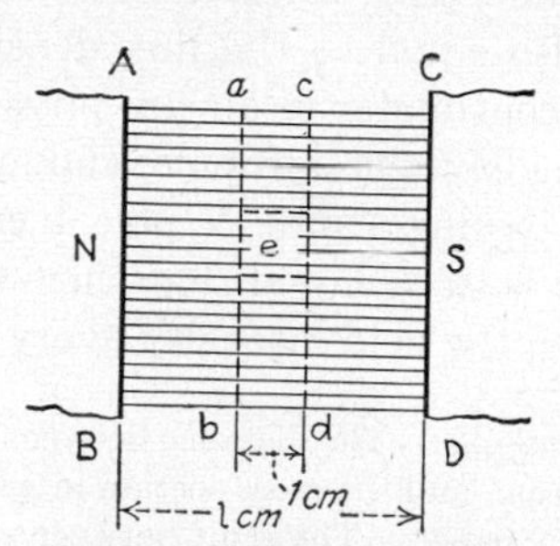

FIG. 201. Field intensity and mmf.

intensity in dynes per unit pole, or oersteds. This may be shown as follows:

In Fig. 201 is shown a portion of a uniform magnetic field in air between two parallel planes AB and CD situated l cm apart. This field might be produced between the poles of an electromagnet or in the center of a long solenoid (pp. 236 and 285). The cross section of the field perpendicular to the paper is A sq cm. The mmf between the planes AB and CD is $\mathfrak{F}$ gilberts. The magnetic flux between planes AB and CD is, by (167),

$$\phi = \frac{\mathfrak{F}}{l/A}. \tag{I}$$

First consider two other planes ab and cd perpendicular to the field and 1 cm apart. The mmf between these planes is $\mathfrak{F}/l$ and the reluctance is $1/A$. Hence the flux $\phi = \frac{\mathfrak{F}/l}{1/A}$ and is the same as that given by (I).

Next consider a centimeter cube e between the planes ab and cd. The mmf across the two opposite faces of this cube, which lie in the planes *ab* and *cd*, is $\mathfrak{F}/l$. The reluctance of the cube is unity. Hence the flux between the opposite faces of the cube *e* is equal to $(\mathfrak{F}/l)/1 = B$ maxwells per sq cm, or gauss.

Since the mmf between any two points is measured by the work in ergs performed in carrying a unit *N* pole between these points, the work done in carrying a unit pole from surface *ab* to surface *cd* is $\mathfrak{F}/l$ ergs. The magnetic field is uniform, and the force on a unit pole is therefore everywhere the same. Since work is equal to the product of force and distance, the force is equal to the mmf divided by the distance, which is unity between the opposite faces of the cube. Hence, the force on a unit pole or the field intensity everywhere between the surfaces *ab* and *cd* is $\mathfrak{F}/l$ dynes. But $\mathfrak{F}/l$ is the mmf *per centimeter length* or *mmf gradient* of this uniform magnetic field.

Thus, *in air*, the field intensity *H*, which is equal to the force in dynes per unit pole, is *numerically* equal to the mmf per centimeter length, and is also equal to the flux density *B*. However, field intensity and mmf per centimeter in air are physically different quantities, field intensity *H* being *force* per unit pole, and mmf per centimeter being the *work* performed in carrying a unit *N* pole 1 cm in the direction of the magnetic field.

It is to be noted that since the field between planes *AB* and *CD* is uniform, the field intensity everywhere in this region is equal to $\mathfrak{F}/l$ oersteds.

Example. The distance between two parallel pole faces, similar to those in Fig. 201, is 10 cm, and the cross section in which the field is uniform is 8 by 5 cm, perpendicular to the paper. The mmf between surfaces *AB* and *CD* is 4,800 gilberts. Determine: (*a*) work done in carrying a unit *N* pole between surfaces *CD* and *AB*; (*b*) reluctance of flux path; (*c*) total flux; (*d*) flux density in gauss; (*e*) mmf per centimeter length of flux path; (*f*) flux in cross section of a centimeter cube perpendicular to field, surfaces of cube being either parallel with or perpendicular to field; (*g*) field intensity in oersteds or dynes per unit pole.

(*a*) Since mmf between two points is defined as work performed in carrying a unit pole between those points, the answer to (*a*) must be 4,800 ergs. *Ans.*

(*b*) $\mathcal{R} = 10/(8 \cdot 5) = 0.250$ cgs reluctance units. *Ans.*

(*c*) $\phi = 4{,}800/0.250 = 19{,}200$ maxwells. *Ans.*

(*d*) $B = 19{,}200/(8 \cdot 5) = 480$ gauss. *Ans.*

(*e*) Mmf per centimeter is $4{,}800/10 = 480$ gilberts. *Ans.*

(*f*) Since the reluctance of a centimeter cube is unity, the flux in the cross section of the cube must be

$$\phi = 480/1 = 480 \text{ maxwells, which is also the flux density } B. \quad \textit{Ans.}$$

(*g*) Since the mmf per centimeter is 480 gilberts, 480 ergs is involved in carrying a unit *N* pole 1 cm in the direction of the field. Since the field is uniform, the force is constant and must be $480/1 = 480$ dynes (force = work/distance). Field intensity is defined as force in dynes per unit pole; hence $H = 480$ oersteds. *Ans.*

It is to be noted that the gauss (*d*), the mmf per centimeter in gilberts (*e*), and the field intensity in oersteds (*g*) are all equal *numerically*.

188. Method of Trial and Error. Magnetic problems cannot always be solved readily by the method used in Sec. 186 (p. 254). This is due to the fact that the permeability (which is a variable but is given in the example as a constant value of 800) is not ordinarily known until the flux density and therefore the answer are known. The answer of course depends in turn on the permeability. If the permeability could be expressed as a function of the flux density, the problem could be solved directly. As a rule, however, the relation of permeability to flux density is not simple, as is shown by Fig. 199, so that a direct solution of the problem is difficult. However, such problems can usually be solved by trial and error as illustrated by the following example:

Example. The iron ring of Fig. 200 and Sec. 186 (p. 254) is made of cast steel whose permeability curve is given in Fig. 199. The air-gap is reduced to 1/16 in. by inserting additional iron. Determine flux and flux density.

Assume the permeability as 900.

$$\mathcal{R}_1 = \frac{18.13 \cdot 2.54}{1.290 \cdot 900} = 0.03966.$$

$$\mathcal{R}_2 = \frac{\frac{1}{16} \cdot 2.54}{1.290} = 0.1231.$$

$$\phi = \frac{471.4}{0.03966 + 0.1231} = 2{,}900 \text{ maxwells.} \quad \textit{Ans.}$$

$$B = \frac{2{,}900}{1.290} = 2{,}245 \text{ gauss.} \quad \textit{Ans.}$$

From Fig. 199, the permeability at this flux density is 830. Therefore $\mathcal{R}_1$ must be recalculated using the new value of permeability:

$$\mathcal{R}_1 = \frac{18.13 \cdot 2.54}{1.290 \cdot 830} = 0.0430.$$

$$\phi = \frac{471.4}{0.0430 + 0.1231} = 2{,}838 \text{ maxwells.}$$

The new value of $B = 2{,}200$ gauss.

As the value of μ corresponding to this flux density is 820, or sufficiently close to the value 830 just used, the last two values of flux and flux density are substantially correct.

With the magnetic problems usually met in practice, the problem is simplified since either the flux or the flux density is known, and it is required to determine the corresponding ampere-turns.

189. Determination of Ampere-turns. It is shown in Sec. 46 (p. 51) that the voltage drop per unit length of a conductor depends only on the *current density* and the resistivity of the conductor. In a similar manner the mmf per unit length depends only on the *flux density* and the reluctivity of the material. This is proved as follows:

From Eq. (168) (p. 254)

$$\phi = \frac{0.4\pi NI}{l/A\mu_r} = \frac{\mathfrak{F}}{l/A\mu_r} = BA.$$

Since $\phi = BA$, where B is the uniform flux density and A is the cross section of the path,

$$\frac{\mathfrak{F}}{l} = \frac{B}{\mu_r}. \tag{I}$$

Multiplying both sides of (I) by l,

$$\mathfrak{F} = \frac{Bl}{\mu_r}. \tag{170}$$

Equation (170) shows that the mmf is equal to the product of the *flux density* and the length of the magnetic path, divided by the permeability of the material. To determine the mmf for a unit length of a circuit,

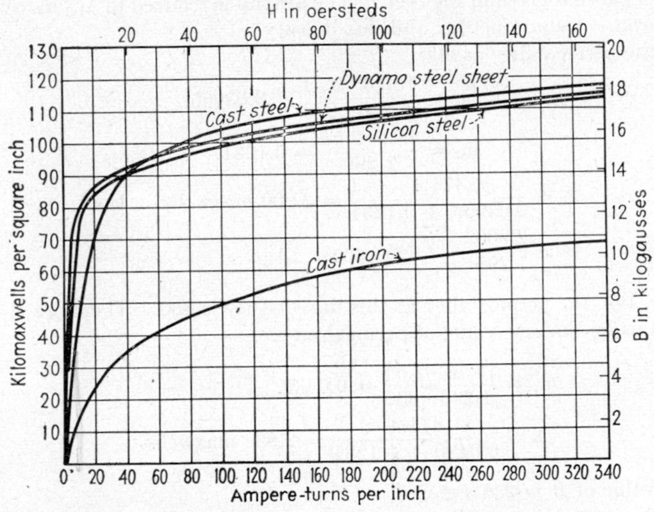

Fig. 202. Typical magnetization curves for iron and steel.

it is necessary to know only the flux density and the permeability. Instead of plotting the permeability as a function of the flux density, the magnetization curve is frequently plotted with ampere-turns per unit length as abscissa and the corresponding flux density as ordinate. This is more convenient and avoids using both 0.4π and the permeability. Such curves are shown in Fig. 202 for various commercial irons and steels used in the manufacture of electrical machinery.

In problems where the flux and the cross section of the magnetic paths are known and it is desired to find the ampere-turns necessary to produce this known flux, the curves just referred to enable the solution to be obtained readily.

190. Ampere-turns for a Simple Air-gap. Let it be required to determine the ampere-turns IN necessary to produce a uniform flux ϕ in a simple air-gap between two parallel planes having areas of A sq cm and spaced a distance of l cm.

The flux $\phi = BA = \dfrac{0.4\pi IN}{l/A}$ [from Eq. (168), p. 254; $\mu_r = 1.0$]

where B is the flux density. Hence,

$$IN = \frac{1}{0.4\pi} Bl = 0.796Bl$$
$$= 0.8Bl \text{ (nearly)} \tag{171}$$

Hence, the ampere-turns for an air-gap depend only on the *flux density* and the *effective length* of gap. [Equation (171) should be compared with Eq. (170).]

Since the dimensions of machines are frequently given in inch units and the operating flux densities are usually given in maxwells per square inch, it is convenient to express (171) in inch units. Let B' be the flux density in maxwells per square inch and l' the length of the gap in inches.

$$B' = (2.54)^2B; \qquad l' = \frac{l}{2.54}.$$

Hence,

$$IN = 0.796 \frac{B'}{(2.54)^2} \cdot 2.54l' = 0.313B'l'. \tag{172}$$

Example. The effective length of the air-gap of a dynamo, after correcting for the effect of the teeth and slots,[1] is 0.25 cm, and the pole faces have an area of 400 sq cm. If the total flux is 2,400,000 maxwells, determine the ampere-turns necessary to produce this flux in the gap.

$$B = \frac{2,400,000}{400} = 6,000 \text{ gauss.}$$

$$IN = 0.796 \cdot 6,000 \cdot 0.25 = 1,194 \qquad \text{[from (171)].} \quad \textit{Ans.}$$

If inch units are used, the area

$$A' = \frac{400}{6.45} = 62.0 \text{ sq in.}$$

$$B' = \frac{2,400,000}{62.0} = 38,710 \text{ lines per sq in.}$$

The length

$$l' = \frac{0.25}{2.54} = 0.09843 \text{ in.}$$

Using (172),

$$IN = 0.313 \cdot 38,710 \cdot 0.09843 = 1,193 \text{ (check).}$$

191. Use of Magnetization Curves. In Fig. 202 are plotted the magnetization curves for common types of magnet iron and steel. Both inch

[1] Methods of making this correction are given in A. S. LANGSDORF, "Principles of Direct-current Machines," Chap. IV, McGraw-Hill Book Company, Inc.

units and cgs units are used for abscissas and ordinates. To illustrate the use of the magnetization curves, the following example is given:

Example. Determine the ampere-turns necessary to produce an air-gap flux of 750,000 maxwells in the electromagnet of Fig. 203. The cores are cast iron, and the yoke and pole pieces are cast steel. Neglect fringing and leakage.
The flux density in the lower yoke is

$$B_1 = \frac{750{,}000}{3 \cdot 4} = 62{,}500 \text{ maxwells per sq in.}$$

The ampere-turns per inch for a density of 62,500 from Fig. 202 (cast steel) is 18. The mean length of flux path is (approximately) 16 in.

$$I_1N_1 = 16 \cdot 18 = 288 \text{ amp-turns,}$$

or 288 amp-turns is required to produce a flux of 750,000 maxwells in the lower yoke.

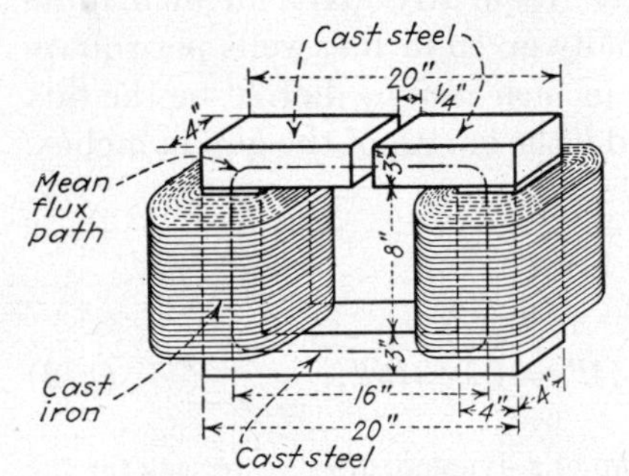

Fig. 203. Electromagnet.

The density in the cores is

$$B_2 = \frac{750{,}000}{4 \cdot 4} = 46{,}900 \text{ maxwells per sq in.}$$

From the curve (cast iron) the ampere-turns per inch = 86.

As there are two cores, the total length is 16 in., neglecting the quarter turn at each corner of the magnetic circuit.

$$I_2N_2 = 16 \cdot 86 = 1{,}376 \text{ amp-turns.}$$

The pole pieces are in every way identical with the yoke, except that the path is 0.25 in. shorter. This small difference if neglected will not introduce an appreciable error, and so for the two pole pieces

$$I_3N_3 = 288 \text{ amp-turns.}$$

For the air-gap [from (172)]

$$I_4N_4 = 0.313 \cdot 62{,}500 \cdot 0.25 = 4{,}890 \text{ amp-turns.}$$

As all the various parts are in series,
The total ampere-turns = 288 + 1,376 + 288 + 4,890 = 6,842. *Ans.*

192. Magnetic Calculations in Dynamos. The magnetic-flux distribution and the flux paths for a multipolar generator are illustrated in Fig. 195 (p. 247). In Fig. 204 the magnetic circuits for the useful flux are indicated by the heavy lines and those for the leakage flux by the lighter lines. It will be noted that the number of magnetic circuits is equal to the number of poles and that each of the poles is common to two magnetic circuits. If two of the poles are considered as being divided by planes *wv* and *xy*, the path *abcdef* constitutes a single magnetic circuit. Each of the other magnetic circuits can be treated similarly. (Distortion of pole flux due to armature reaction, p. 415, might change slightly the positions of the planes *wv* and *xy*.) It will also be noted that each field coil supplies mmf to *two* of the magnetic circuits. For example, field coil *A* supplies mmf for magnetic circuits *abcdef* and *a'b'c'd'e'f'*. However, even though two magnetic circuits share the mmf of each field coil, the *full* mmf of each coil is acting on each circuit. This is readily seen if Kirchhoff's second law, using mmfs rather than emfs, is applied to each magnetic circuit as, for example, *abcdef*. In going round this path, one goes through the mmfs of *two* field coils, *A* and *B*. Hence, the mmfs of *two* field coils act on each of the magnetic circuits, such as *abcdef*.

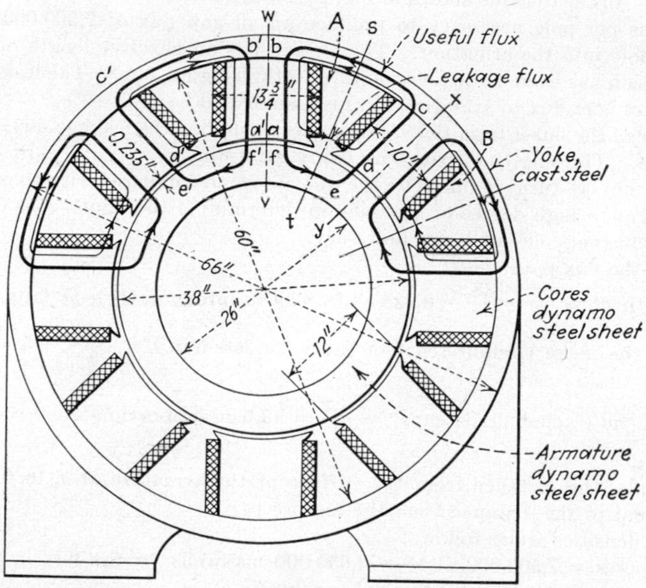

FIG. 204. Eight-pole 400-rpm 250-volt d-c generator. Axial length of armature stampings and pole faces = 16 in.

In the computation of the magnetic circuits of dynamos it is simpler to consider the mmf per pole only. Thus, the magnetic circuit *abcdef* may be considered as being divided into two equal portions by the plane *st*, each of the two field coils *A* and *B* supplying the mmf for each half circuit. In computing the ampere-turns per pole, however, it seems more rational to compute the ampere-turns for the complete magnetic path *abcdef* and to divide this value by 2 to obtain the ampere-turns per pole. This is done in the example which follows.

On account of symmetry, the ampere-turns per pole are the same for the entire dynamo.

The calculation of the exciting ampere-turns is somewhat complicated by the irregular nature of the air-gap, due to the armature teeth, air ducts, fringing, etc. The amount of leakage flux between poles introduces another factor which must be considered.

However, by making some approximations as to leakage and the geometry of the magnetic-flux paths, the relation of flux to ampere-turns may be computed with reasonable accuracy. Below is given an example illustrating the general method of procedure in computing the ampere-turns per pole in a generator. This example is not intended, however, to include the detailed computations such as are found in texts which specialize in dynamo design.

Example. In the dynamo shown in Fig. 204, it is desired to compute the number of ampere-turns per pole necessary to produce an air-gap flux of 7,500,000 maxwells from each pole into the armature. The air-gap has an effective length of 0.235 in., after correction has been made for armature teeth, fringing, etc.[1] The leakage coefficient (ratio of core flux to armature flux) is assumed to be 1.15.

The paths of the fluxes from the various poles, including the leakage flux, are shown in the figure. The lengths of paths are easily determined.

Since the ampere-turns required by the iron are small compared with those required for the air-gap, a high degree of accuracy in determining the dimensions of the iron part of the magnetic circuit is not necessary.

Consider the flux path *abcdef*.

The length $ab = \frac{60 - 38}{2} - 0.235 = 10.8$ in. (approximately); bc (approximately one-eighth the mean circumference of the yoke, less 5 in.) $= \frac{\pi 63''}{8} - 5 = 24.7 - 5 = 19.7$ in.

$$ad \text{ (excluding air-gaps)} = \frac{\pi 32}{8} = 12.6 \text{ in. (approximately).}$$

(For example, the distance from the surface of the armature at a, to f is approximately equal to the distance from the line wv to f.)

The flux densities are as follows:

Flux in cores $= 7{,}500{,}000 \cdot 1.15 = 8{,}630{,}000$ maxwells, as the flux in the core is equal to the armature flux plus the leakage flux.

Flux density in cores $= \frac{8{,}630{,}000}{16 \cdot 10} = 53{,}900$ maxwells per sq in.

This should be increased by about 10 per cent to allow for the thickness of the oxide on the surface of the laminations:

$$53{,}900 \cdot 1.10 = 59{,}300.$$

Flux density in yoke $= \frac{8{,}630{,}000}{2(16 \cdot 3)} = 90{,}000$ maxwells per sq in., as the pole flux divides, one-half going each way in the yoke.

Flux density in armature $= \frac{7{,}500{,}000}{2(6 \cdot 16)} = 39{,}100$ maxwells per sq in.

This must be increased by about 25 per cent to allow for the air-duct space and the oxides between laminations.

This makes the density in the armature

[1] See footnote, p. 259.

$$39{,}100 \cdot 1.25 = 49{,}000 \text{ maxwells per sq in.}$$

The corresponding net area of iron thus becomes

$$0.80 \cdot 2(6 \cdot 16) = 76.8 \text{ sq in.}$$

Hence $B = \dfrac{3{,}750{,}000}{76.8} = 48{,}900$ maxwells per sq in. (*check*).

The air-gap density $= \dfrac{7{,}500{,}000}{16 \cdot 12} = 39{,}100$ maxwells per sq in.

Knowing the above quantities, and utilizing the magnetization curves of Fig. 202, it is a comparatively simple matter to determine the total ampere-turns per pole.

For example, with dynamo steel sheet 4 amp-turns per in. are necessary with 59,300 maxwells per sq in. Hence, for the core *ab*,

$$I_1N_1 = 4 \cdot 10.8 = 43 \text{ amp-turns.}$$

The ampere-turns are then found as follows:

Part	Material	Flux, maxwells	Area, square inches	Flux density, maxwells per square inch	Ampere-turns per inch	Length, inches	Ampere-turns
Core *ab*......	Dynamo steel sheet	8,630,000	160	59,300	4.0	10.8	43
Yoke *bc*......	Cast steel	4,315,000	48	90,000	40.0	19.7	788
Core *cd*......	Dynamo steel sheet	8,630,000	160	59,300	4.0	10.8	43
Gap *de*......	Air	7,500,000	192	39,100	12,240	0.235	2,876
Armature *ef*..	Dynamo steel sheet	3,750,000	76.8	49,000	3.0	12.6	38
Gap *fa*.......	Air	7,500,000	192	39,100	12,240	0.235	2,876
			Total ampere-turns for two poles				6,664
			Total ampere-turns per pole				3,332

As the machine is symmetrical, each complete magnetic circuit requires the same number of ampere-turns per pole. The design of the exciting coils themselves is not difficult.

193. Hysteresis. It is already shown that when the mmf per centimeter or the magnetizing force acting on an iron sample is increased positively from zero, the *normal* magnetization curve results, as is shown by Fig. 198 (p. 253). Also it is shown that as the magnetizing force is increased, the iron becomes more nearly saturated. If, at any point on the normal magnetization curve, the magnetizing force is decreased, it is shown that owing to the delayed unlocking of the domains (p. 202) the values of induction for any given magnetizing force are greater than when the magnetizing force is increasing. For example, in Fig. 205, curve Oa is the *normal* curve. If, after the mmf has reached the value Oa', the magnetizing force is decreased until it reaches zero, the induction now decreases in accordance with the curve ab. When the magnetizing force reaches zero, the induction is not zero but is equal to Ob, or B_r, which is called the *remanence*. Before the flux density can be reduced to zero, the magnetizing force must be reversed in direction. That is, it requires a negative magnetizing force Oc, or H_c, to reduce the induction to zero. The magnetizing force H_c is called the *coercive force*. (These magnetic properties are discussed in connection with permanent magnets, Secs. 201 and 202, pp. 276 and 278.)

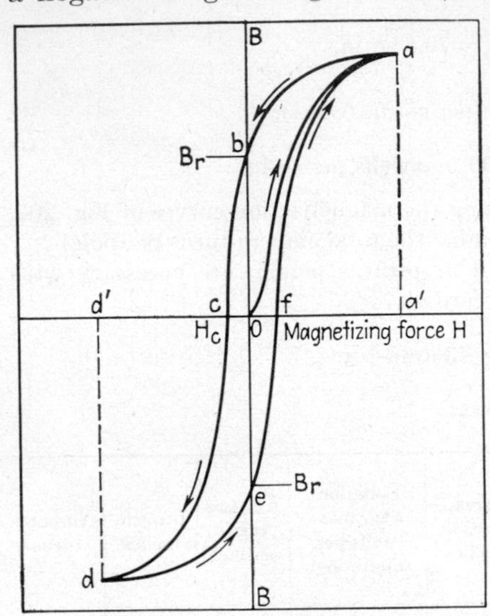

Fig. 205. Hysteresis loop.

If the magnetizing force now be increased in the negative direction to d', where $Od' = Oa'$, the induction will be carried to a negative maximum $d'd$. The negative maximum flux density $d'd$ is equal to $a'a$. If the magnetizing force now is increased toward zero, the curve will pass through point e when the magnetizing force is again zero and the negative remanence $Oe = Ob$. A positive coercive force $Of = Oc$ is necessary to bring the flux density again to zero. When the magnetizing force again becomes Oa', the flux density will return to its original value at a, closing the loop.

It is seen that the induction always lags the magnetizing force. For

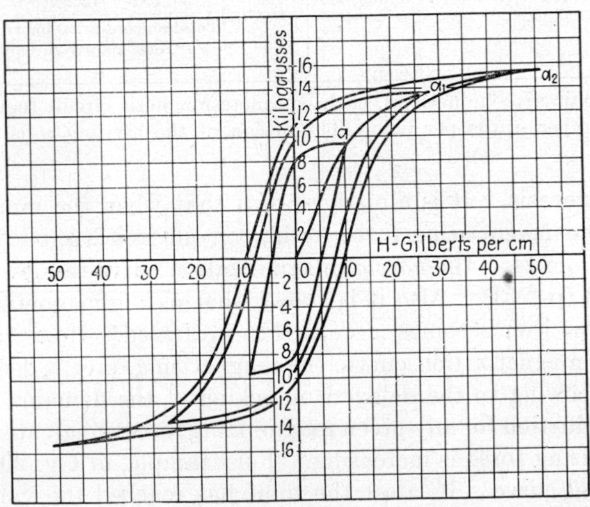

Fig. 206. Hysteresis loops for three maximum flux densities.

example, at b the magnetizing force has reached zero; the induction, however, does not reach zero until the iron has been carried farther along the cycle of magnetization to c. *This lag of the induction with respect to the magnetizing force has been given the name "hysteresis." The cycle of magnetization abcdefa,* Fig. 205, *is called a "hysteresis loop."*

The iron does not return to a previous condition of magnetization without the application of a magnetizing force. For example, it requires a magnetizing force Oc to bring the iron to zero induction at c. (The state of magnetization at c is also different from that at O.) An expenditure of energy is required to carry the iron through the cycle of magnetization. According to the spinning-electron and domain theory, hysteresis loss is caused by the small eddy currents which are induced by the sudden orientations of the domains, the durations of which are about 1/10,000 sec. This theory is substantiated by the fact that the greatest hysteresis loss occurs in the region of the curve, Fig. 149 (p. 202), where the Barkhausen effect is greatest.

If several loops are taken, having different maximum flux densities, they will have the general appearance of the three loops in Fig. 206. The maximum points a, a_1, a_2 all lie along the normal saturation curve Oa_2.

194. Hysteresis Loss. Hysteresis loss is proportional to the area of the hysteresis loop, Figs. 205 and 206. In fact the hysteresis loss may be obtained by finding the area of the loop to scale and dividing by 4π. This gives the loss in ergs per cycle per cu cm.

The relation may be proved as follows: A coil having a total of N turns or n turns per centimeter and wound on an iron core of length l cm and cross section of A sq cm is connected across a potential difference of V cgs volts. The current i (cgs amperes) to the coil is determined not only by the resistance of the coil but by the counter emf $-N\,d\phi/dt = -nl\,d\phi/dt$. The total emf acting on the circuit is therefore $V - nl\,d\phi/dt$ and this is utilized to supply the iR drop in cgs units. That is,

$$V - nl\frac{d\phi}{dt} = iR. \qquad \text{(I)}$$

$$V = iR + nl\frac{d\phi}{dt} \qquad \text{cgs volts.} \qquad \text{(II)}$$

The power

$$Vi = i^2R + nli\frac{d\phi}{dt} \qquad \text{ergs per sec.} \qquad \text{(III)}$$

Vi is the total power input, i^2R is the power which goes to heat the winding, and $nli\,d\phi/dt$ must be the power which goes to store energy in the magnetic circuit. The total stored energy is equal to the integrated product of power and time,

$$W = \int_0^T \left(nli\frac{d\phi}{dt}\right) dt \qquad \text{ergs.} \qquad \text{(IV)}$$

However, $\phi = BA$, where B is the flux density in gauss, and the gilberts per centimeter, $H = 4\pi ni$ (Sec. 187).

These values are substituted in (IV), and the flux density then is integrated between B_1, which is negative, and B_2, giving, Fig. 207,

$$W_1 = \frac{lA}{4\pi}\int_{-B_1}^{B_2} H\,dB \qquad \text{ergs.} \qquad \text{(V)}$$

The integral in (V) gives the area *abcde*0*a*, Fig. 207, shown by horizontal cross-hatching, and when divided by 4π gives the energy in ergs stored per cubic centimeter when H is increased from 0 to H_1. When H is reduced from H_1 to zero, energy is returned from the magnetic field to the electric circuit and is given by

$$W_2 = \frac{lA}{4\pi}\int_{B_3}^{B_2} H\,dB \qquad \text{ergs.} \tag{VI}$$

The integral in (VI) gives the area *cdec*. The total energy stored as H is increased from 0 to H_1 and is then reduced to 0 is $W_1 - W_2$. When H is increased negatively from 0 to $-H_1$ and then reduced to 0, the net energy stored becomes

$$W_3 - W_4 = \frac{lA}{4\pi}\int_{B_3}^{-B_4} -H\,dB + \frac{lA}{4\pi}\int_{-B_1}^{-B_4} -H\,dB \qquad \text{ergs.} \tag{VII}$$

The last term in (VII) is the energy returned from the magnetic field to the electric circuit when H is reduced from $-H_1$ to zero. Hence the total magnetic energy stored per cubic centimeter becomes $(1/lA)$ $(W_1 + W_3 - W_2 - W_4)$ or

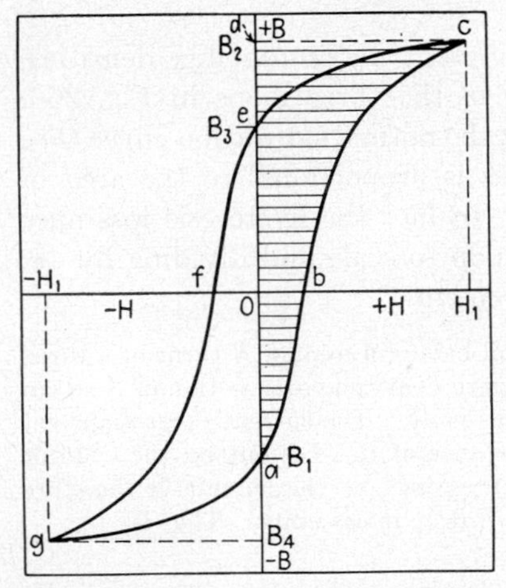

FIG. 207. Hysteresis loss and loop area.

$$W = \frac{1}{4\pi}\left(\int_{-B_1}^{B_2} H\,dB + \int_{B_3}^{-B_4} H\,dB - \int_{B_3}^{B_2} H\,dB - \int_{B_1}^{B_4} H\,dB\right) \qquad \text{ergs.} \tag{173}$$

(173) gives the area of the hysteresis loop *abcefga* divided by 4π and may be generalized as follows:

$$W = \frac{1}{4\pi}\int H\,dB \qquad \text{ergs.} \tag{174}$$

For example, let the area of the smallest loop, Fig. 206, be A sq in. The scale is such that 1 in. on the abscissa scale represents 10 gilberts per cm, and 1 in. on the ordinate scale represent 4 kilogauss. The ergs loss per cycle per cubic centimeter is

$$W_h = \frac{A \cdot 10 \cdot 4{,}000}{4\pi} \qquad \text{ergs.} \tag{175}$$

To convert this energy loss into joules or watt-seconds, divide by 10^7.

The hysteresis loss per cubic centimeter per cycle depends on two factors, the magnetic material and the maximum flux density. The loss within certain limits may be expressed by the Steinmetz law as follows:

$$W_h = \eta B^{1.6}. \tag{176}$$

W_h is the hysteresis loss per cubic centimeter in ergs per cycle, η is a constant depending on the material, and B is the maximum flux density in gauss.

Below are given a few typical values of η.

Hard cast steel	0.025	Sheet iron	0.004
Forged steel	0.020	Silicon sheet steel	0.0010
Annealed cast iron	0.012	Best grade silicon sheet steel	0.00046
		Permalloy	0.0001

Example. Determine the ergs loss per cycle in a core of sheet iron having a net volume of 40 cu cm, in which the maximum flux density is 8,000 gauss.

$W_h = 0.004 \cdot 8{,}000^{1.6}$.

$$\log 8{,}000 = 3.9031.$$
$$1.6 \cdot 3.9031 = 6.2450.$$
$$\log 1{,}757{,}000 = 6.2450.$$

$W_h = 0.004 \cdot 1{,}757{,}000 = 7{,}028$ ergs per cu cm per cycle.
Total loss $W = 7{,}028 \cdot 40 = 281{,}000$ ergs per cycle, or

$$281{,}000 \cdot 10^{-7} = 0.0281 \text{ joule per cycle.} \quad \textit{Ans.}$$

Since the area of the hysteresis loop, divided by 4π, gives the hysteresis loss in ergs per cycle, the hysteresis loss in ergs per second must be equal

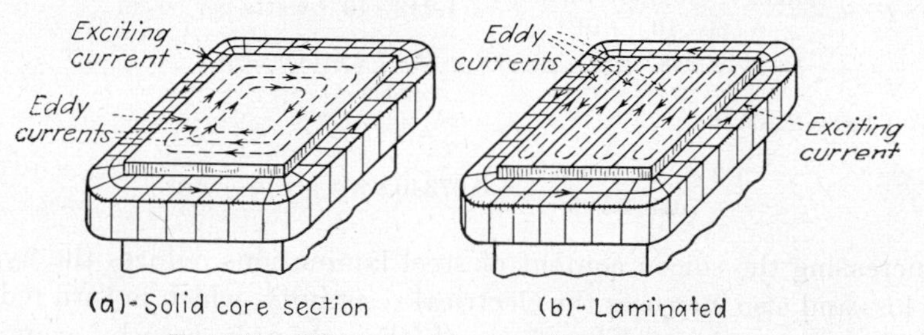

FIG. 208. Effect on eddy currents of laminations.

to the ergs per cycle multiplied by the cycles per second, or frequency. It follows that hysteresis loss is directly proportional to the frequency.

195. Eddy-current Loss. In cores subjected to a varying or an alternating magnetic flux, there exists not only hysteresis loss but eddy-current loss as well. Eddy-current loss is reduced to low values by laminating, the effect of which is shown in Fig. 208. In (*a*), a solid-core section together with the magnetizing coil is shown. The instantaneous direction of the exciting current in the magnetizing coil is counterclockwise. By Lenz's law (p. 299) the direction of the induced current must be such as to *oppose* the inducing current. Hence, the direction of the induced current in the core is clockwise. The effect of laminating is shown in (*b*). Note that the insulation between laminations breaks up the path of the eddy currents shown in (*a*), and the current paths now have much less cross section, making their resistance much higher.

For a given volume of material, eddy-current loss varies as the square of the thickness of the laminations and also as the square of both frequency and flux density. The loss is given quantitatively as follows:

$$P_e = \frac{(\pi t f B_m)^2}{6\rho 10^{16}} \quad \text{watts per cu cm,} \tag{177}$$

where t is the thickness of the lamination in centimeters, f the frequency in cycles per second, B_m the maximum flux density in gauss, and ρ the resistivity in ohm-centimeters. (177) does not always check with measured values since it is assumed that the interlamination conductance is zero. Ordinarily there is some conductance, making the measured values of loss greater.

Example. A transformer core having a total volume of 12,800 cu cm is made of silicon-steel laminations, No. 29 United States standard gage, or 0.014 in. thick. The resistivity is 60 microhm-cm. Determine: (*a*) watts eddy-current loss at a maximum flux density of 10,000 gauss and a frequency of 60 cycles per second; (*b*) watts per pound. The silicon steel has a density of 7.65 g per cu cm.

Using (177),

$$(a)\ P_e = \frac{[\pi(0.014 \cdot 2.54)60 \cdot 10{,}000]^2}{6 \cdot 60 \cdot 10^{-6} \cdot 10^{16}} = 1.248 \cdot 10^{-3} \text{ watts per cu cm.}$$

$$1.248 \cdot 10^{-3} \cdot 12{,}800 = 15.97 \text{ watts.} \quad \textit{Ans.}$$

(*b*) 1 kg = 2.205 lb.

$$\frac{1.248 \cdot 10^{-3} \cdot 1{,}000}{7.65 \cdot 2.205} = 0.07340 \text{ watt per lb.} \quad \textit{Ans.}$$

Increasing the silicon content of steel laminations reduces the hysteresis loss and also increases the electrical resistivity, which in turn reduces the eddy-current loss. The effects of silicon may be seen by examining Table I. Also, increasing the silicon content makes the laminations harder and more brittle, and the cost increases with the silicon content. With dynamos the core losses are not predominant, and with softer grades of steel the punching of pole and armature sheets is facilitated. Hence the content of silicon for dynamo sheet steel varies from about one-fourth of 1 per cent for field cores to 2½ per cent for ordinary dynamo grades. For extra high efficiency motors, 3¼ per cent silicon steel is used, thus approaching the transformer grades. With transformers, the core loss predominates so that high per cent (4 to 5) silicon steel is used, the extra cost being justified by the reduced losses (see Vol. II, Chap. VII).

In order to make a general comparison of the core losses in different grades of iron or steel, the standard has been adopted of watts loss per pound at maximum flux density of 10,000 gauss at 60 cycles. Table I[1] shows in a concise manner the various important properties of some

[1] From "Magnetic Core Materials Practice," Allegheny Steel Company.

TABLE I. PROPERTIES OF COMMERCIAL GRADES OF MAGNETIC CORE MATERIALS AT 10,000 GAUSS
(By courtesy of the Allegheny Steel Company)

Magnetic Core Materials	Silicon content, per cent (1)	B_r Residual flux from 10,000 gauss, maximum (2)	H_c Coercive force from 10,000 gauss, maximum (3)	$H_c \times B_r$ (4)	Hysteresis loss, ergs/cm-cube/cycle, for 10,000 gauss (5)	H†/pound (watt/pound) 60-cycle hysteresis loss for 10,000 gauss (6)	Electrical resistivity, microhms-cm. (7)	P_e/pound (watts/pound) 60-cycle eddy-current loss for No. 29 U.S.S. gauge, for 10,000 gauss (8)	Maximum total core loss, 60 cycles—10,000 gauss, Epstein test, No. 29 U.S.S. gauge (9*)
Full, hard, cold-rolled steel sheets, or strip	....	8,500	5.5	46,700	21,400	7.56	11	0.4	7.96
Hot-rolled, annealed soft-steel sheets	....	8,400	0.86	7,220	3,540	1.25	11	0.4	1.65
Allegheny "Armature"-grade sheet steel	0.5	.....	....	......	2,750	0.958	18	0.356	1.30*
Allegheny "Dynamo"-grade sheet steel	2.5	8,100	0.68	5,510	2,530	0.913	40	0.132	1.01*
Allegheny "Dynamo-Special"-grade sheet steel	3.25	7,300	0.65	4,740	2,030	0.733	48	0.128	0.82*
Allegheny "Radio-Transformer"-grade sheet steel	3.8	.....	....	......	1,890	0.683	56	0.128	0.76*
Allegheny "Transformer 'C'"-grade sheet steel	4.25	8,100	0.4	3,240	1,815	0.658	60	0.114	0.72*
Allegheny "Audio-Transformer 'B'"-grade sheet steel	3.60	8,100	0.4	3,240	1,475	0.532	51	0.128	0.66*
Allegheny "Audio-Transformer 'A'"-grade sheet steel	3.60	8,100	0.4	3,240	1,305	0.472	51	0.128	0.60*
Products from the Research Laboratories									
Pure iron (Yensen—1925)	....	8,600	0.2	1,720	600	0.207	7.64	0.60	0.807
Vacuum-melted 4 per cent silicon iron alloy (Yensen—1925)	....	5,200	0.15	780	500	0.179	55	0.12	0.299
Hipernik (Yensen—1925)	....	7,300	0.05	365	200	0.072	45	0.13	0.202
Permalloy (78 per cent nickel) (Yensen—1925)	....	5,500	0.05	275	200	0.063	25	0.28	0.343

* The values in column (9) which are starred are commercial guarantees which only approximate the total of values in columns (6) and (8). Number 29 U.S.S. gauge is 0.014 in. (14 mils) or 0.0356-cm thick.
† Hysteresis loss.

standard types of magnetic-core materials, as well as of the more perfect laboratory products which are valuable for purposes of comparison.

196. Separation of Iron Losses. The fact that hysteresis and eddy-current losses are different functions of both flux density (or flux) and frequency makes it possible to separate the losses if data for two or more values of flux density (or flux) or of frequency are available. Let P_1 and P_2 be the measured values of power for values of flux ϕ_1 and ϕ_2, the frequency remaining constant. Then,

$$P_1 = K_1\phi_1^{1.6} + K_2\phi_1^2 \quad \text{watts,} \tag{178a}$$
$$P_2 = K_1\phi_2^{1.6} + K_2\phi_2^2 \quad \text{watts,} \tag{178b}$$

where K_1 is a hysteresis coefficient and K_2 an eddy-current coefficient. (178*a*) and (178*b*) are two simultaneous equations which are readily solved for K_1 and K_2.

Since frequency is readily determined and measured, it is preferable to separate the losses by employing two different frequencies, the flux or flux density remaining fixed. Let P_1 and P_2 be the measured values of power for frequencies f_1 and f_2, the flux remaining constant. Then,

$$P_1 = K_hf_1 + K_ef_1^2 \quad \text{watts,} \tag{179a}$$
$$P_2 = K_hf_2 + K_ef_2^2 \quad \text{watts,} \tag{179b}$$

where K_h and K_e are hysteresis and eddy-current coefficients that include the flux ϕ, which is constant. (179*a*) and (179*b*) are readily solved for K_h and K_e.

Example. A sample, weighing 15,000 g, consisting of No. 26 gage (0.0185 in.) dynamo steel, is tested for core loss at a maximum flux density of 10,000 gauss. At 60 cycles per sec the loss is found to be 29.22 watts, and at 30 cycles per sec it is found to be 12.45 watts. Determine: (*a*) K_h and K_e; (*b*) hysteresis loss and eddy-current loss at 30 cycles per sec; (*c*) at 60 cycles per sec; (*d*) hysteresis loss per pound at 60 cycles per sec; (*e*) eddy-current loss per pound at 60 cycles per sec. The density of the steel is 7.58 g per cu cm.

Applying (179*a*) and (179*b*),

$$12.45 = K_h30 + K_e(30)^2. \tag{I}$$
$$29.22 = K_h60 + K_e(60)^2. \tag{II}$$

(*a*) Multiplying (I) by 4 and subtracting (II) from the result,

$$60K_h = 20.58; \qquad K_h = 0.343. \quad \textit{Ans.}$$

Multiplying (I) by 2 and subtracting from (II) gives

$$1{,}800K_e = 4.32; \qquad K_e = 2.40 \cdot 10^{-3}.$$

(*b*) Substituting the values of K_h and K_e in (I) gives

$$12.45 = 0.343 \cdot 30 + 2.40 \cdot 10^{-3}(30)^2 = 10.29 + 2.16 \text{ watts.}$$

Hysteresis loss = 10.29 watts; eddy-current loss = 2.16 watts. *Ans.*

(c) Substituting the values of K_h and K_e in (II) gives

$$29.22 = 0.343 \cdot 60 + 2.40 \cdot 10^{-3}(3{,}600) = 20.58 + 8.64 \text{ watts.}$$

Hysteresis loss = 20.58 watts; eddy-current loss = 8.64 watts. *Ans.*

(d) $\dfrac{20.58}{15{,}000} \cdot \dfrac{1{,}000}{2.205} = 0.6222$ watt. *Ans.*

(e) $\dfrac{8.64}{15{,}000} \cdot \dfrac{1{,}000}{2.205} = 0.2612$ watt. *Ans.*

The losses may also be separated graphically as follows: If either (179*a*) or (179*b*) be written without the subscripts and divided by the frequency f,

$$\frac{P}{f} = K_h + K_e f. \tag{180}$$

(180) is linear, in which the power divided by the frequency, P/f, is a function of the frequency f. If P/f is plotted as ordinates and f as abscissas, K_h is the intercept on the P/f axis and K_e is the slope, $\tan \alpha$, Fig. 209. In the foregoing example at 30 cycles per sec, $P/f = 12.45/30 = 0.415$; at 60 cycles per sec, $P/f = 29.22/60 = 0.487$. These values are plotted as a function of frequency in Fig. 209. The intercept $K_h = 0.343$, and the slope $\tan \alpha = (0.487 - 0.415)/30 = 2.40 \cdot 10^{-3}$.

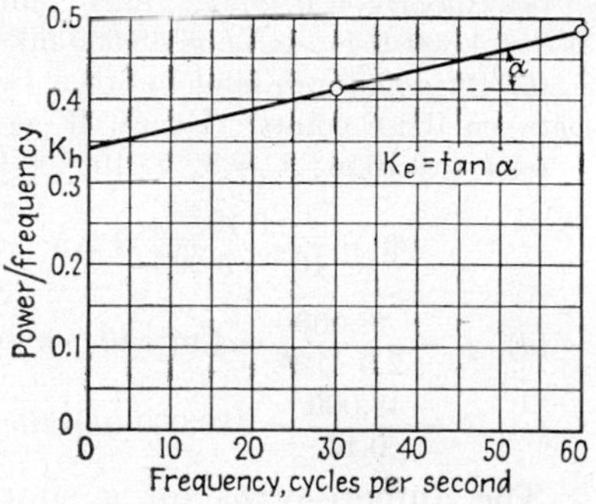

FIG. 209. Separation of hysteresis and eddy-current loss.

UNRATIONALIZED MKS UNITS

197. Law of Magnetic Circuit. It is pointed out (p. 220) that the unrationalized mks system is based on a value $\mu_v = 10^{-7}$ for the permeability of evacuated space. Hence, Eq. (168) (p. 254) is written

$$\phi = \frac{4\pi NI}{l/\mu_r \mu_v A} \quad \text{webers,} \tag{181}$$

where N is turns, I is amperes, l is the length of magnetic circuit in meters, μ_r is *relative* permeability, A is the cross-sectional area of the magnetic circuit in square meters. (The relation $\mu_r \mu_v = \mu$ is often used, where μ is permeability.)

From (181)

$$\phi = BA = \frac{4\pi NI}{l} \mu_r \mu_v A; \qquad B = \frac{4\pi NI}{l} \mu_r \mu_v; \qquad \frac{4\pi NI}{l} = H$$

Hence,

$$B = \mu_r \mu_v H \quad \text{webers per sq m.} \tag{182}$$

Example. The *example*, p. 254, is solved as follows:

$$\mathfrak{F} = 4\pi IN = 4\pi \cdot 1.5 \cdot 250 = 4{,}714 \text{ mks units.}$$
$$l_1 = 45.72 \text{ cm} = 0.4572 \text{ m.}$$
$$l_2 = 0.4763 \text{ cm} = 4.763 \cdot 10^{-3} \text{ m.}$$
$$A_1 = A_2 = 1.290 \text{ sq cm} = 1.290 \cdot 10^{-4} \text{ sq m.}$$

From (181) [also see Eq. (169), p. 254],

$$\phi = \frac{4{,}714}{\dfrac{0.4572}{800 \cdot 10^{-7} \cdot 1.290 \cdot 10^{-4}} + \dfrac{4.763 \cdot 10^{-3}}{1 \cdot 10^{-7} \cdot 1.290 \cdot 10^{-4}}}$$
$$= \frac{4{,}714}{0.4430 \cdot 10^8 + 3.692 \cdot 10^8}$$
$$= 1.140 \cdot 10^{-5} \text{ weber. } \textit{Ans.}$$
$$B = \frac{1.140 \cdot 10^{-5}}{1.290 \cdot 10^{-4}} = 8.837 \cdot 10^{-2} \text{ weber per sq m. } \textit{Ans.}$$

Example. In the example, p. 256, determine: (*a*) mmf in unrationalized mks units; (*b*) work done in carrying a unit pole between surfaces CD and AB; (*c*) reluctance of flux path; (*d*) total flux; (*e*) field intensity in unrationalized mks units.

(*a*) Gilberts = $0.4\pi NI$; mks unrationalized mmf = $4\pi NI$. $0.4\pi NI = 4{,}800$; $NI = 4{,}800/0.4\pi$; $4\pi NI = 48{,}000$ mks units. *Ans.*

(*b*) By definition, mmf between two points is work done in carrying a unit pole between those points. Hence, $W = 48{,}000$ joules. *Ans.*

(*c*) $l = 0.10$ m; $A = 8 \cdot 5 \cdot 10^{-4} = 0.004$ sq m. Hence,

$$\mathfrak{R} = \frac{0.10}{10^{-7} \cdot 0.004} = 2.5 \cdot 10^8 \textit{ unrationalized} \text{ mks units. } \textit{Ans.}$$

(*d*) $\phi = \dfrac{48{,}000}{2.5 \cdot 10^8} = 1.92 \cdot 10^{-4}$ weber. *Ans.*

(*e*) $H = \dfrac{48{,}000}{0.10} = 480{,}000$ *unrationalized* mks units. *Ans.*

The ampere-turns for a simple air-gap [Eq. (171), p. 259] may be determined as follows:

From (181),

$$\phi = \frac{4\pi IN}{l/(10^{-7} \cdot A)} \quad \text{webers.} \tag{183}$$

Hence,

$$IN = \frac{\phi l}{4\pi \cdot 10^{-7} \cdot A} = \frac{Bl \cdot 10^7}{4\pi} \quad \text{amp-turns.} \tag{184}$$

where B is in webers per square meter and l is in meters.

Example. Solve the example, p. 259.

$$l = 0.25 \text{ cm} = 2.5 \cdot 10^{-3} \text{ m}; \qquad A = 400 \text{ sq cm} = 4 \cdot 10^{-2} \text{ sq m};$$
$$\phi = 2{,}400{,}000 \text{ maxwells} = 2.4 \cdot 10^{-2} \text{ weber.}$$
$$B = \frac{2.4 \cdot 10^{-2}}{4 \cdot 10^{-2}} = 0.6 \text{ weber per sq m.}$$

Using (184),

$$IN = \frac{0.6 \cdot 2.5 \cdot 10^{-3} \cdot 10^7}{4\pi} = 1{,}194 \text{ amp-turns. } \textit{Ans.}$$

Hysteresis Loss. A study of the derivation of Eq. (174) in Sec. 194 (p. 266) shows that if V, i, R, ϕ are given in unrationalized mks units, l in meters, n in turns per meter, (III) will be given in joules per sec. Also if A is given in square meters, H in mmf per meter ($H = 4\pi ni$), and B in webers per square meter, Eqs. (IV) to (174) give the hysteresis loss in joules. Hence,

$$W = \frac{1}{4\pi}\int H\,dB \qquad \text{joules per cu m.} \tag{185}$$

That is, the hysteresis loss in joules per cubic meter is the area of the loop multiplied by the scales of abscissas and ordinates and divided by 4π.

Eddy-current Loss. In the unrationalized mks system, Eq. (177) (p. 268) becomes

$$P_e = \frac{(\pi t f B_m)^2}{6\rho} \qquad \text{watts per cu m,} \tag{186}$$

where t is given in meters, f is in cycles per second, B_m is webers per square meter, and ρ is in ohm-meters.

Example. Determine (*a*) in the example, p. 268.

$$t = 0.014 \text{ in.} = 0.014 \cdot 0.0254 = 3.556 \cdot 10^{-4} \text{ m.}$$
$$B_m = 10{,}000 \cdot 10^{-4} = 1 \text{ weber per sq m.}$$
$$\rho = 60\,\frac{10^2}{10^4} \cdot 10^{-6} = 60 \cdot 10^{-8} \text{ ohm-m.}$$
$$P_e = \frac{(\pi \cdot 3.556 \cdot 10^{-4} \cdot 60)^2}{6 \cdot 60 \cdot 10^{-8}} = 1{,}248 \text{ watts per cu m. } \textit{Ans.}$$

RATIONALIZED MKS UNITS

198. Law of Magnetic Circuit. In the rationalized system the unit of mmf is the ampere-turn, and a value of $\mu_v' = 4\pi \cdot 10^{-7}$ is used for the permeability of free space. Hence, Eq. (168) (p. 254) is written

$$\phi = \frac{NI}{l/\mu_r\mu_v'A} \qquad \text{webers.} \tag{187}$$

Example. The example, p. 254, accordingly is solved as follows:

$$\mathfrak{F} = NI = 375 \text{ amp-turns.}$$
$$l_1 = 45.72 \text{ cm} = 0.4572 \text{ m.}$$
$$l_2 = 0.4763 \text{ cm} = 4.763 \cdot 10^{-3} \text{ m.}$$
$$A_1 = A_2 = 1.290 \text{ sq cm} = 1.290 \cdot 10^{-4} \text{ sq m.}$$

From (187) [also see Eq. (169), p. 254],

$$\phi = \frac{375}{\dfrac{0.4572}{800(4\pi \cdot 10^{-7})1.290 \cdot 10^{-4}} + \dfrac{4.763 \cdot 10^{-3}}{1(4\pi \cdot 10^{-7})1.290 \cdot 10^{-4}}}$$
$$= \frac{375}{3.524 \cdot 10^6 + 29.37 \cdot 10^6} = 1.140 \cdot 10^{-5} \text{ weber. } \textit{Ans.}$$

From (187),

$$\phi = BA = \frac{NI}{l}\mu_r\mu_v{}'A; \qquad \frac{NI}{l} = H.$$

Hence,

$$B = \mu_r\mu_v{}'H. \tag{188}$$

Example. Repeat the example, p. 256, using rationalized mks units.
(*a*) $0.4\pi NI = 4{,}800$; $NI = 4{,}800/0.4\pi = 3{,}819$ amp-turns. *Ans.*
(*b*) By definition, $W = 3{,}819$ joules. *Ans.*
(*c*) $\mathcal{R} = \dfrac{0.10}{4\pi \cdot 10^{-7} \cdot 0.004} = 1.989 \cdot 10^7$ *rationalized* mks units. *Ans.*
(*d*) $\phi = \dfrac{3{,}819}{1{,}989 \cdot 10^7} = 1.920 \cdot 10^{-4}$ weber. *Ans.*
(*e*) $H = 3{,}819/0.10 = 38{,}190$ *rationalized* mks units. *Ans.*

The ampere-turns for a simple air-gap [Eq. (171), p. 259] may be determined as follows:

$$\phi = \frac{IN}{l/(4\pi \cdot 10^{-7} \cdot A)} \qquad \text{webers.}$$

$$IN = \frac{\phi l}{4\pi \cdot 10^{-7} \cdot A} = \frac{Bl \cdot 10^7}{4\pi} \qquad \text{amp-turns.} \tag{189}$$

Note that (184) and (189) are identical. (In Figs. 198 and 199 the ordinates and abscissas are also given in rationalized mks units.)

Hysteresis Loss. In Eq. (185) (p. 273), $H = 4\pi nI$. In the rationalized system, $H' = nI$. Hence $H' = H/4\pi$.

Equation (185) then becomes,

$$W = \int H'\,dB \qquad \text{joules per cu m.} \tag{190}$$

That is, the hysteresis loss in joules per cubic meter is the area of the loop multiplied by the scales of abscissas and ordinates.

Eddy-current Loss. In the rationalized mks system the equation for eddy-current loss must be identical with Eq. (186) for the unrationalized mks system (p. 273), since the factors t, f, B_m, and ρ are identical in both unrationalized and rationalized mks systems.

FERROMAGNETIC ALLOYS

Certain alloys of iron and nickel, when properly prepared and heat-treated, have magnetic properties far superior to those of iron itself, particularly at very low flux densities. The most common of these alloys are Permalloy, Perminvar, Hipernik, and Coupernik (also see Sec. 148, p. 196).

199. Permalloy. Permalloy is a term applied to a number of nickel-iron alloys developed by the Bell Laboratories. However, it is usually associated with the alloy having 78.5 per cent nickel and approximately 21.4 per cent iron. The material has abnormally high magnetic properties at low values of magnetizing force, as Fig. 210 shows.

The maximum permeability of ordinary Permalloy is approximately 100,000, although by long-time high-temperature treatments, values as high as 600,000 have been obtained. Permalloy becomes highly saturated in the earth's field alone ($H = 0.45$), so that extreme care must be exercised in testing it. For comparison, in Fig. 210 the *B-H* curve for Armco iron is also given. It will be noticed that only at low values of H is Permalloy superior to Armco iron in its magnetic properties.

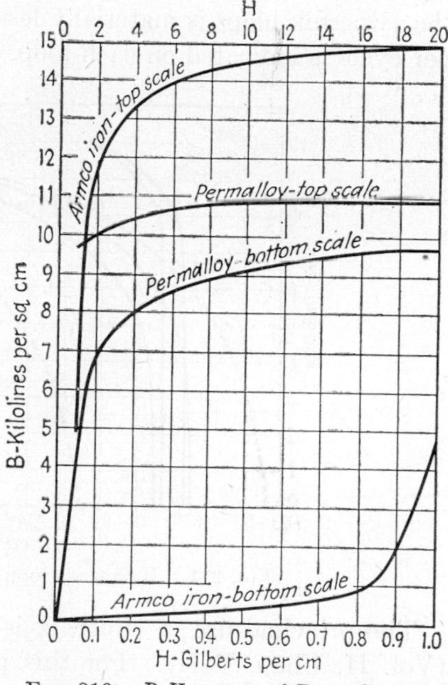

FIG. 210. *B-H* curves of Permalloy and Armco iron.

The hysteresis loop of Permalloy, when carried to a maximum induction of 5,000 gauss, has only one-sixteenth the area of that of iron, and accordingly the hysteresis loss is in the same proportion.

The magnetic properties of Permalloy are very sensitive to heat-treatment, so that it must be carefully prepared and in very thin strips. Also, it is very unstable and may lose much of its high permeability if subjected to magnetic and mechanical shocks. Its principal use at present is in communication work, particularly in the "loading" of submarine cables.[1]

Permalloy powder, or "dust," is mixed with a resinous binder and then compressed under very high pressure to form cores for transformers used at high frequencies in communication work. The fact that the particles are all insulated from one another makes the eddy-current loss practically zero.

Perminvar is an iron-nickel-cobalt alloy which has constant permeability over a wide range of B. Since the area of the hysteresis loop accordingly must be very small, the hysteresis loss is correspondingly small. The permeability is only moderate, being less than half that of Armco iron.

[1] For further details see H. D. ARNOLD, and G. W. ELMEN, "Permalloy, an Alloy of Remarkable Magnetic Properties," *Jour. Franklin Inst.*, May, 1923, p. 621. Reprinted July, 1923, in *Bell System Tech. Jour.*

200. Hipernik. Hipernik is a highly refined 40 to 60 per cent iron-nickel alloy. It is found that, in this type of alloy, impurities of a few hundredths of 1 per cent affect the permeability by several hundred per cent so that in the process of manufacture every trace of impurity must be removed. Ordinarily the permeability reaches values as high as 57,000, which may be determined from Fig. 211, which gives both the *B-H* curve and two hysteresis loops of Hipernik. Under special conditions, the permeability may reach higher values.[1] For comparison, a hysteresis loop for silicon iron is given. It will be noted that the area of the Hipernik loops is materially less than for silicon iron. The ergs loss per cycle is indicated on each loop.

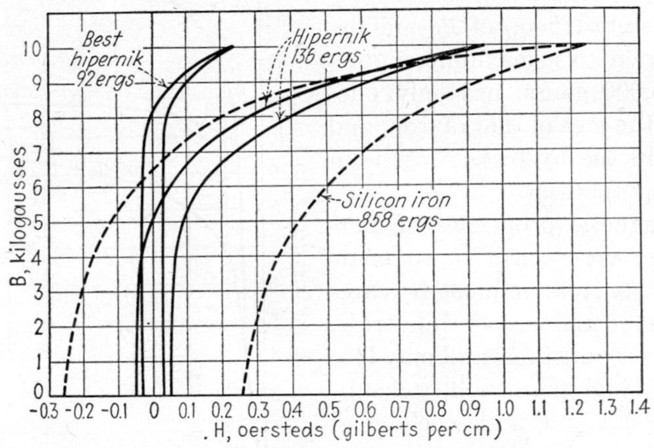

Fig. 211. Hysteresis loops of Hipernik and silicon iron.

The principal use of Hipernik is for the cores of current transformers (Vol. II, Chap. VIII). For this purpose a long ribbon of Hipernik is coiled like a clock spring to form the core, so that waste due to punching is practically eliminated.[1]

Coupernik is an alloy of the same composition as Hipernik, but it is given a different heat-treatment which produces a constant permeability over a wide range of flux density.

201. Permanent Magnets and Hysteresis Loop. In Chap. VI the relation of permanent magnets to the demagnetization curve (p. 223) and the radical improvement made in permanent magnets by the development of the Alnico alloys are discussed briefly. A more detailed analysis of permanent-magnet operation requires a knowledge of the magnetic circuit and hysteresis effects which have just been discussed.

It is already shown that permanent magnets operate on that part of

[1] Yensen, T. D., "Permeability of Hipernik Reaches 167,000," *Elec. Jour.*, June, 1931, p. 386.

the hysteresis loop lying in the second quadrant, Fig. 212. Also it is shown that the stored magnetic energy is proportional to the area of that part of the hysteresis loop under consideration (p. 266). Figure 212 shows the *B-H* curves for typical permanent-magnet materials. The most important criterion of the usefulness of a permanent-magnet material is the stored magnetic energy. This is represented by the areas under the demagnetization curve, Figs. 212 and 213.

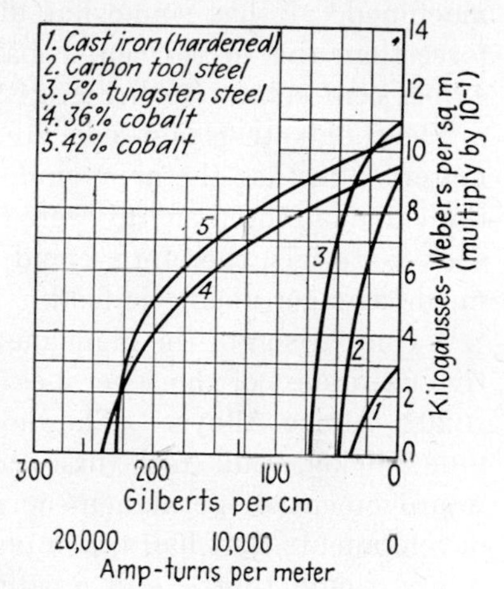

Fig. 212. *B-H* characteristics of permanent-magnet materials.

For a number of years carbon tool steel was the only permanent-magnetic material available. This was followed by a 5 to 6 per cent tungsten-steel alloy (containing also 0.6 to 0.8 per cent carbon and 0.5 per cent manganese). The *B-H* characteristics of several of the permanent-magnet steels are given in Fig. 212. Note that the tungsten-steel alloy has a high value of remanence although the coercive force is not much greater than that for carbon tool steel. The next important material was cobalt-chromium steel (Co 6%, Cr 9%). Although the rema-

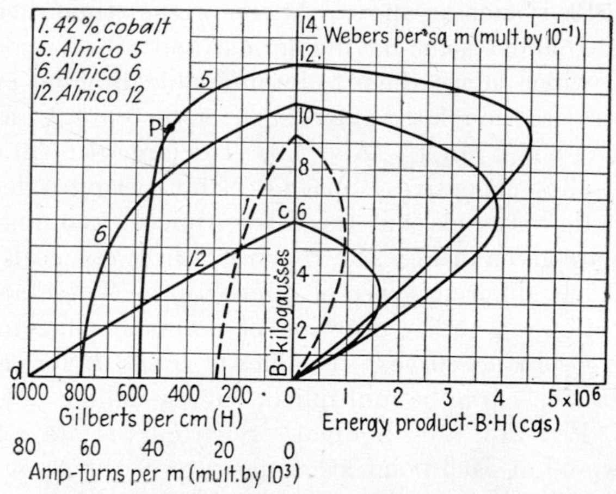

Fig. 213. *B-H* and *B·H* characteristics of Alnico alloys.

nence for this alloy was much less than that for tungsten steel, the coercive force of 210 and the area under the demagnetization curve were both much greater than corresponding values for any of the earlier permanent-magnet materials. The next improvement was 36 per cent *cobalt magnet* steel, Fig. 212, also known as K.S. steel, containing 36 per cent cobalt, 6 per cent chromium, and 4 per cent tungsten. Because of the cobalt content this material is expensive, and it is not readily machined. It has somewhat higher values of remanence and coercive force than the 16 per cent cobalt steel. A further improvement was a 42 per cent cobalt steel, Fig. 212.

The cobalt steels marked a great advance over prior permanent-magnet materials in that the areas under the demagnetization curves and hence the value of stored energy were several times greater. Magnets made of such materials, therefore, could be made much smaller and yet produce much stronger magnetic fields.

A comparison of the demagnetization curves, Fig. 212, shows the relative usefulness of the several earlier permanent-magnet materials.

202. Alnico Alloys.[1] The development of Alnico, an alloy of aluminum, nickel, and steel (first called Alnic), in 1932, marked a radical improvement in permanent-magnet materials that by far exceeded all developments that had taken place up to that time. A short time later it was found that a still greater improvement resulted from replacing part of the nickel with cobalt, and later copper was added. Alnico 6, Fig. 213, is such an alloy (with 1.25 per cent titanium). Later, the important discovery was made that if the alloy were subjected to a magnetizing force during heat-treatment a grain was developed and the magnetic properties in the direction of the grain were greatly increased. Alnico 5, Fig. 213, is such an alloy. At the present time there is a large number of Alnico alloys some having similar and others widely varying characteristics, which adapt them to innumerable different applications. In addition there are the related alloys such as Vectolite, Cunico, Cunife, and Silmanal (Ag 86%, Mn 9%, Al 5%). The large percentage of silver makes this last alloy expensive. Space does not permit a description of all these magnetic materials, but the three Alnicos, 5, 6, and 12, whose characteristics are given in Fig. 213, represent three categories which are required for widely differing types of application. These are described in the next section. Another criterion of permanent-magnet performance is the *energy-product* curve. If values of B and H for each point of the demagnetization curve be multiplied, curves similar to those in the first quadrant, Fig. 213, are obtained. Such curves are called energy product curves and at each point are a measure of the energy per cubic centimeter stored in the magnet. The maximum product of B-H gives the point at which maximum output or optimum operation may be obtained.

[1] For a complete discussion of these alloys and their performance, the article "Performance of the New Alnico Permanent Magnet Materials," by F. W. MERRILL of the General Electric Company, *Elec. Mfg.*, February, 1947, p. 72, is recommended.

For comparison and to illustrate the great superiority of the Alnico alloys over the previous magnetic materials, the demagnetization and energy-product curve for 42 per cent cobalt (shown dotted), the best prior material, are also shown in Fig. 213.

The compositions and important parameters of the three Alnico alloys are given in the accompanying table.

Alloy	Percentage composition						Magnetic properties		
	Al	Ni	Co	Cu	Ti	Fe	B_r	H_c	$B \cdot H$ (max)
5*	8	14	24	3	....	51	12,500	580	$4.5 \cdot 10^6$
6*	8	14	24	3	1.25	49.75	10,500	800	$3.9 \cdot 10^6$
12	6	18	35	..	8.0	33	6,000	1,000	$1.7 \cdot 10^6$

B_r remanence; H_c, coercive force; $B \cdot H$ (max), maximum energy product.
* Directional, *i.e.*, in magnetic field during heat-treatment.

It will be noted that with Alnico 5, when H reaches the value of -500 the induction suddenly drops to zero. This drop off is due to the fact that up to the -500 point the domains remain firmly locked in a direction of easy magnetization and it is possible to unlock only a relatively few. Most of the domains are, however, similar in character, and they all become unlocked almost simultaneously, producing a sudden drop off. This material is highly effective with short fixed air-gaps which would cause it to operate above the point P. As will be shown, this characteristic is, however, highly undesirable if the magnet is to be used in applications where the air-gap may be variable or where the magnetic device may be taken apart. Under these conditions the magnetic induction drops down the steep part of the curve to a low value, and the magnetization cannot be restored to any reasonably high value except by remagnetizing. Alnico 6 is an improvement in this respect in that the sudden drop off is eliminated, the domains responding progressively to the demagnetization force. Alnico 12, which was developed after much research, and which has the highest coercive force for all the Alnicos, is an almost perfect example of progressive unlocking of the domains, the characteristic being almost a straight line.

Many of the Alnico magnets can be made by the sintering process. The constituent powders such as iron, nickel, cobalt, and copper are pressed in a die, any necessary slots, holes, and grooves being made part of the die. The compacted powder is then heated in a hydrogen-atmosphere furnace at a temperature just below the melting point of the constituents. The resulting product is hard and fine-grained but is nonmachinable and must be finished by grinding. Up to the present time it has not been possible to make Alnicos 5, 6, and 12 by this process, but 5 and 6 are made by the sand or precision-casting process. They, too, are nonmachinable and must be ground.

203. Design of Permanent Magnets. The availability of such powerful permanent-magnet materials as the Alnicos has greatly widened the applications of permanent magnets and has brought about a revolution in the design of instruments, meters, radio sets, loudspeakers, magnetos, generators, magnetic chucks, and other devices. It is therefore important to understand the theory of operation and the design of permanent magnets.

The mmf available in the magnet must supply not only the mmf consumed in the magnet itself but also the mmf necessary to send the flux through the exterior circuit, such as soft-iron pole pieces and inserts, and any air-gaps, all of which may constitute a part of the magnetic circuit (see Fig. 165, p. 225). To illustrate the method of designing a permanent magnet, using Alnico 6, and its operation with different air-gaps, the demagnetization curve for Alnico 6 is plotted in Fig. 214. Let it be required to design a magnet to supply ϕ maxwells to an air-gap l_g cm long and A_g sq cm cross section. It is desirable to operate the material at or near the point where the available energy, or energy product, is a maximum. Reference to Fig. 213 shows that this corresponds to a flux density of 6,400 gauss.

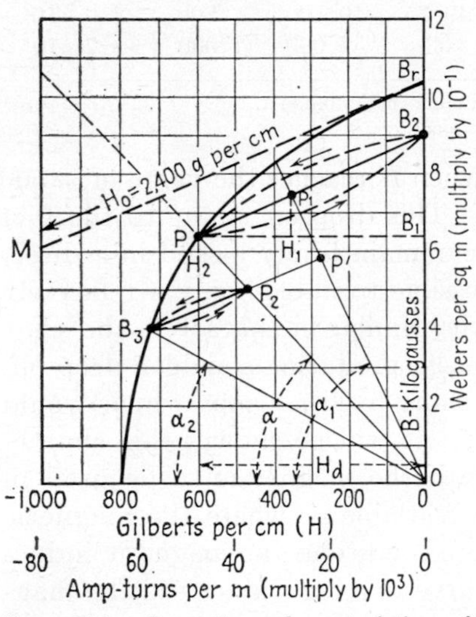

Fig. 214. Operating characteristics of Alnico 6.

The flux density in the air-gap, $B_g = \phi/A_g$. Let L_m and A_m be the length and cross section of the magnet in centimeters and square centimeters. Let H_m be the mmf gradient in the magnet and H_g the mmf gradient in the air-gap, both in gilberts per centimeter. Applying Kirchhoff's second law to the magnetic current,

$$H_m L_m - H_g L_g = 0. \tag{191}$$

Also,

$$\frac{B_g}{B_m} = \frac{A_m}{A_g}. \tag{192}$$

From (191) and (192), and with $H_g = B_g$, numerically, in the air-gap,

$$H_m = \frac{H_g L_g}{L_m} = \frac{B_g L_g}{L_m} \tag{I}$$

and

$$B_m = \frac{B_g A_g}{A_m}. \tag{II}$$

Dividing (II) by (I),

$$\frac{B_m}{H_m} = \frac{B_g A_g/A_m}{B_g L_g/L_m} = \frac{A_g L_m}{A_m L_g} = -\tan\alpha. \tag{193}$$

(193) gives the slope of the line OP, Fig. 214. The line OP is called a *shearing line.* Hence, in order to obtain the point of operation P on the demagnetization curve, draw a shearing line from the origin having a slope of $-A_g L_m/A_m L_g$, and its intersection with the demagnetization curve gives H of the magnet and the flux density at which the magnet operates. Let point P, Fig. 214, be a point of operation on the demagnetization curve, corresponding to flux density B_1. Now assume that when $H = 0$ and $B = B_r$, the mmf applied to the magnet is increased negatively to the value $-H_d$ gilberts per cm. This obviously produces a flux density of B_1 gauss. If the magnet operates at this same flux density of B_1 gauss to produce, for example, flux in an air-gap, the effect of the air-gap must then be equivalent to a demagnetizing mmf of $-H_d$ gilberts per cm in the magnet.

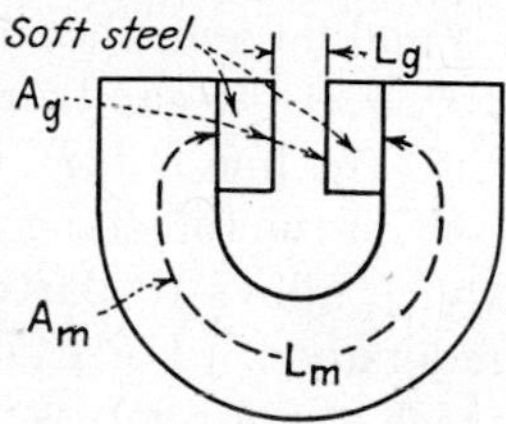

FIG. 215. Alnico magnet.

Example. Design a permanent magnet of Alnico 6 in which the air-gap is 0.6 cm long and has an area of 2 sq cm and the flux in the gap is 15,000 maxwells. The air-gap area is produced by the soft-steel pole pieces, each 2 sq cm area, Fig. 215, in which the mmf drop is negligible. Neglect fringing and leakage flux. Determine: (*a*) cross section of magnet; (*b*) length of magnet; (*c*) slope of shear line, using (193).

(*a*) $B_g = 15{,}000/2 = 7{,}500$ gauss. Figure 213 shows that the maximum value of $B \cdot H$ for Alnico 6 occurs when $B = B_1 = 6{,}400$ gauss. Hence from (192),

$$A_m = 2\,\frac{7{,}500}{6{,}400} = 2.344 \text{ sq cm.} \quad \textit{Ans.}$$

(*b*) Since the gap is air, $H_g = B_g$ numerically. $B_g = 7{,}500$ gauss. Hence, from (191) and Fig. 214,

$$L_m = \frac{7{,}500 \cdot 0.6}{600} = 7.5 \text{ cm.} \quad \textit{Ans.}$$

(*c*) From (193),

$$\frac{B_m}{H_m} = \frac{A_g L_m}{A_m L_g} = \frac{2 \cdot 7.5}{2.344 \cdot 0.6} = 10.67 = -\tan\alpha. \quad \textit{Ans.}$$

Draw a shearing line from the origin which meets the $-H$ abscissa at $-1{,}000$ and the ordinate B at 10,670. This gives $\tan\alpha = -10.67$. The shearing line intersects the curve at P, where $B = 6{,}400$ gauss and $H = -600$ oersteds.

204. Operation of Permanent Magnets. In Fig. 214, the remanence of the magnet would remain at B_r gauss if the magnetic circuit of Alnico remained entirely closed. However, the introduction of the 0.6-cm air-gap reduces the induction from the remanence of B_r to B_1 gauss. If the gap now be closed, as by a keeper, the induction will never return to B_r gauss unless the magnet is remagnetized by an external magnetizing force. The flux density, however, will reach a value B_2 less than B_r, following line PB_2. This line is parallel or nearly parallel to a line B_rM which is tangent to the demagnetizing curve at point B_r and which intercepts the axis of abscissas at a value of $-H_0 = -2{,}400$ gilberts per cm. Actually the magnet will function along the dotted lines between P and B_2, which represent a small area called a *minor hysteresis loop*.

If the magnet is operating at point P and the air-gap is reduced to 0.3 cm, from (193) the shearing line will have a slope, $\tan \alpha_1 = (2 \cdot 7.5)/(-2.344 \cdot 0.3) = -21.33$, and the magnet will operate at point P_1. If the gap be varied between 0.6 and 0.3 cm, the magnet will be stabilized and will operate continuously over the minor loop PP_1.

Let the air-gap now be increased to 1.2 cm. The slope of the new shearing line OB_3 becomes $(2 \cdot 7.5)/(-2.344 \cdot 1.2) = -5.333 = \tan \alpha_2$. The flux density will drop to B_3 gauss, and if the gap be varied between 1.2 and 0.6 cm, the magnet will operate along the minor hysteresis loop B_3P_2. If the gap be reduced to 0.3 cm, the magnet will operate at point P'. The line B_3P_2P' is essentially parallel to line B_rM.

With the foregoing example and analysis, the adaption of the different Alnico alloys to particular types of applications becomes more readily understood. For example, Alnico 6 is best adapted for applications in which the air-gap is variable. That is, the flux density is maintained at a high value when the operation is between points P and P_1. Even when the air-gap is increased to 1.2 cm and the operation is between B_3 and P_2, the magnet still retains a substantial proportion of the flux. This would not be true with Alnico 5 because of the sudden drop off in its induction. Alnico 12 is adapted to applications where the device may be disassembled, as, for example, magneto generators. The operation is essentially along the characteristic *cd*, Fig. 213. Then when the device is reassembled, the initial magnetism is restored. Alnico 5, which, of all the Alnicos, has the highest value of remanence and energy product, should be used only under the conditions of a short fixed air-gap. For example, the alloy should operate at point P, or slightly above, where the energy product is a maximum. If, however, the air-gap is increased by any substantial amount, a study of Fig. 213 shows that the magnet will lose a large proportion of its magnetism because of the sudden drop off in the characteristic. Thus care should be exercised in selecting and applying magnetic alloys for any particular application. In several instances, apparatus has become inoperative owing to a sudden loss of magnetism, caused by using the wrong magnetic alloy.

205. MKS System and Permanent Magnets. Following is an illustration of the application of the rationalized mks system to permanent-magnet design and operation. In Eq. (191) where $H_mL_m = H_gL_g$, $H_g = B_g/\mu_v'$ [See Eq. (188), p. 274]. Hence,

$$H_mL_m = \frac{B_gL_g}{\mu_v'} \tag{194}$$

where H_m is ampere-turns per meter, B_g is webers per square meter, L_g, L_m are the lengths of the gap and magnet in meters, $\mu_v' = 4\pi \cdot 10^{-7}$. In Figs. 212, 213, 214, the abscissas are also given in ampere-turns per meter and the ordinates in webers per square m. (1 gilbert per cm = 79.58 amp-turns per m; 1 weber = 10^8 maxwells.)

Also in (192), B_g and B_m are in webers per square meter and A_m and A_g are in square meters.

In obtaining (193) in the mks system, H_g does not equal B_g, but $H_g = B_g/\mu_v'$. Hence,

$$\frac{B_m}{H_m} = \frac{B_gA_g/A_m}{B_gL_g/\mu_v'L_m} = \frac{\mu_v'A_gL_m}{A_mL_g}. \tag{195}$$

Example. In the example, p. 281, design the magnet, employing the rationalized mks system.

(*a*) The area of the gap is $2 \cdot 10^{-4}$ sq m, and the flux density is $(15{,}000 \cdot 10^{-8})/(2 \cdot 10^{-4}) = 0.75$ weber per sq m. The flux density in the magnet is $6{,}400 \cdot 10^{-4} = 0.64$ weber per sq m (also see Fig. 213).

Hence, from (192),

$$A_m = 2 \cdot 10^{-4} \frac{0.75}{0.64} = 2.344 \cdot 10^{-4} \text{ sq m.} \quad \textit{Ans.}$$

(*b*) From Fig. 214, with Alnico 6, corresponding to $B = 0.64$ weber per sq m, $H_m = 47.8 \cdot 10^3$ amp-turns per m.

Solving (194) for L_m,

$$L_m = \frac{0.75(0.6 \cdot 10^{-2})}{(4\pi \cdot 10^{-7})(47.8 \cdot 10^3)} = 0.075 \text{ m.} \quad \textit{Ans.}$$

(*c*) From (195),

$$\frac{B_m}{H_m} = \frac{(4\pi \cdot 10^{-7})(2 \cdot 10^{-4})(7.5 \cdot 10^{-2})}{-(2.344 \cdot 10^{-4})(0.6 \cdot 10^{-2})} = -1.340 \cdot 10^{-5} = \tan \alpha. \quad \textit{Ans.}$$

206. Magnetizing and Stabilizing. Permanent magnets are magnetized by subjecting them to a magnetizing force of five or six times the maximum $-H_c$ at which they become stabilized (see Figs. 212, 213, 214). The Alnicos require about 3,000 gilberts per cm, or 6,060 amp-turns per in. Owing to the widely different shapes and sizes of Alnico and other types of permanent magnets, they are magnetized by different methods. Horseshoe magnets may be magnetized by placing the magnet (usually several) with a keeper over a single large copper conductor, Fig. 216. A large direct current in the conductor produces a magnetizing force in the direction indicated. Frequently, current in a coil having several turns is used to produce the magnetizing force. Another common method, when the geometry of the magnet permits, is to magnetize it between the pole pieces of a powerful electromagnet. (The magnetic chuck, Fig. 166, p. 226, is magnetized in this manner.)

After being magnetized, magnets will lose some of their magnetization with time. This is due, in part at least, to the gradual unlocking or relaxation of some of the domains. Such aging is particularly undesirable when magnets are used for meters and instruments. Magnets, however, may be stabilized artificially. For example, subjecting them to moderately high temperatures for a number of hours produces stabilization, or aging. Vibration and impact, which may occur in service, will also produce demagnetization. Stabilizing against these effects can be accomplished by subjecting the magnets initially to mechanical vibrations for a short period. If a magnet is to operate along a minor hysteresis loop such as PP_1, Fig. 214, it can be stabilized for this operation by subjecting it to an a-c mmf equal to $H_2 - H_1$ while holding the d-c mmf to $-H_2$ gilberts per cm.

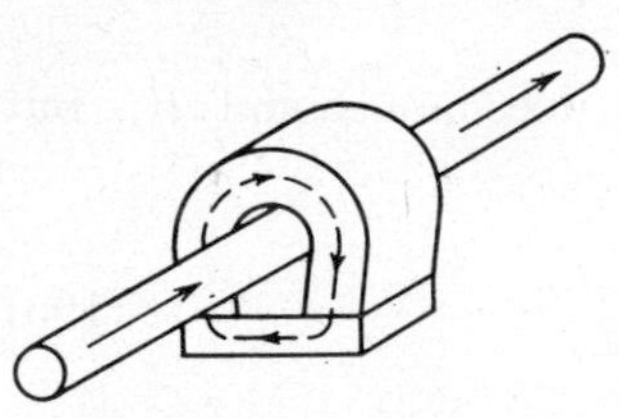

FIG. 216. Magnetizing a horseshoe magnet.

MAGNETIC-FLUX MEASUREMENTS

Magnetic flux cannot be measured by the mere insertion of instruments in a circuit as can electric current, voltage, and power. Magnetic flux is ordinarily measured in two ways: *indirectly* by reading the deflection of a ballistic galvanometer or by the indication of a voltmeter; and *directly* by permeameters of the Koepsel type. The first method depends on the fact that an emf is induced in a coil when the flux linking the coil is changed; the second method depends on the fact that the deflections of Weston-type d-c instruments are proportional to the flux if the current in the moving coil is maintained constant. In the first method, the voltmeter is used if the flux is alternating, the flux being determined by measuring the emf which it induces in a coil of a known number of turns, the voltmeter being of the a-c type (see Vol. II, Chap. VIII).

207. Ballistic Galvanometer. It is shown in Sec. 258 (p. 362) that the ballistic throw of a galvanometer is proportional to the quantity Q of electricity discharged through it, provided that the discharge all takes place before the galvanometer coil has begun to move.

If a galvanometer be connected in series with a coil, Fig. 217, and the flux linking this coil be changed in any manner, an emf is induced in the coil producing a pulse of current through the galvanometer. It can be shown that if the flux is changed by an amount $\Delta\phi$, the quantity of electricity discharged through the galvanometer,

$$Q = N \frac{\Delta\phi}{R} \tag{196}$$

where N is the number of turns in the coil and R is the combined resistance of the coil and galvanometer. Since the galvanometer deflection is proportional to Q, it must also be proportional to the *change of flux*, provided that the resistance R of the entire circuit is kept constant. Therefore, a ballistic galvanometer may be used to measure flux. The change of flux

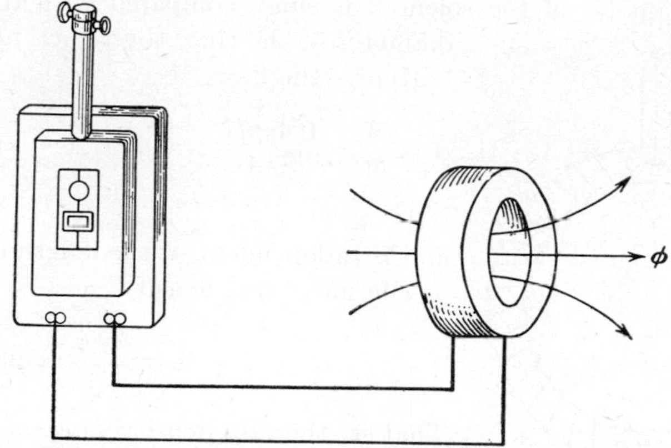

FIG. 217. Ballistic galvanometer used to measure flux.

$$\phi_1 - \phi_2 = KD \tag{197}$$

where ϕ_1 is the initial flux, ϕ_2 the final flux, K the galvanometer constant and D the ballistic deflection of the galvanometer.

208. Standard Solenoid. In order to determine the constant K in (197), a flux of known value is necessary. This flux, which links a secondary coil of known number of turns, is caused to change by a known amount, either by decreasing it to zero or by building it up from zero. Simultaneously, the ballistic deflection of the galvanometer in series with the coil is read. This gives sufficient data for obtaining the galvanometer constant.

The long straight solenoid discussed in Sec. 175 (p. 235) is used to obtain the flux of known value. It is shown that the field intensity at the center of such a solenoid is equal practically to $0.4\pi nI$ oersteds, if the ratio of length to radius of the solenoid is large. (n is the number of turns per centimeter length and I the current in amperes.) Since in air, field intensity is *numerically* equal to flux density, the total flux across the center cross section is $0.4\pi nIA$ maxwells, where A is the cross section in square centimeters. Hence, such a solenoid provides a flux the value of which can be calculated.

The properties of the straight solenoid may also be developed by a consideration of the ring solenoid, Fig. 218, the cross section of which is circular and the core is of nonconducting, nonmagnetic material such as wood. Let the cross-sectional area be A sq cm and the mean circumferential length be l cm, Fig. 218. The solenoid is wound uniformly with n turns per mean circumferential centimeter, and the current in the winding is I amp. The total mmf $\mathfrak{F}$ is obviously $0.4\pi nlI$, and if the cross-sectional diameter of the solenoid is small compared with the internal diameter of the ring, the reluctance is l/A.

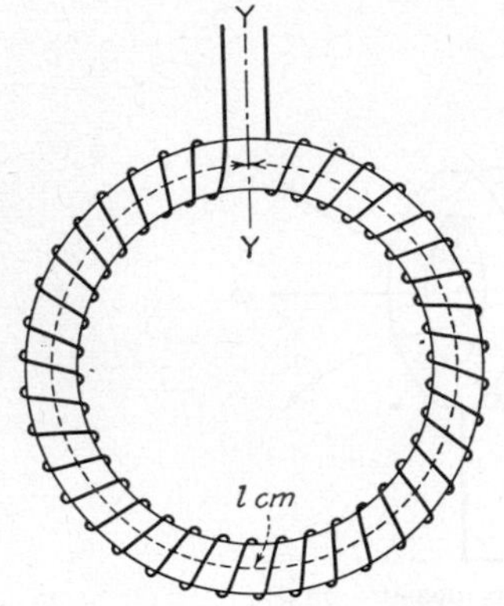

Fig. 218. Ring solenoid.

Hence, the flux

$$\phi = \frac{\mathfrak{F}}{\mathfrak{R}} = \frac{0.4\pi nlI}{l/A} = 0.4\pi nIA \qquad \text{maxwells} \tag{198}$$

and is independent of the length of winding.

The mean flux density

$$B = \frac{\phi}{A} = 0.4\pi nI \qquad \text{gauss.} \tag{199}$$

That is, the flux density *is equal to the mmf per centimeter length* and is also independent of the length of winding.

It will be noted that (199) is identical numerically with Eq. (145*a*) (p. 237), which gives the field intensity at the center of a long, straight solenoid. Equation (198) also gives the flux across the center cross section of a long straight solenoid.

Referring to (198),

$$\phi = \frac{0.4\pi nI}{1/A}.$$

$1/A$ is the reluctance *per centimeter length* of the solenoid, and $0.4\pi nI$ is the mmf *per centimeter length* of the solenoid. Hence, it follows that in such a solenoid the mmf in each unit length is utilized entirely in sending the flux through that unit length.

If the ring solenoid, Fig. 218, be cut along the plane YY and straightened out, a long solenoid is obtained as in Fig. 183 (p. 236) or Fig. 219. The long solenoid, Fig. 219, also has a length of l cm and n turns per centimeter length. The flux, which is shown as acting from right to left within the long solenoid, leaves the left-hand end of the solenoid and spreads, theoretically, over an infinite area and returns to enter the right-hand end. If there were no reluctance exterior to the solenoid, all the mmf within the solenoid would be utilized in overcoming the reluctance of the solenoid, as in the ring solenoid, Fig. 218. Hence, the flux in this solenoid also can be obtained from Eq. (198). Since, in the exterior return path, the flux spreads theoretically over an infinite area, the reluctance is small except for the parts $\mathcal{R}$ near the ends of the solenoid, where the area is finite.

If, however, the reluctance $l \div A$ of the solenoid itself is large compared with $2\mathcal{R}$, the end reluctances, the total mmf of the solenoid may be considered as being utilized in overcoming its own reluctance. Hence, the flux near the center of the solenoid

$$\phi = \frac{0.4\pi nlI}{l/A} = 0.4\pi nIA, \tag{200}$$

the same as Eq. (198). Therefore, the flux ϕ in such a solenoid is equal numerically to the *mmf per centimeter* multiplied by the cross section of the solenoid in square centimeters. It is a simple matter to make such a solenoid, having a known diameter and a known number of turns per centimeter. If the length of the solenoid is 10 times the diameter, (200) is correct within 0.5 per cent, and if the length is 20 times the diameter, the error is only 0.1 per cent.

The error due to the two end reluctances $2\mathcal{R}$ is identical with the error resulting from assuming that a finite solenoid is infinite in length (Sec. 175, p. 236).

In mks unrationalized units, the mmf per meter length of solenoid is $4\pi In$ unrationalized mmf units (= field intensity H_p), where n is the turns per meter. The reluctance of a meter length of solenoid is $1/\mu_v A$, where A is the cross-sectional area in square meters. Hence the flux at the center section,

$$\phi = \frac{4\pi In}{1/\mu_v A} = 4\pi In\mu_v A = \mu_v H_p A = 10^{-7} H_p A \qquad \text{webers.} \tag{201}$$

[See Eq. (160), p. 239.]

In mks rationalized units, the mmf per meter length of solenoid is In amp-turns per m (= field intensity H_p'). The reluctance of a meter length of solenoid is $1/\mu_v' A$. Hence the flux at the center section,

$$\phi = \frac{In}{1/\mu_v' A} = In\mu_v' A = \mu_v' H_p' A = 4\pi \cdot 10^{-7} H_p' A \qquad \text{webers.} \tag{202}$$

[See Eq. (154), p. 239.]

(201) and (202) are equal.

209. Calibration of Galvanometer. To calibrate the galvanometer, connections are made as in Fig. 219, in which a ring test specimen is included as an example. The current in the primary turns of the standard solenoid is obtained from some steady d-c source. Its value is controlled by the rheostat R' and read with the ammeter. A secondary of a known number of turns, n_2, is wound about the solenoid near its center. This secondary is connected in series with the secondary of the test specimen and with the galvanometer G. Both secondaries are always in circuit in order to keep the value of R constant in Eq. (196) (p. 285). A reversing switch Sw is connected in the galvanometer circuit. To calibrate, open switch Sw and close switch S, which energizes the long solenoid without causing the galvanometer to deflect. Close switch Sw and read

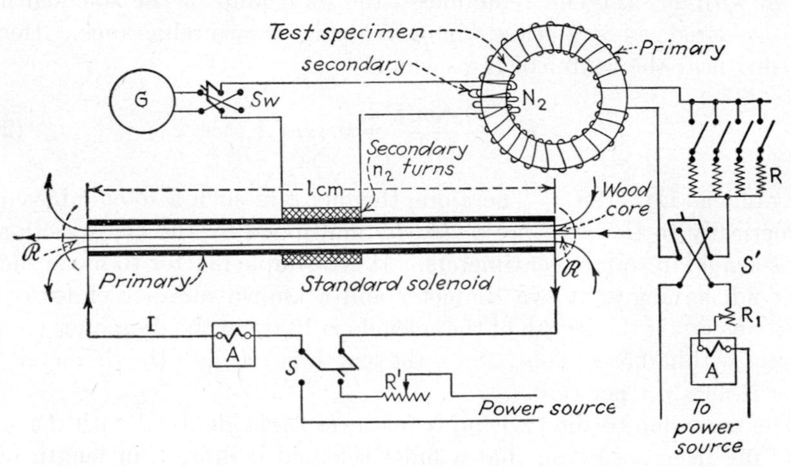

FIG. 219. Standard solenoid with ring sample and galvanometer.

the current I with the ammeter. Then open S, noting the ballistic throw D_1 of the galvanometer. Several check readings should be taken.

When the switch S is opened, the total change of flux $\Delta\phi$ is $0.4\pi nIA$, and the quantity Q_1 is discharged through the galvanometer [Eq. (196)].

$$Q_1 = \frac{n_2\Delta\phi}{R} = n_2\frac{0.4\pi nIA}{R}. \tag{203}$$

When the flux ϕ_2 in the specimen is changed by an amount $\Delta\phi_2$, or from ϕ_2 to ϕ_1, from Eq. (196), the quantity

$$Q_2 = N_2\frac{\Delta\phi_2}{R} = N_2\frac{\phi_2 - \phi_1}{R} \tag{204}$$

where N_2 is the number of secondary turns on the test specimen.

Dividing (204) by (203),

$$\frac{Q_2}{Q_1} = \frac{N_2(\phi_2 - \phi_1)/R}{n_2(0.4\pi nIA/R)} = \frac{N_2(\phi_2 - \phi_1)}{0.4\pi nn_2IA}.$$

$$\phi_2 - \phi_1 = \frac{Q_2}{Q_1}\left(\frac{0.4\pi nn_2IA}{N_2}\right).$$

Since the galvanometer deflections are proportional to the quantities Q_2 and Q_1 [Eq. (197)],

$$\Delta\phi_2 = \phi_2 - \phi_1 = \frac{D_2}{D_1}\left(\frac{0.4\pi n n_2 I A}{N_2}\right)$$
$$= \left(\frac{0.4\pi n n_2 A I}{D_1 N_2}\right) D_2 = K D_2. \tag{205}$$

The quantity in parentheses is the galvanometer constant K in Eq. (197) (p. 285). That is,

$$K = \frac{0.4\pi n n_2 A I}{D_1 N_2} \tag{206}$$

where n is the turns per centimeter in the *primary* of the standard solenoid; n_2 is the total turns in the *secondary* of the standard solenoid; N_2 is the total turns in the secondary of the test specimen; A is the cross section of the standard-solenoid core in square centimeters; I is the current in the primary of the standard solenoid; D_1 is the galvanometer deflection when the primary of the standard solenoid is opened.

Example. An air solenoid 48 in. long has an inside diameter of 1.75 in., a primary winding of 960 turns, and a secondary winding of 2,000 turns. There are 40 turns in the secondary of the test specimen. The galvanometer is connected in series with the secondaries of both the standard solenoid and the test specimen (see Fig. 219). When the current in the primary of the standard solenoid has become steady at 3.82 amp, the circuit is opened and the resulting ballistic deflection of the galvanometer is 12.4 cm. Determine: (*a*) flux density (gauss) in standard solenoid; (*b*) total flux in standard solenoid; (*c*) galvanometer constant; (*d*) flux change in test specimen when ballistic throw of galvanometer is 8.9 cm.

The turns per centimeter length in the standard solenoid,

$$n = \frac{960}{48 \cdot 2.54} = 7.875.$$

The cross section of the standard solenoid $A = (\pi/4)(1.75)^2 \cdot (2.54)^2 = 15.52$ sq cm.

(*a*) From Eq. (199), $B = 0.4\pi \cdot 7.875 \cdot 3.82 = 37.82$ gauss. *Ans.*

(*b*) $\phi = BA = 37.82 \cdot 15.52 = 587.0$ maxwells. *Ans.*

(*c*) Using Eq. (206),

$$K = \frac{0.4\pi \cdot 7.875 \cdot 2{,}000 \cdot 15.52 \cdot 3.82}{12.4 \cdot 40} = 2{,}366. \quad \textit{Ans.}$$

(*d*) $\phi_2 - \phi_1 = \Delta\phi_2 = KD_2 = 2{,}366 \cdot 8.9 = 21{,}060$ maxwells. *Ans.*

210. Yoke Method. In the yoke, or divided-bar, method, which is due to Hopkinson, the test specimen is a cylindrical rod of from ¼ to ½ in. (0.64 to 1.27 cm) diameter and about 20 in. (50.8 cm) long. The rod is in two sections A and B, Fig. 220(*a*), the two ends butting at e. These two ends should have accurately ground flat surfaces so that they make good magnetic contact. The rod fits tightly at both ends into a massive iron yoke Y, whose reluctance is negligible in comparison with that of the rod. The effective length of the rod is taken as l cm, the distance between the inside surfaces of the yoke. The exciting coil PP

is in two sections and has a total of N turns. The flux is determined by means of a small secondary coil S, through which the rod A passes. By means of a spring, the coil S springs out of the yoke when the part A of the rod is withdrawn.

The galvanometer is connected in series with the coil S and the secondary S' of the standard solenoid, Fig. 220(a). The current to the exciting coil is supplied by a battery, or by any source of steady current, through a rheostat R, an ammeter A, and a reversing switch Sw. A voltage divider[1] often gives better adjustment than a series resistor. The mmf in gilberts per centimeter,

$$H = \frac{0.4\pi NI}{l}.$$

To determine some point a on the normal induction curve, the current is increased to a value which gives a mmf ob, Fig. 220(b). The section A

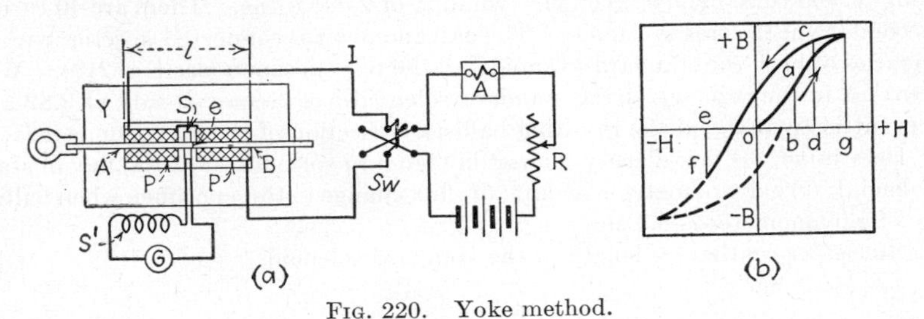

FIG. 220. Yoke method.

of the rod is withdrawn, allowing S to spring out, and the ballistic throw of the galvanometer is read. Since the flux linking the coil S becomes nearly zero when S springs out, the galvanometer deflection must be proportional to the ordinate ba. To determine point c on the hysteresis loop, the excitation is increased to og and then decreased to od. The section A of the rod is again withdrawn and the galvanometer deflection, which is proportional to cd, is read. To determine the point f on the hysteresis loop, the excitation is increased to og, is reduced to zero at o, the reversing switch Sw is thrown, and the excitation is increased negatively to e. The section A of the rod is again withdrawn, and the resulting galvanometer deflection, which is proportional to the ordinate ef, is read.

The galvanometer is calibrated by the method given in Sec. 209. The flux density B is readily determined, knowing the flux ϕ and the cross section A of the rod.

This method is subject to slight errors, due to leakage from the rod to the yoke, imperfect magnetic contacts, and the hysteresis effects in the yoke.

[1] See p. 187.

211. Ring Method. In the ring method of magnetic testing, which was devised by Rowland, the form of the sample is such as to give a closed magnetic circuit. It usually consists of a ring, Figs. 219 and 221, although if the sample cannot be made conveniently into ring form, it may be in the form of a square. For example, a square is readily made from long, rectangular laminations which are made alternately to butt and lap at the joints. If properly made, the joints in this latter case introduce slight error. The connections in the ring method, Figs. 219

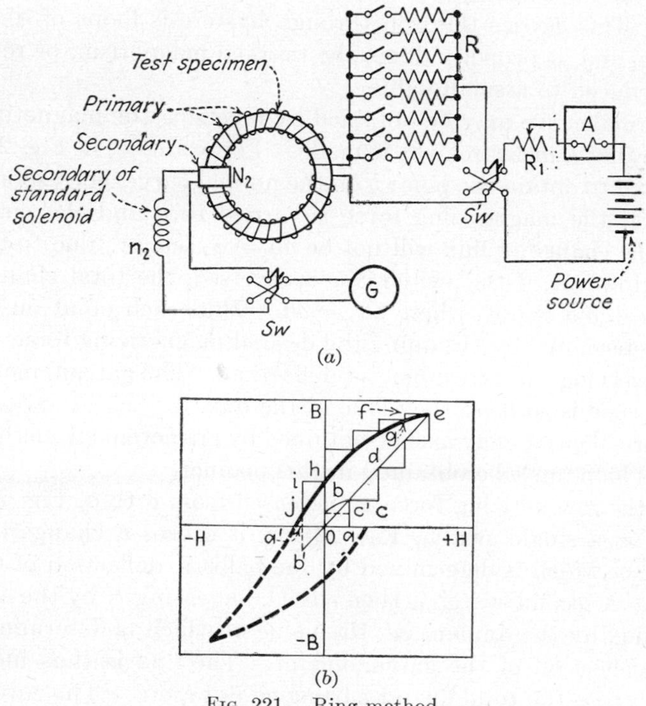

FIG. 221. Ring method.

and 221(*a*), are essentially the same as those for the yoke method, Fig. 220(*a*). The principal difference lies in the procedure in carrying the sample through the magnetic cycle.

The primary is wound uniformly on the ring, Fig. 221(*a*), or along the four sides, if the sample is in the form of a square. The value of *H* is given approximately by dividing the total mmf by the mean length of the sample. The secondary is wound about the specimen in the manner shown in Fig. 219 and Fig. 221(*a*). The success of the experiment depends on the current being quickly changed by definite amounts. Hence, the parallel arrangement of resistors *R*, Fig. 221(*a*), each of which is provided with a switch, is preferable to a sliding-contact resistor. The auxiliary rheostat R_1 is also useful, in that it may be set to correspond to different values of maximum current. A single series resistor, having several switches which short-circuit definite amounts, may also be used to change the current.

Since the sample is a closed iron circuit, there may be initially considerable residual magnetism, or remanence. It is necessary to reduce this residual magnetism to a small value. This is done by reversing the exciting current more or less rapidly by means of switch $S'w$ and at the same time slowly reducing the value of the current to zero with resistors R_1 or R. This carries the iron through hysteresis loops of diminishing amplitude, and, if properly done, the residual magnetism, or remanence, may be reduced to a small value.

The normal curve may be obtained by reversing the magnetizing force each time that a measurement is made. For example, in Fig. 221(b), let it be desired to obtain the point b on the normal curve, corresponding to a flux ϕ_1. If the magnetizing force is carried to a and the circuit then opened, the change of flux will not be $ab = \phi_1$ but bc', due to the remanence. However, if the switch $S'w$ is reversed, the total change of flux will be $ba + a'b' = 2\phi_1$ where $oa' = oa$. Thus each point on the curve may be determined by obtaining the desired magnetizing force, reversing it, and observing the galvanometer deflection. The galvanometer deflection corresponds to *twice* the value of the flux.

The normal curve may also be obtained by an increment method. The hysteresis loop must be obtained in this manner.

When the magnetizing force is increased from o to a, Fig. 221(b), by throwing in a single switch, Fig. 221(a), it causes a change of flux ab, the value of which is determined by the ballistic deflection of the galvanometer. A second switch is then closed, increasing H by the amount bc, and the flux by the amount cd, the value of which is determined by the ballistic deflection of the galvanometer. The flux is thus increased in *increments* to e, the total flux at e being $ab + cd$, etc. The galvanometer measures the *increment* (or *decrement*) of flux between successive magnetizing forces. To obtain points on the hysteresis loop, the magnetizing force is decreased by an amount ef by opening a single switch, Fig. 221(a), and the decrement of flux fg is read with the galvanometer. When the remanence oh is reached, the switch $S'w$ is reversed and a single switch, Fig. 221(a), is closed. This gives a decrement of magnetizing force hi and a corresponding flux decrement ij. The sample is thus carried around the hysteresis loop.

Since the flux at any point is the sum of successive flux increments, a single error vitiates the entire data. It is, therefore, advisable to practice carrying the flux once or twice through the cycle represented by the loop before actually taking data.

Although the ring method gives more precise results than the yoke method, it is more difficult to manipulate and the samples are not of such convenient form. Moreover, the entire data may be rendered worthless by a single error, such as failing to read the galvanometer correctly, inadvertently closing a switch, etc.

212. Koepsel Permeameter. In the preceding two methods of magnetic testing, the measurements are indirect, quite laborious, and involve considerable computation. The Koepsel permeameter is an indicating instrument on whose scale the flux density B in a specimen is read directly, just as current is read on an ammeter scale. The magnetizing force H is

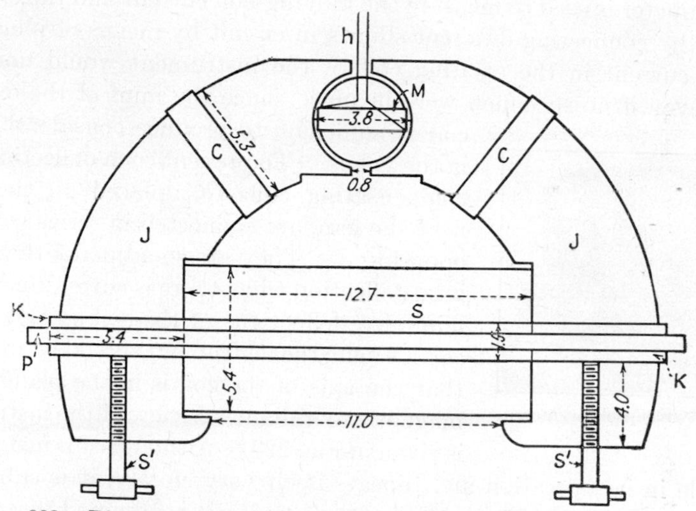

FIG. 222. Diagram of the Koepsel permeameter (dimensions in centimeters).

also read directly by means of an ammeter. The instrument operates on the principle of the Weston ammeter (Sec. 115, p. 145), that is, if a coil carries current in a magnetic field, it tends to assume a position perpendicular to the field. In the ordinary Weston instrument, the flux is constant, and the deflections are practically proportional to the current in the moving coil; in the Koepsel permeameter, the current in the moving coil is constant, and the deflections are practically proportional to the flux in the gap.

The instrument, Fig. 222, consists of two massive soft-iron yokes JJ, a moving coil M which turns in a very short air-gap, two compensating coils CC, and the exciting coil S. The specimen to be tested consists of an iron rod P held into the yokes by iron clamps KK and screws $S'S'$. The test specimen may be square in cross section, or it may be round, the clamps ordinarily being adapted to hold specimens 6 mm (0.236 in.) square or 6 mm diameter.

When the current in the moving coil M is equal to $0.005/A$ amp, where A is the cross section of the test specimen in square centimeters, the instrument reads directly the flux density B in the specimen. The current for the moving coil is supplied by a 4-volt source, such as three or four dry cells in series, and is controlled by a suitable rheostat. This current, when once adjusted, must remain constant. The exciting coil S is wound with 79.6 ($= 100/0.4\pi$) turns per centimeter, and the mmf per centimeter $H = 0.4\pi(100/0.4\pi)I = 100I$ gilberts, where I is the exciting current in amperes. Therefore, the mmf per centimeter may be readily obtained by multiplying the ammeter reading by 100. Ordinarily, the same ammeter is used to measure the moving-coil current and the exciting current, by connecting different shunts in circuit by means of plugs.

With current in the exciting coil S, the instrument would normally deflect even if no specimen were in place, since the mmf of the exciting coil is sufficient to produce considerable flux in the yokes. To prevent such deflection, two compensating coils CC, placed on the yoke near the gap, are connected in series with and opposing S. They are so adjusted that there is no deflection when there is current in S. To minimize deflections of the coil caused by the earth's field, the instrument should be so placed that the axis of the coil is in the plane of the magnetic meridian. A view of the instrument is given in Fig. 223. Although this instrument is simple in its operation and repeats itself very closely, it is subject to some error, particularly at high flux densities. It is assumed that a fixed percentage of the flux in the rod reaches the gap. This fixed percentage may vary as much as 2 per cent, depending on the flux density. Also, because of the reluctance of the air-gap, leakage, etc., the error in H under extreme conditions may be as large as 10 per cent. Correction curves usually accompany the instrument so that the effect of such errors may be reduced. The fact that ordinarily the errors are not large makes the instrument particularly useful in comparing magnetic materials and in detecting nonuniformity.

FIG. 223. Koepsel permeameter.

213. Hysteresis Loop with Cathode-ray Oscilloscope. The methods for obtaining hysteresis loops which so far have been described are point-by-point methods, requiring usually something like 40 sets of data. This is of course a tedious and time-consuming process. If high numerical accuracy is not required, a cathode-ray oscilloscope (CRO) (see Vol. II, Chap. IV) may be used to produce the hysteresis loop dynamically, as well as visually, by a continuous curve, such as is indicated in Fig. 224(b). The connections are shown in Fig. 224(a). In order to obtain complete cycles of magnetizing current which vary rapidly, alternating current is used to produce the magnetizing force H. For accurate results the specimen should be laminated and the frequency should be low in order to make eddy-current effects negligible. It is convenient and more accurate to control the current by a transformer, a variable autotransformer being shown in Fig. 224(a). With a resistor in series for control, the voltage drop across it distorts the voltage applied to the specimen if the current is nonsinusoidal, which is usually true when the iron becomes at all saturated (see Vol. II, 4th edition, Fig. 104, p. 118). A step-down transformer is also convenient if the magnetizing turns on the specimen are few in number. The current is measured by an ammeter A, and the

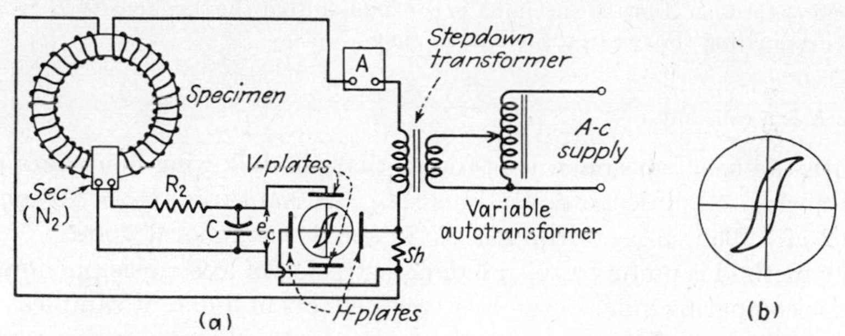

FIG. 224. Dynamic hysteresis loop with cathode-ray oscilloscope.

emf to the H, or X, plates, which deflect the electron beam in a horizontal direction, is taken from a low-resistance shunt Sh. Since the voltage across Sh is proportional to the current I and the magnetizing force H is equal to $0.4\pi nI$, the horizontal deflection will be proportional to H. (n = turns per centimeter of specimen.)

The V, or Y, plates which produce the vertical deflection are supplied by a secondary coil wound on the specimen and having N_2 turns. This secondary is similar to those of Figs. 219 and 221. In order that the vertical deflections shall be proportional to the flux density B, it is necessary to use an integrating circuit consisting of a resistor R_2, having high resistance, and a capacitor C in series. The voltage e_c to the V, or Y, plates is taken from across the capacitor C. The necessity for such a circuit is demonstrated as follows:

Let ϕ be the flux (maxwells) in the specimen, e_2 the emf induced in the secondary, i_2 the secondary current, q the quantity (coulombs) on the capacitor C.

Then,

$$e_2 = -N_2 \frac{d\phi}{dt} \cdot 10^{-8} \qquad \text{volts} \tag{I}$$

$$\phi = -10^8 \frac{1}{N_2} \int e_2 \, dt + K' \qquad \text{maxwells.} \tag{II}$$

The constant of integration K' can be made equal to zero.
Since R_2 is large,

$$i_2 = \frac{e_2}{R_2}; \qquad e_2 = i_2R_2 \text{ (nearly)}. \qquad \text{(III)}$$

Substituting (III) in (II),

$$\phi = -10^8 \frac{1}{N_2} R_2 \int i_2\, dt \qquad \text{maxwells.} \qquad \text{(IV)}$$

The voltage across the capacitor C,

$$e_c = \frac{q}{C} = \frac{1}{C} \int i_2\, dt \qquad \text{volts.} \qquad \text{(V)}$$

The cross section A of the specimen is constant so that the flux density $B = \phi/A$. Hence, comparing (IV) and (V), it follows that

$$B = Ke_c, \qquad \text{(VI)}$$

where K is a constant.

With the usual specimen it is found that the following constants produce normal oscilloscope deflections: $N_2 = 3{,}000$ turns; $R_2 = 10^5$ ohms; $C = 2\ \mu$f. The voltage drop across Sh should be about 3 volts.

The method is useful for visual demonstration of hysteresis phenomena and for comparing quickly the hysteresis effects in different samples. In the manufacture of transformers the method is used to determine rapidly whether or not the cores meet specifications. A normal hysteresis loop is drawn on the CRO screen, and if any core produces a CRO loop which exceeds this in area it is rejected and later re-annealed. A low frequency of a few cycles per second is used in order to make eddy-current effects negligible.

CHAPTER IX

SELF- AND MUTUAL INDUCTANCE

In earlier chapters the current in a circuit has been considered as being determined by sources of emf, such as generators or batteries acting in the circuit, and by resistance. When the current is in the *steady state,* these factors alone do determine the value of the current. If, however, a change in current occurs, it causes a change in the magnetic field associated with the circuit. The change in magnetic field induces an emf in the circuit itself, and this emf is also effective in determining the value of current. Such an emf exists only during the time when the current is *changing.* It does not exist when the current is steady.

A circuit in which a change of current causes an emf to be induced within the circuit itself is said to have *self-inductance,* or frequently, just *inductance.* Methods for determining the effect of inductance in electric circuits are given in the paragraphs which follow.

If an electric circuit is associated with a second circuit, so that a change of current in the second circuit causes a change in the flux linking any of the turns of the first circuit, the two circuits are said to have *mutual inductance.* Mutual inductance is also discussed in the paragraphs which follow.

The effects of inductance are in reality the effects of *induced emf.* As the operation of electrical apparatus, such as generators, motors, and transformers, depends fundamentally on induced emf, an understanding of the principles of induced emf is important.

214. Induced Electromotive Force. If the terminals of an insulated coil, Fig. 225(*a*), be connected to a galvanometer, and a magnetic field be produced through this coil, either by thrusting a bar magnet into the coil or by some other means, the galvanometer will deflect momentarily and then return to rest. This shows that an emf has been induced temporarily in the coil. When the flux through the coil has ceased to change, this emf ceases. If investigation be made, it will be found that the direction of this induced emf is that shown in the figure and that this direction is such that if the emf be allowed to produce a current, this current will tend to push the bar magnet *out* of the coil, or, what is the same thing, will oppose its entering the coil.

If the magnet be withdrawn from the coil, Fig. 225(*b*), the galvanometer will deflect again, momentarily as before, but the deflection is opposite to its direction in the first case. The direction of the induced emf is now such that, if the emf produces a current, this current will tend to *prevent* the magnet from being withdrawn from the coil. The emf in each case is transient and ceases when the *change* of flux through the coil ceases.

If careful measurements be made, the value of this induced emf will be found to be proportional to (1) the number of turns N in the coil; (2) the rate at which the flux linked with the coil changes, $\Delta\phi/\Delta t$.

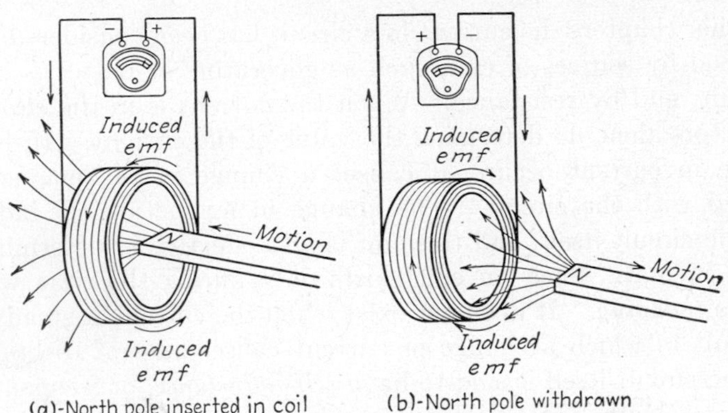

FIG. 225. Induced emf.

The *average* induced emf is given by

$$e = -N\left(\frac{\Delta\phi}{\Delta t}\right)10^{-8} \quad \text{volts,} \tag{207}$$

where $\Delta\phi$ is the incremental change of flux in maxwells occurring in the time increment Δt sec. The factor 10^{-8} changes the flux to webers so that e is in volts.

If $\Delta\phi$ is given in webers, (207) becomes

$$e = -N\left(\frac{\Delta\phi}{\Delta t}\right) \quad \text{volts.} \tag{208}$$

The minus sign indicates that the induced emf is in opposition to the effect which produces it.

$\Delta\phi/\Delta t$ is the average rate of change of flux, so that the induced emf may be said to be proportional to the *number of turns* and the *rate of change of flux.*

Example. A flux of 1,500,000 maxwells links a coil having 350 turns. This flux through the coil is decreased to zero at a uniform rate in 0.2 sec. Determine induced emf during this time interval.

$$e = 350\,\frac{1{,}500{,}000}{0.2}\,10^{-8}$$
$$= 26.25 \text{ volts.} \quad \textit{Ans.}$$

In the foregoing example, the rate of change of flux $\Delta\phi/\Delta t$ is 1,500,000/0.2, or $7.5 \cdot 10^6$, maxwells per sec.

When the flux does not change at a uniform rate, but the rate varies from instant to instant, the induced emf can still be calculated if the *instantaneous* rate of change of flux $d\phi/dt$ is used. This condition occurs, for example, in transformers in which the flux usually varies sinusoidally with time. When the flux is going through zero, its rate of change is a maximum, and when the flux is a maximum, its rate of change is zero (see Vol. II, 4th edition, Fig. 213, p. 246). With instantaneously changing flux, (207) becomes

$$e = -N \frac{d\phi}{dt} 10^{-8} \qquad \text{volts.} \tag{209}$$

and (208) becomes

$$e = -N \frac{d\phi}{dt} \qquad \text{volts.} \tag{210}$$

The fact that the currents produced by induction oppose the effect producing them should be carefully noted, for this principle is manifest in practically all types of electric machinery. This principle was first formulated by Lenz, in a form known as *Lenz's law*,[1] which in effect says:

In all cases of electromagnetic induction, the induced voltages have a direction such that the currents which they produce oppose the effect which produces them.

This law is also based on the law of the conservation of energy. That is, the induced currents are produced at the expense of the mechanical energy required to push the magnet into the coil against their opposition, or the energy required to withdraw the magnet against the opposition of the induced currents, which try to prevent this withdrawal. When an

[1] After Heinrich Friedrich Emil Lenz, 1808–1865. Lenz was born in northern Russia, and there is little record of his early life except that in his early education he studied theology but later changed to the natural sciences and physics. At the age of twenty he made a voyage of investigation round the world as a naturalist, specializing in geology. He made a report on the trip to the Academy of Science, was made professor of physics at St. Petersburg, and was elected to the Academy of Science. It was at this time that he began investigations of electromagnetism, studying carefully the experiments of Faraday. He wrote several papers, including "The Laws Which Govern the Action of a Magnet upon a Spiral When It Is Suddenly Approached or Withdrawn from It," and "The Most Advantageous Method of Constructing Spirals for Magneto Electrical Purposes." Later he made an investigation of the resistance of metals and enunciated a formula giving the change of resistance as a function of temperature. On Nov. 29, 1833, he read a paper, "On the Direction of Galvanic Currents Which Are Excited through Electro Dynamic Induction," which contained the familiar statement, "The electrodynamic action of an induced current opposes equally the mechanical action inducing it," now known as Lenz's law. He was a voluminous writer and in 1864 published a two-volume "Handbook of Physics."

emf is induced in a circuit by a change of current in that circuit, the emf is due to changes in the flux-current linkages of the circuit.

215. Flux-current Linkages and Self-inductance. Current in a conductor produces magnetic flux which completely encircles the conductor, and the current in the conductor completely encircles the flux. Some familiar examples of this are given in Fig. 226, in which the currents and related fluxes are shown.

In Fig. 226(*a*), current in a single turn is shown. The flux which it produces is indicated by the rings. The rings encircle the current, and the current encircles the rings. In (*b*), the current in a thin sheet forming a loop is shown. The flux lines encircle the current, and the current

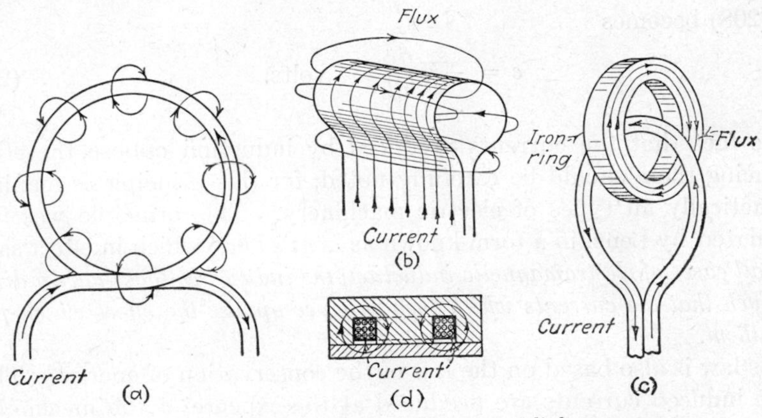

FIG. 226. Illustrations of flux-current linkages.

encircles the flux lines which it produces. A still more striking example is given in (*c*), which shows the current in a loop of wire interlinking a circular magnetic core. Another excellent example of current-flux linkages is given in (*d*), which shows the flux in the magnetic circuit of a lifting magnet linking the current in the exciting coil.

These figures illustrate the fact that a current and the flux which it produces always completely encircle each other. Hence, they are said to *link* each other. This mutual linking action is particularly well illustrated in Fig. 226(*c*).

The product of the turns of conductor and the number of lines of flux linking these turns is called the *flux linkages* of the circuit. These linkages will be given in cgs units if the flux is given in maxwells.

Example. A solenoid has 800 turns. A current of 5 amp in the winding produces a flux of 2,500,000 maxwells. Determine the cgs flux linkages.

$$800 \cdot 2{,}500{,}000 = 20 \cdot 10^8 \text{ flux linkages (cgs units).} \quad \textit{Ans.}$$

When the reluctance of the magnetic circuit is constant (see Sec. 218, p. 304), the number of these *linkages per unit current* is called the *self-inductance*, or just the *inductance*, of the circuit and is represented by the symbol L, implying linkages. The unit of inductance is the henry.[1]

From definition, with constant magnetic reluctance, the inductance

$$L = \frac{N\phi}{I \cdot 10^8} \quad \text{henrys,} \tag{211}$$

where ϕ is the flux in maxwells and I the current in amperes.

It is necessary to divide by 10^8 because 10^8 cgs magnetic lines, or maxwells, are equal to *one* weber in the mks system.

In either the unrationalized or the rationalized mks system, (211) becomes

$$L = \frac{N\phi}{I} \quad \text{henrys,} \tag{212}$$

where ϕ is in webers.

Example. In the foregoing circuit, determine: (*a*) inductance; (*b*) inductance if number of turns is increased to 1,200 other factors remaining unchanged.

(*a*) $L_1 = \dfrac{20 \cdot 10^8}{5 \cdot 10^8} = 4.0$ henrys. *Ans.*

(*b*) With 1,200 turns and the same current of 5 amp the flux will be

$$\frac{1{,}200}{800}\, 2{,}500{,}000 = 3{,}750{,}000 \text{ maxwells.}$$

The new flux linkages are

$$3{,}750{,}000 \cdot 1{,}200 = 4.5 \cdot 10^9.$$

The inductance

$$L_2 = \frac{4.5 \cdot 10^9}{5 \cdot 10^8} = 9.0 \text{ henrys.} \quad \textit{Ans.}$$

Note that the inductance varies as the *square* of the turns.

The henry may be defined as follows: *The henry is the inductance in a circuit in which an electromotive force of one volt is induced by a current changing at the rate of one ampere per second* (also see Eq. (218), p. 304).

[1] After Joseph Henry (1797–1878), an eminent American physicist, who was educated at Albany Academy and prepared himself for the medical profession. However, he became interested in science and in 1825 was elected to the chair of mathematics and natural philosophy at the Albany Academy. With the crudest of apparatus and very little spare time, he made many improvements in electromagnetic apparatus and presented important papers on the subject of electromagnetism.

In 1832 he was elected to the chair of natural philosophy at Princeton University and in 1846 he became secretary and director of the Smithsonian Institution in Washington. He was the first to insulate wire; he invented the spool, or bobbin, winding for electromagnets and the electromagnetic relay which is so widely used for the control of electrical apparatus. His outstanding contribution was his discovery of self-inductance in 1831. Independently of Faraday, he discovered electromagnetic induction. He was voted the foremost American scientist by the National Academy of Scientists.

From (211) and (212) it would appear that the inductance of a circuit is primarily a function of the flux. Also, it might be inferred that inductance is directly proportional to the turns. These two relations are not true, however, under the conditions of constant reluctance because the flux ϕ is proportional to both the turns and the current. That is, $\phi = 0.4\pi NI/\mathcal{R}$, where $\mathcal{R}$ is the reluctance of the magnetic circuit. Hence,

$$L = \frac{0.4\pi N^2}{\mathcal{R}10^8} \quad \text{henrys.} \tag{213}$$

Since $\mathcal{R} = l/\mu A$ (Sec. 186, p. 254),

$$L = \frac{0.4\pi N^2 \mu A}{l10^8} \quad \text{henrys.} \tag{214}$$

Thus, inductance is primarily a property of the geometry of the circuit, the number of turns, and the permeability.

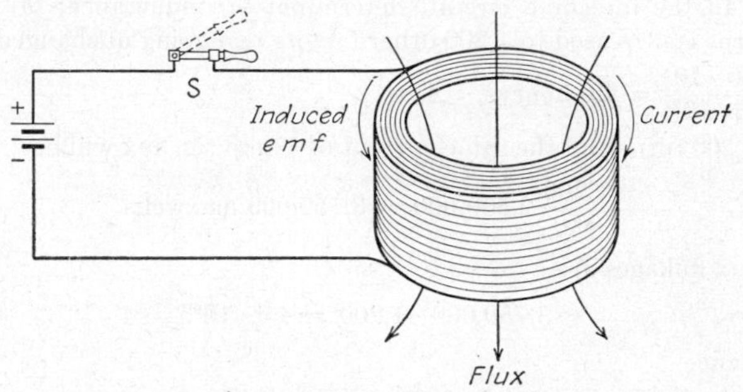

FIG. 227. Relation of emf of self-induction to current.

From (213) and (214) it should be noted that under the conditions of constant reluctance, inductance varies as the *square* of the turns, even though the term N appears in (211) and (212) to the first power only. This is illustrated by the foregoing example.

$$L_2 = 4.0\left(\frac{1{,}200}{800}\right)^2 = 9.0 \text{ henrys.} \quad \textit{Ans. (check)}$$

216. Electromotive Force of Self-induction. If a coil be connected to a battery and a switch S closed, Fig. 227, current will begin to flow in the coil. This current produces a flux linking the coil. As this flux increases it must induce an emf in the coil, the magnitude of which depends on the number of turns in the coil and the rate at which the flux increases. By Lenz's law, and also from a consideration of Fig. 225(*a*), the emf thus induced must have such a direction as to oppose the increase in the flux linking the coil and hence must *oppose* any increase of current. Thus, in Fig. 227, as viewed from the top, the direction of the current in the coil is clockwise, the direction of the flux is downward, and the direction of the induced emf is counterclockwise, or opposite to that of the current. The current cannot, therefore, reach its maximum value at once but is retarded by an emf which the current itself produces. Such an emf, which acts in the same circuit as the current which produces it, is an *emf of self-induction.*

In contrast, the rise of current in a circuit containing resistance only is shown in Fig. 228, the impressed voltage being 10 volts and the resistance 20 ohms. When the switch S is closed, the current reaches its maximum or Ohm's law value of 0.5 amp at once.

With the inductive circuit, the current gradually approaches its Ohm's law value as shown in Fig. 230(*b*) (p. 306). To be exact, it takes an infinite time for the current to reach its Ohm's law value, although in a

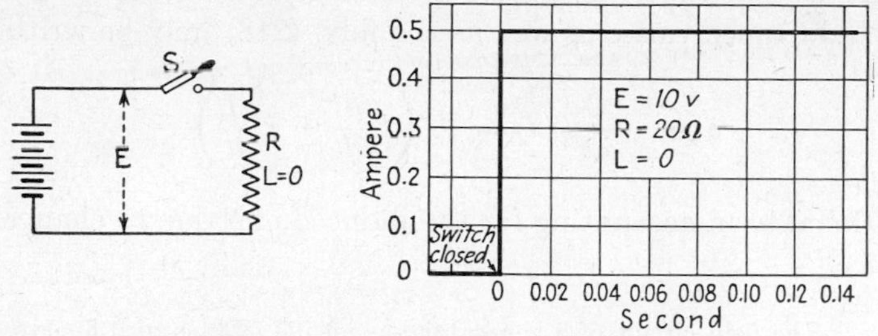

FIG. 228. Rise of current in a noninductive circuit.

comparatively short time it reaches substantially this value. The relation of current to time in an inductive circuit is derived in Sec. 219 (p. 305).

217. Calculation of the Electromotive Force of Self-induction. From Eq. (207) (p. 298) the emf induced in a coil due to a change in the flux linking the coil is

$$e = -N \frac{\Delta\phi}{\Delta t} 10^{-8} \qquad \text{volts,} \tag{215}$$

where N is the number of turns and $\Delta\phi/\Delta t$ the rate at which the flux changes.

Also, from Eq. (211),

$$L = \frac{N\phi}{I} 10^{-8} \qquad \text{henrys.} \tag{216}$$

If ϕ and I are varying, ϕ/I is the rate of change of flux with respect to current. If incremental changes of flux and current be taken, $L\,\Delta I = N\,\Delta\phi\,10^{-8}$. Substituting the value of $N\,\Delta\phi$ in (215),

$$e = -L \frac{\Delta I}{\Delta t} \qquad \text{volts.} \tag{217}$$

If the rate of change of current with respect to time is not constant, the derivative di/dt of current with respect to time must be used. From Eq. (209), $e = -N\,d\phi/dt\ 10^{-8}$ volts, and from Eq. (211), $N\phi 10^{-8} = Li$. Multiplying by -1 and differentiating,

$$-N \frac{d\phi}{dt} 10^{-8} = -L \frac{di}{dt} = e \qquad \text{volts,}$$

and

$$e = -L \frac{di}{dt} \qquad \text{volts,} \tag{218}$$

where L is in henrys.

Hence, the emf of self-induction is equal to the product of the inductance and the rate of change of current with respect to time. The minus sign indicates that this emf *opposes* the change of current.

If the inductance varies as well as the flux, (218) may be written

$$e = -\frac{d}{dt}(Li) = -\left(L \frac{di}{dt} + i \frac{dL}{dt}\right), \tag{219}$$

the additional term accounting for the induced emf due to change in the inductance.

Example. The field circuit of a generator has an inductance of 6 henrys. If the field current of 12 amp is interrupted in 0.05 sec, what is the average induced emf in the field winding?

$$e = -6 \frac{12}{0.05} = -1{,}440 \text{ volts. } \textit{Ans.}$$

218. Self-inductance with Varying Reluctance. When the reluctance of the magnetic circuit is *not constant*, the inductance is equal to the product of the number of turns and the *rate of change of flux* divided by the *rate of change of current* and by 10^8. This relation is derived as follows: Let L now be a *variable* inductance. At any instant the induced emf is

$$-L \frac{di}{dt} = -N \frac{d\phi}{dt} 10^{-8} \qquad \text{volts.} \tag{220}$$

Solving for L gives

$$L = N \frac{d\phi}{di} 10^{-8} \qquad \text{henrys.} \tag{221}$$

The relation is illustrated in Fig. 229. An electric circuit of 500 turns is linked with a magnetic circuit. When the electric circuit is switched across 200 volts, the current increases from zero in the manner shown by curve I in Fig. 229(a). However, with increase of current the iron becomes saturated, as may be seen from the saturation curve of the magnetic circuit in (b). Therefore, as the current becomes greater in value in (a), the rate of increase of flux diminishes with respect to the rate of increase of current. At the instant p, Fig. 229(a), corresponding to 0.0055 sec, the flux is increasing at a rate of $2 \cdot 10^7$ maxwells per sec, and at this same instant the current is increasing at a rate of 200 amp per sec. These rates of increase may be determined from the tangents drawn to the curves at this instant of time.

Example. Determine the value of self-inductance at the instant p. From (220),

$$L = \frac{N\, d\phi/dt}{di/dt} 10^{-8} \qquad \text{henrys.}$$

Hence,

$$L = 500 \frac{2 \cdot 10^7}{200 \cdot 10^8} = 0.5 \text{ henry.} \quad \textit{Ans.}$$

In (b), which shows the saturation curve for this circuit, the point p corresponds to point p in (a). At point p in (b), the rate of change of flux with respect to current, $d\phi/di$, is 10^5 maxwells per amp. Hence, using (221),

$$L = 500 \cdot 10^5 \cdot 10^{-8} = 0.5 \text{ henry, } \textit{Ans. (check)}$$

which value may be determined by the tangent drawn at the point p in (b).

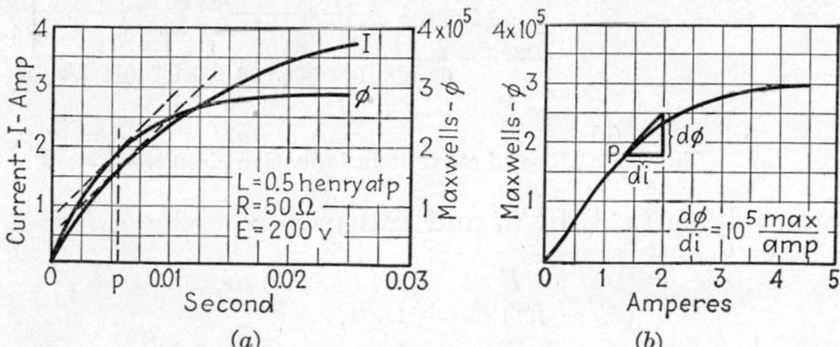

(a) (b)

Fig. 229. Inductance with variable flux-current relation.

In the mks systems (221) becomes

$$L = N \frac{d\phi}{di} \qquad \text{henrys,} \tag{222}$$

where ϕ is in webers.

219. Rise of Current in Inductive Circuit. In Fig. 230(a) is shown a resistance R in series with a self-inductance of L henrys. The inductance itself is assumed to be resistanceless, its actual small resistance being included in R. When the switch S is closed, the circuit is connected suddenly across a potential difference of E volts. Let the instant of closing S be taken as zero time. The current i in amperes may then be found as a function of the time t expressed in seconds.

The applied voltage E must not only supply the resistance drop in the circuit, but it must also *overcome* the emf of self-induction, $-L\, di/dt$. Thus,

$$E = Ri + L \frac{di}{dt} \tag{223}$$

where dt is the differential time. Also, it will be remembered that Ohm's law states that the current in a circuit is equal to the *total* emf divided by the resistance. The total emf acting in the foregoing circuit is $E - L\,di/dt$ so that the current

$$i = \frac{E - L\,di/dt}{R} \tag{224}$$

which is equivalent to (223).

Equation (223) is a linear differential equation of the first order and is readily integrated.

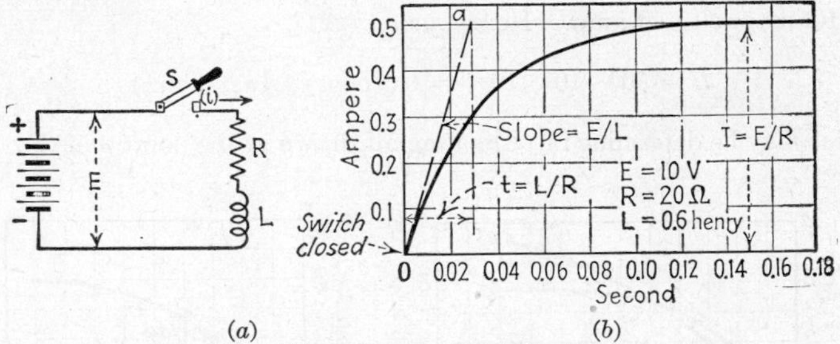

FIG. 230. Rise of current in inductive circuit.

First, multiplying (223) by dt and transposing,

$$E\,dt = Ri\,dt + L\,di,$$
$$(E - Ri)\,dt = L\,di,$$
$$\frac{di}{E - Ri} = \frac{1}{L}\,dt.$$

Integrating,

$$-\frac{1}{R}\log_\epsilon (E - Ri) = \frac{1}{L}t + K$$

where ϵ is the Napierian logarithmic base $= 2.718$ and K is a constant of integration.

$$\log_\epsilon (E - Ri) = -\frac{Rt}{L} - KR.$$

When the time $t = 0$, $i = 0$. This must be true, for if the current rose to any finite value whatsoever in zero time, its rate of change would be infinite and the corresponding emf of self-induction accordingly would be infinite. Hence,

$$K = -\frac{1}{R}\log_\epsilon E,$$

$$\log_\epsilon (E - Ri) - \log_\epsilon E = \log_\epsilon \frac{(E - Ri)}{E} = -R\frac{t}{L},$$

or in exponential form,

$$\frac{E - iR}{E} = \epsilon^{\frac{-Rt}{L}},$$

from which

$$i = \frac{E}{R}\left(1 - \epsilon^{\frac{-Rt}{L}}\right). \tag{225}$$

This is an exponential equation, the graph of which is shown in Fig. 230(*b*) for a circuit in which $E = 10$ volts, $R = 20$ ohms, and $L = 0.6$ henry.

The rate of current increase is large at first and then diminishes until at $t = \infty$ it becomes zero. Theoretically, the current does not reach its Ohm's law value until infinite time. However, it reaches practically this value in a relatively short time.

The rate of change of current at any time t,

$$\frac{di}{dt} = \frac{E}{R}\frac{d}{dt}(1 - \epsilon^{\frac{-Rt}{L}}) = \frac{E}{L}\epsilon^{\frac{-Rt}{L}} \quad \text{amp per sec.} \tag{226}$$

When $t = 0$,

$$\frac{di}{dt} = \frac{E}{L} \quad \text{amp per sec.} \tag{227}$$

That is, at the instant of closing the switch, the current begins to increase at a rate of E/L amp per sec.

A line drawn tangent to the curve at the origin O must have a slope E/L, as shown by line Oa, Fig. 230(*b*). Also, the rate of increase of current at the instant when the switch is closed is found directly from (223), for when $t = 0$, $i = 0$ and $di/dt = E/L$.

Since the current approaches its Ohm's law value gradually and theoretically never reaches this value, the time to reach or even to approach the Ohm's law value cannot be a criterion of the rate of increase of the current. For this reason the time L/R has been chosen as the criterion. This ratio L/R of the inductance in henrys to the resistance in ohms is called the *time constant*, τ, of the circuit and is the time in seconds required for the current to reach 63.2 per cent of its final Ohm's law value. Substituting this value L/R for t in Eq. (225) gives

$$i = \frac{E}{R}[1 - \epsilon^{\frac{-R}{L}\left(\frac{L}{R}\right)}] \quad \text{amp},$$

$$i = \frac{E}{R}\left(1 - \frac{1}{2.718}\right) = 0.632\frac{E}{R} \quad \text{amp.} \tag{228}$$

That is, in the time L/R, or τ, sec the current reaches 63.2 per cent of its final, or Ohm's law, value. This relation is shown in Fig. 230(*b*), in which the time constant is $0.6/20 = 0.03$ sec.

It is to be noted that if the current continues at its initial rate of increase E/L, it will reach its Ohm's law value in L/R sec. That is,

$$i = \frac{E}{L}t = \frac{E}{L} \cdot \frac{L}{R} = \frac{E}{R} \qquad \text{amp.}$$

This is shown by the tangent Oa, Fig. 230(*b*), which intersects the 0.03-sec ordinate at 0.5 amp.

Example. The resistance of a relay is 400 ohms, and the inductance is 0.4 henry. The relay is connected suddenly across 120 volts. Determine: (*a*) equation of current; (*b*) rate at which current begins to increase; (*c*) value of current at 0.0005 sec; (*d*) time constant of circuit; (*e*) value of current corresponding to time in (*d*).

(*a*) Substituting in (225),

$$i = {}^{120}\!/_{400}(1 - \epsilon^{\frac{-400t}{0.4}}) = 0.3(1 - \epsilon^{-1{,}000t}). \quad \textit{Ans.}$$

(*b*) When $t = 0$,

$$\frac{di}{dt} = \frac{E}{L} = \frac{120}{0.4} = 300 \text{ amp per sec.} \quad \textit{Ans.}$$

(*c*) $i = 0.3(1 - \epsilon^{-1{,}000\times 0.0005})$

$$= 0.3(1 - \epsilon^{-0.5}) = 0.3\left(1 - \frac{1}{\sqrt{\epsilon}}\right) = 0.1181 \text{ amp.} \quad \textit{Ans.}$$

(*d*) The time constant $\tau = \frac{L}{R} = \frac{0.4}{400} = 0.001$ sec. *Ans.*

(*e*) $i = 0.3\left(1 - \frac{1}{\epsilon}\right) = 0.3(1 - 0.368) = 0.1896$ amp. *Ans.*

This delayed rise of current in a circuit, due to self-inductance, should be carefully kept in mind, since it accounts for some of the time lag in the operation of relays, trip coils, etc. When a short circuit takes place, there may be considerable delay between the time at which the short circuit occurs and the time of opening of the breaker or switch controlled by the relay. The effect of inductance is also one of the controlling factors in the initial current rush on short circuit.

220. Decay of Current in Inductive Circuit. If an inductive circuit carrying current be short-circuited, the current does not cease immediately, as it does in a noninductive circuit under the same conditions, but continues and does not become zero until an appreciable time after the instant of short circuit. Theoretically, the current becomes zero only after infinite time. This continuation of current, after the applied voltage has been discontinued, is due to the emf of self-induction. The flux linking the coil is due to the current, and when the current decreases, this flux also decreases. The decreasing flux induces an emf in the coil. In the same way that the current due to the induced emf tends to prevent the flux being withdrawn in Fig. 225(*b*) (p. 298), so the emf of self-induction tends to prevent the decrease of the current and the flux. This emf diminishes as the rate of decrease of current and flux diminishes.

A circuit in which inductance and resistance may be short-circuited safely is shown in Fig. 231(*a*). The switch S is arranged to short-circuit the resistance R and the inductance L in series. At the instant of short circuit, the current in R and L is equal to I_0 amp.

A fuse is inserted in series with the battery to protect it from the short circuit. It is possible to solve for the current in the resistance and inductance as a function of time by making $E = 0$ in Eq. (223) (p. 305). However, the circuit is fundamentally a simple one in which an emf, $-L\,di/dt$, is impressed across a resistance R, whence, by Ohm's law,

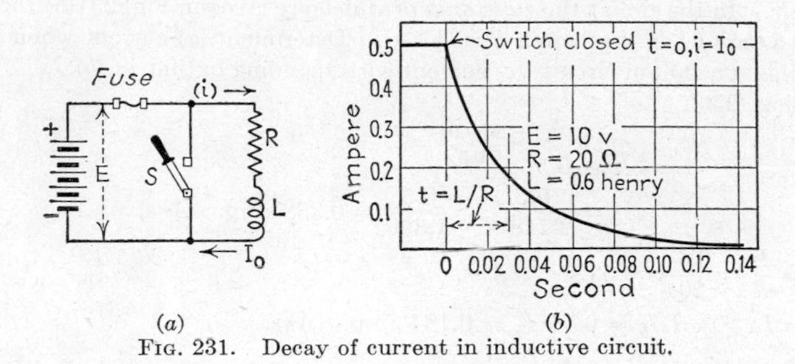

FIG. 231. Decay of current in inductive circuit.

$$iR = -L\frac{di}{dt}, \qquad (229)$$

the minus sign showing that the emf of self-induction is in opposition to the effect producing it (Lenz's law). This equation is readily integrated:

$$\frac{di}{i} = -\frac{R}{L}\,dt,$$

$$\log_\epsilon i = -\frac{Rt}{L} + K,$$

where K is a constant of integration.

When $t = 0$, $i = I_0$. Hence,

$$\log_\epsilon I_0 = K,$$

$$\log_\epsilon \frac{i}{I_0} = -\frac{Rt}{L}.$$

In exponential form, solving for i,

$$i = I_0\epsilon^{-\frac{Rt}{L}}. \qquad (230)$$

(230) is a decaying exponential function. Theoretically, the current becomes zero only after infinite time. It becomes practically zero in a relatively short time. (230) is represented graphically in Fig. 231(*b*) for a circuit in which, prior to short circuit, $E = 10$ volts. R is 20 ohms, and L is 0.6 henry, the same constants as for the circuit of Fig. 230(*b*).

The time constant $\tau = L/R$ is now a criterion of the rate of decay of the current. For example, when $t = \tau = L/R$,

$$i = \frac{I_0}{\epsilon} = 0.368I_0. \tag{231}$$

Example. In the circuit the constants of which are given in Fig. 231(*b*) the current is $I_0 = 0.5$ amp when the switch S is closed. Determine: (*a*) current when $t = 0.01$ sec; (*b*) time constant of circuit; (*c*) current corresponding to time in (*b*).

(*a*) Using (230),

$$i = 0.5\epsilon^{-\frac{20\cdot 0.01}{0.6}}$$
$$= \frac{0.5}{2.718^{1/3}} = \frac{0.5}{1.396} = 0.358 \text{ amp.} \quad \textit{Ans.}$$

(*b*) $\tau = \dfrac{L}{R} = \dfrac{0.6}{20} = 0.03$ sec. *Ans.*

(*c*) $i = I_0\epsilon^{-1} = I_0/\epsilon = 0.368I_0 = 0.184$ amp. *Ans.*

221. Energy of Magnetic Field. To *establish* a magnetic field, energy must be expended. To maintain a constant field does not require an expenditure of energy so far as the *field* is concerned. The energy supplied to the exciting coils of electromagnets is accounted for as heat in the copper and is not concerned with the energy of the magnetic field itself. The energy of the magnetic field is stored as potential energy and is similar to the energy of a raised weight, Fig. 232. Work is performed in raising the weight to its position, but *no expenditure of energy is required to maintain the weight in this position.* The energy of the weight due to its position is Wh ft-lb, where W is the weight in pounds and h is the height in feet through which the weight has been raised above the floor. This energy is available and can be utilized in many ways.

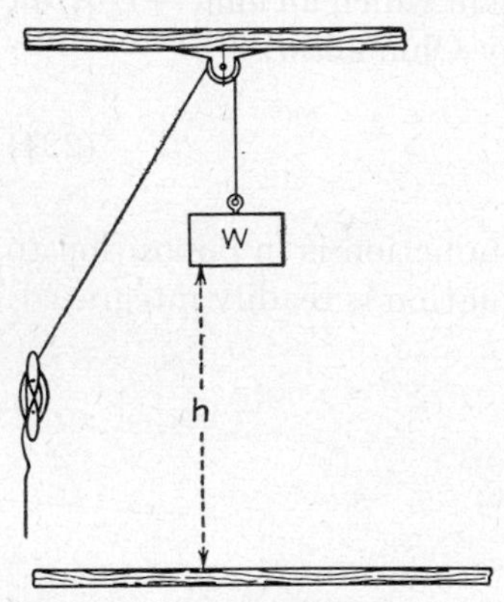

FIG. 232. Energy of suspended weight.

In the same way the energy stored in the magnetic field is available and may make itself manifest in many ways, as, for example, in the arc at the switch contacts. In an a-c circuit all this energy may be returned to the circuit.

The energy of the field in joules or watt-seconds is

$$W = \tfrac{1}{2}LI^2 \qquad (232)^*$$

where L is the circuit inductance in henrys and I is the circuit current in amperes.

Equation (232) is readily derived from the self-inductance relation. Consider the current i in the inductive circuit, Fig. 230(a). Of the energy input, $\int_0^t Ei\,dt$ joules, up to time t, some is dissipated as heat in the resistance $\left(= \int_0^t i^2R\,dt\right)$, and the remainder is stored as energy in the magnetic field. This energy may be determined as follows: When a current is in opposition to an emf, either mechanical power is developed (motor, p. 489) or energy is being stored (charging a battery, Sec. 51, p. 59). In the inductive circuit the current is in opposition to the counter emf $e = -L\,di/dt$, and energy must be stored.

The instantaneous power supplied *to* the inductance is $ie = i(L\,di/dt)$, and the energy

$$W = \int_0^T ie\,dt = L\int_0^I i\,di = \tfrac{1}{2}LI^2. \qquad (232a)$$

(When $t = T$, $i = I$.)

(232) and (232a) show that the energy of the magnetic field is proportional to the *square* of the current. Therefore, if the current can be reduced by a suitable resistance to one-half its initial value before opening a highly inductive circuit, the energy of the arc at the switch contacts can be reduced to one-fourth the value which it would have had without the additional resistance. This fact should be remembered in opening the field circuit of a dynamo.

Example. In a circuit having an inductance of 4 henrys, the current is 10 amp. Determine (a) energy of magnetic field; (b) average power expended by magnetic field when circuit is opened in 0.2 sec.

(a) $W = \tfrac{1}{2} \cdot 4 \cdot 10^2 = 200$ wsec or joules. *Ans.*

(b) $P = \dfrac{200}{0.2} = 1{,}000$ watts $= 1$ kw. *Ans.*

222. Magnetic and Heat Energy. If, after having established the current in the circuit of Fig. 230(a), the switch S be opened, a noticeable arc will appear at the switch contacts. This arc will be much greater in magnitude than that formed at the switch contacts in the circuit of Fig. 228, which has only resistance in the circuit, although the current and

* The resemblance of this expression to that for stored energy in a moving mass should be noted. For example, when a mass M moves with a velocity V, the kinetic energy is $\tfrac{1}{2}MV^2$. With a rotating body having a moment of inertia I and angular velocity ω, the kinetic energy is $\tfrac{1}{2}I\omega^2$.

circuit voltage are the same in both cases. This arcing at the switch contacts may be attributed to two effects of self-inductance.

When the switch is being opened, the current is caused to decrease rapidly. This decrease of current causes an emf of self-induction, $-L\, di/dt$, (Sec. 217, p. 303), which attempts to prevent the decrease of current. The induced emf becomes sufficiently high to start and to maintain an arc of substantial length across the switch contacts. The arc burns the switch contacts and usually causes their rapid deterioration.

Another and probably a better method of considering the phenomenon is from the viewpoint of energy. The energy stored in the magnetic field is $\frac{1}{2}LI^2$ joules. When the current becomes zero, the energy stored in the field must become zero, and by the law of the conservation of energy it must appear elsewhere. In this case it is converted into the heat energy of the arc at the switch contacts.

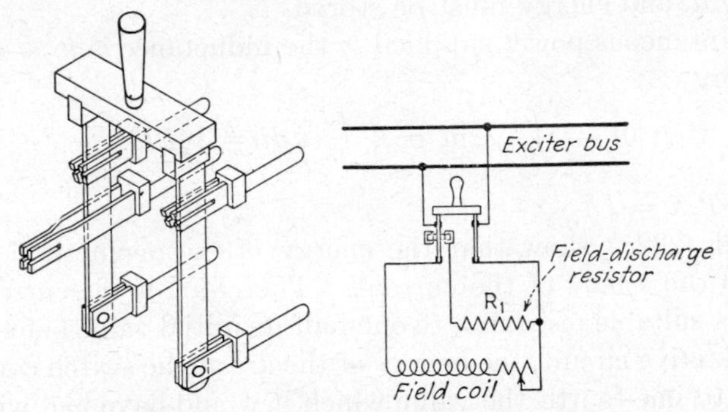

FIG. 233. Field-discharge switch with connections.

The induced emf and the arc resulting from the opening of an inductive circuit may become dangerous from the point of view both of personal injury and of damage to apparatus, as, for example, with the fields of alternators, which are usually separately excited, it being thus necessary to open the circuit when shutting down the alternator. The resulting emf of self-induction has been known to reach such values as to puncture the insulation when the field circuit is opened. To protect the field from puncture, a field-discharge switch, Fig. 233, is often used. At the instant of opening the switch, the field (and the line, temporarily) is in parallel with the field-discharge resistor. The energy of the field is dissipated partly in this resistor rather than in the arc at the switch contacts.

The emf e_f across the field circuit and the field-discharge switch may be computed by the method used in obtaining Eq. (230) (p. 309). The circuit, Fig. 234, is equivalent to that of Fig. 233, R and L being the resistance and inductance of the field circuit, including the field coil and rheostat, and R_1 the resistance of the field-discharge resistor. When the switch is in the closed position, the current to the field circuit $I_0 = E/R$, where E is the exciter-bus voltage. When the switch S is opened, the emf of self-induction $-L\,(di/dt)$ will be acting to send current i around the circuit *abcda*. Since this emf will tend to prolong the current, the direction of i is that of I_0, Fig. 234. At the instant of opening the switch, the current in the field circuit must be I_0, since the current in an inductive circuit cannot change in zero time (p. 306). Writing the circuit equation,

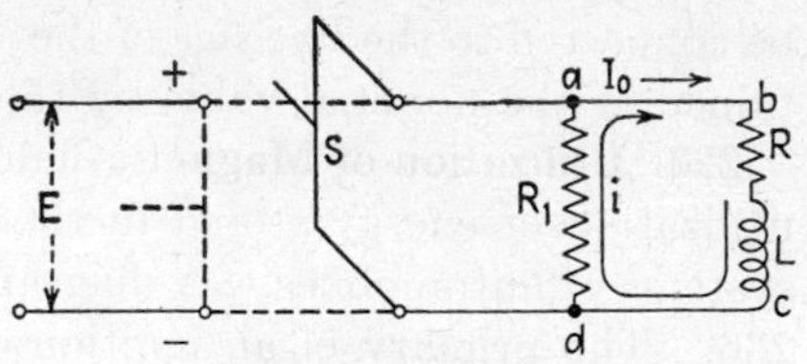

FIG. 234. Field-discharge circuit.

$$-L\frac{di}{dt} = i(R_1 + R),$$

$$\frac{di}{i} = -\frac{R_1 + R}{L}dt,$$

$$\log_\epsilon i = -\frac{R_1 + R}{L}t + K,$$

where ϵ is the Napierian logarithmic base and K is a constant of integration. When $t = 0$, $i = I_0$. Hence,

$$K = \log_\epsilon I_0,$$

$$\log_\epsilon \frac{i}{I_0} = -\frac{R_1 + R}{L}t,$$

$$i = I_0\epsilon^{-\frac{R_1+R}{L}t} \quad \text{amp.} \tag{233}$$

The voltage $e_f = iR_1$. Hence,

$$e_f = I_0R_1\epsilon^{-\frac{R_1+R}{L}t} \quad \text{volts.}$$

$$I_0 = \frac{E}{R}\ \text{amp.}$$

$$e_f = E\frac{R_1}{R}\epsilon^{-\frac{R_1+R}{L}t} \quad \text{volts.} \tag{234}$$

e_f is a maximum when $t = 0$. If $R_1 = R$, the emf across the field is equal to the voltage E.

The fields of shunt generators and motors are usually connected across the armatures, so that when the machine is shut down the field discharges gradually through the armature and a field-discharge switch is unnecessary.

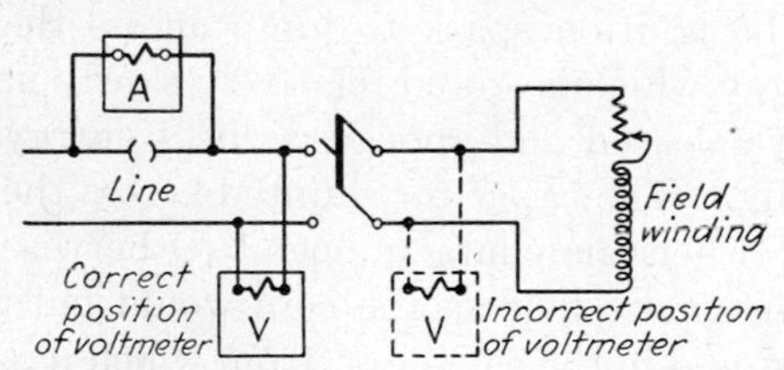

FIG. 235. Position of voltmeter with inductive circuit.

Contact with switches opening inductive circuits, even in the case of very low voltages, should be carefully avoided. There is danger not only of being burned by the arc but also of being injured from the high induced emfs.

In measuring the resistance of an inductive circuit by the voltmeter-ammeter method, the voltmeter, shown dotted, Fig. 235, should never be left connected across the *load side* of the switch. When the switch is opened, there will be an emf of self-induction across the voltmeter which will be several times the voltage of the excitation bus. This is shown by

Eq. (234), in which R_1 will represent the resistance of the voltmeter, which will be several times that of the field circuit. The voltmeter should therefore be disconnected before opening the switch or else should be connected to the *line side* of the switch, since this voltage will be maintained at the nominal value by the generating apparatus of the system.

223. Utilization of Magnetic-field Energy. A common example of the utilization of energy stored in the magnetic field occurs in the ignition systems of automobiles. A diagram of a typical system is shown in Fig. 236. The primary of an ignition coil is connected across the battery in series with the interrupter contacts. The ignition coil consists of a primary winding of relatively few turns and a secondary winding with a comparatively large number of turns on a laminated iron core. The contacts in the interrupter are closed and opened by a rotating cam, the

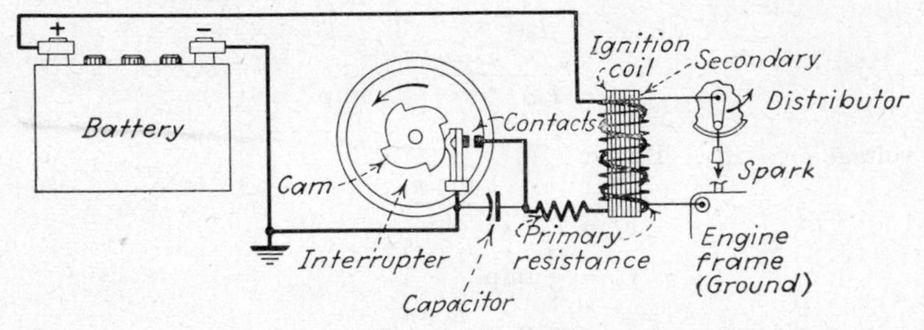

FIG. 236. Automobile ignition system.

number of lobes of the cam corresponding to the number of cylinders. The contacts are closed for a time which is sufficient to permit the flux in the core of the ignition coil to build up to a substantial value. The contacts then open suddenly. This induces a high emf in the secondary ($e_2 = -N_2\, d\phi/dt$), which causes the ignition spark to jump across the points of the spark plug. The energy which is stored relatively slowly in the magnetic field is thus suddenly released and appears as heat energy between the points of the spark plug. The capacitor shunted across the contacts serves to suppress the arc when the contacts open. Otherwise some of the energy stored in the magnetic field of the core would burn the contacts. This energy is now stored in the capacitor, from which it is released when the contacts close again. The resistance in series with the primary has a high temperature coefficient. Hence, when the ignition switch is inadvertently left closed and the contacts happen also to be closed, the primary will not overheat.

This principle of storing energy slowly in a magnetic field and then releasing it suddenly is applied to "make-and-break" ignition used with internal-combustion engines. Two contacts within the cylinder head are in series with a low-voltage source, usually six dry cells, and an "ignition coil." The ignition coil consists of a laminated iron core wound with several turns of wire. It is similar to the core and primary of the ignition coil, Fig. 236. The contacts are made to open and close by means of a cam mechanism. When the contacts are closed, a magnetic field is built up in the ignition coil, thus storing magnetic energy. When the contacts are made to open, this energy appears as a hot spark at the contacts and this spark ignites the explosive mixture in the cylinder.

224. Mutual Inductance. In Fig. 237 are shown two coils A and B. Coil A is connected to a battery through a switch S. Coil B is connected to a galvanometer but not to a source of voltage. Coil B is placed so that its axis is nearly coincident with that of A, and the two coils are close together. When the switch S is closed, current flows in coil A, building up a field which links A. The position of B with respect to A results in a considerable part of the magnetic flux produced by A linking B also. Therefore, if the current in A be interrupted by opening the switch S, or if it be altered in magnitude, a *change of flux simultaneously* occurs in B, inducing an emf in B. This emf is detected by the galvanometer connected across the terminals of B. Upon closing the switch S, the galvanometer will deflect momentarily and then come to zero, showing that a transitory emf has been induced in coil B. On opening the switch S the galvanometer deflection will reverse, showing that the induced emf on opening the circuit is opposite in direction to the emf induced on closing the circuit. Because coil B is in such a relation to A that an emf is induced in B due to the change of flux in A, these two coils are said to possess *mutual inductance*. The induced emf is an emf of *mutual* induction, and its average value, Eq. (215) (p. 303), is

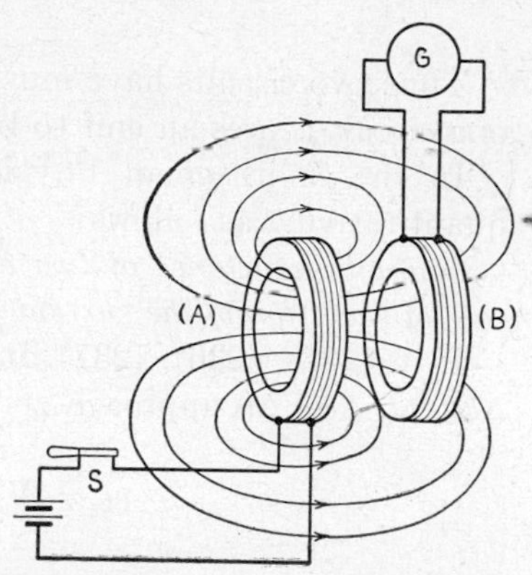

FIG. 237. Mutual inductance between two coils.

$$e_{av} = N_2 \frac{\Delta\phi_2}{\Delta t} 10^{-8} \quad \text{volts} \tag{235}$$

where N_2 is the number of turns in coil B, $\Delta\phi_2$ the change in magnetic flux from coil A which links coil B, and Δt the time in seconds required to change the flux by $\Delta\phi_2$ lines.

Even though coils A and B be brought close together, all the flux ϕ_1, produced by coil A, does not link coil B. Only a certain proportion, k, of ϕ_1 links B, k being less than unity. That is,

$$e_{av} = N_2 \frac{k\Delta\phi_1}{\Delta t} 10^{-8} \quad \text{volts.} \tag{236}$$

k is called the *coefficient of coupling* of the circuits A and B. As N_2 and k are constants for any given geometry of the circuits, and ϕ_1 may be assumed proportional to the current i_1, in coil A, (236) may be written

$$e_{av} = L_{AB} \frac{\Delta i_1}{\Delta t} \quad \text{volts,} \tag{237}$$

where L_{AB} is the *mutual inductance*, or coefficient of mutual induction, in henrys between coil A and coil B, the first letter of the subscript referring to the coil in which the flux linkages originate.

Equating (236) and (237),

$$L_{AB} = kN_2 \frac{\Delta \phi_1}{\Delta i_1} 10^{-8} \quad \text{henrys.} \tag{238}$$

Thus two circuits have mutual inductance when a change of current in one circuit causes an emf to be induced in the other.

In the Smithsonian Physical Tables, mutual inductance is defined quantitatively as follows:

Mutual inductance of two circuits is the emf produced in one per unit rate of variation of the current in the other.

If in (235), (236), (237), instantaneous values are considered, that is, $\Delta\phi_2$, Δt, $\Delta\phi_1$, Δi_1 approach zero as a limit, the three equations become

$$e_2 = N_2 \frac{d\phi_2}{dt} 10^{-8} \quad \text{volts,} \tag{239}$$

$$e_2 = N_2 k \frac{d\phi_1}{dt} 10^{-8} \quad \text{volts,} \tag{240}$$

$$e_2 = L_{AB} \frac{di_1}{dt} \quad \text{volts,} \tag{241}$$

where e_2 is the instantaneous value of the induced emf in coil B.

Example. Coil A, Fig. 237, has 400 turns, and coil B has 600 turns. With 5 amp in coil A, a flux of 500,000 maxwells links with A, and 200,000 of these maxwells link coil B also. All magnetic reluctances are constant. Determine: (*a*) self-inductance of coil A with B open-circuited; (*b*) coefficient of coupling; (*c*) average emf induced in B when flux linking it increases from zero to 200,000 maxwells in 0.5 sec; (*d*) mutual inductance; (*e*) average emf induced in B when current in A increases from zero to 5 amp in 0.5 sec.

(*a*) Using Eq. (216), (p. 303),

$$L_1 = \frac{N_1\phi_1}{I} = \frac{400 \cdot 500{,}000}{5} 10^{-8} = 0.4 \text{ henry.} \quad \textit{Ans.}$$

(*b*) $k = \dfrac{200{,}000}{500{,}000} = 0.4.$ *Ans.*

(*c*) Using (235),

$$e_{av} = 600 \frac{200{,}000}{0.5} 10^{-8} = 2.4 \text{ volts.} \quad \textit{Ans.}$$

(*d*) Using (238),

$$L_{AB} = \frac{0.4 \cdot 600 \cdot 500{,}000}{5} 10^{-8} = 0.24 \text{ henry. } \textit{Ans.}$$

(*e*) Using (237),

$$e_{av} = 0.24 \frac{5}{0.5} = 2.4 \text{ volts. } \textit{Ans.}$$

In (*d*), L_{AB} may also be determined from (*c*) and Eq. (237).

$$2.4 = L_{AB} \frac{5}{0.5}.$$
$$L_{AB} = 0.24 \text{ henry } (\textit{check}).$$

It can be shown that if L_{AB} is the mutual inductance of coil B with respect to A, then L_{BA} is also the mutual inductance of coil A with respect to B. That is, if the rate of change of current in coil B is $\Delta i_2/\Delta t$ amp per sec, an emf is induced in A,

$$e_{av} = L_{BA} \frac{\Delta i_2}{\Delta t} \quad \text{volts,} \tag{242}$$

and for instantaneous values,

$$e_1 = L_{BA} \frac{di_2}{dt}. \tag{243}$$

If the circuit of coil B is closed, then by Lenz's law any current induced in B by a change of current in coil A must be in *opposition* to the current in coil A. That is, if the direction of one current is *clockwise*, that of the other must be *counterclockwise*. The induced current opposes the increase in the flux linking it. Likewise a current in coil B is opposed by any current which it induces in coil A.

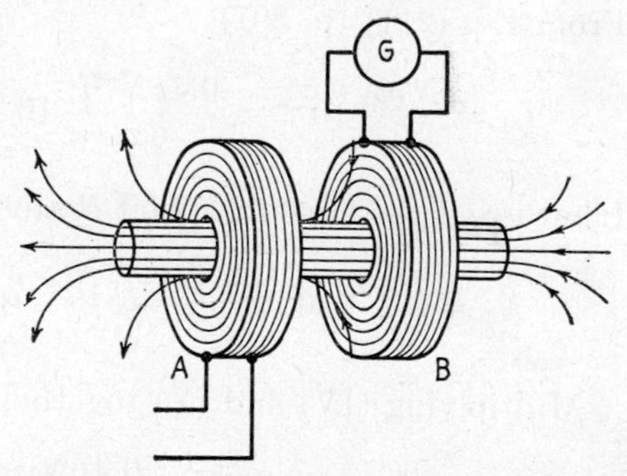

Fig. 238. Effect of iron core on mutual inductance.

The mutual inductance of two circuits may be substantially increased by linking the circuits with an iron core. Thus, if two coils, similar to those shown in Fig. 237, be placed upon an iron core, Fig. 238, the coefficient of coupling k may be made very nearly unity; that is, practically all the flux linking coil A also links coil B.

225. Mutual and Self-inductance. The mutual inductance of two circuits having inductances L_1 and L_2 is

$$L_m = k\sqrt{L_1 L_2} \tag{244}$$

where $L_m = L_{AB} = L_{BA}$ and k is the coefficient of coupling. This may be shown as follows:

In Fig. 239 are shown two coils A and B adjacent to each other on the same magnetic circuit. There are N_1 turns in coil A and N_2 turns in coil B. The reluctance of the magnetic circuit is $\mathcal{R}$ cgs units and is assumed to be constant. Let the current in A alone be i_1 amp.

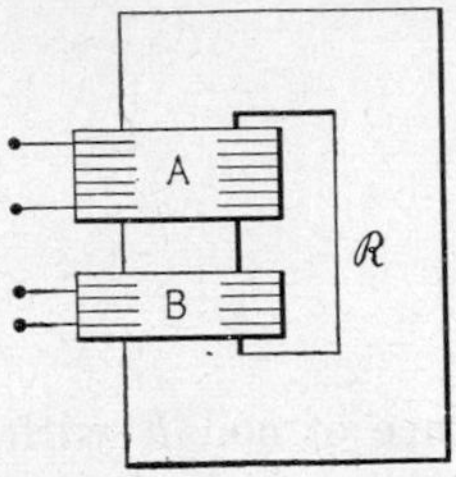

FIG. 239. Self- and mutual inductance of coils on iron core.

The flux in A,

$$\phi_1 = \frac{0.4\pi N_1 i_1}{\mathcal{R}} \quad \text{maxwells.} \tag{I}$$

The flux in B,

$$\phi_2 = k\phi_1 = k\,\frac{0.4\pi N_1 i_1}{\mathcal{R}} \quad \text{maxwells.} \tag{II}$$

The emf induced in B, due to a rate of change of current di_1/dt in A, is

$$e_2 = kN_2 \frac{d\phi_1}{dt} 10^{-8} = k\,\frac{0.4\pi N_1}{\mathcal{R}} N_2 10^{-8} \frac{di_1}{dt} \quad \text{volts.} \tag{III}$$

Hence, from Eq. (241),

$$L_{AB} = L_m = k\,\frac{0.4\pi N_1 N_2}{\mathcal{R}} 10^{-8} \quad \text{henrys.} \tag{245}$$

From Eq. (211) (p. 301),

$$L_1 = \frac{N_1\phi_1}{i_1} 10^{-8} = \frac{0.4\pi N_1^2 i_1}{\mathcal{R} i_1} 10^{-8} = \frac{0.4\pi N_1^2}{\mathcal{R}} 10^{-8} \quad \text{henrys.} \tag{IV}$$

Likewise, if the current in coil B alone is i_2 amp,

$$L_2 = \frac{N_2\phi_2}{i_2} 10^{-8} = \frac{0.4\pi N_2^2 i_2}{\mathcal{R} i_2} 10^{-8} = \frac{0.4\pi N_2^2}{\mathcal{R}} 10^{-8} \quad \text{henrys.} \tag{V}$$

Multiplying (IV) and (V) together and taking the square root,

$$\sqrt{L_1 L_2} = \frac{0.4\pi N_1 N_2}{\mathcal{R}} 10^{-8} \quad \text{henrys.} \tag{VI}$$

From (245) it follows that

$$L_m = k\sqrt{L_1 L_2} \quad \text{henrys.} \tag{246}$$

If the coils A and B are connected in series aiding, the total inductance is

$$L = L_1 + L_2 + 2L_m \tag{247}$$

and, if connected opposing,

$$L = L_1 + L_2 - 2L_m. \tag{248}$$

Equation (247) may be readily proved. Let the current in the two coils in series be i. The total emf induced in the circuit, due to a change of current with respect to time di/dt, is the sum of the emfs due to the self-inductance of the individual coils and the emf induced in each coil due to its mutual inductance with the other. That is,

$$e = \left(L_1 \frac{di}{dt} + L_2 \frac{di}{dt}\right) + \left(L_m \frac{di}{dt} + L_m \frac{di}{dt}\right)$$

$$= (L_1 + L_2 + 2L_m) \frac{di}{dt} = L \frac{di}{dt}.$$

(248) may be proved in a similar manner.

Example. Two coils A and B having 800 and 1,200 turns are linked with a magnetic circuit the reluctance of which is 0.0015 cgs unit. The coefficient of coupling is 0.8, and the current in the two coils in series is 0.5 amp. Determine: (*a*) self-inductance of each coil; (*b*) mutual inductance of two coils; (*c*) total inductance with two coils in series aiding; (*d*) total inductance with two coils in series opposing.

(*a*) $\phi_1 = \dfrac{0.4\pi 800 \cdot 0.5}{0.0015} = 335{,}000$ maxwells.

$L_1 = \dfrac{N_1\phi_1}{i_1} 10^{-8} = \dfrac{800 \cdot 335{,}000}{0.5} 10^{-8} = 5.36$ henrys. *Ans.*

$\phi_2 = \dfrac{0.4\pi 1{,}200 \cdot 0.5}{0.0015} = 502{,}000$ maxwells.

$L_2 = \dfrac{N_2\phi_2 10^{-8}}{i_2} = \dfrac{1{,}200 \cdot 502{,}000}{0.5} 10^{-8} = 12.05$ henrys. *Ans.*

(*b*) Using Eq. (238) (p. 316),

$$L_{AB} = 0.8 \frac{1{,}200 \cdot 335{,}000}{0.5} 10^{-8} = 6.44 \text{ henrys. } \textit{Ans.}$$

Also, using Eq. (244),

$$L_m = 0.8 \sqrt{5.36 \cdot 12.05} = 6.44 \text{ henrys } (\textit{check}).$$

(*c*) Using Eq. (247),

$$L = 5.36 + 12.05 + (2 \cdot 6.44) = 30.29 \text{ henrys. } \textit{Ans.}$$

(*d*) Using Eq. (248),

$$L = 5.36 + 12.05 - (2 \cdot 6.44) = 4.53 \text{ henrys. } \textit{Ans.}$$

226. Stored Energy. If the current in coil A is i_1 amp and that in coil B is i_2 amp, the total stored energy[1] is

$$W = \tfrac{1}{2}L_1 i_1^2 + \tfrac{1}{2}L_2 i_2^2 \pm L_m i_1 i_2 \quad \text{joules.} \tag{249}$$

[1] See LAWRENCE, R. R., "Principles of Alternating Currents," 2d ed., p. 187, McGraw-Hill Book Company, Inc.

The positive sign is used when the mmfs of the two coils are in conjunction, and the negative sign is used when they are in opposition.

Example. In the example, Sec. 225, with the current in coil A equal to 8.0 amp and the current in coil B equal to 5.0 amp, determine total stored energy when (*a*) coil mmfs aid; (*b*) coil mmfs oppose.

$$(a)\ W = \tfrac{1}{2} \cdot 5.36 \cdot 8^2 + \tfrac{1}{2} \cdot 12.05 \cdot 5^2 + 6.44 \cdot 8 \cdot 5$$
$$= 171.5 + 150.6 + 257.6 = 579.7 \text{ joules.} \quad \textit{Ans.}$$
$$(b)\ W = \tfrac{1}{2} \cdot 5.36 \cdot 8^2 + \tfrac{1}{2} \cdot 12.05 \cdot 5^2 - 6.44 \cdot 8 \cdot 5$$
$$= 171.5 + 150.6 - 257.6 = 64.5 \text{ joules.} \quad \textit{Ans.}$$

227. Measurement of Self- and Mutual Inductance. Self-inductance is measured most readily with an impedance bridge (see Vol. II, Sec. 85, p. 121). Mutual inductance also is measured most conveniently with such a bridge. There are several bridge methods of measuring mutual inductance.[1]

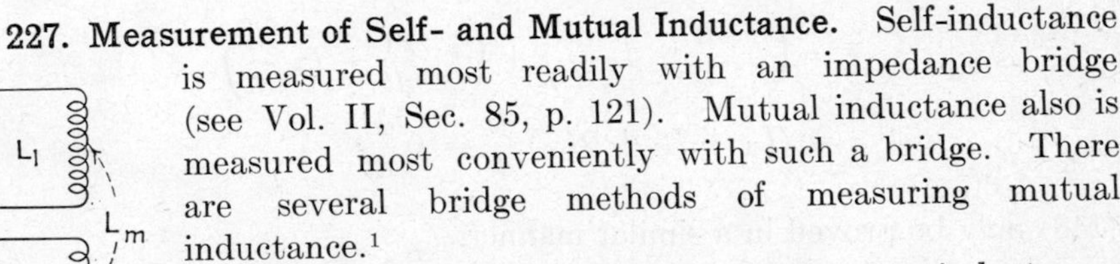

FIG. 240. Measurement of mutual inductance.

Two simple methods are as follows: Let inductances L_1 and L_2, Fig. 240, have mutual inductance L_m. Using an impedance bridge, measure L_1 alone, L_2 alone, and then measure the inductance L with the two connected in series. From Eqs. (247) and (248),

$$L = L_1 + L_2 \pm 2L_m \quad \text{henrys.} \tag{I}$$

If the inductances are aiding magnetically,

$$L_m = \frac{L - (L_1 + L_2)}{2} \quad \text{henrys.} \tag{250}$$

If opposing,

$$L_m = \frac{L_1 + L_2 - L}{2} \quad \text{henrys.} \tag{251}$$

Also, the total inductance L' may be measured with the inductances aiding and then the inductance L'' measured with them opposing. Then,

$$L' = L_1 + L_2 + 2L_m \quad \text{henrys.} \tag{II}$$
$$L'' = L_1 + L_2 - 2L_m \quad \text{henrys.} \tag{III}$$

Subtracting (III) from (II),

$$L_m = \frac{L' - L''}{4}. \tag{252}$$

228. Inductance and Inertia. *Inductance* in the electric circuit is analogous to *inertia* in mechanics. Inertia opposes change of velocity in a mass. When a mass is at rest, inertia opposes the imparting of velocity to it. When a mass is in motion, or has velocity, inertia opposes

[1] See LAWS, F. A., "Electrical Measurements," McGraw-Hill Book Company, Inc.

the bringing of the mass to rest. A flywheel is an excellent example of mechanical inertia. It resists acceleration, and its inertia opposes change of speed. The flywheel thus tends to stabilize the angular velocity of the device with which it is connected, such as a reciprocating steam engine or an internal-combustion engine. Moreover, the energy stored in a moving body is $\frac{1}{2}Mv^2$, where M is the mass and v the velocity. With a rotating mass the stored energy is $\frac{1}{2}\omega^2 I$, where ω is the angular velocity in radians per second and I the moment of inertia (see p. 311). Inertia opposes any attempt to change the stored energy.

Likewise, inductance in the electric circuit has no effect so long as the current is steady. It does, however, oppose any *change* in the current. It opposes the increase of current in a circuit. Likewise, it opposes the

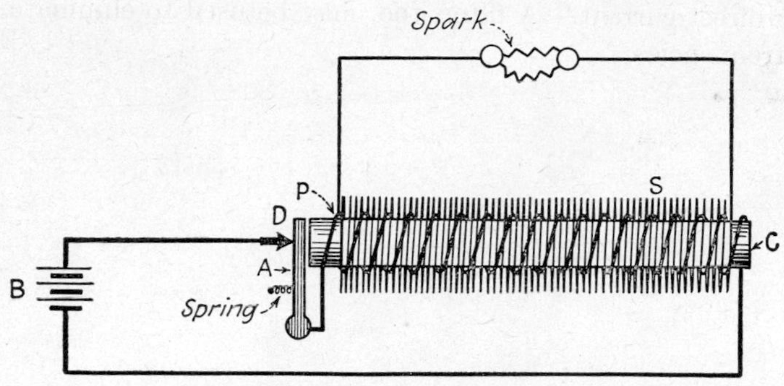

FIG. 241. Induction coil.

decrease of current in a circuit. Hence, inductance frequently can be introduced in order to stabilize electric circuits and electrical devices, such as rectifiers (see Vol. II, Chap. XV). The energy stored in the magnetic field is $\frac{1}{2}Li^2$ joules. Inductance opposes any attempt to change this energy.

229. Induction Coil. A very common example of mutual inductance occurs in the induction coil, Fig. 241. A primary winding P, of comparatively few turns of coarse wire, is wound on a laminated iron core C. This winding is connected to a battery B. The primary current is interrupted by the contact D, against which the iron armature A is held by a spring. When the core C is magnetized by the primary current, the armature A is drawn toward the core and away from D, opening the circuit and causing the flux in the core to drop to zero practically. The spring then pulls the armature A against the contact D, and the cycle is repeated. By this process the flux in the core C is continually being established and then destroyed.

On the same core is placed a secondary winding S, consisting of many turns of fine wire. This winding is thoroughly insulated from the primary winding, but as it is wound on the same core as P, the two coils have a high value of coefficient of coupling. Because of the change of flux in the core, due to the interruptions of the primary current, a high alternating emf is induced in the secondary winding. This induced emf may be considered as due to the mutual inductance existing between the primary and secondary windings. That is, from Eq. (241) (p. 316), the secondary induced emf $e_2 = L_{PS}\, di_1/dt$, where L_{PS} is the mutual inductance between the primary and secondary and i_1 is the primary current.

The induction coil has many practical applications. A common use at present is in obtaining the 90 volts or so for the B battery in automobile radio sets. By means of an induction coil, the 6 volts supplied by the storage battery is converted into an a-c voltage across the secondary. This voltage is rectified by a suitable electronic tube to give the necessary direct current. A filter, too, may be used to eliminate objectionable frequencies.

CHAPTER X

ELECTROSTATICS: CAPACITANCE

Thus far, only the electric current, or electricity in motion, has been considered. However, electricity may also be static, or at rest.

Electricity, though at rest, has important effects on the mediums surrounding it. For example, the design and the applications of insulation, particularly for high voltages, depend on a knowledge of the laws governing static electric charges. Also, the design and operation of transmission lines, the causes of lightning and protection against it involve these same laws. It is the purpose of this chapter to consider some of the laws which govern the behavior of electricity at rest and to determine its effects on the operation of electrical systems.

230. Dynamic and Static Electricity.[1] In Chap. I, Sec. 1 (p. 2), dynamic electricity, or electricity in motion, is discussed with relation to the movement of electrons from atom to atom of the conducting medium. With static electricity, or electricity at rest, the effect of the electrons is as if they were at rest although there may have been an initial movement of electrons with respect to the atoms. Consider first the conditions in the atom itself. When the total charge (negative) of the electrons in an atom is equal to the net positive charge of the nucleus or proton, the atom is said to be in the *uncharged*, or *neutral*, state. If, however, one or more electrons be removed, the atom is said to be *positively charged.* If the removed electrons associate themselves with other neutral matter, this matter is said to be *negatively charged.*

In the dynamic circuit, the applied potential difference causes the electrons in any given group of atoms to pass on to the next group of atoms, thus giving an electric current. Their places are immediately taken, however, by electrons coming from the preceding adjacent group of atoms, which are being acted on by a similar potential difference. Hence, the same number of electrons is always associated with any single atom. If, however, the conducting circuit is not closed, electrons are withdrawn from the positive terminal of the circuit and transferred to the negative terminal. Since the conducting circuit is open, there is no opportunity for the electrons displaced at the positive terminal to be replaced by electrons from adjacent atoms.

If this transfer of electrons is accomplished by a steady source of potential, the positive and negative charges appear to be at rest. For

[1] See Vol. II, 4th ed., Chap. XIII.

example, if the insulated parallel conducting plates A and B, Fig. 242, are connected to the positive and negative terminals of a battery or of an influence machine, the positive terminal of the applied potential will attract, or withdraw, some of the free electrons from electrode A and the negative terminal will repel electrons to electrode B. Hence, the battery, or source of potential, has withdrawn electrons from electrode A and transferred them to electrode B. Thus, plate A has become positively charged, since negative charges have been withdrawn from it, and plate B has become negatively charged. Under these conditions, the charge on the plates is called *static electricity*.

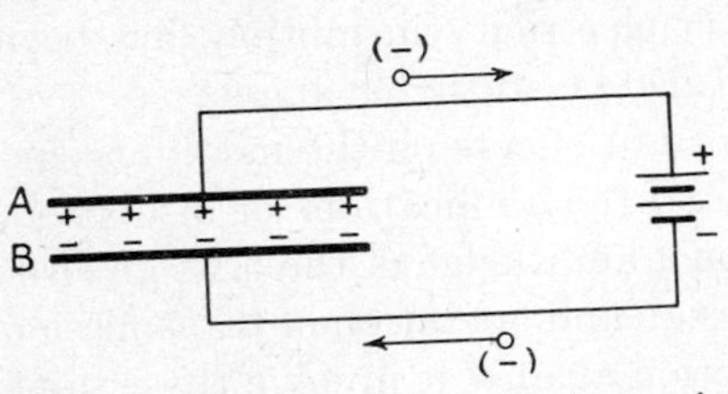

Fig. 242. Transfer of electrons in capacitor plates.

From the preceding brief discussion, it appears that dynamic and static electricity are identical in their ultimate nature. With dynamic electricity, there is a movement of electrons between adjacent atoms of the conductor. With static electricity, free electrons have been displaced from the positive to the negative plate and are maintained in this condition by the electric field. This displacement has the effect of producing a single negative charge on the negative plate and a single positive charge on the positive plate.

The displacement of charges at the positive and negative plates, Fig. 242, is frequently associated with high voltage, particularly if a source such as an influence machine is used. The high voltage and small quantity sometimes convey the impression that static and dynamic electricity are different in nature.

231. Electrostatic Charges. If the terminals of an electrostatic induction machine be connected to two insulated elongated conducting bodies A and B, Fig. 243, the body connected to the positive terminal will be charged with positive electricity and that connected to the negative terminal will be charged with an equal amount of negative electricity. The charge on each body will distribute itself over the entire surface, but the density of the charge will be greatest on the adjacent ends of the two bodies. This is due to the fact that *positive and negative charges attract each other.*

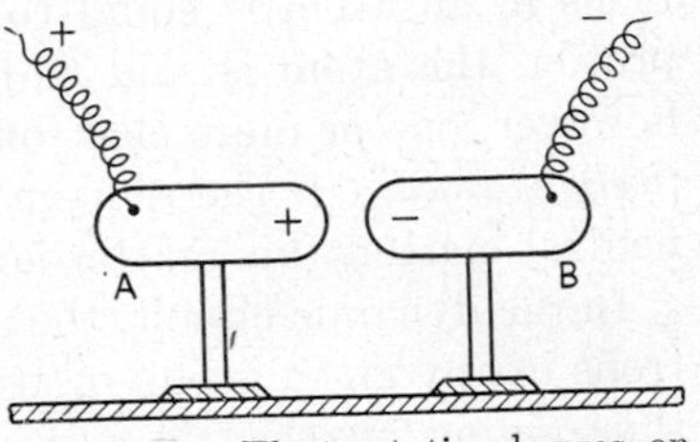

Fig. 243. Electrostatic charges on insulated conducting bodies.

If the two wires from the electrostatic machine be disconnected, the two charges will not be sensibly affected at first. In time they will leak away through the insulating supports.

If the two bodies are free to move, they will come together. If they are connected by a wire, a spark will be observed at the instant that contact is made, showing that, for an instant, there is current from one body to the other. Both of these effects are due to the fact that the positive and negative charges attract each other.

232. Coulomb's Law and Unit Charge. Between the years 1785 and 1789, Coulomb[1] conducted a series of experiments with charged spheres in air and a torsion balance and proved the following law, known as Coulomb's law: *The force acting between two charged bodies in air is proportional to the product of the charges and inversely proportional to the square of the distance between them.*

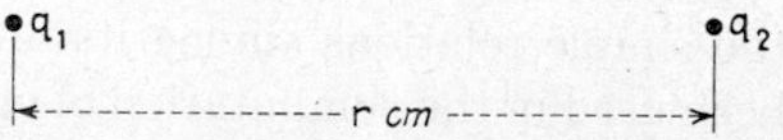

q_1 ——— r cm ——— q_2

FIG. 244. Force between electrostatic charges.

If q_1 and q_2 are two point charges or quantities of electricity in air, Fig. 244, and r is the distance between the charges, Coulomb's law is expressed as follows:

$$\mathbf{F} = \frac{q_1 q_2}{\epsilon_v r^2} \quad \text{units of force.} \tag{253}$$

The quantity ϵ_v is a constant depending on the system of units used. In the cgs electrostatic system the quantity ϵ_v, which is called the *capacitivity* of evacuated space, is taken equal to unity. The capacitivity 1.0006 of air is so nearly equal to unity that it may be taken as unity under most conditions. The unit of force in the cgs system is the *dyne*. If, in (253) $q_1 = q_2 = q$, $q^2 = \epsilon_v r^2 \mathbf{F}$ units of charge squared.

If $\mathbf{F}$ is equal to 1 dyne and r is equal to 1 cm, q is defined as a *unit charge*. Hence, *a unit cgs electrostatic charge (esu) is defined as that charge which, when placed in a vacuum one cm distant from an equal charge, repels it with a force of one dyne.* The unit charge is called the *statcoulomb* and also the esu.

Hence, in (253), if q_1 and q_2 are given in esu and r is in centimeters, $\mathbf{F}$ is in dynes. It is assumed that the charges are concentrated at points.

Example. Two small spheres in air, spaced 14 cm between centers, are charged, respectively, with 2 positive and 5 negative esu. Assume that the charges act as if concentrated at the centers of the spheres. Determine force in dynes acting between spheres.

From (253),

$$\mathbf{F} = \frac{2 \cdot 5}{14^2} = \frac{10}{196} = 0.0510 \text{ dyne.} \quad \textit{Ans.}$$

233. Systems of Electrostatic Units. A general analysis of the systems of units is given on p. 27. In electrostatics there are three systems of units in general use, the cgs electrostatic system, the mks unrationalized

[1] See footnote, p. 29.

system, and the mks rationalized system. As is already stated, in the cgs system the capacitivity of evacuated space ϵ_v is unity, and q_1, q_2 in (253) are so defined that when r is in cm, **F** is given in dynes. In the two mks systems, units of the practical system such as the coulomb, volt, and farad are employed. In the mks unrationalized system the capacitivity of evacuated space, $\epsilon_v = 1.113 \cdot 10^{-10}$, and in the rationalized system the capacitivity, $\epsilon_v' = 8.854 \cdot 10^{-12}$, rather than unity as in the cgs system. In both of these mks systems, the unit of force is the newton (10^5 dynes) rather than the dyne. The relation of ϵ_v and ϵ_v' to the permeability of evacuated space μ_v and μ_v' are discussed on p. 349. Because of the simple relations among its units, the cgs system for a long time has been used in the computation of electrostatic relations. Relations among the units of the several systems are given in Appendix B (p. 581).

234. Electric or Electrostatic Field. It is shown in Chap. VI that the medium in the neighborhood of a magnet appears to be in a stressed condition and that a force acts on an N pole or an S pole placed in such a magnetic field. Likewise, a condition of stress appears to exist in the medium in the neighborhood of an electric charge, and force acts on a positive or a negative charge placed in the medium. This condition of stress makes itself evident if the charges are sufficiently large, and the stress may become so great as to cause mechanical rupture of the medium, followed by an arc discharge (see Sec. 238, p. 332). That stress exists in the neighborhood of electric charges is evident from the fact that pith balls, bits of lint, and similar substances are attracted to the terminals of influence machines and other high-voltage sources.

The region in which the stress exists is called the *electric, dielectric,* or *electrostatic field.* As with the magnetic field, the stress can be represented by lines of force. At each point in the field the direction of the line is that of the force exerted at that point on a positive electric charge. A positive charge, if free, will move along a line of force. Faraday suggested that the electric field be divided into tubes of force, one tube being indicated in Fig. 245. One end of each tube must terminate on a positive charge and the other end on an equal negative charge. The walls of the tube coincide everywhere with the direction of the electric stress. The tube may contain any number of lines, and this number is constant throughout the length of the tube. That is, no lines cross the walls of the tube. The entire electric field is considered as being made up of such tubes. The tubes are assumed to be elastic, tending always to contract and thus to draw the positive and negative charges toward one another, at the same time tending to reduce the dielectric reluctance of the field to a minimum. A line drawn along the center of each tube, Fig. 245, is a dielectric line. The entire field can be considered as made up of such lines. Although the lines do not occupy the entire region, stress must exist in the space between lines, since each line represents a tube of force and the tubes of force do occupy the entire field. In the cgs system the number of lines per square centimeter taken normal to their direction is equal to the field intensity (p. 329). In Fig. 245 the dielectric field between two charged bodies is represented by lines. Note that each line originates at a positive charge and terminates at a negative charge. That is, the lines are not closed. They distribute themselves exactly as the flow- or streamlines of an electric current do or as the lines of force in the magnetic circuit distribute themselves.

A dielectric line of force must always be normal to a conducting surface where it leaves or enters that surface. If this were not true, there would

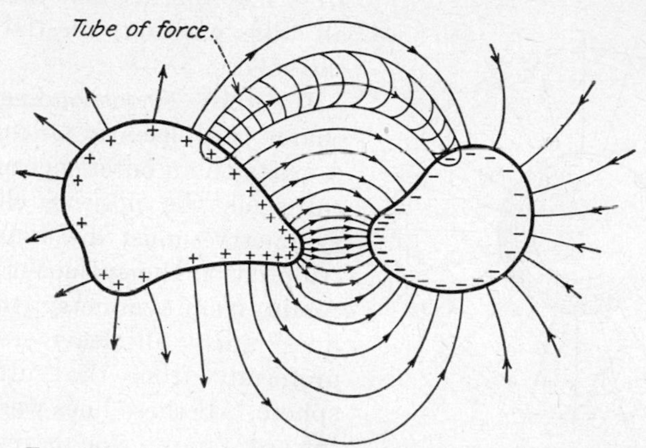

Fig. 245. Electrostatic field between charged electrodes.

be a component of electric force tangential to the conductor at its surface, and the resulting potential difference would produce current. There can be no current, since the *static* condition is assumed. Hence, there cannot be a component of force tangential to the surface of the conductor, and every line must therefore be normal to the surface at the point where it leaves or enters the conductor.

It will also be noted, Fig. 245, that the dielectric-flux lines concentrate in those places where the radius of curvature is least. In these regions, therefore, the electric stress is greatest. In the design of insulation, sharp points and small radii of curvature are avoided so far as possible, so that the electric stress may not become too highly concentrated.

Dielectric flux is denoted by the symbol ψ.

To summarize:

1. *Every line originates on a positive charge and terminates on a negative charge.*

2. *A unit positive charge, if placed at the surface of the positive electrode, will be urged along the lines of force to the negative electrode, with a force in dynes at each point equal to the number of lines per square centimeter at that point, the area being taken normal to the direction of the lines.*

3. *The dielectric field tends to conform itself so that the number of lines is a maximum.*

If a charge is distributed uniformly over the surface of a sphere, so far as the external field is concerned, it acts as if it were concentrated at the center of the sphere.

Figure 246 shows a positively charged[1] isolated sphere in air. The charge must lie wholly on the surface of the sphere. As the individual positive charges repel one another, they will separate as far as possible from one another and therefore must all take positions on the surface of the sphere.

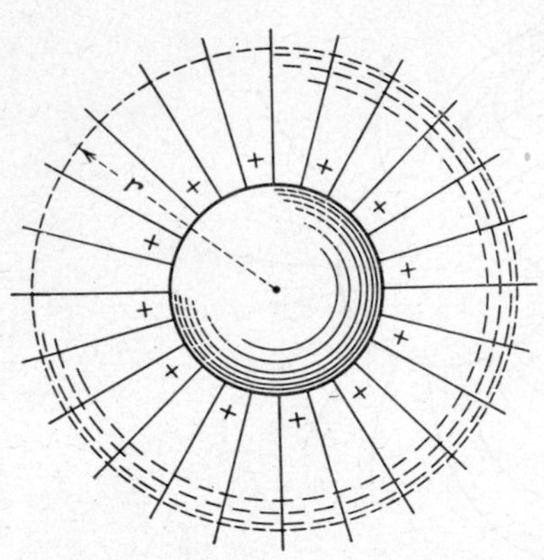

FIG. 246. Isolated charged sphere.

If the corresponding negative charge is sufficiently far removed or if it exists on an outer concentric spherical shell, the positive charge, from symmetry, must be uniformly distributed on the surface of the sphere. Again, from symmetry, the dielectric lines must all leave radially and uniformly from the surface of the sphere. If these lines were continued inward, they would meet at the center of the sphere. Hence, so far as points in space outside the sphere are concerned, the charge has the same effect as if it were concentrated at the center of the sphere.

235. Electrostatic Induction. If a positively charged conducting body A, Fig. 247(a), be brought near a perfectly insulated conducting body B, which initially has no charge, a negative charge b will be found on the end of B nearest A. As B did not have any initial charge and is assumed to be perfectly insulated, no electricity can have left B and none can have reached it, so that the total charge on B must still be zero. Therefore, a positive charge b' must also appear on B at the end farthest from A, and this charge must be equal to charge b. As the charges b and b' are equal and of opposite sign, the total charge on B must still be zero. It will be noted that the negative charge b is as near as possible to the positive inducing charge a, whereas the positive charge b' is as far as

[1] For every positive charge, there must be an equal negative charge. The corresponding negative charge may exist on the walls of the room, on the surface of the earth, or at some remote place.

possible from the positive inducing charge a. This is due to the fact that unlike charges attract and like charges repel.

Charges a and b are *bound charges*, and charge b' is a *free charge*. This may be proved by connecting B to ground, Fig. 247(b). The charge b' will escape to ground and will seek a position as far as possible from a, whereas the two charges a and b will remain.

If a were a negative charge, b would be positive and b' would be negative.

These experiments illustrate the following laws of electrostatics:

Charges of unlike sign attract each other, and charges of like sign repel each other.

A positive charge will induce a negative charge on a body near it.

A negative charge will induce a positive charge on a body near it.

This is similar to magnetic induction, where an N pole induces an S pole, etc. (see Sec. 159, p. 215).

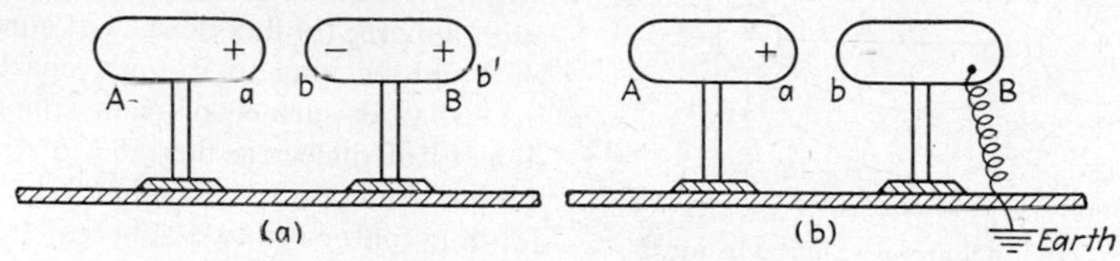

FIG. 247. Electrostatic induction.

236. Field Intensity. In a dielectric field the force on a unit charge is called the *field intensity* and is denoted by **E**.* Field intensity has direction so that **E** is a *vector*. In each of the three systems the force on a charge q is $\mathbf{F} = \mathbf{E}q$ units of force.

Consider the sphere, Fig. 246. If there are $+q$ unit charges, or esu, on the surface of the sphere, then the force on a unit charge or the field intensity **E** at a distance of r cm from the center of the sphere, Fig. 246, is found from Coulomb's law, Eq. (253), by making $q_1 = q$ and $q_2 = 1$.

Thus

$$\mathbf{F} = \frac{q}{\epsilon_v r^2} \quad \text{dynes per unit charge.} \tag{254}$$

[Also see Eq. (256a), p. 334.]

In the cgs system if the medium has a relative capacitivity of $\epsilon_r = 1$, the field intensity is equal to the number of dielectric lines per square centimeter taken normal to their direction, as is described in Sec. 243 (p. 339). Hence, under these conditions the field intensity **E** is equal numerically to the *flux density*, or displacement, D.

If a nonconducting spherical surface of radius r cm be circumscribed about the sphere and concentric with it, the force at each point of the

* The symbol **K** is also used to denote field intensity.

surface will be q/r^2 dynes so that there will be q/r^2 dielectric lines per square centimeter passing through the surface. As the area of the spherical surface is $4\pi r^2$ sq cm, there must be $4\pi r^2(q/r^2)$, or $4\pi q$, dielectric lines passing through the spherical surface. That is, *there must be* $4\pi q$ *lines leaving the charge* q. It follows that 4π *lines leave or enter each unit charge.*

Example. If the charge on the sphere, Fig. 246, is 5.0 positive esu, determine: (*a*) total dielectric lines leaving sphere; (*b*) field intensity at distance of 20 cm from center of sphere.

(*a*) $\psi = 4\pi \cdot 5.0 = 62.83$ lines. *Ans.*

(*b*) $\mathbf{E} = \dfrac{5.0}{20^2} = 0.0125$ dyne per unit charge. *Ans.*

Example. Two spheres A and B, Fig. 248, with radii of 1 cm and 0.5 cm, are spaced 24 cm between centers in air. If the first sphere is charged positively and the second negatively with 20 esu, determine: (*a*) number of dielectric lines leaving each sphere; (*b*) flux density at surface of each sphere, due to its own charge; (*c*) intensity at surface of each sphere; (*d*) density of dielectric flux at a distance of 10 cm from center of sphere A on line joining centers of two spheres; (*e*) force of attraction between spheres.

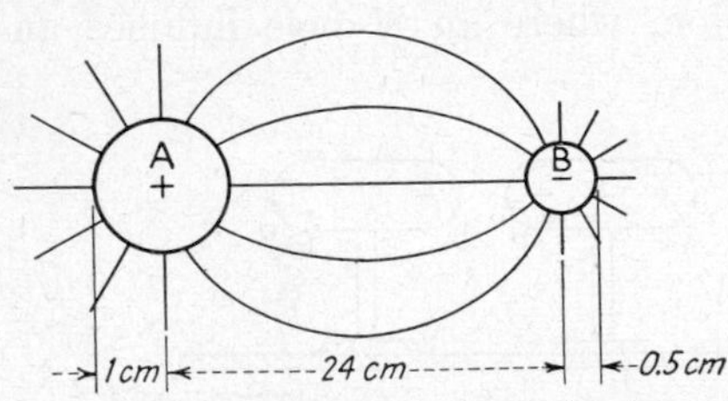

FIG. 248. Charged spheres in air.

Assume the charges to be concentrated at the centers of the spheres.

(*a*) $\psi = 4\pi 20 = 251.3$ lines from or to each sphere. *Ans.*

(*b*) $D_A = \dfrac{4\pi 20}{4\pi(1)^2} = 20$ lines per sq cm. *Ans.*

$D_B = \dfrac{4\pi 20}{4\pi(0.5)^2} = 80$ lines per sq cm. *Ans.*

(*c*) If each sphere were isolated, the field intensity at the surface of each would be given by (*b*) since in air $\mathbf{E} = D$ numerically; but if the spheres are not isolated, the charge on each sphere exerts a force on a unit charge at the surface of the other. This latter force will be a maximum at that point on either sphere which is nearest the other, since the force varies inversely as the square of the distance.

This force at the surface of sphere B due to sphere A, and on the line that joins the centers of the spheres, acts toward the center at B, since the positive charge on A repels a unit positive charge at B. The force on this same positive unit charge, due to the charge on B, acts toward the center of B since the negative charge on B attracts this charge. Hence both forces act in the same direction at this point. Likewise, the charges on both spheres A and B act in the same direction at the point nearest B on the surface of sphere A. Therefore, the force at the surface of each sphere, and hence the field intensity, is a maximum at the points where a line joining their centers intersects their surfaces. Hence,

$$\mathbf{E}_A = 20 + \frac{20}{(23)^2} = 20 + 0.038 = 20.038 \text{ dynes. } \textit{Ans.}$$

$$\mathbf{E}_B = 80 + \frac{20}{(23.5)^2} = 80 + 0.036 = 80.036 \text{ dynes. } \textit{Ans.}$$

(*d*) As the density of the dielectric flux at any point in lines per square centimeter, in air is equal to the force in dynes exerted on a unit positive charge placed at that point,

$$D = \frac{20}{(10)^2} + \frac{20}{(14)^2} = 0.20 + 0.102 = 0.302 \text{ line per sq cm.} \quad \textit{Ans.}$$

(*e*) From Eq. (253),

$$F = \frac{20 \cdot 20}{(24)^2} = 0.6944 \text{ dyne.} \quad \textit{Ans.}$$

It follows that, with an isolated sphere, in air the density of the dielectric lines of force varies *inversely as the square of the distance* from the center of the sphere.

When the distance between two spheres, such as those in Fig. 248, is small compared with their radii, the centers of the charges can no longer be assumed as at the centers of the spheres. Owing to proximity effect, that is, the mutual attraction of the charges, the centers of charge are displaced, each toward the other sphere.

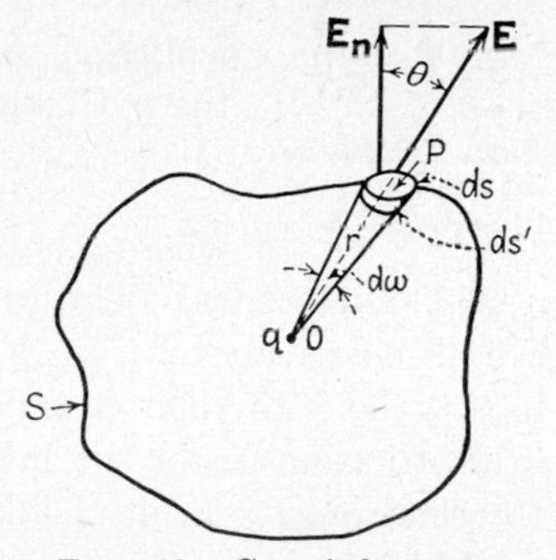

FIG. 249. Gauss' theorem.

Gauss' Theorem. The fact that 4π dielectric lines leave each unit positive charge has been generalized in a theorem by Gauss:[1] *The surface integral of the normal component of the outward electric intensity, over any closed surface in an electric field, is equal to 4π times the total quantity of electricity inside the surface.* This is proved as follows: In Fig. 249 let S be any surface enclosing a quantity q of electricity. Let $d\omega$, a differential solid angle, represent a tube of force enclosing a small cone of flux and intercepting S by the differential area ds. The distance between q and ds is r cm. In the cgs system the field intensity $\mathbf{E}$ at ds is equal to q/r^2 dynes per unit charge. Let $\mathbf{E} = q/r^2$ be the magnitude and direction of the field intensity at ds, and let $\mathbf{E}_n$ be the component of field intensity normal to the surface S at ds. $\mathbf{E}_n = \mathbf{E} \cos \theta$. Let ds' be a differential area perpendicular to $\mathbf{E}_n$. $ds' = ds \cos \theta$. The dielectric lines included within ds and normal to S

$$d\psi = \mathbf{E}_n \, ds = \mathbf{E} \, ds \cos \theta = \frac{q}{r^2} \, ds'.$$

$$\frac{ds'}{r^2} = d\omega.$$

Hence,

$$\psi = q \textstyle\iint d\omega = 4\pi q \text{ dielectric lines.} \quad \text{Q.E.D.}$$

237. Potential Difference. In Sec. 236 field intensity is defined as the force on a unit charge. Under static conditions, potential difference

[1] See footnote, p. 214. Gauss' theorem applies definitely to the cgs system and to the unrationalized mks system. With the rationalized mks system the surface integral is equal to q, the total quantity (see p. 355).

between two points is measured by the *work* done in carrying a positive unit charge between the points and is independent of the path. Work is the product of force and distance. In Fig. 250 let it be required to determine the potential difference between points A and C, the path over which the unit charge is carried being AbC. At any point p the field intensity is **E** units of force per unit charge (dynes per esu in the cgs system), the direction of the field being shown by the vector **E**. Let θ be the angle between ds, a differential length of path, and **E**. Then the potential difference between A and B, which is measured by the work W, is

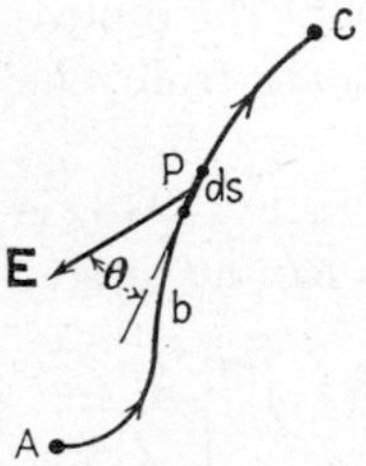

$$V_{AC} = W = \int_A^C \mathbf{E} \cos \theta \, ds. \tag{255}$$

Fig. 250. Line integral of field intensity.

(255) is called the *line integral of the field intensity*. It follows that if the field intensity is uniform over the entire length of path and everywhere has the same direction as the path, then,

$$V = \mathbf{E}d, \tag{255a}$$

where d is the length of the path.

238. Dielectrics. The differences between conductors and insulators are discussed briefly on p. 4 *et seq*. In conductors the electrons are loosely held to their atomic nuclei and so are quite free to pass from atom to atom under the influence of potential difference. In insulators the electrons are firmly held to their atomic nuclei, and it requires a relatively high potential difference to cause even a relatively few electrons to pass from atom to atom. However, the mechanism of conduction of current is the same in insulators and conductors, the differences being one of magnitude. Hence, in considering the properties of an insulating medium relative to the conduction of current, it is called an *insulator*. However, when the behavior of an insulating medium is considered relative to dielectric phenomena such as the number and density of dielectric lines, losses caused by dielectric stress, and resistance to electric breakdown, the medium is called a *dielectric*. For example, air is not a particularly good dielectric so far as flashover is concerned, its dielectric strength being only about 75,000 volts to the inch, but it is one of the best insulators.

Thin samples of rubber will withstand dielectric stresses as high as 450,000 volts to the inch, but they will permit a much greater leakage current than air will permit. That is, rubber is a better dielectric but a poorer insulator than air.

It is stated in Sec. 234 (p. 326) that the dielectric field resembles both the electric circuit and the magnetic field, in that dielectric lines distribute themselves as lines of current flow and magnetic lines do. Irrespective of the magnitude of the current in a conductor, the conductor is not injured mechanically, provided that it can be kept cool. Neither is a magnetic conductor injured, no matter how many magnetic lines exist in it. Dielectric mediums, however, have the property of permitting only a limited number of dielectric lines per unit area without rupture occurring. When the dielectric flux density exceeds this limiting value, rupture occurs and may be followed by a dynamic arc, which burns and chars the dielectric. At the present time, the mechanism of the breakdown of solid and liquid dielectrics is not well understood although several rational theories have been advanced.

The ability of a substance to resist dielectric breakdown is called its *dielectric strength.* This is expressed in volts per unit thickness when the substance is placed between flat electrodes having rounded edges. For example, the dielectric strength of air is approximately 3,000 volts per mm. Rubber and varnished cambric have a much greater dielectric

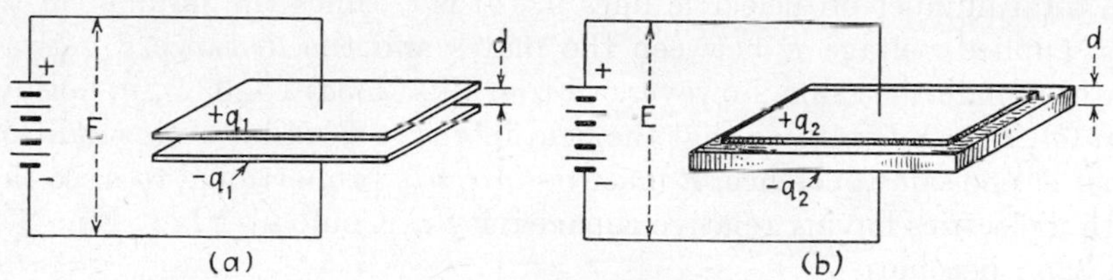

FIG. 251. Effect of solid dielectrics on quantity.

strength than air, an average value for rubber being 16,000 volts per mm, or 400,000 volts per in. Varnished cambric has about twice the dielectric strength of rubber.

The volts per unit thickness impressed across a dielectric is the *voltage gradient.* For example, if 24,000 volts is impressed across 30 mils of insulation, the gradient is 24,000 ÷ 30, or 800, volts per mil. With insulating substances, both the insulation properties and the dielectric properties must be considered.

239. Capacitivity, or Dielectric Constant.[1] In Fig. 251(a) are shown two parallel metallic plates separated by a distance d. When a potential difference E is applied to the plates, a positive charge $+q_1$ is found on the upper plate and a negative charge $-q_1$ is found on the lower plate. If a slab of glass or hard rubber or some other good dielectric be inserted between the plates so as to fill completely the intervening space, Fig. 251(b), the charges $+q_1$ and $-q_1$ will be found to have increased to $+q_2$ and $-q_2$ with the same value E of applied potential difference. The increase in charge must be due to the presence of the glass, rubber, or other dielectric which may have been inserted.

[1] The terms *specific inductive capacity* and *permittivity* are also used although this latter term is now deprecated.

The ratio $q_2/q_1 = \epsilon_r$* is called the *relative capacitivity*, or *dielectric constant*, of the dielectric between the plates.

In the accompanying table are given the relative capacitivities of some of the more common dielectrics.

RELATIVE CAPACITIVITIES[1]

Bakelite	4.5 to 5.5	Paper	2.0 to 2.6
Ebonite	2.8	Paraffin	2.1 to 2.5
Fiber	2.5 to 5	Porcelain	5.7 to 6.8
Glass	5.4 to 9.9	Rubber	2.0 to 3.5
Mica	2.5 to 6.6	Water	81
Oil	2.2 to 4.7	Wood	2.5 to 7.7

[1] For more complete data see "Standard Handbook for Electrical Engineers," 8th ed., Sec. 4, Par. 450 *et seq.*

It will be noted that since q_2 in Fig. 251(*b*) is ϵ_r times q_1 in Fig. 251(*a*), the total number of dielectric lines in (*b*) is ϵ_r times the number in (*a*). The applied voltage E between the plates and the distance d between plates remain the same, however. From Eq. (255*a*) (p. 332), in both (*a*) and (*b*), $E = \mathbf{E}d$ volts, so that the field intensity $\mathbf{E}$ under both conditions must be the same. Hence, $\mathbf{E}$ must be *inversely* proportional to ϵ_r, so that with dielectrics having relative capacitivity ϵ_r, Coulomb's law, Eq. (253) (p. 325), becomes

$$\mathbf{F} = \frac{q_1 q_2}{\epsilon_r \epsilon_v r^2} = \frac{q_1 q_2}{\epsilon r^2} \qquad \text{dynes,} \tag{256}$$

and Eq. (254) (p. 329) becomes

$$\mathbf{F} = \frac{q}{\epsilon_r \epsilon_v r^2} = \frac{q}{\epsilon r^2} \qquad \text{dynes per unit charge,} \tag{256a}$$

where $\epsilon = \epsilon_r \epsilon_v$.

240. Capacitance. Two conductors separated by a dielectric constitute a capacitor. When a potential difference is applied between the plates of a capacitor, electricity is stored in the capacitor, a positive charge being on one plate or set of plates, and an equal negative charge being on the other plate or set of plates. This property of a capacitor to store electricity is called *capacitance*. The mechanism by which these charges are stored is discussed at the beginning of the chapter and is illustrated in Fig. 242 (p. 324).

The performance of a capacitor when connected in an electric circuit is illustrated in Fig. 252, which shows two conducting plates connected to a

* As with μ_v, μ_v' and μ_r (p. 221), ϵ_v, ϵ_v' are quite different physically from ϵ_r. Both ϵ_v and ϵ_v' are *space constants* while ϵ_r is a property of the dielectric and depends on polarization and similar effects.

battery, the plates being separated by a dielectric. There are also a single-pole double-throw (S-P D-T) switch S and a galvanometer G in the circuit. If the switch S be closed to the left, the galvanometer will deflect momentarily and then come back to zero. This indicates that when the switch is closed, a quantity of electricity passes through the galvanometer but that the current ceases almost immediately. The current flows for a time only sufficient to charge the capacitor. After the capacitor has become fully charged, the current ceases because the emf of the capacitor is equal and opposite to that of the battery. As this capacitor emf opposes the current entering the capacitor, it may be considered as a counter emf. Any current after the capacitor has become fully charged is a leakage current through the insulation. If the switch S be opened for a short time and then closed, there will be no deflection of the galvanometer unless there has been leakage.

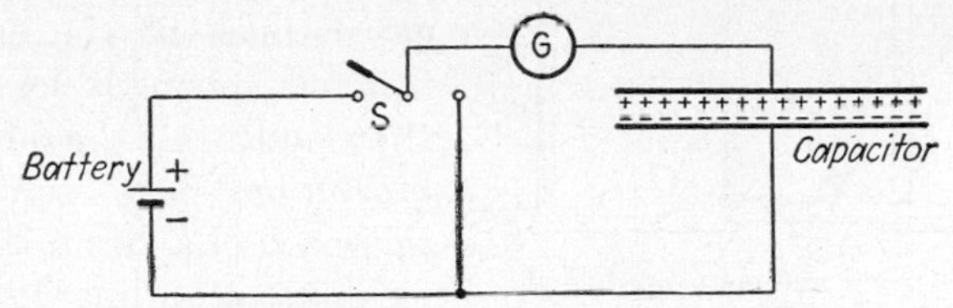

FIG. 252. Charging and discharging a capacitor.

The charging of a capacitor from a battery is not unlike the filling of a tank T from a reservoir R, Fig. 253. When the valve V is first opened, water will rush through the pipe connecting R and T and will continue to flow at a diminishing rate until the level H of the water in the tank T is equal to the level of the water in the reservoir. If the tank does not leak, no water flows through the pipe after the water levels have become equal. In the same manner, the capacitor, Fig. 252, takes current until its potential difference is equal to that of the battery, after which the current ceases. Again, if tank T does not leak, no further flow of water occurs when valve V is closed and then opened.

To prove that electricity has actually been stored in the capacitor, Fig. 252, the switch S may be closed to the right. This short-circuits the capacitor through the galvanometer. The galvanometer now deflects momentarily in a direction opposite to that on charge, showing that the charge now flows *out* of the positive plate. The capacitor now becomes completely discharged, as is shown by there being no longer any deflection of the galvanometer. Also, if the capacitor is not leaky, the ballistic deflection on discharge is the same as that on charge, the quantity of electricity being the same in both cases.

If the voltage of the battery, Fig. 252, be increased, the galvanometer deflection on charge and on discharge will increase also. This is due to the fact that the charge given to the capacitor is proportional to the voltage across its terminals, just as the amount of water in the tank will be proportional to the height H, Fig. 253. The relation between the voltage and the charge in a capacitor is expressed by the equation

$$Q = CE. \tag{257}$$

That is, the charge in a capacitor is equal to the voltage multiplied by a constant C. This constant C is the *capacitance* of the capacitor. The practical unit of capacitance is the *farad*.[1] If C is in farads and E in volts, Q is in coulombs or ampere-seconds.

The farad is too large a unit of capacitance for general use. A capacitor having a capacitance of 1 farad would be prohibitively large. The capacitance of the earth as an isolated sphere is less than one-thousandth of a farad. The *microfarad* (μf), equal to one-millionth of a farad, is the unit of capacitance ordinarily used.

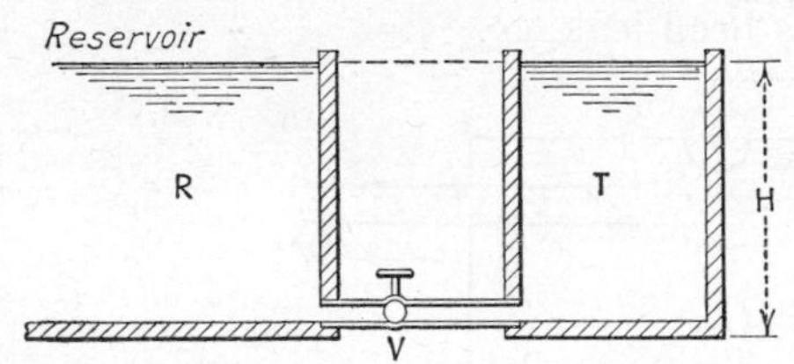

FIG. 253. Reservoir and connected tank.

In radiotelegraph and radiotelephone work, where the capacitances are very small, the microfarad is too large a unit, and the micromicrofarad ($\mu\mu$f $= 10^{-12}$ farad) is used. However, in Eq. (257), and Eqs. (258) and (259), if Q is expressed in *coulombs* and E in *volts*, C *must* be expressed in *farads*.

By transposition, Eq. (257) may be written as follows:

$$C = \frac{Q}{E}. \tag{258}$$

$$E = \frac{Q}{C}. \tag{259}$$

[1] From Michael Faraday, (1791–1867), an English chemist and physicist who was the son of a blacksmith and until 1813 was an apprenticed bookbinder. At the instance of Sir Humphry Davy, he was appointed assistant in the laboratory of the Royal Institution of Great Britain. He was made director in 1825 and in 1833 was appointed Fullerian professor of chemistry for life. Although he made important discoveries in chemistry, his outstanding work was in the field of electricity. He was the first to produce continuous rotation about each other of wires conducting current and magnets (motor action); the first to cause a current in a circuit to be induced by magnetism or by a current in another circuit (generator action and mutual induction). He discovered the two fundamental laws of electrolysis (Sec. 110, p. 134), the effect of magnetism on polarized light, diamagnetism, and made notable contributions to the understanding of electrostatic phenomena, the law of equal and opposite charges and the Faraday tubes of force being typical examples.

As an illustration of the use of the above relations, consider the following example:

Example. A capacitor has a capacitance of 200 μf and is connected across 600-volt mains. If the current is maintained constant at 0.1 amp, how long must it continue before the capacitor is fully charged?

The quantity in the capacitor, when fully charged, is $Q = 0.000200 \cdot 600 = 0.12$ coulomb or amp-sec.

$$0.12 = 0.1t,$$
$$t = 1.2 \text{ sec.} \quad \textit{Ans.}$$

Elastance, S, is the reciprocal of capacitance; that is, $S = 1/C$, and the unit of elastance is the *daraf* (*farad* spelled backward).

241. Capacitors in Parallel. Let it be required to determine the capacitance C of a number of capacitors in parallel, the capacitors having capacitances C_1, C_2, C_3. This arrangement of capacitors is shown in Fig. 254. Let the common voltage across the capacitors be E and the total resulting charge Q. Obviously,

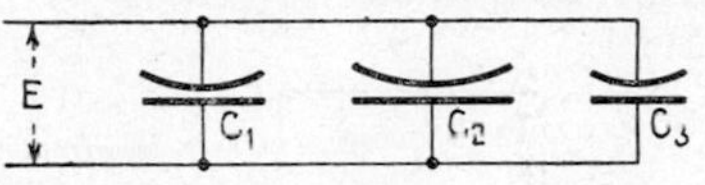

FIG. 254. Capacitors in parallel.

$$Q = CE$$

and

$$Q_1 = C_1E, \qquad Q_2 = C_2E, \qquad Q_3 = C_3E.$$

The total charge

$$Q = Q_1 + Q_2 + Q_3 = CE.$$
$$CE = C_1E + C_2E + C_3E.$$
$$CE = (C_1 + C_2 + C_3)E.$$

Therefore,

$$C = C_1 + C_2 + C_3. \tag{260}$$

That is, if capacitors are connected in parallel, the resulting capacitance is the sum of the individual capacitances.

This is analogous to the grouping of conductances in parallel in the electric circuit.

Example. Three capacitors, having capacitances of 5, 10, 12 μf, are connected in parallel across 600-volt mains. Determine: (*a*) capacitance of single capacitor which could replace combination; (*b*) charge on each capacitor.

(*a*) $C = 5 + 10 + 12 = 27$ μf. *Ans.*

(*b*) $Q_1 = 5 \cdot 600 =$ 3,000 microcoulombs.
$Q_2 = 10 \cdot 600 =$ 6,000 microcoulombs.
$Q_3 = 12 \cdot 600 =$ 7,200 microcoulombs. *Ans.*

Total charge = 16,200 microcoulombs = $27 \cdot 600$ microcoulombs (*check*).

242. Capacitors in Series. In Fig. 255, three capacitors, having capacitances C_1, C_2, C_3, are connected in series across the voltage E.

It is desired to determine the capacitance of an equivalent single capacitor. Let E_1, E_2, E_3 be the potential differences across the capacitors C_1, C_2, C_3. After the voltage E is applied to the system, there will be $+Q$ units of charge on the positive plate of C_1, and, by the law of electrostatic induction, $-Q$ units must be induced on the negative plate of C_1.

Now consider the region a, which consists of the negative plate of C_1, the positive plate of C_2, and the lead connecting them. This system is insulated from all external potentials, since it is assumed that the capacitors have perfect insulation. Before the voltage E is applied to the system of capacitors, no charge exists in the region a. After the application of the voltage, the net charge in this region must still be zero, since perfect insulation is assumed and no charge can enter or leave the region (see Sec. 235, p. 328). Therefore, $+Q$ units must come into existance in order that the net charge in the region a may remain zero $[(+Q) + (-Q) = 0]$. This charge of $+Q$ units will go to the plate of C_2 since it is repelled by the $+$ charge on C_1 just as the charge b', Fig. 247(a) (p. 329), takes a position on the end of the conducting body B as far as possible from the positive inducing charge a. The same reasoning holds for the region b, between C_2 and C_3. Therefore, each of the three capacitors in series has the same charge Q. (This is analogous to resistors in series, each of which must carry the same current if no leakage exists.)

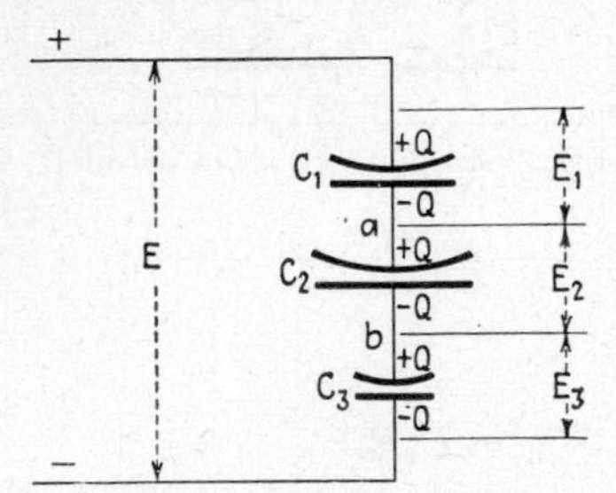

FIG. 255. Capacitors in series.

Consider the voltages E_1, E_2, E_3.

$$E_1 = \frac{Q}{C_1}, \qquad E_2 = \frac{Q}{C_2}, \qquad E_3 = \frac{Q}{C_3} \qquad \text{volts} \qquad \text{[from Eq. (259), p. 336].}$$

The sum of the three capacitor voltages must equal the line voltage.

$$E_1 + E_2 + E_3 = E \qquad \text{volts.}$$

$$E = \frac{Q}{C_1} + \frac{Q}{C_2} + \frac{Q}{C_3} \qquad \text{volts.}$$

Also, $E = Q/C$, as by definition the equivalent capacitor C must have a charge Q.

Substituting this value for E,

$$\frac{Q}{C} = \frac{Q}{C_1} + \frac{Q}{C_2} + \frac{Q}{C_3} \qquad \text{volts.}$$

$$\frac{1}{C} = \frac{1}{C_1} + \frac{1}{C_2} + \frac{1}{C_3} \qquad \text{darafs.} \tag{261}$$

That is, *the reciprocal of the equivalent capacitance of a number of capacitors in series is equal to the sum of the reciprocals of the capacitances of the individual capacitors.*

In assuming for capacitors connected in series that with direct current the potential across each capacitor is inversely proportional to its capacitance, the factor of leakage is neglected. If the capacitors are even slightly leaky, however, there will be current through the series of capacitors and eventually the potential distributes itself according to Ohm's law.

$$E_1 = IR_1, \qquad E_2 = IR_2, \qquad E_3 = IR_3 \qquad \text{volts},$$

where I is the leakage current and R_1, R_2, R_3 are the resistances of the three capacitors.

Example of Capacitors Connected in Series. Consider that the three capacitors of Sec. 241, having capacitances of 5, 10, 12 μf, are connected in series across 600-volt mains. Determine: (*a*) equivalent capacitance of combination; (*b*) charge on each capacitor; (*c*) potential across each capacitor, assuming no leakage.

(*a*) $\frac{1}{C} = \frac{1}{5} + \frac{1}{10} + \frac{1}{12} = 0.3833$ megadaraf.

$C = \frac{1}{0.3833} = 2.608\ \mu\text{f}.$ *Ans.*

(*b*) $Q = 2.608 \cdot 600 = 1{,}565$ microcoulombs, on each capacitor. *Ans.*

(*c*) $E_1 = \frac{1{,}565 \cdot 10^{-6}}{5 \cdot 10^{-6}} = 313.0$ volts.

$E_2 = \frac{1{,}565 \cdot 10^{-6}}{10 \cdot 10^{-6}} = 156.5$ volts.

$E_3 = \frac{1{,}565 \cdot 10^{-6}}{12 \cdot 10^{-6}} = 130.4$ volts. *Ans.*

$E_1 + E_2 + E_3 = 599.9$ volts (*check*).

243. Field Intensity between Parallel Electrodes. Dielectric phenomena in a capacitor, such as the storage of energy and the electrical strength of the dielectric, depend on the intensity of the field within the dielectric.

Consider two parallel conducting electrodes each having an area A sq cm, with a separation which is small compared with the dimensions of their area so that edge effects may be neglected, Fig. 251 (p. 333). Let the dielectric be air. Place a charge $+q_1$ esu on one electrode and a charge $-q_1$ esu on the other electrode. These charges will reside entirely on the adjacent surfaces. The charge per unit area $\sigma = q_1/A$. Since 4π electric lines leave each positive unit charge and terminate on each negative unit charge, there will be $4\pi\sigma$ electric lines per square centimeter between the electrodes. Hence, from definition, the field intensity $\mathbf{E} = 4\pi\sigma$ dynes per unit charge.

The relation may also be developed in the same manner as is used to determine the force adjacent to a magnetized surface (Sec. 162, p. 218).

Since the law relating to the force between unit charges is the same as that relating to unit poles, the force just outside an electrode charged with σ unit charges per square centimeter is $2\pi\sigma$ dynes. The field adjacent to the charged electrode is normal to it (Sec. 234) and is uniform. Hence, the force must be $2\pi\sigma$ dynes per unit charge at any distance from the electrode, so long as the field remains uniform. The field intensity between the two parallel, oppositely charged electrodes is uniform throughout. Each electrode must therefore exert a force of $2\pi\sigma$ dynes on a unit positive charge in the region between the electrodes, so that the total force is $4\pi\sigma$ dynes and the field intensity is

$$\mathbf{E} = \frac{4\pi\sigma}{\epsilon_v} = 4\pi\sigma \qquad \text{dynes per unit charge.} \tag{262}$$

As is stated in Sec. 236 (p. 329), in the cgs electrostatic system $\mathbf{E}$ is numerically equal to D, the electrostatic flux density when the capacitivity ϵ_r of the dielectric is unity, as it is for air. $\mathbf{E}$ corresponds to H, or magnetic-field intensity, in magnetism. Also the fact that $\mathbf{E}$ is equal to D when ϵ_r is equal to unity corresponds to H equal to B when μ_r is equal to unity (see p. 256).

The force of attraction between the electrodes is readily computed. Consider a unit charge on the negative electrode. The positive electrode acts on this charge with a force of $2\pi\sigma$ dynes. The force on each square centimeter of the negatively charged electrode is $2\pi\sigma^2$ dynes, and the force on the entire negative electrode is

$$\mathbf{F} = \frac{2\pi\sigma^2 A}{\epsilon_v} = 2\pi\sigma^2 A \qquad \text{dynes.} \tag{263}$$

When the relative capacitivity of the dielectric is ϵ_r, Fig. 251(b), (262) becomes

$$\mathbf{E} = \frac{4\pi\sigma}{\epsilon_v\epsilon_r} = \frac{4\pi\sigma}{\epsilon_r} \qquad \text{dynes per unit charge.} \tag{264}$$

[See Sec. 239 and Eqs. (256) and (256a), p. 334.]

In the same manner, (263) becomes

$$\mathbf{F} = \frac{2\pi\sigma^2 A}{\epsilon_v\epsilon_r} = \frac{2\pi\sigma^2 A}{\epsilon_r} \qquad \text{dynes.} \tag{265}$$

Substituting σ of (264) in (265) and letting area A be 1 sq cm,

$$\mathbf{F} = \frac{\mathbf{E}^2\epsilon_r}{8\pi} \qquad \text{dynes per sq cm.} \tag{266}$$

[Compare with Eq. (130), p. 219.]

244. Energy Stored in Capacitors. As a charge is stored in a capacitor and a difference of potential exists between the positive and negative electrodes, energy must be stored. The existence of this energy is shown, for example, by the spark which occurs when a capacitor is discharged.

The stored energy may be computed by finding the mechanical work done in charging the capacitor. In Fig. 256, the equal, parallel, flat conducting electrodes A' and B' are separated from each other by an infinitesimal distance. A charge $+q$ esu is placed on B', and a charge $-q$ esu is placed on A'. Since these charges are separated by an infinitesimal distance, no finite work has been done in separating them. The force between the two electrodes is $2\pi\sigma^2 A$, where σ is the density of charge on each electrode in esu per square centimeter and A is the area of each electrode in square centimeters (see Sec. 243). This force is constant so long as the charge is constant and the field between the electrodes is uniform. The electrode B' is now moved away from A' in a direction perpendicular to its plane to a position B, d cm from A' and parallel to A'. The work done in separating the charges $+q$ and $-q$ is the product of force and distance. That is,

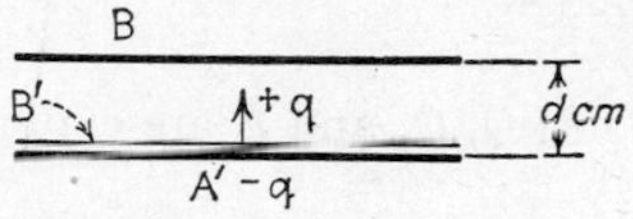

Fig. 256. Charging plate capacitor.

$$w = 2\pi\sigma^2 Ad \qquad \text{ergs.} \tag{I}$$

From Sec. 246 (p. 344), the capacitance of such a capacitor,

$$C = \frac{A}{4\pi d} \qquad \text{statfarads.} \tag{II}$$

Substituting d from (II) in Eq. (I), remembering that $q = \sigma A$,

$$w = \frac{q^2}{2C} \qquad \text{ergs.} \tag{III}$$

If mks units are used, the work is given in joules.

Let the capacitor be further charged by moving another electrode B' from A' to B, bringing an additional charge $+q_1$ to electrode B. There will be two forces to overcome, that due to the separation of charges $+q_1$ and $-q_1$ which is equal to $2\pi\sigma_1{}^2 A$ or $2\pi(q_1/A)^2 A$ and that due to the intensity of the field produced by charges $+q$ and $-q$. This last force is equal to $4\pi\sigma q_1$ or $4\pi(q/A)q_1$. The *total work* is now

$$W = \frac{q^2}{2C} + \frac{4\pi q q_1 d}{A} + \frac{2\pi q_1{}^2 d}{A} \qquad \text{ergs.}$$

Substituting,

$$C = \frac{A}{4\pi d} \qquad \text{statfarads,}$$

$$W = \frac{q^2}{2C} + \frac{qq_1}{C} + \frac{q_1{}^2}{2C} = \frac{1}{2C}(q + q_1)^2 = \frac{1}{2}\frac{Q^2}{C} \qquad \text{ergs,} \tag{267}$$

where $Q = q + q_1$. The same procedure may be followed with additional charges q_2, q_3, etc.

The work may be readily computed using calculus. In Fig. 256, the work done in moving q units through a difference in potential dv (Sec. 237, p. 331) is

$$dw = q\,dv \quad \text{ergs,}$$

and the total work

$$W = \int_0^V q\,dv \quad \text{ergs.}$$

As $q = Cv$,

$$W = C\int_0^V v\,dv = \tfrac{1}{2}CV^2 \quad \text{ergs.} \tag{268}$$

Since $Q = CV$, (267) and (268) may also be expressed as

$$W = \tfrac{1}{2}QV \quad \text{ergs.} \tag{269}$$

If Q, C, and E are expressed in coulombs, farads, and volts,

$$W = \frac{1}{2}\frac{Q^2}{C} \quad \text{joules.} \tag{270}$$

$$W = \tfrac{1}{2}CV^2 \quad \text{joules.} \tag{271}$$

$$W = \tfrac{1}{2}QV \quad \text{joules.} \tag{272}$$

The similarity in form of (271) and the equation for the energy stored in the magnetic field should be noted [see Eq. (232), Sec. 221, p. 311]. The energy stored in the dielectric field is proportional to the square of the *voltage*, whereas the energy stored in the electromagnetic field is proportional to the square of the *current*.

Example. Determine the stored energy in each of the capacitors in series of Sec. 242 (p. 339) and the total stored energy. Using (270),

$$W_1 = \frac{1}{2}\frac{(1{,}565 \cdot 10^{-6})^2}{5 \cdot 10^{-6}} = 0.2449 \text{ joule. } \quad \textit{Ans.}$$

$$W_2 = \frac{1}{2}\frac{(1{,}565 \cdot 10^{-6})^2}{10 \cdot 10^{-6}} = 0.1225 \text{ joule. } \quad \textit{Ans.}$$

$$W_3 = \frac{1}{2}\frac{(1{,}565 \cdot 10^{-6})^2}{12 \cdot 10^{-6}} = 0.1020 \text{ joule. } \quad \textit{Ans.}$$

The total energy $W = \tfrac{1}{2}(1{,}565 \cdot 10^{-6} \cdot 600) = 0.4695$ joule. *Ans.*
Using Eq. (271),

$$W_1 = \tfrac{1}{2} \cdot 5 \cdot 10^{-6} \cdot (313)^2 = 0.2449 \text{ joule } (\textit{check}).$$

Using Eq. (272),

$$W_1 = \tfrac{1}{2} \cdot 1.565 \cdot 10^{-6} \cdot 313 = 0.2449 \text{ joule } (\textit{check}).$$

Energy per Unit Volume of Dielectrics. In Eq. (264) (p. 340), $\sigma = Q/A$. Hence,

$$Q = \frac{\mathbf{E}A\epsilon_r}{4\pi}. \tag{I}$$

From Eq. (255a) (p. 332),

$$V = \mathbf{E}d. \tag{II}$$

Substituting (I) and (II) in (272),

$$W = \frac{1}{2} QV = \frac{\mathbf{E}^2 \epsilon_r Ad}{8\pi} \quad \text{ergs.}$$

$$W_1 = \frac{\mathbf{E}^2 \epsilon_r}{8\pi} \quad \text{ergs per cu cm.} \tag{273}$$

Substituting **E** [Eq. (290) (p. 351)] in (273) with $\epsilon_v = 1$, (273) becomes

$$W_1 = \frac{D^2}{8\pi \epsilon_r} \quad \text{ergs per cu cm.} \tag{273a}$$

Equation (273) may also be derived from Eq. (266) (p. 340). Since the force per square centimeter is equal to $\mathbf{E}^2\epsilon_r/8\pi$ dynes, the work developed by this force through a distance of 1 cm is equal to (273).

245. Calculation of Capacitance. If the geometry is not too complicated, it is possible to calculate the capacitance of a capacitor by either analytical or graphical methods. Capacitance may be computed in terms of the dimensions of the capacitor. The cgs electrostatic system[1] will be used first. It is a simple matter to convert to farads by dividing by[2] $9 \cdot 10^{11}$, the numerical ratio of the units of capacitance of the two systems. The method of procedure is to determine the work done in carrying a unit charge through the field from one electrode to the other. By definition, this gives the potential difference between the electrodes. From Eq. (258) (p. 336), the ratio of charge to potential difference gives the capacitance.

The computation of the capacitance of concentric spherical and coaxial cylindrical capacitors is in part dependent on the fact that *there can be no force in a region totally enclosed by a conductor if there is no charge in the region.* If a force does exist in such a region, there must be lines of force. These lines must begin at a positive charge and end at a negative charge. Also, there must be a difference of potential between the beginning and the end of a line of force. This is impossible under the given conditions, since the entire surrounding conductor is at one potential. If it were not, there would be current, which is contrary to the assumed static conditions.

246. Capacitance of Parallel-electrode Capacitors. The parallel-electrode capacitor is the simplest type of capacitor and is widely used in various forms. Because of its simple geometry, it is easy to calculate

[1] Computation of capacitance in the mks systems is given on pp. 352 and 355, *et seq.*

[2] Actually $8.98645 \cdot 10^{11}$. See Appendix B (p. 581).

the capacitance if the spacing of the electrodes is small compared with their dimensions, making the effect of edge fringing negligible.

In the simple two-electrode capacitor, Fig. 257, the area of each electrode is A sq cm, and the distance between electrodes is d cm. The capacitivity of the dielectric is ϵ_r. A positive charge $+Q$ esu is placed on the upper electrode, and an equal negative charge $-Q$ esu is placed on the lower electrode. The density of charge σ on each electrode is Q/A esu per sq cm.

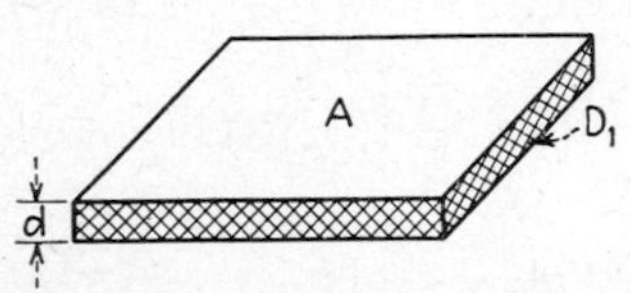

FIG. 257. Capacitance of plate capacitor.

From Eq. (264) (p. 340),

$$\mathbf{E} = \mathbf{F} = \frac{4\pi\sigma}{\epsilon_v \epsilon_r} \quad \text{dynes per unit charge.}$$

Since the field is uniform, the force throughout the region between the electrodes is constant. From Eq. (255a) (p. 332), the work done in carrying a unit positive charge from the negative to the positive electrode is

$$W = \mathbf{E}d = \frac{4\pi\sigma d}{\epsilon_v \epsilon_r} = V, \tag{I}$$

where V is the potential difference between the electrodes. Substituting $\sigma = Q/A$, and since $C = Q/V$ and $\epsilon_v = 1$,

$$C = \frac{\epsilon_r A}{4\pi d} \quad \text{statfarads.} \tag{274}$$

Since the *microfarad* is $9 \cdot 10^5$ times as great as the statfarad, it is necessary to divide (274) by $9 \cdot 10^5$ in order to obtain the capacitance in microfarads. Hence,

$$C = \frac{\epsilon_r A}{4\pi d \cdot 9 \cdot 10^5} \quad \mu\text{f.} \tag{275}$$

The total capacitance of a simple parallel-electrode capacitor of this type cannot be accurately calculated for the following reason: All the electric lines do not lie in the region between the electrodes, as certain lines pass from the back of the positive electrode to the back of the negative electrode, as in Fig. 258(a). This results in the actual capacitance being greater than the value as just calculated. This error may be avoided by using one more electrode in one group than in the other, Fig. 258(b). In this case the area A [Eq. (274)] includes both sides of all electrodes with the exception of the two outside ones. As the charge on both outer electrodes is of the same sign and the electrodes have the same potential, no electric lines can pass between them. An error may occur due to the fringing of the lines near the edges of the electrodes, unless the electrode dimensions are large compared with the distance between electrodes.

Example of Capacitor Design. It is desired to construct a parallel-electrode capacitor having a total capacitance of 8 μf. The electrodes are of tin foil 6 by 8 in. and 1 mil thick. The dielectric is of paper 7 by 9 in. and 2 mils thick, having a capacitivity 3. Determine: (*a*) number of sheets of paper and of tin foil; (*b*) dimensions of capacitor.

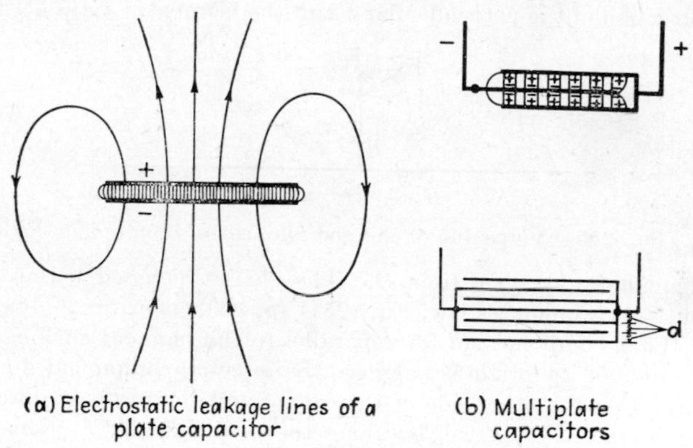

FIG. 258. Parallel-electrode capacitors.

(*a*) The area of each electrode is

$$6 \cdot 8 \cdot (2.54)^2 = 309.7 \text{ sq cm.}$$

The distance between electrodes,

$$d = 0.002 \cdot 2.54 = 0.00508 \text{ cm.}$$

The capacitance between two electrodes [from Eq. (274)],

$$C = \frac{3 \cdot 309.7}{4\pi \cdot 0.00508 \cdot 9 \cdot 10^5} = 0.01617 \ \mu\text{f.}$$

Therefore,

$$\frac{8}{0.01617} = 495 \text{ sections are needed.}$$

These sections are indicated at *d*, Fig. 258(*b*). This means that 496 plates and 495 sheets of paper are necessary.

Thickness:

$$\begin{aligned} \text{Tin foil} &= 496 \cdot 0.001 = 0.496 \text{ in.} \\ \text{Paper} &= 495 \cdot 0.002 = \underline{0.990} \text{ in.} \\ & \qquad\qquad\qquad\quad 1.486 \text{ in.} \end{aligned}$$

Volume of condenser proper = 7 by 9 by 1.49 in. *Ans.*

In addition, outside insulation and a protective covering are necessary.

247. Capacitance of Coaxial Cylindrical Capacitors. Coaxial cylindrical capacitors are in common use. Their widest use is exemplified by the single-conductor cable, particularly the underground power cable with a lead sheath. It is not difficult to compute the capacitance of such a cable. However, before making this computation, the force exerted by a straight, infinitely long charged filament is first determined.

Force Due to Straight Charged Filament. In Fig. 259, a thin straight filament A in air, extending from $-$ infinity to $+$ infinity, is charged with q esu per centimeter length. Let it be required to determine the force exerted by this linearly distributed charge on a unit positive charge at a point P, h cm from the filament. Let the origin O be the intersection of the perpendicular h and the filament. Consider a differential

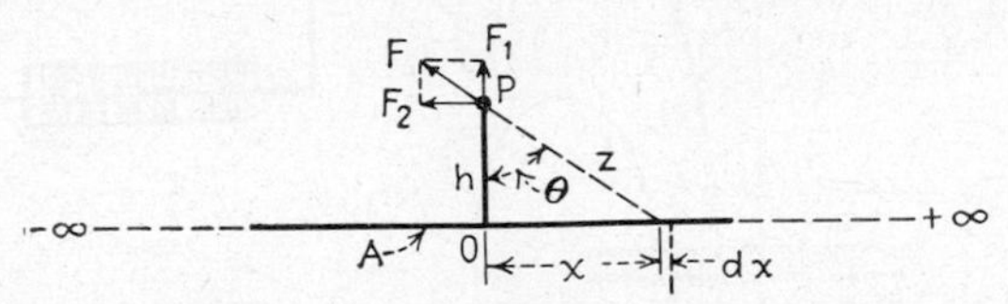

FIG. 259. Force due to charged filament of infinite length.

length of filament dx, at x cm from O. The charge included within the distance dx is $q\,dx$ esu. By Coulomb's law, Eq. (254) (p. 329), it exerts a force $\mathbf{F} = q\,dx/z^2$ dynes at P. Each component of force parallel to the filament such as $\mathbf{F}_2$, due to a charge on one side of the origin is balanced by an equal component due to a charge similarly situated on the other side of the origin, and the resultant force due to the entire charge on the filament will be along the perpendicular h. Hence, the component $\mathbf{F}_1$ in the direction of h, of the force $\mathbf{F}$ needs be alone considered. Force $\mathbf{F}_1$ is equal to $\mathbf{F}\cos\theta = \mathbf{F}(h/\sqrt{x^2+h^2})$. Also, $z^2 = x^2 + h^2$. Let the resultant force be $\mathbf{F}_0$. Difficulty in evaluating the integral is avoided if the integration limits are taken as 0 and ∞ and the integral multiplied by 2. Hence,

$$\mathbf{F}_0 = 2qh\int_0^\infty \frac{dx}{(x^2+h^2)^{3/2}} = 2qh\left.\frac{x}{h^2\sqrt{x^2+h^2}}\right|_0^\infty. \tag{I}$$

Dividing numerator and denominator by x and inserting the limits,

$$\mathbf{F}_0 = \frac{2q}{h}\left.\frac{1}{\sqrt{1+(h^2/x^2)}}\right|_0^\infty = \frac{2q}{h} \quad \text{dynes.} \tag{276}$$

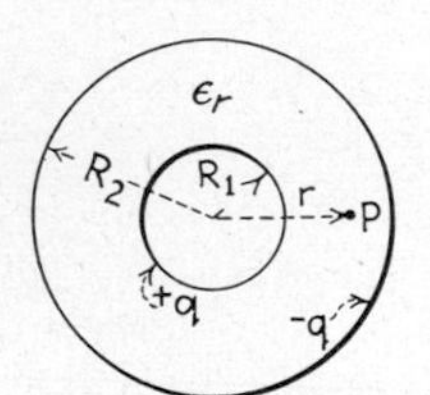

FIG. 260. Coaxial cylindrical capacitor.

If the capacitivity of the dielectric is ϵ_r, the force

$$\mathbf{F}_0 = \frac{2q}{\epsilon_r h} \quad \text{dynes.} \tag{277}$$

(276) should be compared with Eq. (138) (p. 231), which gives the force due to a current in a long, straight conducting filament.

From the symmetry of the charges, the dielectric lines between coaxial cylinders, Fig. 260, must be radial and, if continued inward, will intersect the common axis. Hence it follows that for points external to the inner cylinder the charge on the cylinder acts as if concentrated along the axis, and (276) and (277) may be applied.

Consider the two coaxial cylinders, Fig. 260, in which the radius of the outer cylinder is R_2 cm and the radius of the inner cylinder is R_1 cm. The capacitivity of the insulating medium is ϵ_r. The charge on the inner cylinder is $+q$ esu per centimeter length, and that on the outer cylinder is $-q$ esu per centimeter length. The cylinders are considered as being infinite in length, although even when the ratio of length to radius is only moderately large, the effect is practically that of infinite cylinders. A unit charge is placed at a point P in the dielectric, a distance r cm from the axis. From (277) the force due to the inner cylinder is $2q/\epsilon_r r$ dynes. There can be no force at P due to the charge on the outer cylinder, since P is in a region entirely enclosed by the outer conducting cylinder, the open ends at infinity having no effect. The work done in carrying a unit charge from the surface of the inner cylinder to the outer cylinder, and hence the potential difference,

$$W = V = \int_{R_1}^{R_2} \frac{2q}{\epsilon_r r}\,dr = \frac{2q}{\epsilon_r} \log_\epsilon r \Big|_{R_1}^{R_2} \quad \text{ergs.} \qquad \text{(I)}$$

Inserting the limits and remembering that $\log_\epsilon R_2 - \log_\epsilon R_1 = \log_\epsilon (R_2/R_1)$,

$$V = \frac{2q}{\epsilon_r} \log_\epsilon \frac{R_2}{R_1} \quad \text{statvolts.}$$

Since C_s, the capacitance per centimeter length, is equal to q/V, where q is the esu per centimeter,

$$C_s = \frac{q}{V} = \frac{\epsilon_r}{2 \log_\epsilon (R_2/R_1)} \quad \text{statfarads per cm.} \qquad (278)$$

$$C_s = \frac{\epsilon_r}{2 \cdot 2.303 \log_{10} (R_2/R_1)} \quad \text{statfarads per cm.} \qquad (279)$$

By substituting the microfarad for $9 \cdot 10^5$ statfarads, and changing centimeters to miles, (279) becomes

$$C = \frac{0.0388\epsilon_r}{\log_{10} (R_2/R_1)} \ \mu\text{f per mile.} \qquad (280)$$

The equation in this form is convenient for use with underground cables.

Example. A 1,200-ft length of No. 4 AWG single-conductor rubber-insulated underground cable has a 5/32-in. wall of insulation. The diameter of the conductor is 204.3 mils. The capacitance of the cable is measured and found to be 0.105 μf. Determine capacitivity ϵ_r of the rubber.

$$R_1 = \frac{0.2043}{2} = 0.1022 \text{ in.}$$

$$\tfrac{5}{32} \text{ in.} = 0.1563 \text{ in.}$$

$$R_2 = 0.1563 + 0.1022 = 0.2585 \text{ in.}$$

The capacitance of a mile length,

$$C = \left(\frac{5{,}280}{1{,}200}\right) 0.105 = 0.462 \ \mu\text{f.}$$

Using (280),

$$\epsilon_r = \frac{0.462 \log_{10} (0.2585/0.1022)}{0.0388} = \frac{0.462 \cdot 0.4029}{0.0388} = 4.80. \quad \textit{Ans.}$$

248. Capacitance of Concentric Spherical Capacitors. In Fig. 261 is shown a concentric spherical capacitor. The radius of the inner sphere A is R_1 cm, and the radius of the outer sphere B is R_2 cm. The capacitivity of the dielectric is ϵ_r. A charge of $+q$ esu is placed on the inner sphere and a charge of $-q$ esu on the outer sphere. The potential difference between the spheres is to be determined by carrying a unit charge from sphere A to sphere B. The force at any point P in the dielectric, r cm from the center, due to the charge on the inner sphere, is $q/\epsilon_r r^2$ dynes (see Fig. 246, p. 328). The force at P due to the charge on the outer sphere is zero since point P is within the sphere (Sec. 245, p. 343). Therefore, the potential difference between spheres A and B is

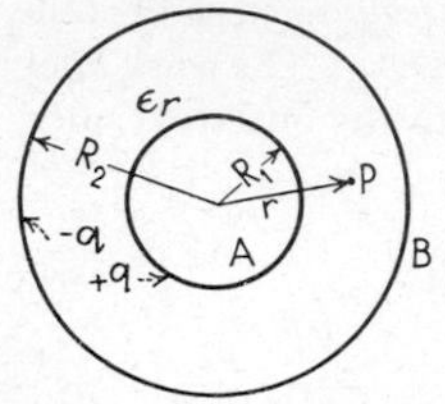

FIG. 261. Concentric spherical capacitor.

$$W = V = \int_{R_1}^{R_2} \frac{q\,dr}{\epsilon_r r^2} = -\frac{q}{\epsilon_r r}\Bigg|_{R_1}^{R_2} = -\frac{q}{\epsilon_r}\left(\frac{1}{R_2} - \frac{1}{R_1}\right).$$

The capacitance

$$C = \frac{q}{V} = \frac{\epsilon_r}{\left(\frac{1}{R_1} - \frac{1}{R_2}\right)} = \epsilon_r \frac{R_1 R_2}{R_2 - R_1} \quad \text{statfarads.} \tag{281}$$

It is interesting to note that if R_2 becomes infinite, the capacitance becomes

$$C = \epsilon_r R_1. \tag{282}$$

That is, the capacitance of an isolated sphere in statfarads is equal to its radius in centimeters, if the sphere is in air ($\epsilon_r = 1$). The capacitance of the earth as an isolated sphere is approximately 720 μf.

249. Capacitance of Parallel Cylinders. Overhead transmission lines usually consist of parallel cylinders. The simplest system is the 2-wire one, which may be a d-c 2-wire system or a single-phase 2-wire system

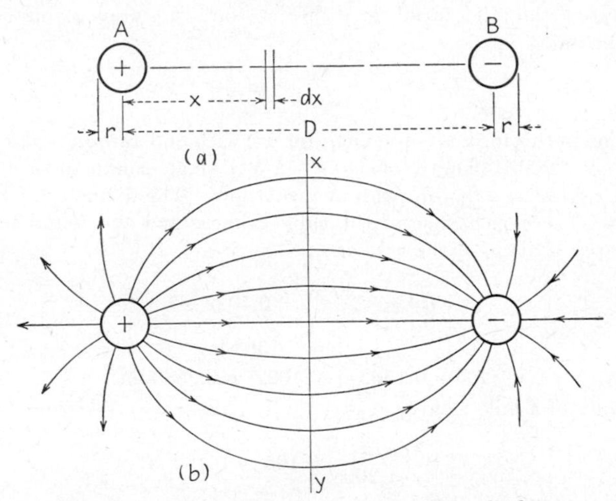

FIG. 262. Capacitance between parallel cylinders.

(see Vol. II, Chap. XIII). With alternating current, if the line is long and the voltage is high, the charging current to the line due to the capacitance between conductors has a marked effect on its performance (see Vol. II, Chap. XIII). The equation for the capacitance between two parallel cylinders is readily computed using Eq. 276 (p. 346).

In Fig. 262(a), the distance between the centers of the conductors is D cm, and the radius of each is r cm. Let the charge on conductor A be $+q$

esu per cm and that on conductor B be $-q$ esu per cm. The potential difference between the two conductors is determined by the work performed in carrying a unit positive charge from the surface of conductor A to the surface of conductor B. Using Eq. (276), the force at x cm from the center of conductor A due to the charge on conductor A is $2q/x$ dynes, and the force due to the charge on conductor B is $2q/(D - x)$ dynes. The work performed, and hence the potential difference, is

$$W = V = \frac{2q}{\epsilon_r \epsilon_v} \int_r^{D-r} \frac{dx}{x} + \frac{2q}{\epsilon_r \epsilon_v} \int_r^{D-r} \frac{dx}{D - x} \tag{I}$$

Since $\epsilon_r = 1$ (air), and $\epsilon_v = 1$,

$$\begin{aligned} V &= 2q[\log_\epsilon x|_r^{D-r} - \log_\epsilon (D - x)|_r^{D-r}] \\ &= 2q\{\log_\epsilon (D - r) - \log_\epsilon r - \log_\epsilon [D - (D - r)] + \log_\epsilon (D - r)\} \\ &= 4q \log_\epsilon \frac{D - r}{r} \quad \text{statvolts.} \end{aligned} \tag{II}$$

$$C = \frac{q}{V} = \frac{1}{4 \log_\epsilon \dfrac{D - r}{r}} \quad \text{statfarads per cm.}$$

$$C = \frac{0.0194}{\log_{10} \dfrac{D - r}{r}} \quad \mu\text{f per mile.} \tag{283}$$

With transmission lines, the capacitance to *neutral* is more frequently used than the capacitance between conductors. In Fig. 262(*b*) a plane xy perpendicular to the plane of the conductors and midway between them cuts all the dielectric lines at right angles. Hence, it is an equipotential surface and, if conducting, would not affect the dielectric field. The capacitance C_n between each conductor and the plane is thus twice the capacitance between conductors. Hence,

$$C_n = \frac{0.0388}{\log_{10} \dfrac{D - r}{r}} \quad \mu\text{f per mile.} \tag{284}$$

With overhead lines r is usually negligible compared with D, and the omission of r in the numerator of the logarithmic function causes scarcely any change in the capacitance. Hence,

$$C_n = \frac{0.0388}{\log_{10} (D/r)} \quad \mu\text{f per mile.} \tag{285}$$

UNRATIONALIZED MKS SYSTEM

In any single system of electrical units the following relations must exist: $\mu_v \epsilon_v = 1/c^2$, where μ_v and ϵ_v are the permeability and capacitivity of free, or evacuated, space, and c is the velocity of light, equal to $3 \cdot 10^8$ m per sec.[1] It is true that in the cgs electromagnetic system $\mu_v = 1$ and in the cgs electrostatic system $\epsilon_v = 1$, but these are two different systems. In either system alone, $\mu_v\epsilon_v = 1/c^2$.* Thus in the mks unrationalized system $\mu_v = 10^{-7}$ so that $\epsilon_v = 10^7/(2.9977 \cdot 10^8)^2 = 1.11279 \cdot 10^{-10}$. The coulomb is equal to $3 \cdot 10^9$ statcoulombs in magnitude.

250. Coulomb's Law. Coulomb's law [Eq. (253), p. 325] thus becomes

$$\mathbf{F} = \frac{q_1 q_2}{\epsilon_v r^2} \quad \text{newtons}\dagger \tag{286}$$

where q_1 and q_2 are in *coulombs*, $\epsilon_v = 1.113 \cdot 10^{-10}$, and r is in meters.

Example. Two positive point charges, one equal to $5 \cdot 10^{-6}$ coulomb and the other equal to $6 \cdot 10^{-6}$ coulomb, are 20 cm apart in air (see Fig. 244, p. 325). Determine force in newtons acting between these charges.

$$\mathbf{F} = \frac{(5 \cdot 10^{-6})(6 \cdot 10^{-6})}{1.113 \cdot 10^{-10} \cdot (0.20)^2} = 6.739 \text{ newtons.} \quad \textit{Ans.}$$

The magnitude of a coulomb is $3 \cdot 10^9$ times that of a statcoulomb. Hence, if the foregoing example is solved in the cgs system,

$$\mathbf{F} = \frac{[(5 \cdot 10^{-6})(3 \cdot 10^9)][(6 \cdot 10^{-6})(3 \cdot 10^9)]}{20^2} = 673{,}500 \text{ dynes,}$$

$$= 6.735 \text{ newtons, } (\textit{check}).$$

If the dielectric has a relative capacitivity of ϵ_r, Eq. (286) becomes

$$\mathbf{F} = \frac{q_1 q_2}{\epsilon_r \epsilon_v r^2} \quad \text{newtons.} \tag{287}$$

[See Eq. (256), p. 334.]

251. Field Intensity and Flux Density. If, in (287), $q_1 = q$ and q_2 is made equal to unity as is done in the cgs system (p. 329), the force *per unit charge* is obtained. As in the cgs system this is defined as the *field intensity* **E** and is given in *newtons per coulomb*, or in *volts per meter*. Thus,

$$\mathbf{E} = \frac{q}{\epsilon_r \epsilon_v r^2} \quad \text{volts per m.} \tag{288}$$

[1] Originally, $3 \cdot 10^8$ m per sec was believed to be the velocity of light, but more precise measurements give the value as more nearly equal to $2.9977 \cdot 10^8$ m per sec. This difference accounts for slight differences in answers obtained by the mks and cgs systems. Actually, the magnitude of a coulomb is $2.9977 \cdot 10^9$ times that of a statcoulomb. Since the *square* of the velocity of light is involved, the error is of the magnitude of 0.2 per cent. Also see Appendix B, p. 581.

* These relations are given in the footnote, Appendix B.

† See footnote, p. 221.

It follows from (288) that the voltage

$$V = \mathbf{E}d \qquad \text{volts,} \tag{289}$$

where d is distance in meters and $\mathbf{E}$ is a vector and is assumed to have the same direction as d.

In the cgs system, flux density and field intensity are equal numerically in evacuated space since $\epsilon_v = 1$. However, in the unrationalized mks system $\epsilon_v = 1.11279 \cdot 10^{-10}$, and, from page 340, the relation of field intensity to flux density,

$$\mathbf{E} = \frac{D}{\epsilon_r \epsilon_v}. \tag{290}$$

Substituting $\mathbf{E}$ of (290) in (288),

$$\frac{D}{\epsilon_r \epsilon_v} = \frac{q}{\epsilon_r \epsilon_v r^2},$$

or

$$D = \frac{q}{r^2} \qquad \text{electric lines per sq m.} \tag{291}$$

If q is a point charge at the center of a sphere of radius r m, Fig. 246 (p. 328), the total flux crossing the surface of the sphere

$$\psi = 4\pi r^2 D \qquad \text{electric lines.} \tag{292}$$

Substituting D of (292) in (291),

$$\frac{\psi}{4\pi r^2} = \frac{q}{r^2},$$

or

$$\psi = 4\pi q \qquad \text{electric lines,} \tag{293}$$

which is the same relation as in the cgs system (p. 330). Hence, the electric flux is proportional to q and is independent of the capacitivity of the medium. Also, 4π electric lines leave or enter each unit charge.

Example. If the charge on the sphere, Fig. 246 (p. 328), is 5.0 positive esu (see example, p. 330), determine: (*a*) total electric flux leaving sphere; (*b*) flux density at distance of 20 cm from center of sphere; (*c*) field intensity at distance in (*b*).

(*a*) $q = \dfrac{5.0}{3 \cdot 10^9} = 1.667 \cdot 10^{-9}$ coulomb.

$\psi = 4\pi \cdot 1.667 \cdot 10^{-9} = 2.095 \cdot 10^{-8}$ electric line. *Ans.*

(*b*) $D = \dfrac{2.095 \cdot 10^{-8}}{4\pi(0.2)^2} = 4.168 \cdot 10^{-8}$ electric line per sq m. *Ans.*

(*c*) Applying (288) using 1.113 for ϵ_v,

$$\mathbf{E} = \frac{1.667 \cdot 10^{-9}}{1.113 \cdot 10^{-10}(0.2)^2} = 374.4 \text{ volts per m.} \quad \textit{Ans.}$$

Also D from (290), ϵ_r being unity,

$$D = 1.113 \cdot 10^{-10}\,(374.4) = 4.168 \cdot 10^{-8} \text{ electric line per sq m } (\textit{check}).$$

Example. In the example, p. 330, determine in mks unrationalized units the maximum field intensity at the surface of each sphere in volts per meter [see (*c*)].

Since 1 coulomb $= 3 \cdot 10^9$ esu, $q = 20/(3 \cdot 10^9) = 6.667 \cdot 10^{-9}$ coulomb.

At surface of sphere A, let $\mathbf{E}_1$ be field intensity due to charge on A and $\mathbf{E}_2$ be that due to charge on B. $\epsilon_r = 1$.

$$\mathbf{E}_1 = \frac{6.667 \cdot 10^{-9}}{1.113 \cdot 10^{-10}(1 \cdot 10^{-2})^2} = 6.00 \cdot 10^5 \text{ volts per m.}$$

$$\mathbf{E}_2 = \frac{6.667 \cdot 10^{-9}}{1.113 \cdot 10^{-10}(23 \cdot 10^{-2})^2} = 0.01111 \cdot 10^5, \text{ or } 1{,}111 \text{ volts per m.}$$

The total field intensity

$$\mathbf{E} = \mathbf{E}_1 + \mathbf{E}_2 = 6.0111 \cdot 10^5 \text{ volts per m.} \quad \textit{Ans.}$$

At surface of sphere B, let $\mathbf{E}_1'$ be field intensity due to charge on B and $\mathbf{E}_2'$ be that due to charge on A.

$$\mathbf{E}_1' = \frac{6.667 \cdot 10^{-9}}{1.113 \cdot 10^{-10}(0.5 \cdot 10^{-2})^2} = 24.00 \cdot 10^5 \text{ volts per m.}$$

$$\mathbf{E}_2' = \frac{6.667 \cdot 10^{-9}}{1.113 \cdot 10^{-10}(23.5 \cdot 10^{-2})^2} = 0.0109 \cdot 10^5, \text{ or } 1{,}090 \text{ volts per m.}$$

The total field intensity,

$$\mathbf{E}' = \mathbf{E}_1' + \mathbf{E}_2' = 24.0109 \cdot 10^5 \text{ volts per m.} \quad \textit{Ans.}$$

Since 1 statvolt = 300 volts,* statvolts per centimeter $= 300 \cdot 100 = 3 \cdot 10^4$ volts per m. Hence, in the example, p. 330,

$\mathbf{E}_A = 20.038$ statvolts per cm $= 300 \cdot 10^2 \cdot 20.038 = 6.0114 \cdot 10^5$ volts per m (*check*).

252. Calculation of Capacitances. Capacitances in the unrationalized mks system are calculated in the same manner as in the cgs system, although the magnitudes of the units are different.

Parallel-electrode Capacitor. Let the area of each electrode, Fig. 257, be A sq m, the distance between the electrodes d m, and the capacitivity of the dielectric ϵ_r. Let $+q$ and $-q$ coulombs be the charges on the two electrodes. Since 4π dielectric lines leave each unit positive charge, the total flux between the electrodes is $4\pi q$ and the flux density,

$$D = \frac{4\pi q}{A} \qquad \text{dielectric lines per sq m.}$$

From (290),

$$\mathbf{E} = \frac{D}{\epsilon_r \epsilon_v} = \frac{4\pi q}{\epsilon_r \epsilon_v A}.$$

From (289),

$$V = \mathbf{E}d = \frac{4\pi q d}{\epsilon_r \epsilon_v A} \qquad \text{volts.}$$

$$C = \frac{q}{V} = \frac{\epsilon_r \epsilon_v A}{4\pi d} = \frac{\epsilon_r (1.113 \cdot 10^{-10}) A}{4\pi d} = \epsilon_r \frac{8.854 \cdot 10^{-12} A}{d} \qquad \text{farads.} \qquad (294)$$

* New value = 299.77. See footnote, p. 350.

Example. A parallel capacitor consists of three plates, two outer ones of the same polarity and one between of the opposite polarity, Fig. 258(*b*) (p. 345). The electrodes are square and have areas of 0.25 sq m. The distance between the plates is 0.3 cm, and the capacitivity of the dielectric is 4. Determine the capacitance of the capacitor.

From (294)

$$C = 2\,\frac{4(1.113 \cdot 10^{-10})0.25}{4\pi 0.003} = 5.903 \cdot 10^{-9} \text{ farad.} \quad \textit{Ans.}$$

Field Intensity Due to Straight Charged Filament. Aside from the units and capacitivities, the equation for the force on a unit charge, or the field intensity, will be identical with Eq. (I) (p. 346). To adapt Eq. (I) to mks units, Eq. (288) (p. 350) is used, field intensity **E** being equal to force **F** on a unit charge.

$$\mathbf{F}_0 = \frac{2qh}{\epsilon_r\epsilon_v}\int_0^\infty \frac{dx}{(r^2+h^2)^{3/2}} = \frac{2q}{\epsilon_r\epsilon_v h} \quad \text{newtons per coulomb,} \qquad (295)$$

where q is in coulombs and x, r, and h are in meters. For air, $\epsilon_r = 1$.

Capacitance of Coaxial Cylindrical Capacitor. The capacitance of a coaxial cylindrical capacitor is found by employing (295) as in Eq. (I) (p. 347), changing the quantities in Eq. (I) to mks units.

$$W = V = \int_{R_1}^{R_2} \frac{2q}{\epsilon_r\epsilon_v r}\,dr = \frac{2q}{\epsilon_r\epsilon_v}\log_\epsilon\frac{R_2}{R_1} \quad \text{volts.}$$

$$C = \frac{q}{V} = \frac{\epsilon_r\epsilon_v}{2\log_\epsilon\frac{R_2}{R_1}} = \frac{\epsilon_r\epsilon_v}{2\cdot 2.303\log_{10}\frac{R_2}{R_1}} = \frac{\epsilon_r\cdot 1.113\cdot 10^{-10}}{4.606\log_{10}\frac{R_2}{R_1}}$$

$$= \frac{2.416\cdot 10^{-11}\epsilon_r}{\log_{10}\frac{R_2}{R_1}} \quad \text{farads per m.} \qquad (296)$$

Example. Determine the capacitance in the example, p. 347, using the value 4.80 for the relative capacitivity ϵ_r.

$$R_1 = 0.1022 \cdot 0.0254 = 0.002596 \text{ m.}$$
$$R_2 = 0.2585 \cdot 0.0254 = 0.006566 \text{ m.}$$

From (296), the capacitance per meter,

$$C_m = \frac{4.80(1.113\cdot 10^{-10})}{4.606\log_{10}(0.006566/0.002596)}$$
$$= \frac{5.342\cdot 10^{-10}}{4.606\cdot 0.4029} = 2.878\cdot 10^{-10} \text{ farad.}$$

Capacitance for 1,200 ft,

$$C = \frac{2.878\cdot 10^{-10}}{3.281}1{,}200 = 1.053\cdot 10^{-7} \text{ farad}$$
$$= 0.1053\ \mu\text{f.*} \quad \textit{Ans. (check)}$$

(1 m. = 3.281 ft.)

* See footnote, p. 350.

Capacitance of Concentric Spherical Capacitors. Equation (281) (p. 348) becomes

$$C = \epsilon_r \epsilon_v \frac{R_1 R_2}{R_2 - R_1} \quad \text{farads.} \tag{297}$$

Capacitance of Parallel-cylinder Capacitor. In Sec. 249 (p. 349), the work in joules, or the voltage in volts, in (I) becomes

$$W = V = \frac{2q}{\epsilon_r \epsilon_v}\left[\int_r^{D-r} \frac{dx}{x} + \int_r^{D-r} \frac{dx}{D - x}\right]$$

$$= \frac{4q}{\epsilon_r \epsilon_v} \log_\epsilon \frac{D - r}{r} \quad \text{volts,}$$

$$C = \frac{q}{V} = \frac{\epsilon_r \epsilon_v}{4 \log_\epsilon \dfrac{D - r}{r}} = \frac{\epsilon_r \cdot 1.113 \cdot 10^{-10}}{4 \cdot 2.303 \log_{10} \dfrac{D - r}{r}}$$

$$= \epsilon_r \frac{1.208 \cdot 10^{-11}}{\log_{10} \dfrac{D - r}{r}} \quad \text{farads per m,} \tag{298}$$

where q is in coulombs and D and r are in meters.

Equations (283), (284), (285) (p. 349) obviously remain unchanged, (298) being comparable with (283).

RATIONALIZED MKS SYSTEM

253. Coulomb's Law. In the mks magnetic system of units, the rationalized system was developed so that the mmf is given in ampere-turns NI rather than $4\pi NI$, and under these conditions the permeability of evacuated space becomes $4\pi \cdot 10^{-7}$. It is stated (p. 349) that in any unified system of electrical units the permeability and capacitivity of evacuated space have the relation $\mu_v \epsilon_v = 1/c^2$, where c, the velocity of light, is $2.9977 \cdot 10^8$ m per sec. Hence, in the rationalized mks electrostatic system, the capacitivity of evacuated space must be

$$\epsilon_v' = \frac{1}{4\pi \cdot 10^{-7} \cdot (2.9977 \cdot 10^8)^2} = 8.854 \cdot 10^{-12}.$$

In determining magnetic-field intensity in the rationalized mks system, it is necessary to multiply μ_v' by 4π (p. 222). Likewise, in order to determine electrostatic-field intensity, it is necessary to multiply ϵ_v' by 4π. The force between two charges then becomes

$$\mathbf{F} = \frac{q_1 q_2}{\epsilon_r (4\pi \epsilon_v') r^2} \quad \text{newtons.} \tag{299}$$

q_1, q_2 are given in coulombs and r in meters.

If $q_1 = q$ and $q_2 =$ unity, the force on a unit charge becomes

$$\mathbf{F} = \frac{q}{4\pi\epsilon_r\epsilon_v' r^2} \, (= \mathbf{E}) \qquad \text{newtons per coulomb, or volts per m.} \qquad (300)$$

In the rationalized mks system, one magnetic line leaves or enters each unit pole. Likewise one electric line leaves or enters each unit charge. Hence, the flux density at a distance r m from a point charge q coulombs,

$$D = \frac{q}{4\pi r^2} \qquad \text{coulombs per sq m.} \qquad (301)$$

By eliminating q from (300) and (301)

$$D = \epsilon_r\epsilon_v'\mathbf{E} \qquad \text{coulombs per sq m,} \qquad (302)$$

which is similar but not equal to Eq. (290) (p. 351).

Example. Using the rationalized mks system, the solution of the example, p. 351, is

(*a*) $\psi = q = 1.667 \cdot 10^{-9}$ coulomb. *Ans.*

(*b*) $D = \dfrac{1.667 \cdot 10^{-9}}{4\pi(0.2)^2} = 3.315 \cdot 10^{-9}$ electric line per sq m. *Ans.*

(*c*) Using (300),

$$\mathbf{E} = \frac{1.667 \cdot 10^{-9}}{4\pi(8.854 \cdot 10^{-12})(0.2)^2} = 374.5 \text{ volts per m.} \quad \textit{Ans.}$$

Since $8.854 \cdot 10^{-12} = (1.113 \cdot 10^{-10})/4\pi$,

$$\mathbf{E} = \frac{1.667 \cdot 10^{-9}}{4\pi \left(\dfrac{1.113 \cdot 10^{-10}}{4\pi}\right)(0.2)^2} = 374.4 \text{ volts per m,}$$

which is the same as (*c*) (p. 351).

In (*b*), using (302),

$$D = 1 \cdot 8.854 \cdot 10^{-12} \cdot 374.5 = 3.315 \cdot 10^{-9} \text{ electric line per sq m } (\textit{check}).$$

254. Calculation of Capacitances. *Parallel-electrode Capacitor.* Let the area of each electrode, Fig. 257 (p. 344), be A sq m, the distance between the electrodes d m, and the capacitivity of the dielectric ϵ_r. Let $+q$ and $-q$ coulombs be the charges on the two electrodes. Since one line leaves each unit positive charge,

$$D = \frac{q}{A}. \qquad (\text{I})$$

From (302) and (I),

$$\mathbf{E} = \frac{D}{\epsilon_r\epsilon_v'} = \frac{q}{A(\epsilon_r\epsilon_v')} \qquad \text{volts per m.}$$

From Eq. (289) (p. 351),

$$V = \mathbf{E}d = \frac{qd}{A(\epsilon_r\epsilon_v')} \qquad \text{volts.}$$

$$C = \frac{q}{V} = \frac{\epsilon_r\epsilon_v' A}{d} = \frac{\epsilon_r(8.854 \cdot 10^{-12})A}{d} \qquad \text{farads.} \qquad (303)$$

Since $\epsilon_v' = \epsilon_v/4\pi$, (303) is identical with Eq. (294) (p. 352).

Field Intensity Due to Straight Charged Filament. In mks rationalized units, Eq. (295) (p. 353) will become

$$\mathbf{F}_0 = \frac{2qh}{4\pi\epsilon_r\epsilon_v'} \int_0^\infty \frac{dx}{(x^2 + h^2)^{3/2}} = \frac{2q}{4\pi\epsilon_r\epsilon_v' h} \qquad \text{newtons per coulomb.} \qquad (304)$$

Since $\epsilon_v' = \epsilon_v/4\pi$, (304) is equal to Eq. (295).

Capacitance of Coaxial-cylindrical Capacitor. Using (304), the work done in carrying a coulomb from the surface of the inner cylinder to the inside surface of the outer cylinder [see Eq. (I), p. 347],

$$W = V = \frac{2q}{4\pi\epsilon_r\epsilon_v'} \int_{R_1}^{R_2} \frac{dr}{r} = \frac{2q}{4\pi\epsilon_r\epsilon_v'} \log_\epsilon \frac{R_2}{R_1} \qquad \text{volts.}$$

$$C = \frac{q}{V} = \frac{4\pi\epsilon_r\epsilon_v'}{2 \log_\epsilon \dfrac{R_2}{R_1}} = \frac{4\pi\epsilon_r \cdot 8.854 \cdot 10^{-12}}{4.606 \log_{10} \dfrac{R_2}{R_1}}$$

$$= \frac{2.416 \cdot 10^{-11}\epsilon_r}{\log_{10} \dfrac{R_2}{R_1}} \qquad \text{farads per m.} \qquad (305)$$

which is identical with Eq. (296) (p. 353).

Capacitance of Concentric Spherical Capacitors. Equation (297) (p. 354) becomes

$$C = 4\pi\epsilon_r\epsilon_v' \frac{R_1 R_2}{R_2 - R_1} \qquad \text{farads.} \qquad (306)$$

Capacitance of Parallel Cylinders. In the rationalized system, Eq. (II) (p. 349) becomes

$$W = V = \frac{4q}{\epsilon_r(4\pi\epsilon_v')} \log_\epsilon \frac{D - r}{r} \qquad \text{volts.}$$

$$C = \frac{q}{V} = \frac{\pi\epsilon_r\epsilon_v'}{\log_\epsilon \dfrac{D - r}{r}} = \frac{\pi\epsilon_r \cdot 8.854 \cdot 10^{-12}}{2.303 \log_{10} \dfrac{D - r}{r}} = \epsilon_r \frac{1.208 \cdot 10^{-11}}{\log_{10} \dfrac{D - r}{r}}$$

$$\text{farads per m,} \qquad (307)$$

which is identical with Eq. (298) (p. 354).

255. Current to Resistance and Capacitance in Series. If a capacitor of C farads capacitance and a resistor of R ohms resistance in series be connected suddenly across a voltage E, Fig. 263, there will be current through the resistor which will charge the capacitor. Theoretically, the voltage across the capacitor will reach the applied voltage E only after infinite time. Actually, however, the time is relatively short. The current to the capacitor and resistor in series may be determined as a function of time.

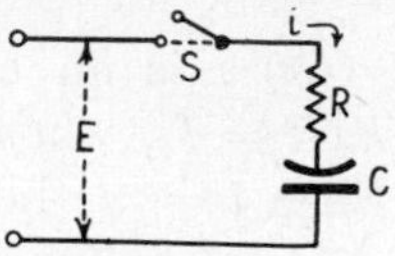

FIG. 263. Capacitor charged through resistor.

The voltage across the capacitor at any instant is q/C volts. After the switch S is closed, Fig. 263, the voltage E not only must supply the resistance drop but also must overcome the counter emf q/C of the capacitor. That is,

$$E = iR + \frac{q}{C} \quad \text{volts.} \tag{I}$$

The quantity $q = \int i\,dt$. Substituting in (I),

$$E = iR + \frac{1}{C}\int i\,dt. \tag{II}$$

Differentiating with respect to t,

$$0 = R\frac{di}{dt} + \frac{i}{C}. \tag{III}$$

Rearranging terms, and integrating,

$$\frac{di}{i} = -\frac{dt}{CR}. \tag{IV}$$

$$\log_\epsilon i = -\frac{t}{CR} + K \tag{V}$$

where K is a constant of integration.

When the time t is zero, the quantity q in the capacitor must be zero, since finite energy cannot be stored in zero time. Hence, when $t = 0$, $q = 0$ and the voltage q/C across the capacitor is zero. Therefore, the line voltage E is equal to I_0R where I_0 is the initial current. Hence at $t = 0$, $i = I_0 = E/R$. Substituting in (V),

$$K = \log_\epsilon \frac{E}{R},$$

$$\log_\epsilon i - \log_\epsilon \frac{E}{R} = \log_\epsilon \frac{i}{E/R} = -\frac{t}{CR}. \tag{VI}$$

Expressing in exponential form,

$$\frac{i}{E/R} = \epsilon^{-\frac{t}{CR}} \tag{VII}$$

and

$$i = \frac{E}{R} \epsilon^{-\frac{t}{CR}} = I_0 \epsilon^{-\frac{t}{CR}} \quad \text{amp.} \tag{308}$$

(308) is an exponential decaying function having an initial value $E/R = I_0$, when $t = 0$. Theoretically, the current becomes zero only when $t = \infty$, but practically it reaches this value in a relatively short time. The function is plotted in Fig. 264 for $E = 200$ volts, $R = 2{,}000$ ohms, $C = 0.00004$ farad $= 40$ μf (see example).

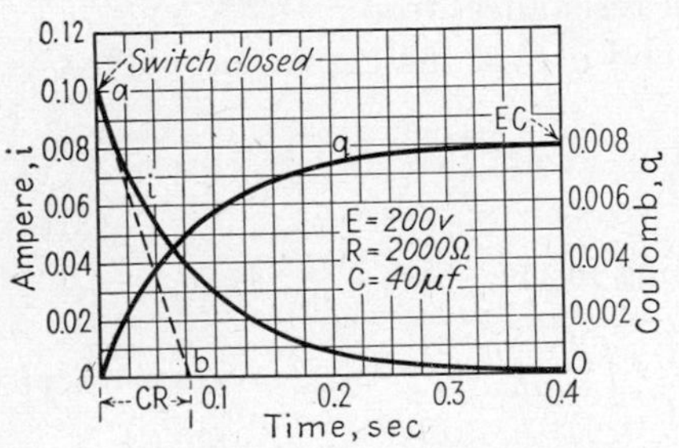

FIG. 264. Charge characteristics of capacitance and resistance in series.

The time constant of the circuit is

$$\tau = CR \quad \text{sec.} \tag{309}$$

Substituting τ for t in (308),

$$i = \frac{E}{R} \epsilon^{-\frac{CR}{CR}} = \frac{E}{R} \frac{1}{2.718} = 0.368 \frac{E}{R} \quad \text{amp.} \tag{310}$$

That is, at time $t = CR = \tau$, the current has dropped to 36.8 per cent its initial value.

After closing the switch, the rate of change of the current from (308) is

$$\frac{di}{dt} = \frac{E}{R}\left(-\frac{1}{CR}\right)\epsilon^{-\frac{t}{CR}} = -\frac{E}{CR^2}\epsilon^{-\frac{t}{CR}} \quad \text{amp per sec.} \tag{311}$$

When $t = 0$, $di/dt = -E/CR^2$. If the current continued to decrease at this rate, it would reach zero in a time equal to the time constant CR. For example, if the uniform rate of change of current $-E/CR^2$ is multiplied by the time CR, the total change of current during this time is $(-E/CR^2)CR = -E/R$. This is equal numerically to the initial current, so that the resulting current is zero (see line *ab*, Fig. 264).

The charge of the capacitor is readily determined by integrating (308). That is,

$$q = \int i\,dt = \frac{E}{R}\int \epsilon^{-\frac{t}{CR}}\,dt = \frac{E}{R}\left(-CR\epsilon^{-\frac{t}{CR}} + K'\right) \tag{I}$$

where K' is a constant of integration. When $t = 0$, $q = 0$ and $K' = (E/R)CR = EC$.

Substituting in (I),

$$q = EC(1 - \epsilon^{-\frac{t}{CR}}). \tag{312}$$

(312) is similar in form to Eq. (225) (p. 307), giving the rise of current in an inductive circuit. It is plotted in Fig. 264.

Since in an uncharged capacitor the counter emf is zero, the current must be infinite at the instant of connection across a constant voltage without series resistance. The duration of the current under this condition is zero. However, the inevitable resistance in the circuit and capacitor prevent the current becoming infinite, though it does reach high values. It is also clear that with any current which is not infinite at the instant of switching, the voltage across any uncharged capacitor is zero.

Example. A capacitor of 40 μf capacitance in series with 2,000 ohms is suddenly connected across a 200-volt source. Determine: (*a*) initial current; (*b*) equation of current as function of time; (*c*) equation of charge as function of time; (*d*) time constant; (*e*) value of current when time is equal to time constant; (*f*) charge on capacitor when time is 0.04 sec; (*g*) energy stored in capacitor in (*f*). (*h*) Plot functions (*b*) and (*c*).

(*a*) Since, at the instant of switching, the voltage across the capacitor is zero, the impressed voltage is utilized entirely in resistance drop. Hence,

$$I_0 = \frac{200}{2{,}000} = 0.10 \text{ amp.} \quad \textit{Ans.}$$

(*b*) Substituting in (308),

$$i = 0.1\epsilon^{-\frac{t}{40 \cdot 10^{-6} \cdot 2{,}000}} = 0.1\epsilon^{-\frac{t}{0.08}} \quad \text{amp.} \quad \textit{Ans.}$$

(*c*) Substituting in (312),

$$q = 200 \cdot 40 \cdot 10^{-6}(1 - \epsilon^{-\frac{t}{0.08}})$$
$$= 0.008(1 - \epsilon^{-\frac{t}{0.08}}) \quad \text{coulombs.} \quad \textit{Ans.}$$

(*d*) $\tau = CR = 40 \cdot 10^{-6} \cdot 2{,}000 = 0.08$ sec. *Ans.*
(*e*) $i = 0.1\epsilon^{-1} = 0.0368$ amp. *Ans.*
(*f*) From (*c*),

$$q = 0.008(1 - \epsilon^{-\frac{0.04}{0.08}}) = 0.008(1 - \epsilon^{-\frac{1}{2}})$$
$$= 0.008\left(1 - \frac{1}{\sqrt{2.718}}\right) = 0.00315 \text{ coulomb.} \quad \textit{Ans.}$$

(*g*) From Eq. (270) (p. 342),

$$w = \frac{1}{2}\frac{Q^2}{C} = \frac{1}{2}\frac{(0.00315)^2}{(40 \cdot 10^{-6})} = \frac{9.92 \cdot 10^{-6}}{80 \cdot 10^{-6}}$$
$$= 0.124 \text{ joule.} \quad \textit{Ans.}$$

(*h*) See Fig. 264.

256. Discharge of Capacitor. In Fig. 265 a capacitor of C farads capacitance has been charged through a resistor of R ohms by closing the switch S upward. The switch S is then thrown downward, disconnecting the line and short-circuiting the resistor and capacitor in series. The voltage across the capacitor at the instant of closing the switch downward is E_0 volts. E_0 may differ from E, owing, for example, to leakage or to the fact that the switch S is closed downward before the capacitor has become completely charged. The capacitor now becomes a diminishing source of emf q/C and is supplying current to the resistor. The direction of the current is the reverse of that on charge. By Ohm's law,

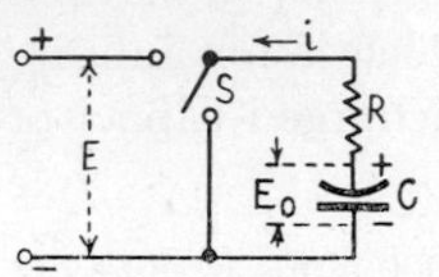

FIG. 265. Capacitor discharged through resistor.

$$-iR = \frac{q}{C} \quad \text{volts.} \tag{I}$$

Since $q = \int i\,dt$,

$$-iR = \frac{1}{C}\int i\,dt \quad \text{volts.} \tag{II}$$

Differentiating and rearranging,

$$-R\frac{di}{dt} = \frac{i}{C}; \quad \frac{di}{i} = -\frac{dt}{CR}. \tag{III}$$

Integrating,

$$\log_\epsilon i = -\frac{t}{CR} + K_0 \tag{IV}$$

where K_0 is a constant of integration.

When $t = 0$, $i = -I_0 = -E_0/R$, so that $K_0 = \log_\epsilon (-I_0)$. Hence,

$$\log_\epsilon \frac{i}{-I_0} = -\frac{t}{CR}. \tag{V}$$

Expressing in exponential form, and solving for i,

$$i = -I_0\epsilon^{-\frac{t}{CR}} = -\frac{E_0}{R}\epsilon^{-\frac{t}{CR}} \quad \text{amp.} \tag{313}$$

(313) is identical in form with (308) except that the current is negative. When $E_0 = E$, (313) becomes the negative of (308). The discharge characteristic for the capacitor and resistor of the example, Sec. 255, is shown in Fig. 266.

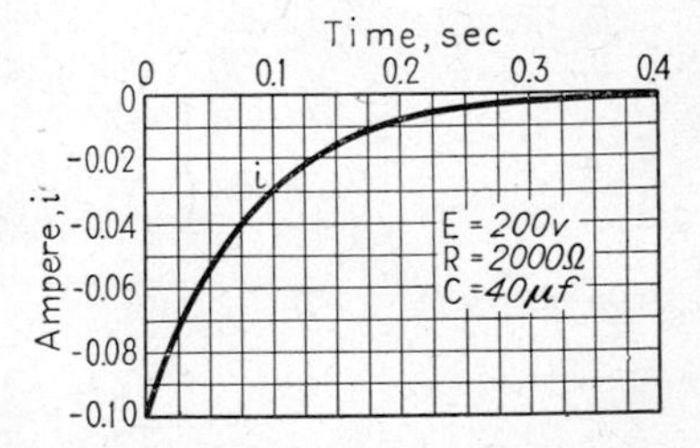

FIG. 266. Discharge characteristic of capacitor and resistor in series.

257. Ionization of Air; Corona. When solid dielectrics are subjected to sufficiently high dielectric stress, they rupture and the dynamic arc which follows chars and disintegrates the dielectric (Sec. 238, p. 332). Although the exact mechanism of the rupture is not understood, undoubtedly there first occurs a destruction of the molecular structure of the medium in some one spot, due to a separation of the electrons from their atomic nuclei, as a result of the high potential gradient.

With gaseous dielectrics such as air, the mechanism of dielectric rupture is much better understood. This is due in part to the fact that the molecular structure of gases is much simpler than that of most other substances. Also, the gas particles are not destroyed by the rupture, and since they are mobile, they can be collected and analyzed even after they have been subjected to rupturing stresses. A gas atom consists of a positive nucleus with one or more minute electric charges or electrons moving in orbits about the nucleus. A hydrogen atom has but one electron; a helium atom has two electrons.

In a dielectric field the electrons of a gas, being negative charges, are attracted to the positive electrode; the positive nuclei, or ions, are attracted to the negative electrode. Hence, the dielectric field tends to separate the electrons from their nuclei. The dielectric forces holding the electrons to their nuclei are so great, however, that a prohibitively high voltage gradient would be necessary to separate them by this effect alone.

There are always some free ions and electrons in any gaseous medium. Under the action of the electric field the ions and, more particularly, the electrons will accelerate. While moving toward the electrodes they will collide with the neutral atoms that happen to be in their paths. These collisions knock other electrons from their nuclei, thus producing more free ions and free electrons. Hence, the process tends to be a cumulative one. When the potential gradient becomes sufficiently great (approximately 30,000 volts per cm[1] for air at 760 mm pressure and at 25°C), the velocities acquired by the ions become sufficiently high to produce ions by collision more rapidly than the ions are withdrawn from the field. The gas is then said to be *ionized*. Ionized gas conducts current but has, notwithstanding, a *very high* resistance. This conduction of current through an ionized gas is a convection phenomenon not unlike the conduction of electricity through an electrolyte (Sec. 109, p. 133). Thus the dielectric strength of the ionized gas has become practically nil. If a source of potential having considerable power behind it is used, rupture of the gas occurs and a dynamic arc follows.

A partial ionization of a gas without complete rupture may be accomplished, if an arrangement somewhat like that shown in Fig. 267 is employed. One electrode, the upper in Fig. 267, is sharp and may be conveniently a needle, the lower one being a flat plate. With the application of voltage, dielectric lines arise between the needle point and the plate. Owing to the sharpness of the needle point, with the corresponding very small radius of curvature, the flux density near it is very high. The density near the plate is much less because of its larger area. Hence, the air in the vicinity of the needle point first becomes ionized, the ionized

[1] This corresponds to 100 cgs electrostatic lines per square centimeter.

region extending at first to line *aa*. Beyond *aa*, the dielectric field is not sufficiently intense to permit further ionization, and the remainder of the air therefore prevents dynamic current. With further increase in potential, the ionized zone may extend to *bb* without complete rupture. Ultimately, however, the potential may reach a value which is sufficient to rupture the non-ionized region, and a dynamic arc follows.

Ionized air at the surfaces of conductors appears as small tufts and streamers, easily visible in the dark. Such ionized air is called *corona* because of its resemblance to solar corona. On the positive conductor the corona is a continuous glow of bluish color. On the negative conductor it consists of reddish tufts or beads. With alternating current corona consists of a more or less continuous glow, reddish blue in color. Corona is also accompanied by a hissing sound, and the odor of ozone is noticed. In the presence of moisture nitrous acid is formed, and this is the basis of one of the methods of producing, by electrical means, nitrates from the nitrogen of the atmosphere. Corona forms on high-voltage apparatus and on transmission lines (see Vol. II, Chap. XIII).

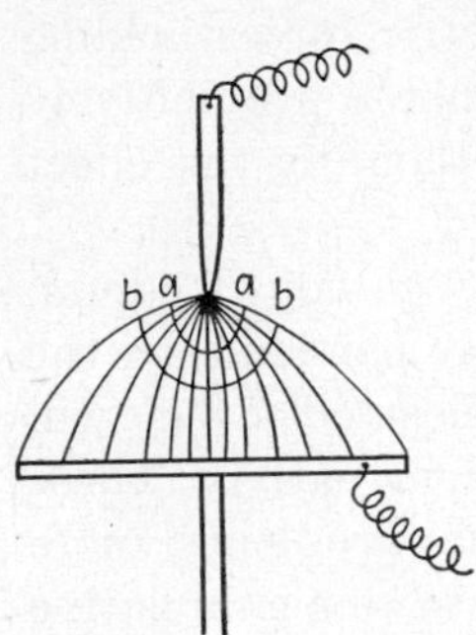

FIG. 267. Dielectric stress lines between a needle point and plate.

MEASUREMENT OF CAPACITANCE

258. Ballistic Method. There are two common methods of measuring capacitance, the d-c, or ballistic, method and the a-c, or bridge, method.

The d-c method employs a galvanometer which is used ballistically. It can be shown that if the moving coil of the ordinary galvanometer has considerable inertia and is properly damped, its maximum throw, due to the impulse produced by the sudden passage of a quantity of electricity through it, is proportional to the quantity.

This assumes that the entire charge passes through the coil before the coil begins to move (see Sec. 207, p. 284). Let D be the maximum galvanometer throw in centimeters. Then,

$$Q = KD \tag{314}$$

where Q is the quantity and K is the galvanometer constant.

To make the measurement, the apparatus is connected as shown in Fig. 268. A battery B supplies the current for the apparatus. The measurement may be made on either charge or discharge of the capacitor, or check measurements may be made using both charge and discharge. If the capacitor is at all leaky, the discharge method is preferable.

When the switch S is closed to the left, the capacitor C_1 is charged through the galvanometer and the maximum throw of the galvanometer is read. Several check readings should be taken. The galvanometer should return immediately to zero. If it shows a steady deflection, a leaky capacitor is indicated. In a corresponding manner the ballistic throw of the galvanometer may be read on discharge by closing switch S to the right after charging. Let D_1 be the deflection of the galvanometer when C_1 is connected, Q_1 the quantity going into the capacitor, and E the voltage across the capacitor. Then, by (314),

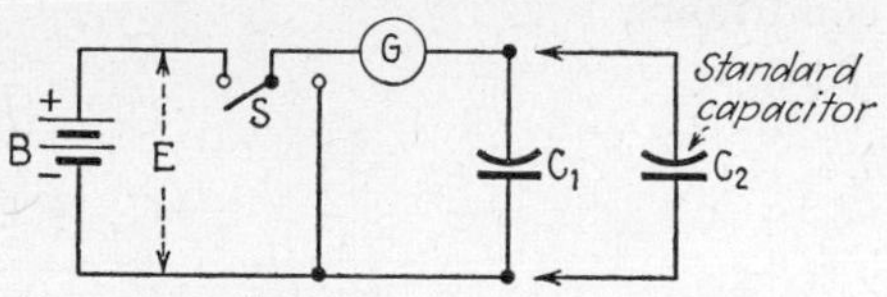

FIG. 268. Ballistic method of measuring capacitance.

$$Q_1 = KD_1,$$

and

$$Q_1 = C_1E,$$

where C_1 is the unknown capacitance. Therefore,

$$C_1E = KD_1. \qquad \text{(I)}$$

If now the standard capacitor C_2 be substituted for the unknown capacitor and another set of readings taken,

$$Q_2 = KD_2,$$
$$C_2E = KD_2. \qquad \text{(II)}$$

Dividing (I) by (II),

$$\frac{C_1E}{C_2E} = \frac{KD_1}{KD_2}.$$

$$C_1 = C_2\frac{D_1}{D_2}. \qquad (315)$$

$E(C_2/D_2)$ is the galvanometer constant.

It is often desirable to use an Ayrton shunt in such measurements, as it gives the apparatus greater range. When such a shunt is used, proper correction must be made for its multiplying power. Also, it is convenient to install either a single-pole or a double-pole double-throw switch so that C_2 may be substituted easily for C_1, and vice versa.

259. Bridge Method. In the bridge method, two capacitors form adjacent arms of a Wheatstone bridge, and two resistors form the other two arms, Fig. 269(a). An a-c supply is preferable. The secondary of an induction coil may be used as the source of power, or a battery with a key may be made to charge and discharge the system as in Fig. 269(b). A telephone is used as a detector except in (b). Let C_x be the unknown capacitance and C_2 a standard which may or may not be adjustable. R_1 and R_2 are two known resistors, one of which should be adjustable unless C_2 is so.

Either C_2 or one of the resistors is adjusted until there is no sound in the telephone, showing that the bridge is in balance. Under these conditions,

$$\frac{C_x}{C_2} = \frac{R_2}{R_1},$$

$$C_x = C_2 \frac{R_2}{R_1}. \tag{316}$$

When a battery is used, a double-contact key K is necessary, Fig. 269(b). K is pressed and released, and until the bridge is balanced, the

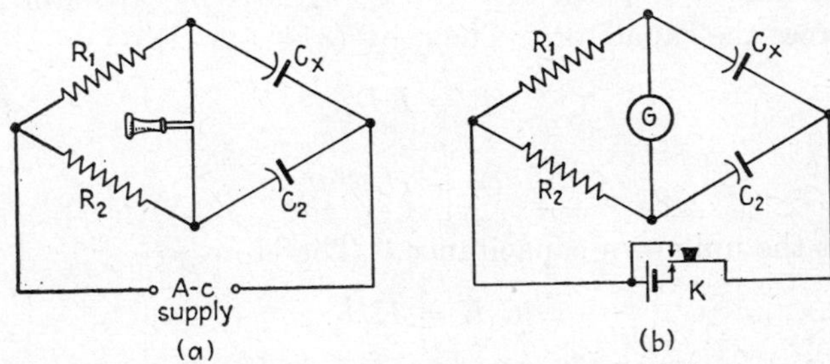

Fig. 269. Bridge methods of measuring capacitance.

galvanometer will deflect both upon charge of the system when the key is pressed, and upon discharge when the key is released. The bridge is balanced when the galvanometer does not deflect on either charge or discharge. (316) is then applicable.

In the above measurements, it is assumed that there is little if any leakage through the capacitors.

260. Location of a Total Disconnection in Cable. In Chap. V, it is shown that a grounded fault in a cable can be located by suitable resist-

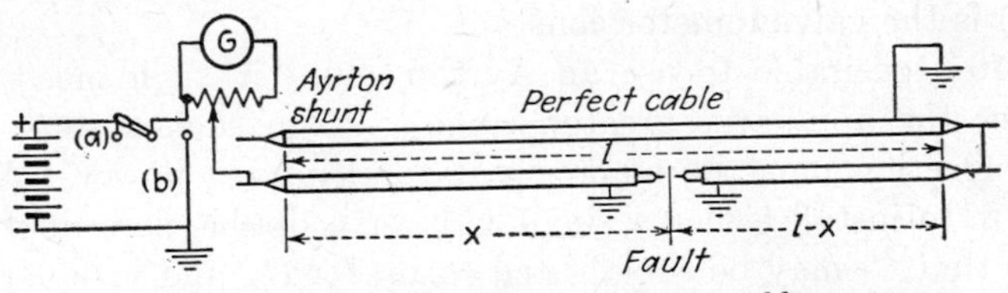

Fig. 270. Locating an open in cable.

ance measurements, such as the Murray and Varley loop tests. If a cable be totally disconnected, and its broken ends remain insulated, these loop tests are impossible. The distance to the fault may now be determined by capacitance measurements. The connections are shown in Fig. 270. The capacitance C_1 of the length x to the fault is first measured by the ballistic method. If a *similar* perfect cable, of length l, parallels the faulty cable, the two are looped at the far end and a measurement is made of the combined capacitance. This capacitance C_2 is the sum of the capacitance of the length l of the perfect cable and the capacitance of the length $l - x$ of the faulty cable. Hence C_2 is the capacitance of the length of cable $l + l - x = 2l - x$.

Let c be the capacitance per foot, assumed to be the same for each cable.

$$C_1 = xc = KD_1 \tag{I}$$

where K is the galvanometer constant and D_1 is the deflection corresponding to C_1.

Likewise,

$$C_2 = (2l - x)c = KD_2. \tag{II}$$

Dividing (I) by (II),

$$\frac{x}{2l - x} = \frac{D_1}{D_2},$$

$$x = l\frac{2D_1}{D_1 + D_2}. \tag{317}$$

The capacitance per unit length and the total capacitance do not enter into the final equation, so that it is not necessary to use a standard capacitor for the calibration of the galvanometer. The capacitances of the various lengths are proportional to the galvanometer deflections when corrected for the setting of the Ayrton shunt.

(I) and (II) may also be solved giving x as a function of C_1 and C_2.

$$x = l\frac{2C_1}{C_1 + C_2}. \tag{318}$$

The bridge method can be used to measure C_1 and C_2, and the distance to the fault may then be calculated.

CHAPTER XI

THE GENERATOR

Definition. An electric generator is a machine which transforms mechanical power into electric power.[1] This is accomplished by means of an armature carrying conductors on its surface which act in conjunction with a magnetic field. Electromotive force is induced by the relative motion of the armature conductors and the magnetic field, and when current is delivered to an external circuit, electric power is supplied by the armature.

In the d-c generator the field is usually stationary, and the armature rotates. In most types of a-c generator, the armature is stationary, and

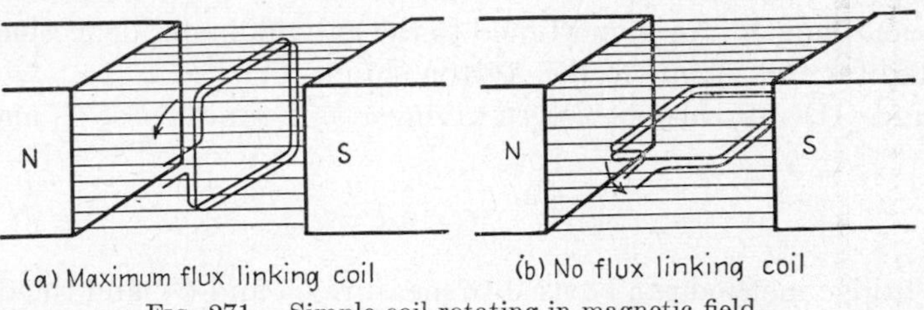

FIG. 271. Simple coil rotating in magnetic field.

the field rotates. Either the armature or the field may be driven by mechanical power applied to its shaft.

261. Generated Electromotive Force. It is shown in Chap. IX that if the flux linking a coil is varied, an emf $e(-N\, d\phi/dt)(10^{-8})$ volts is *induced* in the coil. The action of the generator is based on this principle. The flux linking the armature coils is varied by the relative motion of armature and field.

In Fig. 271 a coil rotates in a uniform magnetic field produced by an N pole and an S pole. In Fig. 271(a) the plane of the coil is perpendicular to the magnetic field, and the maximum possible flux links the coil. Let this flux be ϕ maxwells.

If the coil be rotated counterclockwise a quarter of a rotation, it will lie in the position shown in (b), and as the plane of the coil is parallel to the direction of the flux, no flux links the coil. Therefore, in a quarter

[1] ASA Definitions of Electrical Terms, 1941 edition, 10.10.050.

rotation the flux which links the coil has been decreased by ϕ lines. The average emf induced in the coil during this period is, therefore,

$$E_{av} = N\frac{\phi}{t}10^{-8} \qquad \text{volts} \quad \text{[Chap. IX, Eq. (207), p. 298]}$$

where N is the number of turns in the coil and t is the time required for a quarter rotation. But $t = 1/4s$, where $s = rps$. Therefore, the average induced emf during a quarter revolution is

$$E_{av} = 4Ns\phi10^{-8} \qquad \text{volts.} \tag{319}$$

If the flux is given in webers (Φ), the emf is

$$E_{av} = 4Ns\Phi \qquad \text{volts.} \tag{320}$$

In the windings of rotating machinery the armature coils overlap one another, and the change of flux linking each coil, during the rotation of the armature or field, is not clearly defined. Hence, it is usually more convenient to consider the emf induced in each coil as the sum of the emfs induced in each of two active coil sides, the sides of the coil forming the end connections having no appreciable emfs induced in them. The emf induced by a conductor of length l cm cutting a flux of density B gauss at a velocity of v cm per sec is

$$e = Blv10^{-8} \qquad \text{volts,} \tag{321}$$

provided that B, l, v are mutually perpendicular. If not, (321) must be multiplied by the sine of the angle between any two of the three quantities B, l, v.

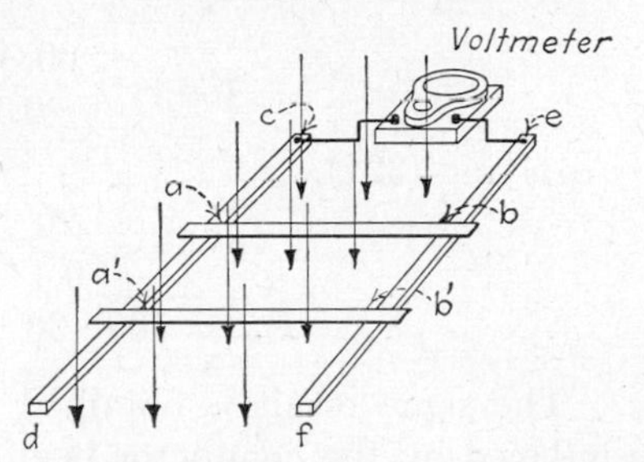

FIG. 272. Conductor cutting uniform magnetic field.

If B is in webers per square meter, l in meters, and v in meters per second, (321) becomes

$$e = Blv \qquad \text{volts.} \tag{322}$$

Although the relation $e = (-N\,d\phi/dt)(10^{-8})$ volts is the more fundamental equation for induced emf and is universally applicable, the same induced emf will be obtained if (321) and (322) are correctly applied, as is shown by the following:

Consider the conductor *ab*, Fig. 272, free to slide along two parallel metal rails *cd* and *ef* spaced *ab* cm apart. The rails are connected at one end by a voltmeter. A uniform magnetic field, of density B gauss, passes perpendicularly through the plane of the rails and conductor.

Let the conductor *ab* move parallel to itself at a uniform velocity v to the position $a'b'$. While this movement is taking place, the voltmeter will indicate a certain voltage. This voltage may be attributed to either of two causes:

1. As conductor *ab* moves to position *a′b′*, the flux linking the conducting loop formed by *ce*, the rails, and *ab* is increased, because of the increasing area of this loop.

2. An emf is generated in the conductor *ab* since it cuts the magnetic field.

The fact that the same emf is obtained by either (1) or (2) is illustrated by the use of numerical quantities. Let the flux density, Fig. 272, be 100 gauss, the distance *ab*, 30 cm, and $aa' = bb' = 20$ cm. The conductor *ab* moves at a uniform velocity v to position *a′b′* in 0.1 sec. Determine the emf across *ce*.

The change of flux linking the coil is

$$\phi = 30 \cdot 20 \cdot 100 = 60{,}000 \text{ maxwells.}$$

This change occurs in 0.1 sec.

By Eq. (207) (p. 298),

$$E_{av} = 1 \frac{60{,}000}{0.1} 10^{-8} = 0.006 \text{ volt.}$$

Applying (321),

$$v = \frac{20}{0.1} = 200 \text{ cm per sec.}$$

$$E_{av} = 100 \cdot 30 \cdot 200 \cdot 10^{-8} = 0.006 \text{ volt.}$$

The same result is obtained whether the emf is considered as being induced by the conductor itself *cutting* the field or as being induced by the change in flux *linking* the coil.

Similarly, the emf developed by the coil in Fig. 271 may be attributed to the emfs generated in the conductors on opposite sides of the coil by their *cutting* of magnetic flux. These conductors are connected in series by the end conductors, or connectors, which in themselves generate no appreciable emf. The direction of the emfs developed in the coil sides are such that these emfs are additive.

To distinguish between the two different concepts, an emf which is considered as being induced by change of flux linkages is called a *transformer emf*, whereas an emf which is considered as being induced by the cutting of flux by a conductor is called a *speed emf*. Frequently, both emfs may be induced simultaneously, as in the armature of the single-phase induction motor (Vol. II, Chap. X). It is stated that Eqs. (321) and (322) must be *properly* applied if the correct value of emf is to be obtained. At different times, conditions, supposedly anomalous, are cited to show that these equations are *not* always applicable. For example, while a conductor is cutting flux, the flux itself which links the coil may vary owing to a change in magnetic reluctance or to other causes. Accordingly, unless the transformer emf due to this change in flux linkage is taken into consideration, an incorrect value of induced emf is obtained.

262. Direction of Induced Electromotive Force. Fleming's Right-hand Rule. A definite relation exists among the direction of flux, the direction of motion of the conductor, and the direction of emf induced in the conductor.

A convenient rule for determining this relation is the *Fleming right-hand rule.* In this rule the fingers of the *right* hand are utilized as follows:

Set the forefinger, the thumb, and the middle finger of the right hand at right angles to one another, Fig. 273. If the *forefinger points along the lines of flux and the thumb in the direction of motion of the conductor, the middle finger will point in the direction of the induced emf.*

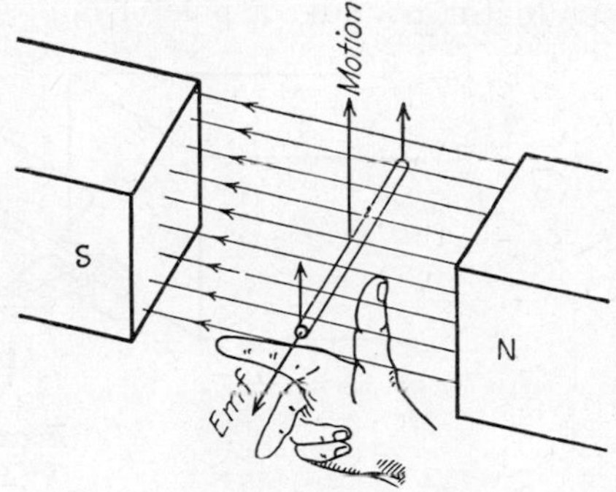

Fig. 273. Fleming's right-hand rule.

This rule is illustrated by Fig. 273. (Also see Fig. 381, p. 482.)

263. Electromotive Force Generated by Rotation of a Coil. A coil of a single turn is shown in Fig. 274(*a*). The coil rotates in a counterclockwise direction at a uniform speed in a uniform magnetic field. As

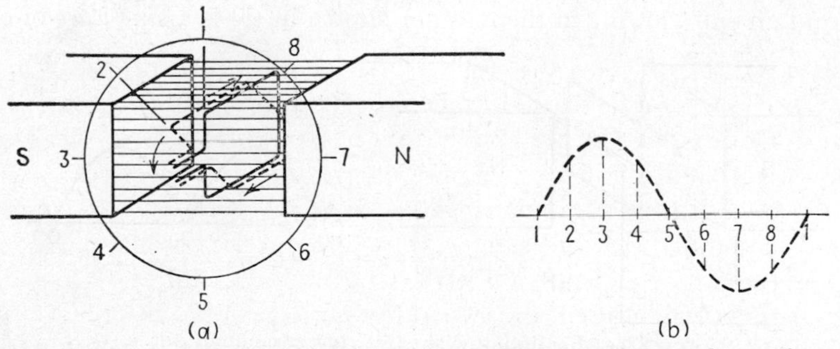

Fig. 274. Electromotive force induced in coil rotating at constant speed in uniform magnetic field.

the coil assumes successive positions, the emf induced in it changes. When it is in position 1, the emf generated is zero, for in this position neither active conductor is *cutting* magnetic lines but is moving parallel to these lines. (When the coil is in this position, the rate of change of *flux linkages* is zero.) When the coil reaches position 2 (shown dotted), its conductors are cutting across the lines *obliquely* and the induced emf has a value indicated at 2 in Fig. 274(*b*). When the coil reaches position

3, the conductors are cutting the lines *perpendicularly* and are cutting therefore at the maximum possible rate. Hence, the induced emf is a maximum when the coil is in this position. At position 4, the induced emf is less, due to a lesser rate of cutting. At position 5, no lines are being cut, and, as in 1, there is no induced emf. In position 6, the direction of the induced emf in the conductors will have reversed, as each conductor is under a pole of opposite sign to that for positions 1 to 5.

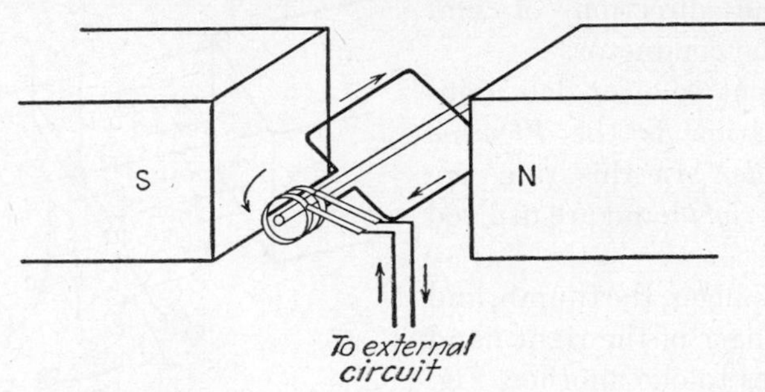

FIG. 275. Current taken from rotating coil by means of slip rings.

The induced emf increases to a negative maximum at 7 and then decreases until the coil again reaches position 1. After this the coil merely repeats the cycle. The region corresponding to positions 1 and 5 in which the plane of the coil is perpendicular to the direction of the flux and in which no emf is induced in the coil by rotation is called the *neutral zone*.

Since the induced emf reverses in direction cyclically, it is an *alternating* emf and an emf varying in the manner shown in (*b*) is a *sine wave* of emf.

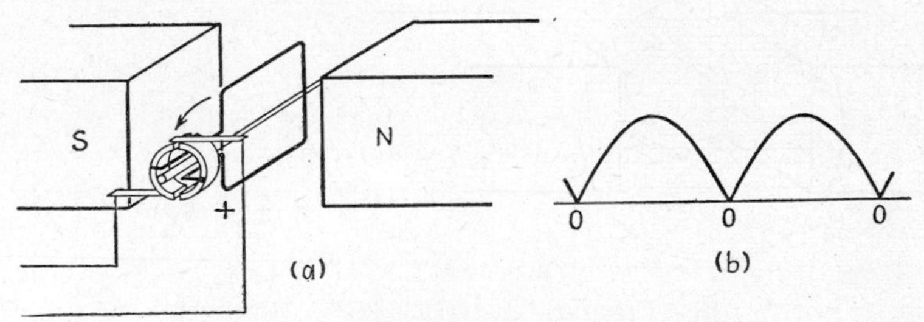

FIG. 276. Rectifying with split ring or commutator.

This alternating emf may be impressed on an external circuit by means of two *slip rings*, Fig. 275. Each ring is continuous and is insulated from the other ring and from the shaft. A metal or a carbon brush rests on each ring and conducts the current from the coil to the external circuit (see Vol. II, Chap. I).

If direct current is desired, that is, one whose direction is always the same, such rings cannot be used. The coil current must be alternating, since the emf which produces it is alternating, as shown in Fig. 274(*b*).

The current must be rectified before it enters the external circuit. This rectification can be accomplished by using a split ring, Fig. 276(*a*). Instead of two rings, as in Fig. 275, only one ring is used. This is split by saw cuts at two points diametrically opposite, and the ends of the coil are connected to the sections or segments so produced.

A consideration of Fig. 276(*a*) shows that as the direction of the current in the coil reverses, the connections to the external circuit are simultaneously reversed. Therefore, the direction of current in the external circuit is not changed. The brushes pass over the cuts in the ring when the coil is perpendicular to the magnetic field, or in the so-called *neutral zone*, and no emf is being induced, as at points 1 and 5 of Fig. 274. These neutral points are marked 0-0-0 in Fig. 276(*b*).

Comparing Fig. 274(*b*) with Fig. 276(*b*), it is seen that the negative half of the wave has been reversed and made positive.

An emf with zero value twice in each cycle, Fig. 276, could not be used commercially for d-c service. Also, a single-coil machine would have a small output for its size and weight. The emf wave of Fig. 276 may be made less pulsating by the use of two coils and four commutator segments, Fig. 277(*a*). This gives an *open-circuit* type of winding, since it is impossible to start at any one commutator segment and return to this segment by following through the entire winding. In this particular winding the full emf generated in each coil is not utilized, as one coil passes out of contact with the brushes at points *a*, *a*, *a*, Fig. 277(*b*), and the emf shown by the dotted lines is not used.

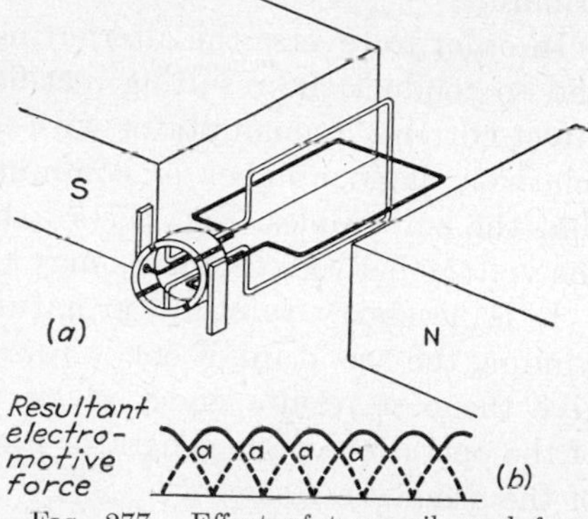

Fig. 277. Effect of two coils and four commutator segments on emf wave.

264. Armature. In Sec. 263 it is shown that in a generator there must be conductors which cut a magnetic field and that a commutator must be provided for reversing the induced currents at the proper time and for conducting them to the external circuit. These elements are supplied by the armature. Also, the armature must be designed so that the power output of the generator is sufficiently great in proportion to the weight and cost to justify the generator economically.

The commercial armature must have a core of iron which not only carries the copper conductors through the magnetic field but also forms part of the magnetic circuit. Without the iron core the magnetic field would be so weak that little power output would result. The armature consists of a cylindrical core of iron laminations (p. 399) mounted on a shaft so that it may rotate in the magnetic field, which is produced by the field winding located on the field poles. The faces of the poles are practically coaxial with the armature, and the lengths of the air-gaps in the magnetic circuit are relatively small, thus making the magnetic reluctance relatively small.

The conductors are placed in slots on the surface of the armature (p. 378). This construction is advantageous in that the conductors are held firmly in position, and the teeth permit a short air-gap to be used. Every effort is made to place as much copper as possible in the slots, since the generator output is proportional to the active copper. Also, the conductors must be placed and connected so that their emfs are additive and the full induced emf is delivered to the brushes. Except in the smallest machines, air ducts are provided for ventilating the armature.

In order to reverse the alternating current induced in the conductors, and to conduct the resulting rectified current to the external circuit as direct current, a commutator with appropriate brushes is necessary. A relatively large number of commutator segments is essential in order that the emf ripples, Fig. 277(*b*), shall not be too pronounced and that the voltage between segments may not be so high that flashover occurs.

It is necessary to study armature construction and the methods of winding the armature, if one is to select the type of armature which will give the best results under given conditions. Also, an understanding of the operation of the generator itself depends on a thorough knowledge of the armature assembly.

265. Gramme-ring Winding. The coils and conductors which constitute the armature winding must be interconnected so that the desired induced emf and current output will be produced efficiently and economically. This may be accomplished by different designs of windings, as will be shown later. The design and manner of connecting armature windings are better understood if the principles of power generation and of commutation are well known.

The gramme-ring type of armature was used with the early generators, and although it has long been obsolete, the simplicity of the winding and the fact that there are no crossings of conductors make it advantageous in illustrating the principle of the operation of armatures. Also, the electrical and magnetic effects in the armature are identical qualitatively with those of the modern drum type of winding.

In Fig. 278(*a*) is shown a 2-pole type. The armature core consists of a hollow cylinder, or ring, made up of iron laminations, with insulated wire wound spirally about the ring, with taps taken from the wire at regular intervals and connected to commutator segments. Note that the winding is continuous, hence is *closed*, and that the coils between brushes are all connected in series. A connection is brought from each coil to a commutator segment as shown. In Fig. 278(*a*) the coils at *A* and *B* are shown as being connected instantaneously to the brushes through their corresponding commutator segments. By applying Fleming's right-hand rule (Sec. 262) the induced emfs are inward under the *N* pole and outward under the *S* pole so that in the complete winding the emfs in the halves of the winding are in opposition. The arrows show the direction of the induced emf in different parts of the winding.

If the armature and its relation to the pole pieces are symmetrical, the emf induced in the upper half of the winding between the points

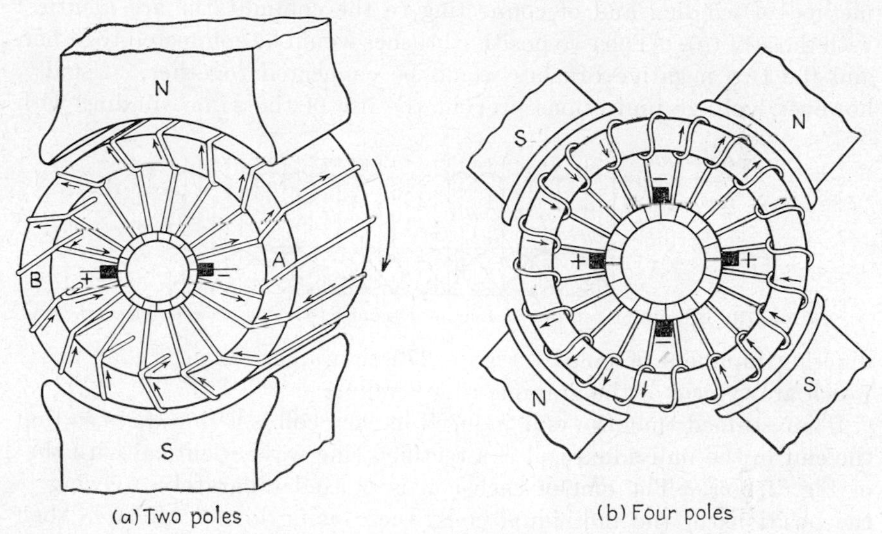

FIG. 278. Gramme-ring windings and pole pieces.

A and *B* and that induced in the lower half between the same two points are opposite and equal. The resultant emf around the armature is therefore zero. An emf exists, however, between points *A* and *B*, and since they are connected directly to the brushes, a substantial emf exists between the brushes. It is also to be noted that as the armature rotates and the points *A*, *B* and the commutator segments to which they are connected move away from the position of direct connection to the brushes, shown in Fig. 278(*a*), other similar coils and segments take their places. Hence, with constant speed and constant flux from the pole pieces, the emf between the brushes will remain constant, except for the small fluctuations caused by the successive segments coming in contact with the brushes and then leaving them (see Fig. 279).

Also note that the coils at *A* and *B*, which at the instant are connected to the brushes and hence are undergoing commutation, are in the region between the poles where they are cutting no flux. Accordingly they are in the neutral zone corresponding to positions 1 and 5, Fig. 274, and no emf is being induced in them. The coils A and B are, therefore, merely acting as connections from the active conductors to the commutator and brushes. They are also short-circuited by the brushes, and were any substantial emf being induced in them, the current in the coils would be large, since their resistance and that of the brushes is low. (See Sec. 299, p. 429, for further discussion of commutation.)

An advantage of the gramme-ring winding is that theoretically the same winding is adapted to any number of poles. This is illustrated by Fig. 278(*b*), which shows a 4-pole gramme-ring winding. Note that the method of winding and of connecting to the commutator are identical with those of (*a*). The two positive brushes would be connected together, and the two negative brushes would be connected together. Usually, however, voltage limitations prevent the use of the same winding with

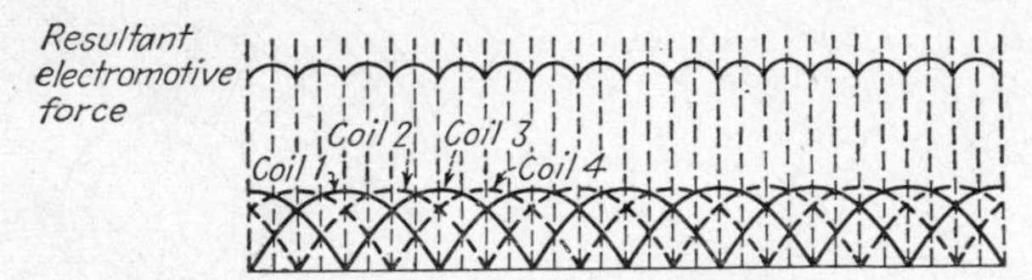

FIG. 279. Resultant emf due to four series-connected coils between brushes.

differing numbers of poles. Figure 279 shows the induced emf waves which are typical of the gramme-ring winding.

It is assumed that the emf induced in each coil is a sine wave so that the emf in the individual coil is a rectified sine wave identical with that of Fig. 276(*b*). The emf of each coil is plotted separately. Owing to the positions of the individual coils, these emfs do not all have their zero value at the same time, nor do they reach their maximum value at the same time. Since in both Figs. 278(*a*) and (*b*) the coils between brushes are in series, the emf between brushes is the *sum* of the emfs induced in the individual coils. Hence, except for the brief interval when a coil is short-circuited by a brush during the commutation period, each coil is contributing emf at all times.

The fact that the emf between the negative and the positive brushes is the sum of the induced emfs in those coils which are in series between the brushes is illustrated in Fig. 279, which is representative of the conditions in Fig. 278(*b*). A study will show that there are four active coils in series between each pair of positive and negative brushes. Hence, the resultant emf at any instant is the sum of these individual emfs at this instant. The resultant emf should be compared with the resultant emf obtained with the open-coil winding, Fig. 277, in which the resultant emf does not equal the sum of the individual emfs but consists of the tops of the individual waves. It will be noted that a fairly smooth resultant emf is obtained with four coils, the "ripples" being noticeable but small. As the number of coils is increased the ripples become almost unnoticeable. A gramme-ring winding is a *closed-coil* winding, since it is possible to start at any one point in the winding and return to the same point by passing continuously through the winding. Although the gramme-ring winding is shown in Figs. 278(*a*) and (*b*) as lying on the surface of the armature, in practice the conductors are usually placed in slots. As has been stated, the gramme-ring winding is no longer used. This is due to the fact that the conductors which lie inside the ring cut practically no flux and hence act merely as connectors for the active conductors. Because of the small proportion of active conductor, a relatively large amount of copper is required for a given output. In small machines, there is not sufficient room to carry the inactive conductors back through the armature core (see Fig. 306, p. 400). In a gramme-ring winding, formed coils cannot be used, and this makes the winding expensive.

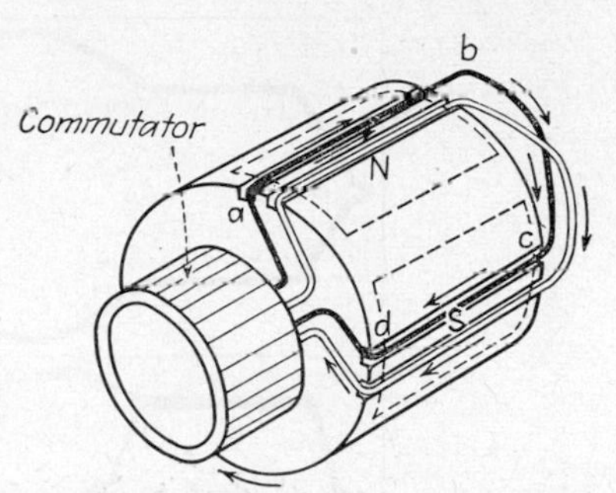

FIG. 280. Two coils in place on a 4-pole drum-wound armature.

266. Drum Winding. The objections to the ring-type winding are overcome by the use of the drum winding. The conductors of this winding all lie in slots in the surface of the armature and are connected to one another by front and back connectors or coil ends (*ad* and *bc*, Fig. 280, are coil ends). The two principal advantages of the drum winding are that, with the exception of the end connections, all the armature copper is "active," that is, it cuts flux and so is active in generating emf; and with the exception of small units and armatures having semiclosed slots, Fig. 309(*d*) (p. 402), the coils can be preformed and insulated before being placed on the armature, thus reducing the cost of winding.

The requirements which a winding should meet are that the winding be closed, or continuous, that is, that it be a closed-coil winding in order that all the coils shall be "active" except during the brief commutation period. Under these conditions the emf between brushes is the sum of the emfs induced in all the coils which lie between the brushes, Fig. 279. Those parts of the coils such as *ad* and *bc*, Fig. 280, called "end connections," which connect the active lengths of conductors *ab* and *dc* in series should not be too long in proportion to the total length of coil. The emfs induced in the two sides of any coil should be additive so that when one side of a coil lies under the center of an *N* pole, the other side must lie at or near the center of an *S* pole. In order to obtain economy in winding, the coils should be preformed and insulated before being placed on the armature. This necessitates a 2-layer winding, Fig. 283. The coils usually are wound on machine-driven forms which give them the proper shape, and the turns are then bound together, usually with cotton tape. The ends are left bare so that they may be soldered later to the commutator bars. The coils are then dipped in some insulating compound such as asphaltum and are then dried (see Fig. 281). For very high-temperature operation, other materials, such as mica and paper tape, fiberglas tape, and silicone-impregnated insulation are used.

The slots are lined with insulation, and the conductors are held firmly by fiber or other nonconducting wedges in the larger machines, Fig. 309 (p. 402), and by binding wires in the smaller machines. These con-

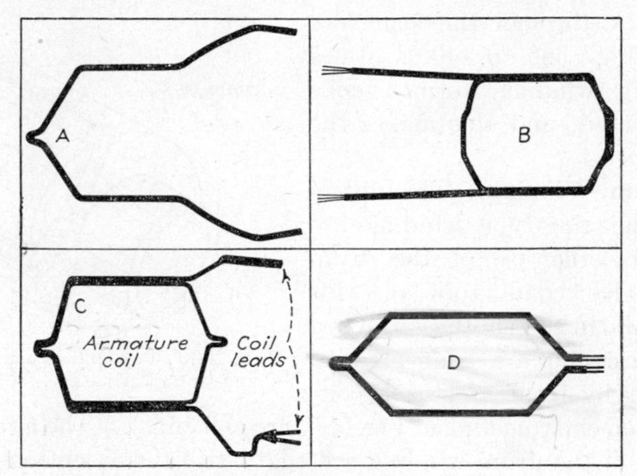

FIG. 281. Formed armature coils.

structions are much better mechanically than with the conductors on the surface of the armature. On the other hand, as the coils are embedded in iron, they have relatively high self-inductance. This makes satisfactory commutation more difficult, and the flux pulsations due to the armature teeth give pole-face and tooth losses. The *pole pitch* is the periphery of the armature divided by the number of poles and accordingly is the distance on the periphery of the armature between centers of adjacent poles, Fig. 312 (p. 406).

In order that the emf induced in the coil be a maximum, other conditions being fixed, the span of the coil should be equal to the pole pitch. However, the span may be reduced to as much as eight-tenths the pole pitch without any serious reduction in the induced emf. When this is done, the winding is called a *fractional*-pitch one. This type of winding effects a substantial saving in the copper of the end connections and improves commutation, owing to the lesser mutual inductance between coils.

Usually, one side of every coil lies in the top of one slot, and the other side lies in the bottom of some other slot at a distance of approximately one pole pitch along the armature. Thus, at least two coil sides occupy each slot. Frequently, however, two or more coils are taped together to form a multiple coil (Sec. 269) in which the several coil sides occupy the top of one slot and the other sides occupy the bottom of some other slot at a distance of approximately one pole pitch. This type of winding is called a *2-layer* one and is now used almost universally. It permits the end connections to be easily made as the coil ends can be bent around one another in a systematic manner, passing from the bottom to the top layer by means of the peculiar twist in the ends of the coils.

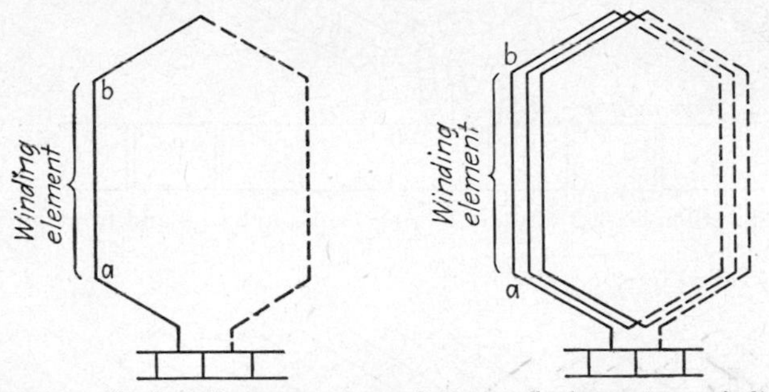

Fig. 282. Single coil representing a 3-turn coil of armature winding.

267. Lap Winding. In the simple-lap type of drum winding, the coil connection is made from one segment, through the two sides of a coil and thence *back* to the next adjacent segment, from which similar connection is made to the next coil, etc., Fig. 280. A study of Fig. 280 shows that the number of commutator segments must be equal to the number of armature coils.

In the study and design of windings, the group of wires which constitutes the side of a single coil, and which is almost always wrapped with tape as a unit, is considered as being a *winding element.* Such winding elements are shown at *ab* and *dc* in Fig. 280 and at *ab* in the two coils in Fig. 282. Even when there are several conductors in a coil side, they will be shown as a single element in the wiring diagram, Fig. 282. Obviously there will be twice as many of these elements as there are coils. The number of elements that the coil advances on the back of the armature is the *back pitch* of the winding, Fig. 284, and will be denoted by y_b, Fig. 294(a), (p. 389). This back pitch is determined by the span of the connection *bc*, Fig. 280. The number of elements spanned on the commutator end of the armature is called the *front pitch* and will be designated by y_f.

This may be *greater or less* than the back pitch *but not equal* to it. If it be greater, the winding is *retrogressive;* that is, it advances in a counter-clockwise direction when viewed from the commutator end. If the front pitch be less than the back pitch, the winding is *progressive;* that is, it advances in a clockwise direction when viewed from the commutator

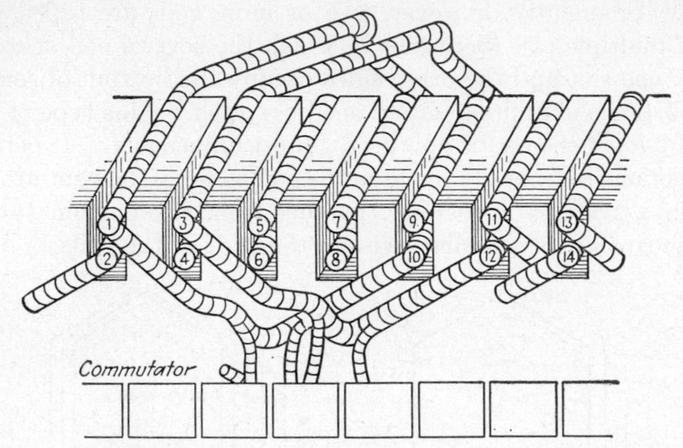

Fig. 283. Simplex lap winding having back pitch of 9 and front pitch of 7.

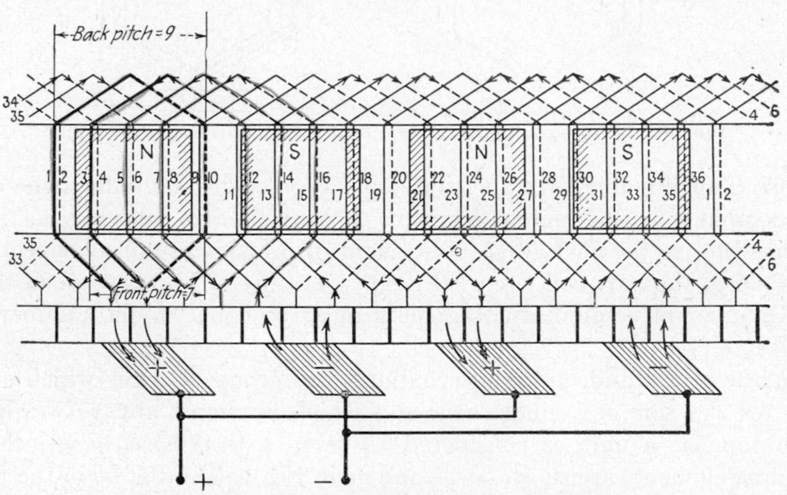

Fig. 284. Development of 4-pole lap winding.

end. This is illustrated in Figs. 283 and 284. Element 1 is connected on the back of the armature to element 10. Therefore, the back pitch $y_b = 9$. Element 10 is then connected back to 3 on the front of the armature, the connection being made at the commutator segment. Therefore, the front pitch $y_f = 7$. This winding is therefore *progressive.*

As nearly all windings are now 2-layer ones, only this type of winding will be considered. The elements lying in the tops of the slots are given odd numbers and those in the bottoms of the slots even numbers, Fig. 283. If one side of a coil lies in the bottom of a slot, the other side must lie in the top of some other slot. Hence y_b and y_f must both be *odd*. If y_b and y_f were both even, all the elements would lie *either* in the tops of the slots or in the bottoms of the slots and it would thus be impossible for one side of a coil to lie in the bottom of a slot and the other side of the same coil to lie in the top of some other slot. Hence y_b and y_f must both be odd if the winding is to be properly placed on the armature.

It follows that the front and back pitches must differ from each other by 2. That is,

$$y_b = y_f \pm 2. \tag{323}$$

The average pitch is

$$y = \frac{y_b + y_f}{2}. \tag{324}$$

The plus sign in (323) shows that the winding is progressive, that is, progresses in a clockwise direction when viewed from the commutator end. The minus sign shows a retrogressive winding whose advance is in a counterclockwise direction when viewed from the commutator end.

268. Commutator Pitch. It is noted (p. 377) that the number of commutator segments is equal to the number of coils. Therefore, the number of commutator segments

$$N_c = N = \frac{Z'}{2}$$

where Z' is the total number of winding elements on the surface of the armature and N is the number of coils.

From Figs. 283 and 284 it is seen that the winding advances *one commutator segment for each complete turn.* Hence, in such a winding, the commutator pitch $y_c = 1$.

In designing a winding it is necessary that the opposite sides of each coil lie under poles of different polarity so that the two emfs induced in the coil sides may be additive. Hence, the average pitch should be nearly equal to the number of elements per pole.

The three fundamental conditions to be fulfilled by a *lap winding* are:

1. *The pitch must be such that the opposite sides of a coil lie under unlike poles.*
2. *The winding must include each element once and only once.*
3. *The winding must be reentrant, i.e., must close on itself.*

Example. Assume that the armature of a 4-pole dynamo has 18 slots. Design a 2-layer lap winding having two elements per slot.

There are 36 elements. The average pitch should be nearly equal to $36 \div 4 = 9$. The back pitch can be made equal to 9.

$$y_b = 9; \quad y_f = 7.$$

Starting at 1, the winding will progress as follows:

1–10–3–12–5–14–7–16–9–18–11–20–13–22–15–24–17–26–19
28–21–30–23–32–25–34–27–36–29–2–31–4–33–6–35–8–1.

This is a *winding table*. It is useful in checking the winding. By inspection it may be determined whether each element is included once, and only once, and whether the winding closes at the same element, 1 in this case, at which it began. The winding is shown in Fig. 284 as if it were split axially and laid out flat. It will be noted that the brushes rest on segments to which are connected elements, 1 and 19, for example, which lie midway between the poles. That is, the brushes are connected to conductors in which practically no emf is being induced.

269. Multiple Coils. In dynamos of larger ratings it is often necessary to place several coil sides or elements in a single slot, usually four, six, or eight. More than eight elements per slot is rarely used. The reason for placing several elements in a single slot is as follows:

The commutator segments must not be too few in number. The average voltage between adjacent segments cannot safely exceed 15 volts or thereabouts, because of danger of flashover, and this voltage should preferably be less than this limiting value. Therefore, the number of segments is determined by the voltage between brushes, and there must be enough segments between positive and negative brushes to make the voltage between adjacent segments well below the flashover value. Moreover, with too few segments the emf ripple may become objectionable, Fig. 277(*b*) (p. 371). Hence, in many dynamos with the necessary number of commutator segments, if two elements per slot were used, one in the top layer and one in the bottom layer, a large number of slots would be necessary. This would reduce the size of the slots and make the space factor (ratio of the copper cross section to the slot cross section) low. Also, the tooth root would be so narrow that the teeth would be mechanically weak. By placing more than two elements in each slot the number of slots is reduced, and larger slots result. This also reduces the cost of winding.

Two, three, or four individual coils are taped together to form a single coil, as shown at *B* in Fig. 281. Such a coil is called a *multiple coil* and may be more specifically designated as a double coil, triple coil, etc. Such a single coil may be placed as a unit in the appropriate slots. The armature of Fig. 307 (p. 401) shows three coil leads protruding from the insulation of each of the multiple coils, indicating a triple coil.

The numbering and connections of the elements are in no way different from those already described in the case of only two elements per slot.

The selection of the pitch, where several elements per slot are used, is more restricted than with two elements per slot.

Assume that a 6-pole machine has 72 slots and six elements per slot. The total number of elements on the armature surface

$$Z = 72 \cdot 6 = 432.$$

The pitch should be approximately

$$y = \frac{432}{6} = 72.$$

Let

$$y_b = 71,$$
$$y_f = 69.$$

If this back pitch is used, a coil must reach from element 1 to element 72, Fig. 285. Then the next element 3, which is taped to element 1, will

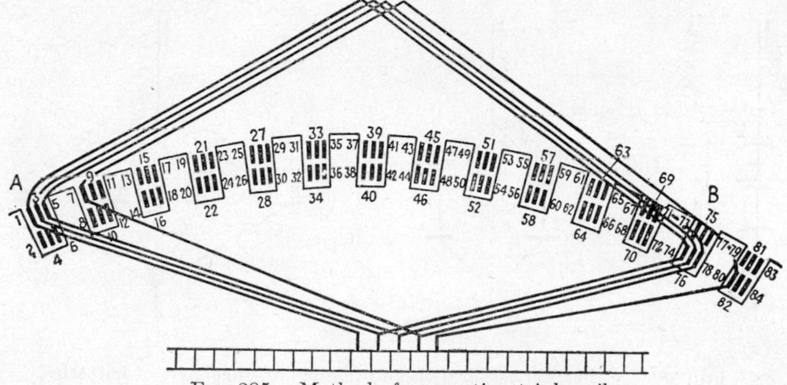

FIG. 285. Method of connecting triple coil.

reach to element 74. These two coils, therefore, span different distances on the armature, since elements 72 and 74 lie in different slots. Hence, although the left-hand sides of these two coils and element 5 are taped together as a unit, the right-hand elements cannot be taped together, since they lie in different slots. This can be seen from a study of Fig. 285. Under these conditions, if one group of coil sides of two or more coils lie in one slot and the other group of coil sides lie in different slots, the coil as a whole is called a *split coil.*

In practice, it is desirable, if any number of coil sides are to be placed together in the top of any slot, that their opposite sides shall all be placed together in the bottom of some other slot. This makes it possible to tape all these coils together and place them as a unit in both slots.

Therefore, if in the above case $y_b = 73$ and $y_f = 71$, the coil containing element 1 will connect from the upper *left-hand* side of slot A to the lower *left-hand* side of slot B, that is, from element 1 to element 74. Element 3 will connect from the center and top of slot A to the center and bottom of slot B, and element 5 will connect from the upper right-hand side of slot A to the lower right-hand side of slot B. As all three coils now span the same distance on the armature, they will be equal in size, form, etc. Moreover, the three single coils can be taped together to form a *triple coil* and placed in the two slots as a unit. Therefore, if the sides of three adjacent coils are in the top of a slot, their other sides should lie together in the bottom of some other slot. This condition is secured by making the back pitch 1 greater than a multiple of the number of coil sides or elements per slot. For example, in the illustration just given, y_b is equal to 73, that is, 1 greater than 72, and 72 is a multiple of 6.

Coils taped together and placed in the slots in the foregoing manner are called *multiple coils*.

270. Paths through Armature. In Fig. 286(a) are shown four battery cells in series. Each has an emf rating of 2 volts, a current rating of

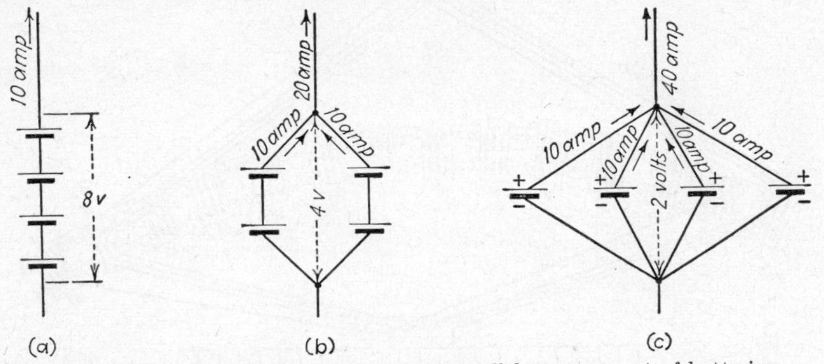

FIG. 286. Series, series-parallel, and parallel arrangement of batteries.

10 amp, and a power rating of 20 watts. When the four cells are connected in series aiding, the emf rating of the battery becomes 8 volts, the current rating 10 amp, and the power rating 80 watts. With this series connection there is but one current path through the battery. If the four cells be arranged in two groups of two in series as in (b), the result is two paths for the current through the battery, the emf rating is 4 volts, the current rating 20 amp, and the power rating is $4 \cdot 20 = 80$ watts.

If the four cells be arranged in parallel, as in (c), the result is four paths for the current, the emf rating is 2 volts, the current rating is 40 amp and the power rating remains 80 watts.

Let Z be the number of equal cells in a battery, e the emf rating per cell, i the current rating per cell, and P' the paths through the battery.

Then, the emf rating of the battery,

$$E = \frac{Ze}{P'} \quad \text{volts.} \tag{325}$$

The current rating

$$I = P'i \quad \text{amp.} \tag{326}$$

The power rating

$$P = EI = Zei \quad \text{watts.} \tag{327}$$

It is to be noted that the power rating is independent of the manner of connecting the batteries, so long as all act in conjunction to supply current to the external circuit.

These relations among the cells of a battery also apply to the conductors in an armature. Each conductor is a source of emf, and in the normal machine these emfs are all equal. These conductors may be connected in different combinations so that there are two, four, or more

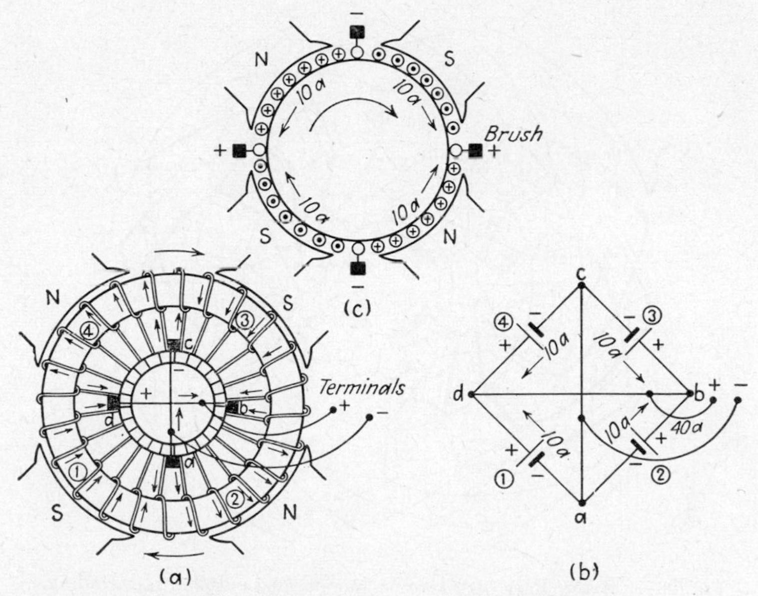

FIG. 287. Four paths in parallel through armature.

current paths through the armature. In the usual type of winding there must be at least two paths through the armature. The emf and current rating of the armature as a whole are determined by (325) and (326), where e and i are the emf and current ratings of each conductor. Moreover, as with the battery, the power rating of the armature is independent of the manner of connecting the conductors, if all act in conjunction to supply current to the external circuit.

To determine the number of parallel paths through an armature, start at one of the terminals, as, for example, the negative, and see how many different paths through the armature it is possible to follow in order to reach the positive terminal.

The simplest arrangement of conductors occurs in the gramme-ring winding. Figure 287(a) shows such a winding for a 4-pole machine.

Starting at the − terminal, one path may be followed by going to brush *a*, through the winding at 1 to brush *d*, and then to the + terminal.

A second path is obtained by going to brush *a*, through path 2 to brush *b*, and then to the + terminal.

A third path is obtained by going to brush *c*, through path 3, then through brush *b* to the + terminal.

A fourth path is obtained by going to brush *c*, through path 4 to brush *d*, then to the + terminal.

This makes four separate paths between the − and + terminals, these paths being in parallel.

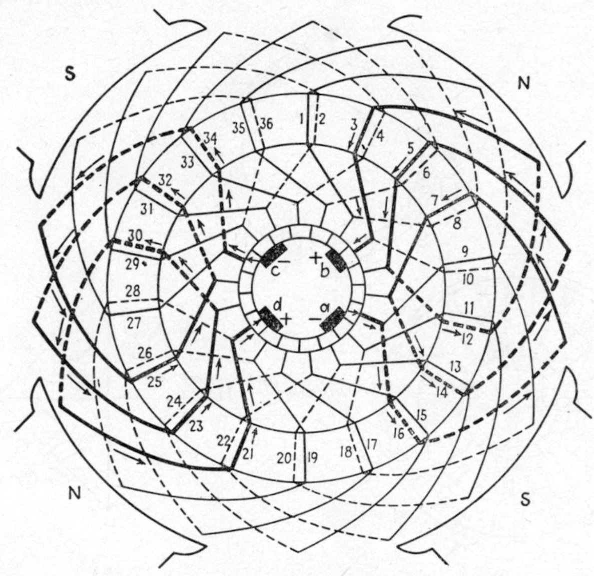

FIG. 288. Heavy lines show two of four parallel paths in lap winding.

Assume that there are 10 amp per path and 20 volts between brushes. The armature may be considered as equivalent to four batteries connected as in Fig. 287(*b*), each battery delivering 10 amp at 20 volts. Battery 1 corresponds to path 1, battery 2 to path 2, etc.

It is seen that the four batteries are connected in parallel because their four positive terminals are connected together and their four negative terminals are connected together. The total current delivered will be 40 amp at 20 volts. In a similar manner each path in the gramme-ring winding will deliver 10 amp, making 20 amp per brush, or 40 amp per terminal. The potential difference between brushes will be 20 volts.

The paths through a drum winding are not so easy to follow as those through a ring winding since the end connections cross one another as the winding spirals along the armature surface. Figure 288 shows developed in circular form the 18-slot drum winding of Fig. 284 (p. 378). For the sake of simplicity two paths are shown in heavy lines, one from brush *a* to brush *b*, the other from brush *c* to brush *d*. These constitute two paths. By tracing through the lighter lines, two more paths may be found, one between brushes *c* and *b*, the other between brushes *a* and *d*, making four paths in all.

In all simplex lap windings there are as many paths through the armature as there are poles.

271. Multiplex Windings. Figure 289 shows a 36-slot 4-pole winding, in which every alternate slot is filled. There are two coil sides per slot.

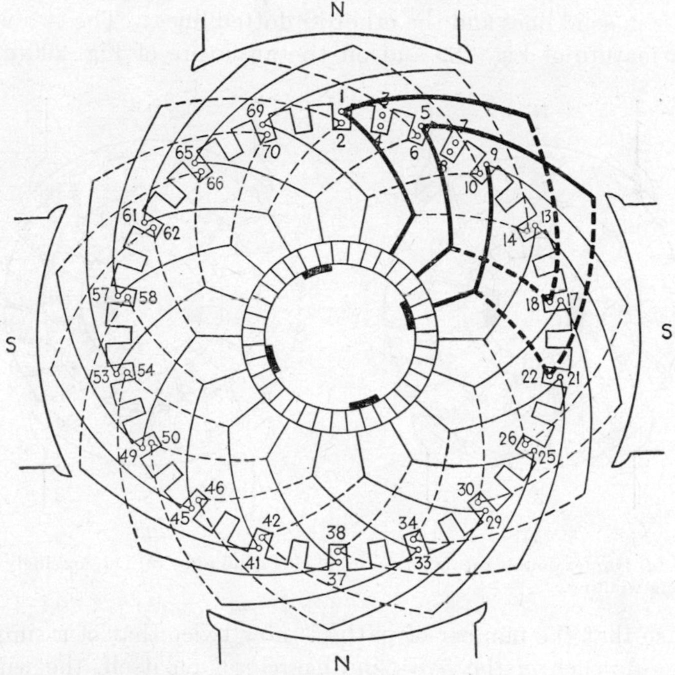

FIG. 289. Duplex doubly reentrant lap winding, one winding only being shown.

The back pitch y_b is 17, and element 1 connects to element 18 on the back of the armature. Element 18 then connects to 5 on the front of the armature, making the front pitch $y_f = 13$. Instead of returning to the element differing by 2 from the initial coil side, the return is made to an element differing by 4 from the initial coil side. Likewise, from element 5, connection is made at the back of the armature to element 22 and thence back to 9. Elements 3, 4 and 7, 8 are not connected to this winding. Furthermore, only alternate commutator segments are utilized. It is seen that this winding closes on itself after going once around the armature; that is, this winding is reentrant and is in itself complete in the same manner as any simplex 18-slot winding, Fig. 288.

As this winding uses only alternate slots and alternate commutator segments, another winding, the duplicate of the first, can be placed in the vacant slots, this second winding having the same front and back pitch as the first, and being connected to the commutator segments not utilized by the first. This second winding will also close on itself and is reentrant.

These two windings are separate, and are insulated from each other on the armature but are connected together electrically by the span of the carbon brushes on the commutator. This condition is more clearly shown in the simple gramme-ring winding of Fig. 290(*a*), where one winding is in solid lines and the other in dotted lines. The two windings on the armature of Fig. 289 and on the armature of Fig. 290(*a*) are in

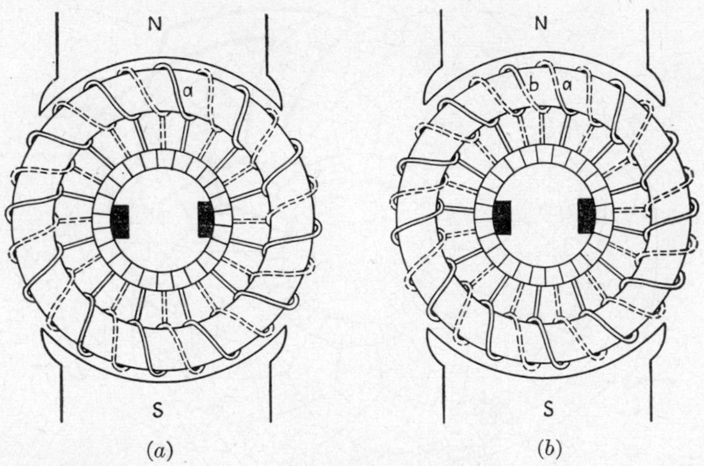

FIG. 290. (*a*) Duplex doubly reentrant gramme-ring winding. (*b*) Duplex singly reentrant gramme-ring winding.

parallel, so that the number of paths is now twice that of a simplex lap winding. As each of the two windings closes on itself, the winding is *doubly reentrant.* With this type of winding it is necessary that the brush span at least two commutator segments.

When there are two such windings in parallel, the winding is *duplex*. Therefore, this is a *doubly reentrant duplex winding.* Three or more such windings can be placed on an armature, making the winding triplex, quadruplex, etc., the number of such windings being the multiplicity of the winding.

Let m = the multiplicity of the winding. The number of paths p' in a lap winding is

$$p' = mp \tag{328}$$

where p is the number of poles.

The relation between back and front pitch is

$$y_b = y_f \pm 2m. \tag{329}$$

This should be compared with Eq. (323) (p. 379), where $m = 1$.

If the number of slots and hence of coils, Fig. 289, be odd, that is, if there are 35 or 37 coils and commutator segments, the winding will not close after having gone once around the armature but will return one slot, or two elements, to the right or to the left of the element at which it started. If there are more than four elements per slot, the winding may return to the same slot at which it started, but removed by two elements from the element at which it started. Therefore, this winding does not close, or become reentrant, after having passed once around the armature but must pass around once again before closing. This is illustrated in

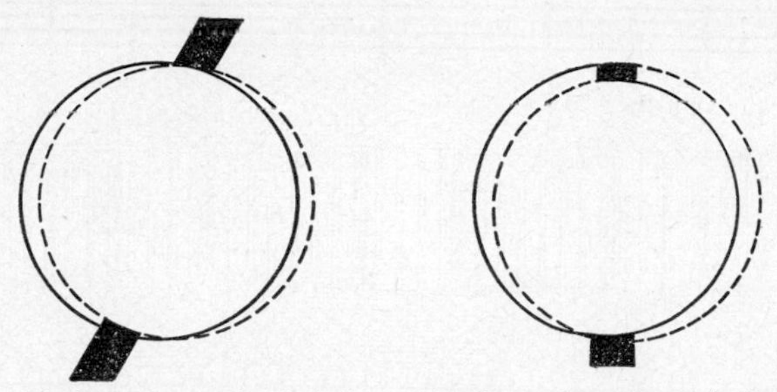

FIG. 291. Duplex windings in diagrammatic form.

Fig. 290(*b*). The initial winding shown with the solid line starts at *a*. After passing once around the ring armature it does not close at *a*, as does the winding in Fig. 290(*a*), but terminates at *b*, one element removed from *a*. The second winding, shown dotted, starts at *b* and after passing once around the armature, closes at *a*. Although the winding passes around the armature twice, it closes only once and so is *singly* reentrant. Therefore, this is a *singly reentrant duplex* winding. The singly reentrant and the doubly reentrant windings are the same electrically. Their difference is best illustrated by the two simple diagrams of Fig. 291.

From the foregoing it is seen that with duplex lap windings the commutator pitch $y_c = 2$; with triplex windings $y_c = 3$; etc.

272. Equalizer Connections in Lap Windings. Lap windings may consist of several paths in parallel, the parallel connections being made through the brushes. If several batteries are connected in parallel and their emfs are not equal, currents circulate among the batteries, even when no external load is being supplied. This means a constant loss of energy and heating of the batteries.

The same condition exists in generator armatures. Because of very slight inequalities in the air-gaps, due to wearing of the bearings, lack of mechanical alignment, etc., there may be slight differences of emf in the different paths through the armature. These differences of emf will cause currents to circulate between different points in the armature, and these currents must go through the brushes even when no current is being delivered by the generator. To relieve the brushes of this extra current, several points in the armature which should be simultaneously at the same potential are connected together by heavy copper bars or equalizers. These currents then circulate between the different points in the armature without going through the brushes.

The action of the equalizer connections, however, differs from that of the brushes. The equalizing currents through the brushes are direct cur-

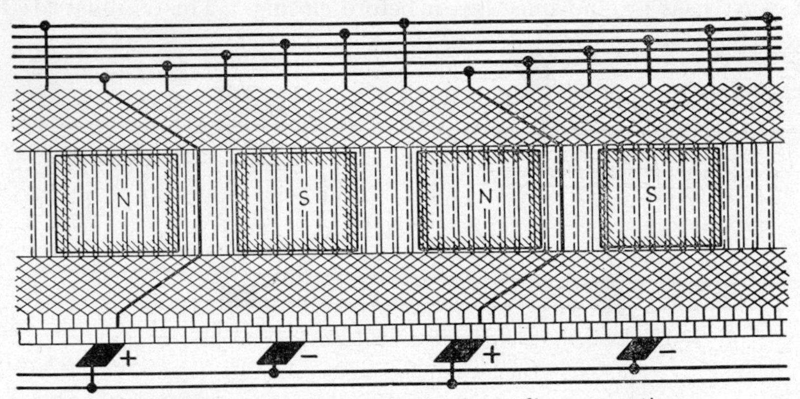

Fig. 292. Simplex lap winding with equalizer connections.

rents, which bring the different paths to equality of voltage by the IR drops which these currents produce in the different armature paths. The currents through the equalizer connections are alternating currents. These alternating currents produce mmfs which react on the poles of the generator in such a manner that they oppose the flux where it has increased and act in conjunction with the flux where it has decreased. Hence, the circulatory currents tend to bring the *induced* emfs in every path to equality. They accomplish the equalization of voltage without the heating which the brush currents would produce.[1]

To make these equalizer connections, the number of coils should be a multiple of the number of poles, and the coils per pole should be divisible by some small number as 2 or 3. As an example, assume an 8-pole generator having 12 slots per pole and 2 coil sides per slot. There will be 96 slots and 192 coil sides. The number of coil sides per pole will be

[1] See Moore, A. D., "Theory of the Action of Equalizer Connections in Lap Windings," *Elec. Jour.*, December, 1926, p. 624.

24. Let $y_b = 25$ and $y_f = 23$. A portion of the winding is shown in Fig. 292. Note that every fourth coil is connected to an equalizer. The coils that are connected to the same equalizer occupy the same positions relative to the poles. (See the two half coils drawn with heavy lines.) This is necessary as such coils at any instant should be generating the *same* emf. Note in Fig. 292 that the two segments under the two positive brushes are connected together by an equalizing connection.

Theoretically, every coil should be connected to an equalizer, but as this would require an undue number of equalizers, it is sufficient, practically, to connect every third or fourth coil. This is the reason why the number of coils per pole should be divisible by a small number, as 2, 3, or 4. Figure 293 shows a large d-c armature with the equalizer connections at the back of the armature.

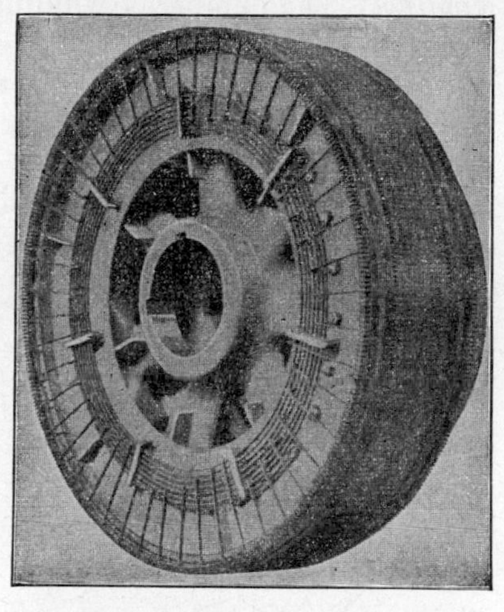

FIG. 293. Direct-current armature with equalizer connections. (*General Electric Company.*)

273. Wave Winding. It is shown that with the *lap* winding an element under one pole is connected directly to an element which occupies a nearly corresponding position under the next pole. This second element is then connected *back* again to an element under the *original* pole, but removed two or more elements from the initial one. This is shown in Fig. 294(*a*), where element *ab* under an *N* pole is connected to element

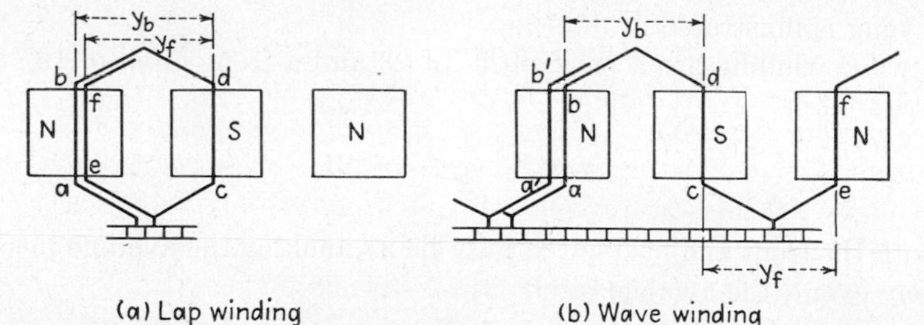

FIG. 294. Lap and wave windings.

cd having a corresponding position under the adjacent *S* pole. Element *cd* is then connected back to *ef*, which is adjacent to *ab* under the original *N* pole. Obviously it would make no difference so far as the direction and magnitude of the induced emf in the winding are concerned if the connection, instead of returning to the same *N* pole, advanced *forward* to the next N pole, as in Fig. 294(*b*). The winding then passes successively every N pole and S pole before it returns to the original pole, as shown at $a'b'$ in Fig. 294(*b*). The winding after passing once around the armature reaches element $a'b'$ lying under the same pole as the initial element ab. When a winding advances from pole to pole in this manner, it is a *wave winding*. The number of winding elements spanned by the end connections on the back of the armature is called the *back* pitch and is denoted by y_b in Fig. 294(*b*). This is similar to the corresponding term in the lap winding, Fig. 294(*a*). The number of elements which the end connections span on the commutator end of the armature is the *front* pitch and is denoted by y_f. This should also be compared with Fig. 294(*a*). As in the lap winding, y_f and y_b must both be odd in order that one side of a coil may lie in the top of a slot and the other side in the bottom of a

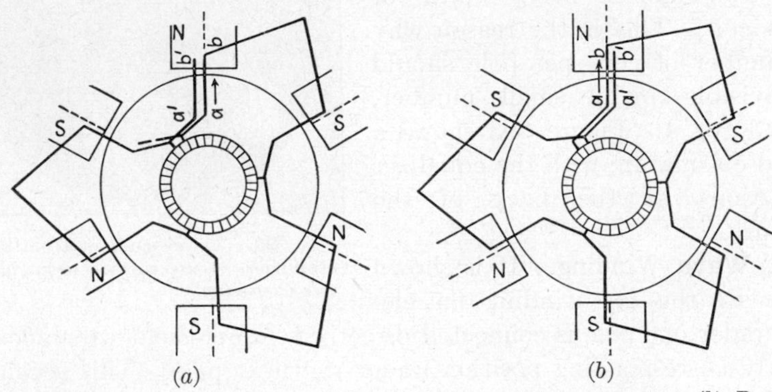

FIG. 295. (*a*) Retrogressive wave winding—34 commutator segments. (*b*) Progressive wave winding—32 commutator segments.

slot. Unlike the lap winding, y_f may equal y_b in the wave winding. The foregoing is illustrated as follows:

A wave winding has a back pitch of 23 and a front pitch of 19. The average pitch

$$y = \frac{23 + 19}{2} = 21.$$

Both the front and back pitch may be 21, making the average pitch 21. In any event, the average pitch

$$y = \frac{y_b + y_f}{2} \tag{330}$$

may be either even or odd.

When the winding viewed from the commutator end falls in a slot to the left of its starting point as $a'b'$, Figs. 294(*b*) and 295(*a*), after passing once around the armature, the winding is *retrogressive*. If, on the other hand, it falls to the right of its starting point, Fig. 295(*b*), it is *progressive*.

The wave winding is much more restricted in its relation to the number of slots and coils than the lap winding, for the following reason: In a simplex wave winding, after having gone once around the armature, the winding must fall *two* elements either to the right or left of the element at which it started. Thus in Fig. 295(*a*), if there are two elements per slot and element *ab* lies in the bottom of one slot, element *a'b'* must lie in the bottom of the slot next to *ab*. As there are two elements in each slot, elements *ab* and *a'b'* must differ from each other by 2.

Let y be the average pitch. Assume that the winding closes after going once around the armature, which, of course, it should not do as this would constitute a short circuit. Then,

$$py = Z$$

where p is the number of poles and Z the number of coil sides or elements. But the winding must *not* close after passing once around; in fact, it must

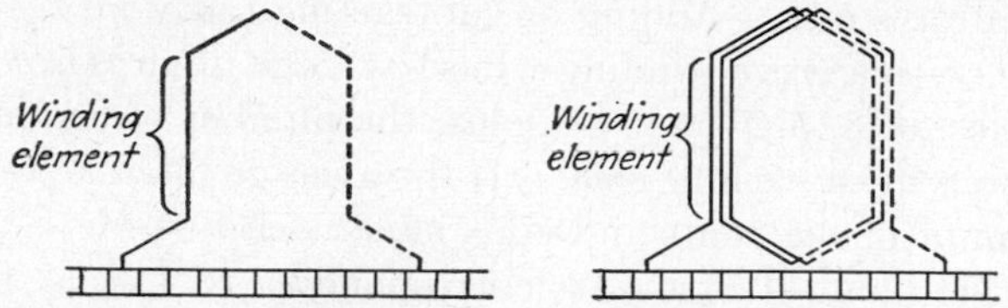

FIG. 296. Single-turn coil representing a 3-turn coil for winding diagram.

not close until every slot is filled. Therefore, after having gone once around the armature, the product py cannot equal Z but must be $Z \pm 2$. That is,

$$py = Z \pm 2,$$

or

$$y = \frac{Z \pm 2}{p}. \tag{331}$$

The plus sign indicates a *progressive* winding and the minus sign a *retrogressive* winding.

As an illustration, assume that a 4-pole armature has 63 slots and four elements per slot, making 252 winding elements. Let the average pitch be 63, the front and back pitch being 63. As in the lap-winding diagrams, a single-turn coil will be used to represent a coil having several turns, Fig. 296. Starting at element 1, the winding will advance as follows:

1–64–127–190–(253 or 1).

That is, the winding will close on itself after having gone once around the armature, which condition constitutes a short circuit and makes the winding impossible. (The method by which a winding may be placed in these slots will be shown later, p. 393.) Therefore, a simplex wave winding is impossible in a 4-pole machine if 252 winding elements are to be included.

Let N_c be the number of commutator segments, which is also the number of coils.

$$N_c = \frac{Z}{2}; \qquad Z = 2N_c.$$

Let

$$p_1 = \text{pairs of poles} = \frac{p}{2}; \qquad p = 2p_1.$$

Substituting in (331)

$$y = \frac{2N_c \pm 2}{2p_1};$$

$$N_c = p_1 y \mp 1. \tag{332}$$

If p_1 and y are odd, the product p_1y is odd, as the product of two odd numbers is always odd. Adding or subtracting unity makes N_c even.

Therefore, with a wave winding whose average pitch is *odd* and having 6, 10, 14 poles, or 3, 5, 7 pairs of poles, the number of commutator segments and coils must each be *even*. If the average pitch is *even*, the number of commutator segments and coils must each be *odd*.

On the other hand, if p_1 is *even*, corresponding to 4, 8, or 12 poles, the product p_1y is always even, so that N_c must be *odd*. That is, when the pairs of poles are *even*, the number of commutator segments must be *odd*. The application of (332) is illustrated in Fig. 295. There are 6 poles and the average commutator pitch y is 11. Applying (332), $N_c = 3 \cdot 11 + 1 = 34$ and $N_c = 3 \cdot 11 - 1 = 32$. The 34 segments are shown in Fig. 295(a), which gives a retrogressive winding, and the 32 are shown in (b), which gives a progressive winding. N_c is even in either case.

274. Commutator Pitch. It is seen from a study of Fig. 295 that the commutator pitch in a wave winding is quite different from that in a lap winding. In both (a) and (b) the commutator pitch $y_c = 11$ segments. The commutator pitch *cannot* be equal to the total number of segments divided by the pairs of poles, for if this were the case the winding would close on itself after one passage around the armature. For example, if the total number of segments in Figs. 295(a) and (b) be divided by the pairs of poles, there results $11\frac{1}{3}$ and $10\frac{2}{3}$. The difference between 11, the actual commutator pitch, and these quantities represents the creepage of the wave winding. This creepage is necessary in order that the winding shall not close on itself after one passage around the armature.

This gives another limitation of the wave winding and shows why the 252-element (126-coil) winding just considered is impossible. The number of coils must be *odd* in a 4-pole winding. However, if one coil were omitted, making 250 elements, the winding would progress as follows:

1–64–127–190–(253 or 3)
–66–129–192–5, etc.

That is, the winding would advance by 2 elements after each passage around the armature, which condition makes the winding possible. The omission of a coil reduces the number of commutator segments and coils from 126 to 125, an odd number. If the armature stampings were standard, having 126 slots, the winding would be possible by omitting 1 coil. This coil would be inserted in the slots just the same as the other coils, except that its ends would not be connected to the commutator segments but would be taped and thus insulated from the main winding. The coil would serve only as a filler and is a "dummy coil." In this case there would be a slight "creeping" of the winding with respect to the commutator, as shown in Fig. 297. This is a *forced* winding.

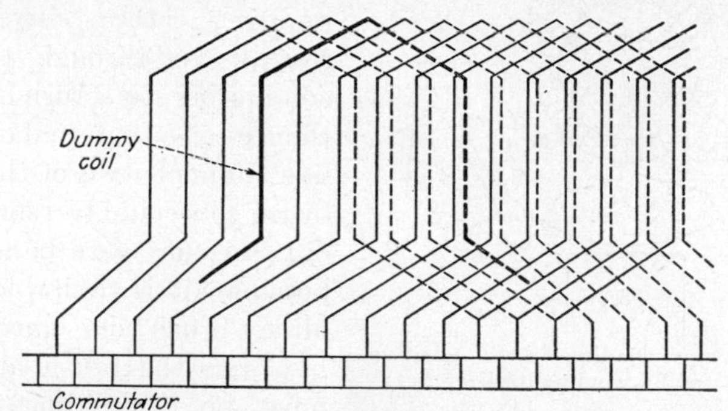

FIG. 297. Dummy coil and "creeping" in forced wave winding.

If the coils in a wave winding consist of more than one turn, they will have the ends brought out and connected in the manner shown in Fig. 281 (p. 376) and in Fig. 296. When coils for a wave winding are formed, the ends must be spread as in *A*, *B*, and *C*, Fig. 281. With the lap winding the coil ends are taped in close to each other so that they may be connected to adjacent commutator segments, Fig. 283 (p. 378). (With a duplex winding the ends connect to alternate segments, etc.)

275. Number of Brushes. Figure 298 shows a wave winding after a single passage around the armature. It starts at positive brush *a* and returns to this brush after advancing once around the armature. This is a 6-pole winding in a machine having 44 commutator segments. The pitch is found from (332):

$$44 = 3y \mp 1.$$

$$y = \frac{44 + 1}{3} = 15,$$

using the plus sign. This is also equal to the number of commutator segments by which the winding advances per *pair* of poles, or each time that it is connected to the commutator. Therefore, the segment connections, starting with 1, are 1–16–31–2–17, etc., as in Fig. 298. The winding ends one segment beyond the starting point for each complete passage around the armature, showing that the correct pitch has been chosen.

There are three positive brush sets *a*, *b*, *c*, and also three negative brush sets, the same number that would be used with a lap winding. Note that the three positive brush sets, *a*, *b*, *c*, are connected together *directly* by the winding. Moreover, the conductors which connect these three brush sets all lie between the poles in the neutral plane, where they are not cutting magnetic flux and are for the instant, therefore, dead conductors. Hence, if brush sets *b* and *c* were removed, the current could readily go through these dead conductors to brush set *a* and thence to the external circuit. In like manner, two of the negative brush sets could be removed without serious disturbance. When possible, it is desirable to utilize all six brush sets, since with only two sets the brush area per set must be three times the value when all six brush sets are used. This would mean that the commutator must be nearly three times as long as before.

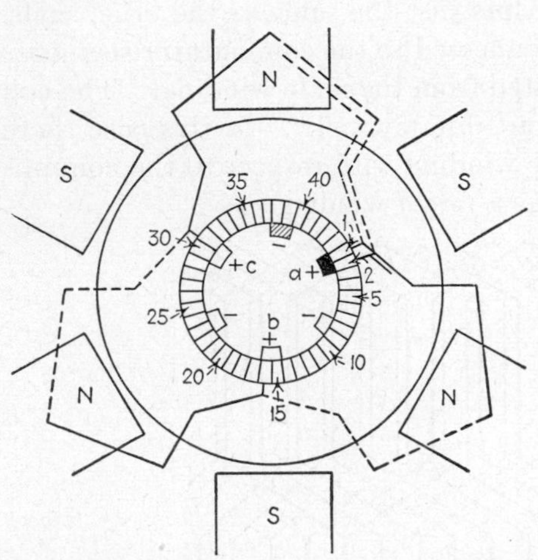

FIG. 298. Wave winding—three positive brushes connected by winding itself.

In a wave winding only two brush sets are necessary, regardless of the number of poles, although it is usually desirable to use the same number of brush sets as poles.

There are cases, however, where it is desirable to use only two brush sets. The best example is in railway motors where it would be difficult to obtain access to four or six brush sets. By means of a small handhole in the motor casing, it is a comparatively simple matter to reach two brush sets located on the top of the commutator.

276. Paths in Wave Winding. In a simplex wave winding there are always *two* parallel paths, regardless of the number of poles. Figure 299 shows a 4-pole 17-slot simplex wave winding, having two coil sides per slot. One of the paths is shown by heavy lines. Approximately half the winding is heavy, the other half constituting the other path. (The coils short-circuited by the brushes are not included.) A wave winding may be duplex, triplex, or have any degree of multiplicity, just as the lap winding may.

The number of paths through the armature depends only on the degree of multiplicity and not on the number of poles. A simplex wave winding always has two paths, a duplex winding four paths, etc.

It is interesting to compare the current and voltage of an armature for the various ways of connection. Consider the armature of a 6-pole dynamo. When connected as a simplex lap winding let its emf be 300 volts and the armature current per terminal be 120 amp. The accompanying table gives the values of current and emf obtainable when the winding is changed, the total number of armature conductors remaining fixed.

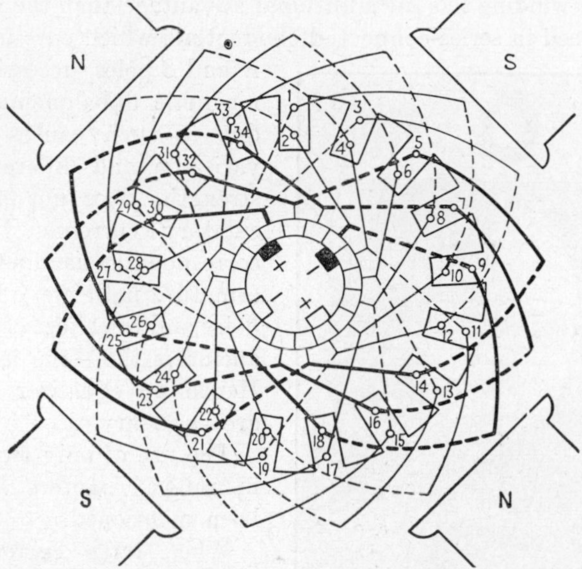

Fig. 299. Seventeen-slot 4-pole simplex wave winding; back pitch = 9, front pitch = 7; one of two parallel paths shown heavy.

	Paths	Volts	Amperes	Kilowatts
Simplex lap	6	300	120	36
Duplex lap	12	150	240	36
Triplex lap	18	100	360	36
Simplex wave	2	900	40	36
Duplex wave	4	450	80	36
Triplex wave	6	300	120	36

Note that in this particular machine the triplex wave winding gives the same result as the simplex lap winding. The kilowatts capacity is not affected by the connection used. These relations should be kept in mind when it is desired to change the voltage and current rating of an armature, either by reconnecting the winding or by rewinding the armature.

277. Uses of the Two Types of Winding. A wave winding has the advantage that it gives a higher emf with a given number of poles and armature conductors. It is used, therefore, in small machines, especially those designed for 600-volt circuits. In this case a lap winding would result in a very large number of small conductors. This, in turn, means a higher winding cost and less efficient utilization of the space in the slots.

The wave winding has an additional advantage that the emf in each path is induced in series-connected conductors, which pass under *all* the *N* and *S* poles successively. Any magnetic unbalancing, therefore, due to such causes as air-gap variation and difference in pole strength, does not produce circulatory currents, because the corresponding conductors of every armature path move by the same poles and the effect of such unbalancing is the same in each path. Hence no equalizer connections are necessary.

Fig. 300. Rolled-steel yoke with welded feet and terminal box. (*Westinghouse Electric Corporation.*)

The use of only two brush sets in railway motors has already been mentioned.

When large currents are required, the lap winding is more satisfactory, since it gives a larger number of paths. As 200 amp per path is practically the limit, a large number of paths must be used where large current output is desired. This is particularly true for large engine-driven multipolar generators.

DYNAMO CONSTRUCTION

278. Frame and Cores. The frame, or yoke, of a dynamo has two functions. It is a portion of the magnetic circuit (see Figs. 194 and 195, pp. 246 and 247), and it acts as a mechanical support for the machine as a whole. In small machines, where weight is of little importance, the yoke is often made of cast iron. The feet almost always form a part of the casting. Except in dynamos of small size, however, the modern method of forming the yoke is to roll a steel slab around a cylindrical mandrel and then to weld the slab at the bottom. Figure 300 shows a yoke so fabri-

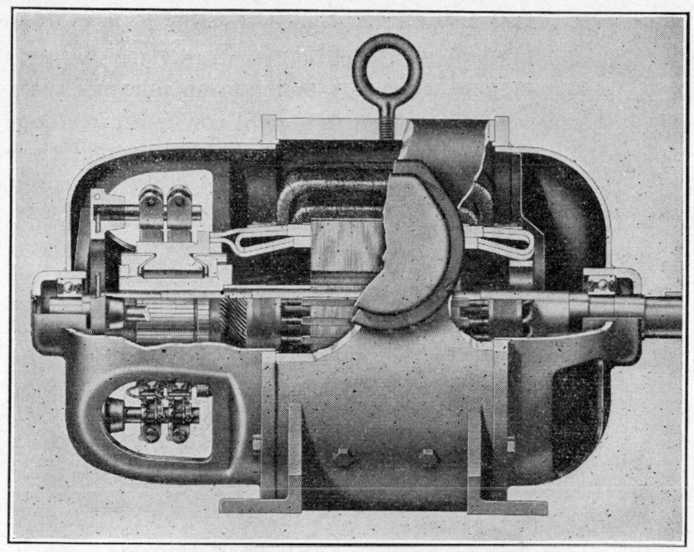

FIG. 301. Cutaway view of complete dynamo with yoke of Fig. 300. (*Westinghouse Electric Corporation.*)

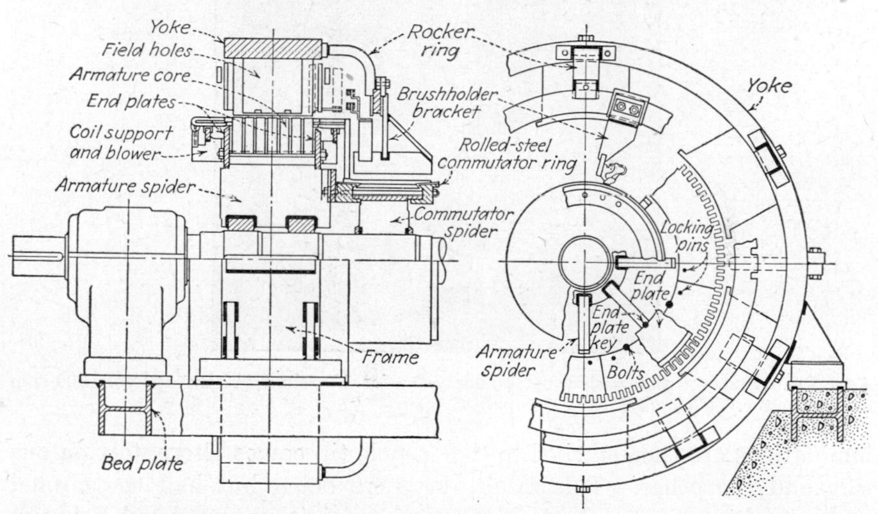

FIG. 302. A typical fabricated d-c machine assembly. (*Westinghouse Electric Corporation.*)

cated with the feet and terminal box welded to it. A cutaway view of the complete generator is shown in Fig. 301. In large dynamos, the field frame, the feet, and the bedplate are fabricated from steel, Figs. 302 and 303. In such dynamos the yoke, or the field frame, is fabricated in two pieces which are bolted together as shown in the figures. This facilitates shipment and also permits the armature to be removed by means of an overhead crane.

279. Field Cores and Shoes. Although in the past cast steel and forged steel have been used for the field cores, in modern designs the field cores are built up of annealed sheet-steel laminations riveted together under hydraulic pressure. The complete field core with windings is held by cap screws to the frame, the threads of which extend through the frame and tap into the pole cores, Figs. 303 and 306. To minimize the distortion of the flux due to armature reaction (Secs. 293, 294, 295), each lamination is sometimes made with only a single pole tip, Fig. 304. These

FIG. 303. Stator frame with brush-holder yoke for 12-pole 2,300-kw 600-volt 500-rpm d-c generator. (*General Electric Company.*)

laminations are then stacked so that a pole tip comes alternately on one side and the other. This results in there being but half the normal amount of iron in a pole-tip cross section, giving a saturated pole tip, which assists commutation.

An advantage of pole cores built up of laminations is that eddy-current losses in the pole faces are minimized (p. 526). When solid pole cores are used, it is usually necessary to have laminated pole shoes.

280. Field Coils. The field coils are usually wound with magnet wire (Appendix J, p. 594). If cotton insulation is used, the coils are dried in a vacuum and then impregnated with an insulating compound. The outer cotton insulation is often protected by tape or cord. In the larger machines, an air space is often left between layers for ventilating purposes. Another method is to wind the shunt coil on a metal spool, Fig. 305. Such a spool is readily removed from the pole core. The series winding is usually of bare copper strap, wound edgewise and spaced away from the shunt winding to assist ventilation, Fig. 305.

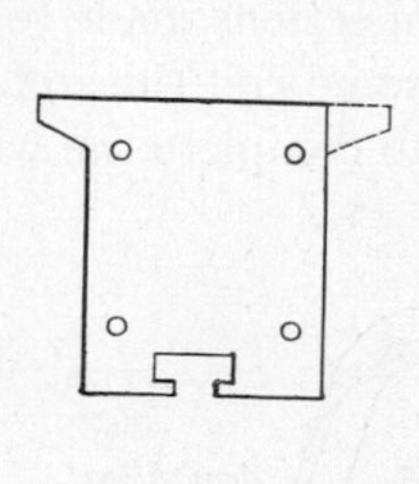

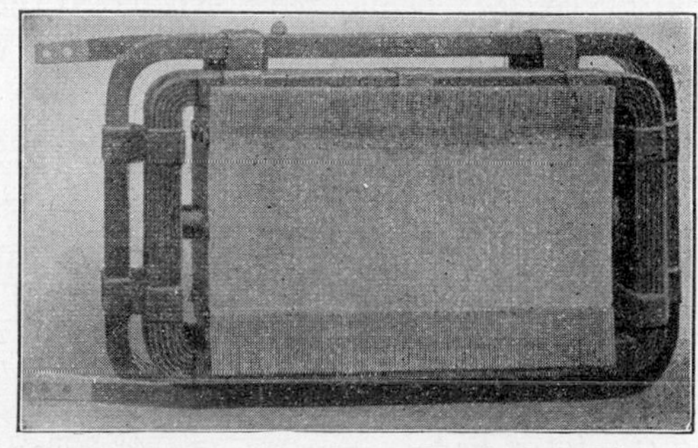

Fig. 304. Field core lamination, and pole piece assembled. (*Westinghouse Electric Corporation.*)

281. Armature. The armature is made of sheet-steel disks (14 to 25 mils thick) punched out by a die (also see p. 268). The slots may be cut by the die, or they may be punched with a slotting machine. In small motors the stampings are keyed directly to the shaft. The laminations may be perforated to permit air to pass through the armature axially and out radially for ventilation.

Fig. 305. Shunt-field coil and edgewise series winding.

In machines of medium size, the stampings are assembled and keyed to an armature spider, which is in turn keyed to the shaft, Fig. 306. This reduces the amount of sheet steel necessary and at the same time permits a free passage of air through the center of the armature. Usually in armatures, spacers are used to form ventilating ducts. In the armatures of Figs. 306 and 308 there is a single ventilating duct at the center of the laminations. The air, which flows axially within the spider, is thrown out through the ventilating ducts by centrifugal action. The stampings are usually clamped together by end plates held by through bolts. These end plates serve sometimes as supports for the overhang of the armature coils.

In Fig. 307 is shown an armature in the process of being wound, triple coils, Fig. 285 (p. 381), being used. Note that the coil sides of the bottom layer have all been placed in the slots and their connections made to the risers of the commutator bars. There are shown some coil sides of the top layer which are about to be placed in the slots to complete the wind-

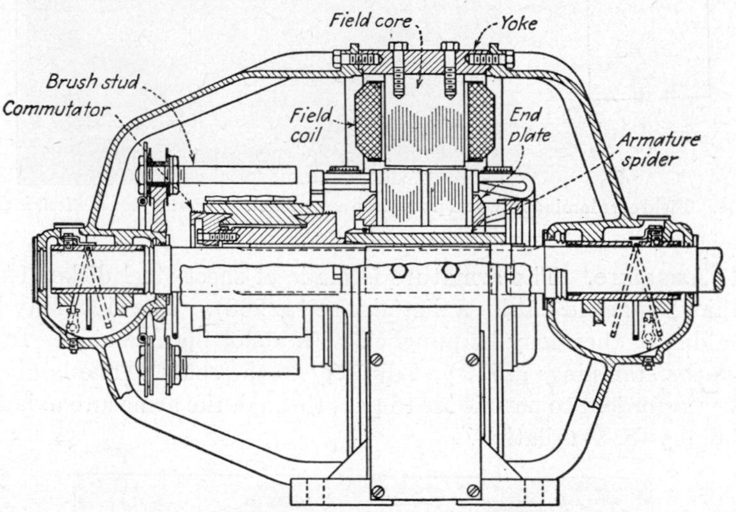

Fig. 306. Direct-current generator with shield bearings. Longitudinal section. (*General Electric Company.*)

ing. In Fig. 308 is a front (commutator) view and a back view of a completed armature.

When the armature becomes greater than 38 in., or so, in diameter, it is not economical to punch out a complete ring. Such armatures are made up of segments similar to those in Fig. 302, each segment lapping the joint in the next layer. The segments are either dovetailed to the armature spider or are clamped between the two end plates by through bolts, and the end plates are in turn keyed to the armature spider, Fig. 302. In the fabricated construction of Fig. 302 the spider arms are welded to the hub rings, the welds being shown in heavy black.

The slots may be straight-sided, Fig. 194 (p. 246), in which case the conductors are held in the slots by binding wires. In the larger machines the conductors are held in the slots by hard-fiber wedges, Fig. 309. The slots must be well insulated, as grounds are troublesome and expensive to

Fig. 307. Partly wound armature showing method of assembling coils. (*Reliance Electric and Engineering Company.*)

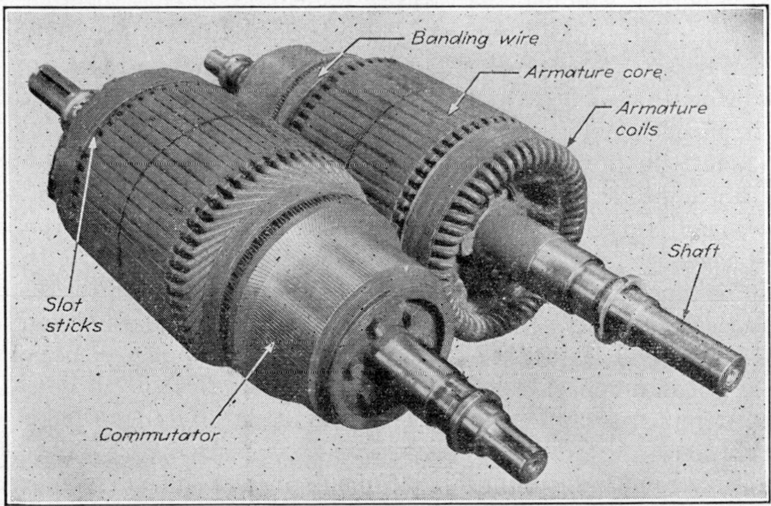

Fig. 308. Front and back view of a completed armature. (*Reliance Electric and Engineering Company.*)

repair. A layer of a hard substance, such as fish paper, fiber, or press-board, should be placed next to the laminations, Fig. 307. This layer, in turn, should be lined with varnished cambric or muslin. In Fig. 309(*a*) is shown the arrangement of triple coils in a slot, a fiber wedge being used to hold them in the slot. In Fig. 309(*b*) two coil sides of 12 turns each are held by a fiber wedge. In Fig. 309(*c*) is shown the type of slot used by the Reliance Electric and Engineering Company, in which a hard-fiber wedge and a hard-fiber separator are used.

The conductors are usually either single cotton-covered (scc), double cotton-covered (dcc), or enamel and cotton. Fiberglas, treated with organic varnishes, and silicone are also used for conductor insulation where the operating temperature is abnormally high, as in railway motors. Also, mica tape is sometimes used where the temperature is high.

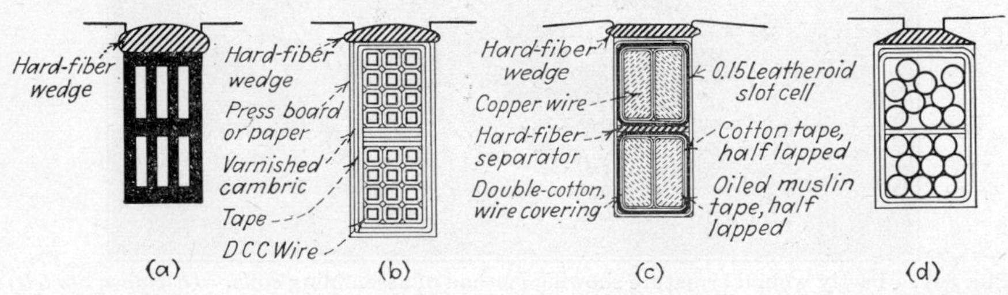

FIG. 309. Types of slot. (*a*) Open slot containing triple coil. (*b*) Open slot containing two coil sides, 12 turns per coil. (*c*) Slot used by Reliance Electric and Engineering Company. (*d*) Semiclosed slot and "mush" winding.

In the normal winding, the turns of the coil are bound together with cotton tape, and the coil unit so formed is dipped in impregnating varnish and baked. This process may be repeated as many as three or four times before the coil is ready to be placed in the slot. Two or more coils may be taped together to form multiple coils (p. 380).

To reduce the flux irregularities due to the tufts of flux from the tooth faces which produce pole-face losses (p. 526), a semiclosed slot, Fig. 309(*d*), may be used. Because of the restricted slot opening, the individual coil sides must be placed in the slot one by one. Hence the coil cannot be taped as a unit, and the coil ends must be taped after the coils are placed in the slots. Except under special conditions, usually in fractional-horsepower motors, the expense of winding prevents the use of this type of slot in d-c machines.

282. Commutator. The commutator is made of wedge-shaped segments of hard-drawn or drop-forged copper, insulated from one another by thin layers of built-up mica cut from segment plate. The segments are held together by clamping flanges, Fig. 310, which pull the segments inward when the flanges are drawn together by either through bolts or cap screws. These flanges are prevented from short-circuiting the segments by two collars or rings of built-up mica, Fig. 310. This type of construction is shown by the commutators of the machines in Figs. 301 and 306.

The leads from the armature coils may be soldered into small longitudinal slits in the ends of the segments, or the segments may have risers, Figs. 301, 302, 306, 307, 308, 310, to which these leads are soldered.

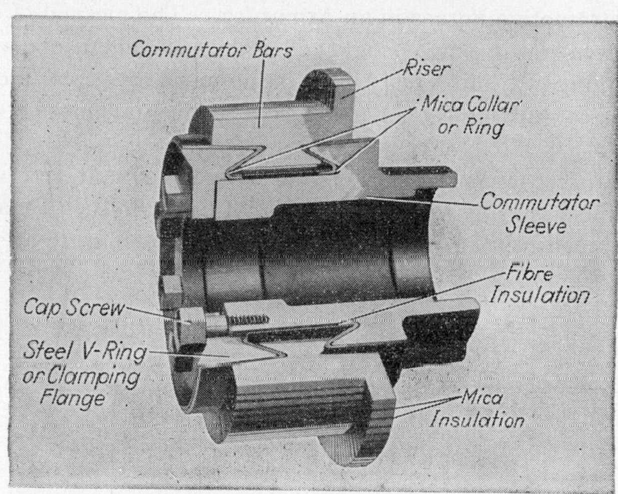

FIG. 310. Commutator construction. (*Reliance Electric and Engineering Company.*)

283. Brushes. The function of the brushes is to carry the current from the commutator to the external circuit. They are usually made of carbon, although in very low-voltage machines they may be made of copper gauze or patented metal-carbon compounds. The brush holder is fastened to the brush stud, Fig. 306, and holds the brush in its proper position on the commutator. The brush stud is insulated from the rocker arm by means of an insulating bushing and washer, Fig. 306. The brush should be free to slide in its holder in order that it may follow any irregularities in the commutator. The brush is made to bear down on the commutator by a spring. The pressure should be from 1 to 2 psi. To decrease the electrical resistance, the upper portion of the brush is copper-plated, Fig. 88 (p. 136), and this plating is connected to the brush holder by a pigtail made of copper ribbon. A brush-holder bracket attached to the stator frame is shown in Fig. 302.

CHAPTER XII

GENERATOR CHARACTERISTICS

284. Electromotive Forces in an Armature. The method of determining the average emf in simple single-coil and 2-coil generators is discussed at the beginning of Chap XI. Also it is shown that the emf induced in a single conductor cutting the magnetic field at right angles is $e = Blv10^{-8}$ volt [Eq. (321), p. 367], or $e = Blv$ [Eq. (322)].

The armature core forms part of the magnetic circuit and carries the conductors mechanically through the magnetic field in such a manner that emfs are induced in them. The windings on the armature are arranged

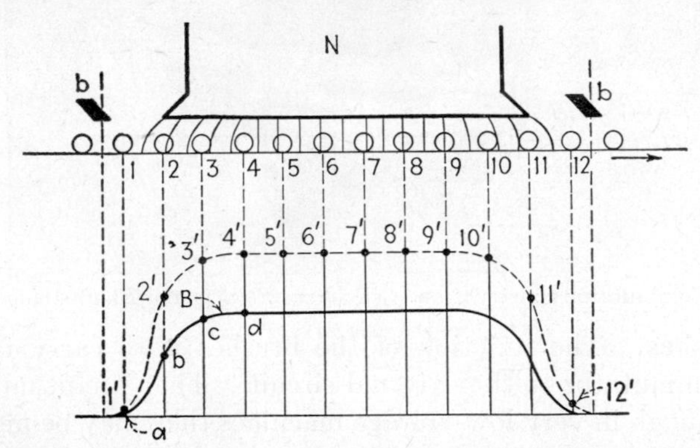

FIG. 311. Electromotive force induced in conductors between brushes.

so that certain groups of conductors are in series between brushes, care being taken in making the connections that no induced emfs are in opposition. The induced emf between brushes can be determined in terms of flux per pole, speed, number of armature conductors, parallel paths, etc.

In the elementary generators, Figs. 271 and 274 (pp. 366 and 369), the emf varies sinusoidally with time because simple coils rotate in a uniform magnetic field. In commercial generators these conditions usually do not exist. Instead of being uniform the field has a maximum density directly under the poles. The density diminishes irregularly between poles, becoming zero at some place in the region between poles, Fig. 312. Commercial generators also have closed-coil windings, and a number of conductors in series are distributed over the armature surface.

Consider Fig. 311, which shows a portion of an armature under an N pole and moving from left to right. The flux entering the armature from this north pole is also shown. Below, the curve B shows the flux density along the armature. That is, the ordinate at each point gives the *flux density* at that point, expressed preferably in lines per square centimeter. The total flux per pole is given by the area under the curve multiplied by the effective length of the armature. Midway between poles this flux density is zero, and under the pole, where the air-gap is practically uniform, the flux density is practically uniform.

In Fig. 311 are also shown 12 conductors (1, 2, . . . , 12) on the surface of an armature included in one pole pitch and which, at the instant shown, lie under an N pole. They may represent the conductors of a ring winding, Figs. 278(a) and (b) (p. 373), or one layer of a lap or of a wave winding, Figs. 288 and 299, (pp. 384 and 395). A study of Fig. 278 shows that if they represent the conductors of a ring winding, they are all connected in series between a positive and a negative brush. If they represent a single layer of a simplex lap or of a wave winding, the other coil side of each conductor, which is in series with it, lies at this instant in the same, or in nearly the same, position relative to an S pole.

It follows that if the sum of the emfs in the conductors of this group can be determined, it will be equal to the sum of the emfs induced in the conductors of similar groups which, at this same instant, lie under the other poles. The emf between brushes will then be equal to the sum of the emfs induced in all the conductors on the armature, divided by the number of parallel paths, as will be shown later.

The emf induced in a single conductor at any instant is given by Eq. (321) (p. 367):

$$e = Blv10^{-8} \qquad \text{volts.}$$

If the speed is constant, the induced emf in any single conductor is proportional to the flux density B in which that conductor finds itself. For example, conductor 2 finds itself in a field whose density is given by ordinate b. The emf induced in this conductor will be given by the ordinate $2'$, which is equal to ordinate b multiplied by a constant of proportionality. Likewise, the emf induced in conductor 3 is given by ordinate $3'$, which is equal to ordinate c multiplied by the same constant of proportionality. Conductor 1 lies in the interpolar space, where the flux density, given by ordinate a, is low, and the emf is given by ordinate $1'$. From similar reasoning it is seen that the total emf induced in this group of conductors is given by the sum of all the ordinates $1'$ to $12'$. It is also seen that if a smooth curve be drawn through points $1'$ to $12'$, it is identical in shape with the curve B, being equal to B multiplied by the constant of proportionality. The sum of all the ordinates $1'$ to $12'$ is equal to the total emf induced in this group of conductors. This total emf is also equal to the average value of these ordinates multiplied by the number of ordinates, 12 in this case.

The emf ordinates, Fig. 311, give the emfs in the various conductors which at the instant shown happen to be lying between the two brushes *bb*. Since the conductors are all moving, these ordinates likewise give the emf induced in any single conductor as it takes successive positions 1, 2, etc., between brushes *bb*. Hence it follows that the total emf induced in this group of conductors is given by the average emf *per conductor* multiplied by the number of conductors. Further, it follows that the curve giving the variation with time of the emf in a single conductor, as it cuts a flux at constant speed, is of the same shape as the flux-density curve.

In Fig. 312 are shown two N poles and one S pole of a generator. For simplicity, the armature surface is shown as if it were rolled out flat. The flux-density curve is given below. The positive ordinates of the flux-distribution curve are N-pole flux entering the armature, and the negative ordinates are flux leaving the armature and entering an S pole. The total flux leaving an N pole is given by the area under one of the positive parts

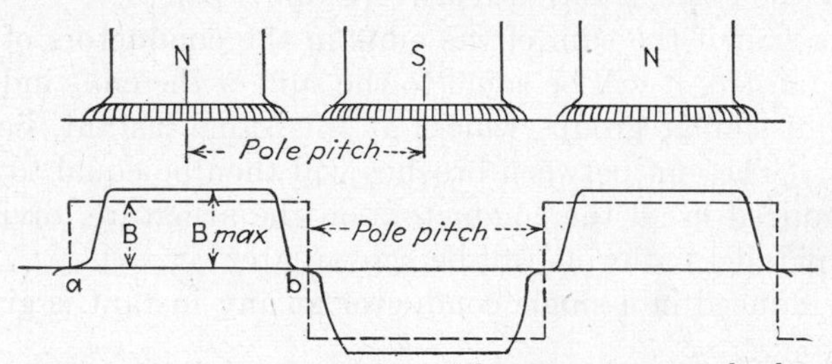

FIG. 312. Flux distribution of d-c generator at no load.

of the flux-distribution curve multiplied by the axial length of the pole. Similarly, the total flux leaving the armature and entering an S pole is given by the area of one of the negative parts of the flux-distribution curve multiplied by the axial length of the pole. The maximum flux density is given by the ordinate B_{max}.

Each positive part and each negative part of the curve may be replaced by a rectangle having the same area, as shown by the dotted line, Fig. 312. The height of this rectangle will be B maxwells per sq cm, which is equal to the *average* value of the flux density over an entire pole pitch. Let it be required to determine the average emf induced in a single conductor as it passes through the flux of successive poles.

Let the total flux leaving an N pole or entering an S pole be ϕ maxwells. Let l be the active length of the conductor in centimeters, s the speed of the armature in *rps*, and P the number of poles.

When the conductor passes through the distance *ab*, or one pole pitch, the average induced emf, by Eq. (321) (p. 367) and from the foregoing, is

$$E_{av} = Blv10^{-8} \qquad \text{volts,}$$

where B is the *average* flux density per pole pitch, l the active length of the conductor in centimeters, and v the velocity of the conductor in centimeters per second.

$$v = \frac{ab}{t} \qquad \text{cm per sec,}$$

where t is the time required for the conductor to travel the distance ab, equal to the pole pitch.

$$E_{\text{av}} = \frac{Bl(ab)}{t} 10^{-8} = \frac{\phi}{t} 10^{-8} \qquad \text{volts,}$$

since $Bl(ab)$ gives the total flux cut by the conductor between the points a and b and is therefore equal to ϕ, the flux per pole in maxwells.

The time

$$t = \frac{1}{sP} \qquad \text{sec.}$$

Therefore, the average emf per conductor is

$$E_{\text{av}} = \frac{\phi}{1/sP} 10^{-8} = \phi sP 10^{-8} \qquad \text{volts.}$$

If there are Z such conductors and P' paths through the armature, there must be Z/P' such conductors in series [see Eq. (325), p. 382].

Hence the total induced emf between brushes is

$$E = \frac{\phi sPZ}{P'10^8} \qquad \text{volts.} \tag{333}$$

If the speed S is given in rpm, (333) becomes

$$E = \frac{\phi SPZ}{60P'10^8} \qquad \text{volts.} \tag{334}$$

If the flux per pole Φ is given in webers, (334) becomes

$$E = \frac{\Phi SPZ}{60P'} \qquad \text{volts.} \tag{335}$$

Example. A 900-rpm 6-pole generator has a simplex lap winding. There are 300 conductors on the armature.

The poles are 10 in. square, and the average flux density is 50,000 maxwells per sq in. Determine the emf induced between brushes.

$$\phi = 10 \cdot 10 \cdot 50{,}000 = 5{,}000{,}000 \text{ maxwells.}$$
$$s = {}^{900}\!/_{60} = 15 \text{ rps.}$$
$$P = 6.$$
$$P' = 6 \text{ (see Sec. 270, p. 382).}$$
$$E = \frac{5{,}000{,}000 \cdot 15 \cdot 6 \cdot 300}{6 \cdot 10^8} = 225 \text{ volts.} \quad \textit{Ans.}$$

In the mks systems the flux Φ is equal to 0.05 weber. Using (335),

$$E = \frac{0.05 \cdot 900 \cdot 6 \cdot 300}{60 \cdot 6} = 225 \text{ volts. } \textit{Ans.}$$

285. Saturation Curve. Equation (334) may be written as follows:

$$E = \left(\frac{PZ}{60P'10^8}\right)\phi S \qquad \text{volts.} \tag{336}$$

The quantity within the parentheses is constant for a given machine and may be denoted by K.

Therefore,

$$E = K\phi S. \tag{337}$$

The induced emf in a dynamo is directly proportional to the flux per pole and to the speed. If the speed be kept constant, the induced emf is directly proportional to the flux per pole ϕ.

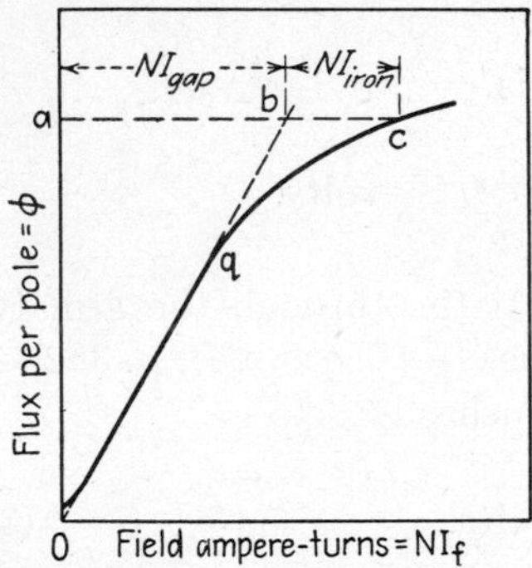

FIG. 313. Saturation curve.

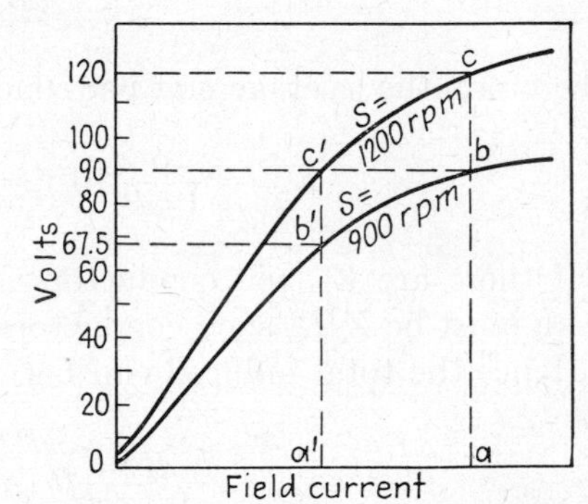

FIG. 314. Saturation curves for two different speeds.

The flux is produced by the field ampere-turns, and as the turns on the field remain constant, the flux is a function of the field current. It is not directly proportional to the field current because of the varying permeability of the magnetic circuit.

Figure 313 shows the relation between the field ampere-turns and the flux per pole, or the *saturation curve.* The flux does not start at zero, ordinarily, but at some value slightly greater, owing to the residual magnetism in the magnetic circuit. For low values of field ampere-turns the saturation curve is practically a straight line since most of the reluctance of the magnetic circuit is in the air-gap. At the point q the iron begins to become saturated, and the curve falls away from the straight line.

The number of field ampere-turns for the air-gap and for the iron can be approximately determined for any point on the curve.

Let it be required to determine the ampere-turns for the gap and for the iron at the point c. From the origin, draw ob tangent to the saturation curve, and also draw the horizontal line *ac*. The line *ob* is the magnetization curve of the air-gap, if the reluctance of the iron at low saturation be neglected. Therefore, the ampere-turns required by the gap are equal to *ab*, and those required by the iron are equal to *bc*.

From (337) the induced emf is proportional to the flux, if the speed is maintained constant. Therefore, if the induced emf be plotted with field current as abscissas, a curve similar to that of Fig. 313 is obtained. This is shown in Fig. 314, and the ordinates differ from those of Fig. 313 only by a constant quantity *KS*. Two curves are shown in Fig. 314, one plotted for 1,200 rpm and the other for 900 rpm. The curves are similar, any ordinate of the lower curve being 900/1,200 of the value of the corre-

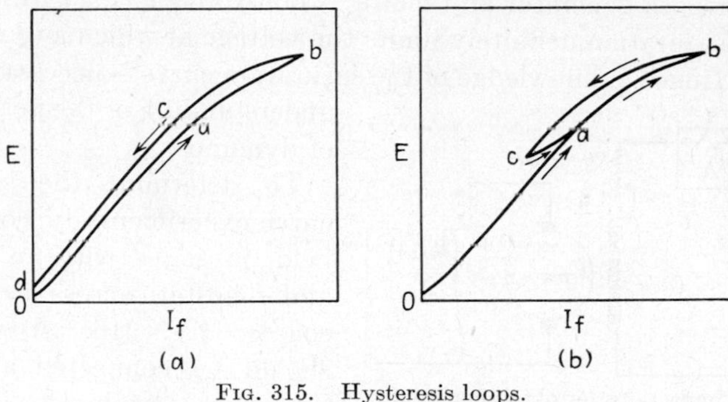

FIG. 315. Hysteresis loops.

sponding ordinate of the upper curve. Thus, at ordinate *ac*, equal to 120 volts,

$$\frac{ab}{ac} = \frac{900}{1{,}200} = \frac{90 \text{ volts}}{120 \text{ volts}}.$$

Also at ordinate $a'c'$, equal to 90 volts,

$$\frac{a'b'}{a'c'} = \frac{900}{1{,}200} = \frac{67.5 \text{ volts}}{90 \text{ volts}}.$$

If the saturation curve of a generator for one speed has been determined, saturation curves for other speeds may be readily found by the proportionality method just indicated.

286. Hysteresis. The saturation curve *oab*, Fig. 315(*a*), is determined for *increasing* values of the field current. If when point *b* is reached the field current be decreased, the curve will not retrace its path along the curve *bao*. For any given field current, the corresponding induced emf will now be greater than it was for *increasing* field currents. This is shown by the curve *bcd*. This effect is due to hysteresis in the iron (see Sec. 193, p. 263).

Figure 315(*b*) shows the effects obtained when the curve is carried up along the path *oab*, back to *c*, and at *c* the field current is again increased, the curve ultimately coming back to *oab* at the point *a*.

It is evident that for any given value of field current there may be more than one value of flux. The value of flux for any given field current depends on whether the field current was *increased* until it reached the value in question or whether it was *decreased*. This characteristic of the magnetic circuit should be kept in mind, for the operating characteristics of both generators and motors are affected to a considerable degree by hysteresis in their magnetic circuits.

287. Experimental Determination of Saturation Curve. The saturation curve of a dynamo has important effects on the operating characteristics for both generator and motor. For example, Figs. 313, 314, 315 show that saturation definitely limits the voltage at which a dynamo can operate. Hence, a knowledge of the saturation curve is necessary for the understanding of the performance of dynamos.

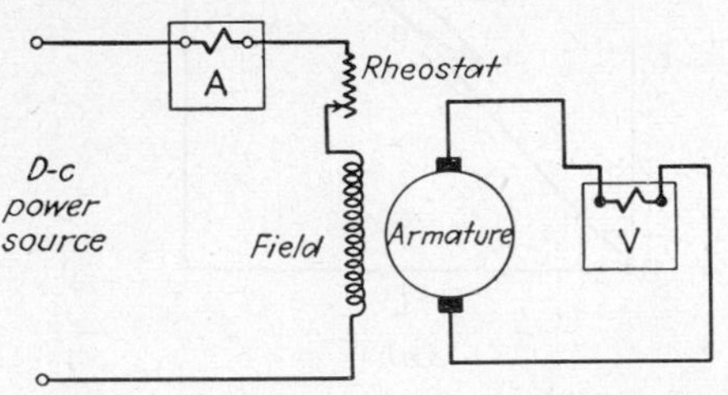

Fig. 316. Connections for obtaining saturation curve.

To determine the saturation curve experimentally, connect the field, in series with an ammeter and rheostat, across a d-c power source, Fig. 316. A voltmeter should be connected across the armature terminals. The ammeter measures the field current, plotted as abscissa; the voltmeter measures induced armature emf, plotted as ordinate. As the voltage drop within the armature due to the voltmeter current is negligible, the terminal volts and the induced emf are identical under these conditions. During the experiment the speed should be determined each time that the other readings are taken (see p. 520). If the speed cannot be maintained constant, corrections can be made for any variation, using the method of Sec. 285 (p. 408).

When the saturation curve of a shunt generator is determined, it may be difficult to obtain a sufficiently high resistance to reduce the field current to its lower values. A voltage divider, Fig. 317(*a*), allows field currents as low as zero to be obtained without using excessive resistance. Such a connection is easily made with the well-known three-point type of field rheostat, Fig. 317(*b*).

In determining the saturation curve experimentally, the field current should be varied continuously in *one direction*, either up or down, Fig. 315(*a*). Otherwise, minor hysteresis loops will be introduced, Fig. 315(*b*).

The field current in this experiment should be obtained from a source other than the generator itself, for two reasons. If the generator excites its own field, the induced emf and field current are interdependent. Hence, any adjustment of field current causes a change in induced emf, which in turn changes the field current. This makes it difficult to adjust the field current to a definite value. Also, a voltage drop exists in the armature due to field current. The voltmeter does not indicate, therefore, the true induced emf, although the error is slight.

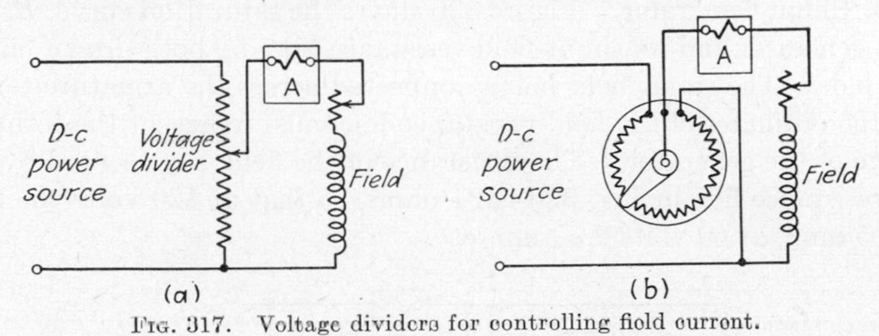

FIG. 317. Voltage dividers for controlling field current.

288. Field-resistance Line. By Ohm's law, the current in a simple circuit of constant resistance is proportional to the voltage. If the voltage be plotted as a function of current, Fig. 318, a straight line results, passing through the origin. For example, if the resistance of a field circuit be 50 ohms, the current will be 2 amp when the voltage is 100 volts; 1.5 amp when the voltage is 75 volts; and 1 amp when the voltage is 50 volts. This relation is shown in curve II, Fig. 318. Curve I shows the resistance line for 80 ohms field resistance. It will be noted that at 80 volts the current is 1.0 amp, at 40 volts it is 0.5 amp, etc. Curve III shows the same relation for a field resistance of 40 ohms.

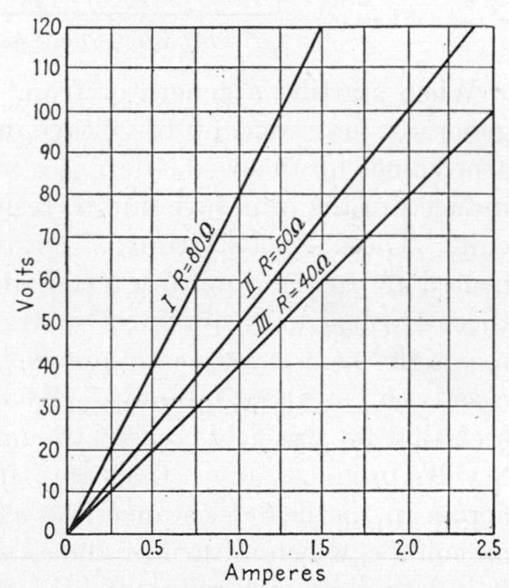

FIG. 318. Field-resistance lines.

It will be noted that the higher the resistance the greater the slope of the resistance line. In fact the slope of the line is equal to the field resistance in ohms, since the tangent of the angle which the line makes with the axis of abscissas is E/I.

289. Types of Generators. There are three general types of d-c generator, the shunt, the compound, and the series. In the shunt type the field circuit is connected across the armature terminals, usually in series with a rheostat, Fig. 319. The shunt field, therefore, must have a comparatively high resistance in order that it may not take too great a proportion of the generator current. The compound generator is similar to the shunt but has an additional field winding connected in series with either the armature or the load, Fig. 356 (p. 452). The series generator is excited entirely by a winding of comparatively few turns connected in series with the armature and load (see p. 461).

290. Shunt Generator. Figure 320 shows the saturation curve, E, of a shunt generator and its shunt-field resistance line, I_f, both drawn on the same plot. The shunt field being connected across the armature terminals, the ordinates of the field-resistance line must represent the terminal voltage of the generator. The resistance of the field, represented by the field-resistance line in Fig. 320 is 24 ohms, so that at 120 volts the field takes 5 amp, at 60 volts 2.5 amp, etc.

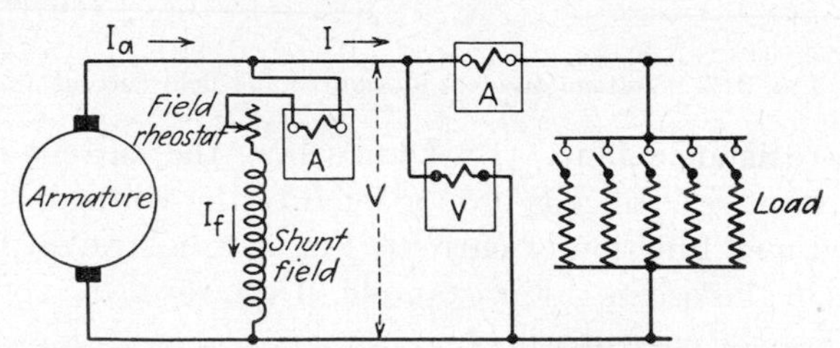

FIG. 319. Shunt-generator connections.

When starting a generator from rest, the induced emf is zero. The generator may come up to voltage in the following manner: As the generator comes up to speed, there is a small emf *oa*, Fig. 320, about 4 volts, induced in the armature due to residual magnetism in the magnetic circuit. These 4 volts also exist across the field, because the field is connected across the armature terminals. The value of field current due to these 4 volts can be obtained by drawing a horizontal line from *a* until it meets the field-resistance line at *b*. The field current in this particular case is *ob′*, or about 0.2 amp. By consulting the saturation curve, it is seen that for this field current the induced emf *b′c* is about 8 volts. The 8 volts produces about 0.33 amp in the field, as is seen by projecting across to the field resistance line at *d*. This field current *od′* produces an emf *d′e*, which in turn produces a higher value of field current. Thus it is seen that each value of field current produces an emf in excess of the previous value, and this increased emf in turn increases the field current, or the action is cumulative. The emf continues to build up until point *f* is reached, where the field-resistance line crosses the saturation curve. The generator cannot build up beyond this point for the following reasons:

Consider a point *k* above *f* on the field-resistance line. This point represents a field current *og′* of about 5.3 amp. To produce this field current requires a voltage $g'k$ of about 128 volts. But this field current of 5.3 amp produces an induced emf $g'g$ of only 122 volts. If 128 volts is required to produce the field current of 5.3 amp and the generator can produce only 122 volts at this field current, it is obvious that the generator cannot build up to the point k.

The generator will not build up in the large discrete increments shown by the dotted line, Fig. 320. The flux cannot change instantly so that the indication of a voltmeter connected across the generator terminals will increase gradually and smoothly.

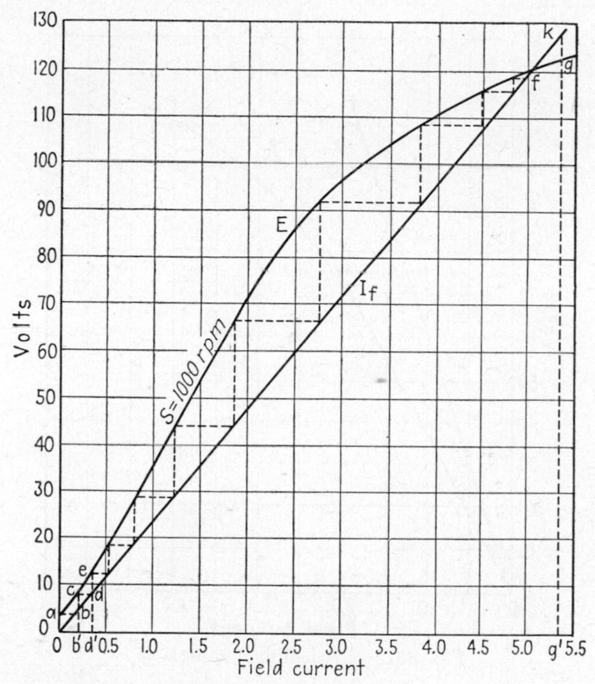

FIG. 320. Method of shunt generator building up.

The building up of the generator, Fig. 320, may also be considered from the point of view of analytic geometry. The emf E of the saturation curve is a function of field current. That is,

$$E = f(I_f) \qquad \text{volts.} \tag{I}$$

Neglecting the small voltage drop in the armature due to the field current,

$$I_f = \frac{E}{R_f} \qquad \text{amp,} \tag{II}$$

where R_f is the resistance of the field circuit.

If (I) and (II) are solved simultaneously, the values of voltage and field current to which the generator builds up are obtained. However, it is difficult to express (I) as an analytic function. The solution of two simultaneous equations can be obtained, however, by the intersection of their graphs. This gives the point *f*.

It is evident that saturation of the iron prevents a generator from building up indefinitely.

291. Critical Field Resistance. If the resistance of the field circuit, Fig. 320, be increased to 60 ohms, the field-resistance line will be represented by *oa*, Fig. 321. This line crosses the saturation curve at point *a′*,

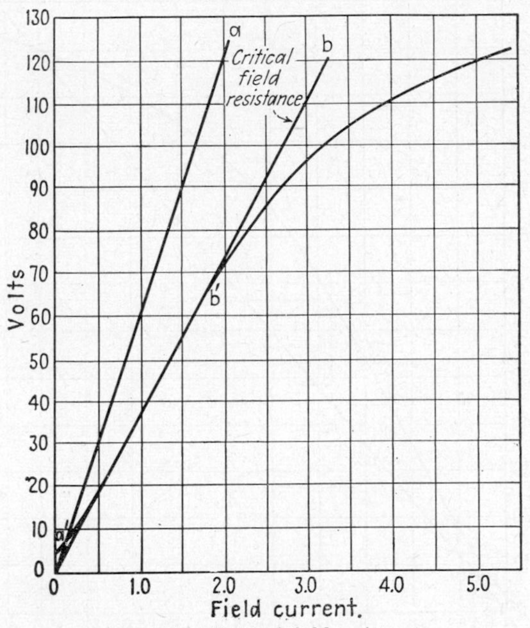

FIG. 321. Critical field resistance.

corresponding to about 6 volts. Therefore, with this value of field resistance, the generator will not build up beyond *a′*. If the field-circuit resistance be slowly decreased until the field-resistance line reaches *ob*, tangent to the saturation curve, the generator will begin to build up continuously without further decrease in the resistance of the field circuit. It will stop building up at the point *b′*. The value of the field resistance, corresponding to *ob*, which makes the field-resistance line tangent to the saturation curve is called the *critical field resistance*. In this particular case, the critical field resistance is 120 ÷ 3.25, or 36.9 ohms. If the field resistance exceeds the critical value, the generator cannot build up.

292. Failure to Build Up. If a generator fails to build up, the cause may be one or more of the four following:

1. The shunt field may be connected in such a way that the initial current through it on starting is in such a direction as to "buck" or reduce the residual magnetism, instead of increasing it. Under these conditions, the generator cannot build up. To test for this, open the field circuit. If the voltage rises when the field is opened, the field current is bucking the residual magnetism and the field should be reversed. If opening and closing the field circuit produce no effect on the voltmeter, it may be assumed that the field circuit is open.

2. The field resistance may be greater than the critical field resistance. In this case, the procedure is to reduce the field resistance until the generator builds up.

3. Imperfect brush contact may cause high resistance from commutator to brush. Since the field is the only load across the armature, poor brush contact is equivalent to high resistance in the field circuit. The effect is the same as that shown by the resistance line *oa*, Fig. 321, and the generator cannot build up to any substantial voltage. Low current density causes high brush-contact resistance (Sec. 301, p. 434). High contact resistance may be determined by exerting slight pressure on the individual brushes.

4. There may be no residual magnetism in the generator, owing to jarring or to too long a period of idleness. If the armature circuit is not open and the voltmeter is known to be all right, the absence of residual magnetism will be indicated by the voltmeter not reading. To remedy the difficulty, it may be necessary to connect the field terminals temporarily across a separate power supply in order to build up the residual magnetism. This is called *flashing* the field. If the generator has a series field, a convenient method is to connect a low-voltage source, such as a storage battery or even a dry cell, across the series field. This may produce enough magnetism to cause the generator to begin to build up. One or two trials may be necessary in order to secure the proper polarity.

293. Armature Reaction. Figure 322(*a*) shows the flux from the field poles through the armature of a bipolar generator when there is no current in the armature conductors. This flux is produced entirely by the ampere-turns of the field. Moreover, it is distributed symmetrically with respect to the polar axis, that is, the center line of the N and the S poles. The neutral plane, which is a plane perpendicular to the direction of the flux, coincides with the geometrical neutral of the system. At the right in Fig. 322(*a*) is shown a vector F which represents in magnitude and direction the mmf producing this flux. At right angles to this vector F is the neutral plane.

In Fig. 322(*b*) there is no current in the field coils, but the armature conductors are shown as carrying current. This current is in the same direction in the armature conductors as it would be were the generator under load. The direction of current is the same in all the conductors that lie under one pole. The direction of the current is into the paper on the left side of the armature. (This current direction may be checked by Fleming's right-hand rule, Sec. 262, p. 369.) The mmfs of these con-

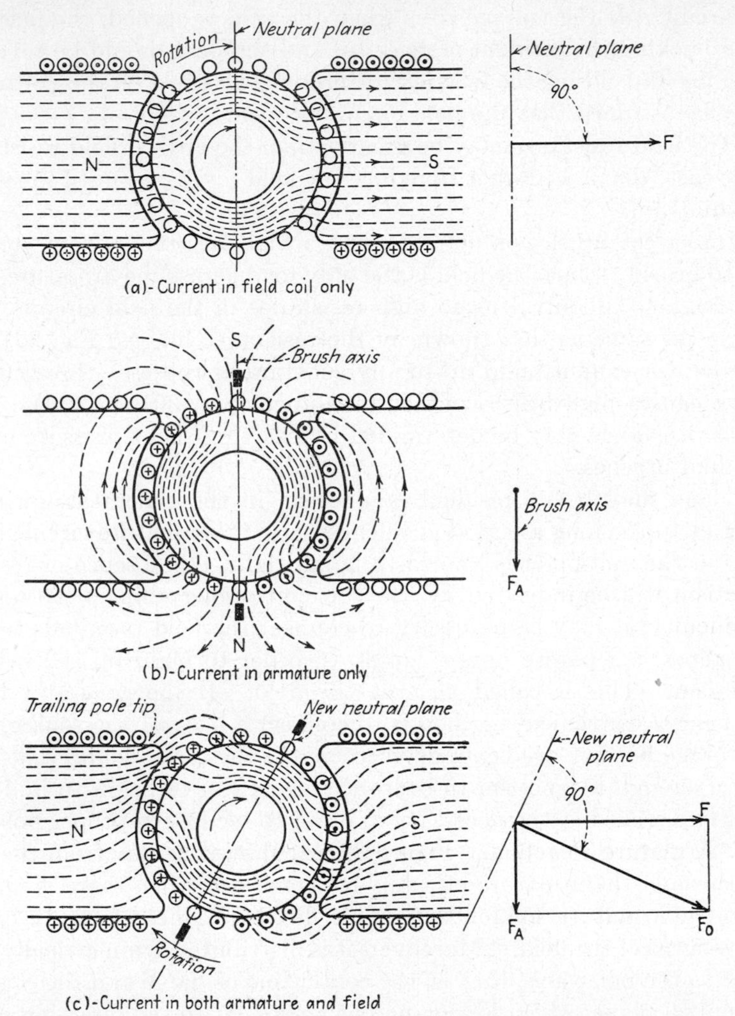

Fig. 322. Effect of armature reaction on field of generator.

ductors combine to send flux *downward* through the armature, as shown in the diagram, this direction being determined by the corkscrew rule. The direction of current in the conductors on the right-hand side of the armature is shown as being out of the paper. Their mmfs also combine to send flux *downward* through the armature. That is, the mmfs of the ampere-conductors on both sides of the armature combine in such a manner as to send flux downward through the armature. The direction of this flux is perpendicular to the polar axis. To the right of the figure, the armature mmf is represented in magnitude and direction by the vector F_A.

Figure 322(*c*) shows the result obtained when the field current and the armature current are acting simultaneously, which occurs when the generator is under load. The armature mmf crowds the symmetrical field flux shown in (*a*) into the upper pole tip in the N pole and into the lower pole tip in the S pole. As the generator armature is shown rotating in a clockwise direction, it will be noted that the flux is crowded into the *trailing* pole tip in each case. On the other hand, the flux is weakened in the two *leading* pole tips.

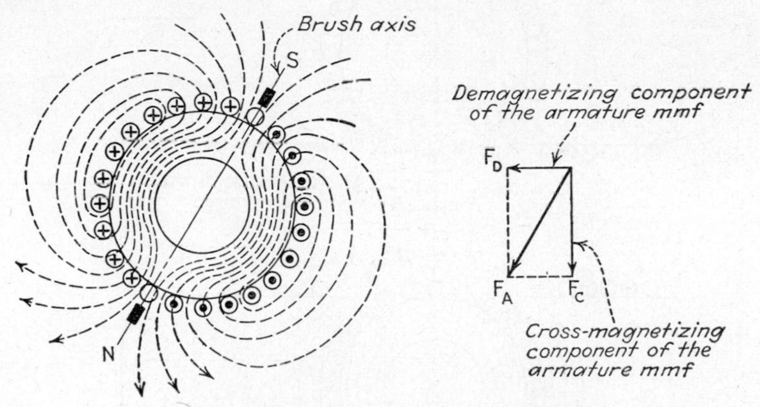

FIG. 323. Relation of armature flux to brush axis.

The effect of the armature current is to displace the field in the direction of rotation of the generator. *It should be kept in mind that the flux is not pulled around by the mechanical rotation of the armature.*

To the right of Fig. 322(*c*) the effect of armature reaction is shown by vectors. The field mmf vector F and the armature mmf vector F_A combine at right angles to form the resultant-field mmf vector F_0. The direction of F_0 is downward and to the right, which corresponds to the general direction of the resultant flux in the drawing. The neutral plane must be at right angles to F_0, provided that the direction of the resultant flux is the same as that of the resultant mmf.

As the neutral plane is perpendicular to the resultant field, it will be noted that it too has been advanced. It is shown in Chap. XI that the brushes should be set so that they short-circuit the coil undergoing commutation as it passes through the neutral plane. When the generator delivers current, the brushes should be set a little ahead of this neutral plane, as will be shown later. If the brushes are advanced to correspond to the advance of the neutral plane, all the conductors to the left of, but between, the two brushes must still carry current into the paper and those to the right must carry current out of the paper. The result is shown in Fig. 323. *The direction of the armature field moves with the brushes. Its axis always lies along the brush axis.* Therefore F_A, instead of pointing vertically downward, now points downward and to the left, as is shown by the vector. F_A may be resolved into two components, F_D parallel to the polar axis and F_C perpendicular to this axis. Since the geometrical distributions about the armature of these three mmfs are quite different

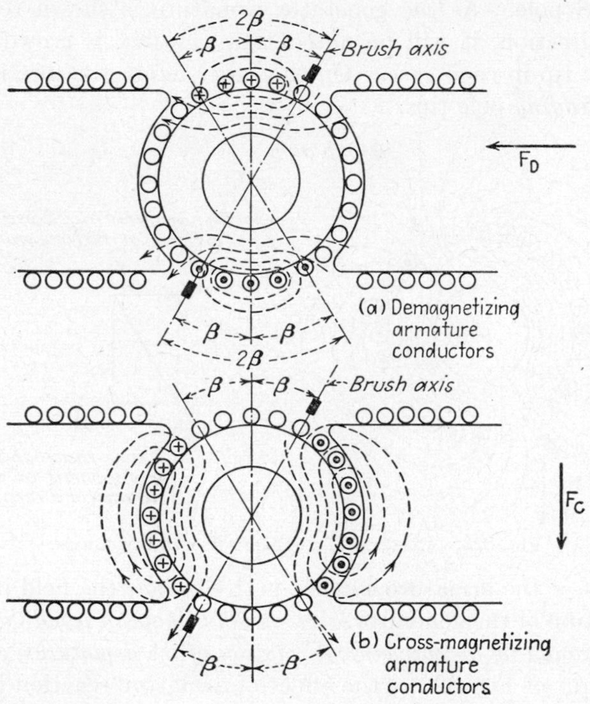

FIG. 324. Demagnetizing and cross-magnetizing *components* of armature reaction.

from one another (see Fig. 331), a coefficient must be applied to each in order to make F_A equal to the vector sum of F_D and F_C.[1]

It will be noted that F_D acts in direct opposition to F, the main field, Fig. 325. Therefore, it tends to reduce the total flux and so is called the *demagnetizing component* of armature reaction. F_C acts at right angles to F, producing distortion, and is called the *cross-magnetizing component* of armature reaction.

The exact conductors which produce these two effects are shown in Fig. 324. In (*a*) the brushes are shown as advanced by an angle β to

[1] If the mmfs are distributed *sinusoidally* along the armature, they may be represented correctly by vectors and combined accordingly. For example, see Vol. II, 4th ed., Fig. 178, p. 198.

correspond to the advance of the neutral plane. All the conductors within the angle 2β, at both the top and bottom of the armature, carry current in such a direction as to send a flux through the armature from right to left. This may be checked by the corkscrew rule. These conductors thus act in direct opposition to the main field and are called the *demagnetizing armature conductors*. Their mmf is represented by the component F_D, Fig. 323.

Figure 324(*b*) shows the flux produced by the conductors not included within twice the angle of brush advance. The direction of this flux is downward and perpendicular to the polar axis. These conductors cross-magnetize the field. The mmf producing this flux is represented by the component F_C, Fig. 323.

It should be remembered that the number of demagnetizing and cross-magnetizing *ampere-turns* is equal to one-half the number of the corresponding *ampere-conductors*.

Example. A 4-pole generator has 288 surface conductors. The armature is lap-wound, and the armature current is 120 amp. The brushes are advanced 15 space degrees. Determine demagnetizing and cross-magnetizing armature ampere-turns.

Twice the angle of brush lead is 30 space degrees. There are four brushes, so that the total number of degrees covered by the demagnetizing conductors is 120°. Therefore one-third the conductors on the armature, or 96 conductors, are demagnetizing conductors.

As the armature is lap-wound, there are four paths through it. The current per path $= 120 \div 4 = 30$ amp.

Demagnetizing *ampere-conductors* $= 30 \cdot 96 = 2{,}880$.

Demagnetizing *ampere-turns* $= 2{,}880 \div 2 = 1{,}440$. *Ans.*

The number of cross-magnetizing conductors must be two-thirds of the conductors on the armature. Therefore, the number of cross-magnetizing *ampere-turns* is

$$\frac{192 \cdot 30}{2} = 2{,}880. \quad Ans.$$

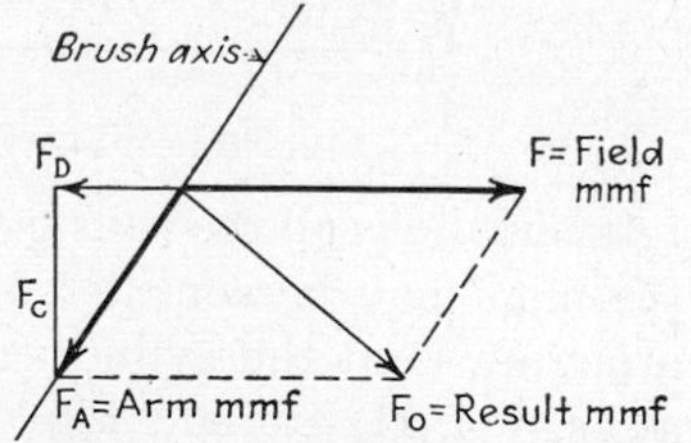

FIG. 325. Resultant of armature and field mmfs.

Figure 325 gives the mmf diagram. F is the field mmf, and F_A is the armature mmf acting along the brush axis after the brushes have been advanced. F_0 is the resultant of the two, being less than F owing to the demagnetizing component of F_A. F_A can be resolved into two components at right angles to each other: F_D, the demagnetizing component of the armature mmf; and F_C, the cross-magnetizing component of the armature mmf. Owing to the fact that F_C and F_D are produced by distributed windings and F is produced by the field coils, the space distributions of all three mmfs are quite different, Figs. 326 and 331. Hence, quantitatively, F_A is only equal to the vector sum of F_D and F_C when each mmf has been multiplied by a coefficient which corrects for space distribution.[1]

294. Mmf of Distributed Windings. Armature reaction occurs in multipolar dynamos in the same manner as in bipolar dynamos, which has just been described. To the eye, however, the mmf and flux distributions may appear different. The analysis of the reactions in a multipolar dynamo is based on the mmfs and fluxes produced by a distributed winding.

With the usual electromagnet, the exciting coils all act on the same magnetic circuit. To be sure, there are local leakage paths associated with single coils and parts of single coils, but a large proportion of the

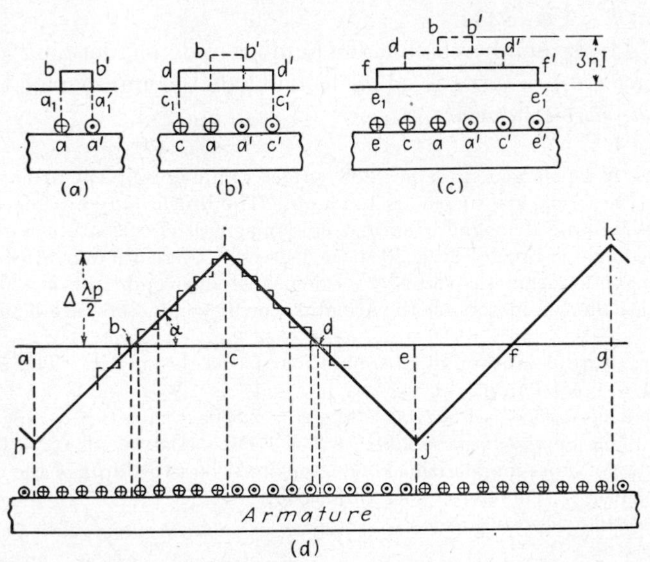

FIG. 326. Magnetomotive force of distributed winding.

total flux links all the coils (see Fig. 193, p. 246). Under these conditions the mmf may be considered as *concentrated*. However, with the usual armature (and the cylindrical-type rotor used with synchronous generators, Vol. II, 4th ed., Fig. 160, p. 175) the mmf is *distributed* over the armature surface and its effects must be determined accordingly.

In Fig. 326(a) consider two coil sides a,a' on the surface of the armature. (For simplicity the slots are omitted.) Let there be n conductors in every coil side, and let the current per conductor be I amp. Also, for the moment, neglect the width of each coil side, that is, assume that the ampere-conductors act as if they were concentrated at the center of the coil side. With the given direction of current, inward in a and outward in a', the mmf which they produce will be *downward* into the armature.

[1] See footnote, p. 418.

Since flux entering the surface of the armature, Fig. 312 (p. 406), has been shown by positive ordinates, the mmf produced by coil aa' will be given by the rectangle $a_1bb'a_1'$. Now add two more coil sides cc', as in (*b*), each having a mmf equal to that of a and a'. Their mmf will be given by the rectangle $c_1dd'c_1'$, and the resultant mmf produced by the four coil sides $caa'c'$ is given by the area $c_1dbb'd'c_1'$. In (*c*) two more similar coil sides ee' are added, their mmf is given by the rectangle $e_1ff'e_1'$, and the resultant mmf is given by the area $e_1fdbb'd'f'e_1'$. The total height of the rectangle is $3nI$ amp-turns.

In (*d*) are shown the ampere-conductors on the surface of an armature extending over three pole pitches *ac*, *ce*, *eg*, the armature surface being shown as a plane. By continuing the process of (*a*), (*b*), (*c*), noting that the direction of the flux produced by the ampere-conductors in the belt *bd* is downward and is represented by positive ordinates, the mmf distribution is represented by the stepped broken lines. However, since on the usual armature there is a large number of ampere-conductors, closely spaced, the current is actually distributed over the entire coil side and is not concentrated at its center, so that the corners of the mmf wave of the coil are more or less rounded. Also, the resultant flux fringes at the edges of the tooth faces. These two effects make the actual distribution of mmf and flux along the armature surface quite smooth and the mmf distribution can be represented by smooth lines such as *hi*, *ij*, *jk*. Note that these lines cross the zero axis at the midpoints, such as *b*, *d*, *f*, of the conductor belts in which the current in all the conductors is in the same direction. Also note that the maximum positive and negative values occur at the points in the conductor belts where the direction of the current reverses, as at *a*, *c*, *e*, *g*. This same effect is noted in (*a*), (*b*), (*c*). It follows that, aside from the small irregularities due to the conductors being placed in slots, the armature mmf increases uniformly from zero at the center of a unidirectional current belt to a maximum at the point where the current direction reverses.

The maximum values of the mmfs, such as *ah*, *ci*, *ej*, *gk*, in ampere-turns are equal to the number of ampere-conductors in half a pole pitch. Let Δ be the ampere-conductors per peripheral inch, Z the total number of conductors on the surface of the armature, I the current in each conductor, and D the diameter of the armature in inches.

$$\Delta = \frac{ZI}{\pi D} \quad \text{amp-conductors per in.} \tag{338}$$

Then the values of *ah*, *ci*, *ej*, *gk*, with the proper signs, are equal to $\Delta(\lambda_P/2)$, where λ_P is the pole pitch in inches.

The slope of the armature-mmf lines, such as that of *hi*, is equal to Δ amp-conductors per in. With the convention used, the slope is positive when the direction of the current in the conductor belts is inward and negative when the direction is outward.

295. Armature Reaction in Multipolar Machines. In Fig. 327 the armature and the field poles of a multipolar generator are shown, the armature being shown as a flat surface, for convenience.

In (*a*) are shown the alternate *N* and *S* poles, together with the magnetic flux entering and leaving the armature. There is no current in the armature conductors. In (*b*) the flux-density curve, giving the flux distribution, is shown. Note that it is symmetrical about the polar axis, is substantially constant under the pole face and drops off gradually at the edges, owing to fringing. It falls to zero and reverses in the interpolar spaces. The neutral plane is the region where the flux is zero and under no-load conditions is midway between the poles.

Figure 328(*a*) shows the armature conductors carrying current, the field current being zero.

Below in (*b*), shown dotted, is the armature mmf distribution, which is drawn in accordance with that of Fig. 326(*d*). The mmf is zero under the centers of the pole faces and is maximum at the brush axes, the brushes being at the centers of the interpolar spaces. The flux produced by the armature mmf acting alone is shown in (*a*) and corresponds to the armature flux of Fig. 322(*b*). The armature conductors between the lines *qr* and *st* may be considered as constituting a pancake coil, the current being into the paper in the conductors on the left and out of the paper in the conductors on the right. Midway between *qr* and *st*, at *oo′*, the mmf is maximum, as the mmfs of all the conductors on both sides are acting in conjunction at this point. This point of maximum mmf coincides with the maximum *i* of the mmf curve in (*b*).

The mmf directly under the pole centers is zero, since for every ampere-conductor on one side of the pole axis there is a symmetrically spaced ampere-conductor on the other side carrying an equal current in the *same* direction. The net mmf at the pole center, due to all such ampere-conductors, thus is zero. These points of zero mmf in (*a*) coincide with points *b, d, f* of zero mmf shown by the dotted mmf curve in (*b*). Comparison should also be made with Fig. 326(*d*).

If the reluctance of the air-gap were uniform, the flux density produced by the armature mmf would be represented by a curve identical in shape with the mmf curve. Owing to the high reluctance of the interpolar space, the *flux-density* curve has not the same shape as the mmf curve but droops in the interpolar space, Fig. 328(*b*).

The resultant flux density at each point is found by adding the two flux-density curves of Figs. 327 and 328, as is done in Fig. 329. *This*

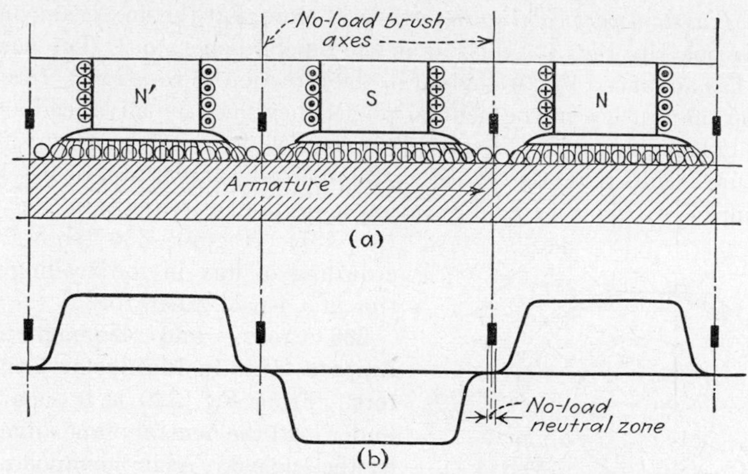

FIG. 327. Field flux density in a multipolar generator.

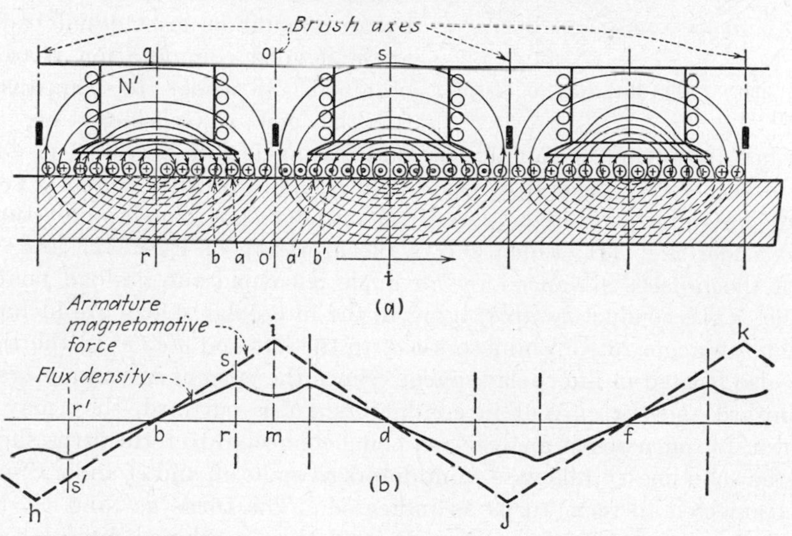

FIG. 328. Flux density due to armature reaction in multipolar generator.

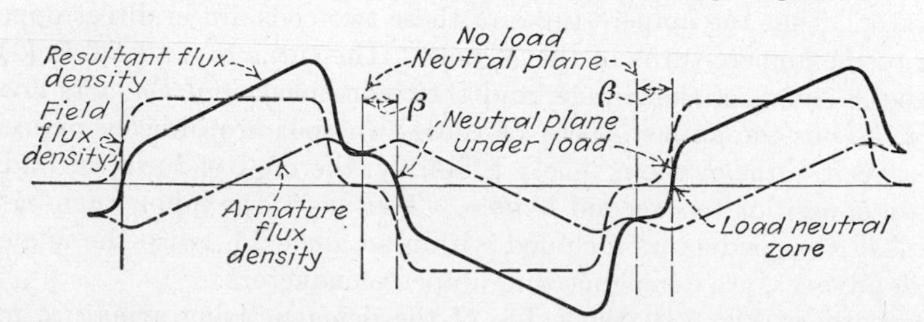

FIG. 329. Resultant flux density found by combining field flux density (Fig. 327) and armature flux density (Fig. 328).

assumes constant permeability in the iron. Note that the flux peaks on the trailing pole tip, Fig. 329, just as in the bipolar generator. The neutral plane has advanced by an angle β in the direction of rotation. In order to keep the brushes in the neutral plane, they must be advanced as the neutral plane advances. It should also be noted that with current in the armature conductors, the width of the neutral zone is practically zero. This makes satisfactory commutation more difficult to obtain, Sec. 302 (p. 437). Figure 330 shows the crowding of flux in the trailing pole tips in a 4-pole generator.

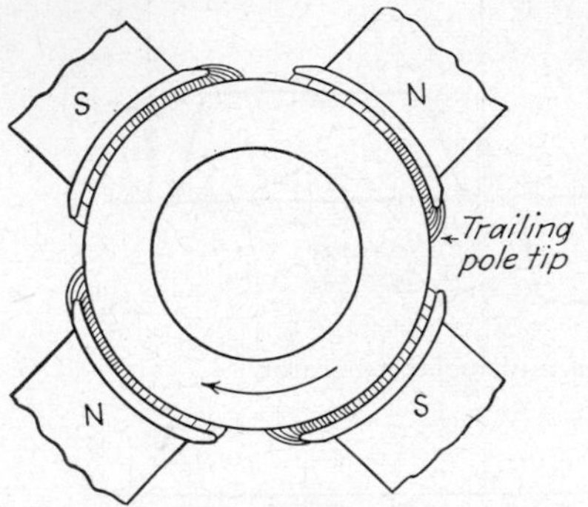

FIG. 330. Field distortion in 4-pole generator.

296. Cross- and Demagnetizing Ampere-turns in Multipolar Generators. From Fig. 329 it is seen that under load the neutral plane advances by the angle β. As in the bipolar generator, the brushes must be advanced by an amount at least equal to this angle if good commutation is to be obtained. In order to compensate for the emf of self-induction, the brushes are advanced actually beyond this angle (see Sec. 300, p. 432). As in the bipolar generator, the advance of the brushes converts some of the cross-magnetizing ampere-turns into demagnetizing ampere-turns.

Consider Fig. 331, which shows the armature of Figs. 327 and 328 with the brushes advanced by an angle β beyond the no-load neutral plane. The conductors *abcd*, lying in the interpolar space, are included within an angle 2β. Conductors $b'a'$ to the left and $d'c'f'e'$ to the right are also located in interpolar space. Since the current in conductors *ab* is inward and the current in conductors $a'b'$ is outward, they may be shown, for purposes of analysis, as being connected to form turns shown by the solid lines. Likewise, conductors *cd* and $c'd'$, and *ef* and $e'f'$, may be connected to form turns as indicated. The turns aa' and bb' link the magnetic circuit of the N pole, and their combined mmf F_D acts upward. Thus the ampere-turns of these two coils are in direct opposition to the ampere-turns of the N pole. The turns cc' and dd' link the magnetic circuit of the S pole, and their combined mmf F_D' acts downward. Thus the ampere-turns of these two coils are directly opposing the ampere-turns of the S pole. Similarly, the mmf of turns ee' and ff' acts in opposition to a second N pole. Thus, as in the bipolar generator, Fig. 324, the conductors included within an angle 2β, twice the angle of brush advance, are demagnetizing ampere-conductors.

Beneath, in Fig. 331, the value of the demagnetizing armature mmf is plotted as a function of distance along the armature and is shown by the solid line.

In Fig. 331, the armature conductors not included within twice the brush angle β are connected with dotted lines to form turns. Except for the omission of the demagnetizing ampere-conductors included within the angles 2β, the positions and currents of these conductors are identical with those on the armature of Fig. 328. Their mmf graph, shown beneath in Fig. 331 by the dashed line, is similar to that of Fig. 328, with the effect of the demagnetizing ampere-conductors omitted. The mmf is zero at the centers of the pole faces and is a maximum across the interpolar spaces. Accordingly, the mmf acts transversely to the direction of the

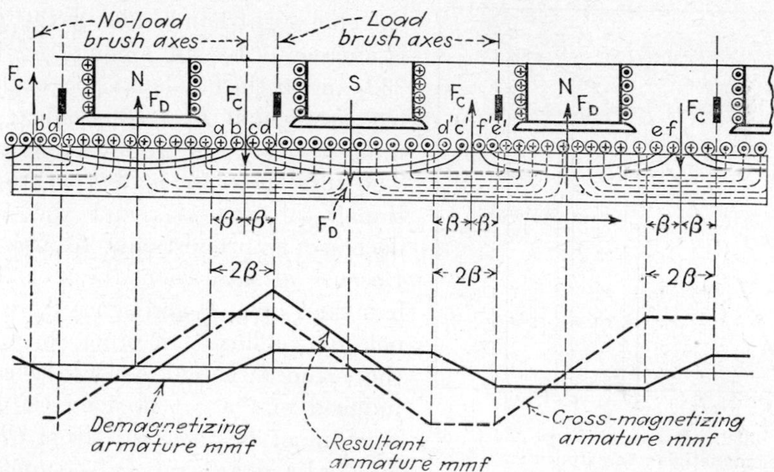

FIG. 331. Cross- and demagnetizing ampere-turns in multipolar generator.

flux in the armature core, and the ampere-turns must be cross-magnetizing as in Fig. 328, where the brushes are in the no-load neutral plane. At each interpolar space, the cross-magnetizing mmf is denoted by F_C.

Thus the rules used with bipolar generators for separating demagnetizing and cross-magnetizing ampere-conductors apply to multipolar generators.

If the cross-magnetizing and demagnetizing mmf graphs, Fig. 331, are combined, the resulting armature mmf graph is identical with that in Fig. 328, except that the graph as a whole has moved to the right by the angle β, with the movement of the brushes. The peaks of the graph still coincide with the brush positions. For simplicity, only a small portion of the resultant armature mmf is shown in Fig. 328.

297. Demagnetizing Effect of Cross-magnetizing Ampere-turns. Even with the brushes in the no-load neutral, Fig. 328(a), some demagnetization by the armature takes place owing to the effects of saturation produced by the *cross-magnetizing* ampere-turns. In Fig. 332, flux density B in the air-gap is plotted as a function of the field ampere-turns per pole N_fI_f. With current in the armature conductors, Figs. 328(*a*) and (*b*), the mmf at the right-hand side of the left-hand pole N' is increased by an amount rs, and at the left-hand side it is decreased by an equal amount $r's'$. The effect on the flux distribution is shown in Fig. 329 and also in Fig. 332. With no armature current, and hence at no load, the magnetic circuit is operating at a field mmf OF, Fig. 332, producing a uniform flux density FD over the pole face. With current in the armature the mmf rs, Figs. 328(*b*) and 332, is added to OF and $r's'$ is subtracted. The flux density at the extreme right-hand side of the pole is increased by an amount fc, Fig. 332, and at the left-hand side, neglecting any small hysteresis effect, the mmf is decreased by an amount eb. The total increase in flux is proportional to area A_1, and the total decrease is proportional to area A_2. Because of saturation, the area A_1 is less than area A_2 and hence there is a net *loss* of flux. In order to obtain the same flux and hence the same induced emf as at no load the field mmf must be increased from OF to OF', or by an amount g. The mmf OF' must be so chosen that it is at the center of a new area $a'b'c'd'$, which is equal in area to rectangle $aefd$, which is a measure of the no-load flux.

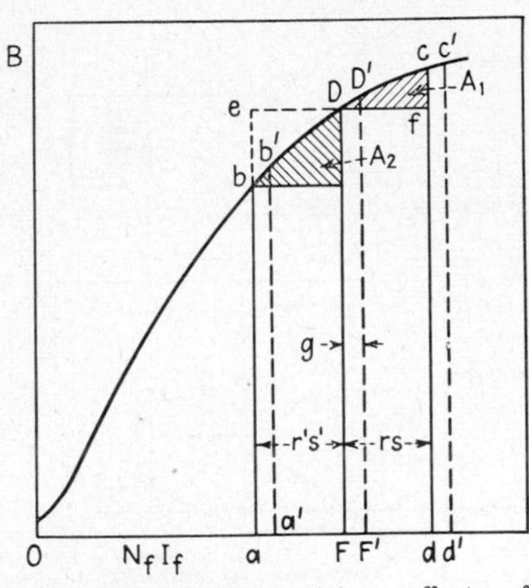

Fig. 332. Demagnetizing effect of cross-magnetizing ampere-turns.

298. Compensating Armature Reaction. If the armature mmf becomes too large in comparison with the field mmf, a tendency toward instability in both generators and motors (see Sec. 329, p. 490) results. For example, if the armature mmf $r's'$ acting on the left-hand side of the pole N', Figs. 327 and 328(*a*) and (*b*), becomes greater than that part of the field mmf which is utilized in the gap and the teeth, the polarity of the left-hand side of the pole, as well as that of the other poles, will become *reversed*, which tends to produce instability. Moreover, the increased distortion of the field makes commutation more difficult, tends to produce instability in the speeds of motors, and is conducive to commutator flashovers. Hence it is desirable to maintain the mmf per field pole reasonably strong as compared with the armature mmf.

A study of Figs. 322(*b*) and 328(*a*) shows that the flux produced by the armature mmf crosses the air-gap twice. Hence, by increasing the length of the air-gap, reluctance to the armature flux is increased, and the armature flux for a given armature mmf decreases. The reluctance to the main flux is also increased, and in order to maintain the field flux at its original value, it is necessary to increase the field ampere-turns. Hence, the main flux is brought back to normal, but the armature-reaction flux is reduced. It is to be noted that the ratio of field to armature ampere-turns has been increased. *Thus the ratio of field ampere-turns to armature ampere-turns is the basic criterion of armature reaction.* Dynamos with a long air-gap, and thus a high ratio of field to armature ampere-turns, are said to have a "stiff field." The increased field ampere-turns increase the field copper and the field loss. By the use of commutating poles (Sec. 302, p. 437), however, modern dynamos operate satisfactorily with relatively short air-gaps.

A practical method, when laminated pole cores are used, is to use a stamping having but one pole tip, Fig. 304 (p. 399). These are alternately reversed when the core is built up. This leaves spaces between the pole-tip laminations, and the pole tips have but one-half the cross section of iron along their lengths. Therefore, the pole tip becomes highly saturated and its permeability greatly reduced. This tends to prevent the flux from crowding into the trailing tip. Actually, the magnetic circuit for the armature flux becomes highly saturated, whereas that for the main flux is scarcely affected.

Commutating poles (Sec. 302) are used to neutralize the effects of armature reaction and produce the correct commutating flux *in the neutral zone only*. With commutating poles it is possible to reduce the air-gap, and hence the ratio of field to armature ampere-turns, and yet obtain satisfactory commutation. This results in a saving in field turns and in a reduction in field copper loss. The greater armature reaction, however, produces a greater distortion of the flux under the poles, Fig. 329, with corresponding disadvantages. With large machines such as the generators and motors used in rolling mills, and which are subjected continuously to sudden overloads, high armature reaction tends to produce instability and flashover. Hence, it is frequently desirable to neutralize the armature mmf over the entire pole arc.

Since the mmfs which produce the armature flux are in a different location from those which produce the main flux, it is possible, without affecting the main field, to neutralize the armature mmfs by opposing mmfs.

In order to be effective, these compensating mmfs at every point should be equal in magnitude and opposite in direction to those of the armature. This is accomplished by a compensating winding placed in slots in the pole faces, Fig. 333. The direction of current in the pole-face conductors is opposite to the direction of current in the armature conductors lying directly across the air-gap. The pole-face ampere-conductors are also made equal to the armature ampere-conductors on the opposite side of the air-gap so that the armature mmf under each pole face is practically compensated. The commutating poles, Fig. 333, compensate only the armature mmf which acts in the commutating zone, Figs. 344 and 346 (pp. 438 and 439). The foregoing method of compensation is also used

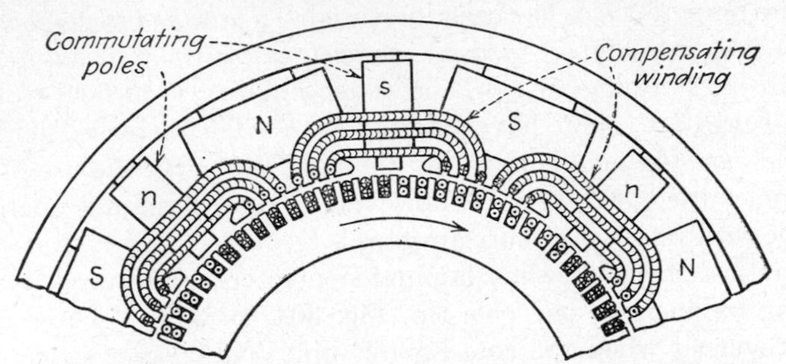

Fig. 333. Pole-face winding to compensate armature reaction.

in the a-c series motor, in which armature reaction is particularly objectionable (see Vol. II, 4th edition, Fig. 297, p. 361).

Example. The diameter of the armature of a 500-kw 250-volt 6-pole generator is 30 in., its length 13 in., and there are 108 slots. The winding is simplex lap with a single turn per coil and two coil sides per slot. The ratio of pole arc to pole pitch is 0.65. The length of air-gap is 0.25 in., but taking into account the slot openings and teeth it may be considered as having an effective length of 0.30 in. With 25 per cent overload, determine: (*a*) minimum ampere-turns per pole for teeth and gap necessary to prevent reversal of flux at pole tip; (*b*) average flux density in air-gap under these conditions. Neglect shunt-field current in computing armature current.

(*a*) Rated current = 500,000/250 = 2,000 amp.

25% overload, current = 2,500 amp.

Since there are six parallel paths in armature,

$$\text{Current per coil side} = 2{,}500/6 = 416.7 \text{ amp.}$$

$$\text{Current per slot} = 833.4 \text{ amp.}$$

$$\text{Slot pitch} = \frac{30\pi}{108} = 0.8727 \text{ in.}$$

From Eq. (338) (p. 421),

$$\Delta = \frac{833.4}{0.8727} = 954.9 \text{ amp per peripheral in.}$$

$$\text{Pole pitch} = \frac{30\pi}{6} = 15.71 \text{ in.}$$

$$\text{Pole arc} = 15.71 \cdot 0.65 = 10.21 \text{ in.}$$

Mmf at pole tip (p. 421),

$$954.9 \cdot 10.21/2 = 4{,}875 \text{ amp-turns.} \quad \textit{Ans.}$$

[This is equal to $r's'$, Fig. 328(*b*), p. 423.]

(*b*) Using Eq. (172) (p. 259),

$$4{,}875 = 0.313B' \cdot 0.3$$
$$B' = 51{,}900 \text{ maxwells per sq in.} \quad \textit{Ans.}$$

Although Δ is given in amp-conductors per peripheral inch, the answer is given in *ampere-turns*, since for each ampere-conductor, such as a, between planes qr and oo', Fig. 328(a), there is a similar ampere-conductor a' between planes st and oo' with current in the reverse direction. These two conductors as well as other pairs, such as b and b', form complete turns and, with their currents, become *ampere-turns*.

Note that when the load on the generator is greater than 125 per cent rated load, the flux does reverse at the leading pole tips. The advantages of the compensating winding, Fig. 333, then become apparent.

299. Commutation. It has been shown that the emf induced in any single coil of a d-c generator is alternating. In order that the current to

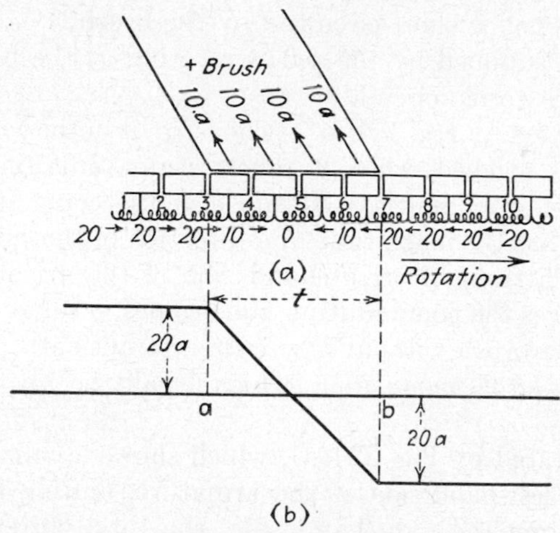

FIG. 334. Current in coil undergoing commutation—ideal conditions.

the external circuit may always be in the same direction, a commutator is necessary. During the brief interval when a coil is short-circuited by a brush the current must be reversed from its full positive value to its full negative value, or vice versa. Figure 334 shows the change of current in an armature coil as it approaches and recedes from a brush. It is assumed that ideal commutation is being realized. That is, the current, as it leaves the commutator, is distributed uniformly over the brush. Accordingly, in each coil, the current change or reversal from maximum positive to maximum negative value is uniform. This is called *straight-line* commutation. The load is such that the current in each path of the armature is 20 amp, and 40 amp leaves the armature by this one brush.

When in positions 1, 2, 3, each coil, and therefore any one particular coil in its successive positions, carries 20 amp. As the brush covers four commutator segments, and the current distribution is uniform, 10 amp must go into the brush from each segment. Therefore, in moving from 3 to 4, the coil must lose the 10 amp from segment 3 into the brush. Hence, in position 4 the coil carries only 10 amp.

Before reaching position 5, the coil gives up another 10 amp so that the current is zero when the coil reaches position 5. When the coil reaches position 6, the direction of the current is reversed, owing to the fact that the current enters the brush from the right-hand armature path. The current reaches 20 amp in position 7 and remains 20 amp in positions 8, 9, 10.

Therefore, commutation consists of two parts:

1. Reversing the current in any coil from its full positive value to an equal negative value, or vice versa. This reversal must take place in the very short time interval required for a segment to pass under the brush, or the time that a coil is short-circuited by the brush.

2. The current supplied by the paths meeting at the brush must be conducted to the external circuit.

Part 1 is illustrated by Fig. 334(b). The current in the coil is +20 amp until the brush is reached, when it reverses at a uniform rate until it reaches a value of −20 amp at the end b of the commutation time t. The current then has the magnitude and direction of the current which is entering the brush from the right-hand side of the armature. Hence, each coil as it leaves the commutating zone comes in series with the coils at the right of the brush without any current transient. This mode of current reversal is *ideal commutation*, which usually is only approximated in practice.

Part 2 is illustrated by Fig. 334(a), which shows a current of 20 amp coming from the left-hand side of the armature, uniting with an equal current coming from the right-hand side, the total current of 40 amp being conducted to the external circuit by the positive brush.

Ideal commutation, Fig. 334(b), is only approximated in practice. There are two causes preventing its complete realization.

It will be noted that when the coil is in positions 4, 5, 6, it is short-circuited by the brush. If any emf is induced in the coil while in these positions, the current will be large, since the resistance of the short-circuited path is very low. This resistance consists merely of the resistance of the coil plus the contact resistance of the brush, the contact resistance constituting the greater portion of the total resistance. Figure 335 shows assumed currents of 15 and 5 amp in coils 4 and 5, due to emfs induced in 4 and 5 while they are short-circuited by the brush.

If the local short-circuit currents of Fig. 335 be superposed on those of Fig. 334(a), the current distributes itself over the brush in the manner shown in Fig. 336. There are 45 amp entering by one section of the brush and 5 amp leaving by another section. Therefore, the brush must carry 50 amp instead of 40 amp, and in one segment there are 20 amp, or twice the current existing under the ideal conditions of Fig. 334. This will tend to produce undue heating and undue sparking under the heel of the brush.

Figure 336(*b*) shows the manner in which the current in the coil varies under these new conditions. Instead of dropping uniformly from 20 amp,

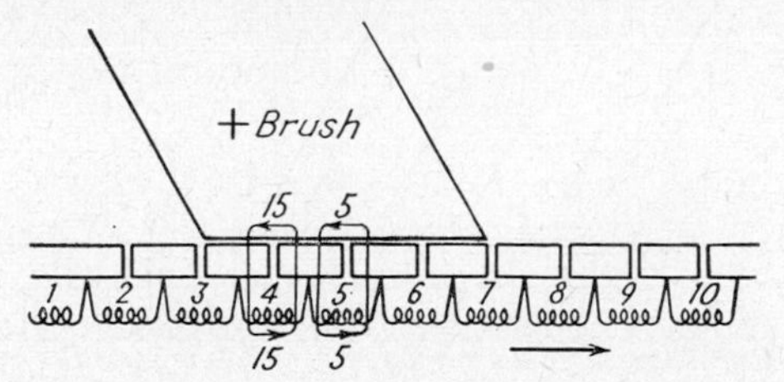

Fig. 335. Short-circuit currents through brush.

it first *rises* to 25 amp before starting to reverse. It will be noted that the time for reversing from +20 amp to −20 amp has been reduced from time t to time t_1, making commutation more difficult. The conditions of Fig. 336 occur when the brush is too far back of the neutral plane and emfs are induced in the coils as they undergo commutation.

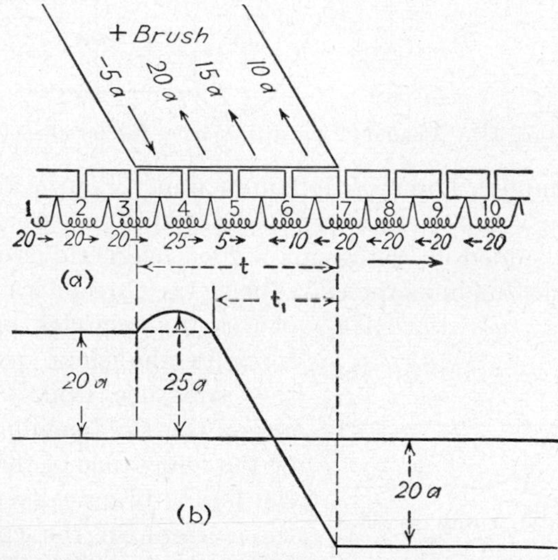

Fig. 336. Change of current in coil when brushes are too far back of neutral plane.

If the brushes are placed too far ahead of the neutral plane, short-circuit currents flow under the toe of the brush, resulting in the current distribution and commutation curve of Fig. 337(*b*). This condition produces undue sparking under the toe of the brush.

If the brushes are too wide, both the heel and the toe of the brush will short-circuit coils in which emfs are induced, resulting in the commutation curve of Fig. 338. Moving the brushes either backward or forward does not improve matters in this case. The remedy is a narrower brush.

The curves of Figs. 334(*b*), 336(*b*), 337(*b*), and 338 are called *commutation curves.*

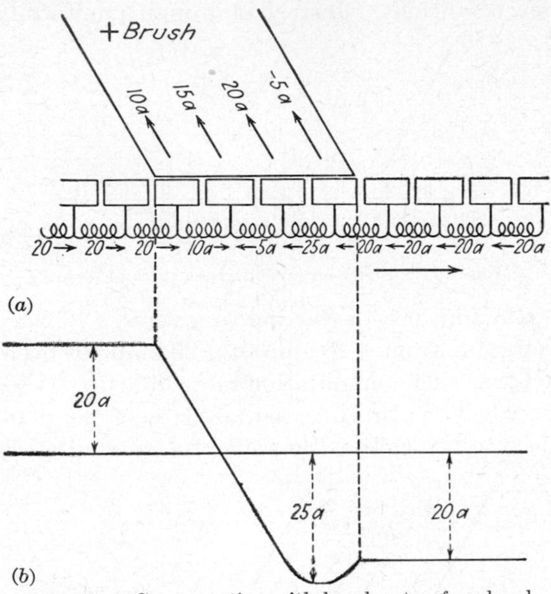

Fig. 337. Commutation with brushes too far ahead.

300. Electromotive Force of Self-induction. Figure 339(*a*) shows an armature coil just as it is entering the commutation zone. The slot conductors are embedded in iron giving a good magnetic circuit, and therefore considerable flux links the coil, due to the current in the coil. Most of this flux encircles, or links, the coil sides in the slots, passing through the armature iron, the teeth, and across the slot opening. Since most of the reluctance of the path is in air, the flux is practically proportional to the current in the coil. When the coil is just entering the commutating zone, the general direction of the flux is upward through the coil, Fig. 339(*a*). Since the flux is practically proportional to the current in the coil, the values of flux, as the coil passes through the commutating zone, follow the law of the current, Figs. 334(*b*), 336(*b*), 337(*b*), 338.

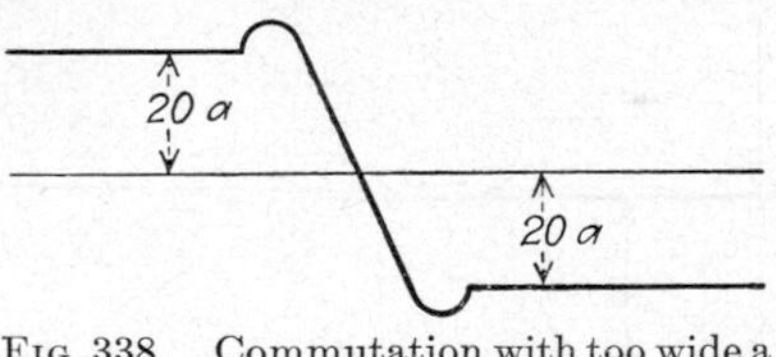

Fig. 338. Commutation with too wide a brush.

Let ϕ_c be the magnitude of the total flux linking the coil. In Fig. 339(*b*) the coil is shown just after it has left the commutating zone. The current in the coil has the same value as in Fig. 339(a), but its direction is reversed. The flux linking the coil has still the magnitude ϕ_c, but its direction is also reversed. Therefore, in the time t sec required for a segment to go through the commutating zone, the flux has changed by

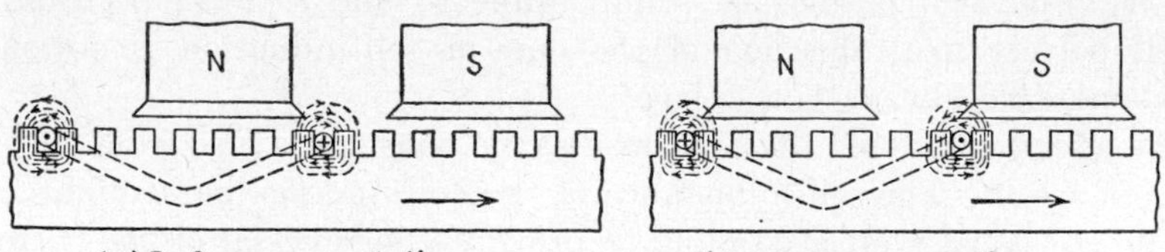

FIG. 339. Change of flux through coil undergoing commutation.

$2\phi_c$ lines. This is shown in Fig. 340, where ideal commutation is assumed. This change of flux induces an emf

$$e_c = -N \frac{d\phi_c}{dt} 10^{-8} \qquad \text{volts} \qquad \text{[Eq. (209), p. 299].}$$

When ideal commutation takes place, Fig. 340,

$$e_c = -N \frac{2\phi_c}{t} 10^{-8} \qquad \text{volts} \qquad \text{[Eq. (207), p. 298],}$$

N being the number of turns in the coil.

This emf, with its proper direction shown in Fig. 340, is an emf of *self-induction.* That is, flux produced by the current in the coil itself links the coil, and the coil has self-inductance. During the time that an emf is induced in the coil, the coil is short-circuited by the brush. The emf is acting in a circuit of very low resistance, and unless this emf is in large measure neutralized, it will produce a large short-circuit current through the commutator and brush, resulting in severe sparking. If the brushes are set so that the coils undergoing short circuit are in the geometrical neutral, where they are cutting no flux and hence have no induced emf due to rotation, there will still be the emf of self-induction and severe sparking will result.

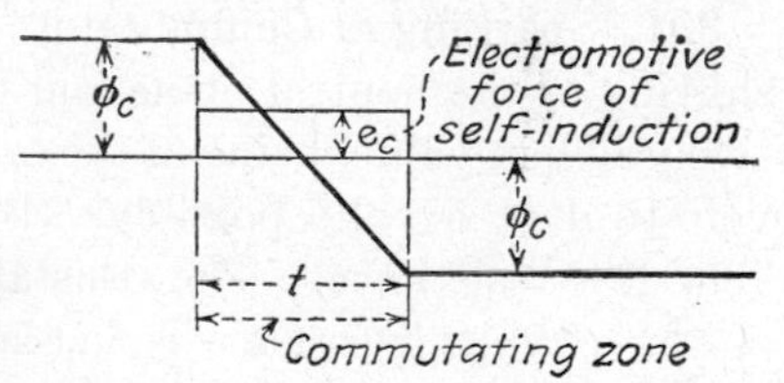

FIG. 340. Electromotive force of self-induction in coil undergoing commutation.

In order to neutralize this emf of self-induction in a generator without commutating poles, it is necessary to set the brushes *ahead* of the neutral plane so that the sides of the short-circuited coils find themselves in a field of the same polarity as that which they enter on leaving the commutating zone, Fig. 329. Under these conditions the emf induced by rotation is in opposition to the emf of self-induction. By choosing a correct position for the brushes, the emf induced by the cutting of the field can be made theoretically to neutralize the emf of self-induction, making the net emf in the coil zero and thus eliminating sparking. Actually, owing to the slope of the flux-density curve in the fringe of the pole (see B_1, Fig. 344, p. 438), it is impossible to find a brush position for which perfect neutralization of the emf of self-induction is obtained. Some sparking always takes place.

The effect of moving the brushes may be considered also from another point of view. The self-inductance of the coil undergoing commutation acts as electrical inertia, tending to prevent the reversal of the current. The direction of the emf induced by the cutting of the pole flux in advance of the neutral plane is the same as the direction which the reversed current is about to assume. Hence, by moving the brushes ahead, the emf induced in the coil by the cutting of the pole flux helps the current to reverse.

Thus in a *generator* under load it is necessary that the brushes be kept *in advance* of the neutral plane in order to obtain satisfactory commutation.

Practically all modern generators and motors have commutating poles, and this movement of the brushes with change of load therefore is unnecessary. However, there is still in operation a large number of generators and motors with no commutating poles. The function of the commutating pole is best understood when the effects of armature reaction and brush position on commutation are known.

301. Sparking at Commutator. The emfs induced in a coil due to the shifting of the neutral plane and to its own self-inductance are comparatively low in value, being of the order of magnitude from a few tenths of a volt to 4 or 5 volts possibly. But they are acting in a circuit having very low resistance. The resistance of a single coil is low so that most of the circuit resistance is in the brush contact. If the brush-contact resistance is too low, the short-circuit current may reach such values as to produce severe sparking at the brushes. On the other hand, a brush with low contact resistance is desirable from the standpoint of conducting the current to the external circuit with minimum contact loss.

Copper brushes have a very low contact resistance, but when they are used the short-circuit currents are excessive. Therefore, their application is limited to low-voltage high-current dynamos. Copper gauze, rolled and pressed into a rectangular cross section, is often used. Another disadvantage of using copper brushes is that they "cut" the commutator mechanically. These disadvantages have been overcome in considerable measure by brushes of a graphite-copper composition which have low resistance and do not abrade the commutator.

Carbon brushes have a much higher contact resistance than copper and thus limit the short-circuit currents, giving much more satisfactory commutation. In addition, they are more or less graphitic in composition and lubricate the commutator to a degree. Unusually hard carbon brushes may cut the commutator. Different grades of carbon are required for different operating conditions.

The passage of the current from the commutator to the brush is more of an arc phenomenon than one of pure conduction. A careful examination will show myriads of minute arcs existing between the brush surface and the commutator. The voltage drop between the commutator and the brush, instead of being proportional to the current (as it would be with linear conduction), is substantially constant and is equal to about 1 volt per brush. Bits of copper may be found in the *positive* brush because of the arcing. The character of an arc stream depends on the material of the electrodes. When copper is positive and carbon is negative, the characteristics of the arc stream are different from those when carbon is positive and copper is negative. For this reason the voltage drop across the *negative* brush is *greater* than that across the *positive* brush, owing to the commutator copper being positive in one case and negative in the other. The resistance of the armature circuit, *including brushes*, diminishes with increasing current.

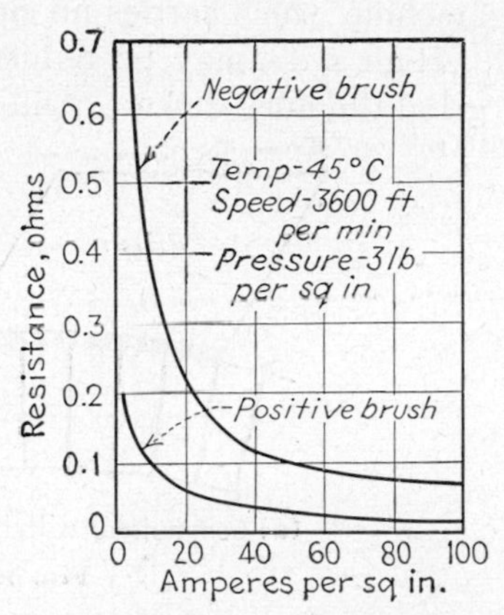

FIG. 341. Contact-resistance characteristics of carbon brushes.

These relations are illustrated in Fig. 341,[1] which shows the variation of contact resistance for positive and negative brushes when operating on copper rings. All these facts substantiate the arcing theory.

Another proof of the theory is "high mica." After a machine has been in operation for a considerable time, it often happens that the mica insulation between the commutator segments protrudes above the surface of the commutator, resulting in high mica, Fig. 342(*a*). It was supposed at one time that this was due to mica being harder than copper, which resulted in the wearing away of the copper more readily than the mica. The fallacy of this supposition is evident. Even though mica is harder than copper, the two must always wear down evenly, for the brush cannot

[1] From HESSLER, VICTOR P., "The Effect of Various Operating Conditions upon Electrical Brush Wear and Contact Drop," *Iowa Eng. Expt. Sta. Bull.* 122, Iowa State College. The negative-brush characteristic was taken from Fig. 60 and the positive-brush characteristic was plotted from the data of Fig. 59 in the paper.

grind the copper until it comes in contact with it. Hence, the brush must grind down the mica before it can touch the copper, if high mica is due to mechanical abrasion alone.

The rational explanation of high mica is given in detail by B. G. Lamme in a paper presented before the American Institute of Electrical Engineers.[1] The copper is not worn away, as was formerly supposed, but is carried away by the minute arcs that exist between the brush and the commutator, as in Fig. 342(*a*). This may be proved by running two similar machines for the same period of time, one of the machines delivering current and the other having no current in brushes and commutator. High mica will ultimately appear on the commutator which carries current, whereas it will be found impossible to produce high mica on the machine which carries no current.

High mica may be reduced by the use of fairly hard brushes which grind the mica down. Amber mica appears to be softer than white mica

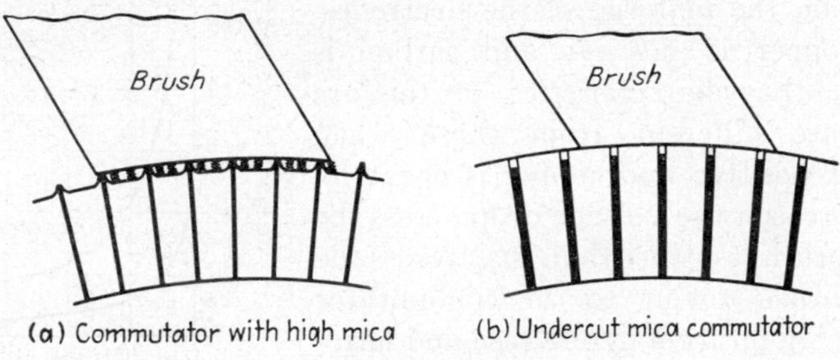

FIG. 342. Brush on commutator.

and is often preferred for commutator-segment insulation. In modern practice the mica is undercut by many manufacturers, that is, the top of the mica is below the commutator surface, as in Fig. 342(*b*). There is some disadvantage in this construction, in that small bits of copper, carbon, and dirt collect in the grooves and may ultimately short-circuit the segments. However, these grooves can be cleaned out easily.

The result of any arcing under the brush is to pit the commutator. As irregularities and depressions in the commutator tend to prevent intimate contact between the brush and commutator, arcs of increasing magnitude will be formed. The deeper the depressions, or the higher the mica, the larger and more vigorous these arcs become. Hence, any condition which produces sparking and so roughens the commutator increases the sparking and roughening, these being cumulative actions. If a commutator is sparking badly and the cause of the sparking is not corrected, the commutator will deteriorate rapidly and soon will become inoperative.

[1] LAMME, B. G., "Physical Limitations in D.C. Commutating Machinery," *Trans., AIEE*, Vol. 34, Part II, p. 1739, 1915.

The brushes should be fitted very carefully to the commutator surface by grinding with sandpaper, or "sanding in," in the manner shown in Fig. 343. Carbon on the surface of the commutator should be removed with an oily cloth. *Do not use waste.* A slightly roughened commutator may be partially smoothed with fine sandpaper. *Do not use emery,* as the particles of emery are conducting and may short-circuit the commutator bars. If the commutator is grooved by the brushes or is otherwise in poor condition, it should be turned down in a lathe.

Fig. 343. Proper method of fitting brushes.

Other difficulties, such as loose mica and loose segments, are more serious in character. It is often possible to rectify these last difficulties by tightening up the commutator clamp bolts.

302. Commutating Poles (Interpoles). Figure 344 shows the geometrical neutral or no-load neutral plane and the neutral plane of a generator when under load. It is to be noted that this figure is taken from Fig. 329 (p. 423). If the brushes remain in the no-load neutral plane, there will be severe sparking under load conditions, because of the flux density B_2, due to armature reaction and existing in the neutral zone. The brushes will not commutate properly even if advanced to the load neutral plane. This is due to the fact that the emf of self-induction exists in the coils undergoing short circuit, even if the emf due to the cutting of the pole flux is zero. The brushes must be advanced so that the short-circuited coils are cutting the flux density B_1 of the next pole, as in Fig. 344, in order that a speed emf may be induced which will balance the emf of self-induction. It will be noted that this position is in the fringe of the next pole flux. As a very slight movement of the brushes in either direction brings a very marked change in the flux density, it is difficult to obtain good commutation under these conditions. In fact it may be impossible to obtain satisfactory commutation because of the steepness of the flux-distribution

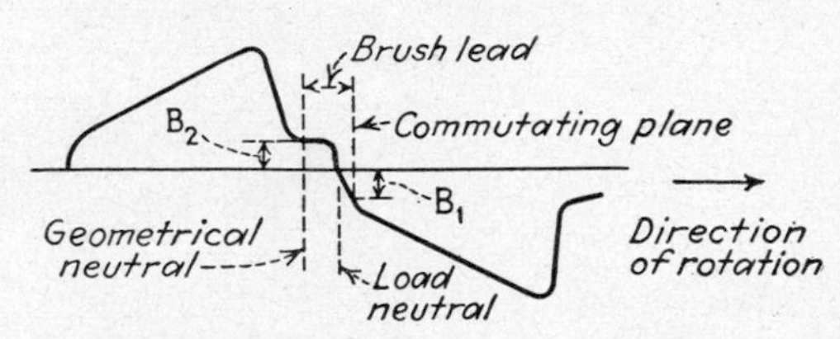

FIG. 344. Brush advance to proper commutating plane.

curve. When the best position of the brushes is obtained, the trailing tip of each brush may be in too strong a field and the leading tip in too weak a field.

If a flux density having the same value as B_2, but opposite to it in direction, can be produced in the geometrical neutral, it is clear that the flux density in the neutral plane can be brought to zero notwithstanding armature reaction. If a flux density of a value $B_2 + B_1$ is produced, satisfactory commutation is obtained without moving the brushes. It is the function of commutating poles to produce the required flux density in the neutral zone.

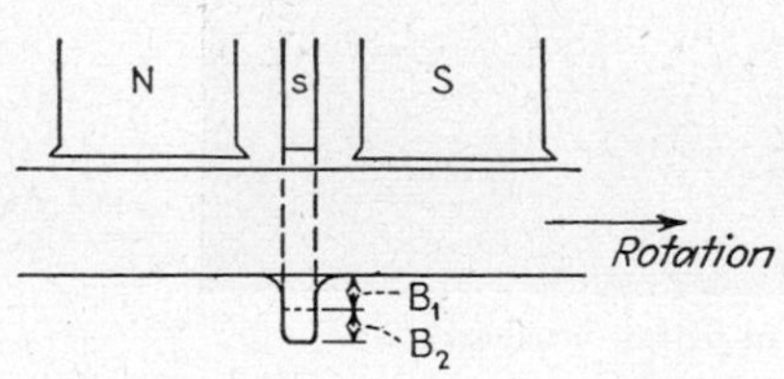

FIG. 345. Flux density produced by commutating pole alone.

Commutating poles are narrow poles located between the main poles. They produce flux in the commutating zone which is of such magnitude that reasonably good commutation is obtained. For example, in Fig. 345 the commutating pole must first produce a flux density equal to B_2 so as to neutralize in the neutral zone the increase of flux density due to armature reaction. It must also produce an additional flux density B_1 in order to counteract the emf of self-induction in the coil undergoing commutation. This commutating-pole flux density is shown in Fig. 345. The pole producing it at this point must be an S pole. Figure 346 shows the resultant flux obtained by combining Figs. 344 and 345.

As the armature reaction and the emf of self-induction in the coils undergoing commutation are both proportional to the armature current, the flux density necessary to compensate for them, produced by the commutating poles, must also be proportional to the armature current. Therefore, the commutating poles are wound with a few turns of comparatively heavy wire and are connected in series with the armature, as in Fig. 347. The air-gap between the commutating poles and the armature is large, so that at all loads the commutating-pole flux is nearly proportional to the armature current.

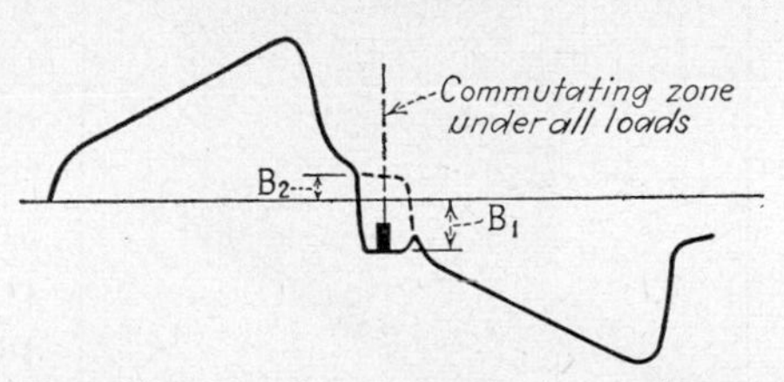

FIG. 346. Resultant of main flux and commutating-pole flux with load.

It should be noted that the sequence of poles in the direction of rotation in a generator is *NsSn*, where the capitals refer to the main poles and the small letters refer to the commutating poles. Figure 348 shows a commutating pole with its winding.

In Fig. 349 the frame and poles of a dynamo are shown. The arrangement and connections of both main and commutating poles are clearly indicated (also see Fig. 303, p. 398).

It is possible to use only two commutating poles in a 4-pole dynamo. This comes from the fact that, with the usual windings, when one side of a

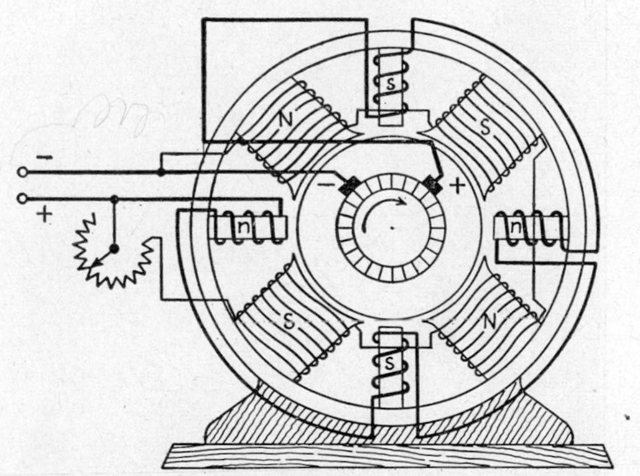

FIG. 347. Connections of shunt field and commutating poles.

coil is under an *N* pole, the other side is under an *S* pole. Hence, by using a single commutating pole for each pair of main poles, this single pole having twice the magnetic strength of each of the two commutating poles which it replaces, the correct emf for commutation is induced in the coil. With a wave winding, a single commutating pole would suffice, irrespective of the number of poles, if it could be made of sufficient magnetic strength (see Fig. 298, p. 394). In practice, however, the number of commutating poles is usually made equal to the number of main poles.

Fig. 348. Commutating pole and winding. (*Reliance Electric and Engineering Company.*)

Commutating poles are so designed that they produce a flux density of greater magnitude than is necessary. Formerly, the method of obtaining the correct density was to shunt the entire commutating-pole circuit by a low resistance, the resistance being adjusted until the best condition of commutation was obtained. Modern practice is to dispense with such shunt resistance and to adjust the effect of the commutating poles by the use of shims between the commutating poles and the yoke.

Commutating poles increase the leakage flux between the main poles. For this reason the main-pole arc, normally 0.70 the pole pitch, is reduced

Fig. 349. Frame and poles of dynamo, showing arrangement of commutating poles. (*Reliance Electric and Engineering Company.*)

to 0.65 the pole pitch or less, Figs. 347 and 349. Also, the commutating poles must be made very narrow, and at moderate values of overload they usually become saturated. It is for this reason that the air-gaps are made relatively large so that the commutating-pole flux will tend to remain proportional to the armature current.

The distinction between the action of commutating poles and of compensating windings, Fig. 333 (p. 428), should be kept in mind. Both are connected in series with the armature and with both the mmfs act to neutralize armature reaction, the commutating poles, however, supplying additional mmf so as to counteract the emf of self-induction in the coils undergoing commutation. Also, the commutating poles act only locally in the commutating zone and thus have negligible effect on the armature reaction which occurs over the remainder of the armature periphery.

The number of ampere-turns on the commutating poles which are necessary to neutralize the armature reaction mmf *im* in the neutral zone, Fig. 328(*b*) (p. 423), are equal to $\Delta\lambda_p$, where Δ is the armature ampere-conductors per peripheral inch (p. 421) and λ_p is the pole pitch.

Example. With the generator and its load in the example, p. 428, determine ampere-turns on each commutating pole which are necessary to neutralize armature mmf in neutral zone.

Δ = 954.9 amp-conductors per peripheral in.; pole pitch = 15.71 in.

Required ampere-turns,

$$(NI)_c = 954.9 \cdot 15.72 = 7{,}500 \text{ amp-turns.} \quad Ans.$$

In addition there must be sufficient ampere-turns on the commutating pole to produce a flux density B_2, Figs. 345, 346. The speed emf induced in the armature by the flux corresponding to B_2 neutralizes the emf of self-induction.

303. Shunt-generator Characteristics. If a shunt generator, after building up to voltage, be loaded, the terminal voltage will drop. This drop in voltage will increase with increase in load. Such a drop in terminal voltage is undesirable, especially when it occurs in generators which supply power to incandescent lamps.

It is important to know the voltage at the terminals of a generator for each value of current that it delivers, because the ability to maintain its voltage under load conditions determines in large measure the suitability of a generator for a specified service.

The relation between the terminal volts and the current which a generator delivers is called its *characteristic*. When the relation is between the *terminal* volts and the current to the load, it is called the *external* characteristic. The *internal*, or *total*, characteristic is the relation between induced emf in the armature and armature current (see Sec. 305, p. 445). Unless otherwise specified, the term *shunt characteristic* refers to the external characteristic.

To test a generator to determine the relation of terminal volts to load current, it is connected as in Fig. 319 (p. 412). The generator is self-excited, and a voltmeter is connected across its terminals to measure the terminal volts. An ammeter is connected in the line to measure the load current. In performing this test, it is often desirable to connect an ammeter in the field circuit so that the value of field current, as load is applied, may be determined.

In starting the test, rated load should first be applied and the field current adjusted until rated voltage is obtained. It is desirable to run the generator under these conditions for 20 min or longer in order to give the field opportunity to approach its ultimate operating temperature (see Fig. 423, p. 543). The load should then be removed and the no-load volt-

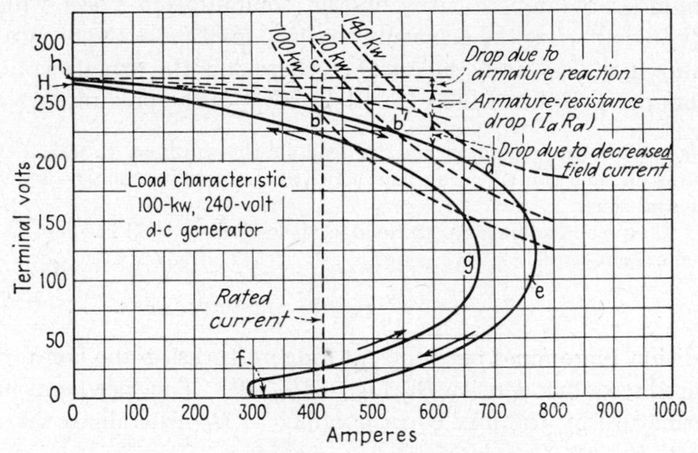

FIG. 350. Load characteristic of shunt generator.

age read on the voltmeter. The field rheostat should remain unchanged. The load should then be gradually applied, and at frequent intervals, the load current I, the terminal voltage V, and the field current I_f recorded. The speed of the generator should be maintained constant throughout. If the readings be plotted as in Fig. 350, the shunt characteristic is obtained. If the load be carried far enough, the terminal voltage will begin to decrease rapidly, as shown at point d and beyond, Fig. 350. This is called the *breakdown* point and the generator is said to "unbuild." Further application of load results in a very rapid decrease of voltage, and beyond a certain point any attempt at increase of load results in a *decrease* of current rather than an increase, as at point e in Fig. 350. The load may even be carried to short circuit as at f, and yet the current will actually decrease as this short-circuit condition is approached. At short circuit the field is short-circuited, and any current is due merely to the residual magnetism of the generator.

If the external resistance now be increased, the voltage will rise slowly and will ultimately reach a value not far below that at which it started, Fig. 350. The fact that the voltage follows a different curve when the short circuit is removed is due primarily to hysteresis. When the load is being applied, the voltage is dropping and the iron is on the part of the cycle represented by *c*, Fig. 315(*a*) (p. 409). When the voltage starts to increase, the return curve is along the path *a*, Fig. 315(*a*). On path *a* there is less flux for a given field current than on path *c*, and consequently less emf is induced in the armature. This fact, together with a lesser field current resulting from the lower terminal voltage, accounts for the return curve *fgH* lying below *hbb′de*, Fig. 350.

In practice, generators are operated only on the portion *hbb′* of the characteristic, Fig. 350. This figure shows the load characteristic of a 100-kw shunt generator, carried to short circuit and return. The rated current is 100,000 ÷ 240 = 417 amp. The generator field rheostat is set so that the terminal voltage is 240 volts when the generator is delivering 417 amp.

There are three reasons for the drop in voltage of a shunt generator under load.

1. The terminal voltage is less than the induced emf by the resistance drop in the armature. That is, the terminal voltage

$$V = E - I_a R_a \qquad \text{volts,} \tag{339}$$

where E is the induced emf, I_a the armature current, and R_a the armature resistance.

Example. The emf induced in the armature of a shunt generator is 600 volts. The armature resistance is 0.1 ohm. Determine terminal voltage when armature current is 200 amp.

Applying (339),

$$V = 600 - (200 \cdot 0.1) = 600 - 20 = 580 \text{ volts.} \quad \textit{Ans.}$$

2. Armature reaction weakens the field and so reduces the induced emf.

3. The drop in terminal voltage due to 1 and 2 results in a decreased field current. This in turn results in a decreased induced emf.

The effect of each of these three factors is shown in Fig. 350.

It might appear that the voltage of the generator would drop to zero, practically, of its own accord when the load is first applied, because the foregoing cycle is cumulative. That is, a lesser terminal voltage results in a weaker field, a weaker field results in a lesser induced emf, and therefore a lower terminal voltage, which still further reduces the field, etc. The cycle *would* result in the terminal volts reaching zero, if the iron were not saturated in some degree. If a 10 per cent drop in terminal voltage resulted in a 10 per cent drop in flux, the generator would be unable to supply any substantial load. However, at or near rated voltage, a 10 per cent drop in terminal voltage and thus in field current results probably in a 2 or 3 per cent drop in flux, due to saturation and hysteresis, as in Fig. 315(*a*) (p. 409). Therefore, a generator when operating at high saturation maintains its voltage better than when operating at low saturation.

This is illustrated in Fig. 351, which shows two saturation curves for a 230-volt generator, one at 900 rpm and the other at 1,200 rpm. If the no-load voltage of the generator in each case is 230 volts, the generator will be operating at point (*a*) on the 1,200-rpm curve, at point (*b*) on the 900-rpm curve. As point (*b*) corresponds to a much higher saturation of the armature and field iron than (*a*), the generator will maintain its voltage better at 900 rpm than at 1,200 rpm, as shown by the characteristics in Fig. 351. (The effect of saturation is further discussed in Sec. 306.)

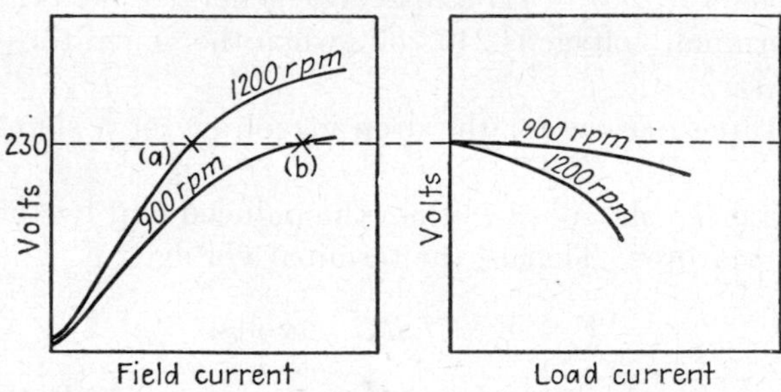

Fig. 351. Relation of shunt characteristics to speed.

Three constant-power curves, for 100 kw, 120 kw, and 140 kw, are shown in Fig. 350. Since power $P = VI$, each curve is a rectangular hyperbola ($xy = k$). Note that the maximum power which the generator can deliver is about 130 kw at point d. For values of current greater than at point d the power decreases. The generator is then *unstable* since attempt to take greater power by decreasing the load resistance results in the generator delivering *less* power.

304. Generator Regulation. The ability of a generator to maintain its voltage under load is a measure of its suitability for constant-potential service. The *regulation* shows quantitatively the change in terminal voltage from rated load to no load.

Regulation is defined in the American Standard C50[1] as follows:

2.130. The regulation of a direct-current generator is the change in voltage when the load is reduced from rated load to zero, expressed in per cent of rated-load voltage. For separately excited generators the excitation shall remain constant during the test, and for self-excited generators the external resistance in the field circuit shall remain constant.

[1] ASA C50, 1943, "Rotating Electrical Machinery."

Regulation may also be stated by giving numerical values of the voltage at no load and rated load. In some cases it is advisable to state regulation for intermediate loads by either of the above methods.

The regulation of direct-current generators refers to changes in voltage corresponding to gradual changes in load and does not relate to the comparatively large momentary fluctuations in voltage that frequently accompany instantaneous changes in load.

2.132. (*a*) *Method of Applying Load.* In making regulation tests, unless otherwise specified, the load shall be increased to the rated load and the regulation observed with decreasing load.

(*b*) *Speed.* Generators shall be tested at rated speed, allowing for the change in speed inherent in the prime mover.

(*c*) *Excitation.* The regulation shall be determined under such conditions as to maintain the field adjustment constant at a value which gives a rated-load voltage at rated-load current. These conditions are as follows: In the case of separately excited fields, constant excitation; in the case of self-excited machines, constant setting of field rheostats.

It is further specified that the generator shall have reached its final temperature and that the temperature shall be maintained as nearly constant as possible during the test.

As an example, the regulation of the generator whose characteristic is shown in Fig. 350 (p. 442) is

$$\frac{270 - 240}{240} = 0.125, \text{ or } 12.5\%.$$

305. Total Characteristic. The *shunt* characteristic is the relation between *load* current and *terminal* volts. The *total* characteristic is the relation between *armature* current and *induced* volts.

The armature current differs from the load current by the field current. The armature current

$$I_a = I + I_f \tag{340}$$

where I is the load current and I_f the shunt-field current.

The induced volts

$$E = V + I_aR_a \tag{341}$$

where V is the terminal voltage and R_a the armature resistance, including brush and brush-contact resistance. The total characteristic is the curve showing the relation of I_a and E. It may be found graphically from the shunt characteristic as follows:

Let qr, Fig. 352, be the shunt characteristic. Draw the field-resistance line oa, as is done in Figs. 320 and 321 (pp. 413 and 414). The line will have the *appearance* of being nearly vertical, owing to the fact that the abscissas are plotted to armature-current scale. The horizontal distances from the OY axis to line Oa give the value of field current for each value of terminal voltage. By adding these distances horizontally to the shunt characteristic, the total current is given by the resulting characteristic *qe*. For example, at point *c* on the shunt characteristic, the distance *c′d′* is added horizontally at *cd*, giving point *d* on the characteristic *qe*.

The armature-resistance-drop line *Ob* is then plotted, assuming that the brush-contact resistance is constant. The voltage drop in the armature is then proportional to the current. It is necessary merely to determine the drop *e′f′* at some value of current *Oe′*. That is, the voltage drop

$$e'f' = (Oe')R_a.$$

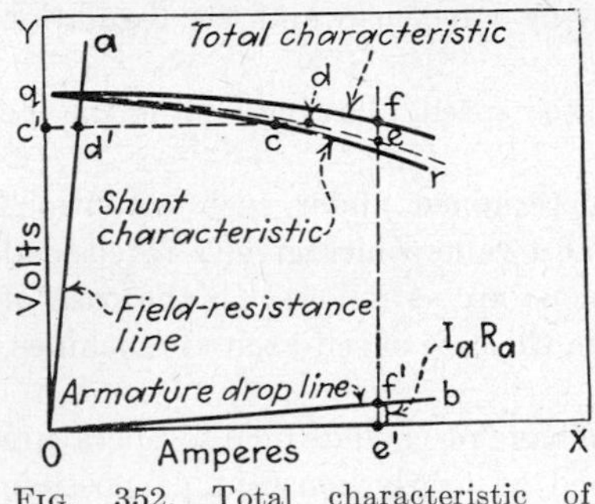

FIG. 352. Total characteristic of shunt generator.

Draw the line *Of′b*. The vertical distances from the *OX* axis, *Oe′* to *Of′*, give the armature drop for each value of current. Adding these drops to the characteristic *qe*, as *ef* = *e′f′* is added at the point *e*, the total characteristic *qf* is obtained.

The total *induced* emf multiplied by the total, or armature, current gives the total power developed by the armature. All of this power is not available, however, for two reasons.

1. Some of this power is lost in the armature itself, appearing as $I_a^2R_a$ loss in the armature copper and in the brushes.
2. Some of the armature output is consumed in heating the shunt field.

Example. A 20-kw 220-volt shunt generator has an armature resistance of 0.07 ohm and a shunt-field resistance of 200 ohms. Determine power developed in armature when it delivers its rated output.

Rated current

$$I = \frac{20{,}000}{220} = 90.9 \text{ amp}$$

Field current

$$I_f = \frac{220}{200} = 1.1 \text{ amp.}$$

Armature current

$$I_a = 90.9 + 1.1 = 92.0 \text{ amp.}$$

Induced volts

$$E = 220 + (92.0 \cdot 0.07) = 226.4 \text{ volts.}$$

Power developed in armature,

$$P = 226.4 \cdot 92.0 = 20{,}830 \text{ watts} = 20.83 \text{ kw.} \quad \textit{Ans.}$$

The same result may be obtained by adding power losses as follows:

Field loss

$$P_f = \frac{(220)^2}{200} = 242 \text{ watts.}$$

Armature loss

$$P_a = (92.0)^2 \cdot 0.07 = 592 \text{ watts.}$$

Power developed in armature,

$$P = 20{,}000 + 242 + 592 = 20{,}834 \text{ watts} = 20.83 \text{ kw } (check).$$

Current in the armature of a generator develops a motor torque, or countertorque (p. 483), which tends to drive the armature in the *reverse* direction. The prime mover, such as a motor, steam turbine, or water wheel, must overcome this countertorque. Thus this countertorque is the reaction in the generator which causes the prime mover to develop the energy necessary to drive the generator (also see Sec. 325, p. 482).

306. Relation of Shunt Characteristic to Saturation Curve. It is pointed out in Sec. 303 (p. 443) that the shunt characteristic depends on

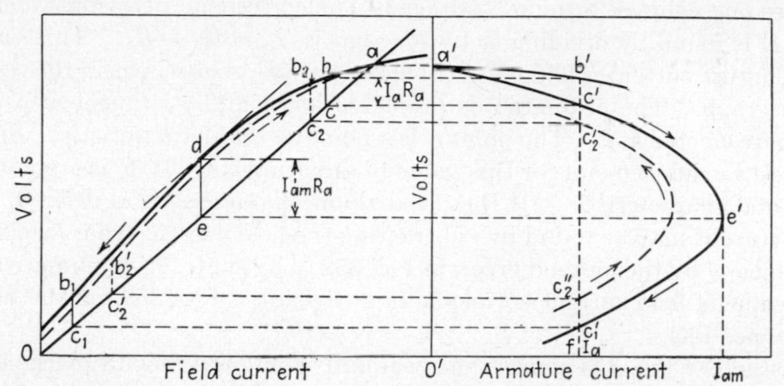

FIG. 353. Relation of shunt characteristic to saturation curve—no armature reaction.

the degree of saturation of the magnetic circuit and hence on that part of the saturation curve at which the generator is operating. A method for determining the shunt characteristic directly from the saturation curve and the field-resistance line is as follows:

a. Armature Reaction Negligible. Assume first that the armature reaction is so small as to be negligible. This condition often occurs with generators having commutating poles in which the brushes remain in the geometrical neutral. Figure 353 shows the saturation curve of a shunt generator taken at some definite speed. The dotted line is taken with increasing values and the solid line with decreasing values of field current. The field-resistance line is Oa, and the generator will build up along the dotted line to point a, neglecting the small drop in the armature due to the field current. Hence, (neglecting field current) a' on the right-hand plot will be the generator terminal voltage when the armature current is zero. With the application of load, two effects cause the terminal voltage to drop, the resistance drop I_aR_a in the armature and the decreased field current due to the lessened terminal voltage. The armature reaction is assumed to be negligible.

When the generator has reached a condition of stability, two conditions must be fulfilled. The induced emf must lie on the descending portion of the saturation curve adb_1, as at some point b; the corresponding terminal voltage must lie on the field-resistance line at point c, since the field-circuit terminals are connected directly to the armature terminals. Moreover, points b and c must have the same abscissa, for the field current which gives the induced emf b is also produced by the terminal voltage corresponding to c. Furthermore, the distance bc must be equal to I_aR_a, since the difference between the induced emf and the terminal voltage is equal to the armature-resistance drop. That is, the induced emf E at b is equal to the terminal voltage V at c plus the I_aR_a drop [see Eq. (341)]. Hence, c gives one value of terminal voltage. The corresponding armature current I_a is found by dividing bc by R_a; that is, $I_a = bc \div R_a$. This value of armature current is laid off at $O'f$ along the axis of abscissas in the right-hand graph. The ordinate c is projected horizontally to meet at c' the ordinate erected at f. The point c' is a point on the characteristic. Since b gives the induced emf for this value of armature current, b' is a point on the total characteristic. If the usual shunt characteristic is desired, the load current may be found by subtracting the field current from I_a, either graphically by the method given in Fig. 352 or by subtracting numerically the value of field current corresponding to point c, Fig. 353, on the field-resistance line.

A study of Fig. 353 shows that ordinarily there is a second place, as at b_1c_1, where bc may be fitted vertically between the saturation curve and the field-resistance line. Hence, there must be two values of terminal voltage corresponding to the same value of armature current. The load current will be slightly different in the two cases, since the values of field current are not the same. Point c_1', on the lower portion of the characteristic, gives the second value of terminal voltage corresponding to the given value of armature current.

The maximum value of armature current may be found by drawing a tangent to the saturation curve at d parallel to the field-resistance line. The corresponding value of armature current I_{am} is found by dividing the vertical distance de by the armature resistance. This gives point e' on the characteristic.

With constant armature resistance, the distances bc, de, etc., are proportional to the armature current. Hence, the abscissas for the characteristic may be found also by drawing a number of vertical lines between the saturation curve and the field-resistance line, determining the armature current for each of these lines by scaling. That part of the load curve fgH, Fig. 350, which begins at short circuit may be similarly determined. For example, in Fig. 353, b_2c_2 equal to bc is fitted between the dotted ascending saturation curve and the field-resistance line Oa, giving point c_2' on the load curve. Also, $b_2'c_2'$ equal to b_2c_2 gives point c_2'' for the same value of current but for the lower value of voltage.

As is pointed out in Sec. 301 (p. 434), the armature resistance is not constant but is a function of the armature current. An error results in assuming the armature resistance to be constant. Also, the ordinates of the saturation curve depend so much on the previous magnetic history of the iron that the curve does not ordinarily repeat itself accurately. A small percentage change in either the saturation curve or the field-resistance line makes a much larger percentage change in their difference. Therefore, as would be expected, characteristics obtained by this method may not be exactly the same as those obtained by test, but they are suffi-

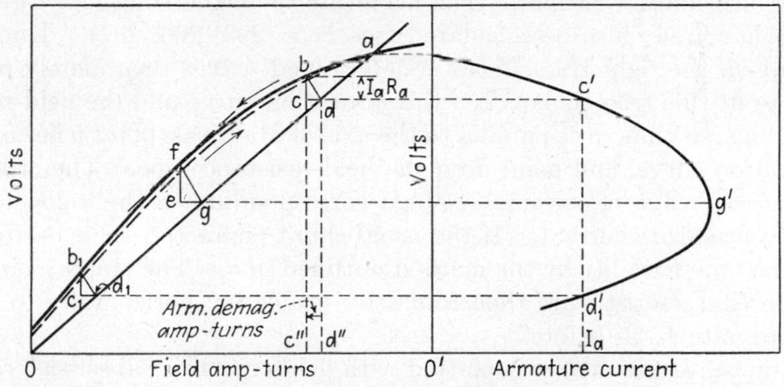

FIG. 354. Relation of shunt characteristic to saturation curve—armature reaction included.

ciently close to give a near approximation to the actual performance of the generator.

It is shown in Fig. 351 (p. 444) that if the speed be increased with the same no-load voltage, the load voltage is less for each value of armature current. The reason for this is shown by Fig. 353. If the speed be increased and the no-load voltage be maintained constant by increasing the field resistance, the distances bc, de will be decreased. Hence, for any given terminal voltage, the armature current will be decreased, resulting in a more drooping characteristic.

b. Armature Reaction Not Negligible. In Fig. 354 let $abfb_1$ be the descending saturation curve with field *ampere-turns* as abscissas and oa the field-resistance line with field ampere-turns as abscissas rather than field current. Consider a terminal voltage dd''. Point d must be on the field-resistance line since the field is connected across the armature terminals. If there were no demagnetizing action of the armature, the induced emf corresponding to the field ampere-turns Od'' would lie on the saturation curve vertically over *d*, as *b* lies over *c* in Fig. 353. Under load, the armature reduces the total ampere-turns of the magnetic circuit by an amount $d''c''$, where $d''c''$ is equal to the armature demagnetizing ampere-turns (see Secs. 293, 296, 297, pp. 415, 424, 425). Hence, the *net* ampere-turns acting on the field are given by Oc''. The corresponding induced emf must be $c''b$.

The condition that the terminal voltage must be equal to the induced emf minus the I_aR_a drop must be fulfilled. Hence, *bc* must be equal to the I_aR_a drop in the armature, where *cd* is equal and parallel to $c''d''$. Therefore, triangle *bcd* must have such a position that point *b* lies on the saturation curve, point *d* lies on the field-resistance line, and *cd* is parallel to the axis of abscissas. To determine the two sides of triangle *bcd*, side *bc*, or the I_aR_a drop, may be calculated as in *a* (p. 448), using the desired value of armature current. The armature demagnetizing ampere-turns per pole *cd* may also be calculated (see Secs. 293, 296, 297). Knowing *bc* and *cd*, the right triangle *bcd* is determined. It is then merely necessary to fit this triangle between the saturation curve and the field-resistance line, so that *cd* is parallel to the axis of abscissas, point *b* lies on the saturation curve, and point *d* on the field-resistance line. The ordinate $d''d$ is the value of terminal voltage corresponding to the value of the chosen armature current. If the usual shunt characteristic is desired, it may be found readily by the method outlined in *a*. The points c' and d_1' on the characteristic are then found by projecting horizontally to meet the ordinate I_a, as before.

If the saturation curve is plotted with field current as abscissas, rather than with field ampere-turns, it is merely necessary to divide the armature demagnetizing ampere-turns by N_f, where N_f is the number of shunt-field turns per pole, in order to use the given scale of abscissas.

Other values of armature current may be found as follows: If the armature resistance be assumed constant, both the sides *bc* and *cd* of triangle *bcd* are proportional to the armature current. Hence, the triangles for all values of armature current are similar, and when fitted properly between the saturation curve and the field-resistance line, their corresponding sides are parallel. Therefore, the hypotenuses are parallel to one another. That is, *fg* is parallel to *bd*, etc. To determine the armature current for the terminal voltage corresponding to *g*, draw *fg* parallel to *bd*, intersecting the saturation curve at *f*. The armature current will be equal to *fg* to the same scale as *bd*. Triangle *feg* is drawn to correspond to the maximum value of armature current, the tangent drawn to the saturation curve at *f* being parallel to the field-resistance line. Point g' on the characteristic is found by projecting horizontally to meet the ordinate corresponding to the value of armature current determined from *fg*. If it be desired to obtain that part of the characteristic which gives the return from short circuit, such as $c_2''c_2'$, Fig. 353, the dotted saturation curve for increasing values of field current is used, Fig. 354, and the procedure described in *a* followed.

This method is subject to the same errors as those of *a*, that is, the armature resistance changes with the current and there are some variations in the saturation curve. On account of saturation, particularly of the pole tips and armature teeth, the effects of armature reaction cannot be determined with high precision. However, a moderately close approximation to the performance of the generator can be obtained with the two methods.

307. Compound Generator. The drop in terminal voltage with load, which is characteristic of the shunt generator, makes this type of generator undesirable where constancy of voltage is essential. This applies

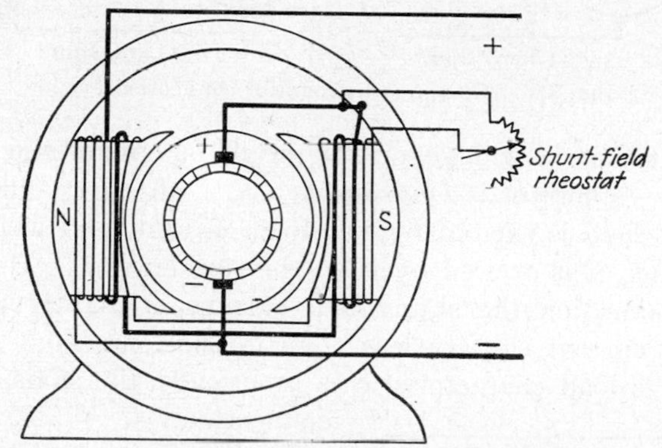

FIG. 355. Connections of compound generator (short-shunt).

particularly to lighting circuits, where a very slight change of voltage makes a material change in the candlepower of incandescent lamps. A generator may be made to produce a substantially constant voltage, or even a rise in voltage as the load increases, by placing on the field core a few turns which are connected *in series* with either the load or the armature. These turns are connected so as to *aid* the shunt turns when the generator delivers current, Fig. 355. As the load increases, the current through the series turns also increases and, therefore, the flux increases. The effect of this increased flux is to increase the induced emf. By adjustment of the series ampere-turns, this increase in induced emf may be made to balance the combined drop in voltage due to armature reaction and to armature resistance. Since the terminal voltage usually remains either substantially constant or increases with load, the field current does not decrease as the load increases. Therefore, of the three causes for the drop in terminal voltage with the shunt generator—namely, armature reaction, armature-resistance drop I_aR_a, and decrease in field current, Fig. 350,—the series-field ampere-turns compensate for the effects of the first two, and the last does not occur. In fact, with the overcompounded generator (below), there is an actual *increase* in shunt-field current with load.

The shunt field may be connected directly across the armature terminals, Fig. 356(a), in which case the generator is *short-shunt*. If the shunt

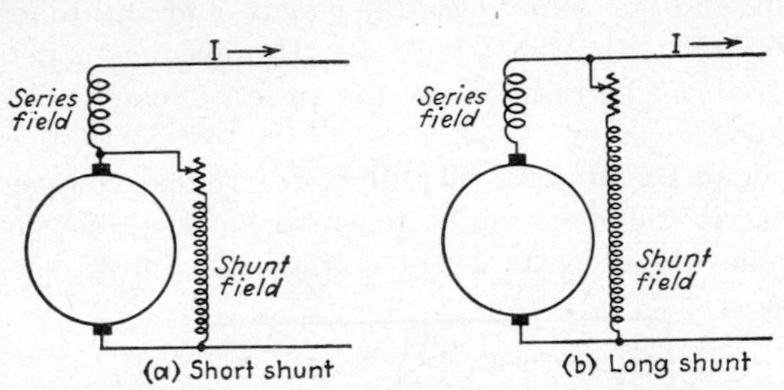

Fig. 356. Compound-generator connections.

field be connected across the generator terminals outside the series field, Fig. 356(b), the generator is *long-shunt*. With the short-shunt connection, the series field is excited by the load current, and with the long-shunt connection, it is excited by the armature current. Hence, in the short-shunt connection the shunt-field current is slightly greater and the series-field current slightly less than in the long-shunt connection. Accordingly, the load characteristic is practically the same with either connection.

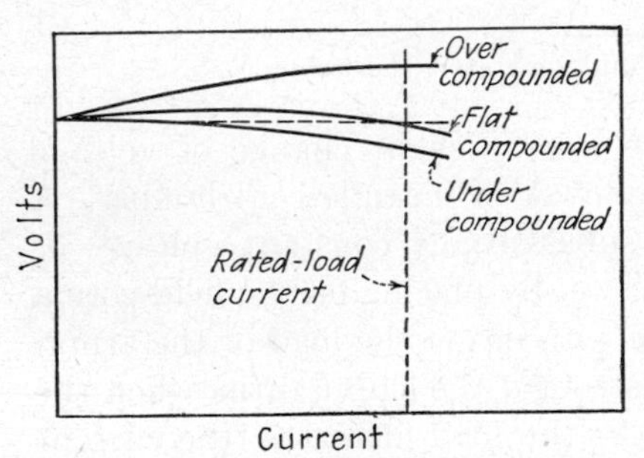

Fig. 357. Compound-generator characteristics.

If the effect of the series turns is to produce the same voltage at rated load as at no load, the machine is *flat-compounded*, Fig. 357. It is seldom possible to maintain a constant voltage for all values of current from no load to rated load. The tendency is first for the voltage to rise and then to drop, reaching the same voltage at rated load as at no load. The shape of the characteristic is due to the saturation of the iron, so that the series ampere-turns do not increase the flux at full load proportionately as much as they do at light load (see Sec. 308). When the rated-load voltage is greater than the no-load voltage, the machine is *overcompounded*. When the rated-load voltage is less than the no-load voltage, the machine is *undercompounded*. Generators are seldom undercompounded.

Flat-compounded generators are used principally in isolated plants, such as hotels and office buildings. The size of the conductors in the distribution system of such plants is determined almost entirely by underwriters' requirements as to safe current-carrying capacity. Wires conforming to these requirements are usually of such size that only a very small voltage drop takes place between the generator and the various loads.

Overcompounded generators are used where the load is located at a considerable distance from the generator. As the load increases, the voltage at the load tends to decrease, owing to the voltage drop in the feeder. If, however, the generator voltage rises just enough to balance this feeder drop, the voltage at the load remains constant.

Example. Consider the conditions shown in Fig. 358(*a*). A certain load is 4,000 ft distant from the generator. The load is supplied over a 500,000-cir-mil feeder. The no-load voltage of the generator is 500 volts. It is desired to maintain the load

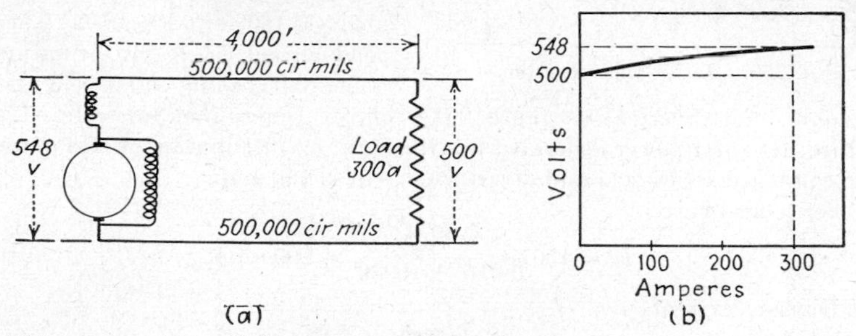

FIG. 358. Overcompounded generator maintaining constant voltage at end of feeder.

voltage at a substantially constant value of 500 volts from no load to the maximum demand of 300 amp. Determine characteristic of generator.

If the feeder operated at "normal" density, the current would be 500 amp, or 0.001 amp per cir mil (Sec. 46, p. 51) and the drop would be 0.01 volt per ft, making a total drop of 80 volts.

The actual drop is

$$(300 \div 500)80 = 48 \text{ volts.}$$

The generator terminal voltage should rise from a no-load value of 500 volts to 548 volts when 300 amp is being delivered to the load, Fig. 358(*b*).

Compound generators are usually wound so as to be somewhat overcompounded. The degree of compounding can then be regulated by shunting more or less current from the series field. To do this a low-resistance shunt, called a *diverter*, is used, Fig. 359.

Compound generators which supply 3-wire distribution systems usually have two series-field windings, one connected to each side of the armature. There are two separate series windings on each pole, one winding being connected to the positive terminal and the other to the negative terminal of the generator, Fig. 430 (p. 549).

In a compound generator, the induced emf in the armature is

$$E = V + I_s R_s + I_a R_a \tag{342}$$

where V is the terminal voltage, I_s the series-field current, I_a the armature current, and R_s and R_a the resistance of the series field and armature. If a diverter is used, R_s is the equivalent parallel resistance of the series field and diverter, and I_s is the combined current in the series field and diverter. In a long-shunt generator, $I_s = I_a$.

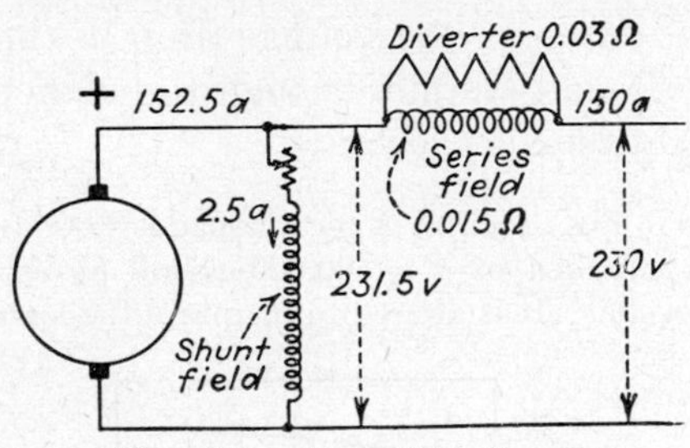

FIG. 359. Series-field diverter.

Example. In a compound generator, connected short-shunt, the terminal voltage is 230 volts when the generator delivers 150 amp, Fig. 359. The shunt-field current is 2.5 amp, armature resistance 0.032 ohm, series-field resistance 0.015 ohm, and diverter resistance 0.030 ohm. Determine: (*a*) induced emf in armature; (*b*) total power generated in armature; (*c*) distribution of this power.

The combined series-field and diverter current is 150 amp.

(*a*) Series-field current

$$I_s = 150 \frac{0.030}{0.015 + 0.030} = 100 \text{ amp.}$$

Diverter current

$$I_d = 150 \frac{0.015}{0.015 + 0.030} = 50 \text{ amp.}$$

Combined equivalent resistance of series field and diverter,

$$\frac{1}{R'} = \frac{1}{0.015} + \frac{1}{0.030}; \qquad R' = 0.010 \text{ ohm.}$$

Voltage drop in series field and diverter,

$$E' = 150 \cdot 0.010 = 1.50 \text{ volts.}$$

Armature current

$$I_a = 152.5 \text{ amp.}$$

Induced emf

$$E = 230 + 1.5 + 152.5 \cdot 0.032 = 236.4 \text{ volts.} \quad \textit{Ans.}$$

(*b*) Total power generated,

$$P_a = 236.4 \cdot 152.5 = 36{,}050 \text{ watts} = 36.05 \text{ kw.} \quad \textit{Ans.}$$

(*c*) Armature loss

$$P_a' = 152.5^2 \cdot 0.032 = \quad 744 \text{ watts.} \quad \textit{Ans.}$$

Series-field loss

$$P_s = 100^2 \cdot 0.015 \quad = \quad 150 \text{ watts.} \quad \textit{Ans.}$$

Diverter loss

$$P_d = 50^2 \cdot 0.030 \quad = \quad 75 \text{ watts.} \quad \textit{Ans.}$$

Shunt-field loss

$$P_{sh} = (230 + 1.5)2.5 = \quad 579 \text{ watts.} \quad \textit{Ans.}$$

Power delivered

$$P = 230 \cdot 150 \quad = \underline{34{,}500} \text{ watts.}$$

$$\text{Total} = 36{,}048 \text{ watts } (\textit{check}).$$

308. Relation of Compound Characteristic to Saturation Curve. The characteristic of the compound generator may be determined from the

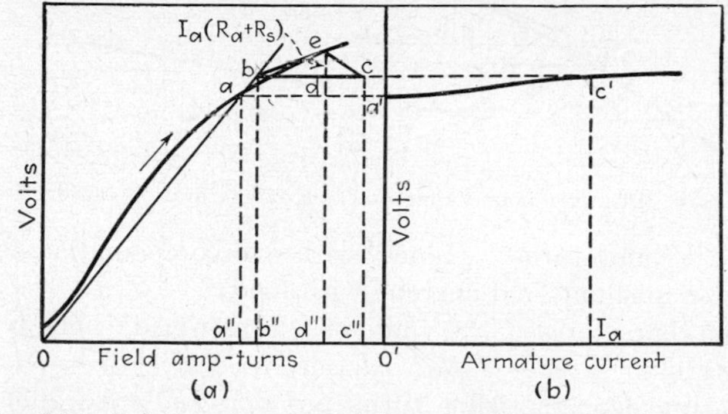

FIG. 360. Relation of compound characteristic to saturation curve.

saturation curve and field-resistance line just as with the shunt generator. In Fig. 360(*a*) is shown the saturation curve of a compound generator, plotted with shunt-field ampere-turns per pole as abscissas, and *Oa*, the field-resistance line, with field ampere-turns as abscissas rather than field current. Assume that the generator is long-shunt, so that the armature and series-field currents are the same. At no load, the voltage drop in the armature and series field, due to the shunt-field current, may be neglected. Moreover, this small drop is offset at no load by the series ampere-turns due to the shunt-field current in the series field. Thus at no load the terminal voltage is the emf at the intersection of the field-resistance line with the saturation curve at *a* and is shown as $O'a'$ in (*b*).

Consider a value of terminal voltage bb''. Since bb'' represents *terminal* voltage, point *b* must lie on the field-resistance line. The corresponding shunt-field ampere-turns are given by Ob''. Let *bc* equal the series-field ampere-turns per pole, I_aN_s, where I_a is both the series-field and the armature current, the generator being connected long shunt. N_s is the number of series turns per pole. The *total* ampere-turns per pole must be the sum of the shunt ampere-turns Ob'' and the series ampere-turns $b''c''$, giving total ampere-turns Oc''. Were it not for the demagnetizing ampere-turns, the induced emf would be found on the saturation curve at the point of intersection with ordinate $c''c$. The armature demagnetizing ampere-turns are given by cd or $c''d''$. These must be subtracted from the total ampere-turns Oc'' in order to obtain the *net* field ampere-turns per pole Od''. Hence, the induced emf is equal to $d''e$.

As before, the terminal voltage bb'' must be equal to the induced emf minus the $I_a(R_a + R_s)$ drop, where R_s is the resistance of the series field. Hence, ed is equal to $I_a(R_a + R_s)$.

At no load the shunt-field ampere-turns are equal to Oa'', Fig. 360(a), and under the given conditions of load they have increased to Ob'', an

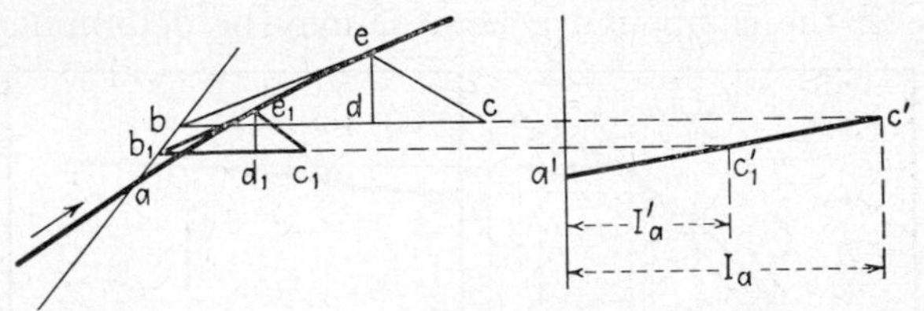

FIG. 361. Compound characteristic and saturation curve.

increase of $a''b''$ amp-turns. Hence, with overcompounding there is an actual increase in shunt-field current with load.

To plot the characteristic, the value of I_a is assumed. The triangle bec is then determined; $bc = I_aN_s$; $cd = I_aN_D \div P'$; $ed = I_a(R_a + R_s)$. (N_D = armature demagnetizing turns per pole; P' = parallel paths in armature.) The triangle bec is so placed that bc is parallel to the axis of abscissas, point e lies on the saturation curve, and point b lies on the field-resistance line. The line bc is extended to the right to meet the ordinate erected at I_a, giving c' as a point on the characteristic. If it is desired to plot the load current as abscissa, the field current may be subtracted, either graphically or numerically, its value ($ob'' \div N$) being determined from the saturation curve (see p. 448).

The method of determining some other point c_1' on the characteristic is indicated in Fig. 361, which shows the upper portion of the saturation curve of Fig. 360(a) to larger scale. Assume that point c_1' corresponds to an armature current $I_a' = \frac{1}{2}I_a$. The triangle $b_1e_1c_1$, similar to bec, is drawn, each side being one-half the length of the corresponding side of triangle bec. Triangle $b_1c_1e_1$ is placed so that side $b_1d_1c_1$ is parallel to the axis of abscissas, e_1 lies on the saturation curve, and b_1 lies on the field-resistance line. The point c_1' on the characteristic is found as before by extending the line $b_1d_1c_1$ to meet the ordinate at I_a'.

If the load current is being increased, *oae*, Fig. 360(*a*), and ae_1e, Fig. 361, must be the saturation curve taken with *increasing* values of field current; if the load current is being decreased, *oae*, Fig. 360(*a*), and ee_1a, Fig. 361, must be the saturation curve taken with *decreasing* values of field current.

If the saturation curve at ae_1e, Fig. 361, has curvature, the characteristic $a'c_1'c'$ will not be a straight line [see Figs. 357 and 358 (*b*), pp. 452 and 453]. If I_a is the rated armature current of the generator and the generator is flat-compounded, points *a* and *b* coincide (Figs. 360 and 361).

In Figs. 360 and 361 the abscissas are ampere-turns. If the abscissas are shunt-field current, it is merely necessary to multiply the series-field ampere-turns and the armature ampere-turns by N_s/N_{sh} to adapt them to the scale of shunt-field current. (N_{sh} = shunt-field turns per pole.)

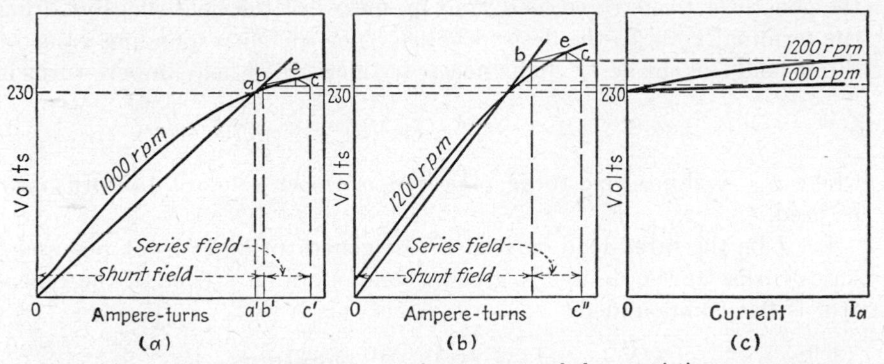

FIG. 362. Effect of speed on compound characteristic.

309. Effect of Speed. Figure 362(*a*) shows the saturation curve of a 230-volt compound generator connected long-shunt taken at 1,000 rpm. The shunt-field rheostat is adjusted so that the generator builds up to a no-load voltage of 230 volts, and the corresponding number of shunt-field ampere-turns is given by Oa'. When load is applied to the generator, in accordance with Sec. 308, Figs. 360 and 361, the mmf of the field is increased by the series-field ampere-turns an amount I_aN_s, or *bc*, Fig. 362(*a*). Also, if the generator is overcompounded, the shunt-field ampere-turns are increased by the amount $a'b'$. From Sec. 308, the terminal voltage $c'c$ for any given value of armature current I_a is obtained by placing the triangle *bce* so that *b* is on the field-resistance line and *e* is on the saturation curve. Now let the same generator be speeded up to 1,200 rpm, and let the no-load terminal voltage still be 230 volts, Fig. 362(*b*). For the same value of armature current I_a, the triangle *bce* remains unchanged. When it is now fitted to the field-resistance line and saturation curve, the terminal voltage becomes $c''c$, which is considerably greater than $c'c$ in (*a*). Accordingly, the load characteristic for 1,200 rpm lies above the one for 1,000 rpm, Fig. 362(*c*). (Armature current rather than load current is plotted.) The greater increase in terminal voltage at the higher speed is obviously due to the lesser saturation of the iron at the higher speed. Note that the effect of speed on the compound characteristic is just the reverse of the effect of speed on the shunt characteristic, Fig. 351 (p. 444). This is due to the fact that in each case saturation tends to prevent change of flux.

310. Determination of Series Turns; Armature Characteristic. It is often desired to determine experimentally the number of series turns necessary to be placed on the poles of a shunt generator in order to make it either flat-compounded or to give it any desired degree of compounding.

To make the determination, adjust the no-load voltage to the desired value, and let the corresponding value of shunt-field current be I_1. Load the generator to its rated load, and by means of the field rheostat bring the terminal volts to the desired value. Let the corresponding value of shunt-field current be I_2. The necessary increase of field ampere-turns is

$$(I_2 - I_1)N_{sh}$$

where N_{sh} = shunt-field turns. Either turns per pole or total turns may be used.

Let I be the rated-load current of the generator and N_s the necessary series turns for the desired degree of compounding. Then, if the generator is flat-compounded,

$$N_sI = (I_2 - I_1)N_{sh} \quad \text{amp-turns.}$$

$$N_s = \frac{(I_2 - I_1)}{I} N_{sh} \quad \text{turns.} \tag{343}$$

If the generator is overcompounded, the increase in voltage with load produces an increase in the shunt-field current (p. 456) and hence a part of the increase in ampere-turns required to produce the overcompounding is supplied by the shunt field. Let I_3 be the increase in shunt-field current due to overcompounding. This is equal to $a''b''$, Fig. 360(*a*) (p. 455), divided by N_{sh}. Hence,

$$(I_2 - I_1)N_{sh} = N_sI + N_{sh}I_3 \quad \text{amp-turns,}$$

or

$$N_s = \frac{(I_2 - I_1 - I_3)N_{sh}}{I} \quad \text{turns.} \tag{344}$$

Eq. (344) also applies to undercompounded generators if the sign of I_3 is reversed, since it now represents a decrease in field current.

Since, in (343) and (344) I is the *rated-load* current, the equation applies to the *short-shunt* connection, for with this connection the series field is directly in series with the load. If it were desired to use (343) and (344) with the *long-shunt* connection, the experiment should be conducted with the ammeter in the armature circuit. The armature current I_a should then be substituted for the load current I. Little difference would be noticed in the two cases since the shunt-field current rarely exceeds 3 per cent of the armature current and the differences due to hysteresis

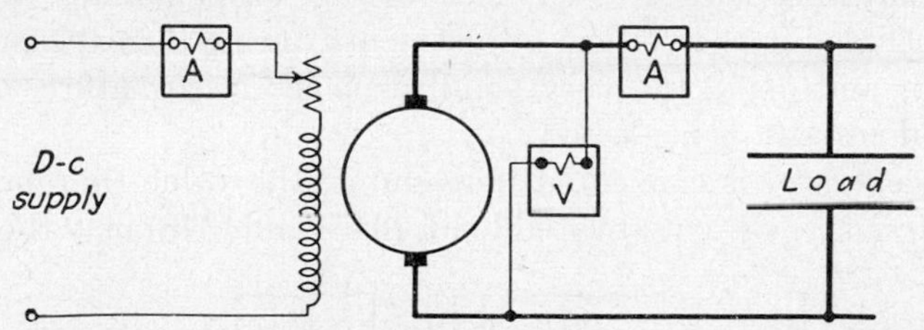

FIG. 363. Connections for obtaining armature characteristic.

in the magnetic circuit of the generator would probably exceed any effect due to the particular shunt-field connection.

The number of series turns for flat compounding may be obtained also by means of the armature characteristic. The load is applied to the armature in the usual way. It is preferable to excite the field separately, as shown in Fig. 363. Load is applied, and the terminal voltage is maintained constant by means of the shunt-field rheostat. Corresponding values of field current and armature current are noted. When the two are plotted, Fig. 364, the resulting curve is the *armature characteristic*. Owing to saturation the rate of increase of field current is greater for the higher values of armature current.

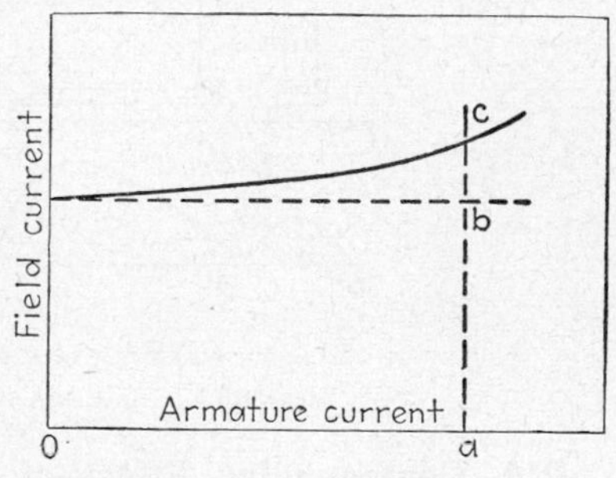

FIG. 364. Armature characteristic.

The shunt-field ampere-turns necessary to maintain constant voltage across the armature terminals are given by $N_{sh}(bc)$. If Oa is the rated-load current and the generator is connected short-shunt, the number of series turns for flat compounding, with reference to the voltage at the *armature terminals*, is

$$N_s = N_{sh} \frac{bc}{Oa} \quad \text{turns.} \tag{345}$$

Because of the drop in the series field the voltage at the *generator terminals* is slightly less than the value given by (345) for flat compounding. If the series-field resistance be known, the field current ac, Fig. 364, may be changed to a value ac' (not shown in Fig. 364) which at rated load gives a voltage equal to the no-load voltage plus the series-field drop. The series turns for flat compounding then take the value

$$N_s = N_{sh} \frac{bc'}{Oa} \quad \text{turns.} \tag{346}$$

If commutating poles are used, their voltage drop, like that in the armature, is included in the voltage adjustments during the experiments. In both (345) and (346), the very small drop in the armature, due to the shunt-field current, is neglected.

If the generator is connected long-shunt, the value Oa represents the value of *armature* current at rated load, (345) and (346) may then be used.

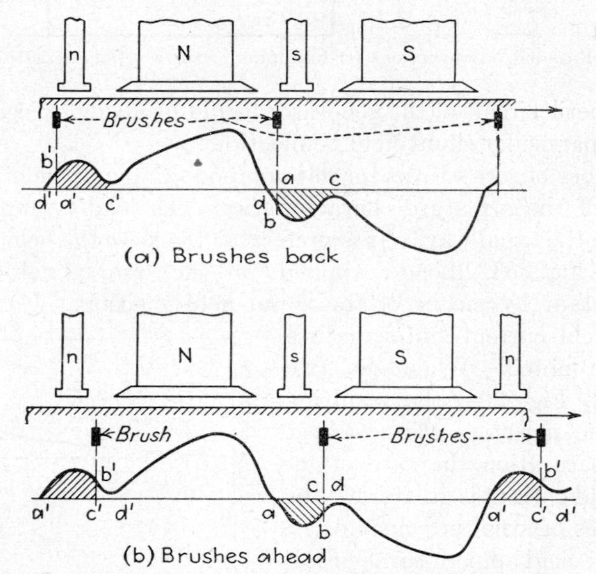

FIG. 365. Compounding effect of commutating poles.

311. Compounding Effect of Commutating Poles. Flux enters and leaves the armature through the commutating poles (Figs. 345 and 346, pp. 438 and 439), and the magnitude of this flux is nearly proportional to the armature current. If the flux from each commutating pole divides equally on the two sides of the conductor connected to the commutator segment directly under the center of the brush, there is negligible compounding effect of the commutating poles. Practically, it is not always possible to place the brushes in this ideal position.

It also happens frequently that when the brushes are adjusted to give what appears to be the best commutation conditions, their positions may be such that a coil side to which the brush is connected at the instant is at one side of the commutating-pole flux, Figs. 365(a) and (b), rather than at the center of this flux. For example, in (*a*) the brushes are back of the center of the commutating-pole flux. Consequently the portion *abc* of this flux adds to the *S*-pole flux between brushes, and the portion *a'b'c'* adds to the *N*-pole flux. The small area *abd* subtracts from an *N*-pole flux, and the small area *a'b'd'* subtracts from an *S*-pole flux. The net effect, however, is to increase the flux between brushes, and the commutating poles tend to overcompound the generator.

If, on the other hand, the brushes are moved ahead of the center of the commutating-pole flux, as in (*b*), the flux corresponding to the area *abc* will subtract from an *N*-pole flux and the flux corresponding to the area *a'b'c'* will subtract from an *S*-pole flux. The small flux areas *bcd* and *b'c'd'* add to *S*-pole and *N*-pole flux, respectively. Thus, the net effect of the commutating poles in this case is to compound the generator differentially. This is usually undesirable, and some care should be taken, therefore, in determining the brush position. Thus the commutating poles may have the effect of a series winding on the operating characteristics of a generator. These compounding effects may become distinctly detrimental in the operation of a motor.

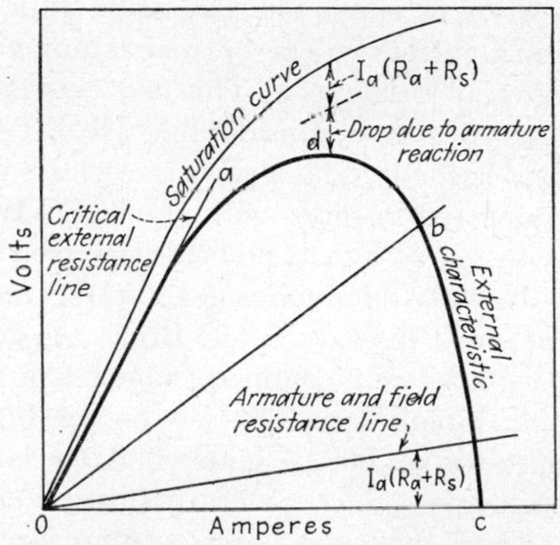

FIG. 366. Series-generator characteristic.

312. Series Generator. In the series generator the field winding is connected in series with the armature and the external circuit. It consists necessarily of comparatively few turns of wire having sufficiently large cross section to carry the rated current of the generator.

The series generator in most instances is used for constant-current work, in distinction to the shunt generator, which maintains constant potential. Figure 366 shows the saturation curve of a series generator and also its external characteristic. The saturation curve differs in no way from that of the shunt generator. Also, at low saturation the external characteristic is similar in shape to the saturation curve. The voltage at each point on the characteristic is less than that shown by the saturation curve, by the amount due to the drop through the armature and field $I_a(R_a + R_s)$ and the drop due to armature reaction. The curve reaches a maximum beyond which armature reaction becomes so great as to cause the curve to drop sharply, and the terminal voltage drops rapidly to zero. Series generators are designed to have a very high value of armature reaction.

The generator builds up as follows: If the series field is connected in such a manner that the current due to residual magnetism aids this magnetism, the generator will build up, provided that the external resistance equals or is less than that indicated by the external-resistance line *Oa*. The line *Oa* is called the *critical external-resistance line*. As the external resistance decreases, the external-resistance line swings down to the right, as is discussed for the shunt generator in Sec. 288 (p. 411). The line *Ob* is such a line. It would be practically impossible to operate with an external resistance corresponding to the line *Oa*, or to any line cutting the curve to the left of *d*, as a small increase in external resistance would swing the resistance line away from the curve, resulting in the dropping of the load. The generator is designed to operate along the portion *bc* of the characteristic, which corresponds to substantially constant current. The current is not affected by a considerable change in external resistance. This may be seen by swinging the external-resistance line *Ob* over a considerable arc. To obtain close regulation, the series field is shunted by a rheostat, whose resistance is controlled by a solenoid connected in series with the line. In this way the current delivered by the generator may be held very nearly constant.

In early days series generators were used to supply arc lamps in series for street lighting. The Brush arc generator and the Thomson-Houston generator were common examples of such machines. Both of these have open-circuit armatures (see Sec. 263, p. 371). As the voltage on the commutator is 2,000 to 3,000 volts, the commutators have wide gaps between segments. Such generators have long since become obsolete.

Until 1937, the Thury system[1] was used in Europe to transmit power at high voltage with direct current. The voltage, which was as high as 50,000 volts, was obtained by connecting several series generators in series and transmitting at constant current. The voltage increased with the load. Each generator had two commutators, one at each end of the armature. The potential ran as high as 5,000 volts per commutator. Regulation was obtained by shunting the fields. The power was utilized by series motors connected in series with the line at the desired points.

313. Series Booster. Series generators are occasionally used as boosters on d-c feeders. When the voltage drop on a particular feeder becomes excessive, it may be more economical to install a booster and utilize it at peak load than to invest in more copper. The booster is a series generator operating on the straight portion of the saturation curve, the terminal voltage being proportional to the current. Likewise, the voltage drop in the feeder is proportional to the current in the feeder. If the generator be connected in series with the feeder, Fig. 367(*a*), and

[1] See "Standard Handbook for Electrical Engineers," 8th ed., Sec. 13, p. 1171, McGraw-Hill Book Company, Inc.

adjusted properly, its terminal volts may be made always equal to the drop in the feeder, Fig. 367(*b*), and the voltage at the load may be maintained constant. The booster is direct-connected to a shunt motor which takes its power from the bus bars. If the driving power should in any way be removed, the series generator will reverse and operate as a motor. The speed of a series motor without load is practically unlimited, and it will run away and tear itself to pieces. Therefore, such a booster

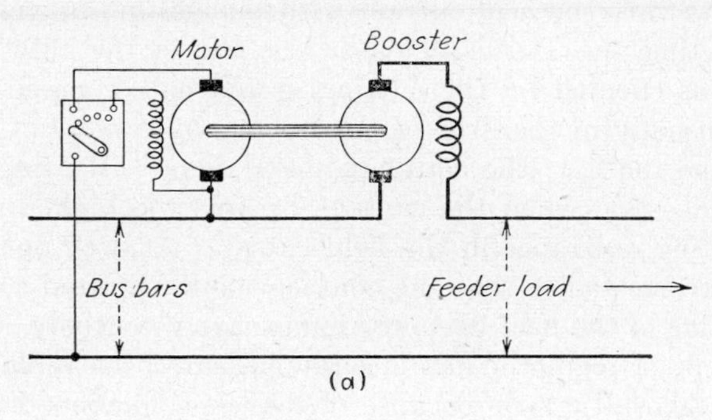

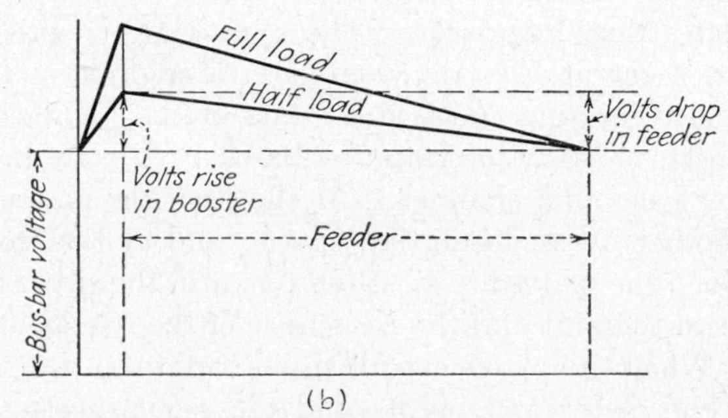

FIG. 367. Series booster.

should never be belt-driven and should have some device to prevent its running away.

314. Effect of Variable Speed on Characteristics. When a generator is being tested to determine its characteristic or its regulation, it is assumed that the generator speed is maintained at a constant value, the rated speed of the generator. Any drop in voltage resulting from a drop in speed of the prime mover or driving motor is not chargeable to the generator. In practice, a drop in speed with load in the case of the prime mover is often unavoidable, and the regulation of the generator is made to include the voltage drop due to this decreased speed. In writing specifications, the regulation of the generator *when driven by its prime mover should be specified.* Speed correction applied to the characteristics of generators is quite involved, because of the many factors which enter.

AUTOMATIC VOLTAGE REGULATORS

It is pointed out that the voltage of a generator varies with the load, speed, etc. By means of an automatic regulator, the voltage of a generator can be maintained constant even under rapid fluctuations of load. In addition, compensation may be made for line drop. These automatic regulators usually operate through the field of the generator or the field of an exciter to vary the field current with changes in line voltage.

For a long time the Tirrill regulator was almost the only type used. Regulation was effected by the cutting in and out of resistance in the field circuit, usually in the field of the exciter, by contacts. When the voltage became too low, the contacts closed, short-circuiting a portion of the field rheostat; when the voltage became too high, the contacts opened, inserting resistance in the field circuit. At each operation, the regulator overcorrected so that the contact points vibrated continuously and the time lag of the field current produced an essentially steady voltage. This type of regulator has in large measure been replaced by the direct-acting rheostatic type because of the lesser likelihood of contacts sticking and also because of lesser maintenance.

315. Direct-acting Regulator. The type GDA regulator, manufactured by the General Electric Company, is a direct-acting rheostatic type with the regulating rheostat as part of the regulator itself. The rheostat consists of stacks of graphite plates, each plate being pivoted at the center by a metallic member. At the back the plates are separated from one another by an insulating spacer, and at the front by a silver button. When the plates are all tilted forward, the silver buttons form a continuous short circuit and the resistance of the regulating rheostat is a minimum. When the plates are all tilted backward, the current path is through all the plates and pivots and the regulating resistance of the rheostat is a maximum. The value of the regulating resistance thus depends on the number of plates that are tilted either backward or forward.

A diagram of the regulator is shown in Fig. 368. A U-shaped iron core 2 is magnetized by a coil 1, connected across the generator terminals in series with a resistor and voltage-adjusting rheostat. A torque armature of iron 3 tends to align itself between the poles of the iron core 2 but is restrained by the spring 4. The torque system actuates an adjustable link 5, which in turn operates the rheostatic element through the equalizing bar 6. In order to prevent oscillations, a dashpot 7 is connected to the torque-system shaft through a leaf spring 8, acting as a lever. The spring 8 permits a rapid instantaneous movement of the mechanism at the instant a change in voltage occurs. The plate 9 and screws 10 are for purposes of adjustment.

The regulator is normally at rest. If a drop in generator voltage occurs, the current in coil 1 decreases and the flux is weakened. The spring 4 overcomes the torque of the armature 3, and the shaft rotates in a clockwise direction, causing a downward pull on the link 5. This causes some of the plates to tilt forward, thus cutting out some of the resistance in the generator-field circuit. The voltage rises, and equilibrium between

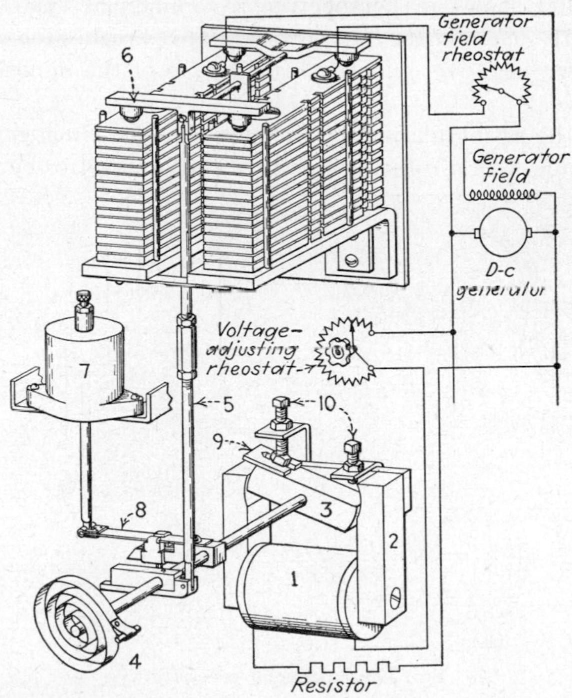

Fig. 368. Schematic drawing and diagram of type GDA generator-voltage regulator. (*General Electric Company.*)

the spring and armature is restored. The reverse process occurs with an increase in generator voltage.

SPECIAL TYPES OF GENERATOR

316. Unipolar, or Homopolar, Generator.[1] In the ordinary d-c generator, an alternating emf is generated, and the resulting current must be rectified or commutated. In the unipolar generator, however, a unidirectional emf is generated and no commutator is necessary.

The principle of the unipolar generator is that of Faraday's disk dynamo, Fig. 369(*a*). If a disk be rotated between the poles of a magnet, an emf is induced between the center and rim of the disk. Current can be

[1] For a more complete discussion see "Standard Handbook for Electrical Engineers," 8th ed., Sec. 8, Par. 197 *et seq.*, McGraw-Hill Book Company, Inc.

taken from the disk by placing a brush at the center and another at the rim. The disk shown in Fig. 369(*a*) would not be practicable because the emf is induced at one portion of the disk only, and current can circulate through the disk even when the external circuit is open. If an annular pole be used, Fig. 369(*b*), an equal emf is induced along each radius of the disk and the current has no return path in the disk itself.

Figure 369(*c*) shows in perspective a commercial type of unipolar generator with one-quarter cut away. The brushes *bb* are of one polarity, shown negative, and the brush (*a*) is of the opposite polarity, shown positive.

A hole in the casing allows access to brush (*a*). Such generators are sometimes made with a rotating cylinder and are said to be of the axial type.

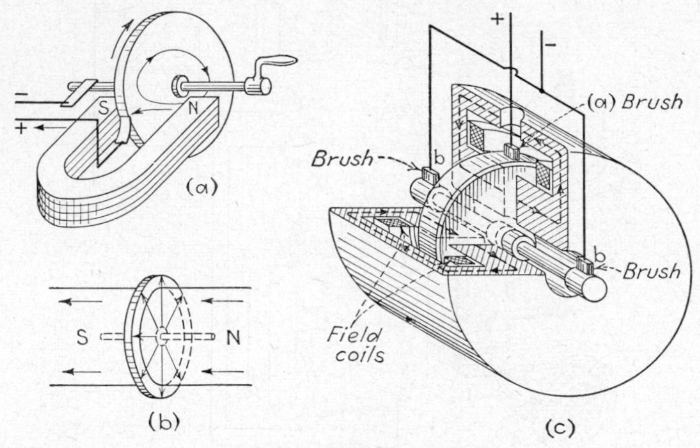

Fig. 369. Unipolar generator.

The chief disadvantage of the unipolar type of generator is the very low emf induced, even at high speeds. It is necessary to connect several disks in series in order to obtain commercial values of voltage. The generator in Fig. 369(*c*), having an armature diameter of about 20 in. and running at 3,000 rpm, would give only about 40 volts. Another disadvantage is the difficulty of conducting the current from the disk at the high speeds at which these generators are necessarily run. Their field of application is that of a high-speed, turbo-driven generator, designed for high currents at low voltages. Because of the superiority of coil-wound generators, the use of the unipolar generator has been very limited.

317. Third-brush Generator. In some types of small generator, particularly those which operate at variable speed, such as automobile generators, advantage is taken of armature reaction to regulate the current. Were an ordinary shunt or compound generator used in an automobile to charge the battery, the generator would be lightly loaded at low speeds and too heavily loaded at the higher speeds.

A common method of regulating automobile generators is the third-brush method, in which the shunt field is connected between one of the main brushes and a small third brush located between the two main brushes, Fig. 370. In the figure, A is the positive main brush, and B is the negative main brush, which is usually grounded to the frame of the car or engine.

The auxiliary, or third, brush C is placed at an angle of about 60° from brush B in the direction opposite to the direction of rotation. The shunt field is connected between the brush C and the positive brush. In Fig. 370(a) the flux through the armature under light-load conditions is shown

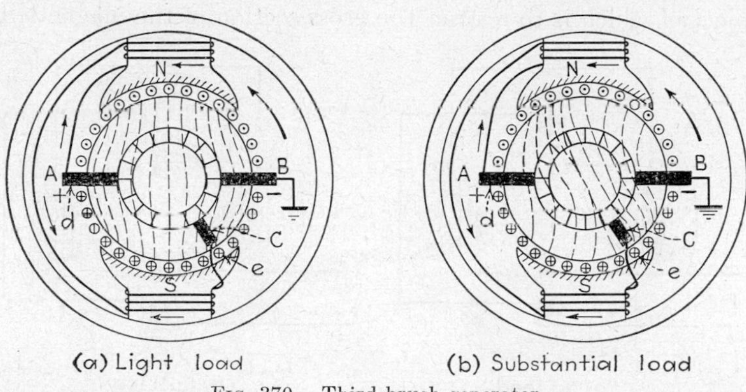

Fig. 370. Third-brush generator.

diagrammatically. There is negligible armature reaction [see Fig. 322(a), p. 416]. The voltage across the field will be substantially the emf induced in the conductors connected in series between d and e, which cut the flux included between brushes A and C.

If the speed of the generator increases, other factors remaining constant, the emf will increase and the generator will deliver a greater current. This current, however, distorts the magnetic field in the direction of rotation, Fig. 370(b) [also see Fig. 322(c), p. 416]. The effect is to transfer the flux from between conductors d and e to the region between brushes C and B. Since the total emf between conductors d and e, and hence the voltage across the field, is proportional to the flux between conductors d and e, the effect of the increased speed will be compensated in part at least by the lesser flux and the current will increase only slightly if at all. A study of Fig. 370(b) shows that the current may be increased by moving the third brush C in the direction of rotation and the current may be decreased by moving it against the direction of rotation.

When such generators are used to charge batteries, as in automobiles, there should be a cutout relay which connects the battery to the generator only after the generator has built up to a voltage slightly higher than that of the battery. If the generator slows down, this relay opens when the current reverses and begins to flow from battery to generator.[1]

318. Diverter-pole Generator.[2] The diverter-pole generator is a compound generator in which the voltage is controlled by shunting more or less of the main flux away from the armature by means of a magnetic shunt. The characteristics thus obtained have certain advantages over those of the usual compound generator, particularly for battery charging. Diagrams of the generator at no load and at full load are shown in Fig. 371. Small diverter poles D are placed midway between the main poles, and each diverter pole is connected to a main pole by means of a magnetic bridge B. In each magnetic bridge there is a longitudinal slot S', the object of which is to restrict the cross section of the magnetic bridge

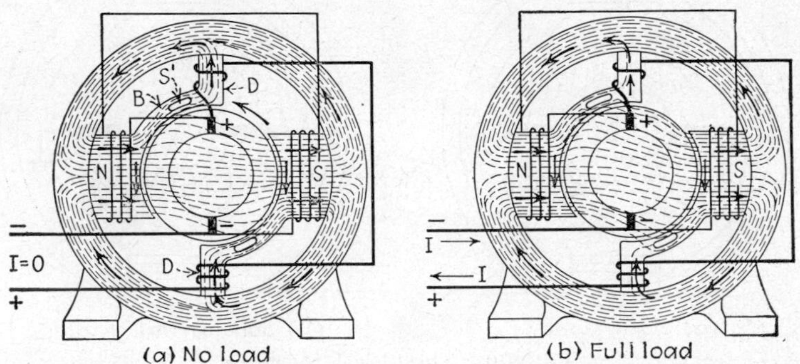

Fig. 371. Magnetic-flux distribution in diverter-pole generator.

at that point and thus to cause the iron at the slot S' to be easily saturated. Series turns are wound on the diverter pole, the winding being in such a direction as to produce a polarity which is the same as that of the main pole to which the diverter pole is connected.

The no-load conditions are shown in Fig. 371(a). The excitation of the diverter poles is zero, and a considerable portion of the main flux is shunted to the yoke by the diverter pole, the shunting effect being limited by the saturation in the bridge at slot S'. The effect of the slot may be considered also from the point of view of magnetic potential. The considerable drop in magnetic potential through the saturated portion S' of the bridge raises the magnetic potential of the main pole face with respect to the armature and thus causes a substantial portion of the total flux to enter the armature from the bridge itself.

[1] See Dawes, C. L., "Industrial Electricity," Part I, McGraw-Hill Book Company, Inc.

[2] Smith, E. D., "The Diverter Pole Generator," *Trans. AIEE*, Vol. 47, p. 1412, October, 1928

In Fig. 371(*b*) the magnetic conditions of the generator under load are shown. The series turns on the upper diverter pole act to drive the flux downward and therefore to force the leakage flux, which went through the diverter pole, into the bridge and down into the armature. This action may also be considered from the point of view of magnetic potential. The series ampere-turns act to raise the magnetic potential of the bridge, and as a result more flux will enter the armature.

Typical characteristics of this type of generator, operating shunt or self-excited and separately excited, are shown in Fig. 372. The flat nature of the characteristics should be noted.

The principal use of this generator is in the charging of storage batteries. It is not open to the objection of the shunt generator, in which

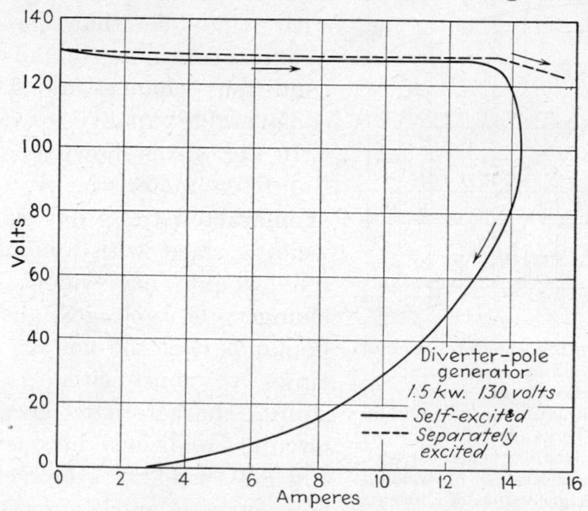

FIG. 372. Load characteristic of diverter-pole generator.

the voltage drops with load, or of the compound generator, the characteristics of which are convex, due to saturation (Fig. 357, p. 452). The linear characteristic of the diverter-pole generator is due to the fact that, with increase of load, additional flux is not added to the main pole to saturate it, but leakage flux is merely diverted into the armature. Unlike the straight-compound type, this generator will not run away when it accidentally "motors." The series turns cannot cause any reversal of flux in the main field because the restricted sections of the bridge limit the flux which can go through the bridge. Moreover, flux from the diverter poles into the armature is limited by the saturation of these poles themselves. As these poles act along the brush axis, they have little effect on the emf in the armature. The diverter poles also have the advantage that they provide along the brush axis a flux of the correct polarity for assisting commutation and hence act like commutating poles.

319. Electric-welding Generators. Electric welding is now widely used in the fabrication of iron and steel. Because of the steady stream of ions between anode and cathode, a d-c arc is more easily maintained than an a-c arc and is preferred for many types of welding. The characteristics of the arc-welding generator must be adapted to meet the special conditions determined by the arc.

The generator must be able to operate intermittently from open circuit, before the arc is struck, to short circuit, which occurs when the arc is struck or when globules of molten metal short-circuit the arc. The volt-ampere characteristics of the generator must be such that the arc is stable. The length of arc, and hence the current and voltage, vary rapidly with time so that the generator operates continuously under transient conditions, changes taking place with considerable rapidity.

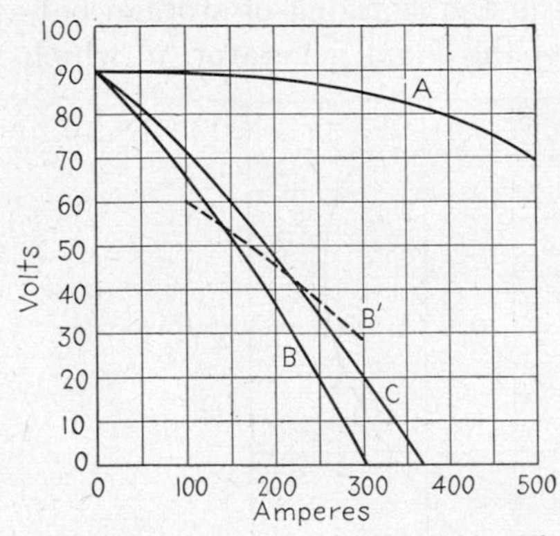

FIG. 373. Operating characteristics of shunt and arc-welding generators. *A*. Conventional shunt generator. *B*. Steady-state characteristic of welding generator. *B′*. Dynamic or transient characteristic of welding generator. *C*. Steady-state characteristic of welding generator with larger values of current.

In Fig. 373 is shown a conventional shunt characteristic *A*. This type of characteristic is not suited to arc welding since, with welding, the current would vary widely with small changes of voltage, and the arc demands that the voltage shall go at times to short circuit. When the shunt characteristic goes to short circuit, conditions become unstable, Fig. 350 (p. 442). However, the characteristics *B* and *C* are well adapted to arc welding. In each of these characteristics the voltage at no load is 90 volts, which is well above the voltage, about 45 volts, necessary to maintain an arc. The currents at short circuit are nominal and definite. Compared with a conventional characteristic such as *A*, in *B* and *C* the current varies only moderately with voltage, so that the arc is stable and the current can be controlled by the operator.

It is to be noted that *B* and *C* are steady-state characteristics. That is, the value of the voltage for each value of current is determined after conditions have become steady.

In practice, the generator would not ordinarily operate according to characteristic *B* or *C*, because of the transient conditions of the arc. Consider the usual shunt generator. The load characteristic is determined by the armature-resistance drop, the variation in field current due to change in terminal voltage, and the armature reaction (p. 443). As time is required to change a magnetic field (p. 320), the change in flux due to armature reaction cannot occur immediately with a sudden change of load. Therefore, at the instant that a new value of current is reached, the terminal voltage will not be that corresponding to the steady-state value. These same magnetic relations exist in the welding generator. For example, with rapidly increasing load a portion of the *transient characteristic* corresponding to the steady-state characteristic B may be B'. The characteristic B' is not well adapted to welding.

Moreover, a change of flux in the magnetic circuit induces currents in the iron and in the field circuit. By Lenz's law (p. 299), these induced currents oppose any change in the flux producing them. Hence, the induced currents cause an additional retardation in the change of flux with change in load and also cause a further increase in the departure of the dynamic from the steady-state characteristic.

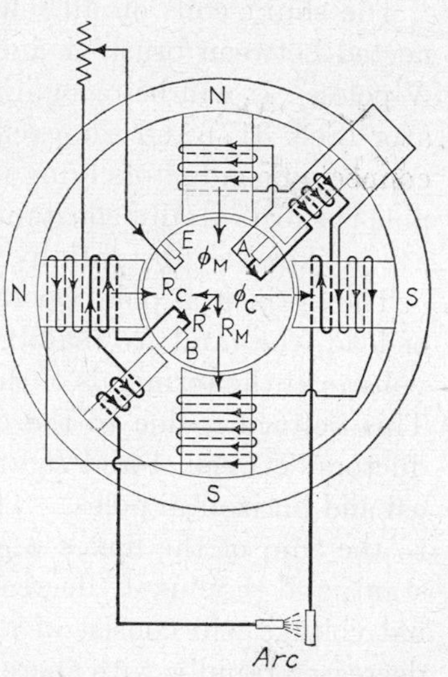

Fig. 374. Arc-welding generator. (*General Electric Company.*)

In welding generators, these difficulties are overcome in part by laminating the magnetic circuit so as to reduce the induced currents in the iron. An inductance or reactor is frequently connected in series with the load. The inductance opposes change in current (p. 321). Actually, with change of current, the emf of self-induction acts in such a direction as to bring the transient characteristic B' in closer proximity to the steady-state characteristic B.

To overcome the effect of the transient change in field current produced by the change in flux, the inductance in series with the load is sometimes provided with a secondary connected to a winding on the magnetic circuit. The direction of this winding is such that its induced current is in opposition to that induced in the field winding and hence practically counteracts the effect of change in current in the field winding.

There are many special types of welding generators designed to give the required characteristics under transient as well as under steady-state conditions. The General Electric type WD generator[1] is such a type, and the design is such that an inductance or a reactor for stabilizing the arc is not required. A diagram of the generator with connections is shown in Fig. 374. Four main poles are shown, but the two N poles

[1] Hornby, F. B., "Control of Transients in Welding Generators," *Trans. AIEE*, Vol. 53, p. 1598, 1934. Also see *Elec. Eng.*, December, 1934, p. 1598, and April, 1935, p. 441.

and the two S poles are adjacent to each other, and thus this is in reality a 2-pole generator, the two main poles being split. The brushes A, B lie along the geometrical neutral, and commutating poles act along the same axis. Let ϕ_M be the flux in the poles along the vertical axis and ϕ_C be the flux in the poles along the horizontal axis. The armature mmf R lies along the brush axis (p. 418). R may be resolved into two components, R_C in opposition to ϕ_C, and R_M in conjunction with ϕ_M. Hence, armature reaction reduces the flux ϕ_C and tends to increase the flux ϕ_M. However, the poles along the vertical axis are operated at high saturation, and the added mmf R_M has little effect on ϕ_M.

The shunt coils on all four poles are in series, and the circuit is connected between brush A and a third brush E midway between the two N poles. It will be recognized that this constitutes a third-brush generator (Sec. 317) and the excitation voltage is that induced in the series-connected conductors lying under the upper N pole. The flux ϕ_M in this pole is substantially constant at all loads, and hence the shunt-field voltage is likewise substantially constant at all loads.

The horizontal poles operate at low saturation. Hence, with increase of load, the mmf R_C readily reduces ϕ_C and may even reverse it. The voltage at the terminals of the generator is that between brushes A and B. This voltage is due to the emf induced in *all* the series-connected conductors between A and B, and hence in the conductors under both vertical and horizontal poles. Therefore, the terminal voltage is proportional to the sum of the fluxes ϕ_M and ϕ_C. The flux ϕ_M is substantially constant, and the flux ϕ_C decreases as the load increases. Hence, the terminal voltage will consist of a steady component and a component which decreases rapidly with increase of load. For example, if at no load the emf due to ϕ_M and ϕ_C is 45 volts each, the terminal voltage is 90 volts. If, at nearly half load, the emf due to ϕ_C is 5 volts, the terminal voltage is 50 volts. Hence, under such conditions, the generator characteristic becomes similar to B and C, Fig. 373.

Inductance in the shunt-field circuit reduces the transient induced current which causes flux lag. In this type of generator the flux ϕ_M changes only slightly. The turns about the vertical poles, however, do give inductance to the entire shunt circuit and hence reduce induced currents. Obviously this inductance is due to the leakage flux in the coils about the vertical poles. Inductance is also produced by the armature-flux linkages. The horizontal poles offer a path of low reluctance for the armature flux and thus increase the armature inductance. These inductances, due to field and armature, are sufficient to stabilize the arc without the use of an external reactor.

Different characteristics such as B and C, Fig. 373, adapted to different types of welding, are obtained by means of the series winding shown, together with the taps which cut turns in and out as is found necessary. The series winding opposes the shunt coils. The generator also has commutating poles which are excited by a series winding.

320. Amplidyne. The Amplidyne, manufactured by the General Electric Company, is a rotating amplifier and consists of a d-c generator in which a small amount of power supplied to excite the field is amplified by a large ratio in the generator output. The ordinary, separately excited d-c generator can be used as a power amplifier since the terminal voltage can be made essentially proportional to the field current if the iron is operated on the straight portion of the saturation curve. As the power to the field is only from 1 to 3 per cent of the rated output, a small change in the power to the field can be made to produce a large proportionate change in the power output. However, a much larger ratio of output power to input power can be obtained with the Amplidyne, since, within the machine, a second stage of amplification is produced by the effect of armature reaction.

Consider Fig. 375(*a*), which shows diagrammatically a conventional 2-pole d-c generator delivering power to a load. The excitation flux ϕ_M is produced by the main poles, which are excited by a control winding W, which, for convenience, is shown on one pole only. The armature produces a cross-magnetizing flux ϕ_A along brush axis BB (see Fig. 322, p. 416). The design is such that ϕ_A is practically equal to ϕ_M.

Assume that the power to the excitation winding is 100 watts and that the generator output is 100 amp at 100 volts, or 10,000 watts. This corresponds to a load resistance of 1 ohm. Accordingly, the power amplification ratio is 100 to 1. Assume that the excitation power is now reduced from 100 to 1 watt. If constant excitation voltage is assumed, the excitation current is also 0.01 its former value and the generator voltage and current output are now 1 volt and 1 amp. Both the excitation flux ϕ_M and the armature flux ϕ_A will be reduced to 0.01 their original values, as is indicated in Fig. 375(*b*).

The armature flux ϕ_A, however, may be restored to its original value, practically, if the load is removed and the brushes BB are short-circuited. If it is assumed that the armature and brush resistance are approximately 0.01 the load resistance of 0.01 ohm, which is practically true, the armature current and hence the armature flux ϕ_A will now be equal to their original values. The excitation current and the excitation flux ϕ_M, however, are now only 0.01 their original values. This condition is indicated in Fig. 375(*c*), the weight of the lines indicating the magnitudes of the quantities which they represent.

The relatively large armature flux ϕ_A is now available for producing emf and power output. In order to utilize this flux two brushes $B'B'$, whose axis is at right angles to ϕ_A and also to the axis of brushes BB, are added, Fig. 375(*d*). Since the magnitude of ϕ_A is essentially that of the original ϕ_M, the voltage between brushes $B'B'$, will be 100 volts and the current to the load can be 100 amp. Thus, with only 1 watt, or 0.01 the original value of excitation current, the original 10,000 watts, or 10 kw,

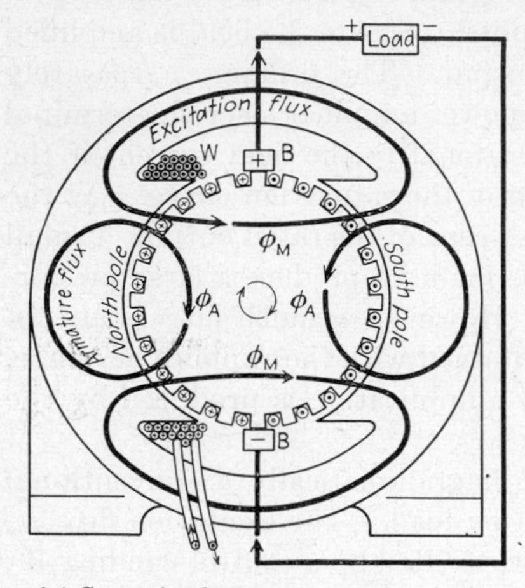

(*a*) *Conventional generator, normal excitation*

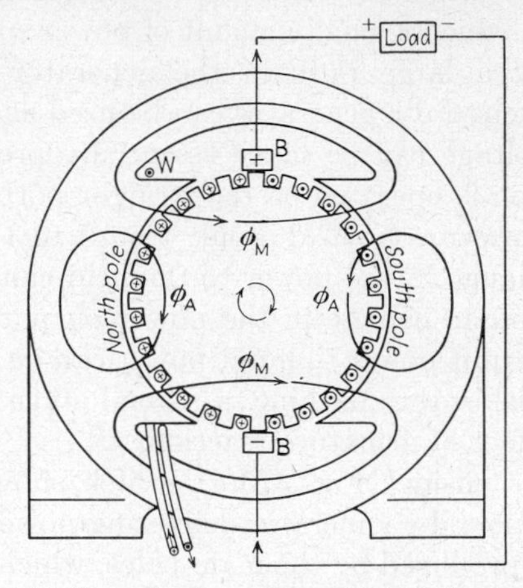

(*b*) *Conventional generator, excitation reduced*

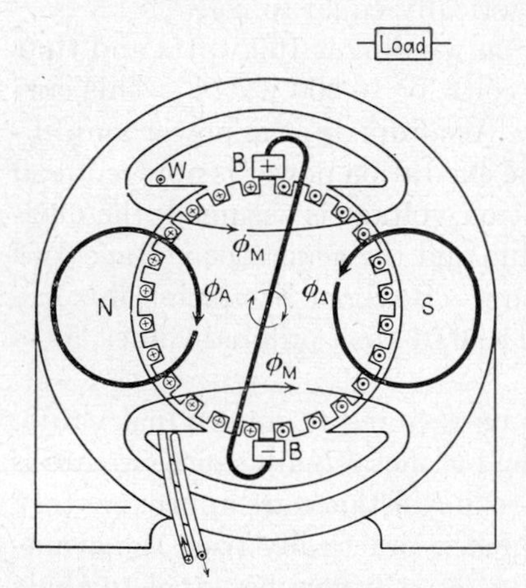

(*c*) *Conventional generator, armature flux restored*

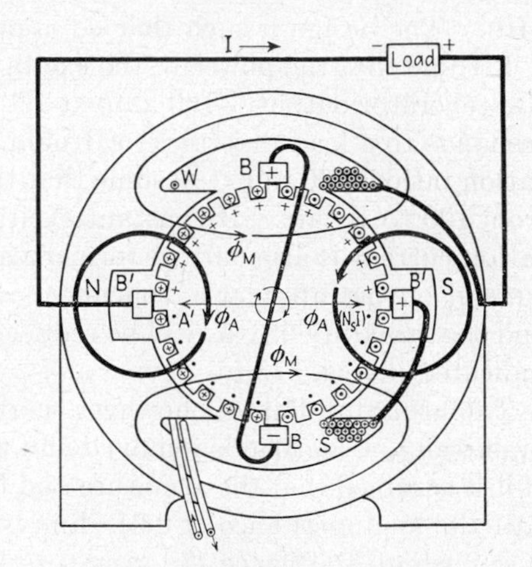

(*d*) *Amplidyne with its fields*

Fig. 375. Amplidyne. (*General Electric Company.*)

output is now obtained. In a conventional generator, there would be large short-circuit currents in the armature conductors short-circuited by brushes $B'B'$, since these conductors would be cutting some of the flux ϕ_M provided by the main poles. However, by making cavities in the pole faces of the main poles, Fig. 375(*d*), the flux in the commutating zone is reduced to a small value, thus practically eliminating the short-circuit commutation currents.

The armature-reaction mmf A' produced by the load current I acts along the brush axis $B'B'$, Fig. 375(d). Were this mmf not compensated, it would oppose and might even annul the mmf produced by the control winding W and all control would be lost. Accordingly, a winding S, having N_S turns, in series with the load to produce a mmf N_SI, always opposite and equal to A', is necessary. For simplicity the winding S is shown as wound on one pole only though actually wound on both poles. In Fig. 375(d), the directions of the currents in the armature conductors, produced by the main poles, are shown by the crosses and dots on the conductors themselves. The directions of the currents produced by the load currents are shown by the crosses and dots beneath the slots. Using clock-face terminology, note that from 9 to 12 o'clock and from 3 to 6

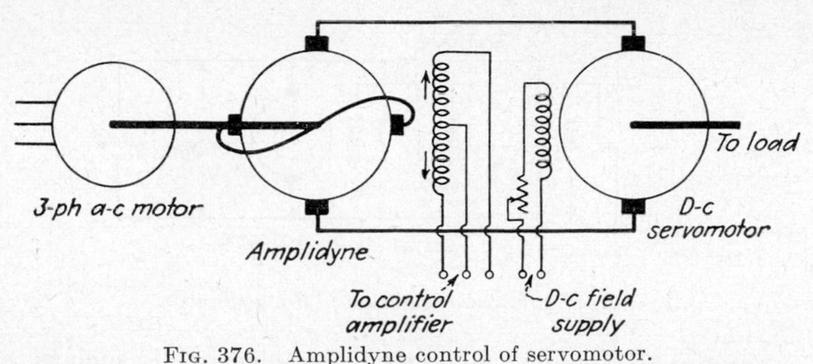

Fig. 376. Amplidyne control of servomotor.

o'clock slot and load currents are in the same direction and from 12 to 3 o'clock and from 6 to 9 o'clock these currents are in opposition.

Assume that the excitation current to the field winding is doubled. The input power is increased from 1 watt to 4 watts, but the Amplidyne voltage is now 200 volts and the current 200 amp, and the output is now 40,000 watts, or 40 kw. Thus, an increase of only 3 watts in the input increases the output by 30,000 watts, an amplification of 10,000 to 1. With Amplidynes of large ratings, amplifications as high as 250,000 to 1 are obtainable.

The Amplidyne has a relatively quick over-all response, the time constant (p. 307) being $\frac{1}{20}$ to $\frac{1}{4}$ sec.

The Amplidyne is driven ordinarily by an a-c motor, Fig. 376. It has wide uses, particularly in regulation and control systems. For example, the Amplidyne might supply the power to a motor which actuated either the azimuth or elevation of an antiaircraft gun or the large guns on a battleship. A Selsyn (Vol. II, Chap. XI) by actuating a rheostat in the control field could so control the output of the Amplidyne that the motor (with others) similarly controlled would keep the guns on the target. By using the Amplidyne as an exciter of a d-c or a-c generator and making the control-field current responsive to the terminal voltage of the generator, an effective voltage regulator is obtained.

Figure 376 shows in simple form the connections of an Amplidyne controlling the output of a d-c motor. The load and the short-circuited brushes are displaced 90° from those in Fig. 375(d). The Amplidyne field is controlled by a control amplifier, and, being in two sections, the direction of the field current and hence the polarity of the Amplidyne output may be reversed. The speed of the motor may be held constant, or it may be caused to vary in a predetermined manner by "signals" supplied to the Amplidyne field by the control amplifier.

321. Rototrol. Like the Amplidyne, the Rototrol, manufactured by the Westinghouse Electric Corporation, is a rotating amplifier which is capable of regulating any electrical quantity such as voltage, current,

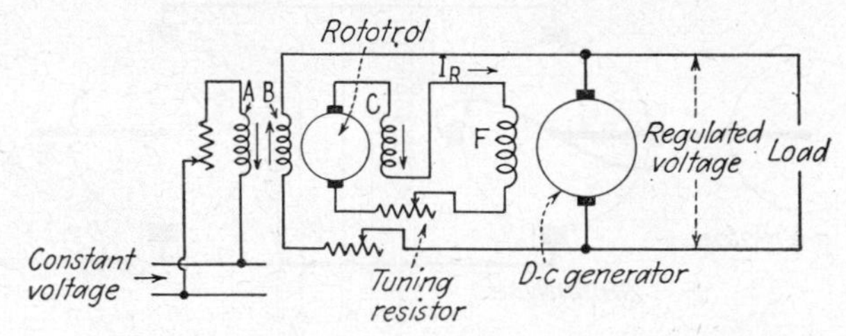

Fig. 377. Rototrol regulation of d-c generator.

power, or any quantity which can be measured electrically such as torque, speed, tension, or position. It is fundamentally a d-c generator with a number of field windings which can be connected in several ways depending on the required regulating function. A common function of the Rototrol is to regulate voltage, and Fig. 377 shows the connections for regulating the terminal voltage of a d-c generator.

In Fig. 377, A and B are two field windings which are similar to the usual shunt winding. Winding A, in series with a rheostat, is connected to a constant-voltage source and is called the *pattern* field. Winding B, in series with a rheostat, is connected across the voltage to be regulated and is called the *pilot* field. A third field winding C, having N_c turns, in series with the Rototrol armature, is called the *self-energizing* field. Fields A and C act in conjunction and field B acts in opposition to fields A and C, as is indicated by the arrows. The Rototrol operation depends on the interaction among these three fields. Pattern field A sets a pattern, in this case a constant voltage. Pilot field B measures the quantity under regulation and compares it with the pattern. Self-energizing field C, in series with the Rototrol armature, provides the ampere-turns for the excitation of the Rototrol.

The generator field F and a tuning resistor are also connected in series with field C.

The method of operation is explained by reference to Fig. 378, in which OH is the saturation curve. The Rototrol ordinarily operates on the straight part of the curve. Let voltage V_1 be the generator terminal voltage which it is desired to hold constant. The line OD gives the relation of the ampere-turns, $I_R N_c$, produced by the self-energizing field C, and the voltage across the entire series circuit including the fields C and F, the tuning resistor, and the Rototrol armature. If the abscissas were the current in field C, rather than ampere-turns, OD would be a resistance line. When the Rototrol is put into operation, the mmf provided by field A will start the generator building up. This will produce current in both windings B and C, the current in C being the Rototrol armature current

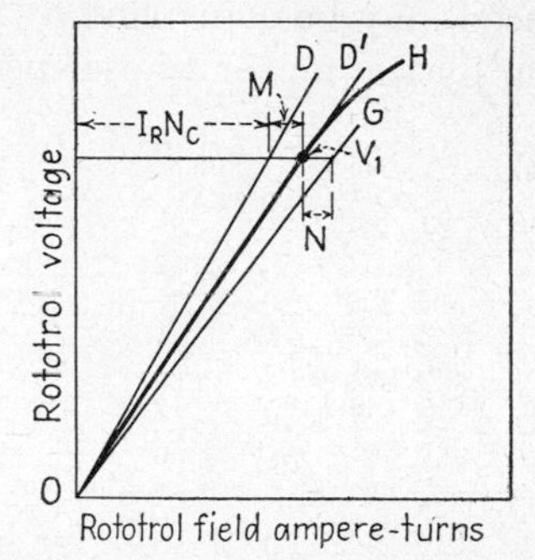

FIG. 378. Rototrol saturation curve and resistance lines.

I_R. When the generator builds up to voltage V_1, winding C produces $I_R N_c$ amp-turns and the remainder M must be supplied jointly by fields A and B. If, however, the resistance of the tuning resistor is decreased until line OD intersects the point V_1 on the saturation curve, shown by line OD', all the ampere-turns are now supplied by the self-energizing field C and the resultant ampere-turns of windings A and B become zero.

Assume that an increased load on the generator causes its voltage V_1 to drop. Accordingly, the current in field B will decrease proportionately. The resultant ampere-turns of fields A and B will no longer be zero, but those produced by field A will predominate. This will increase the ampere-turns of the Rototrol field, resulting in increased Rototrol terminal voltage and accordingly increased current in field C. This action will continue until the generator terminal voltage reaches its regulated value V_1 and the resultant ampere-turns of windings A and B again go to zero.

If the voltage of the generator increases, the increased current in field B will reduce the total ampere-turns, reducing the Rototrol terminal voltage and accordingly the current in field C until the resultant ampere-turns of windings A and B again become zero.

If the resistance of the circuit of field C becomes too low, the line OD' will swing to position OG. The ampere-turns N will then be the resultant of fields A and B, the effect of field B predominating. As a matter of fact, the Rototrol will operate satisfactorily if the resultant ampere-turns of field windings A and B are not exactly zero when equilibrium is reached. Thus in Fig. 378, operation could be in accordance with either line OD or line OG, provided that M or N were not much more than 5 per cent of the total ampere-turns.

For controlling current or torque (hence tension in winding operations) the pilot field B can be connected across the commutating-pole field of the regulated machine so that the current in the pilot field B is then proportional to armature current. Unless adjustment is made, there will be some error due to the change in resistance of the commutating-pole field with temperature. Speed may be controlled by supplying the pilot field B by a magneto driven by the motor whose speed is to be regulated.

CHAPTER XIII

THE MOTOR

It is stated in Chap. XII that a generator is a machine for converting mechanical energy into electrical energy.

In a similar way the motor is a machine for converting *electrical* energy into *mechanical* energy. The same machine, however, may be used either as motor or generator.

322. Principle of the Motor. Figure 379(a) shows a magnetic field of uniform strength or intensity in which is placed a straight conductor that carries no current, the conductor being perpendicular to the direction of

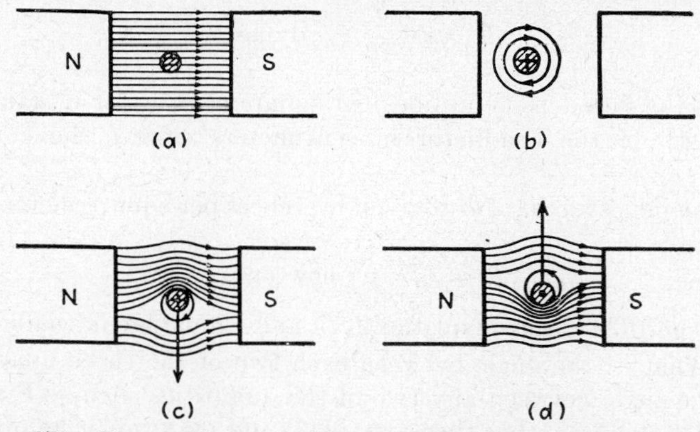

FIG. 379. Force acting on conductor carrying current in magnetic field.

the field and to the plane of the paper. In (b) the conductor is shown as carrying a current into the paper, but the field due to the N and S poles has been removed. A cylindrical magnetic field now exists about the conductor due to the current in it. The direction of this field, which may be determined by the corkscrew rule, is clockwise.

Figure 379(c) shows the resultant field obtained by combining the main field and that due to the current. The field due to the current in the conductor acts in conjunction with the main field above the conductor, but opposes the main field below the conductor. The result is to crowd the flux into the region directly *above* the conductor and to reduce the flux density in the region directly *below* the conductor.

It will be found that a force acts on the conductor, trying to push the conductor *down,* as shown by the arrow.

It is convenient to think of this phenomenon as due to the crowding of lines on one side of the conductor. Magnetic lines of force may be considered as acting like elastic bands under tension. These lines always are endeavoring to contract to minimum length. The tension in these lines on the upper side of the conductor tends to pull it down as shown in the figure.

If the current in the conductor be reversed, the crowding of lines will occur *below* the conductor, which will tend to move it *upward*, Fig. 379(*d*).

The operation of the electric motor depends on the principle illustrated by Fig. 379. A conductor carrying current in a magnetic field tends to move at right angles to the field.

323. Force Developed on Conductor Carrying Current. The force acting on a conductor carrying a current in a magnetic field is directly proportional to three quantities: the strength of the field, the magnitude of the current, and the length of the conductor lying in the field. The force in *dynes* is given by

$$\mathbf{F} = Bl\frac{I}{10} \quad \text{dynes} \tag{347}$$

where B is the flux density in lines per square centimeter or gauss, l the active length of the conductor in centimeters, and I the current in amperes.

Using the mks system, if B is given in webers per square meter and l in meters,

$$\mathbf{F} = BlI \quad \text{newtons.} \tag{348}$$

In (347) and (348) the quantities **F**, B, and I must be mutually perpendicular. That is, the angle between each two of the three quantities is 90°. If the angle between any two of the quantities such as **F** and B,B and I, and I and **F** is other than 90°, (347) and (348) must be multiplied by the sine of that angle.

The relation is developed as follows:

In Sec. 173 (p. 233, Eq. 141), it is shown that the force on a unit pole at the center of a circular turn of radius R cm carrying current I' abamp is

$$H_c = \frac{2\pi I'}{R} \quad \text{dynes.} \tag{I}$$

The force per centimeter length of the turn

$$\mathbf{F}_1 = \frac{2\pi I'}{R(2\pi R)} = \frac{I'}{R^2} \quad \text{dynes.} \tag{II}$$

The turn itself must be acted on by an opposite and equal force. The flux from the unit pole is 4π maxwells (p. 214). The flux density at the surface of a sphere of R cm radius is

$$B = \frac{4\pi}{4\pi R^2} = \frac{1}{R^2} \quad \text{gauss.} \tag{III}$$

This must be the flux density at the circular turn. Substituting in (II) the value of R^2 from (III),

$$\mathbf{F}_1 = BI' \quad \text{dynes.}$$

The force on a length of l cm is

$$\mathbf{F} = BlI' \quad \text{dynes,} \tag{349}$$

$$\mathbf{F} = Bl\frac{I}{10} \quad \text{dynes} \quad \text{[Eq. (347)]} \quad Q.E.D.$$

where I is in amperes. Flux density B, length of conductor l, and force $\mathbf{F}$ are mutually perpendicular.

Example. A rectangular flat coil of 20 turns lies with its plane parallel to a magnetic field (see Fig. 383), the flux density in the field being 3,000 gauss. The axial length of the coil is 8 in. The current is 30 amp. Determine the force in pounds which acts on each side of the coil [see arrows in Fig. 383(*a*), p. 483].

$$B = 3{,}000 \text{ gauss}$$
$$l = 8 \cdot 2.54 = 20.32 \text{ cm.}$$
$$I = 30 \text{ amp.}$$
$$\mathbf{F} = 3{,}000 \cdot 20.32 \cdot {}^{30}\!/_{10} = 182{,}900 \text{ dynes.}$$

As there are 20 turns,

$$\mathbf{F}_1 = \mathbf{F}_2 = 20 \cdot 182{,}900 = 3{,}658{,}000 \text{ dynes.}$$
$$\frac{3{,}658{,}000}{981} = 3{,}729 \text{ g.}$$
$$= 3.729 \text{ kg.}$$
$$3.729 \cdot 2.204 = 8.219 \text{ lb.} \quad \textit{Ans.}$$

In mks units,

$$B = 0.3 \text{ weber.}$$
$$l = 0.2032 \text{ m.}$$

From (348),

$$\mathbf{F} = 0.3 \cdot 0.2032 \cdot 30 = 1.829 \text{ newtons.}$$
$$\mathbf{F}_1 = \mathbf{F}_2 = 20 \cdot 1.829 = 36.58 \text{ newtons.}$$

From Appendix A (p. 579),

$$36.58 \text{ newtons} = 36.58 \cdot 0.2248 = 8.223 \text{ lb.} \quad \textit{Ans.}$$

324. Fleming's Left-hand Rule. The relation among the direction of a magnetic field, the direction of motion of a conductor in that field, and the direction of the *induced* emf in the conductor is given by Fleming's *right-hand* rule (see Sec. 262, p. 369).

In a similar manner, the relation among the direction of a magnetic field, the direction of a current in that field, and the direction of the resulting *motion* of the conductor carrying the current can be determined by using Fleming's *left-hand* rule.

Fleming's *left-hand* rule:

With the forefinger, middle finger, and thumb mutually perpendicular, point the forefinger in the direction of the field or flux, the middle finger in the direction of the current in the conductor, and the thumb will point in the direction in which the conductor tends to move. This is illustrated in Fig. 380.

Another convenient method for determining this relation is to make use of the fact that the crowding of the magnetic lines behind the conductor tends to push it along. It is necessary merely to sketch the main field and the lines about the conductor, as in Fig. 381(*a*). It is evident that the lines will be crowded at the right of the conductor so that in a motor the direction of motion is to the left.

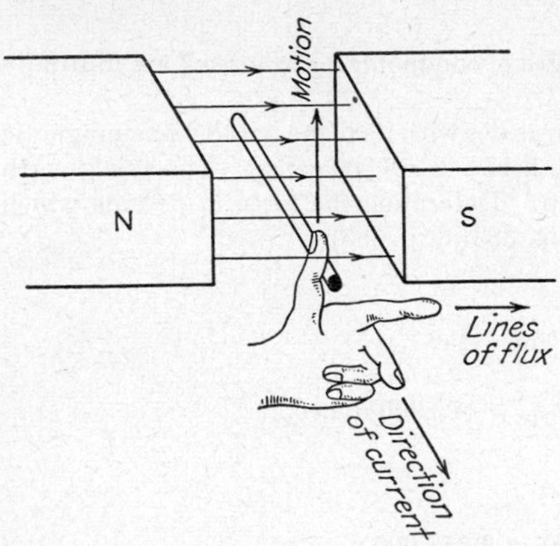

Fig. 380. Fleming's left-hand rule.

In Fig. 381(*b*) is shown a similar condition for a generator. In this case the conductor, as a generator, moves to the right. Hence, in a generator the conductor must move *against* a force tending to oppose its motion, and so the conductor requires a mechanical driving force to keep it in motion. This driving force is supplied by the prime mover to which the generator is connected.

325. Torque. When an armature, a flywheel, or any other device is rotating about its center, a tangential force is necessary to produce and maintain rotation. This force may be developed within the machine itself, as in a motor or steam engine, or it may be applied to a driven device such as a pulley, Fig. 382, a shaft, a generator, or driving gears.

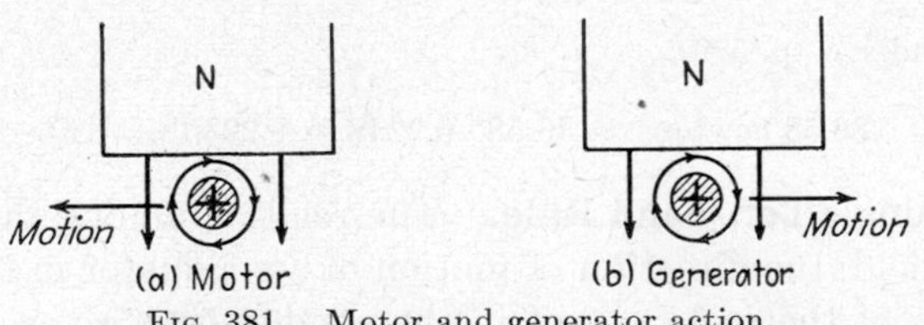

Fig. 381. Motor and generator action.

The total effect of the force is determined not only by its *magnitude* but also by its *arm*, or radial distance from the center of the pulley or gear to the line of action of the force.

The product of this force and its perpendicular distance from the axis is called *torque*.

Torque may also be considered as a mechanical couple tending to produce rotation. Its value is expressed in units of force and distance.

In the English system, torque is usually expressed in pound-feet. (This distinguishes it from foot-pounds, which represent *work*.)

In the cgs system the unit of torque is the dyne-centimeter (a very small unit), and in the metric system the unit is the kilogram-meter.

Example. A belt is driving a 36-in. pulley, Fig. 382. The tension in the tight side of the belt is 90 lb, and that is the loose side is 30 lb. Determine torque applied to pulley.

The two sides of the belt are acting in opposition, so that the net pull on the rim of the pulley is

$$90 - 30 = 60 \text{ lb.}$$

This force is acting 18 in., or 1.5 ft, from the center of the pulley. Therefore, the torque

$$T = 60 \cdot 1.5 = 90 \text{ lb-ft.} \quad Ans.$$

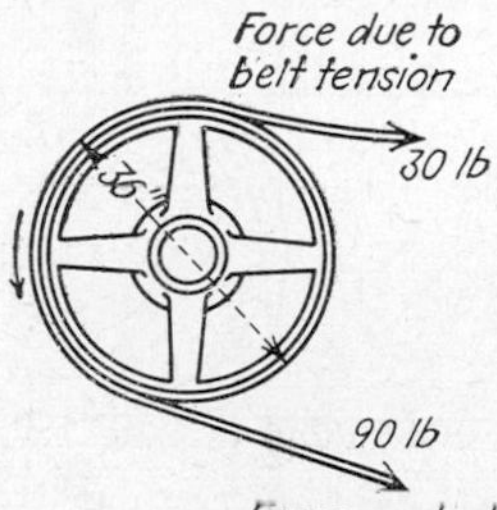

FIG. 382. Torque developed by belt.

326. Torque Developed by a Motor. Figure 383(*a*) shows a rectangular coil of a single turn, whose plane lies parallel to a magnetic field. The direction of the current in the left-hand side of the coil is into the paper, and in the right-hand side it is out of the paper. Therefore, the left-hand conductor tends to move downward with a force $\mathbf{F}_1$, and the right-hand conductor tends to move upward with an equal force $\mathbf{F}_2$. As the current in each of the conductors is the same and they lie in magnetic fields of the same strength, force $\mathbf{F}_1 = \mathbf{F}_2$. Both forces act to develop a

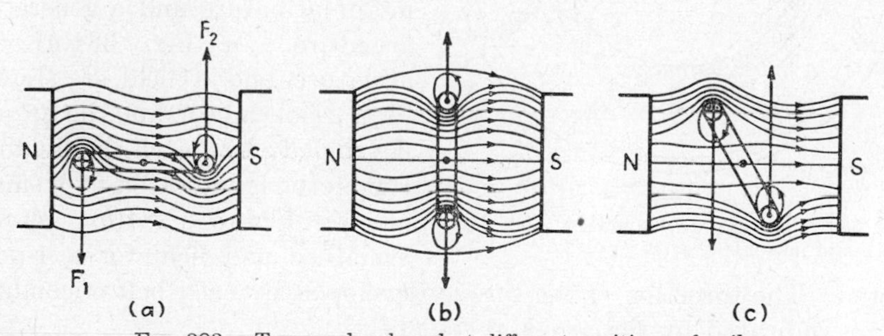

FIG. 383. Torque developed at different positions of coil.

torque which tends to turn the coil in a counterclockwise direction. In Fig. 383(*a*) the coil is in the position of maximum torque because the perpendicular distance from the coil axis to the forces acting is a maximum.

When the coil reaches the position (*b*), neither conductor can move any farther without the coil itself spreading. This is a position of zero torque because the perpendicular distance from the coil axis to the line of action of the forces is zero.

If, however, the current in the coil be reversed when the coil reaches position (*b*) and the coil be carried beyond the dead center, as in (*c*), a torque is developed which tends to continue to turn the coil in the counterclockwise direction.

To develop a continuous torque in one direction, the current in each coil on the armature must be reversed as the coil is passing through the position of zero torque. A commutator is therefore necessary. This is analogous to using a commutator with a generator so that the current in the external circuit may be unidirectional.

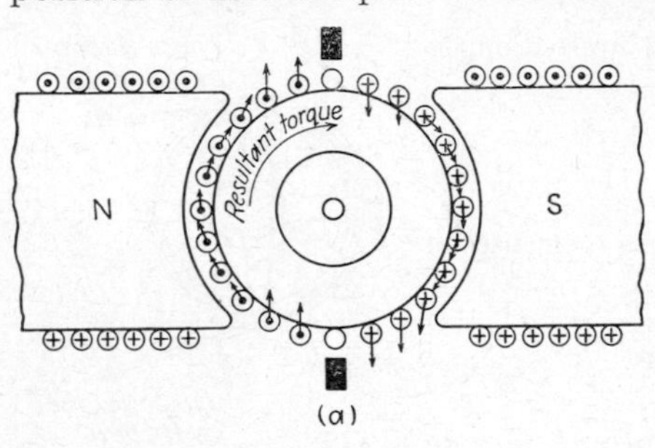

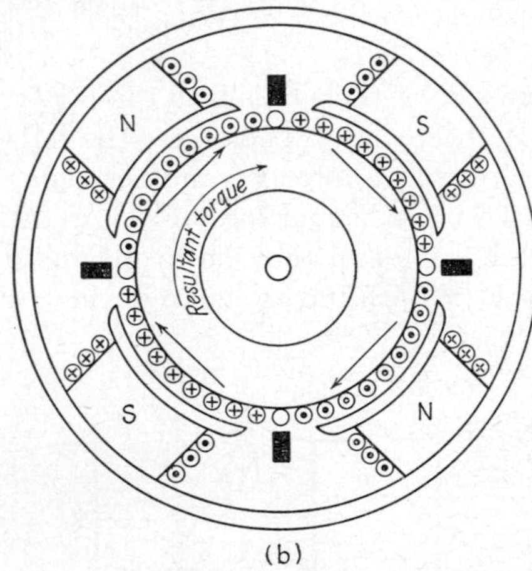

FIG. 384. Torque developed by belt conductors in motor armatures.

A single-coil motor, like that shown in Fig. 383, would be impracticable as it has dead centers and the torque which it develops is pulsating. A 2-coil armature would eliminate the dead centers, but the torque developed would still be more or less pulsating in character.

The best results are obtained when a large number of coils is used, just as in the armature of a generator. In fact there is no difference in the construction of a motor armature and a generator armature. In Fig. 384(*a*) an armature and a field are shown for a 2-pole motor, and the torque developed by each individual conductor is indicated by a small arrow. Figure 384(*b*) shows armature and field for a 4-pole motor. The direction of the torque developed by each belt of conductors is indicated by the arrow at that belt.

In armatures of this type only a small portion of the total number of coils is undergoing commutation at any one instant. Therefore, the variation in the number of active conductors is so slight that the torque developed is substantially constant for constant values of armature current and of main flux.

From Eqs. (347) and (348), the torque developed by an armature is

$$T = K_t' Z I_a \phi \tag{350}$$

where K_t' = a constant, involving the number of poles, the parallel paths through the armature, the diameter of the armature, the choice of units, etc.

Z = number of conductors on the surface of the armature.

I_a = current to the armature, amp.

ϕ = flux from one N pole entering the armature.

Equation (350) is derived as follows:

From Eq. (347) the force on each conductor $\mathbf{F} = Bl(I/10)$ dynes, where I is the amperes per path. The sum of the forces on Z conductors is $ZB_{av}l(I/10)$ dynes, where B_{av} is the average flux density over any pole pitch (see B, Fig. 312, p. 406). The corresponding torque is

$$T = \left(\frac{d}{2}\right)\left(ZB_{av}l\frac{I}{10}\right) \quad \text{dyne-cm} \tag{I}$$

where d is the diameter of the armature in centimeters.

The flux entering the armature from one N pole,

$$\phi = B_{av}l\left(\frac{\pi d}{P}\right) \tag{II}$$

where P is the number of poles.

Substituting in (I) the value of B_{av} from (II), and $I_a = IP'$, where P' is the number of parallel paths,

$$\begin{aligned} T &= \frac{d}{2}Z\left(\frac{\phi P}{l\pi d}\right)l\frac{I_a}{10P'} \quad \text{dyne-cm.} \\ &= \frac{P}{20\pi P'}ZI_a\phi \quad \text{dyne-cm.} \\ &= K_t'ZI_a\phi \quad \text{dyne-cm.} \quad \text{Q.E.D.} \end{aligned}$$

where K_t' is a constant of proportionality and is equal to $P/(20\pi P')$.

The torque in pound-feet is found by dividing by $445{,}000 \cdot 2.54 \cdot 12$. Hence,

$$T = 0.117\frac{P}{P'}ZI_a\phi \cdot 10^{-8} \text{ lb-ft.} \tag{351}$$

For any particular machine Z is fixed, so that the torque

$$T = K_tI_a\phi \tag{352}$$

where K_t is a new constant.

That is, in a given motor, *the torque is proportional to the armature current and to the strength of the magnetic field.*

This is a very important relation to keep in mind, for by its use the variation of torque with load in the different types of motors can be readily determined.

Example. When a motor armature is taking 50 amp from the line, it develops 60 lb-ft torque. The field strength is reduced to 75 per cent of its original value and the current increases to 80 amp. Determine new value of torque.

If the current remained constant, the new value of torque, due to weakening the field, would be

$$0.75 \cdot 60 = 45 \text{ lb-ft.}$$

Due to the increase in the value of current, however, the final value of torque will be

$$(8\%_{50})45 = 72 \text{ lb-ft.} \quad \textit{Ans.}$$

It must be remembered that the torque expressed by the above equations is the *electromagnetic* torque or the *internal* torque developed by the armature. The torque available at the pulley will be slightly less than this, owing to the torque lost in overcoming friction and windage and in supplying the iron losses of the armature.

327. Counter Electromotive Force. The resistance of the armature of the ordinary 10-hp 110-volt motor is about 0.05 ohm. If this armature were connected directly across 110-volt mains, the current, by Ohm's law, would be

$$I = \frac{110}{0.05} = 2{,}200 \text{ amp.}$$

This value of current is not only excessive but unreasonable, especially when one considers that the rated current of such a motor is in the neighborhood of 90 amp. When a motor is in operation, the *current through the armature is evidently not determined by its ohmic resistance alone.*

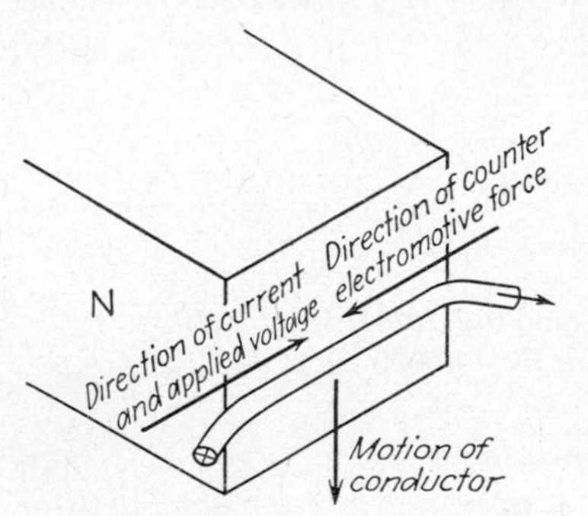

FIG. 385. Relation of direction of currents and voltages in motor conductor.

The armature of a motor is in every way similar to that of a generator. The conductors on its surface, in addition to carrying current and so developing torque, are cutting flux. Therefore, they *must* be inducing emf.

Consider Fig. 385 which shows a conductor on the armature of a motor, moving downward in front of an N pole. In order to move downward, the current in this conductor must be inward or from left to right, Fig. 383(c).

If the right-hand rule be applied to determine the direction of the emf *induced* in this conductor, due to its downward motion, Fig. 385, it will be found to be acting from right to left, or in opposition to the current.

If the direction of the induced emf in any conductor on a motor armature be similarly determined, it will be found to act always in *opposition* to the current. That is, it *opposes* the current entering the armature. This induced emf is called the *counter electromotive force*, or *back electromotive force*. As the counter emf opposes the current it must also oppose the applied, or terminal, voltage. Therefore, the net emf acting in the armature circuit is the difference of the applied voltage and the counter emf. Let V equal the applied voltage and E the counter emf. The net voltage acting in the armature circuit is

$$V - E.$$

The armature current follows Ohm's law and is

$$I_a = \frac{V - E}{R_a} \tag{353}$$

where R_a is the armature resistance.

This equation may be transposed and written

$$E = V - I_aR_a. \tag{354}$$

This should be compared with Eq. (341) (p. 445), which is the similar equation for a generator.

In a generator the induced emf is equal to the terminal voltage *plus* the armature-resistance drop. In a motor the induced emf is equal to the terminal voltage *minus* the armature-resistance drop. The counter emf must always be less than the terminal voltage if the direction of current is *into* the armature at the positive terminal.

Example. Determine the counter emf of a 10-hp motor when the terminal voltage is 110 volts and the armature current is 90 amp. The armature resistance is 0.05 ohm.

$$E = 110 - (90 \cdot 0.05) = 110 - 4.5 = 105.5 \text{ volts.} \quad \textit{Ans.}$$

An interesting experiment for demonstrating the existence of counter emf is shown in Fig. 386. A lamp bank is connected in series with the armature of a shunt motor. First close switch S_2, which closes the field circuit. Then close S_1. At the instant of closing S_1 the lamps will burn brightly, being practically up to candlepower. As the armature speeds up, these lamps will become dimmer and dimmer, showing that the armature is generating a *counter* emf which opposes the line voltage and so results in less voltage for the lamps. When the armature is up to speed, the lamps will be very dim. If, however, the field switch S_2 now be opened, the flux and, therefore, the counter emf will be reduced to zero, practically, which will be shown by the lamps again coming up to full candlepower. (In practice, when a motor is in operation, *the field circuit should not be opened under any conditions whatsoever.*)

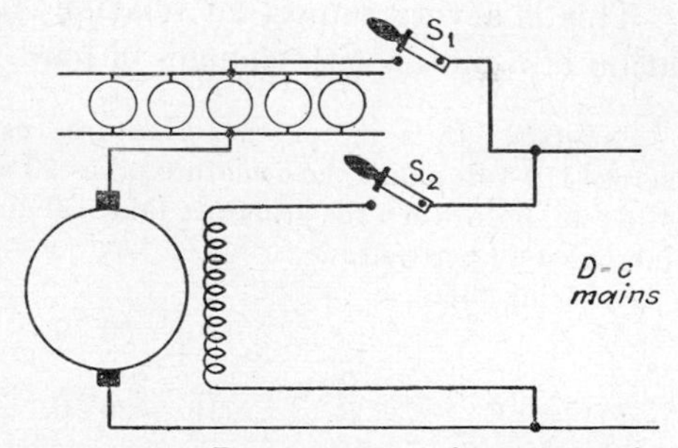

FIG. 386. Demonstration of counter emf.

Equation (334) (p. 407) for the induced emf in a generator will obviously apply to a motor. That is, the counter emf

$$E = \frac{\phi SPZ}{60\,P'10^8} \quad \text{volts}$$

where ϕ is the total flux entering the armature from one N pole, S is the speed of the armature in rpm, P is the number of poles, Z is the number of conductors on the surface of the armature, and P' is the number of parallel paths through the armature.

As Z, P, P', and 10^{-8} are all constant for any given motor, the counter emf is

$$E = K_1\phi S,$$

which is identical with Eq. (337) (p. 408), with K_1 substituted for K.

Solving for speed,

$$S = K\frac{E}{\phi} \tag{355}$$

where $K = 1/K_1$.

The speed of a motor is directly proportional to the counter emf and inversely proportional to the field flux.

Substituting for E in (355) its value given in (354), the speed becomes

$$S = K\frac{V - I_aR_a}{\phi}. \tag{356}$$

This is a very important relation, for it shows the law of speed variation of a motor with changes of load.

Example. In a motor the armature resistance is 0.1 ohm. When connected across 110-volt mains the armature takes 20 amp, and its speed is 1,200 rpm. Determine its speed when the armature takes 50 amp from these same mains, with the field increased 10 per cent.

Applying (356),

$$\frac{S_2}{S_1} = \frac{K\dfrac{110 - 50 \cdot 0.1}{\phi_2}}{K\dfrac{110 - 20 \cdot 0.1}{\phi_1}} = \frac{\dfrac{105}{\phi_2}}{\dfrac{108}{\phi_1}} = \frac{105}{\phi_2} \cdot \frac{\phi_1}{108},$$

$$S_1 = 1{,}200.$$

Therefore,

$$S_2 = 1{,}200\,\frac{105}{108} \cdot \frac{\phi_1}{\phi_2}.$$

But

$$\phi_2 = 1.10\phi_1.$$

Therefore,

$$S_2 = 1{,}200\,\frac{105}{108}\left(\frac{\phi_1}{1.10\phi_1}\right) = 1{,}061 \text{ rpm.} \quad \textit{Ans.}$$

Although, from (355), the speed decreases when the field is strengthened, it might appear that the stronger field would produce a greater torque [Eq. (352)], which would accelerate the armature to a higher speed. Momentarily, however, the speed of the armature cannot change appreciably, due to its inertia. The strengthened field increases the counter emf E. Since the difference between the terminal voltage V and the counter emf E is small, a small proportionate increase in E causes a large proportionate decrease in current [Eq. (353), p. 487]. Hence the current I_a in Eq. (353) decreases more than ϕ increases, and the torque therefore *diminishes*. The speed of the armature will drop, therefore, and ultimately reach such a value that the electromagnetic torque will be in equilibrium with the torque required of the armature under the changed conditions. The new value of speed will be that given by (356).

For example, assume that the I_aR_a drop is $0.1V$, where V is the terminal voltage.

From Eq. (353), the current

$$I_a = \frac{V(1 - 0.9)}{R_a} = \frac{0.1V}{R_a}.$$

The flux ϕ is suddenly increased by 5 per cent, and the speed is assumed to remain constant for the moment. The induced emf E' now equals $1.05E$, and the new value of current

$$I_a' = \frac{V(1 - 0.9 \cdot 1.05)}{R_a} = \frac{0.055V}{R_a} = 0.55I_a.$$

The flux ϕ has been increased by 5 per cent, and the current has decreased by 45 per cent. The momentary torque is

$$T' = 1.05 \cdot 0.55T = 0.58T$$

where T is the original torque. Hence the speed of the armature will decrease until the current has attained such a value that its reaction with the new value of flux brings the electromagnetic torque into equilibrium with the load and friction torques.

328. Counter Electromotive Force and Mechanical Power. Let the input to a motor armature be VI_a watts. A part P_a of this power is lost in heating the armature.

$$P_a = I_a^2R_a \qquad \text{watts}$$

where R_a is the armature resistance. The remainder of the power VI_a must appear as mechanical power P_m. This follows from the law of the conservation of energy. That is,

$$\begin{aligned} P_m &= VI_a - I_a^2R_a \\ &= (V - I_aR_a)I_a \qquad \text{watts.} \end{aligned}$$

But $V - I_aR_a$ is the counter emf of the motor [Eq. (354), p. 487]. Hence,

$$P_m = EI_a \quad \text{watts.} \tag{357}$$

Hence, *the mechanical power developed within the armature of a motor is equal to the product of the counter emf and the armature current.* The power available at the pulley is slightly less, since some of this internal power is accounted for by friction, windage, and iron losses; that is, it is lost as stray power (see p. 530).

Example. Determine the mechanical power developed in the armature of the motor given in the example on p. 487. The counter emf is 105.5 volts, and the armature current is 90 amp. Hence, the mechanical power developed within the armature, or the internal power,

$$P_m = 105.5 \cdot 90 = 9{,}495 \text{ watts. } \textit{Ans.}$$
$$= 12.73 \text{ hp. } \textit{Ans.}$$

329. Armature Reaction and Brush Position in a Motor. Figure 387(*a*) shows a motor armature carrying current, the directions of the currents in the armature conductors corresponding to clockwise rotation and to an N pole at the left. Due to the armature ampere-turns, a mmf F_A is produced in the armature and the direction of flux produced by this mmf is upward and at right angles to the polar axis. Figure 387(*b*) shows the vectors representing the magnitudes and directions of the armature mmf F_A and the field mmf F. By adding these two mmfs vectorially, the resultant mmf F_0 is obtained. The total flux produced by F_0 is distorted as shown in Fig. 387(*c*). It will be noted, that (1) the flux has been crowded into the *leading* pole tips and (2) the neutral plane perpendicular to the resultant field has moved *backward.* Therefore, in a motor it is necessary to move the brushes *backward* with increase of load, whereas in a generator they are moved *forward.* Were it not for the emf of self-induction (see Sec. 300, p. 432), the brush axis would coincide with the neutral plane. Owing, however, to the necessity of counteracting this emf of self-induction, the brushes are set behind this load neutral plane, Fig. 387(*c*). That is, in both motor and generator it is necessary to set the brushes beyond the load neutral plane in order to counteract the emf of self-induction.

This backward movement of the brushes in a motor is accompanied by a demagnetizing action of the armature on the field, as shown in Fig. 387(*d*), where F_D is the demagnetizing component of F_A and F_C is the cross-magnetizing component. (*Cf.* Figs. 322 and 323, pp. 416 and 417, for the generator.) Therefore, as the load is increased on a motor, the armature reaction tends to increase the motor speed. In fact, instances have been known where motors with short air-gaps (producing high armature reaction) have run away when the load was applied. For this reason most shunt, and even compound, motors have a "stabilizing" winding consisting usually of 1½ turns on each pole in series with the armature and aiding the shunt-field ampere-turns. This prevents weakening of the field through armature reaction which might be caused by an increase in load, thus securing speed stability.

With multipolar motors, the field and armature mmfs are similar to those shown in Figs. 327, 328, 329, 331 (pp. 423 and 425), except that

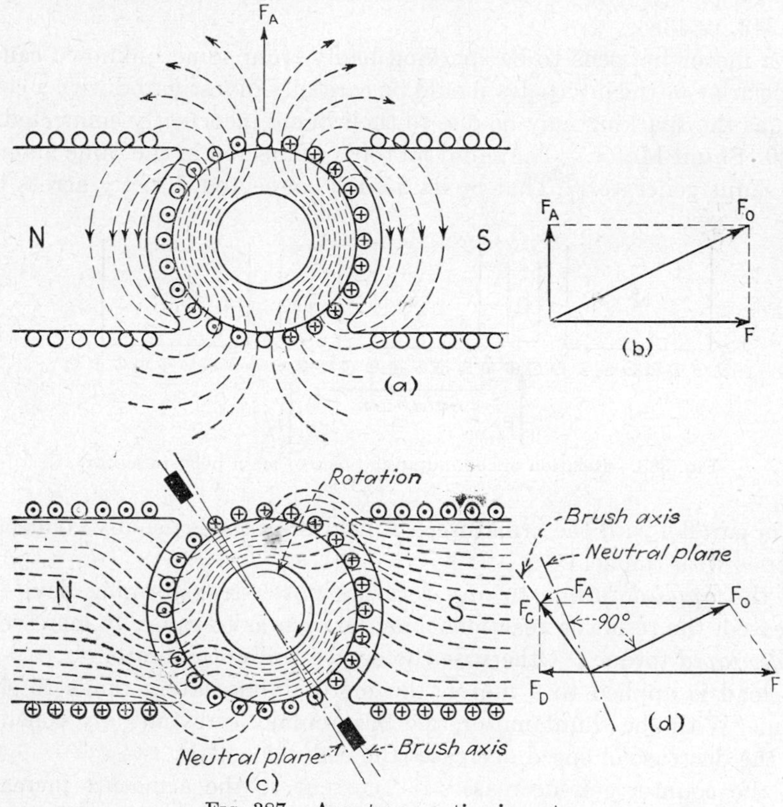

FIG. 387. Armature reaction in motor.

the graphs of armature mmf are reversed in sign. The cross-magnetizing and the demagnetizing ampere-turns can be separated in the manner shown in Fig. 331. For heavy-duty combined with variable-speed and quick-reversing operations, such as occur in rolling mills, it is imperative to compensate the armature mmf over the entire pole pitch. This is accomplished with pole-face windings, in combination with commutating poles, in the same manner as with generators, Fig. 333 (p. 428).

Figure 388 shows the armature conductors of a motor carrying current and moving under successive N and S poles. The directions of the currents correspond to a direction of rotation from left to right. These directions are such that the armature reaction F_A in the first interpolar space is *upward* (see Fig. 328, p. 423). Therefore, if a commutating pole is to be used, it must be an *n* pole, in order to oppose this mmf of the armature by tending to send a flux downward into the armature. F_A' must likewise be opposed by an *s* pole. Therefore, in a motor, the relation of main poles and commutating poles, *in the direction of rotation,* is *NnSs,* or opposite to the corresponding relation for a generator (see Fig. 345, p. 438).

If a motor happens to be sparking badly from some unknown cause, the polarity of the interpoles should be carefully investigated with a compass, as the sparking may be due to their being incorrectly connected.

330. Shunt Motor. The shunt motor is connected in the same manner as a shunt generator. That is, its field is connected directly across the

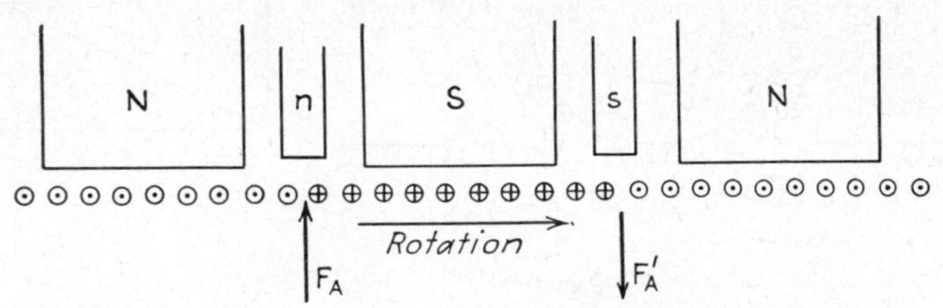

FIG. 388. Relation of commutating poles to main poles in motor.

line in parallel with the armature. A field rheostat is usually connected in series with the field.

If the *applied* torque to any rotating power-transforming device is increased, the resulting reactions must be such as to cause an increase in the *developed* torque. Otherwise the device will not operate.

If load is applied to a motor, the motor immediately tends to slow down. With the shunt motor, the flux remains substantially constant and the decrease of speed decreases the counter emf E.

If the counter emf decreases, the current to the armature increases [see Eq. (353), p. 487]. This continues until the increased armature current produces sufficient torque to meet the demands of the increased load. Therefore, the shunt motor is always in a condition of stable equilibrium, since the reactions caused by a change of load always adapt the power input to the changed load conditions.

The suitability of a motor for any particular duty is determined almost entirely by two factors, the variation of its *torque* with load, and the variation of its *speed* with load.

In the shunt motor the flux is substantially constant. Therefore, from Eq. (352) (p. 485) the electromagnetic torque will be nearly proportional to the armature current. For example, in Fig. 389, when the armature current is 30 amp, the motor develops 40 lb-ft torque; and when the current is 60 amp, the motor develops 80 lb-ft torque. That is, when the current doubles, the torque doubles.

The speed of a motor varies according to Eq. (356) (p. 488), where

$$S = K\frac{V - I_aR_a}{\phi}.$$

In the shunt motor, K, V, R_a, and ϕ are all substantially constant. Therefore, the only variable is I_a. As the load on the motor increases, I_a increases and the numerator of the fraction decreases. As a rule the denominator changes only by a small amount. The speed of the motor will drop with increase of load, Fig. 390. As I_aR_a is ordinarily from 2 to 6 per cent of V, the percentage drop in speed of the motor is of the same order of magnitude. For this reason the shunt motor is considered a constant-speed motor, even though its speed does drop slightly with increase of load.

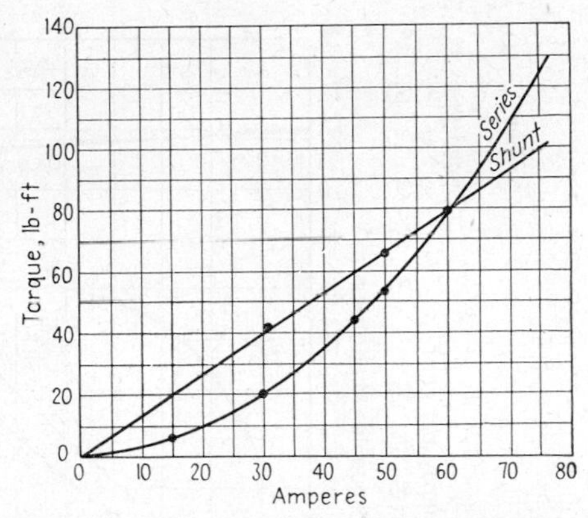

FIG. 389. Shunt and series motors; torque-current characteristics. (Electromagnetic or internal torque.)

Owing to armature reaction, ϕ ordinarily decreases slightly with increase of load, and this tends to maintain the speed constant. Occasionally, the armature reaction is sufficiently great to give a rising speed characteristic with increase of load.

The change in speed between rated load and no load of a d-c motor is a criterion of its performance, particularly if the motor is of the essentially constant-speed type, such as the shunt motor. In the American Standard C50, change of speed is specifically defined as "regulation" and is given in per cent of rated-load speed.

Speed regulation is defined as follows:[1]

Speed Regulation of Direct-current Motors. The speed regulation of a constant-speed, direct-current motor is the change in speed when the load is reduced from rated load to zero, expressed in per cent of rated-load speed. The regulation shall be determined with rated voltage and at the final temperature attained at operation under rated load for the time specified in the rating.

The regulation of a direct-current motor refers to the change between no-load speed and the speed obtained with an unvarying load on the motor, and does not

[1] ASA C50, "Rotating Electrical Machinery," 1943 edition, 2.140.

relate to transient periods in which comparatively large fluctuations in speed accompany rapid changes in load.

That is, in Fig. 390, the speed regulation is

$$\frac{ca - ba}{ba} = \frac{cb}{ba}.$$

Example. The speed of a shunt motor falls from 1,100 rpm at no load to 1,050 rpm at rated load. Determine its speed regulation.

$$\text{Regulation} = \frac{1{,}100 - 1{,}050}{1{,}050} = 0.0476, \text{ or } 4.76\%. \quad \textit{Ans.}$$

The speed regulation is a measure of the ability of a motor to maintain its speed when load is applied.

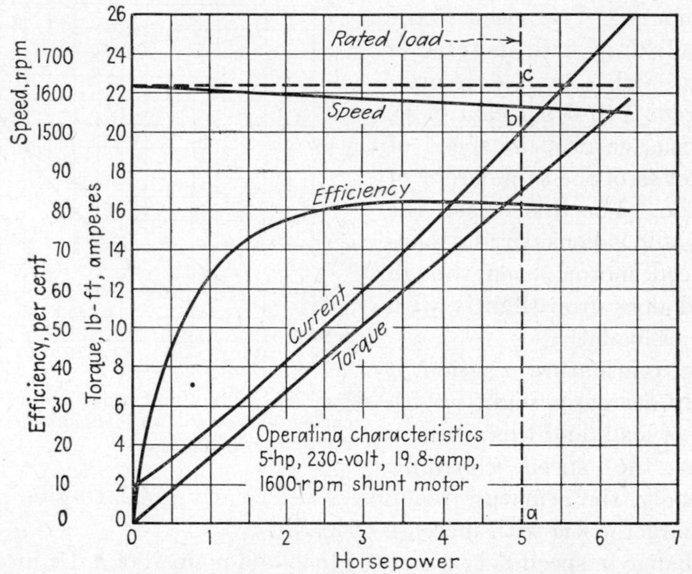

FIG. 390. Typical shunt-motor characteristics.

Figure 390 shows the four essential characteristics of a shunt motor, namely, torque, speed, current, and efficiency, each plotted as a function of horsepower output. The effect of machine losses on efficiency will be discussed in the next chapter. It will be noted that the shunt motor has a definite no-load speed. Therefore it does not run away when the load is removed, provided that the field circuit remains closed.

Shunt motors are used where a substantially constant speed is required, as in machine-shop drives, spinning frames, or blowers. No type of motor is better adapted than the shunt motor to speed control and to speed adjustment. Hence, it is also used where the speed must be varied or must be adjustable. With *adjustable* speed, the speed is set at the desired value and then remains substantially constant as the load varies.

An engine lathe is an excellent example of adjustable-speed operation. Different sizes of cuts require different speeds. However, when the speed for a definite cut has been fixed, the speed should remain substantially constant (also see p. 500).

There is an erroneous impression that shunt motors have low starting torque. This is undoubtedly due to the fact that the ordinary starting box is designed for starting under light load only. Although such boxes will safely allow 125 per cent full-load current on the first notch, they quickly overheat if this value of current is sustained sufficiently long to bring the motor with its load up to speed.

Torque is proportional to the product of current and flux [Eq. (352), p. 485]. The motor is started with full-field excitation (Sec. 333, p. 501). Hence, the motor on starting can develop full-load torque, or even 150 per cent and over of full-load torque provided that the starting rheostat can carry the requisite current.

When motors are started under load, a controller (Sec. 336, p. 505) rather than a starting box is provided. In a controller, the resistors are designed to carry continuously full-load and overload currents.

In modern shunt motors, the shunt-field ampere-turns and hence the shunt-field loss are made small by making the air-gap short. The short air-gap causes high armature reaction (see Fig. 407, p. 511), but good commutation is obtained with commutating poles. It is shown (p. 490) that, owing to high armature reaction, there is a danger that with increasing load the armature mmf may overcome the field mmf, causing the motor to run away, and that, to prevent this, a few series turns aiding the shunt turns are wound on each pole. Although such a motor might be considered a compound motor, the series turns are so few that the characteristics are actually those of a shunt motor, and such machines are considered as shunt motors.

331. Series Motor. In the series motor, the field is connected in series with the armature, Fig. 391. The field has comparatively few turns of wire, and this wire must be of sufficient cross section to carry the rated armature current of the motor.

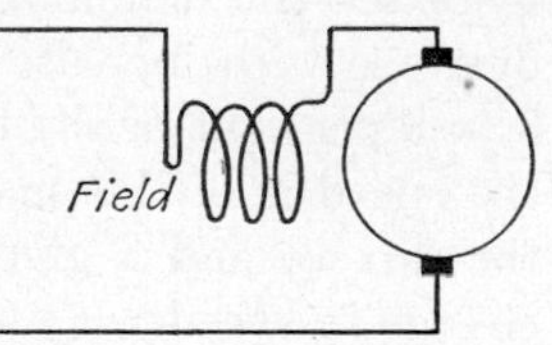

Fig. 391. Connections of series motor.

In the series motor the flux ϕ depends entirely on the armature current. If the iron of the motor is operated at moderate saturation, the flux will be almost directly proportional to the armature current. Therefore, the expression for torque, $T = K_t I \phi$ [Eq. (352), p. 485] can be written as

$$T = K_t' I^2 \tag{358}$$

if ϕ is assumed to be proportional to I, K_t' being a constant.

The torque then is proportional to the *square* of the armature current, Fig. 389. When the current is 30 amp, the torque is 20 lb-ft; at 60 amp, the torque is 80 lb-ft. That is, doubling the armature current results in quadrupling the torque. Note that as the current increases above 60 amp, the torque rises very rapidly. This characteristic of the series motor makes its use desirable where a large increase in torque is desired with a moderate increase in current. In practice, saturation and armature reaction both tend to prevent the torque increasing as rapidly as the square of the current.

When Eq. (356) (p. 488) is applied to the series motor, the speed

$$S = K \frac{V - I_a(R_a + R_s)}{\phi} \tag{359}$$

where K is a constant, V the terminal voltage, I_a the motor current, R_a the armature resistance including brushes, R_s the series-field resistance, and ϕ the flux entering the armature from an N pole. R_s, the resistance of the series field, is now added to the armature resistance in order to obtain the total motor resistance. Both I_a and ϕ vary with the load.

As the load increases, the voltage drop in the field and armature resistance increases, this voltage drop being proportional to the current. Therefore, the counter emf and the numerator of (359) become less, which tends to decrease the speed, although, as with the shunt motor, the decrease due to this factor is only a few per cent. The flux ϕ in the denominator, however, increases almost *directly proportional to* the current. Hence, an increase in current decreases the numerator and increases the denominator of (359), and the speed of the motor must decrease with increase of load. The resistance drop ordinarily is from 3 to 8 per cent of the terminal voltage V so that its effect in decreasing the speed is of this magnitude. The speed is inversely proportional to the flux ϕ, and a given change in ϕ produces the same proportionate change in speed.

When the load torque is increased, the reactions are as follows: There must be a drop in speed, at least momentarily, since load torque exceeds electromagnetic torque, and, for the instant, current and flux have not changed. This reduces the counter emf, and the difference between terminal voltage and counter emf increases. Hence, the current increases and causes field flux and electromagnetic torque to increase. The speed and current will then adjust themselves until electromagnetic torque is equal to the sum of load torque and loss torque and equilibrium is reached. Since electromagnetic torque increases nearly as the square of the current, the increase of current with the same increase in torque is less than with a shunt motor.

When the load torque is decreased, the armature accelerates, at least momentarily, increasing the counter emf, since, for the moment, current and flux have not changed. Accordingly, current and field flux will decrease, and electromagnetic torque will also decrease. Speed and current will adjust themselves until equilibrium is reached.

If the load be removed altogether, ϕ becomes extremely small, resulting in a very high speed. It is dangerous to remove the load from series motors, as their armatures are almost certain to reach speeds where centrifugal action will wreck them.

Figure 392 shows the characteristic curves of a 5-hp series motor plotted with horsepower as abscissa. The torque curve concaves upward for the reasons just stated. The speed varies practically inversely as the current. At large values of current the speed is low, and at small values of current

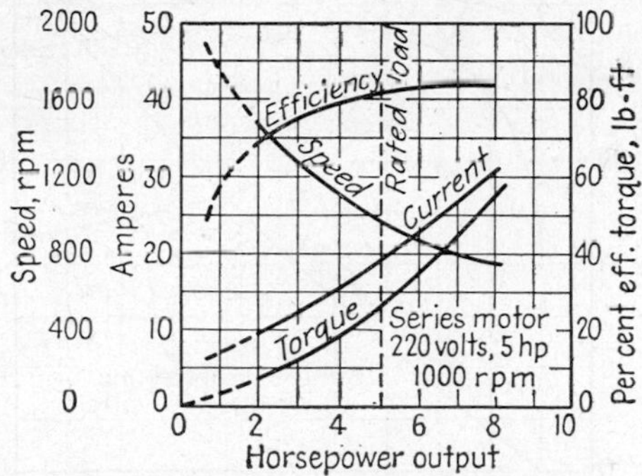

FIG. 392. Typical series-motor characteristics.

the speed is high. The characteristics cannot be determined for small values of current because the speed becomes dangerously high.

The efficiency increases rapidly at first, reaches a maximum, and then decreases. This is due to the fact that at light loads the friction and iron losses are large compared with the load. The effect of these losses becomes less as the load increases. The field and armature loss varies as the *square* of the current (I^2R), so that these losses increase rapidly with the load. The maximum efficiency occurs when the friction and iron losses are practically equal to the copper losses. These characteristic curves should be carefully compared with the corresponding curves for the shunt motor, Fig. 390.

Series motors are used for work which demands large starting torque, such as streetcars, locomotives, or cranes. In addition to the large starting torque, there is another characteristic of series motors which makes them especially desirable for traction purposes. Assume that a shunt motor is used to drive a streetcar. When the car ascends a grade, the shunt motor maintains the speed of the car at approximately the same value that it has when the car is running on level ground. The motor therefore tends to take an excessive current. A series motor, on the other hand, automatically slows down on such a grade, because of the increased current demand. It therefore develops more torque at reduced speed. The drop in speed allows the motor to develop a large torque with but a moderate increase of power. Hence, the rating of a series motor would be less than that of a shunt motor under the same conditions.

When the characteristics of railway motors are plotted, the curves refer to the output at the track and not at the motor shaft. Figure 393 gives such characteristics for a 500-volt 75-hp General Electric railway motor. It will be noted that tractive effort is plotted rather than torque. The speed of the car in mph is given rather than the rpm of the motor arma-

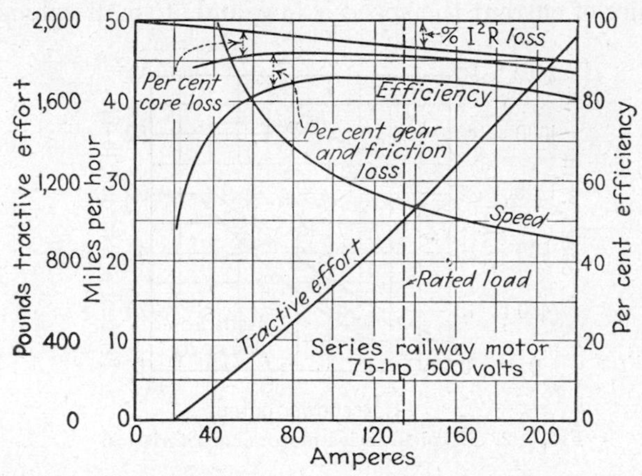

Fig. 393. Typical characteristics of a 75-hp series railway motor.

ture. These curves differ from those for torque and rpm obtained at the pulley by a constant of proportionality, determined by the gear ratio and by the diameter of the driving wheels. There is a loss of torque in the gears. The efficiency curve is the efficiency at the rails. These characteristic curves resemble the curves of Fig. 392. Figure 394 shows a General Electric series motor, designed for a diesel-electric locomotive, as viewed from the axle side. The handhole through which access to the brushes is obtained is shown covered at the left.

332. Compound Motor. A shunt motor may have an additional series-field winding in the same manner as a shunt generator. This winding may be connected so that it aids the shunt winding, in which case the motor is said to be *cumulative compound;* or the series winding may oppose the shunt winding, in which case the motor is said to be *differential compound.*

The characteristics of the cumulative-compound motor are a combination of shunt and series characteristics. As the load is applied, the séries turns increase the flux, causing the torque for any given current to be greater than it would be for the shunt motor. On the other hand, this increase of flux causes the speed to decrease more rapidly than it does in

Fig. 394. Transportation series motor designed for use on diesel-electric locomotive. (*General Electric Company.*)

the shunt motor. These characteristics are shown in Fig. 395. Values are given for electromagnetic torque or torque developed within the armature. The cumulative-compound motor develops a high torque with sudden increase of load. It also has a definite no-load speed, so does not run away when the load is removed.

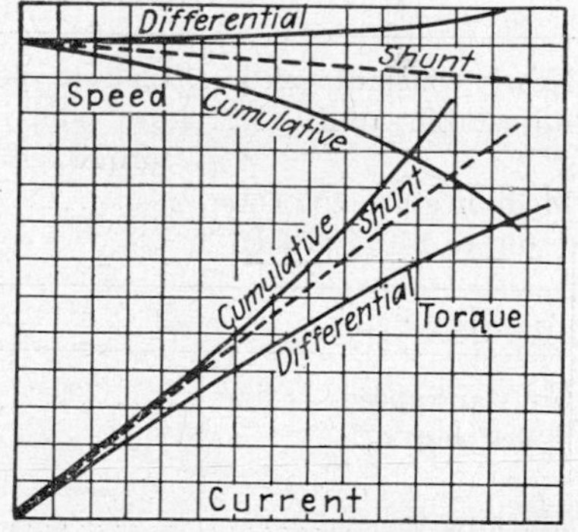

Fig. 395. Electromagnetic torque (developed) and speed characteristics of shunt and compound motors.

The field of application of the cumulative-compound motor lies principally in driving machines which are subject to sudden applications of heavy load, such as occur in rolling mills, shears, or punches. This type of motor is used also where a large starting torque is desired, but where a straight series motor cannot be used conveniently. Cranes and elevators are representative of such loads. In elevators, the series turns are usually short-circuited when the motor reaches running speed.

Another advantage of the cumulative-compound motor for suddenly applied loads is that the motor automatically undergoes a substantial drop in speed when the load is applied, Fig. 395. Accordingly, much of its stored kinetic energy becomes available for supplying a part of the increased load, thus reducing the electrical load on the motor as well as the peaks on the power system. The available kinetic energy is frequently increased by the use of a flywheel, particularly with rolling-mill motors.

In the *differential*-compound motor, the series field opposes the shunt field so that flux is decreased as load is applied. This results in the speed remaining substantially constant or even increasing with increase of load. This speed characteristic is obtained with a corresponding decrease in the rate at which the torque increases with load. Such motors are used where a very constant speed is desired. Because of the substantially constant speed of the shunt motor, there is little occasion to use the differential-compound motor. Moreover, since the field is weakened with increase of load, there is a tendency to speed instability and the motor running away. In starting a differential-compound motor, the series field should be short-circuited, as the large starting current in the series field may be sufficient to overbalance the shunt-field ampere-turns and to cause the motor to start in the wrong direction. Typical torque and speed curves of the differential-compound motor are shown in Fig. 395.

SUMMARY OF MOTOR APPLICATIONS

Shunt	Differential-compound	Cumulative-compound	Series
		Characteristics	
Nearly constant speed	Constant speed	Varying speed	Varying speed
Adjustable speed	Low starting torque	Adjustable varying speed	Adjustable varying speed
Medium starting torque (up to 150% rated)	....	High starting torque	Very high starting torque
		Applications	
Constant-speed line shafting	....	(Intermittent high-torque loads)	Traction
			Electric locomotives
			Diesel-electric locomotives
Machine tools	....	Shears	
Blowers	....	Punches	Rapid-transit systems
Centrifugal pumps	....	Presses	
Reciprocating pumps	....	Elevators	Trolley cars and buses
Woodworking	....	Conveyers	
Paper machines	....	Stokers	Cranes
Printing presses	....	Rolling mills	Hoists
			Conveyers

To reverse the direction of rotation in any motor, either the armature alone or the field alone must be reversed. If both are reversed the direction of rotation remains unchanged. Therefore, in so far as the direction of rotation of the motor is concerned it is immaterial which line is positive.

MOTOR STARTERS

333. Three-point Box. It is shown in Sec. 327 (p. 486) that if a 10-hp 110-volt motor is connected directly across 110-volt mains, the resulting current is 110 ÷ 0.05, or 2,200, amp. Such a current is far too large for both the motor and the power system. Hence, resistance must be connected in series with the motor *armature* when starting. This resistance may be gradually cut out as the armature comes up to speed and develops a counter emf.

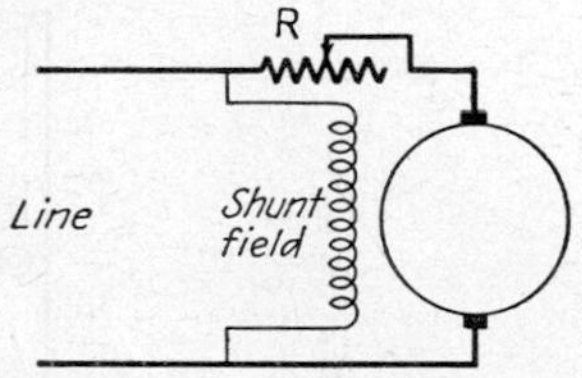

Fig. 396. Resistance used for starting.

Figure 396 shows the use of a simple resistor R for starting a shunt motor. It will be noted that this resistor is in the *armature* circuit and that the field is connected directly across the line and outside the resistor R. If the field were connected across the armature terminals, putting the resistor R in series with the *motor*, there would be little or no voltage across the field at starting. There would be little torque developed, and difficulty in starting would be experienced.

Figure 397 shows a three-point starter. This does not differ fundamentally from the connections shown in Fig. 396. One line connects directly to an armature terminal and a field terminal tied together. It makes no connection whatever with the starting box. The other line goes to the line terminal of the starting box, which is connected directly to the starting arm. The starting arm moves over contacts set in the slate front of the starting box. These contacts connect with taps distributed along the starting resistor. The armature terminal of the starting box, which is the right-hand end of the starting resistance, is connected to the other armature terminal of the motor. The field connection in the starting box is connected from the first starting contact, through the holdup magnet, to the field terminal of the box. This field terminal is connected directly to the other terminal of the shunt field.

When the starting arm makes connection with the first contact, the field is connected directly across the line and at the same time the entire starting resistor is put in series with the armature. As the starting arm is moved, the starting resistor is gradually cut out. When the arm reaches the running position, the starting resistor is all cut out, and, to ensure good contact, the line and armature conductors frequently are connected directly by a laminated copper brush, Fig. 397. The path of the field current is now from the starting arm back through the starting resistor. The resistance of this resistor is so low, compared with the resistance of the field circuit, that it has no material effect on the value of the field current. A spring tends to pull the starting arm back to the starting position. When the arm reaches the running position, it is held against the action of this spring by a soft-iron magnet or holdup magnet, connected in series with the shunt field. A soft-iron armature is often attached to

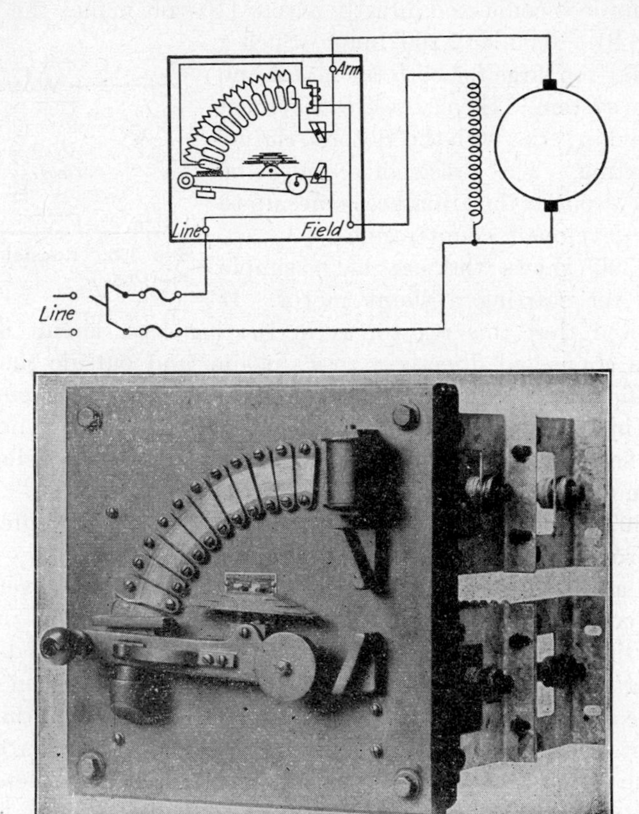

FIG. 397. Three-point starting box.

the starting arm as shown in the figure. If, for any reason, the line is without voltage, the starting arm will spring back to the starting position. Otherwise, if the voltage returned to the line after a temporary shutdown, the stationary motor armature would be connected directly across the line and a short circuit would result.

The advantage of connecting the holdup coil in series with the shunt field is that, should the field circuit become opened, the arm springs back to the starting position and so prevents the motor running away.

334. Four-point Box. The three-point starting box cannot be used to advantage on variable-speed motors having field control. Such motors frequently have a speed variation of 5 to 1. This results in the field current having approximately the same range. The holdup magnet may be too strong, therefore, at the higher values of field current and too weak at the lower values. To obviate this difficulty a four-point box is used, Fig. 398. It is similar to the box shown in Fig. 397, except that the holdup

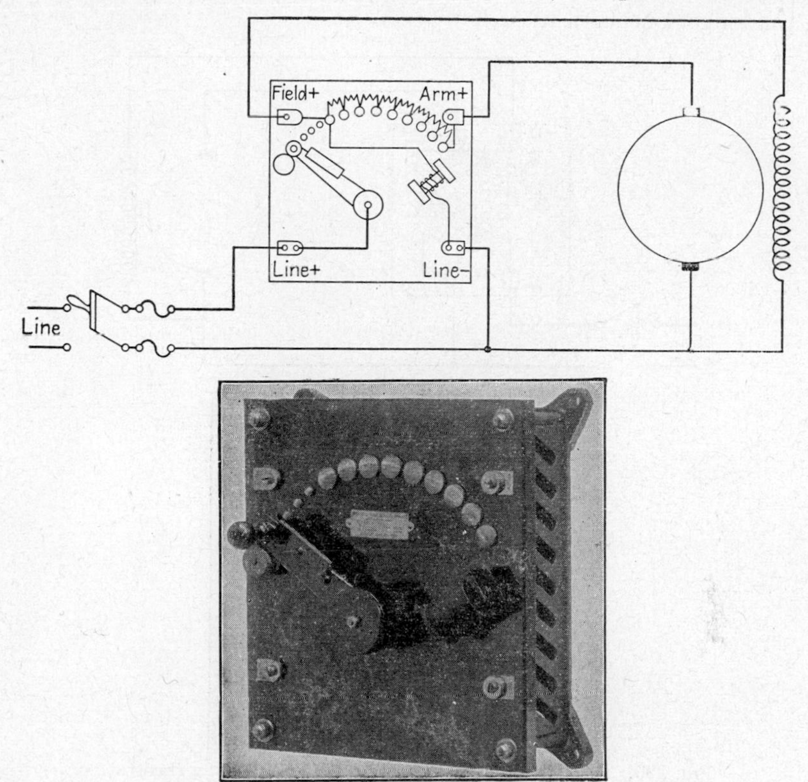

FIG. 398. Connections for a four-point starting box.

coil is of high resistance and is connected *directly across the line*. The only difference in the connection is that the "line−" terminal must be connected to the side of the line which runs directly to the common armature and field terminals. When the voltage leaves the line, the holdup coil becomes dead and allows the arm to spring back to the starting position.

Sometimes the field rheostat is contained within the starting box. For example, in Fig. 399, it is connected between the contacts in the two upper rows. The box then has two arms. The shorter arm connects to the lower row of contacts and cuts out the armature starting resistor in the ordinary manner. This arm is pushed forward by the longer arm.

During the starting period the field rheostat is short-circuited by the finger *S* moving over the metallic sector, Fig. 399. When the starting resistance is all cut out, the shorter arm is held by the magnet and the short circuit of the field rheostat is removed by this arm pushing *S* to the right of the sector. The longer arm, which has no spring, inserts resistance in the field circuit when moved backward. If the voltage goes off, the magnet becomes de-energized and the shorter arm springs back, carrying the longer one with it.

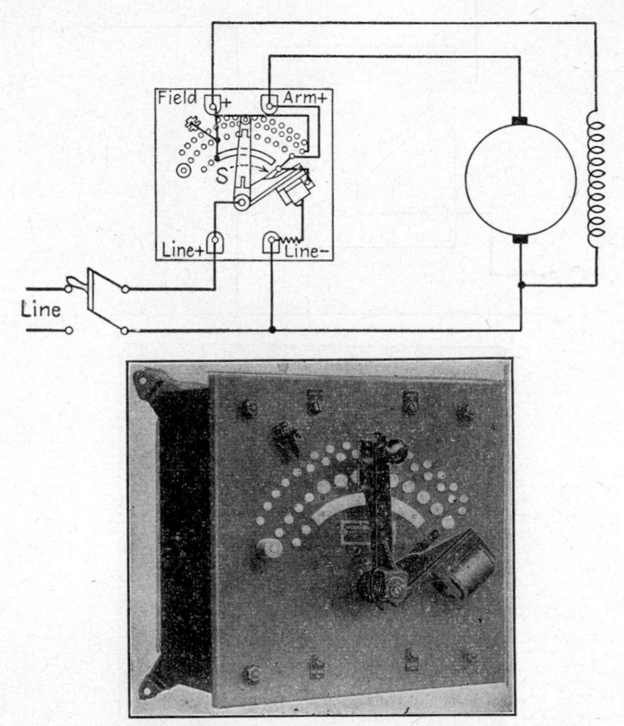

Fig. 399. Westinghouse starting and speed-adjusting rheostat.

In stopping a motor, the *line switch* should always be opened rather than throwing back the starting arm. With shunt motors, the line switch can be opened with no appreciable arc, since the motor develops a counter emf nearly equal to the line voltage and the net voltage across the switch contacts is small. The electromagnetic energy stored in the field does not appear at the switch but is discharged gradually through the armature. On the other hand, if the starting arm is thrown back, the field circuit is broken at the last contact button. Owing to the inductive nature of the field, this results in a hot arc which burns the contact. To prevent the contact from being burned, a small finger breaks the arc, Fig. 399.

335. Series-motor Starters. The series-motor starter needs no shunt-field connection. There are two principal types, one having a no-voltage release, Fig. 400(*a*), and one having a no-load release, Fig. 400(*b*). In the no-voltage-release type, the holdup coil is connected directly across the line and releases the arm when the voltage goes off the line. In the no-load-release type, the holdup coil consists of a few turns in series with the motor. When the motor current falls below a determined value, the starting arm is released. This last type is particularly adapted to series motors where there is a possibility of the load dropping to such a low value that the motor speed may become dangerous.

336. Controllers. Controllers are used where the operation of the motor is continually under the direct control of an operator, as in street-

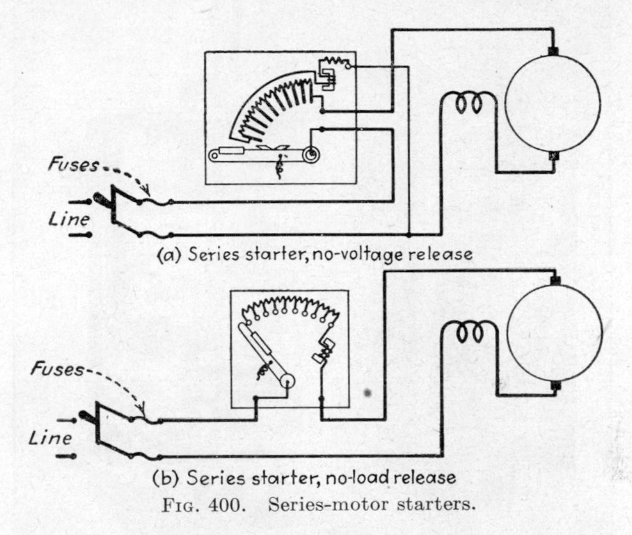

Fig. 400. Series-motor starters.

car, crane, and elevator motors. The controller must be more rugged than the starting box, since the controller is used for continual starting, stopping, and reversing the motor. A typical controller is shown in Fig. 401. Such controllers usually have an external resistor which is cut in and out by fingers in the controller. A shunt-motor field rheostat may also be incorporated within the controller. Controllers are usually fitted with a "reverse," so that the motor may be run in either direction. The controller, Fig. 401, contains both the shunt-field resistor and the reverse.

337. Automatic Starters. Automatic starters are often used. They have many advantages over the hand-operated starter. They cut out the starting resistor at a definite rate, so that the blowing of fuses and the opening of circuit breakers, due to too great an acceleration, are avoided. In many installations where a motor is used intermittently, it may be started and stopped by merely pushing "start" and "stop" buttons. Operators will be more likely to shut the motor down when the power is not being used, because of the ease with which starting and stopping are effected. In the larger sizes of motors, especially when extremely rapid operation is necessary, as in rolling mills, only automatic starters can give satisfactory results. Two or three, or even more, start and stop buttons may be located in different positions in a shop so that at least one button is always readily accessible.

A typical automatic starter is shown in Fig. 402. A front view of the mechanism, without cover, and in the "off" position, is shown in Fig.

Fig. 401. Compound revolving-drum controller with finger-type field control. (*Cutler-Hammer, Inc.*)

402(*a*). The wiring diagram is shown in (*b*). When the start button is pushed, the solenoid is energized through the circuit *ab*213*d*. The solenoid, shown at the lower right in (*a*) closes contacts C, C_1 and opens C_2. The closing of contact C connects the shunt-field circuit directly across the line terminals $L1$ and $L2$ and also connects the armature, commutating poles, series field, and the starting resistor in series across $L1$ and $L2$. The closing of C_1 maintains the solenoid circuit closed through *abc*13*d* when the contact at 2 is released. The opening of C_2 inserts resistance in the solenoid circuit and thus reduces heating. Much less flux, and hence current, in the solenoid is required to hold the contacts closed than is required to close them initially.

After the closing of contact C the time-closing contacts TC_1 and then TC_2 close in sequence, there being a time delay between the closing of all three contacts. The time between the closing of successive contacts is regulated by the timing mechanism, shown enclosed at the lower left in

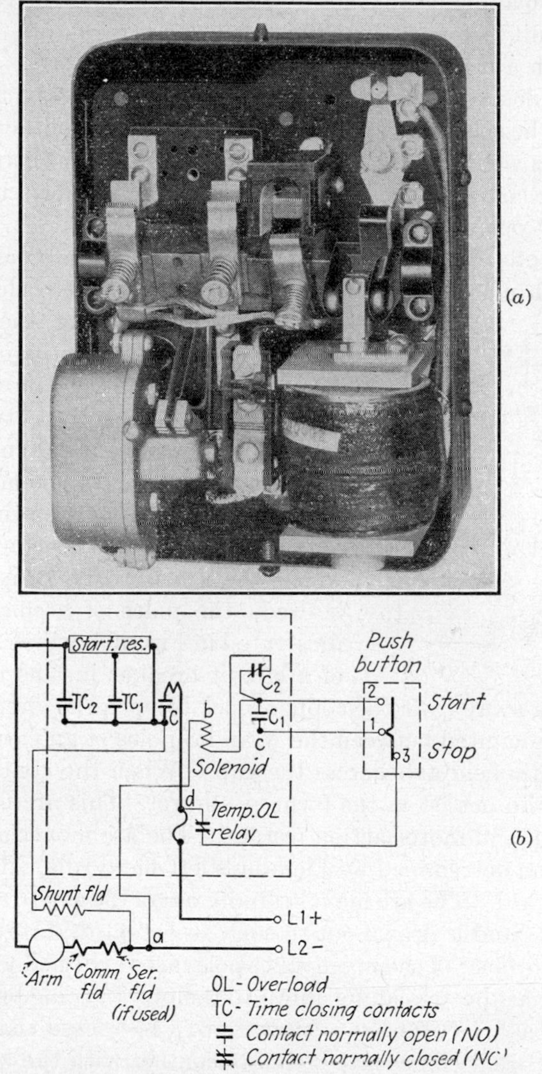

FIG. 402. Magnetic controller for automatic starting. (*General Electric Company.*)

(*a*), which is regulated by an escapement. Each contactor can close only in accordance with the time determined by the timing mechanism. Contact TC_1 short circuits a part of the starting resistor, and after contact TC_2 closes, the starting resistor is entirely short-circuited and the motor armature in series with the commutating and series fields is connected directly across the line. A temperature-time overload relay is also shown at *d* in (*b*). This is a bimetallic thermostat placed near a small resistor in series with the motor armature. There is considerable heat storage. The relay is so adjusted that if an overload continues the relay opens the solenoid circuit before injury can occur to the motor. Contact C is equipped with a magnetic blowout (Sec. 338).

When it is desired to shut the motor down, the stop button is pressed, which opens the solenoid circuit at 3, permitting the contacts in the armature circuit as well as C_1 to open. Instead of a push-button switch, the motor may be controlled by a float switch, a pressure switch, or any other automatically operated switch.

338. Magnetic Blowouts. Controllers and circuit breakers are often equipped with magnetic blowouts whose function is to elongate the arc resulting from opening the circuit, thus causing the arc to be extinguished quickly. The arc is also made to move out rapidly from the space directly between the contacts so that burning of the current-carrying surfaces, due to the persistence of the arc, is materially reduced. The principle of blowouts is as follows: The contacts between which the arc is to be broken are placed between the poles of a magnet. This is illustrated in Fig. 403, which shows the pole of a circuit breaker just as the brush contact is moving away from the copper block to open the circuit. The contact brush is mounted between the N and S poles of an electromagnet, so that a magnetic field acts across the gap. When the contacts open, the current tends to persist in the form of an arc. This arc finds itself in a magnetic field, and motor action results. The arc moves across the field in the direction determined by Fleming's left-hand rule. In Fig. 403 the motion is upward. The arc moves rapidly out of the gap to the upper edges of the contacts and is drawn out to such an extent that it ruptures easily.

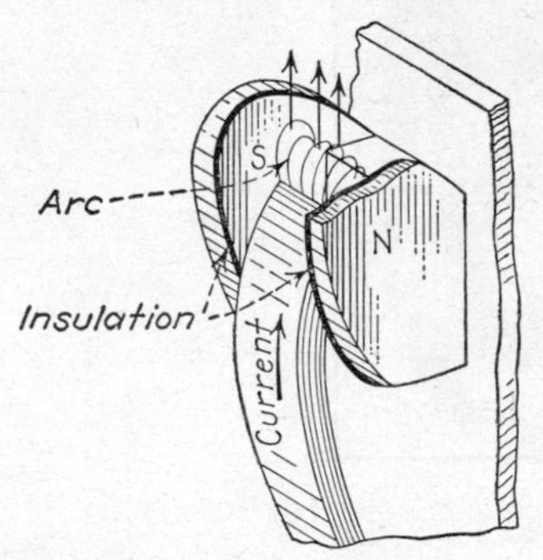

Fig. 403. Magnetic blowout.

The inner surfaces of the magnets or pole faces are lined with insulation, Fig. 403, so that the arc cannot jump to them. In some breakers of high interrupting capacity, the arc is blown into a restricted channel called an *arc shute*. There it comes into intimate contact with the walls of the arc shute, where it is cooled and rapidly de-ionized.

SPEED CONTROL

In the equation for motor speed, $S = KE/\phi$ [Eq. (355), p. 488], there are but two factors that can be changed to secure speed control without making changes in the motor construction, namely, the counter emf E and the flux ϕ.

339. Armature-resistance Method. In this method, the speed control is obtained by connecting a resistor directly in series with the motor *armature*, keeping the field across full-line potential, Fig. 404(a). Because of the voltage drop in this resistor, the counter emf E is changed. A wide range of speed can be obtained by this method, and at the same time the motor will develop any desired torque over its operating range, for the *torque* depends only on the *flux* and armature *current*.

The principal objections to this method of speed control are that an excessive proportion of power is lost in the armature series resistor and the speed *regulation* is very poor. In Fig. 404(b) are the speed-load curves of a shunt motor with and without resistance in series with the armature.

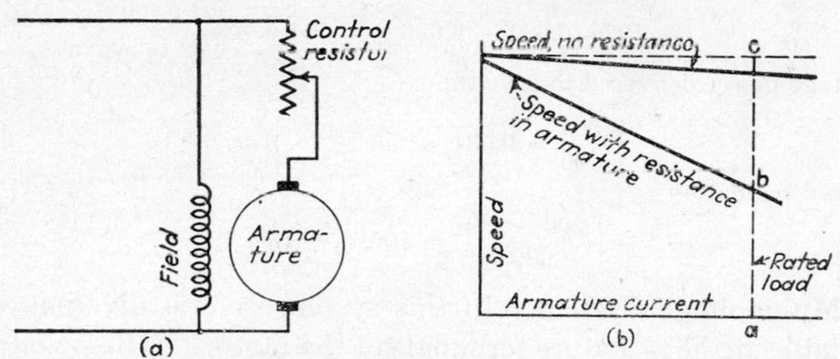

Fig. 404. Speed control and regulation—armature-resistance method.

The speed-load curve with armature series resistance shows that half speed is obtained at rated load. Note that the speed at no load rises to a value which is practically equal to the speed of the motor when there is no armature series resistance. In this case the speed regulation with resistance which is equal to cb/ba is about 100 per cent. About 50 per cent of the power supplied to the armature circuit is lost in the series resistor. Without series resistance the speed regulation is the usual 3 or 4 per cent.

Another objection to this method is that the control resistor must have sufficient carrying capacity for rated and overload current of the motor, and provision must be made for dissipating the large amount of heat developed in the resistor.

Example. A 220-volt 7-hp motor has an armature resistance of 0.25 ohm. When running without load at 1,200 rpm, the armature takes 6 amp. Determine: (a) resistance which should be connected in series with armature to reduce speed of motor to 600 rpm with 30 amp to the armature; (b) power lost in resistor; (c) percentage of power to armature circuit which is available at armature terminals; (d) speed regulation. Neglect armature reaction.

(*a*) E_1 (at no load) $= 220 - (6 \cdot 0.25) = 218.5$ volts.

$$E_2 \text{ (at 600 rpm.)} = \frac{600}{1{,}200} 218.5 = 109.3 \text{ volts.}$$

$$\text{Total } (R + R_a) = \frac{220 - 109.3}{30} = \frac{110.7}{30} = 3.69 \text{ ohms.}$$

Subtracting armature resistance,

$$R = 3.69 - 0.25 = 3.44 \text{ ohms.} \quad \textit{Ans.}$$

(*b*) Power lost in series resistor,

$$P_1 = (30)^2 \cdot 3.44 = 3{,}096 \text{ watts.} \quad \textit{Ans.}$$

(*c*) Power delivered to armature circuit,

$$P_2 = 220 \cdot 30 = 6{,}600 \text{ watts.}$$

Power delivered to armature,

$$P_3 = 6{,}600 - 3{,}096 = 3{,}504 \text{ watts.}$$

Percentage power delivered to armature,

$$\frac{3{,}504}{6{,}600} = 0.531, \text{ or } 53.1\%. \quad \textit{Ans.}$$

(*d*) Speed regulation

$$\frac{1{,}200 - 600}{600} = 100\%. \quad \textit{Ans.}$$

340. Multivoltage System. In this system several different voltages are available at the armature terminals of the motor. These voltages are often supplied by a balancer set, Fig. 405. The shunt field of the motor is

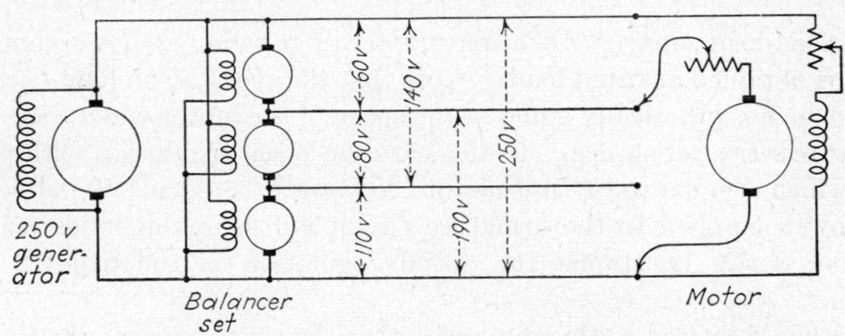

FIG. 405. Multivoltage speed control.

connected permanently across a fixed voltage, and, with the 4-wire system shown, six voltages are available for the armature. Intermediate speed adjustments can be made with a limited field control. Owing to the necessity of having a balancer set, or its equivalent, and because of the large number of wires necessary, this system is little used in this country for ordinary power drive.

341. Ward Leonard System. In this system, Fig. 406, variable motor voltage is obtained by means of a separate generator G driven by a motor

M_1. By varying the field of the generator, the desired voltage across the motor terminals M_2 is obtained. The motor field is connected across the supply mains in parallel with the fields of the other two machines. In Fig. 406, M_1 is a motor driving generator G. G, in turn, supplies variable voltage to the armature of motor M_2, whose speed is to be varied. This system is very flexible and gives close adjustment of speed as well as good speed regulation. The chief disadvantages are the low over-all efficiency of the system, especially at light loads, and the necessity of having two extra machines. This system is used where fine speed adjustment and

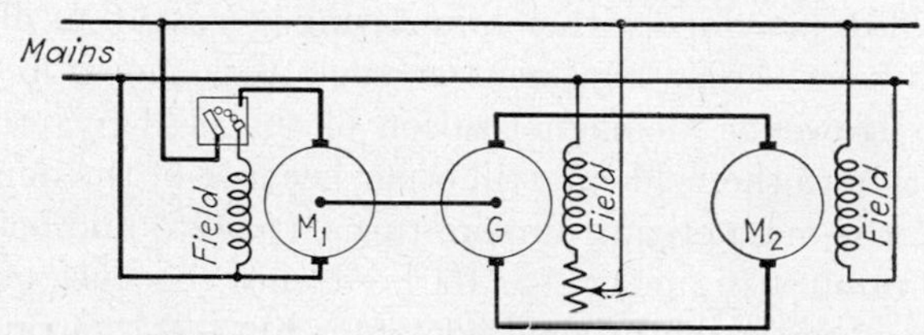

Fig. 406. Ward Leonard system of speed control.

smooth acceleration are required. One common application is in elevators.

Since the power supply is usually a-c, the motor M_1 can be an a-c motor, commonly an induction or a synchronous motor. Under these conditions a small d-c exciter or other d-c power source is necessary for the field excitation of G and M_2.

Both the Amplidyne and Rototrol (Secs. 320 and 321, pp. 473 and 476) are used to supply variable voltage for motor speed control. Figure 376, (p. 475) shows a specific application.

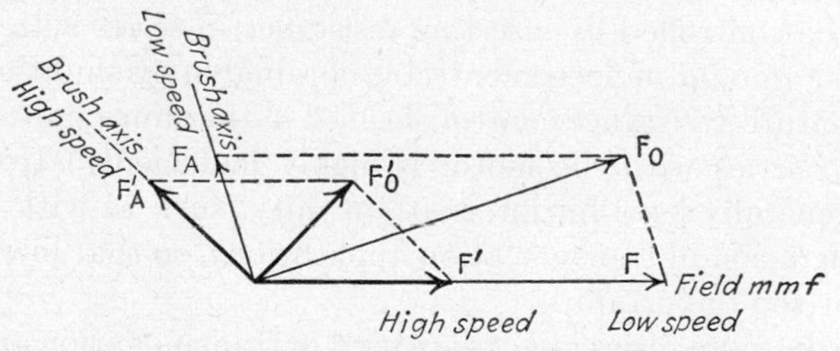

Fig. 407. Effect of weak field on brush position.

342. Field Control. In the foregoing methods of speed control, the armature voltage is varied. Change of speed also may be obtained by varying the flux ϕ by means of a field rheostat, [Eq. (355), p. 488]. This method is very efficient so far as power is concerned, and for any particular speed adjustment the speed regulation from no load to full load is excellent. The range of speed obtainable by this method with the ordinary motor is limited by commutation difficulties. Referring to Fig. 407, F is the field mmf at low speed, and F_A is the corresponding armature mmf. The resultant mmf is F_0. If it be attempted to double the speed of the motor by weakening its field, then, neglecting saturation, the new field mmf will be F'. It is now necessary to move the brushes farther backward, and the armature mmf will be F_A'. The resultant mmf is F_0'.

It is evident that the neutral plane has been moved backward to a considerable extent, the demagnetizing component of the armature mmf has increased, and the armature mmf is about equal to the field mmf. In addition to severe sparking at the commutator, the strong armature mmf may so weaken the main field that the motor tends to run away. Nearly all motors are now provided with commutating poles so that displacement of the brushes from the no-load neutral, such as is shown in Fig. 407, is unnecessary. However, demagnetization of the field by too strong an armature relative to the field can still occur because of the demagnetizing action of the cross-magnetizing ampere-turns, (p. 425) and because of the mmf of the commutating poles, (p. 460). Hence, because of the risk of instability, speed variation by field control is limited to a ratio of 5 or 6 to 1.

343. Lincoln Motor. In the Lincoln Motor, made by the Reliance Electric and Engineering Company, the flux entering the armature is varied by moving the rotating armature in and out of the field structure. As the armature is moved out of the field, the length of armature-conductor cutting flux is reduced. Therefore the armature must rotate faster in order to develop the requisite counter emf. This gives smooth speed control over wide ranges, ratios as high as 10 to 1 being obtained. These motors are provided with commutating poles.

344. Series-motor and Series-parallel Control. The speed of a series motor may be controlled by inserting resistance in series with the motor, and a limited amount of speed control is obtainable by shunting the field. As with armature-resistance control of speed in the shunt motor, inserting resistance in series with the motor is highly inefficient. However, the method is generally used for intermittent duty, such as with hoists, and during acceleration in transportation applications, so that low power efficiency is not too important.

When two or more series motors are used in transportation applications, such as in electric locomotives, rapid-transit trains, trolley cars, and buses, speed control may be obtained by combining series resistance with series and parallel connections of the motors. By this method, in a two-motor car, two different speeds can be efficiently obtained. The motors are first connected in series through a starting resistor R, as in Fig. 408(a). This resistor is gradually cut out by the controller as the car comes up to speed, and then each motor receives one-half the line voltage. This is the first running position. For any given value of armature current each motor will run at half its rated speed. As there is no external resistance in the circuit, the motors are operating at an efficiency very nearly equal to that obtainable with full-line voltage across the terminals of each motor. Since torque is a function of motor current only, each motor can develop any value of torque up to the values which it develops when connected across full voltage.

When it is desired to increase the speed of the car, the two motors are connected in parallel and in series with a portion of the resistor R. This resistor is gradually cut out, and when the running position is reached, each motor receives full-line voltage, as in Fig. 408(*b*).

In a four-motor car, the motors are usually divided into two groups, each group consisting of two motors which are always in parallel. In starting, these two groups are connected in series, each group taking the place of the single motor of a two-motor car. This starting condition is

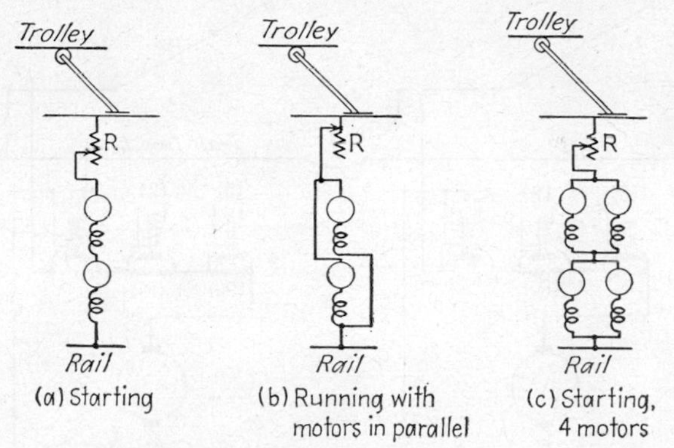

FIG. 408. Series-parallel control of series motors.

shown in Fig. 408(*c*). When the full-speed running position is reached, both groups are connected in parallel across the line. Each motor then receives full-line voltage.

345. Multiple-unit Control. In the heavier electric cars and locomotives, the currents become so large that direct platform control is out of the question from the standpoint of size of controller, safety, and expense. Moreover, when cars are operated in trains, it is necessary that the motors on all the cars shall be under a single control and that each control operation shall take place simultaneously on all cars.

In the multiple-unit system, all the heavy-current switching is done by solenoid-operated contactors located beneath the car. Compressed air is usually employed to operate the contactors and circuit breakers, the air being admitted and exhausted from the cylinders by means of small magnet valves energized by the train line.

The *train line*, which runs the entire length of the train, Fig. 409, is made continuous through plug and socket connectors located in the car couplers. The wires of this train line receive their power through the master controller operated by the motorman. As this train-line current is of the magnitude of 2.5 amp, a small platform controller can be used. Another distinct advantage of this system is that the rate of cutting out the starting resistance during the acceleration period is outside the control of the motorman, being accomplished by automatically operated contactors which close in sequence at the proper times. This ensures uniform acceleration and eliminates the opening of the car circuit breakers and the shocks to the equipment caused by the too great changes in acceleration which may occur when manual operation is used.

Figure 409 shows the underlying principle of the system, no attempt being made to give the many details which must necessarily accompany

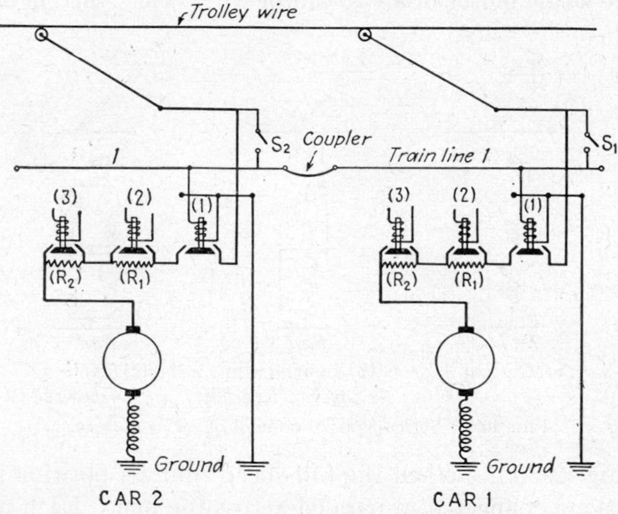

FIG. 409. Principle of multiple-unit control.

such a system. Each car has its own trolley or third-rail shoe for collecting the current. A train line of small wires runs the entire length of the train, the connections being made through the couplers between cars. This line usually consists of six wires. Solenoids, which operate contactors, usually by means of compressed air, are connected across the train lines. Some of the contactors are operated directly by the controller in the hands of the motorman, and others operate automatically after the manual controller has been turned in the desired position. For example, in Fig. 409 are shown two motors, one in each car. One line of the train line is shown running between cars and connected by the coupler. It is assumed that the train is to be operated from car 1. If the switch S_1 in the controller of car 1 be closed, train line 1-1 becomes alive. This energizes relay (1) in each car, and both relays simultaneously close the motor circuits, the starting resistors R_1, R_2 being in series with the motors. As the motors "pick up," the current drops and relay (2) in each car becomes automatically energized and the starting resistors R_1, R_1 are short-circuited in each car. Then the next set of relays becomes energized in a similar manner, until all starting resistance is cut out and the motors are across the line.

In the complete system there are six train lines, some of which cause reverse, change from series to parallel, etc. The great advantage of this system is that every motor on the train can be operated from either of the two controllers on any one car, all the motors are controlled simultaneously, the acceleration cannot exceed a certain value regardless of the motorman, and as there are driving wheels on every car, high accelerations can be obtained. This system is also used extensively on single cars.

346. Dynamic and Regenerative Braking. It is often desirable to brake a motor when it is being driven by its load, as in the case of descending elevators and crane loads. This is often done by using a controller which connects the field across the line and at the same time puts a resistance load across the armature terminals. This produces generator action and therefore retards the armature. If series motors are used, their fields must be connected across the line in series with resistance. Such braking is not effective for completely stopping the motor armature, as the braking action diminishes proportionally to the speed of the armature.

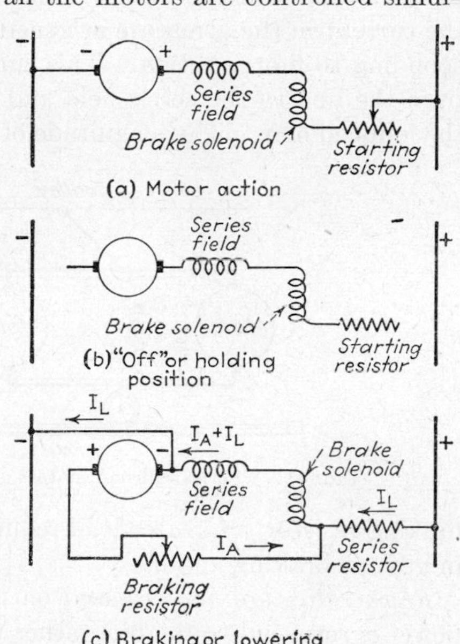

Fig. 410. Dynamic braking.

Dynamic braking for a series motor is illustrated in Fig. 410. In (*a*) the motor is shown connected for raising the load. When the load reaches the desired position, the armature circuit is broken by means of the controller, as in (*b*). This de-energizes the brake solenoid, resulting in the brake being set (see Fig. 188, p. 242) and so holding the load in position. To lower the load, the operator, by means of the controller, makes the connections in (*c*). A series resistor in circuit allows initially just enough current I_L to energize and disengage the brake solenoid. This current also produces flux in the series field of the motor, and its path is to the negative side of the line without having then gone through the armature and thus without having produced any motor action. Since the load is being lowered, the armature is rotating in a direction opposite to that which it had when the load was being raised. The torque which now produces the rotation is supplied by the load. This rotation of the armature in the magnetic field produced by the series winding causes an emf to be induced in the armature, and as a closed external path is provided, a current I_A results. Application of both right- and left-hand rules shows that, since the direction of the field is the same as it was with motor action and the direction of rotation is opposite, the direction of the current in the armature as generator must be the same as that corresponding to motor action. This current reinforces the small current I_L from the line to the series field and hence determines the magnitude of the induced emf. The magnitude of the load is regulated by varying the

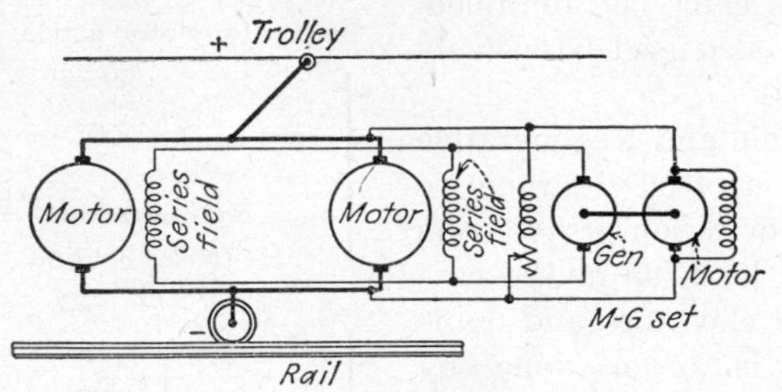

FIG. 411. Series railroad motors connected for regenerative braking.

braking resistor. Greater load requires greater torque and hence results in greater braking action.

Regenerative braking is based on this same principle, except that the power is returned to the line rather than being lost in resistance.

Series and overcompounded generators when operated in parallel with a constant-potential system are unstable (see Sec. 364, p. 547). Hence, when series motors are used for regenerative braking, as in railroad operation, the series fields are separately excited in parallel from a low-voltage motor-generator set, Fig. 411. Such a system is used on the electric locomotives of the Chicago, Milwaukee, St. Paul and Pacific Railroad.

347. Motor Testing—Prony[1] Brake. It is often necessary to determine the efficiency of a motor at certain definite loads and frequently over its entire range of operation. A knowledge of the efficiency may be necessary, as in the case of an acceptance test; further, the motor may be used as a power-measuring device for determining the power taken by some machine, such as a generator, pump, or blower. Knowing the

[1] After Baron de Gaspard Clair François Marie Riche Prony (1755–1839), French engineer, mathematician, and physicist.

motor input, which can be measured with ammeter and voltmeter, and also knowing the motor efficiency, the output for any given input can be computed. This output will be the power delivered to the generator, the pump, etc.

The most common method of making direct measurements of efficiency in motors up to about 50 hp is to use a prony brake. Such brakes are made in various forms. In their usual forms such brakes have strong tendencies to vibrate and chatter, making the reading of the pointer on

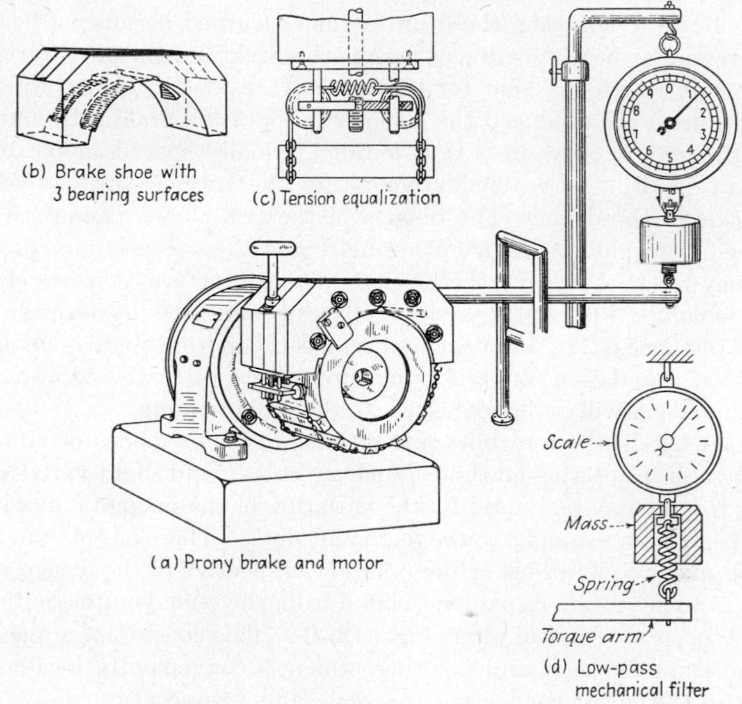

Fig. 412. Prony brake.

the brake scale difficult; sometimes the pointer is actually unreadable. A brake designed by Professor P. M. Honnell,[1] now in use at the U.S. Military Academy at West Point, has several special features which make the brake practically vibration-free, the load being at the same time smoothly adjustable to any desired value. The brake and some of the details of construction are shown in Fig. 412. The complete brake and brake drum, together with the motor under test, are shown in (*a*). The main elements are a brake shoe, a lightweight torque arm, a scale sus-

[1] Formerly lieutenant colonel, U.S. Military Academy at West Point, now professor of electrical engineering, Washington University, St. Louis, Mo. See "The Prony Brake," *Jour. Eng. Education*, Vol. 36, November, 1945.

pended from a vibration-free support, and a mechanical vibration filter connecting the torque arm to the scale. The brake shoe is constructed of four pieces of maple shaped as shown in (*a*) and bolted together. Although the brake shoe may be fitted accurately to the drum at room temperature, the drum surface becomes warped at the higher temperatures existing during the dissipation of mechanical energy. To ensure that the shoe will always ride on the drum without a tendency to slide sideways, the shoe bears on only three small surfaces, two in the rear on the edges of the drum and the one in front on the center line of the drum, Fig. 412(*b*). Even when the drum becomes warped because of heating, the three-point bearing surfaces permit the brake to continue to ride on center. It was found that for friction surfaces hard maple, lubricated with machine oil, produced the smoothest operation practically immune from the effects of water. Five parallel, equally spaced maple blocks fastened solidly to two chains constitute the friction surfaces on the underside of the drum. The tension in the two chains is equalized by the use of two pulleys and a coil spring, Fig. 412(*c*), thus minimizing any tendency to chattering by the blocks. The torque arm consists of light ¾-in. conduit filled with sand to introduce internal hysteresis. The torque distance is 2 ft. For the best results the motor should be mounted on a solid foundation, preferably concrete, since otherwise vibrations of the foundation will be introduced into the scale reading.

Even with all the foregoing precautions, resonant modes of vibration are inherent in rotating machines, such as motors, and slight variations in motor torque may be caused by the variation of the magnetic flux in the air-gaps due, for example, to the teeth and slots. These factors can cause high-frequency vibrations of the pointer irrespective of the design of the brake. Such vibrations can be isolated from the scale pointer by the use of a low-pass mechanical filter, Fig. 412(*d*). This consists of a mass suspended from the scale and a spring, which is conveniently located in a recess in the mass, connecting the scale and torque arm. For a 5-hp brake, a mass of 10 lb and a spring requiring 10 lb per in. of tension give maximum effectiveness.

Load can be smoothly and uniformly applied by the hand adjusting screw shown in (*a*) which acts to increase the tension in the chains supporting the maple blocks.

The zero or tare reading is obtained by releasing the adjusting screw until the maple blocks are free of the brake drum and inserting a ¼-in. brass rod, shown dotted in (*a*), in a half-round slot in the brake shoe. This lifts the brake shoe from the drum and provides a balancing surface.

No provision is made for holding the torque arm level since it is found that if it is level at full load, the slight angular displacement at lighter loads introduces no appreciable error.

Brakes of this type are cooled ordinarily by pouring water into the hollow brake drum. The water prevents the drum from becoming excessively hot. As the maximum temperature which water can reach in the open air is 100°C, the drum temperature cannot much exceed this. The heat developed in the drum is utilized in converting the water into steam. As a considerable number of heat units is required to convert a small amount of water into steam, a moderate amount of water will keep the drum comparatively cool.

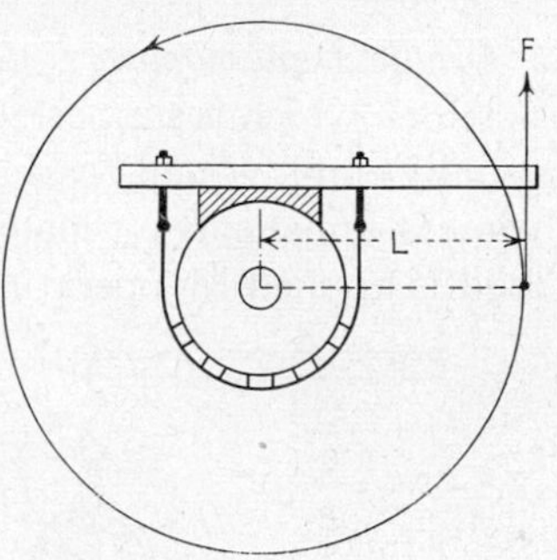

Fig. 413. Work developed by a prony brake.

To determine the equation for the horsepower absorbed by such a brake, consider Fig. 413. Let F be the net force in pounds acting at a perpendicular distance L ft from the center of the drum. First assume that the drum is stationary and that the arm is pulled around the drum by means of the force F. The distance per revolution through which the force F acts is $2\pi L$ ft. The work done in one revolution of this arm around the drum is the product of force and distance $= F(2\pi L)$ ft-lb.

The work done in S revolutions $= F(2\pi L)S$ ft-lb.

If S is the rpm, the horsepower

$$\text{Hp} = \frac{2\pi(FL)S}{33{,}000}.$$

But FL is the torque T; therefore,

$$\text{Hp} = \frac{2\pi TS}{33{,}000}. \tag{360}$$

$$\frac{2\pi}{33{,}000} = 0.0001904.$$

Therefore,

$$\text{Hp} = 0.0001904TS. \tag{361}$$

Obviously, the same amount of work is done on the brake surface whether the drum is stationary and the arm rotates or the arm is stationary and the drum rotates. Therefore, (360) and (361) apply to brakes of the type shown in Figs. 412 and 413. It will be noted that in this particular type of brake the horsepower is independent of the diameter of the drum.

Example. In a brake test of a shunt motor, ammeter and voltmeter measuring the input read 34 amp and 220 volts. The speed of the motor is found to be 910 rpm, and the balance on a 2-ft brake arm reads 27.2 lb. The tare weight of the arm is found to be +2.3 lb. Determine: (*a*) output of motor; (*b*) efficiency at this load.

(*a*) Net reading of balance $= 27.2 - 2.3 = 24.9$ lb.
Torque $T = 24.9 \cdot 2 = 49.8$ lb-ft.
Hp output $= 0.0001904 \cdot 49.8 \cdot 910 = 8.629$ hp. *Ans.*
(*b*) Output $= 8{,}629 \cdot 746 = 6{,}437$ watts.
Input $= 220 \cdot 34 = 7{,}480$ watts.

$$\text{Eff } \eta = \frac{6{,}437}{7{,}480} 100 = 86.06\%. \quad \textit{Ans.}$$

Cradle Dynamometer. A cradle dynamometer is a rotating electrical machine which is supported by its shaft on trunnions, Fig. 414, and which usually employs ball bearings. When coupled to a motor shaft it is a convenient apparatus for loading the motor and measuring its output. The load is applied by operating the dynamometer as a d-c generator with a resistor load. By combining the adjustment of the resistor load with the field rheostat, smooth and fine adjustment of the load is readily obtainable. Separate excitation is preferable. The torque is measured by means of a torque arm attached to the frame of the machine, which restrains it from turning, combined with a scale for measuring force.

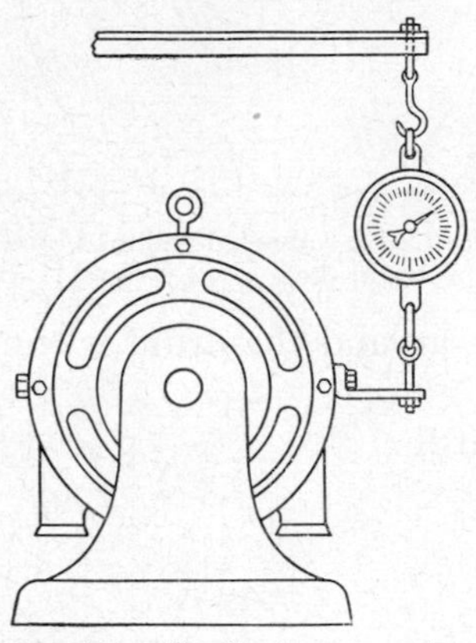

Fig. 414. Cradle dynamometer.

The dynamometer may also operate as a motor to drive a generator, pump, blower, or similar devices. Since the torque and speed of the dynamometer are readily measured, the input to the driven device is readily computed. The friction of the bearings introduces a small error which, with ball bearings, is usually negligible. The cradle dynamometer is ordinarily used for loads not exceeding 100 hp.

348. Measurement of Speed. The measurement of the speed of machines is much simpler as a rule than the measurement of torque. The most common method is to use a simple revolution counter having a conical rubber tip which fits into the countersink of the shaft. There are several types of speed counters available, some of which combine a stop watch with the revolution-counter mechanism. However, speed counters do not give instantaneous speed, but rather average speed over a given period of time.

Tachometers indicate instantaneous speed. There are mechanical tachometers, where the indicator is actuated by centrifugal action. This type should be carefully checked on each occasion of use, as it is especially subject to error after having been in service for some time.

A simple and convenient as well as accurate type of tachometer is the combination of a d-c magneto and a voltmeter. In the magneto, the flux is produced by permanent magnets and so is constant. Therefore, the emf induced in the magneto armature is directly proportional to the speed. If this emf be measured with a voltmeter, the voltmeter reading multiplied by a constant gives the speed directly. Since the voltmeter is a constant-resistance load on the magneto, the voltmeter reading will always be proportional to the speed even should it produce a small resistance drop in the magneto armature. Practically all tachometer magnetos include a voltmeter which is calibrated directly in rpm. However, as a precaution, it is usually desirable to check one or two points on the scale with a speed counter and stop watch.

349. Dynamotor. The dynamotor is defined as follows:

> A dynamotor[1] is a machine which combines both motor and generator action in one magnetic field, either with two armatures or with one armature having two separate windings.

The two windings of the dynamotor armature, when the machine has but a single armature, may or may not lie in separate slots. The machine is used ordinarily to convert d-c power from one voltage to another. One winding develops motor action and causes rotation; the other winding develops generator action and delivers electrical energy. Since the motor and generator currents are in opposite directions, the net armature ampere-turns will be small, being just sufficient to overcome the torque due to rotational losses. Hence, there is but slight armature reaction.

As both windings cut the same magnetic field at the same speed, their induced emfs must be directly proportional to their turns. The emf ratio cannot be changed by changing the field excitation. If, for example, the field is strengthened, the motor conductors as well as the generator conductors are cutting more magnetic flux. Although the generator induced emf will be proportional to this increased value of flux, the speed will decrease to a value that is inversely as the flux (motor action) so that the induced emf in each winding will remain unchanged. If the field is weakened, the speed will increase and again the induced emfs do not change. The ratio between volts at the two commutators is affected to some extent by the armature-resistance drops.

Dynamotors can be used in place of motor-generator sets only when voltage regulation is of no great importance. They are used in the operation of signal systems such as fire-alarm and telephone systems. They are also used for telephone-ringing systems, the generator armature being provided with slip rings for supplying current at from 16 to 19 cycles per sec.

[1] ASA Definitions of Electrical Terms, 1941 edition, 10.10.450.

CHAPTER XIV

LOSSES; EFFICIENCY; OPERATION

350. Dynamo Losses. A part of the energy given to any motor or generator is lost within the machine itself, being converted into heat and wasted. Not only is this energy lost, but there is the further objection that it heats the machine and so limits its output. If the energy loss in the machine becomes excessive, the resulting temperature rise may injure the insulation.

As motor and generator are similar, they have the same types of losses throughout. Therefore, the following applies to either motor or generator.

The losses in d-c rotating machinery are enumerated in ASA Standard C50,[1] together with recommendations for determining these losses.

Schedule of Losses. The following losses are, or may be, present in direct-current generators and motors. They shall be included in determining the efficiency, except as otherwise specified in subsequent paragraphs.

Type of Loss	Description
(a) Shunt-field Loss (See 2.106)	I^2R loss in shunt-field windings.
(b) Rheostat Loss (See 2.107)	I^2R loss in rheostat controlling shunt-field current.
(c) Exciter Losses (See 2.108)	Electrical and mechanical losses in machines supplying excitation.
(d) Friction and Windage Loss (See 2.109)	Mechanical power necessary to drive unexcited machine at rated speed.
(e) Brush-friction Loss (See 2.110)	Mechanical loss due to brushes.
(f) Ventilating Loss (See 2.111)	Power input to ventilating system in addition to windage loss.
(g) Core Loss (See 2.112)	Loss due to magnetic field at no-load rated voltage corrected for effect of IR drop.
(h) Armature I^2R Loss (See 2.113)	I^2R loss in armature windings.
(i) Series Winding I^2R Loss (See 2.114)	I^2R loss in series windings and shunts, if any.
(j) Brush-contact Loss (See 2.115)	Electrical loss in brushes and contacts.
(k) Stray-load Loss (See 2.116)	Losses due to eddy currents in the copper and additional core loss in the iron, produced by distortion of the magnetic flux by load current except that due to IR drop; and short-circuit loss of commutation.

[1] ASA, "Rotating Electrical Machinery," approved Mar. 29, 1943, 2.105 to 2.116.

Losses (a), (b), (h), (i), (j) are electrical losses and can be determined by electrical measurements. It is specified that for efficiency calculations, (**2.104**), all resistances shall be corrected to 75°C. For copper,

$$R = \frac{(234.5 + 75)R_t}{234.5 + t} = \frac{309.5R_t}{234.5 + t}$$

where R is the resistance at 75°C, and R_t the resistance at t°C.

Where series-field shunts or diverters are used, their resistances, corrected to 75°C, should be included.

(a) (**2.106**) **Shunt-field I^2R Loss.** The shunt-field I^2R loss shall be the product of the measured resistance (in ohms) of the field winding corrected to 75°C, and the square of the field current (in amperes).

(b) (**2.107**) **Rheostat Loss.** Unless otherwise agreed upon, all losses due to field rheostats shall be charged against the plant of which the machine is a part and not against the machine.

(c) (**2.108**) **Exciter Loss.** Unless otherwise agreed upon, exciter losses are charged against the plant.

(d) (**2.109**(**a**)) **Friction and Windage Loss.** The friction and windage loss, excluding brush friction, is the power required to drive the unexcited machine at normal speed with its brushes lifted.

(e) (**2.110**) **Brush-friction Loss.** (a) Experience has shown that wide variations are obtained in tests of brush friction made at the factory before the commutator and brushes have received the smooth surfaces that come after continued operation. Conventional values of brush friction, representing average values of many tests, shall, therefore, be used as follows:

	Watts per sq in. of brush contact surface per 1000 ft per min peripheral speed
Carbon and graphite brushes..........	8.0 watts
Metal-graphite brushes...............	5.0 watts

(f) (**2.111**) **Ventilating Loss.**

(a) General. The power required to circulate the gas through the machine and ventilating system, if one is provided, whether by self-contained or external fans, shall be charged against the machine, except as specified below.

(g) (**2.112**) **Core Loss.** The core loss shall be taken as the difference in power required to drive the machine at normal speed, when excited to produce a voltage at the terminals corresponding to the calculated internal voltage, and the power required to drive the unexcited machine at the same speed.

The internal voltage shall be determined by correcting the rated terminal voltage for the resistance drop only.

(h) (**2.113**) **Armature I^2R Loss.** The armature I^2R loss shall be the product of the resistance (in ohms) of the armature winding, as measured with direct current and corrected to 75°C, and the square of the armature current (in amperes).

(i) (**2.114**) **Series-field Windings**[1] I^2R **Loss.** The series-field windings I^2R loss shall be the product of the measured resistance (in ohms) of the field windings, corrected to 75°C, and the square of the current (in amperes) in the series-connected field windings. The I^2R loss at 75°C of any shunts used across these fields shall be included.

(j) (**2.115**) **Brush-contact Loss.** A voltage drop for all brushes of each polarity shall be used in determining brush-contact loss as follows:

Carbon and graphite brushes, shunts attached.........	1 volt
Carbon and graphite brushes, without shunts..........	1½ volts
Metal-graphite brushes, shunts attached..............	¼ volt

The drop shall be taken the same for all loads.

(k) (**2.116**) **Stray-load Loss.** The stray-load losses shall be taken as one per cent of the ouput.

(a) *Shunt Field.* The loss in the winding itself is readily determined by measuring the current with an ammeter and the voltage across the winding with a voltmeter. Furthermore, it may be agreed to include the rheostat loss with that of the field. The shunt-field loss

$$P_f = VI_f, \qquad (362)$$

where V is either the voltage across the winding or that across the winding and rheostat.

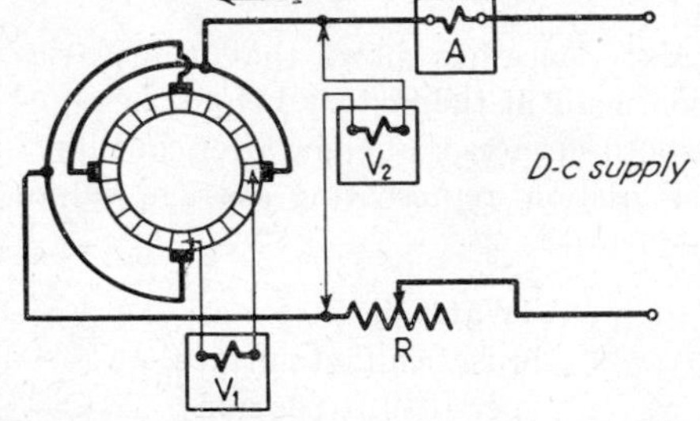

Fig. 415. Measurement of armature resistance.

(h) *Armature.* The resistance of the armature is frequently measured by the voltmeter-ammeter method (p. 155). Typical connections are shown in Fig. 415. The resistor R is inserted to limit the current to the stationary armature. If the requirements of (h) are to be met, the resistance of the armature *copper* only should be measured. Accordingly, the low-reading voltmeter V_1 is connected to the commutator segments which are directly under brushes of opposite polarity. Thus, the brush and brush-contact resistances are excluded. It is desirable to make measurements with the armature in three or four different positions.

In many tests, however, it is not necessary to separate the armature-copper resistance and the brush and brush-contact resistance, but all these resistances may be combined into a single resistance. Under these conditions the voltmeter, such as V_2, may be connected to the machine terminals, Fig. 415. Again, it is desirable to make measurements with the armature in three or four different positions in order to obtain an

[1] Includes commutating-field winding.

average resistance. As the low-reading scale of the voltmeter is used ordinarily in making this measurement, the instrument may be injured on opening the circuit, owing to the emf of self-induction of the armature. Also, poor contact between the commutator and brushes might put full line voltage across the low-reading voltmeter V_2. Therefore, either voltmeter should be disconnected when the circuit is opened or closed and also when the armature is turned.

351. Core Loss. The core loss under (g) is the eddy-current and hysteresis loss in the iron of the dynamo produced by the changes in the direction and the magnitude of the flux which result from the relative motion between armature and field. A large proportion of the core loss occurs in the armature iron.

A. Eddy Currents. As the armature iron rotates in the same magnetic field as the copper conductors, emfs are also induced in it. Iron is a good conductor of electricity, and were the iron a solid mass, Fig. 416(*a*), the current paths would be short and of large cross section. Hence,

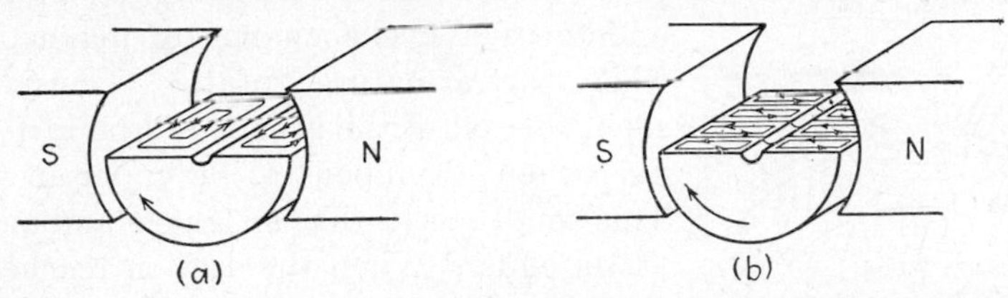

FIG. 416. Eddy currents in armature iron without and with laminations.

under these conditions large currents would be induced in the armature iron. These currents would produce so great a power loss that the armature would overheat even without any useful load. By laminating the armature iron, Fig. 416(*b*), the paths of these currents are broken up by the insulating effect of the oxides on the surfaces of the laminations, and the magnitudes of the eddy currents are reduced. A study of Fig. 416(*b*) shows that the length of the path for each eddy current is in the direction of the laminations and the cross section of the current path, which is determined by the thickness of the laminations, is only a very small fraction of that in (*a*). Thus the laminations not only break up the paths of the eddy currents shown in (*a*), but the resistance of the paths is greatly increased. Hence, the eddy currents and the resulting loss are greatly reduced. Although silicon steel has less eddy-current, as well as hysteresis, loss, dynamo steel, Fig. 202 (p. 258), is used for rotating machinery because of its better mechanical characteristics, silicon steel being somewhat brittle; also, dynamo steel is less expensive. The thickness of laminations for dynamos is usually 0.0172 in. and is much less proportionally than is indicated in Fig. 416(*b*) [see Eq. (177), p. 268].

Note that although the laminations break up the eddy-current paths, they do not interpose reluctance in the magnetic circuit, since their direction is the same as that of the magnetic flux. Because of the oxides on the surfaces of the laminations the ratio of net iron to the total volume of the laminations is about 0.9.

Eddy currents are proportional to both speed and flux. As the loss varies as the square of the current (I^2R), *eddy-current loss varies as the square of both speed and flux.*

Example. The eddy-current loss in a dynamo is 600 watts when the total flux is 2,000,000 maxwells per pole and the speed is 800 rpm. Determine the loss when the flux is increased to 2,500,000 maxwells and the speed is increased to 1,200 rpm.

$$P_e = 600 \cdot \left(\frac{2,500,000}{2,000,000}\right)^2 \cdot \left(\frac{1,200}{800}\right)^2 = 2,109 \text{ watts. } \textit{Ans.}$$

B. Hysteresis. It is shown in Chap. VIII that when iron is carried through a cycle of magnetization (Sec. 194, p. 265) an energy loss results proportional to the area of the hysteresis loop. The iron in an armature undergoes a cyclic change of magnetization when the armature rotates. Consider the small section of the armature iron at (*a*), Fig. 417, when it happens to be under an *N* pole. This small section has an *n* pole and an *s* pole at its ends. When the section reaches position (*b*), its poles have become reversed, as shown. Practically all the armature iron is continually going through similar cycles of magnetic reversals. Therefore, there results a hysteresis loss in the armature iron as the armature rotates. This loss is directly proportional to the speed and is proportional to the 1.6 power of the maximum flux density, by the Steinmetz formula [Eq. (176), p. 266]. *Laminating the iron does not affect the hysteresis loss.*

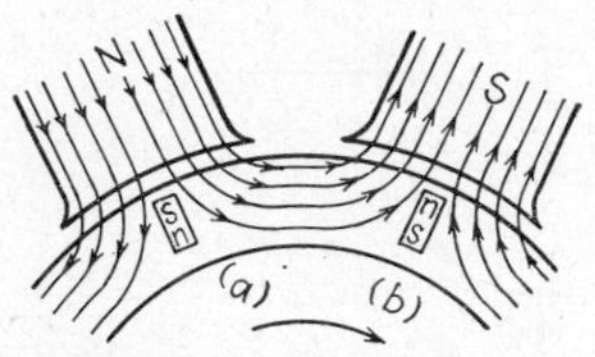

FIG. 417. Reversal of magnetic flux in armature iron.

C. Pole-face Loss. The flux enters and leaves the armature in tufts through the teeth as has already been shown, Figs. 194 and 195 (pp. 246 and 247). As these tufts of flux pass across the pole face, they produce flux pulsations in the pole face. These pulsations induce eddy currents in the pole face, in the manner shown in Fig. 418. This results in a power loss. Hysteresis loss also accompanies these flux pulsations. The eddy-current loss is reduced by laminating the pole faces (see Fig. 304, p. 399). However, the flux pulsations penetrate more deeply into the

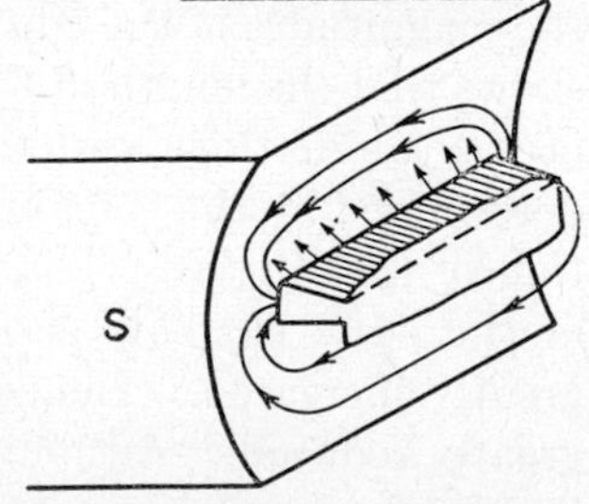

FIG. 418. Pole-face loss due to tufts of flux from teeth.

laminated pole cores than with solid cores, for with the latter the eddy currents have a screening effect.

Note that the foregoing core losses are a function of both flux and speed. They are also supplied mechanically in that they produce a torque which opposes rotation.

352. Efficiency. The efficiency of a machine is the ratio of output to input. Thus,

$$\text{Efficiency} = \frac{\text{output}}{\text{input}}. \tag{363}$$

This may be written also in either of the following ways:

$$\text{Efficiency} = \frac{\text{output}}{\text{output} + \text{losses}}. \tag{364}$$

$$\text{Efficiency} = \frac{\text{input} - \text{losses}}{\text{input}}. \tag{365}$$

Therefore, if the losses in a machine be known, the efficiency may be found for any given input or output.

As electrical rather than mechanical quantities are ordinarily used in efficiency determinations, (364) is used for generators (output is electrical) and (365) for motors (input is electrical).

Efficiency can be determined by measuring simultaneously the output and input and taking the ratio [(363)]. However, this is often difficult and impracticable. Although with a generator it is a simple matter to measure the output with electrical instruments, it is difficult to measure the input since this involves the measurement of torque. If an electrical dynamometer (p. 520) happens to be available, the measurement is simplified but such dynamometers ordinarily are special equipment. With motors, the input is readily measured with electrical instruments and the output can be measured by means of a prony brake (p. 516) or a dynamometer. However, except in the smaller ratings it is difficult to absorb the energy in a prony brake, and again a dynamometer is special equipment, with a rating limited to 100 hp. With either motor or generator, particularly with the larger ratings, it is frequently impossible to supply and absorb the energy involved in the test.

Moreover, when (363) is used, any percentage error in either output or input produces an equal percentage error in the efficiency. Since the efficiency of electrical apparatus is high, there is usually little difference between output and input and (363) does not give high precision. In both (364) and (365), except at light loads, the losses are small compared with either the output or the input, and any percentage error in the losses affects the efficiency by only a fraction of this percentage. Hence, in most cases (364) or (365) is to be preferred in the determination of the efficiency of electrical apparatus.

Example. The current to a shunt motor is 37.5 amp at 230 volts. The total motor losses are 1,180 watts. Determine efficiency.

Using (365)

$$\eta = \frac{(230 \cdot 37.5) - 1{,}180}{230 \cdot 37.5}$$

$$= \frac{8{,}625 - 1{,}180}{8{,}625} = 0.862, \text{ or } 86.2\%. \quad \textit{Ans.}$$

353. Efficiency from Losses. To illustrate the determination of efficiency from losses, the following example is given: D-c compound generator, long-shunt, 12 kw, 240 volts, 1,200 rpm. At 75°C, shunt-field resistance 210 ohms, armature resistance 0.252 ohm; commutating-field resistance 0.033 ohm, series-field resistance 0.0293 ohm. The friction and windage (*d*) and the brush-friction losses (*e*) are combined. The rheostat loss (*b*) will be included in the shunt-field loss (*a*). There are no exciter losses (*c*) or ventilating losses (*f*).

The data for output, losses, and input are given in Table II. The load was adjusted to values of current in column (1), and the corresponding terminal voltages are given in (2). The product of (1) and (2) gives the output in watts (3). The shunt-field resistance is 210 ohms, and the field current, I_f in (4), was determined by dividing (2) by 210. Column (5) gives the shunt-field-circuit loss. The armature current, as well as the commutating-field current and the series-field current, each equal to I_a, is found by adding (1) and (4). The internal emf E in (7) is assumed arbitrarily to be the sum of (2) and the product of I_a and the sum of R_a, R_c, R_s.[1] The armature, commutating-field, and series-field losses are given in (8), (9), (10). The brush-contact loss P_B (11) is obtained by multiplying the brush contact drop of 2 volts [see (j), 2.115] by I_a. The stray-load loss P_{SL} (12) is 1 per cent of the output.

The core loss was determined from the differences in output of a small motor when driving the generator with the field excited and then with it unexcited. The core loss at any one load is the no-load core loss thus measured when the generator is excited so that the no-load emf is the same as the calculated internal, or induced, emf [column (7)], at the given load. The friction and windage plus brush friction P_{FW} were determined from the difference in power output of a small motor, which drove the generator first with the generator connected to it mechanically with the brushes pressing on the commutator and then with the generator disconnected. The total loss P_{LS} (15) is the sum of columns (5), (8), (9), (10), (11), (12),

[1] In accordance with ASA Standard C50 the brush-contact voltage is not included in the determination of E in (7).

TABLE II. GENERATOR LOSSES AND EFFICIENCY

I	V	VI	I_f	VI_f	I_a	E	$I_a{}^2R_a$	$I_a{}^2R_c$	$I_a{}^2R_s$	P_B	P_{SL}	P_{CL}	P_{FW}	P_{LS}	P_{IN}	Eff
(1)	(2)	(3)	(4)	(5)	(6)	(7)	(8)	(9)	(10)	(11)	(12)	(13)	(14)	(15)	(16)	(17)
70	235.0	16,450	1.119	263.0	71.12	257.4	1,274.6	166.9	148.1	142.2	164.5	153.2	256.6	2,569.1	19,019	0.865
60	238.0	14,280	1.133	270.0	61.13	257.2	941.7	123.3	109.5	122.3	142.8	133.0	256.6	2,099.2	16,379	0.872
50	240.0	12,000	1.143	274.3	51.14	256.1	658.9	86.3	76.6	102.3	120.0	152.0	256.6	1,727.0	13,727	0.874
40	241.8	9,672	1.151	278.3	41.15	254.7	426.6	55.9	49.6	82.3	96.7	150.6	256.6	1,396.6	11,069	0.874
35	242.0	8,470	1.152	278.8	36.15	253.4	329.4	43.1	38.3	72.3	84.7	149.4	256.6	1,252.6	9,723	0.871
30	242.3	7,269	1.154	279.6	31.15	253.1	244.5	32.0	28.4	62.3	72.7	149.0	256.6	1,125.1	8,394	0.866
25	242.0	6,050	1.152	278.8	26.15	250.7	172.3	22.6	20.0	52.3	60.5	146.6	256.6	1,009.7	7,060	0.857
20	241.5	4,830	1.150	277.7	21.15	248.1	112.7	14.8	13.1	42.3	48.3	144.0	256.6	909.5	5,740	0.841
15	240.0	3,600	1.143	274.3	16.14	245.1	65.6	8.6	7.6	32.3	36.0	141.0	256.6	817.0	4,417	0.815
10	238.2	2,382	1.134	270.1	11.13	241.7	31.2	4.1	3.6	22.3	23.8	137.6	256.6	749.3	3,131	0.761
5	237.0	1,185	1.129	267.6	6.13	238.8	9.5	1.2	1.1	12.3	23.2	134.6	256.6	706.1	1,891	0.626
0	236.0	0	1.124	265.2	1.12	236.4	0.3	.....	.....	2.2	23.6	132.5	256.6	680.4	680	0

TABLE III. MOTOR LOSSES AND EFFICIENCY

V	I	VI	I_f	VI_f	I_a	E	$I_a{}^2R_a$	$I_a{}^2R_s$	P_B	P_{SL}	P_{CL}	P_{FW}	P_{LS}	P_{OU}, watts	P_{OU}, hp	Eff
(1)	(2)	(3)	(4)	(5)	(6)	(7)	(8)	(9)	(10)	(11)	(12)	(13)	(14)	(15)	(16)	(17)
240	50	12,000	1.085	260.4	48.91	226.1	602.8	78.9	97.8	104.6	120.0	256.6	1,521.1	10,479	14.05	0.873

I, Amperes output for generator, input for motor; V, terminal voltage; VI, output or input; I_f, shunt-field current; VI_f, shunt-field-circuit loss; I_a, armature, commutating-field, series-field current; E, internal emf; R_a, armature resistance; R_c, commutating-field resistance; R_s, series-field resistance; P_B, power in brush-contact resistance; P_{SL}, stray-loss power; P_{CL}, core-loss power; P_{FW}, brush-friction and windage power; P_{LS}, total losses; P_{IN}, power input; P_{OU}, power output. All quantities are in mks, or practical, units.

(13), (14). The power input P_{IN} (16) is the sum of (3) and (15). The efficiency Eff (17) is (3) divided by (16).

The measured values of the armature resistance and of the shunt-, commutating-, and series-field resistances were corrected to 75°C (see 2.104, p. 523).

Example. Compute the losses and efficiency at rated load of 50 amp. Columns (1), (2), (3), Table II, are obvious.

$$I_f = {}^{240}\!/_{210} = 1.143 \text{ amp.}$$

(5) $240 \cdot 1.143 = 274.3$ watts.
(6) $I_a = 50 + 1.14 = 51.14$ amp.
(7) $E = 240 + 51.14(0.252 + 0.033 + 0.0293) = 256.1$ volts [see (g)].
(8) $(51.14)^2 0.252 = 658.9$ watts.
(9) $(51.14)^2 0.033 = 86.3$ watts.
(10) $(51.14)^2 0.0293 = 76.6$ watts.
(11) $51.14 \cdot 2 = 102.3$ watts.
(12) $P_{SL} = 0.01(12{,}000) = 120.0$ watts.
(13) 152 watts (measured when driven by small motor and excited to make $E = 256.1$ volts) [see (g), 2.112].
(14) Measured [see (d) (2.109)(a)].
(15) $P_{LS} = 274.3 + 658.9 + 86.3 + 76.6 + 102.3 + 120.0 + 152.0 + 256.6 = 1{,}727.0$ watts.
(16) $P_{IN} = 12{,}000 + 1{,}727 = 13{,}727$ watts.
(17) Eff $= 12{,}000/13{,}727 = 0.874$.

Losses and Efficiency in Motor. Let it be required to determine the losses and output of the foregoing generator as a shunt motor at rated input of 50 amp at 240 volts as is done in Table III. The shunt-field resistance at 75°C for this condition of motor operation was measured and found to be 221.2 ohms.

To determine the stray-load losses, P_{SL} in (11), it is necessary to employ trial and error since the output is not known until all the losses are known. One trial, however, is ample. The tabulation of data is given in Table III.

Columns (1), (2), (3) are obvious.
(4) $I_f = 240/221.2 = 1.085$ amp.
(5) $VI_f = 240 \cdot 1.085 = 260.4$ watts.
(6) $50 - 1.09 = 48.91$ amp.
(7) $E = 240 - 48.91(0.252 + 0.033) = 240 - 13.9 = 226.1$ volts [see (g) (2.112)].
(8) $(48.91)^2 0.252 = 602.8$ watts.
(9) $(48.91)^2 0.033 = 78.9$ watts.
(10) $48.91 \cdot 2 = 97.8$ watts.
(11) $P_{SL} = 0.01 \cdot 10{,}479 = 104.8$ watts.
(12) $P_{CL} = 120$ watts measured corresponding to 226.1 volts [see (g), 2,112].
(13) P_{FW} (measured) $= 256.6$ watts.
(14) $P_{LS} = 260.4 + 602.8 + 78.9 + 97.8 + 104.8 + 120.0 + 256.6 = 1{,}521.3$ watts.
(15) Power output, $P_{OU} = 12{,}000 - 1{,}521 = 10{,}479$ watts.
(16) Hp $= 10{,}479/746 = 14.05$.
(17) Eff $= 10{,}479/12{,}000 = 0.873$

354. Stray Power. The detailed division of losses given in Sec. 350 (p. 523) is necessary when d-c generators and motors are required to meet ASA standards. Very frequently, however, it is desirable to determine losses and efficiency of some particular machine under actual operating conditions, which usually do not involve temperatures as high as 75°C. Also, the calculation of efficiency can be considerably simplified by combining some of the nonelectrical losses in the ASA schedule (p. 530 *et seq.*).

Note that the losses under (a), (b), (h), (i), (j) are *electrical* losses, and if (b) be excluded, they become copper losses. All the foregoing losses are readily measured with electrical instruments. Usually (c) and (f) can be excluded. Also note that the losses (d), (e), (g) are functions of speed or speed and flux and are supplied *mechanically*. These three losses may be termed *stray power*. It follows that if the speed and flux are the same under two or more conditions of operation, the stray power must also be the same. This fact makes it possible to measure, under no-load conditions, the value of stray power which exists under load conditions. Since the electrical losses are readily calculated, it becomes possible to determine all the losses and thus the output and efficiency of d-c machines.

From Eqs. (364) and (365) (p. 527), efficiencies are as follows:

For a generator,

$$\eta = \frac{VI}{VI + I_a^2R_a + I_C^2R_C + I_S^2R_S + \text{S.P.} + P_{SL}}. \tag{366}$$

For a motor,

$$\eta = \frac{VI - (I_a^2R_a + I_C^2R_C + I_S^2R_S + \text{S.P.} + P_{SL})}{VI}. \tag{367}$$

where V is the terminal volts, I the line current, I_a the armature current, R_a the armature resistance including brush-contact resistance, I_C and R_C the commutating-field current and resistance, I_S and R_S the series-field current and resistance, S.P. the stray power, and P_{SL} the stray-load loss.

Example. A 250-kw 230-volt compound generator is delivering 800 amp at 230 volts. The shunt-field current is 12 amp. The armature resistance is 0.007 ohm, and the series-field resistance is 0.002 ohm. The stray power at this load is 5,500 watts. The generator is connected long-shunt. Determine generator efficiency at this load:

Output $= 230 \cdot 800 = 184{,}000$ watts.

Shunt-field loss	$= 230 \cdot 12$	$= 2{,}760$ watts.
Armature loss	$= 812^2 \cdot 0.007$	$= 4{,}615$ watts.
Series-field loss	$= 812^2 \cdot 0.002$	$= 1{,}319$ watts.
Stray power		$= 5{,}500$ watts.
Stray-load loss, $0.01 \cdot 184{,}000$		$= 1{,}840$ watts.
	Total loss	$= 16{,}034$ watts.

$$\text{Eff} = \frac{184{,}000}{184{,}000 + 16{,}034} = \frac{184{,}000}{200{,}034} = 0.920, \text{ or } 92.0\%. \quad \textit{Ans.}$$

355. Measurement of Stray Power. In order to duplicate the stray-power loss, it is necessary merely to duplicate the speed and flux under whatever conditions the machine operates. The speed is readily duplicated. It is not easy to measure the flux directly, but from Eq. (337) (p. 408), where $E = K\phi S$,

$$\phi = \frac{1}{K}\left(\frac{E}{S}\right). \tag{368}$$

Hence, if E/S is duplicated under two or more conditions, the flux must be the same in each.

To measure stray power, the machine, whether it be a motor or a generator, is run light (without load) as a motor, as in Fig. 419. The field, in series with a rheostat, is connected across the line.

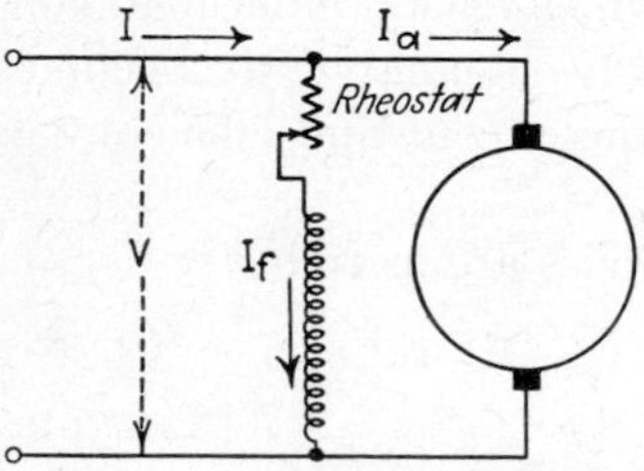

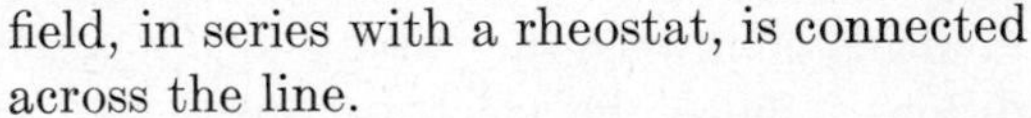

FIG. 419. Determination of stray power in a dynamo.

The total power input to the machine is

$$VI = V(I_a + I_f) = VI_a + VI_f$$

where V is the terminal voltage, I the line current, I_a the armature current, and I_f the field current.

The total power input VI is distributed as follows: Part goes to supply the field loss, part supplies the armature $I_a{}^2R_a$ loss, and the remainder is the stray power (S.P.), the output being zero. Therefore,

$$VI_a + VI_f = VI_f + I_a{}^2R_a + \text{S.P.}$$

$$\text{S.P.} = VI_a - I_a{}^2R_a. \tag{369}$$

The *stray power* is equal to the total input to the *armature* minus the armature-resistance loss.

Example. A shunt generator when running light as a motor at 1,000 rpm takes 12 amp from 115-volt mains. The field current is 7 amp, and the armature resistance is 0.03 ohm. Determine stray-power loss of the machine at this particular value of flux and speed.

The armature current $I_a = 12 - 7 = 5$ amp.

The stray power S.P. $= 115 \cdot 5 - (5)^2 0.03 = 575 - 0.75 = 574$ watts. *Ans.*

Note that the armature $I_a{}^2R_a$ loss is practically negligible in this case.

It follows from (368) that if E and S under load conditions be duplicated at no load the flux will be the same. Since stray power is a function of flux and speed, it also follows that the stray power under load and no-load conditions will be the same.

Example. Assume that the foregoing generator is delivering 100 amp at 110 volts and 1,000 rpm. The field current is 7.0 amp. Determine: (*a*) stray power under this condition of load; (*b*) efficiency.

(*a*) The induced emf

$$E = 110 + (107 \cdot 0.03) = 113.2 \text{ volts.}$$
$$S = 1{,}000 \text{ rpm.}$$

To make the adjustments of E and S, the generator is run as a motor, connected as in Fig. 420. The rheostat R is first adjusted so that V_1 is equal to 113.2 volts, the small armature voltage drop under these conditions being negligible. The field rheostat is then adjusted to give a speed of 1,000 rpm. The machine is operating at the same value of speed and flux as it did under the given load. Therefore, the stray power is the same in the two cases. The current I_a is 4.8 amp, and $V_1 = 113.2$ volts. (This neglects the small drop in the armature, $4.8 \cdot 0.03$.) The stray power

$$\text{S.P.} = 113.2 \cdot 4.8 - (4.8)^2 0.03 = 542.7 \text{ watts.} \quad \textit{Ans.}$$

(*b*) From (366) (p. 531),

$$\text{Output under load} = 110 \cdot 100 = 11{,}000 \text{ watts.}$$

$$I_a{}^2R_a = (100 + 7)^2 0.03 = 343.5 \text{ watts.}$$
$$VI_f = 110 \cdot 7 = 770.0 \text{ watts.}$$
$$\text{S.P.} = 542.7 \text{ watts.}$$
$$\text{Stray-load loss, } P_{SL} = 0.01 \cdot 11{,}000 = 110.0 \text{ watts.}$$
$$\text{Total losses} = 1{,}766.2 \text{ watts.}$$

$$\eta = \frac{11{,}000}{11{,}000 + 1{,}766} = \frac{11{,}000}{12{,}766} = 0.862, \text{ or } 86.2\%. \quad \textit{Ans.}$$

356. Stray Power as Function of Flux and Speed. It is shown (p. 531) that stray power is a function of speed and flux. At no load, the flux is a function of field current. However, only at no load can flux be considered as a function of field current. Because of hysteresis, even under these conditions there can be different values of flux for a given value of field current. Also, when a machine is under load, the flux is a function not only of field current but of armature reaction as well. Accordingly, it is more accurate to determine the value of flux from Eq. (368) (p. 532), in which $\phi = (1/K)(E/S)$.

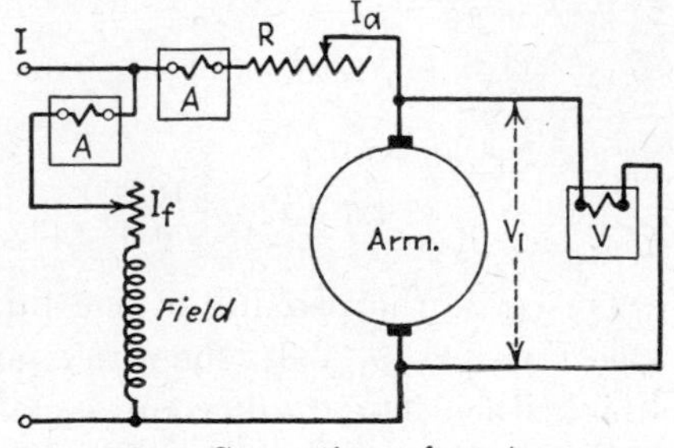

Fig. 420. Connections for stray-power measurement.

For any given machine, K is constant. Hence, the stray power is a function of E/S and S; that is,

$$\text{S.P.} = f'\left(\frac{E}{S}, S\right). \tag{370}$$

If the ratio E/S and S are the same for two different operating conditions, the stray power must be the same, neglecting the changes in the shape of the flux-distribution curve which account for a part of the stray-load losses. The following example illustrates the application of (370):

Example. A 20-kw 220-volt shunt generator, having an armature resistance of 0.096 ohm, is delivering 85 amp at 222 volts. Its speed is 920 rpm, and the field current is 2.24 amp. Determine: (*a*) no-load conditions under which generator must be operated (as motor) in order that its no-load stray power may be equal to that which exists under given conditions of operation; (*b*) value of stray power if armature input at no load is 4.02 amp at 230.4 volts; (*c*) efficiency of generator under given operating conditions.

(*a*)
$$E = 222 + (85 + 2.24)0.096 = 230.4 \text{ volts.}$$
$$\frac{E}{S} = \frac{230.4}{920} = 0.250.$$

Although the dynamo is a generator, it is operated as a motor to determine its stray power. The connections are shown in Fig. 420. The *field* rheostat is adjusted until the terminal voltage divided by the speed is equal to 0.250. The armature-resistance drop is negligible at no load. The speed is then adjusted by means of the *armature* rheostat R until it is 920 rpm. Changing the armature rheostat does not change the flux and hence does not change the ratio E/S.

(*b*) From Eq. (369), the stray power is

$$\text{S.P.} = 230.4 \cdot 4.02 - (4.02)^2 0.096 = 926.2 \text{ watts.} \quad \textit{Ans.}$$

(See Fig. 421)

(*c*) Output = 222 · 85 = 18,870 watts.

$$I_a{}^2R_a = (85 + 2.24)^2 0.096 = 730.7 \text{ watts.}$$
$$VI_f = 222 \cdot 2.24 = 497.3 \text{ watts.}$$
$$\text{S.P.} = 926.2 \text{ watts.}$$
$$\text{Stray-load loss, } 0.01 \cdot 18,870 = 188.7 \text{ watts.}$$
$$\text{Total losses} = 2,342.9 \text{ watts.}$$

$$\text{Eff } \eta = \frac{18,870}{18,870 + 2,343} = 0.882, \text{ or } 88.2\%. \quad \textit{Ans.}$$

Owing to the peaking of the flux curve caused by armature reaction (see Fig. 329, p. 423), the stray-power loss will be slightly greater than it is with a flat-top flux curve, even though the total areas under the two curves are the same. This is due to the fact that the stray-power losses are not directly proportional to the flux density but vary to a power higher than the first power.

357. Stray-power Curves with Constant Flux. Let it be required to plot a series of stray-power curves covering the maximum probable range of operation of a dynamo as both motor and generator. Stray power is a function of two quantities, S and E/S, or flux. In order to plot the complete function in a plane, it is customary to hold one of the quantities at some constant value while the other is varied. The first quantity is then held constant at some other value while the second again is varied. This procedure is repeated until the desired range of operation is obtained.

With stray power, it is convenient to maintain the flux E/S constant and to determine the stray power as a function of speed S, Fig. 421. Usually, three curves for three different values of flux are sufficient. The range of operation depends on the particular conditions under which the dynamo is to be operated.

The maximum value of flux occurs when E is a maximum and S is a minimum. E is a maximum for generator operation at overload.

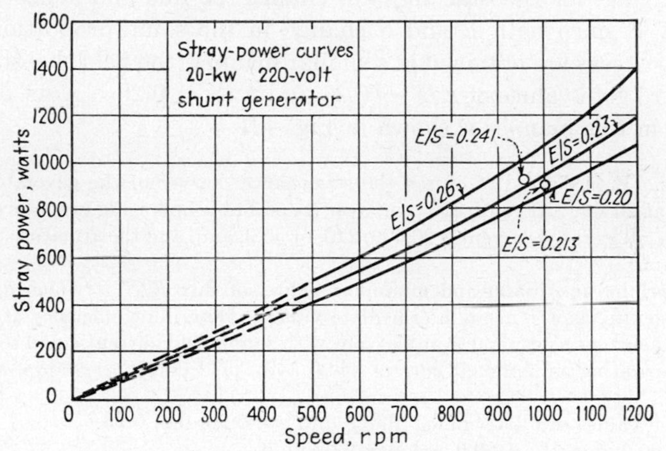

FIG. 421. Stray power as function of flux and speed.

Assume 25 per cent overload. The rated current is 90.9 amp. Assume 2 amp for the field current.

$$E_1 = 220 + (113.6 + 2)(0.096) = 231.1 \text{ volts.}$$

The dynamo probably will not operate at less than 900 rpm. Hence, the maximum value of flux is determined by

$$\frac{E}{S} = \frac{231.1}{900} = 0.26 \text{ (nearly).}$$

The minimum value of flux occurs when E is a minimum and S is a maximum. E is a minimum under motor operation at overload. Assume 25 per cent overload.

$$E = 220 - 116(0.096) = 209.0 \text{ volts (nearly).}$$

Assume that the motor speed will not exceed 1,050 rpm. Hence, the minimum value of flux is determined by

$$\frac{E}{S} = \frac{209.0}{1{,}050} = 0.2 \text{ (nearly).}$$

An intermediate value of flux would be determined by $E/S = 0.23$.

To obtain the three curves, the connections of Fig. 420 are used, the machine being operated as a motor in all the stray-power tests. It may be necessary to excite the field from a source greater than 220 volts in order to obtain the maximum value of flux.

The field rheostat is adjusted until $E/S = 0.26$, and a run is made with varying speed. The speed is varied by means of the armature rheostat R. Changing this rheostat does not change the flux and hence does not change E/S since both E and S change in the same proportion. The other two curves are obtained in a similar manner, the field rheostat being adjusted to give values of $E/S = 0.23$ and $E/S = 0.20$. A set of curves obtained in this manner is shown in Fig. 421.

Example. It is desired to obtain the stray-power curves of the generator of Sec. 356, rated at 20 kw, 220 volts, 920 rpm, over its probable operating range as generator and motor. The rated current is 20,000/220, or 90.9, amp and the armature resistance is 0.096 ohm.

(*a*) Determine maximum and minimum values of flux E/S at which dynamo is likely to operate, as well as an intermediate value. Determine efficiency at (*b*) rated voltage and current as generator at 950 rpm with shunt-field current equal to 1.8 amp; (*c*) when operating as motor at current of 80 amp, field current 1.5 amp, and speed 1,000 rpm.

(*a*) These values are determined above and are 0.26, 0.2, 0.23.

(*b*) $I = 90.9$ amp; $I_a = 90.9 + 1.8 = 92.7$ amp.

$E = 220 + 92.7 \cdot 0.096 = 228.9$ volts.

$E/S = 228.9/950 = 0.241$

Interpolating between curves $E/S = 0.23$ and 0.26 on the 950-rpm ordinate, Fig. 421, S.P. = 920 watts. From (366),

$$(92.7)^2 0.096 = 824.9 \text{ watts.}$$
$$220 \cdot 1.8 = 396.0 \text{ watts.}$$
$$\text{S.P.} = 920.0 \text{ watts.}$$
$$P_{SL} = 0.01(20{,}000) = 200.0 \text{ watts}$$
$$\text{Total loss} = 2{,}340.9 \text{ watts.}$$

$$\text{Eff} = \frac{20{,}000}{20{,}000 + 2{,}341} = 0.895, \text{ or } 89.5\%. \quad \textit{Ans.}$$

(*c*) $I_a = 80 - 1.5 = 78.5$ amp.

$E = 220 - 78.5 \cdot 0.096 = 212.5$ volts.

$E/S = 212.5/1{,}000 = 0.2125$ or 0.213 (nearly).

Interpolating between curves $E/S = 0.20$ and 0.23 on the 1,000-rpm ordinate, Fig. 421, S.P. = 900 watts.

$$(78.5)^2 0.096 = 591.6 \text{ watts.}$$
$$220 \cdot 1.5 = 330.0 \text{ watts.}$$
$$\text{S.P.} = 900.0 \text{ watts.}$$
$$P_{SL} = 0.01(15{,}622) = 156.2^* \text{ watts.}$$
$$\text{Total} = 1{,}977.8 \text{ watts.}$$

* Trial and error.

From (367),

$$\text{Input} = 220 \cdot 80 = 17{,}600 \text{ watts.}$$
$$\text{Output} = 17{,}600 - 1{,}978 = 15{,}622 \text{ watts.}$$
$$\text{Eff} = \frac{15{,}622}{17{,}600} = 0.888, \text{ or } 88.8\%. \quad \textit{Ans.}$$

Since stray power is a small proportion of the total input of a dynamo, errors in its determination produce much smaller proportionate errors in the efficiency.

358. Opposition Test—Kapp Method. The objection to the foregoing stray-power methods of measuring losses is that the dynamo is not under load when the losses are being measured, so that their values may be in error. If two similar dynamos are available, their losses may be determined when both dynamos are loaded, and yet the power source supplies only the *losses* of the two dynamos. The connections for making such a test are shown in Fig. 422.

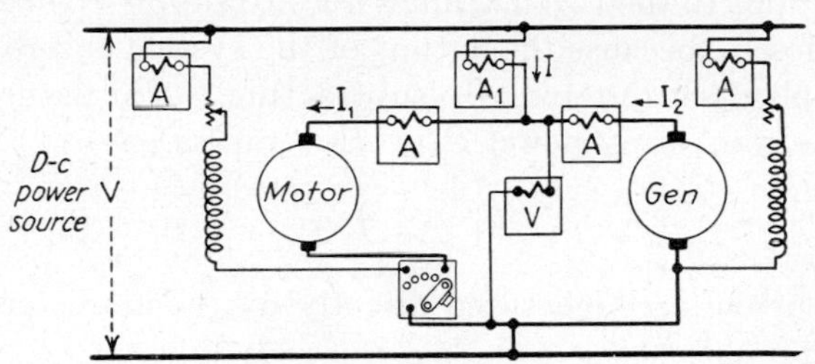

Fig. 422. Kapp opposition method for determining losses.

The two similar dynamos are coupled together mechanically and are then connected to the line, as shown. The motor should have a starting box. Five ammeters are used, one in each field, one in each armature circuit, and one in the line supplying the two armatures. The fields are connected directly to the line so that their currents are not indicated by the ammeter A_1.

The operation of the set is as follows: The motor supplies mechanical power to the generator. This in turn supplies electrical power to the motor. The power delivered by the generator is less than that required by the motor, owing to the losses in the two machines. Therefore, this deficit must be made up by the line which supplies the current I.

The total input to the two armatures is VI.

This power is distributed as follows:

Motor-armature loss $= I_1^2R_1$.
Generator-armature loss $= I_2^2R_2$.
Motor stray power.
Generator stray power.

R_1 and R_2 are the resistances of motor and generator armature, including brush-contact resistances.

As the generator field is necessarily stronger than that of the motor because it requires the higher internal voltage, its stray power will be greater than that of the motor, as stray power increases with increase of flux. As a close approximation, the total stray-power loss may be divided between the two machines in proportion to their induced emfs.

Let E_1 equal the motor induced emf and E_2 the generator induced emf.

$$E_1 = V - I_1R_1.$$
$$E_2 = V + I_2R_2.$$

Let P_1 and P_2 be the values of stray power in the two machines. Then,

$$\frac{P_1}{P_2} = \frac{E_1}{E_2}. \tag{371}$$

The total input to the two machines goes to supply their armature and stray-power losses, because the output of the system is zero and the field power is supplied separately. By subtracting the armature losses from the input, the total stray power $P_1 + P_2$ remains.
That is,

$$P_1 + P_2 = VI - I_1^2R_1 - I_2^2R_2. \tag{372}$$

The field currents are measured directly by the ammeter in each field circuit.

The advantages of this method are that each dynamo is operating under load conditions so that the stray-load losses are included in the measurement; the regulation of each dynamo may be determined; the power source needs supply only the losses.

The principal disadvantage is that the method requires two similar dynamos. The assumptions made in regard to the stray-power distribution may be slightly in error.

The dynamos are brought into operation by first starting the motor, using the starting box. Then the generator voltage is made equal to the motor terminal voltage, and the generator terminals are connected directly across the motor terminals, exactly as generators are connected in parallel. Care should be taken that the polarity is correct. The generator field is strengthened and the motor field weakened until the desired conditions of load and speed are obtained.

Example. Two similar 120-volt 7.5-hp. motors are connected in the manner shown in Fig. 422. The armature resistance of each is 0.12 ohm. The fields are adjusted so that the motor current I_1 is 57 amp, and the generator current I_2 is 45 amp. Under these conditions the power source is supplying a current I of 12 amp at 120 volts. Determine stray power of each machine under these conditions.

Power supplied by line,

$$P = 120 \cdot 12 = 1{,}440 \text{ watts.}$$
$$I_1^2R_1 = 57^2 \cdot 0.12 = 390 \text{ watts.}$$
$$I_2^2R_2 = 45^2 \cdot 0.12 = 243 \text{ watts.}$$
$$\text{Total} = 633 \text{ watts.}$$

Total stray power = 1,440 − 633 = 807 watts.

$$E_1 = 120 - (57 \cdot 0.12) = 113.2 \text{ volts.}$$
$$E_2 = 120 + (45 \cdot 0.12) = 125.4 \text{ volts.}$$

The motor stray power

$$P_1 = \frac{113.2}{113.2 + 125.4} 807 = 383 \text{ watts.} \quad \textit{Ans.}$$

The generator stray power

$$P_2 = \frac{125.4}{113.2 + 125.4} 807 = 424 \text{ watts.} \quad \textit{Ans.}$$

Knowing the stray power and the armature and field losses, the efficiency is readily calculated.

359. Performance of D-C Machines. The accompanying tables give efficiencies and other performance data of d-c machines. The data are typical but do not necessarily represent the performance of all machines having these ratings.

PERFORMANCE OF D-C MOTORS
(Westinghouse Electric Corporation)

Hp	Speed, rpm	Wt, lb	Eff, %, Load ½	Eff, %, Load ¾	Eff, %, Load Full
¾	1,150	85	69	74	75
¾	1,750	85	71	75	76
1	1,750	85	72	75	77
2	1,750	155	74	79	81
3	1,750	165	77	81	82
5	1,750	195	77	80	83
10	1,750	545	82	85	86
25	1,750	980	84.5	86.5	87.5
50	850	1,830	84.0	87	89
100	850	2,925	88	89	90.5

COMPOUND-WOUND GENERATORS WITH COMMUTATING POLES, 1,750 RPM

Kw	Volts	Amp	Eff, % Load ½	¾	Full
5	125	40	77.0	80.5	82.0
10	125	80	80.0	83.0	85.0
25	125	200	84.0	86.5	88.0
50	125	400	83.0	86.0	88.0
100	125	800	87.0	88.5	90.0
200	125	1,600	88.0	90.5	91.0
400	250	1,600	91.7	91.9	91.7
1,000	250	4,000	92.1	92.6	92.1

DISTRIBUTION OF LOSSES, CONSTANT-SPEED STABILIZED SHUNT MOTORS, 230 VOLTS, 1,750 RPM
(General Electric Company)

	Loss, watts					
	Horsepower					
	1½	3	5	10	25	60
Shunt field	52	75	90	105	220	240
Friction and windage	25	40	60	130	420	570
Brush friction	10	25	35	70	180	375
Core loss	40	70	130	245	590	895
Armature	90	150	240	340	425	1,000
Commutating field	20	30	50	70	130	330
Brush contact	10	25	35	75	180	425
Stray-load loss*	11	22	37	75	187	448
Total losses	258	437	677	1,110	2,332	4,283

* Conventional value—not test.

360. Ratings and Heating. Practically all power apparatus, whether it be steam engines, gas engines, or dynamos, has a definite power rating. The rating is determined by the manufacturer and is supposed to give the power which the apparatus can safely or efficiently deliver under specified conditions. It is interesting to consider what, in general, determines the rating of various power devices.

Both a steam engine and a steam turbine are usually rated at the load for which their *efficiency* is a maximum. These two types of prime mover can carry a large overload without difficulty but at reduced efficiency.

Owing to the excessive weights and costs, large gas engines are usually rated as high as possible, which is near the point at which they cease to operate. Their thermal efficiency is ordinarily so much greater than that of the steam engine or turbine that the question of weight is more important than the question of efficiency.

Electrical apparatus is usually rated at the load which it can carry without *overheating*. *Commutation* may at times limit the output of d-c machines.

When organic insulation, which is used almost entirely for the insulation of electrical machinery, is subjected to higher temperatures, it deteriorates with time, both electrically and mechanically. In time the insulation becomes dry and brittle, which usually results ultimately in physical disintegration. There is direct correlation between electrical strength and mechanical strength.

Insulation does not usually fail immediately on reaching a critical temperature, but only when the gradual mechanical deterioration impairs the electrical strength so that it falls below the critical value. Insulation life is also dependent to a considerable extent on the access of oxygen, moisture, dirt, and chemicals.[1]

The temperature limits on which the rating of electrical machines and apparatus is based are largely determined by the character of the insulating materials used. For the purpose of establishing temperature limits, insulating materials are classified into five categories in Table 4-60 of AIEE Standard No. 1. Of the five categories the temperature limits of only classes A and B have been specified for electrical machines.[2]

2.052 *Class A Insulation Defined.*[2] Class A insulation consists of: (1) cotton, silk, paper, and similar organic materials, when either impregnated or immersed in a liquid dielectric; (2) molded and laminated materials with cellulose filler, phenolic resins, and other resins of similar properties; (3) films and sheets of cellulose acetate and other cellulose derivatives of similar properties; and (4) varnishes (enamel) as applied to conductors.

2.053 *Class B Insulation Defined.*[2] Class B insulation consists of mica, asbestos, fiber glass, and similar inorganic materials, in built-up form with organic binding substances. A small proportion of Class A materials may be used for structural purposes only.

From the results of experience and laboratory tests, limiting temperatures, called "hottest spot temperatures," have been assigned to the various insulating materials. These values of hottest spot temperatures for the different insulation classifications are given in Table 4-61 of AIEE

[1] For complete discussion see AIEE Standard No. 1, "General Principles upon Which Temperature Limits Are Based in the Rating of Electrical Machinery and Apparatus," June, 1947.

[2] ASA Standard C50-1943, p. 9. See footnote, p. 522.

Standard No. 1. These values are useful as a point of reference in selecting the observable temperature rise in standards for rating and testing.

For class A the limiting value of temperature, or hottest spot, is 105°C and for class B, 130°C. With 40°C ambient temperature the limiting rise for class A is 65°C and for class B is 90°C.

In ASA Standard C50-1943, "Table 1—Limiting Observable Temperature Rise," of which Table IV is an abridgment, are given the limiting temperatures for different parts of machines, such as armature windings, field windings, cores, etc., for the class A and class B insulation. The method of temperature measurement is also included. There are two methods specified, thermometer and resistance methods. In the thermometer method (2.054) temperature is determined by mercury or alcohol thermometers, by resistance thermometers, or by thermocouples, any of these instruments being applied to the hottest part of the machine accessible to the mercury or alcohol thermometer.

TABLE IV. LIMITING OBSERVABLE TEMPERATURE RISE, °C

Machine part	Method of temperature determination	General-purpose generators, motors, and generators for electrolytic service, class A*	Totally enclosed fan-cooled, explosion-proof, waterproof, etc., dust-tight, etc., motors		Generators having a nominal rating at end of 2-hr overload	
			Class A*	Class B*	Class A*	Class B*
Armature and all windings other than field and bare copper	Thermometer	40	55	75	55	75
Shunt-field windings	Thermometer	40	..	..	55	75
	Resistance	50	60	80	65	85
Cores and mechanical parts in contact or adjacent to insulation	Thermometer	40	..	..	55	75

* Insulation.

The bulbs of thermometers must be covered by felt pads cemented to the machine, or by oil putty, cotton waste, or other material suitable for the purpose, applied in such a way as not to interfere with the normal ventilation of the machine (2.056).

361. Resistance Method. In the resistance method the temperature is determined by comparison of the resistance to be determined with the resistance at a known temperature (2.055). This method is given in

Chap. I (p. 19). With field windings it is merely necessary first to measure their resistance after they have been standing for a sufficiently long time in a room of known temperature to have acquired that temperature. Any of the several methods (pp. 155 to 171) may be used, although the voltmeter-ammeter method is the most common. In using this method, the measurements should be made quickly so that the measuring current will not heat the winding appreciably above the initial temperature (see Fig. 423).

The voltmeter must be connected across the shunt-field winding itself and must not include the field rheostat since change in resistance of the *copper* is being measured. Likewise, measurements with series fields cannot be used for temperature determination if the fields are provided with shunts, or diverters.

Example. With an ambient temperature of 30°C, the resistance of the field of a shunt generator increases from 104 to 112 ohms. Determine its temperature rise.

Using Eq. (16) (p. 21),

$$\frac{112}{104} = \frac{234.5° + t_2}{234.5° + 30°}.$$

$$234.5 + t_2 = 264.5(^{112}\!/_{104}) = 284.9°.$$

$$t_2 = 50.4°.$$

$$\text{Temperature rise} = 50.4° - 30.0° = 20.4° \quad \textit{Ans.}$$

ASA Standard C50 (2.064) specifies that the "temperature test shall be continued until the temperature rises during test shall have attained a steady final value; or until sufficient evidence is available to show that the temperature rises would not exceed the requirements of the standards if the test were prolonged until the attainment of steady final values."

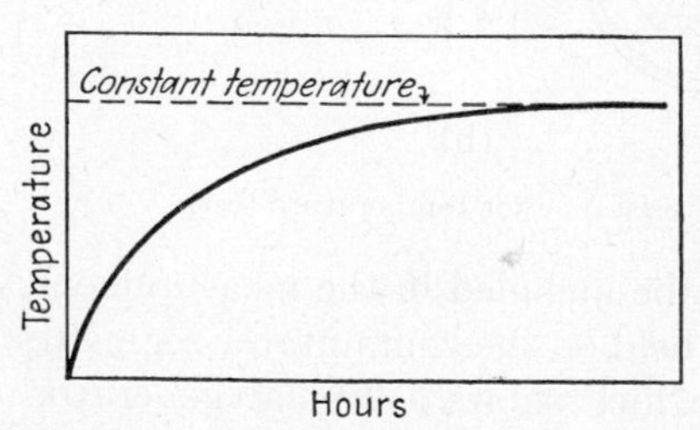

FIG. 423. Curve of temperature rise with time, for dynamo.

If temperature rise be plotted as a function of time, a curve similar to that of Fig. 423[1] is obtained, which was determined for a shunt field. Such a curve is readily obtainable by leaving the voltmeter and ammeter connected in circuit permanently and taking readings at the desired intervals. At the beginning of the test the curve rises rapidly, since at that time there is but a slight difference of temperature between the field coils and the room. Therefore, but a small amount of heat is dissipated by the coils, and as a result the temperature rises rapidly. As the difference between the coil temperature and the room temperature increases, more and more heat is dissipated by the coils, and the temperature rises less

[1] This curve is similar in character with the curve giving the rise of current with time in an inductive circuit (see Fig. 230(*b*), p. 306).

rapidly. Therefore, the rate of temperature increase becomes less as the time increases. This is illustrated by the curve of Fig. 423. When the curve becomes practically horizontal, the total heat developed in the coils is equal to the heat dissipated by the coils and the coils have reached a constant temperature. Similar curves would be obtained for other parts of the machine.

Care must be taken in measuring the armature resistance when determining temperature rise. The object of this measurement is not to determine the resistance for use in the calculation of loss, but to determine the *change of resistance in the armature copper, due to change of temperature.* Therefore, it is essential that the resistance of the *copper alone* be measured and that the current path through the copper be the same in every measurement. To exclude all resistance except that of the copper, the

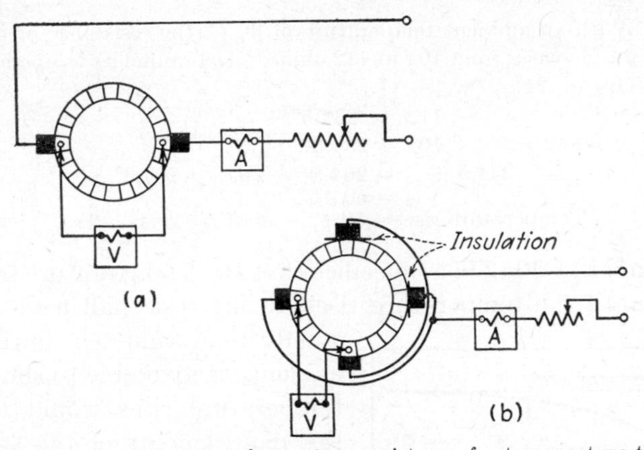

FIG. 424. Measurement of armature resistance for temperature test.

brush and contact resistances must not be included in the measurement. Therefore, the voltmeter leads must be held on the commutator segments inside the brushes, as in Fig. 424(a), which shows a bipolar generator. Moreover, these segments should be marked, and in every subsequent measurement they should be directly under the same brushes. This ensures the same conducting path for each measurement.

When this type of measurement is made on a multipolar armature, the *division* of current in the various paths is determined in part by the brush-contact resistance. This is apparent from a study of Fig. 415, p. 524. The current I divides between the two brush sets, and hence the division of current will in part be determined by their resistances. To make certain that in the different resistance measurements the current paths remain unchanged, two brushes may be insulated, Fig. 424(b). Under these conditions the current paths are not symmetrical, but the division of current is determined by the copper resistance itself and not by brush-contact resistance. With an odd number of pairs of brush sets the current paths will be symmetrical if diametrically opposite brush sets conduct the current to the commutator.

In measuring the shunt-field resistance, the voltmeter should be connected directly across the winding so as to exclude the drop in the field rheostat.

In addition to measuring the temperature of the windings, the rise of temperature of bearings and of commutator should be measured with a thermometer.

In many modern dynamos, thermocouples are inserted in the windings and are connected to millivoltmeters on the switchboard, so that the operator can determine the hot-spot temperatures at any time.

362. Parallel Operation of Shunt Generators. In most power plants it is necessary, or at least desirable, that the power be supplied by several small units rather than by a single large unit.

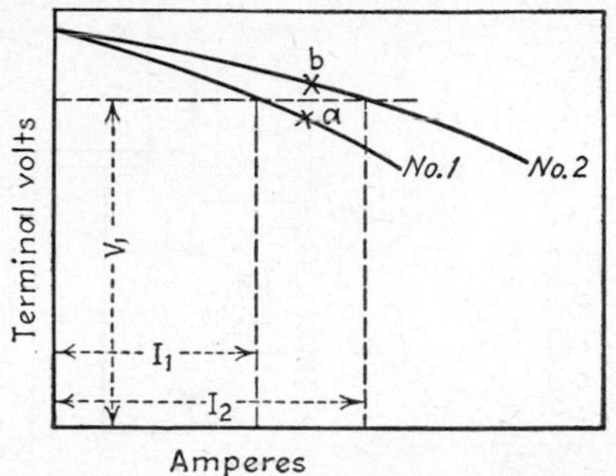

FIG. 425. Characteristics of shunt generators in parallel.

(*a*) Several small units are more reliable than a single large unit, for if one of the small units is disabled the entire power supply is not cut off. (*b*) The units may be connected in service and taken out of service to correspond with the load on the station. This keeps the units loaded up to their rated capacity and increases the efficiency of operation. (*c*) A unit can be repaired more readily if there are several in the station. (*d*) Additional units may be installed to correspond with the growth of station load. (*e*) The station load may exceed the capacity of any single available unit.

Shunt generators, because of their drooping characteristic, are particularly well suited for parallel operation. In Fig. 425 are shown the characteristics of two shunt generators, designated as No. 1 and No. 2. It will be noted that generator 1 has the more drooping characteristic. If the two generators are connected in parallel, Fig. 426, their terminal voltages must be the same, neglecting any very small voltage drop in the connecting leads. Therefore, for a common terminal voltage V_1, Fig. 425, generator 1 delivers I_1 amp, and generator 2 delivers I_2 amp. That is, the generator with the more drooping characteristic carries the smaller load.

Assume that some condition arises which temporarily causes generator 1 to take more than its share of the load. This condition might arise from a temporary increase in the speed of its prime mover, or it might be occasioned by a momentary change of load on the system. If the increased current persisted after normal conditions were restored, generator 1 would tend to operate at some point *a* on its characteristic. This results in a drop in its terminal voltage, which tends to make it take *less* load. Moreover, at the time that generator 1 takes more load, generator 2 must take less load, the total load remaining constant, and accordingly generator 2 will tend to operate at some point *b* on its characteristic. This will raise its terminal voltage and cause it to take more load. Therefore, any tendency of one generator to take more than its share of the load results in changes of voltage in the system which oppose this tendency. Hence, shunt generators in parallel may be said to be in *stable* equilibrium. The reactions of the system are such as to hold the generators in parallel.

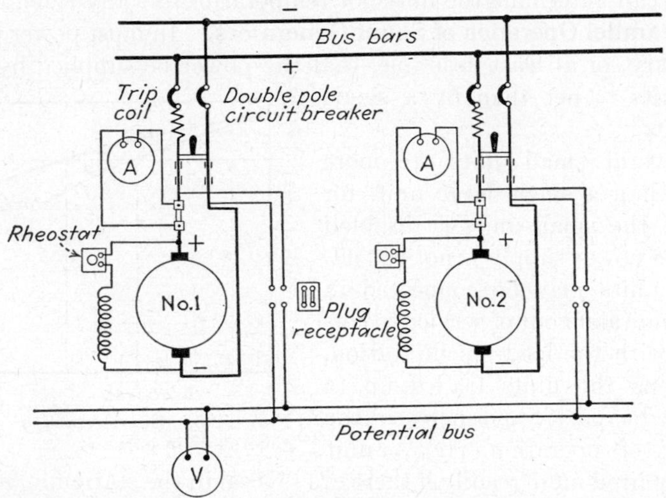

FIG. 426. Connections for parallel operation of shunt generators.

Moreover, if any *change* of load on the system occurs, each generator must supply some of the increase or decrease of load.

363. Connections of Shunt Generators in Parallel. The connections for operating shunt generators in parallel are shown in Fig. 426. Each generator should have its own ammeter. A common voltmeter is sufficient for all the generators. The individual generators can be connected to the voltmeter or potential bus through suitable plug connectors or selective switches. Assume that generator 2 is out of service and that generator 1 is supplying the load. It is desired to put No. 2 in service. The prime mover of No. 2 is started and the generator is brought up to speed. Its field is then adjusted so that its voltage is just equal to that of the bus bars, which condition may be determined by the voltmeter. The breaker and switch are now closed and No. 2 is connected to the system. Under these conditions, however, it is not taking any load, as its *induced* emf is just equal to the bus-bar voltage, and there can be no current between points at the same potential. That is, the generator is "floating" on the bus bars. Its induced emf must be greater than the voltage of the bus bars in order that it may deliver current. Therefore, the field of No. 2 is strengthened until the generator takes its share of the load. It may be necessary to weaken the field of generator No. 1 at the same time in order to maintain constant the bus-bar voltage.

To take a generator out of service, its field is weakened and that of the other generator is strengthened until the load of the first generator is zero. The breaker and then the switch are opened, clearing the generator. Connecting in and removing a generator from service in this manner prevents any shocks or disturbance to the prime mover or to the system.

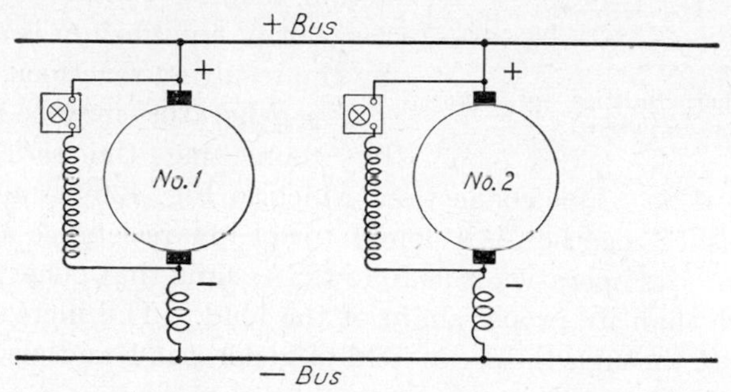

Fig. 427. Compound generators in parallel.

If the field of one generator be weakened too much, power will be delivered to this generator, which will then run as a motor and tend to drive its prime mover.

It is evident that if shunt generators are to divide the load properly at all points, *their characteristics must be similar in form and each must have the same voltage drop from no load to full load.*

364. Parallel Operation of Compound Generators. Figure 427 shows two overcompounded generators connected to bus bars, positive and negative terminals being properly connected as regards polarity. Each generator is taking its proper share of the load. Two such compound generators operating in parallel are in *unstable equilibrium.* For example, assume that for some reason generator 1 takes a slightly increased load. The current in its series winding must increase, which strengthens its field and raises its emf, thus causing it to take still more load. On the other hand, as the system load is assumed to be fixed, generator 2 will at the same time drop some of its load, resulting in a weakening of its series field and a consequent further dropping of its load. Almost instantaneously No. 1 will be driving No. 2 as a motor, and the circuit breaker of at least one of the generators will open.

This condition is also illustrated by Fig. 428, which shows the individual characteristics of the two generators. Assume that the generators are operating at voltage V_1, which corresponds to currents I_1 and I_2. Assume that generator 1 delivers a slightly increased load. Its voltage will then tend to rise to some point a. This increased voltage causes the generator to deliver more load, the effect is cumulative, and almost instantaneously a circuit breaker opens.

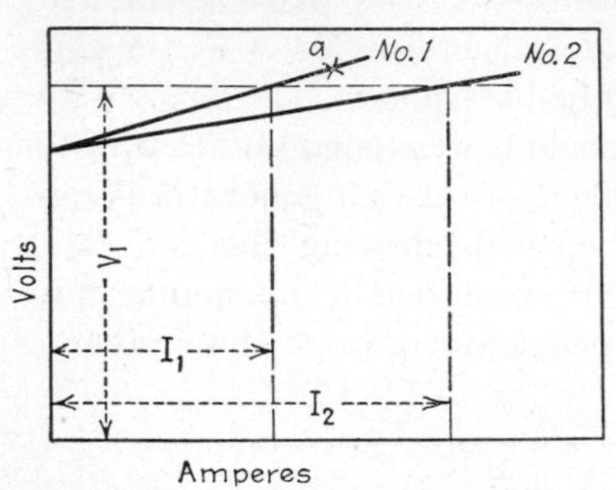

Fig. 428. Characteristics of compound generators in parallel.

Hence, compound generators operating under these conditions are in *unstable* equilibrium. That is, any action tending to throw the generators out of equilibrium is accentuated by the resulting reactions.

The generators may be made stable by connecting the series fields in parallel, Fig. 429. This connection, which in Fig. 429 connects the two negative brushes together, is a conductor of low resistance and is called the *equalizer*. Its operation is as follows: Assume that generator 1 starts to take more than its proper share of the load. The increased current will go in part through the series field of generator 1 and also, by means

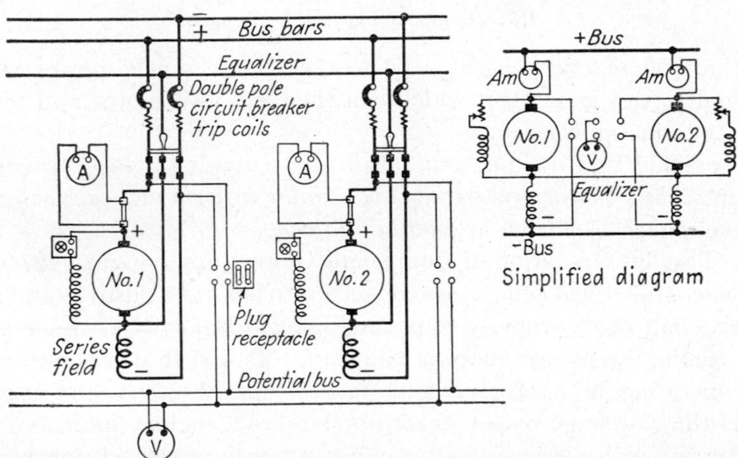

Fig. 429. Typical connections for two compound generators operating in parallel.

of the equalizer, will go in part through the series field of generator 2. Therefore, both generators are affected in a similar manner and No. 1 cannot take the entire load.

To maintain the proper division of load from no load to full load, the following conditions must be satisfied:

a. The regulation of each armature must be the same.

b. The series-field resistances must be inversely proportional to the generator ratings.

It is not always possible to adjust compound-generator characteristics by means of series-field diverters so that the generators, while in parallel, divide the load properly. Assume, Fig. 429, that the series field of generator 1 is shunted by a diverter. If the equalizer and bus bar have negligible resistance, this diverter shunts the series field of generator 2 as well as that of generator 1. Therefore, the diverter merely drops the characteristic of the entire system but does not affect the *division* of load. The proper load adjustments may be made by means of a resistor of low resistance *in series* with one of the series fields.

It should be noted that the desired division of load among either shunt or compound generators for any given external load may be

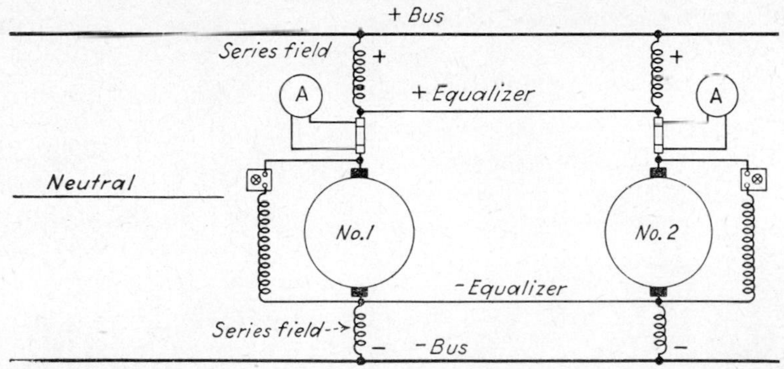

Fig. 430. Compound generators requiring two equalizers (neutral connection to generators omitted).

obtained by adjusting their shunt-field rheostats. However, it is usually desirable that this division remain constant at all loads, especially if an operator is not in continuous attendance. Therefore, it is desirable that shunt and compound generators operating in parallel shall have similar characteristics.

A compound generator with a single series field usually has a 3-pole switch, one blade of which connects the equalizer, Fig. 429. If a 3-wire generator (see p. 566) having two series fields is to be connected, a 4-pole switch is necessary, as there are two equalizers, Fig. 430. The load ammeter in a compound generator should always be connected between the *armature* terminal and the bus bars, Fig. 430. If it is connected in the series-field circuit, the ammeter may not indicate the generator current, owing to the fact that some of the generator current may be going through the equalizer.

Compound generators are put in service and taken out of service in the same manner as shunt generators, that is, the load is adjusted and shifted by means of the shunt-field rheostat.

Sometimes, however, when the switch for the incoming generator is closed after the generator emf has been made equal to the voltage of the bus bars, the generator immediately supplies a substantial load. A study of Fig. 429 shows that the two right-hand switch blades connect the series field of the incoming generator in parallel with those of the generators already connected to the bus bars. Hence, the series field of the incoming generator immediately takes current, and its emf is increased above the voltage of the bus bars, resulting in its supplying load. If this condition is serious, the switching may be arranged so that the two right-hand contacts of the switches are first closed, the generator emf made equal to the bus-bar voltage, and then the left-hand contact closed.

CHAPTER XV

TRANSMISSION AND DISTRIBUTION OF POWER

365. Power-distribution Systems. Under modern conditions, most central stations generate power on a large scale as alternating current and transmit this power as alternating current. Even when large d-c loads are to be supplied, such as to electrolytic plants, the power is almost always generated as alternating current and converted to direct current in the locality or localities at which it is to be utilized. An important reason for generating power as alternating current is that a-c generators can be constructed in large high-speed units having ratings as high as 200,000 kw, which are economical in cost per kilowatt and also in operation. On account of commutation, it is difficult to construct a d-c generator of a rating much higher than 5,000 kw, and such units must operate at low speed, which necessitates large, heavy machines (see Vol. II, Chap. 1, Sec. 1). Another important reason for using alternating current is that the voltage may be efficiently raised and lowered by means of transformers. This enables the obtaining of high voltages, which are essential to the economical and efficient transmission of power, and also the obtaining of lower voltages, such as 2,300, 600, 230, 115 volts, at which power is generally utilized.

Direct-current power must be generated at comparatively low voltages in units of relatively small power ratings, and there is no economical method of raising the voltage for transmission and lowering it for utilization. At present there are no commercial high-voltage d-c systems. The Thury high-voltage d-c system (p. 462) was in operation in France for a number of years, but was abandoned in 1937.

At the present time, general d-c distribution is used in the downtown districts of a few large cities. This system is still employed chiefly because it is a development of the past which cannot be changed readily to alternating current without prohibitive expense. However, in such cities new extensions are usually alternating current, the low-voltage network[1] being generally used. In the early days of power distribution, the primary reason for selecting direct current for the downtown sections of large cities was that continuity of service was of the highest importance and direct current enabled the use of a storage-battery reserve which can be readily maintained and immediately put into service should the power

[1] Vol. II, 4th ed., p. 496.

supply into the area be interrupted. The storage battery can also be used as a voltage regulator. Direct-current motors are admirably adapted to elevators and printing presses, which form an important part of the power load in a city (see Vol. II, 4th ed., Sec. 1, and pp. 456 and 496).

Other advantages of direct current are the absence of inductive and capacitive effects, present with alternating current, and the absence of eddy-current losses in cable sheaths and of skin effect in large underground conductors. Hence, large single-conductor cables can be used.

366. Power Systems. Nearly all d-c power now is obtained from large a-c power systems by the use of converting apparatus. This is illustrated by Fig. 431, which shows a typical power system, no attempt being made to show such details as instruments, switches, and circuit breakers.

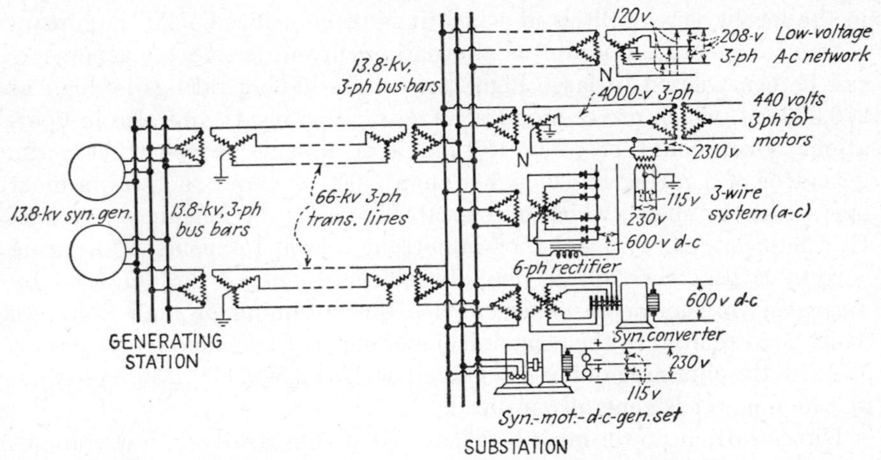

Fig. 431. Typical power system.

The analyses of the 3-phase connections and voltages are given in Vol. II, particularly in Chap. XIII (also see Vol. II, Sec. 1, p. 1). The generating station, Fig. 431, may be either steam or hydroelectric. Two 3-phase synchronous generators in parallel are delivering power to the 13.8-kv (13,800-volt) bus bars. The power is stepped up by transformers to 66 kv for transmission, and at the substation it is stepped down to 13.8 kv for distribution. The 66 kv used for transmission, although typical, is given only for illustration. Other voltages such as 110, 132, 164, and 220 kv are commonly used, depending on the transmission distance, economics, and other factors.

Since a-c distribution is now predominant, two typical a-c systems are shown at the substation, the low-voltage a-c network in which the power is stepped down at or near the load center from 13,800 volts to a 208/120-volt 3-phase system. Lamp and other 120-volt loads are connected from the 3-phase wires to the neutral N, and 3-phase 208-volt motor loads are connected to the 3-phase wires.

In the second a-c system the 13,800-volt power is stepped down to 4,000 volts, 3-phase, for distribution. The voltage to the neutral N is 2,310 volts, and transformers with a 10 to 1 ratio connected between phase wires and neutral give the 230/115-volt 3-wire systems. For motor loads, step-down transformers connected to the 4,000-volt phase wires give 230, 440, and 575 volts, 3-phase power, for motors, 440 volts being shown.

There are also shown three common methods for converting a-c power to d-c power. The 6-anode mercury-arc rectifier rectifies the a-c voltage to give 600 volts d-c, after the voltage has been stepped down to the proper value by transformers. The 600-volt d-c power would probably be used for electric railways or for electrolytic purposes. Also a synchronous converter is shown, a rotating machine which converts the a-c power to d-c power after the voltage is stepped down by transformers to the proper value. This d-c voltage is also 600 volts, but synchronous converters are used commonly to convert to 230 volts d-c. A synchronous-motor–d-c-generator set is also shown for converting the a-c power to 230-volts d-c. Although all three methods are in common use, the rectifier is being favored when the d-c voltage is 600 volts and higher because of its higher efficiency and lesser weight.

367. Voltage and Weight of Conductor. *The weight of conductor varies inversely as the square of the voltage*, when the power transmitted, the distance, and the loss are fixed.

Let it be required to transmit power P at voltage V_1 and current I_1 over conductors having resistance R_1.

The current

$$I_1 = \frac{P}{V_1}.$$

The power loss

$$P_1 = I_1^2 R_1.$$

Assume that the voltage is raised to V_2, power, distance, and loss remaining fixed.

The current

$$I_2 = \frac{P}{V_2}.$$

The power loss

$$P_2 = I_2^2 R_2 = P_1.$$

Therefore,

$$I_1^2 R_1 = I_2^2 R_2.$$

$$\frac{R_1}{R_2} = \left(\frac{I_2}{I_1}\right)^2 = \frac{(P/V_2)^2}{(P/V_1)^2} = \frac{V_1^2}{V_2^2}. \qquad (373)$$

That is, the conductor resistance varies *directly* as the square of the voltage. But the volume or the weight of a conductor of given length varies *inversely* as the resistance.

Let the weight of copper in the two cases be W_1 and W_2.

$$\frac{W_1}{W_2} = \frac{V_2^2}{V_1^2}. \tag{374}$$

Therefore, the conductor weight varies inversely as the square of the voltage, when power, distance, and loss are fixed.

If the voltage of as ystem is *doubled,* the weight of the conductor is *quartered,* other conditions being the same.

Example. 50 kw is delivered at a distance of 500 ft at 110 volts over a 400,000-cir-mil feeder. Determine: (*a*) power loss; (*b*) power loss with 220 volts at load.

(*a*) $I_1 = \frac{50,000}{110} = 454.5$ amp.

If the cross section of the cable were 454,500 cir mils (see Sec. 47, p. 53), the loss would be $454,500 \cdot 1,000 \cdot 10^{-5}$ watts $= 4,545$ watts. Actually the loss is

$$\left(\frac{454.5}{400}\right)^2 \cdot 1,000 \cdot 10^{-5} \cdot 400,000 = 5,164 \text{ watts.} \quad \textit{Ans.}$$

(*b*) $I_2 = \frac{50,000}{220} = 227.27$ amp.

The loss is

$$\left(\frac{227.27}{400}\right)^2 \cdot 1,000 \cdot 10^{-5} \cdot 400,000 = 1,291 \text{ watts.} \quad \textit{Ans.}$$

The loss in (*b*) is one-fourth that in (*a*). Therefore, a 100,000-cir-mil feeder, having just one-fourth the weight of the feeder in (*a*), would transmit the same power the same distance with the *same loss.*

368. Distance and Weight of Conductor. *The weight of conductor varies inversely as the square of the voltage,* when the power transmitted, the voltage, and the loss are fixed. Let the voltage and power of two systems be V volts and P watts. Let the current, resistance, and length of line in one system be I_1 amp, R_1 ohms, and l_1 units of length. Let the corresponding quantities in the second system be I_2 amp, R_2 ohms and l_2 units of length. Let $\mathcal{V}_1$ and $\mathcal{V}_2$ be the volumes of the conductors in the two systems, and let ρ be the resistivity of the conductors and A_1 and A_2 their respective cross sections.

$$R_1 = \rho \frac{l_1}{A_1} \quad \text{ohms}; \qquad R_2 = \rho \frac{l_2}{A_2} \quad \text{ohms.} \tag{I}$$

Since the voltage V, power P, and power loss I^2R in the two systems are equal,

$$I_2 = I_1; \qquad I_1^2R_1 = I_2^2R_2.$$

Therefore, $R_1 = R_2$. Hence

$$\rho \frac{l_1}{A_1} = \rho \frac{l_2}{A_2}. \tag{II}$$

Substituting

$$A_1 = \frac{\mathfrak{V}_1}{l_1} \qquad \text{and} \qquad A_2 = \frac{\mathfrak{V}_2}{l_2} \tag{III}$$

in (II) and rearranging,

$$\frac{\mathfrak{V}_2}{\mathfrak{V}_1} = \frac{l_2^2}{l_1^2}. \tag{375}$$

Weight obviously is proportional to volume.

369. Size of Conductors. In transmitting or distributing power by direct current, four factors must be considered in determining the size of conductor.

1. The conductors must be able to carry the current without overheating.

This is particularly important with inside wiring where fire risk exists. Tables of the permissible current-carrying capacity of conductors are given in the Appendixes G and I (pp. 591 and 593).

2. The voltage drop to the load must be kept within reasonable limits. This is particularly important when incandescent lamps constitute the load.

3. The conductors must be of sufficient mechanical strength. This is important when the conductors are strung on poles. It is not advisable to use conductors smaller than No. 8 AWG for pole lines.

4. The economics of the problem must be considered. Increasing the size of conductor means higher investment costs but less energy loss in transmission. That size of conductor should be chosen which makes the cost of the energy loss plus the interest on the investment a minimum. This may be modified in view of the considerations stated in 1, 2, and 3.

CONSTANT-POTENTIAL DISTRIBUTION

370. Distribution Voltages. From 110 to 120 volts has been found to be the most satisfactory voltage for incandescent lighting. It is not so high as to be dangerous to persons. Incandescent-lamp filaments for voltages much in excess of 120 volts become so long and of so small a cross section that they are fragile. An even lower voltage than this would be desirable from the standpoint of the filament, but a lower voltage would be accompanied by an increase in the required weight of copper. Therefore, 110 to 120 volts has been standardized for lighting and for domestic use as being the most desirable when all factors are taken into consideration. Six hundred volts is commonly used for trolley distribution, because it is not so high as to give operating difficulties and saves considerable copper as compared with systems of lower voltage. At the present time, 1,200, 2,400, and even 3,000 volts d-c are used at the trolley in railway electrification, these higher voltages being for trunk-line electrification, not for municipal traction.

371. Distributed Loads. Feeders conduct the power in bulk from the bus bars to load centers from which it is distributed to the consumers through the mains (p. 566). Hence, with feeders the load is almost always concentrated at the end although at times there may be one or two intermediate loads (see Figs. 31 and 32, pp. 49 and 50). With mains, however, the loads are usually distributed more or less uniformly, Figs. 432(*a*), (*b*), (*c*), in which lamp loads are given as examples.

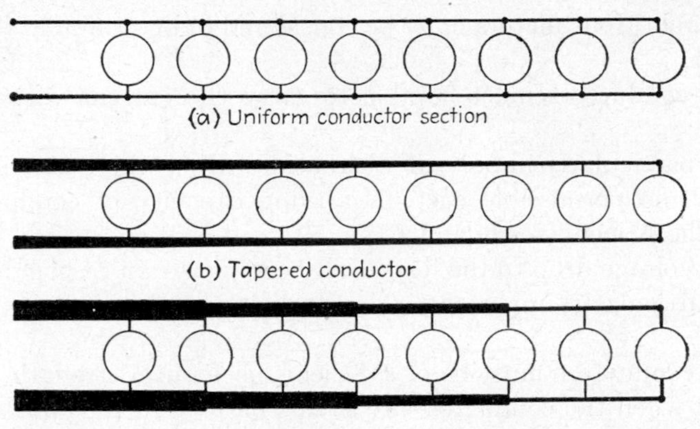

FIG. 432. Conductor cross section of distributing system of mains.

The conductors may be of uniform cross section throughout their entire length, Fig. 432(*a*). This system is used where the mains are short and the voltage drop is small.

The minimum weight of conductor for a given voltage drop is obtained when the mains are uniformly tapered, Fig. 432(*b*).

As it is impracticable to have a uniformly tapering conductor, a conductor of constant cross section is run for a part of the distance, followed by another uniform conductor of lesser cross section, and so on, Fig. 432(*c*). A good rule to remember is that the current *density* in each section should be the same. For example, the first section may consist of a 250,000-cir-mil conductor, carrying 200 amp; assume the second section carries 150 amp; it should be a $^{150}/_{200} \cdot 250{,}000 = 187{,}500$ cir-mil conductor. Ordinarily, 4/0 wire would be used for this second section.

372. Systems of Feeding. In order that a number of lamps may operate at essentially the same voltage without using an excessive amount of copper, the *return-loop*, or *anti-parallel*, system, Fig. 433(*a*), may be used.

The two feeding conductors are connected to opposite ends of the load. This system allows all the lamps to operate at nearly the same voltage, and yet the voltage drop in the feeding wires may be large.

The objection to the return-loop system is the extra length of wire required. This objection is often overcome by arranging the loads in the manner shown in Fig. 433(*b*), the *open-spiral* system. Where large groups of lamps are switched off and on at the same time, as in theaters

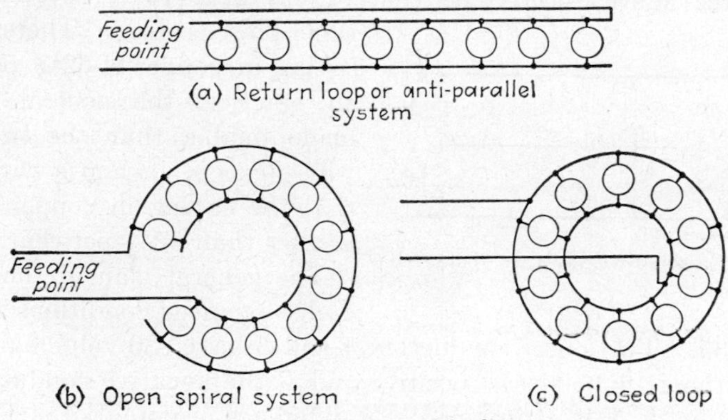

FIG. 433. Systems of feeding.

and auditoriums, it is often possible to arrange the lamps in this way.

The open spiral may be closed at its ends, resulting in the *closed-loop* system, Fig. 433(*c*).

373. Series-parallel System. Doubling the voltage of a system results in reducing the weight of conductor to one-fourth its initial value. If 115-volt lamps be arranged so that two are always in series, Fig. 434, the system may be operated at 230 volts. The conductor section will then be one-fourth that required for straight 115-volt distribution. The obvious disadvantages of the series-parallel system are that lamps can be switched only in groups of two, and if one lamp burns out, the lamp to which it is connected ceases to operate. Also, both of the lamps in series must be of the same voltage and current rating. It is obvious that this system is entirely unsuited to the usual 115-volt appliances.

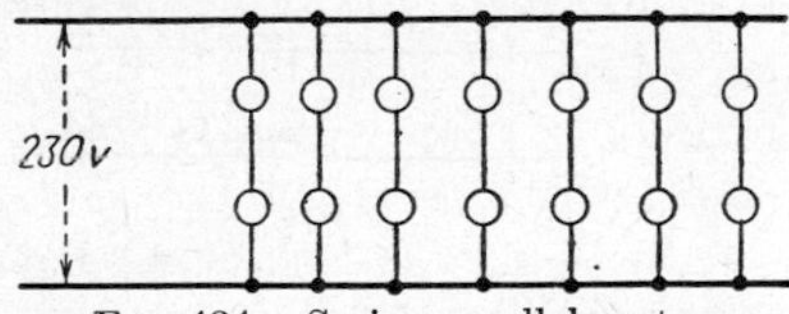

FIG. 434. Series-parallel system.

EDISON THREE-WIRE SYSTEM

374. Advantages of Edison Three-wire System. The objections to the series-parallel system may be eliminated by running a third conductor, a *neutral*, between the two outer conductors, a method invented by

Edison. This neutral maintains all the lamps and other loads at approximately 115 volts. The advantage of a higher voltage in reducing the weight of conductor is secured by the use of this system. If there were no neutral conductor, the 230-volt system would require one-fourth the weight of conductor of an equivalent 115-volt system. If it be assumed that the neutral of the Edison system is of the same cross section as the two outer conductors, the total weight of conductor for the Edison system is three-eighths, or 37½ per cent, of that for a 115-volt system of the same power rating. Therefore the saving in copper is 62½ per cent. In practice, the neutral can be made smaller than the two outer wires (except in house wiring), so that the saving in copper is even greater than 62½ per cent.

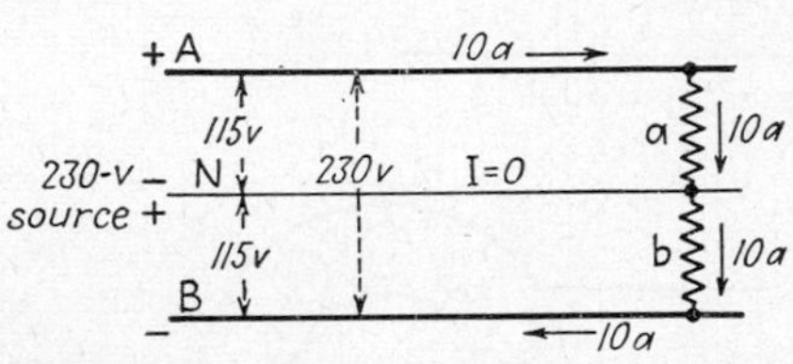

Fig. 435. Edison 3-wire system—balanced loads.

The general plan of the system under balanced conditions is shown in Fig. 435. Two outer conductors A and B have 230 volts maintained between them, A being the positive and B the negative conductor. A third conductor N is maintained at a difference of potential of 115 volts from each of the two outer conductors. Hence, N must be negative with respect to A and positive with respect to B: that is, the direction of current is from A to N and from N to B.

Another advantage of the system is that two values of voltage are available. The 115 volts is well adapted to lamps and appliances, whereas 230 volts is better adapted to motors.

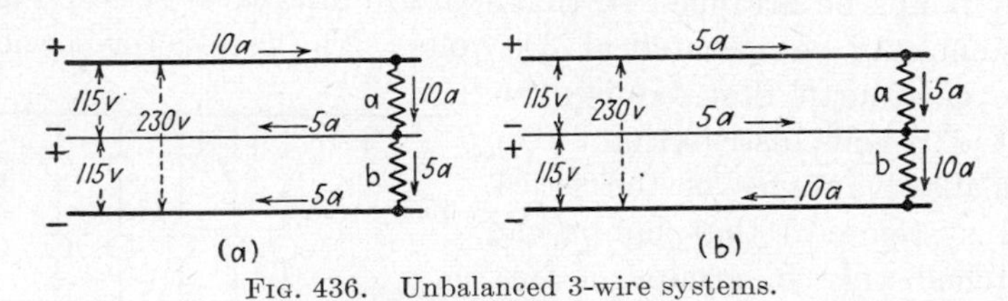

Fig. 436. Unbalanced 3-wire systems.

375. Balanced and Unbalanced Loads. Figure 435 shows the conditions which exist when the load on each side of the system is the same. Each of the loads a and b takes 10 amp. The 10 amp taken by load a goes through to load b and then back through conductor B to the source. This is equivalent to a series-parallel system, as both loads are equal and in series. Under these conditions the loads are balanced, and the current in the neutral conductor is zero.

Figure 436(a) shows the conditions existing when the load a on the positive side of the system is 10 amp and the load b on the negative side is 5 amp. Under these conditions the extra 5 amp taken by load *a* must go *back* through the neutral to the generator or source. Therefore there are 5 amp returning to the generator in the neutral.

In Fig. 436(*b*) the load *b* is 10 amp, and load *a* is 5 amp. Under these conditions the extra 5 amp must go *out* to the load through the neutral. Note that the direction of current in the neutral may be either toward the power source or away from the power source depending on which load is the greater. Therefore, if an ammeter is used in a neutral, it should be of the zero-center type. Moreover, note that the neutral carries the *difference* of the currents taken by the two loads. In practice the loads are usually so disposed that they are nearly balanced. Ten per cent unbalancing, that is, a neutral current which is 10 per cent that in the outer conductors, is usually allowed in the larger systems, while in smaller systems the unbalance may at times reach 25 per cent. The current in the neutral is ordinarily much smaller than that in the outer conductors and a much smaller conductor can be used safely. In practice the neutral is usually grounded.

376. Effect of Opening Neutral. In practice, it is desirable to keep the neutral of the 3-wire system closed under *all* conditions. The reason for this is illustrated by the following example:

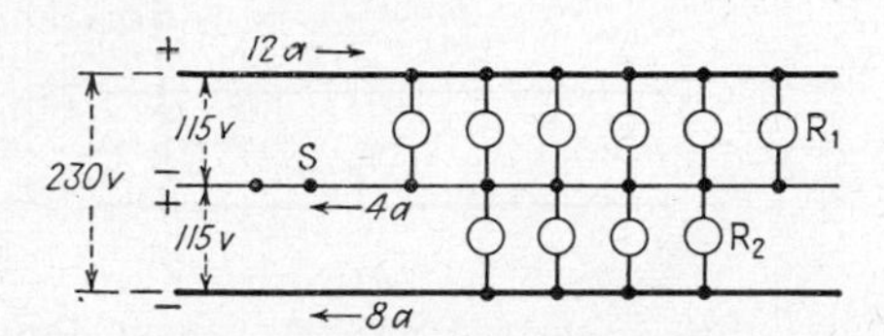

FIG. 437. Effect on balance of 3-wire system of opening neutral.

Figure 437 shows two lamp loads on a 3-wire system. The load on the positive side consists of six lamps each taking 2 amp, making a total of 12 amp. The load on the negative side consists of four lamps each taking 2 amp, making this load 8 amp. The voltage across each load is 115 volts so that the resistance R_1 of the positive load is

$$R_1 = {}^{115}\!/_{12} = 9.58 \text{ ohms.}$$

The resistance of the negative load is

$$R_2 = {}^{115}\!/_{8} = 14.38 \text{ ohms.}$$

If the neutral be opened at the point S, the two loads R_1 and R_2 are in series and must take the same current. The total resistance $R = R_1 + R_2 = 23.96$ ohms.

There is now 230 volts across these two loads in series, so that the current

$$I = \frac{230}{23.96} = 9.60 \text{ amp.}$$

The voltage across load R_1 is

$$V_1 = 9.60 \cdot 9.58 = 91.96 \text{ volts.}$$

The voltage across load R_2 is

$$V_2 = 9.60 \cdot 14.38 = 138.04 \text{ volts.}$$

This assumes that the resistance of the lamp filaments does not change. Note, however, that the larger bank of lamps is operating at a reduced voltage, resulting in a substantial decrease in the lumens output of the lamps, and that the smaller bank is operating considerably above rated voltage, which would result in the burning out of the lamps in a short time.

For this reason the neutral of the 3-wire system is almost always grounded, and when circuit breakers are used, there is rarely a pole in the neutral conductor. Also, in modern building and house wiring, no fuses are used in the neutral conductor.

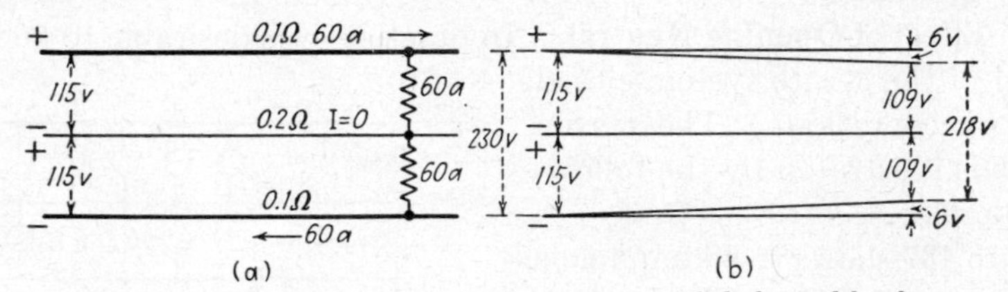

FIG. 438. Voltage drop in 3-wire system with balanced loads.

377. Voltage Unbalance. The voltage on the two sides of a 3-wire system may be considerably unbalanced if the loads on the two sides of the system are unequal.

In Fig. 438(a) there is a load of 60 amp on each side of the system. The resistance of each outer conductor is 0.1 ohm and of the neutral is 0.2 ohm. The applied voltage is 230 volts across the two outer conductors.

As the two loads are equal, there is no current in the neutral conductor. Therefore, the voltage drop per conductor for the outers is

$$e = 60 \cdot 0.1 = 6.0 \text{ volts.}$$

The voltage across each load is 109 volts. There is no voltage drop along the neutral, as it carries no current. Figure 438(b) shows a plot of the voltage distribution.

Assume that the loads are 100 amp on the positive side of the system and 20 amp on the negative side, Fig. 439(a). This represents the same total amperes as in Fig. 438.

The drop in the positive conductor,

$$e_1 = 100 \cdot 0.1 = 10 \text{ volts.}$$

The drop in the neutral,

$$e_2 = 80 \cdot 0.2 = 16 \text{ volts.}$$

Voltage across positive load,

$$V_1 = 115 - 10 - 16 = 89 \text{ volts.} \quad Ans.$$

The drop in the negative conductor,

$$e_2 = 20 \cdot 0.1 = 2 \text{ volts.}$$

Voltage across negative load,

$$V_2 = 115 - 2 + 16 = 129 \text{ volts.} \quad Ans.$$

There is now 40 volts difference between the voltages on the two sides of the system.

Under these conditions, the voltage across the load on the negative side is *greater* than the voltage on the negative side of the system at the sending end, or power source. This rise in voltage from power source to

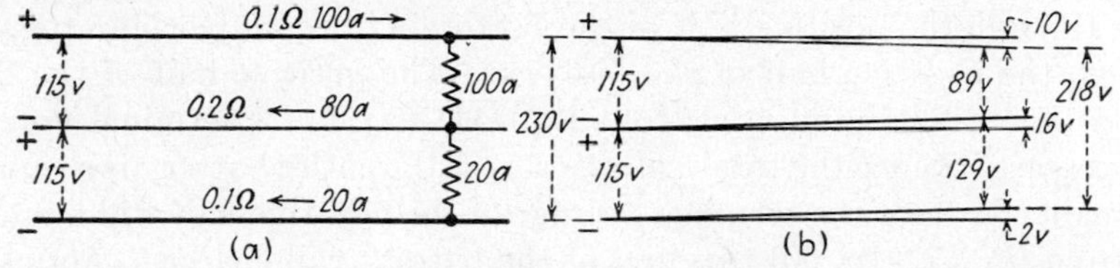

FIG. 439. Voltage unbalance in 3-wire system with unbalanced loads.

load is due to the direction of the drop in the neutral. Figure 439(*b*) shows these conditions graphically. Note in Fig. 438(*b*) and in Fig. 439(*b*) that the voltage across the outer conductors, 218 volts, is the same. This follows from the fact that the total current load is the same in each case.

When motor loads are to be connected to a 3-wire system, they are usually connected between the two outer conductors rather than between an outer conductor and neutral in order that they shall not produce any voltage unbalancing. In fact some power companies will not permit motor loads exceeding 1 hp to be connected to neutral.

METHODS OF OBTAINING THREE-WIRE SYSTEM

There are several methods of obtaining a 3-wire system.

378. Two-generator Method. Two shunt generators may be connected in series, Fig. 440. The positive terminal of one should be connected to the negative terminal of the other; that is, the generators are in series between the outers. Both generators may be driven by the same prime mover. When connected in this manner, each generator supplies the load on its own side of the line only. The obvious objection to this method is that two separate generators are required.

379. Storage Battery. A *storage battery* may be "floated" across the line, Fig. 441. The neutral wire is connected to the mid-point of the battery. When the load is unbalanced, that half of the battery on the more heavily loaded side will discharge and the other half will be charged. Assume for the moment that there are no losses in the battery. The

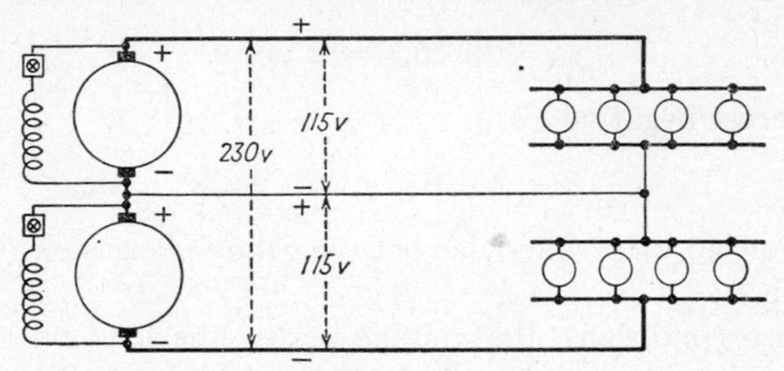

Fig. 440. Two generators supplying 3-wire system.

10 amp returning through the neutral will then divide equally, 5 amp going through the positive half of the battery and the other 5 amp going through the negative half of the battery. The positive half of the battery is then discharging, and from Eq. (44) (p. 55) its terminal voltage will decrease. Since the total voltage across the entire battery is assumed to remain constant, the terminal voltage of the negative half will increase and from Eq. (52) (p. 60) this half of the battery will charge. Actually,

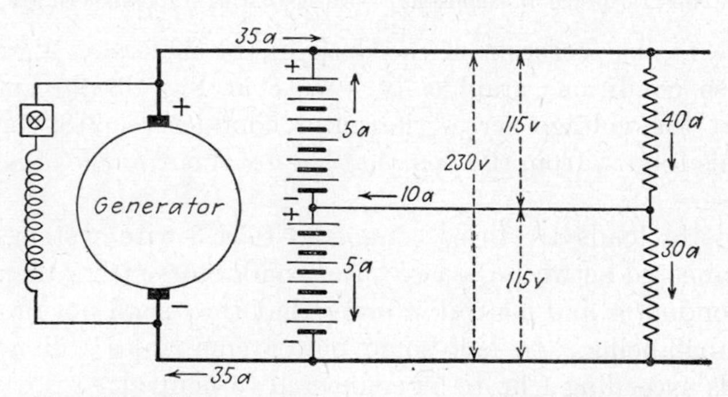

Fig. 441. Storage battery giving neutral in 3-wire system.

owing to losses in the battery, more current will go through the negative half of the battery than through the positive half, and the generator current will be greater than 35 amp. This is illustrated with the balancer set (Sec. 380) and by Prob. 770 (p. 721). Hence, in order that such a system may operate, the voltages to neutral must become unbalanced when there is neutral current in the system. On account of their initial cost and the cost of maintenance, storage batteries are rarely used for the sole purpose of obtaining a neutral. However, central-station stand-by batteries, when floating on a 3-wire system, incidentally provide an additional neutral for the system.

380. Balancer Set. A balancer set is a common method of obtaining the neutral. This set consists of two dynamos mechanically coupled together. They are connected in series across the outer conductors, and

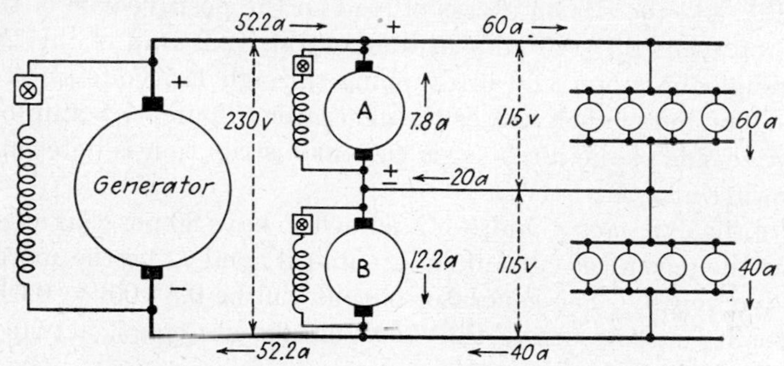

Fig. 442 Balancer set giving neutral in 3-wire system.

the neutral is brought to their common terminal, Fig. 442. With little or no unbalance in current, both dynamos operate as motors. With any appreciable unbalance, one dynamo operates as motor to drive the other as generator to supply a part of the unbalanced current.

The action of this set may best be illustrated by the hydraulic analogy shown in Fig. 443. Water is supplied by the canal A. This water falls over a weir into canal B and may be made to do useful work. All this water is not needed at the other point of utilization D between the canal B and the tailrace C. Some of the water which is not needed at D passes to C through the water wheel shown in the figure. This water wheel is belted to a centrifugal pump operating between B and A. In virtue of the water passing through the water wheel some of the water in the canal B is pumped back to A by the pump, where it may be utilized again. The water wheel corresponds to the motor, or dynamo B, Fig. 442, and the centrifugal pump to the generator, or dynamo A.

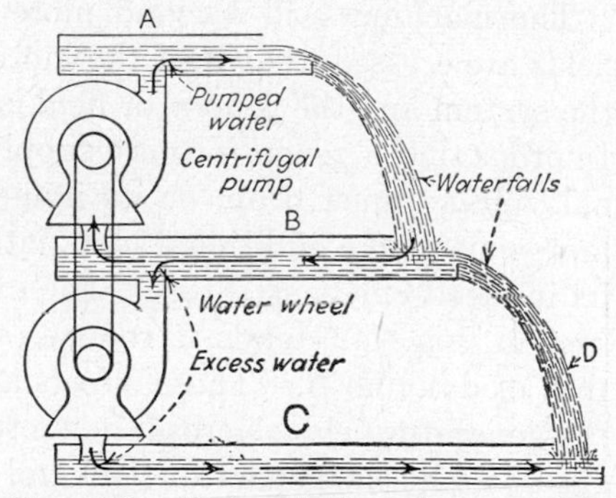

Fig. 443. Water-wheel analogue of balancer set.

If in Fig. 443 more water is required at D between canals B and C than can be supplied by the weir at A, the centrifugal pump may act as a water wheel and the water wheel as a pump. Some of the extra water required at D will be supplied through the upper machine operating as a water wheel and discharging into B. In so doing the upper machine drives the lower machine as a pump. The lower machine then pumps water from C back to B to supply the remainder of the water required at D. This condition corresponds to an excess of load on the negative side of the system of Fig. 442.

If in Fig. 442 there is an excess of load on the positive side of the system, as represented by 20 amp in the neutral, 12.2 amp of this 20 amp goes through the motor and in dropping through 115 volts gives up its energy. The motor then causes the generator to pump 7.8 amp back to the positive side of the line. This current distribution is determined in the following manner:

Each of the dynamos A and B is assumed to have 80 per cent efficiency. Let I_1 be the generator current in dynamo A, and I_2 be the motor current in dynamo B. The generator output will be $0.8 \cdot 0.8 = 0.64$ times the motor input. Assuming that the voltages are equal, actually they will be slightly unbalanced,

$$115I_2 \cdot 0.64 = 73.6I_2 = 115I_1.$$
$$I_1 + I_2 = 20.$$

Solving,

$$I_1 = 7.8 \text{ amp.}$$
$$I_2 = 12.2 \text{ amp.}$$

The machines will respond more readily to unbalanced loads if their fields are crossed, that is, if the motor field is across the generator side of the system and the generator field is across the motor side of the system. In order that a generator may supply additional current, either its terminal voltage must drop, or its induced emf must rise. In order that a motor may take additional load, either its terminal voltage must rise, or its induced emf must drop. The excess load on the positive side of the system, Fig. 442, tends to reduce the field of dynamo A and to increase that of dynamo B. These effects are the reverse of what is desired. If the generator field is across the motor side of the line, the increased voltage is across the generator field and will raise the generator induced emf. Therefore, its terminal voltage need not drop so much to take care of unbalanced currents.

A much better method, however, is to use a series field with each machine. The series fields should be so connected that the dynamo acting as generator is cumulatively compounded and that acting as motor is differentially compounded. If, for example, the greater load is on the positive side of the system, the emf of this machine, which is acting as a generator, is increased by the action of the series field. On the other hand, the emf of the machine on the negative side, which is acting as a motor, is decreased by the action of its series field. Hence, the machine on the positive side can function as a generator, and the machine on the negative side as a motor, without there being any change in terminal voltage. With the greater load on the negative side, it follows that the machine on this side of the system will be cumulatively compounded as a generator, and the other differentially compounded as a motor, and the system can function without the voltages to neutral becoming unbalanced.

Figure 444 shows standard connections for a balancer set with series fields. The machines are started in series, with the neutral switch *S* open and the shunt fields in series across the line. When the machines are up to speed, the neutral switch *S* is closed. If the voltages on the two sides

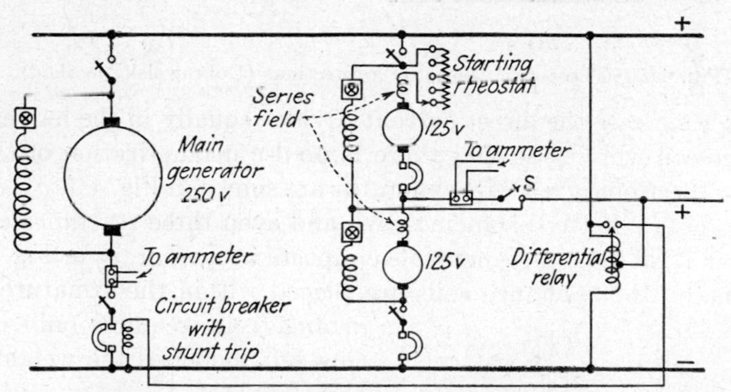

FIG. 444. Connections of 3-wire system using balancer set.

of the system become widely different, the currents in the halves of the differential relay become unbalanced. This relay then closes the tripping-coil circuit of the main generator breaker, resulting in the main generator circuit opening, even though *its* load is not excessive. This prevents injury to apparatus connected between the outer conductors and neutral, due to its being subjected to improper voltage.

381. Three-wire Generator. The 3-wire-generator, or Dobrowolsky, method is an efficient means for obtaining a neutral. The details of the method can be understood better after alternating currents and the synchronous converter have been studied.[1] The principle of the method is as follows: Alternating current is generated in a d-c armature, as is shown in Chap. XI (p. 369). If slip rings be employed, alternating current is obtained from the generator. A reactance coil wound on an iron core, therefore having high inductance and offering high impedance to alternating current, is connected across the slip rings. The center of this inductance, or reactance, coil is at the electrical center of gravity of the

[1] See Vol. II, Chap. XII.

voltages in the armature. Further, the inductance coil offers very little resistance to direct current. Therefore, if the neutral be connected to the center of this coil, the voltage to either brush from the neutral will be the same. Moreover, any current returning through the neutral can enter the armature readily through the reactance coil. Also, current going out over the neutral can leave the armature through the reactance

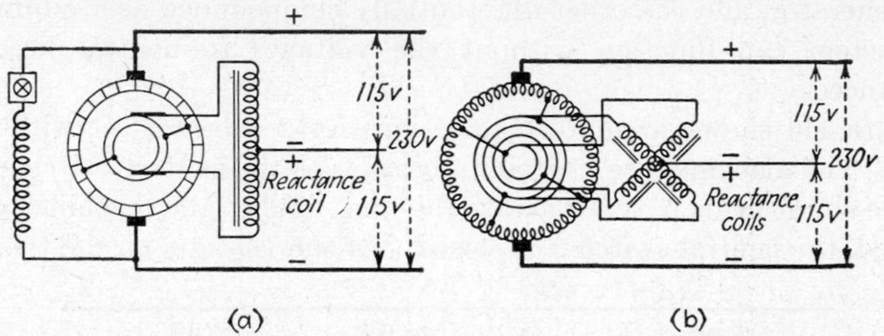

Fig. 445. Three-wire generator connections (Dobrowolsky method).

coil. In each case the direct current divides equally in the halves of the reactance-coil winding so that there is no d-c magnetization of the iron.

The connections of a 3-wire generator are shown in Fig. 445(a). Sometimes, to obtain better balancing, two and even three reactance coils are employed. All have their neutrals connected together, as in Fig. 445(b). Occasionally, the reactance coils are placed within the armature. This arrangement requires only one slip ring but increases the weight of the armature.

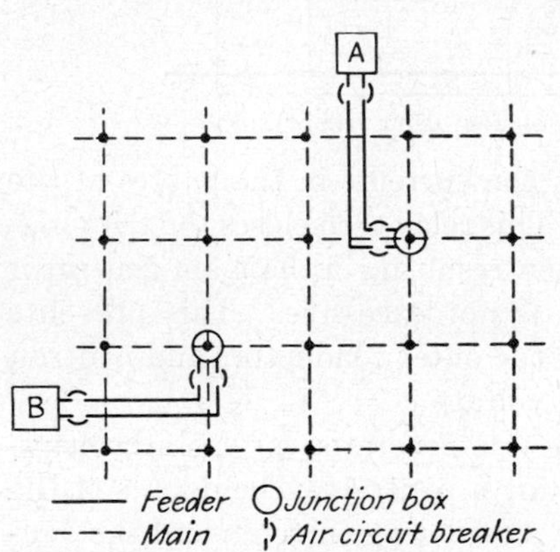

Fig. 446. Direct-current distribution network.

The Edison 3-wire system may be extended to 4-, 5-, 6-, and 7-conductor systems (see Fig. 405, p. 510). The complications and number of conductors prevent these multiconductor systems being extensively used.

Direct current is still used in isolated plants, particularly in industries where d-c power is desirable or essential, as in electrochemical processes, variable-speed motor drives, etc. The distribution system is essentially the same as for utilities, but on a much smaller scale.

382. Direct-current Distribution System. In the thickly settled city districts where direct current is still used, the distribution system consists of a network of mains to which the consumers' services are connected. In Fig. 446 is shown a one-line diagram of a typical system. The network is supplied at various points, called *centers,* by feeders connected to the d-c bus bars at the d-c substation. The center consists of a junction box which contains bus bars to which the mains are connected, usually through fuse links.

In Fig. 446, two feeders connect each substation, A and B, to a junction box. An air circuit breaker is shown at the station end and the load end of each feeder. On account of the necessity for continuity of service, the circuit breakers do not trip on straight overload, but only when a failure occurs in the cable itself. One method of effecting the tripping action is to run control wires, similar to the pressure wires, Fig. 447, to operate the breakers. A failure in the cable produces current to ground in the control wires, which trips both circuit breakers.

In order that the voltages of the centers may be determined and so maintained at the desired values, pilot, or pressure, wires run back to the station voltmeter. By means of a dial switch, the operator is able to read the voltages at the various centers. Figure 447 shows the cross section of a concentric 1,000,000-cir-mil cable. The outer and inner conductors are the outer conductors of the Edison 3-wire system. The neutral is usually a separate conductor of much smaller cross section, or there may be one large neutral common to several feeders and mains. The three pilot, or pressure, wires are connected one to each outer conductor and one to the neutral at the feeding point. If the operator finds that the voltage is too low at the feeding point, he connects a feeder to a bus bar of higher voltage. A substantial voltage drop can occur in such feeders, as no loads are taken off at intermediate points.

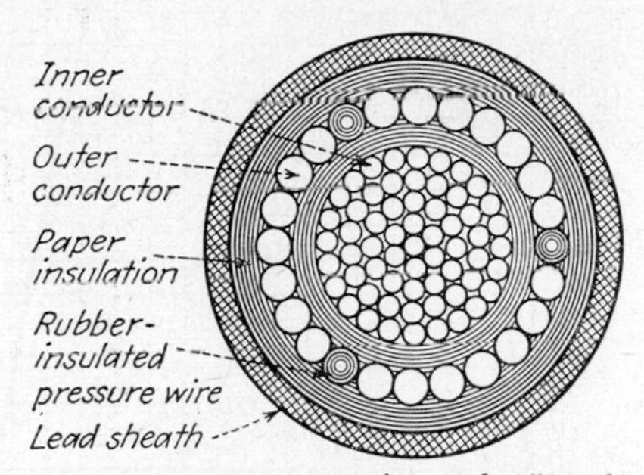

FIG. 447. Cross section of 250-volt 1,000,000-cir-mil concentric cable.

In practice, the following are the percentage drops usually allowed: in feeders, 5 to 10 per cent; in the distribution mains, 3 per cent.

383. Maximum Power over a Feeder. In Sec. 50 (p. 57), it is shown that the maximum power which a battery can deliver occurs when the external resistance is equal to the internal resistance of the battery. Under these conditions the voltage drop within the battery is equal to its terminal voltage. This same rule applies to any condition where a constant-voltage source is supplying a concentrated load through a fixed resistance. Consider a d-c feeder, or transmission, line which is fed from constant-voltage bus bars. The line resistance is constant. As load is applied at the end of the line, the current I increases and the voltage V at the load decreases, as is shown in Sec. 44 (p. 49). The power delivered is VI. This power will increase so long as I increases faster than V

decreases. When the load voltage V is equal to one-half the sending-end voltage, VI is a maximum. Further decrease in the load resistance results in V decreasing faster than I increases, and the power therefore decreases with further increase in I. This relation is shown in Fig. 448. The following example is given to illustrate these conditions:

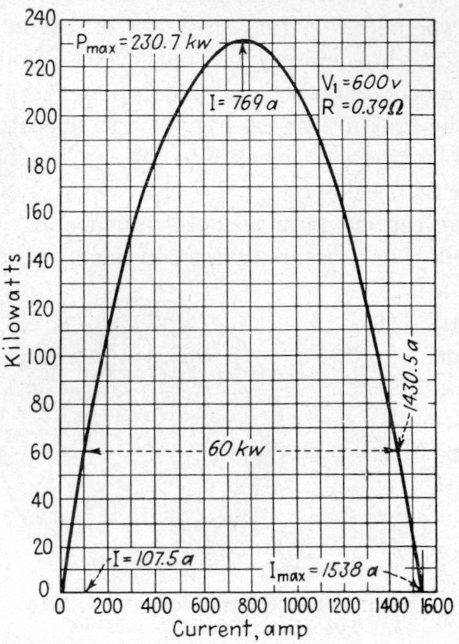

Fig. 448. Power and current over feeder.

Example. A power station supplies 60 kw to a load over 2,500 ft of 000 2-conductor copper feeder the resistance of which is 0.078 ohm per 1,000 ft. The bus-bar voltage is maintained constant at 600 volts. Determine: (*a*) current; (*b*) voltage at load; (*c*) efficiency of transmission; (*d*) maximum power which can be transmitted; (*e*) maximum current which can be supplied.

(*a*) Total resistance $R = 5 \cdot 0.078 = 0.39$ ohm.

Let I be the current and V the voltage at the load:

$$60{,}000 = VI. \qquad \text{(I)}$$

$$V = 600 - 0.39I. \qquad \text{(II)}$$

Substituting V from (II) in (I),

$$60{,}000 = (600 - 0.39I)I.$$

$$0.39I^2 - 600I = -60{,}000. \qquad \text{(III)}$$

Dividing (III) by 0.39,

$$I^2 - 1{,}538I = -153{,}800. \qquad \text{(IV)}$$

This is a quadratic equation and must have two roots. Hence, two values of current will satisfy the given conditions. Completing the square and solving,

$$I^2 - 1{,}538I + (769)^2 = -153{,}800 + (769)^2.$$

$$(I - 769)^2 = 437{,}600.$$

$$I - 769 = \pm\sqrt{437{,}600}.$$

$$I = 769 \pm 661.5$$

$$= 1{,}430.5, \text{ or } 107.5 \text{ amp.}$$

Both values of current satisfy (I) and (II), but if the larger value of current were used, the efficiency would be too low. Hence, the current

$$I = 107.5 \text{ amp.} \quad \textit{Ans.}$$

(*b*) $V = 600 - (0.39 \cdot 107.5) = 600 - 41.9 = 558.1$ volts. *Ans.*

$P = 558.1 \cdot 107.5 = 60{,}000$ watts, or 60 kw (*check*).

(*c*) $\eta = \dfrac{558.1}{600} = 0.930$, or 93.0%. *Ans.*

(*d*) Repeating (I), (II), (III), (IV) with power represented by P,

$$P = VI = (600 - 0.39I)I. \qquad \text{(V)}$$

$$0.39I^2 - 600I = -P.$$

Dividing by 0.39 and completing the square ($591{,}400 = \overline{769^2}$),

$$I^2 - 1{,}538I + 591{,}400 = 591{,}400 - 2.564P.$$
$$I - 769 = \pm\sqrt{2.564}\sqrt{230{,}700 - P}.$$
$$I = 769 \pm 1.6\sqrt{230{,}700 - P}.$$

If the power P exceeds 230,700 watts, the quantity under the radical is negative, the radical is an imaginary quantity, and the current is the sum of a real and an imaginary quantity, showing that this condition is impossible. Hence, the maximum value which the power P can have is 230,700 watts, or 230.7 kw.

Since, under these conditions, the radical is zero, the two roots of the equation are equal. Hence, the current I has but a single value and is equal to 769 amp (see Fig. 448).

The voltage at the load,

$$V = 600 - (769 \cdot 0.39) = 600 - 300, \text{ or } 300 \text{ volts.}$$

The maximum power which can be transmitted,

$$P_m = 300 \cdot 769 = 230{,}700 \text{ watts, or } 230.7 \text{ kw.} \quad \textit{Ans.}$$

Under these conditions, one-half the power is lost in the line, and the efficiency is 50 per cent. This corresponds to the similar condition for batteries (p. 58).

The value of maximum power is more readily determined by the use of calculus. Let V_1 be the bus-bar voltage, V the load voltage, I the current, r the total line resistance, and P the power to the load. Then,

$$V = V_1 - Ir.$$
$$P = VI = V_1I - I^2r.$$

Taking the first derivative of the power with respect to the current, and equating to zero to obtain the condition for maximum power,

$$\frac{dP}{dI} = V_1 - 2Ir = 0,$$
$$Ir = \frac{V_1}{2},$$

and

$$V = V_1 - Ir = V_1 - \frac{V_1}{2} = \frac{V_1}{2}. \tag{376}$$

(e) The maximum current occurs when the load is short-circuited. That is,

$$I = \frac{600}{0.39} = 1{,}538 \text{ amp.} \quad \textit{Ans.}$$

The power supplied to the load under these conditions must be zero since the voltage at the load is zero.

To illustrate further these relations between power and voltage, the curve, Fig. 448, is given. Current is plotted as abscissa and power as ordinate. Different values of current are assumed, substituted in (V), and the equation solved for the power P. The power must be zero when the current is zero (voltage V a maximum) and when the voltage V is zero (current a maximum). It is clear that for any given value of power, except the maximum, there are two different values of current. The maximum power is 230.7 kw and occurs when the current is 769 amp. At this point both roots of the quadratic equation are equal. In practice the power transmitted is usually a small proportion of the maximum power, as can be seen by the position of the 60-kw point on the curve, Fig. 448.

Also the other solution of (IV), $I = 1{,}430.5$ amp, is found at the second intersection of the characteristic with the 60-kw ordinate.

384. Electric-railway Distribution. Electric-railway generators are generally compounded, the series field being on the negative side. The negative terminal is usually connected directly to ground or to the rail through a switch. The positive terminal feeds the trolley through an ammeter, a switch, and a circuit breaker.

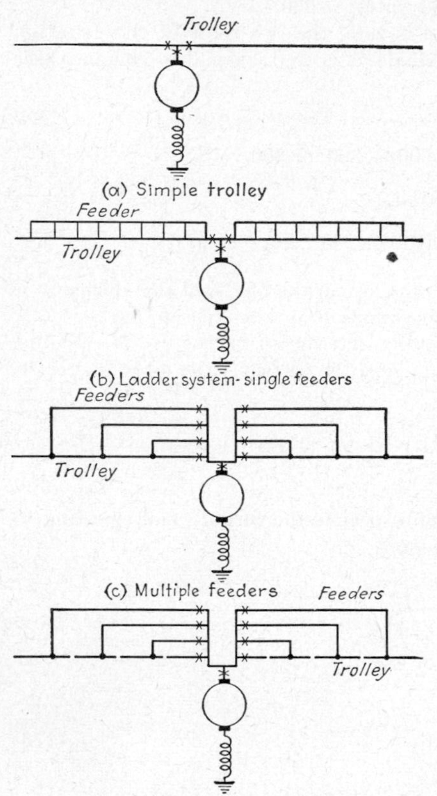

FIG. 449. Methods of feeding trolley system.

On short lines, with light traffic, the trolley alone may suffice to carry the current to the car, Fig. 449(*a*). Except in small installations, the trolley is not of sufficient cross section to supply the required power and at the same time to keep the voltage drop within the necessary limits. As the size of the trolley wire is limited by the trolley wheel, it cannot be conveniently increased. The same result as increasing the size of the trolley may be obtained by running a feeder in parallel with the trolley and connecting the feeder to the trolley at short intervals, Fig. 449(*b*). This is called the *ladder system* of feeding. The trolley and feeder together may be considered as forming a single conductor.

Where the density of traffic requires several feeders, better results are obtained by connecting the feeders in the manner of Fig. 449(*c*). Each feeder is protected by a circuit breaker.

The objections to the preceding methods of feeding are that trouble, due to a ground, for example, at any point on the trolley, involves the entire system. In cities where traffic is particularly dense, it is not permissible to take chances of having the entire system shut down because of a ground at one point only. Therefore, the trolley is sectionalized, Fig. 449(*d*). In this method the trolley is divided into insulated sections, each of which is supplied by a separate feeder. Trouble in one section is not readily communicated to the other sections. This increased reliability is obtained at the expense of efficiency in the use of the copper, as the feeders are unable to assist one another. In the preceding systems this mutual assistance exists.

In (*d*), when the trolley wheel passes over the insulation between sections, the motorman is required to move the controller to the "off" position, after which he may move it rapidly back to the "full-speed" position. Were the controller left in the full-speed position, even a small voltage difference between sections would cause a large momentary current to the motors. This is due to the fact that the difference between the terminal voltage and the induced emf is small, and a small change in either makes a large proportionate change in their difference. Unless

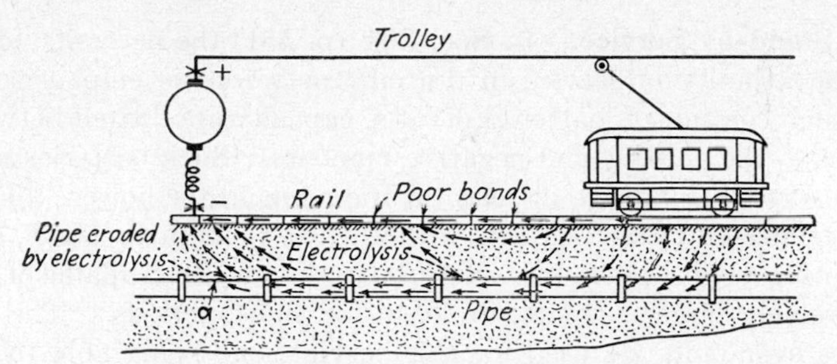

Fig. 450. Electrolysis by earth currents.

resistance is introduced in the armature circuit, the change in current will be large [see Eq. (353), p. 487].

The foregoing methods of supplying power to trolley systems also apply equally well to trolley-bus systems, to third-rail systems, and to d-c railroad electrification.

385. Electrolysis by Earth Currents. Most trolley systems use the track as the return conductor for the current taken by the car. The paths of the return currents are not only through the tracks themselves, for the currents, by spreading through the earth, seek the paths of least resistance by which they may return to the negative terminal of the station generator. Such currents in spreading through the earth follow such low-resistance conductors as water pipes, gas pipes, and cable sheaths, Fig. 450. The fact that current *enters* and flows in these conductors does no harm. However, such currents must ultimately leave these conductors, etc., as at *a*, Fig. 450. In leaving, they tend to carry the metal of the pipe into electrolytic solution, which ultimately results in the pipe being eroded away. To decrease the effects of electrolysis, several expedients have been used. Two of the most successful are the following. (*a*) Provide a return path of as low a resistance as possible. This is done by good bonding and by using insulated negative feeders, that is, heavy copper feeders that are carried back to the negative bus from various points along the track. Figure 450 indicates how poor rail bonds may cause the current to leave the track and enter the pipe. In some cities the total permissible drop in the ground-return circuit must not exceed 10 to 15 volts. (*b*) Discourage the entering of the current into the pipes by inserting occasional insulating joints in the pipes.

In testing for electrolysis, the usual method is to measure the voltage existing between the track and the water pipes (as at a hydrant). The magnitude of this voltage indicates roughly the magnitude of the current from one to the other. The polarity shows the direction of the current. For example, if the track is positive to the pipe, the direction of current must be from the track to the pipe.

APPLICATIONS OF STORAGE BATTERIES TO POWER SYSTEMS

386. Stand-by Service. In Sec. 365 (p. 551) the necessity for maintaining continuity of service in d-c city networks is emphasized. To secure such continuity, batteries of large capacity are floated between the neutral and the positive and negative bus bars. Such batteries also provide for any sudden large increase in the demand for power. They are solidly connected to the bus bars without fuses, circuit breakers, or other interrupting devices in circuit. Such batteries must be capable of delivering extremely large currents, at least for short periods. The largest batteries ever built are used for this service, one being able to deliver 37,000 amp to the 250-volt bus bars for 10 min.

In order that the floating battery may discharge when required, it is necessary with constant bus-bar voltage to increase the battery emf. The most common method of controlling the discharge of batteries under these conditions is by means of end-cell switches (Sec. 391).

The batteries may be charged by a separate motor-generator set after being disconnected from the bus bars, or they may be charged from the bus bars by a booster generator. Shunt generators are well suited for battery charging but require frequent adjustments of the field rheostat. Because of its constant-voltage characteristics, the diverter-pole generator (p. 468) is now widely used. The number of cells used in stand-by service is usually 150, which at 2.15 volts per cell gives 322.5 volts total. This permits a large discharge rate without the terminal voltage decreasing to too low a value.

Duty cycles of stand-by batteries are relatively light, and the batteries are installed in the business districts of cities where space is valuable. Hence, the pasted-plate type of battery is used because of its high-discharge rate and smaller size.

387. Regulating Duty. There are d-c installations which may be supplied by a d-c generator, synchronous converter, or a rectifier, where continuity of service justifies the use of a floating battery for emergency operation. In addition, however, the battery may assist in absorbing the fluctuations of load and thus reduce the rating of the necessary electrical apparatus, which otherwise would need to be of sufficient rating to carry the load peaks: that is, when the load exceeds the average, the battery discharges and carries the excess. When the load is below the average, the battery is charged.

For example, in Fig. 451 is shown a typical load curve for a central station. From before midnight until 6 A.M. the load is comparatively light, consisting for the most part of street lights, some few commercial loads such as fans and pumps, and a small residential and commercial lighting load. This constitutes a "valley" of the load curve. Just

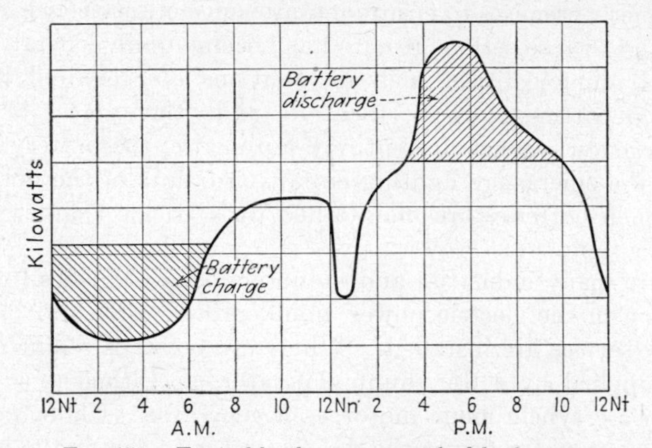

FIG. 451. Typical load curve smoothed by battery.

before 6 A.M. the load begins to increase rapidly, owing to the beginning of activities by the population, the starting of streetcar service (if it is supplied by this system), and also the starting up of commercial loads by various industries.

A distinct valley occurs between 12 M. and 1 P.M., due to the lunch hour. The afternoon peak occurs between 5 and 6 P.M., particularly in winter, when the late afternoon lighting load is superposed on the commercial and streetcar loads. The smaller load in the evening consists for the most part of household and other lighting.

The ratio of average to maximum load is the *load factor*. Obviously, a large load factor is desirable.

Example. A station delivers 192,000 kwhr in a day, and its peak load is 20,000 kw. Determine daily load factor.

$$\text{The average load} = \frac{192{,}000}{24} = 8{,}000 \text{ kw.}$$

$$\text{The load factor} = \frac{8{,}000}{20{,}000} = 0.40, \text{ or } 40\%. \quad \textit{Ans.}$$

With a d-c station, theoretically the battery floated across the bus bars could discharge on the peak of the load curve and be charged during the valley, Fig. 451. However, even with a battery already floating on the bus bars, this is not economical, for the saving in kilowatts capacity of generating apparatus is more than offset by the more rapid deterioration of the battery caused by repeated charging and discharging. On the other hand, in a few small isolated plants, a battery is used to smooth out the load curve, as indicated in Fig. 451. Also, batteries floating across the bus bars may absorb small fluctuations of load, but in this type of duty the charging and discharging is so light that it causes negligible deterioration of the battery.

388. Emergency Light and Power. The installation of a battery on the consumer's premises to ensure maintenance of service where an interruption might cause serious results has become quite general. In many states and municipalities, such installations are required by law for hospitals, department stores, theaters, and other places of assembly. Such emergency systems are entirely automatic, the battery being connected to the emergency lighting circuit on failure of the normal power source. Such batteries are maintained by a trickle charger, usually of the rectifier type.

There are many industrial and manufacturing processes for which an interruption in the electric power would prove costly and batteries for emergency service are installed. Where a-c power is required, it is frequently supplied by a d-c shunt generator, operating as a motor and driving an a-c synchronous motor as a generator. Under normal conditions, the a-c motor drives the d-c generator to charge the battery.

Fig. 452. Resistance control of battery discharge.

389. Resistance Control. In controlling the load taken by a generator connected to the bus bars, it is necessary to change its induced emf by changing the field current. It is not possible to adjust the emf of a storage battery in this manner. One method of controlling the output of the battery is by having the battery emf several volts higher than the bus-bar voltage and by inserting a resistor in series with the battery, Fig. 452. By adjusting this resistor, the load delivered by the battery may be controlled. The disadvantage of this method is the loss of power and the voltage drop in the resistor, which varies with the load. Even with constant load, the resistor must be adjusted occasionally to compensate for the drop in battery emf during discharge.

Example. It is desired to discharge a storage battery, consisting of 115 cells, each having an emf of 2.1 volts and an internal resistance of 0.001 ohm, into 220-volt bus bars so that the battery delivers 100 amp. Determine the value of resistance to which the series resistor must be adjusted.

Total battery emf

$$E = 115 \cdot 2.1 = 241.5 \text{ volts}$$

Bus-bar voltage

$$V = 220 \text{ volts.}$$

The battery resistance

$$r = 115 \cdot 0.001 = 0.115 \text{ ohm.}$$

Let R equal the added external resistance.

$$100 = \frac{241.5 - 220}{0.115 + R}.$$

$$100R = 21.5 - 11.5 = 10.0.$$

$$R = 0.10 \text{ ohm.} \quad \textit{Ans.}$$

390. Counter-electromotive-force Cells. It is characteristic of storage cells, of either the lead or the alkaline type, that when being charged, their terminal voltage does not change greatly over a wide range in the value of the charging current. This principle is utilized in controlling the current delivered by a battery.

A few cells are connected at an end of the battery so that their emfs oppose the current. The rate of discharge is regulated by the number of cells in circuit, and some means, such as an end-cell switch, Fig. 453, is provided for switching the cells in and out of circuit. Since such cells are not required to store energy, they are made up of plain lead or nickel plates and the appropriate electrolyte. In lead cells a counter emf of from 2.25 to 2.50 volts per cell is developed and in the nickel-alkaline cell the counter emf is approximately 2.00 volts. The advantage of this method over resistance control is that the opposing, or control, emf is substantially independent of changes in load.

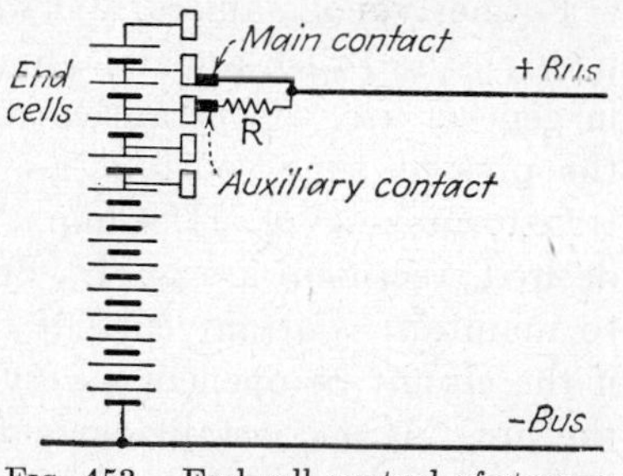

FIG. 453. End-cell control of storage battery.

391. End-cell Control. A battery consists usually of a sufficient number of cells to give an emf exceeding by an ample margin that of the bus bars. The emf of the battery, and hence its load, may be controlled by cutting in or out the cells at the end of the battery.

It is essential to do this without opening the circuit. For this purpose a switch is used similar to that shown in Fig. 453. The main contact is connected to the auxiliary contact by a resistor R. When sliding from one battery contact to the next, the auxiliary contact maintains the circuit connections through the resistor R. Were there zero resistance between the main contact and its auxiliary contact, the individual cells would be dead-short-circuited during the transition period. The resistor R is usually so chosen as to permit the normal battery current during the transition period. In Fig. 453 the position of the switch is that corresponding to the transition period. The end-cell switches become rather massive in large battery installations and are often operated by a motor-driven worm. This also permits remote control.

The end cells, not being in continuous service, are discharged to a lesser degree than the main battery cells. Therefore the end cells require individual attention on charging.

392. Series Distribution. In the parallel system of distribution, the loads are all independent of one another. That is, a load applied at any one point does not affect any of the other loads, provided that the voltage does not change. In the series system the loads are all in series with one another so that the current in each load is the same. Therefore, if the circuit of any one load be opened, the current to all the other loads will be interrupted. As this is not permissible in practice, a load must be *short-circuited* when it is desired to remove it from service.

Formerly, constant current was supplied by series generators (Sec. 312, p. 461), the Brush-arc and Thomson-Houston generators being the types in general use. Constant-current d-c generators are now obsolete. At the present time constant a-c current is supplied by constant-current transformers (Vol. II, Chap. VIII), and if constant direct current is desired, rectifiers are used. Such constant-current power sources tend to maintain constant current under all conditions of load. Therefore, if the circuit be opened, a very high resistance is introduced, usually in the arc. If a constant current is maintained across a high resistance, a high voltage results. If an actual open circuit does occur, the power source will still attempt to maintain constant current and the voltage will reach dangerously high values. For this reason, the lamps in constant-current systems are protected by a thin disk of paper between the lamp terminals (film cutout). If the lamp burns out, the high voltage across this paper punctures it and so prevents the opening of the circuit.

The advantage of the series system is the small amount of copper required. This is due to the fact that the copper carries only the current of a single load. As the loads are in series, the resulting voltage is high. Therefore, this system is applicable only to outside work, such as street lighting, because it would ordinarily be dangerous to have such high voltages in buildings.

Another important advantage of the series lighting system is that incandescent lamps on a constant-current system maintain a high lumen efficiency (about 97 per cent) throughout their life, while the lumen efficiency of the constant-voltage incandescent lamp drops to a value of about 79 per cent at the end of its rated life. The lumen efficiency will continue to decline to much lower values if the lamps are not replaced. The power to an incandescent lamp is I^2R, and, with the continual evaporation of the filament which occurs in service, R increases. Since, in the series lamp, the current I is maintained constant, the power to the lamp and hence the filament temperature increase, which nearly compensates for the blackening of the inside of the lamp. For the multiple lamp the power is E^2/R, where E is the voltage across the lamp. As R increases with the reduction of filament cross section, the power

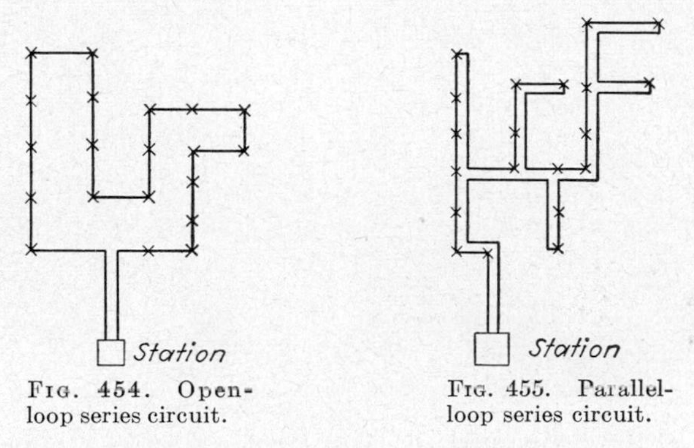

FIG. 454. Open-loop series circuit.

FIG. 455. Parallel-loop series circuit.

decreases. Hence, the reduction in wattage and blackening of the glass act in conjunction to reduce the lumens.

There are two general methods of connecting such series loads. In the open-loop system, Fig. 454, the circuit is connected to the loads without reference to the separation of the two conductors. This system is economical of copper.

In the parallel-loop system the outgoing and return conductors are always kept near each other, Fig. 455. This system requires more copper than the open-loop system but facilitates testing for faults and reduces the inductive effect on neighboring circuits.

QUESTIONS AND PROBLEMS

QUESTIONS ON CHAPTER I

Resistance

1. Name the principal factors which make electrical energy so useful and so important, with particular reference to flexibility, generation, transmission, and applications.

2. Describe the mechanism of current, or the flow of electricity, according to modern theory. In what important respect does the atomic structure of insulators differ from that of conductors?

3. Discuss the principal ways by which resistance manifests itself in an electric circuit in which there is current. According to modern theory, how may the power loss in resistance be accounted for by the action of electrons? What is the mechanical analogue of resistance?

4. In what way, so far as atomic structure is concerned, do insulators differ from conductors?

5. Name the three general classes into which conductors may be divided. For each class describe the mechanism of conduction.

6. What substances are the best conductors? What substances are insulators? Discuss any boundary which may exist between conductors and insulators. Compare the relative resistivities of a good conductor and a good insulator.

7. Name and define the unit of resistance. Define a megohm; a milliohm; a microhm.

8. With constant cross section, how does the resistance of a homogeneous substance vary with its length? With constant length, how does the resistance of a homogeneous substance vary with its cross section? What factor other than the geometrical shape of a body of given resistivity determines its resistance?

9. Define volume resistivity. Upon what factor does it depend? If the volume of a given substance is fixed, how does the resistance vary with the length? with the cross section?

10. What is conductance, and how does it vary with length and with cross section? Distinguish between conductance and conductivity.

11. How is the resistance determined for a current path if the cross section varies with the length? Cite a simple example of such a path. What is the relation of the total resistance of a circuit to the resistances of its individual parts when these are connected in series?

12. What is the relation of the total conductance of a circuit to the conductances of its individual parts when these are connected in parallel? From this relation show how resistances connected in parallel may be combined into an equivalent resistance.

13. What is the meaning of the term *mil?* What is a square mil? A circular mil? What relation does one bear to the other? When is the circular mil usually chosen as the unit of cross section? What are its advantages over such units as the square mil and the square inch? What is the relation between the number of circular mils in a circular cross section and its diameter?

14. Define a circular-mil-foot. What is its approximate resistance for copper? How may the resistance of a copper wire be determined if its length in feet and its cross section in circular mils be known?

15. Define a circular-mil-inch. What is its resistance for copper at 60°C? For what types of resistance calculations is this unit of resistivity very convenient?

16. Name the different units in which the mass and volume resistivities of the International Annealed Copper Standard are expressed. What is the approximate per cent conductivity of commercial copper in terms of the standard?

17. What is the approximate per cent volume conductivity, in terms of the copper standard, of hard-drawn aluminum conductor? Similarly, what is the per cent *mass conductivity* of the aluminum conductor?

18. What is meant by resistivity specifications? What resistivity standard is most commonly used for determining the resistivity of a copper specimen?

19. For what purposes are resistor materials used? Compare the general properties and the applications of the nickel-chromium, the chromium-nickel-steel, and the ferro-nickel alloys. What is their approximate volume conductivity in terms of that of copper?

20. What is manganin, and what is the particular property which makes it useful?

21. How is the resistance of most of the unalloyed metals affected by temperature? What is *temperature coefficient of resistance?* How is it used? How is the temperature coefficient of resistance at any initial temperature determined?

22. At what temperature would the resistance of copper be zero if the resistance decreased at the same rate that it decreases within ordinary ranges of temperature? How may this result be used to solve problems involving resistance and temperature?

23. Define semiconductors, stating their general range of resistivities. What is the nature of their temperature coefficients of resistance? Define a varistor; a thermistor. Name some of the substances of which semiconductors are made. State some of the applications of thermistors.

24. What is the basis of the American wire gage (AWG)? What relations do the diameters of successive gage numbers bear to one another?

25. In the AWG what are the relations between the cross sections of wires differing by three gage numbers? by one number? by two numbers? How do these relations enable one to determine readily the resistance and weight of any given size of wire? What is the resistance of 1,000 ft of No. 10 wire? What is the weight of 1,000 ft. of No. 10 wire? Of No. 2 wire?

26. Why is stranding necessary with the larger sizes of wire? What is the gage number of the largest size of solid copper wire? State the relation of the number of wires in successive layers of a stranded cable and the number of wires in standard cables.

27. What are the best conductors among the metals? State an application where silver may be used advantageously. Which of the metals is most commonly used as a conductor? Give reasons. Compared with copper, what are the advantages and the disadvantages of aluminum as a conductor? When are iron and steel used as conductors? Explain.

PROBLEMS ON CHAPTER I

Resistance

1. The resistance of a cylindrical brass conductor, 0.5 cm diameter and 3 m long, is 0.0108 ohm. Determine resistance of a cylindrical conductor of the same material at the same temperature, and having a diameter of 0.25 cm and a length of 8 m.

2. The diameter of a cylindrical conductor A is 6 mm, and its length is 2 m. The diameter and length of a cylindrical conductor B of the same material as A are 3 mm and 1 m. The resistance of conductor B is 0.02 ohm. Determine resistance of conductor A, its temperature being the same as that of B.

3. The resistance of a 10-ft length of resistor material having a cross section of 0.00204 sq in is 4.1 ohms. The resistance at the same temperature of a 12-ft length of the same material is 7.7 ohms. Determine its cross section in square inches.

4. The resistivity of copper is 1.724 microhm-cm at 20°C. Determine for copper, at the same temperature, the resistance (*a*) between opposite faces of an inch cube; (*b*) of a wire 1 ft long and 0.001 in. in diameter (cir-mil-ft); (*c*) of a rod 1 m long and having a diameter of 1 mm.

5. The resistance of a 200-ft length of a copper-bronze alloy at 20°C is 1.46 ohms, and its diameter is 0.0508 in. At the same temperature, determine the resistivity in (*a*) centimeter units; (*b*) circular-mil-foot units.

6. The resistivity of standard copper at 20°C is 0.6788 microhm-in. Determine the resistance at the same temperature of 500 ft of No. 8 AWG solid copper conductor which has a diameter of 0.128 in.

7. A copper bus bar is built of two copper bars 50 ft long, each having a cross section of 5 by ¼ in. The two bars are spaced 0.5 in between adjacent surfaces, and they are connected in parallel. The resistivity of the copper is 0.738 microhm-in. at the operating temperature. Determine: (*a*) resistance of bus bar; (*b*) total weight, if weight of an inch cube of copper is 0.3214 lb.

8. Repeat (*a*), (*b*), Prob. 7, for an aluminum bus bar of the same length but now being made up of two aluminum bars each 6 by ½ in. cross section. The density of copper is 8.89 g per cu cm, and that of aluminum is 2.70. The resistivity of aluminum at the operating temperature is 1.113 microhm-in.

9. The resistivity of a ferric-chromium-aluminum alloy is 51.0 microhm-in. A sheet of the material is 15 in. long, 6 in. wide, and 0.014 in. thick. Determine resistance between (*a*) opposite ends; (*b*) opposite sides.

10. The cross section of No. 6 AWG copper wire is 13.30 sq mm, and the resistivity of copper at 20°C is $1.750 \cdot 10^{-6}$ ohm-cm. Determine length in meters of a No. 6 wire to give a resistance of 0.06 ohm at 20°C.

11. It is desired to obtain a resistance of 22.1 ohms with a 120-in. length of nickel-chromium-alloy ribbon which has a resistivity of 640 ohms (cir-mil-ft). Determine: (*a*) cross section in circular mils; (*b*) thickness if width of ribbon is 0.065 in.

12. The cross section of an 89.9-lb (per yd) third rail is 8.83 sq in., and the resistivity of the steel is 4.80 microhm-in. Neglecting the effect of joints, determine resistance of 1 mile of such rail.

13. A 1,000-ft length of No. 8 AWG copper wire has a resistance of 0.628 ohm at 20°C. Determine resistance of this same mass of copper if it were drawn down to one-half the cross section.

14. A cylindrical copper rod having a diameter of 0.40 in. has a resistance of 0.00264 ohm. Taking the resistivity of copper as 1.745 microhm-cm at 20°C, determine: (*a*) length of rod in feet; (*b*) resistance of rod when it is drawn down to one-third the initial diameter, the volume remaining unchanged. Assume that the resistivity of the copper is not affected by the drawing process.

15. The density of copper is 8.89 g per cu cm, and the resistivity is 1.724 microhm-cm. Determine length in meters and resistance of 12 kg of copper, the cross section of which is 2.09 sq mm.

16. A solid cylindrical aluminum rod has a diameter of 0.5 in. and weighs 23 lb. The density of aluminum is 2.70 g per cu cm (= 0.0974 lb per cu in.). Determine: (*a*) length; (*b*) diameter to which it should be drawn to give resistance of 1.07 ohm if volume remains unchanged; (*c*) circular mils in (*b*).

17. The resistivity of a commercial quality of copper is 0.686 microhm-in. at 20°C. Determine cross section in square inches and circular mils and resistance at 20°C of 121 lb of this copper when the length is 600 ft. The weight per cubic inch of copper is 0.321 lb.

18. The conductivity of aluminum is 353,600 mho-cm^{-1} at 20°C. Determine: (*a*) conductance and resistance at 20°C of an aluminum bus bar 6 by ½ in. and 42 ft long; (*b*) weight in pounds and in kilograms. The density of aluminum is 2.70 g per cu cm.

19. In Prob. 18 determine, for a bus bar of copper having the same conductance: (*a*) width if thickness is 0.375 in.; (*b*) weight. The conductivity of the copper is 566,000 mho-cm^{-1}, and the density is 8.89 g per cu cm.

20. The cross section of No. 6 AWG wire is 0.02062 sq in., and the resistivity at 25°C of the copper is 0.6794 microhm-in. Determine the conductance of 850 ft of such wire.

21. The resistance of a sample of "medium-strength" bronze trolley wire is measured in order to determine its resistivity. The cross section is circular, and the diameter is 0.460 in. (No. 0000); the resistance of a 38-in. length is found to be $2.392 \cdot 10^{-4}$ ohm at a temperature of 20°C. Determine: (*a*) resistance per foot; (*b*) resistivity in ohm-inches; (*c*) resistivity in ohm-centimeters; (*d*) conductivity as a per cent of that of the International Copper Standard (1.7241 microhm-cm).

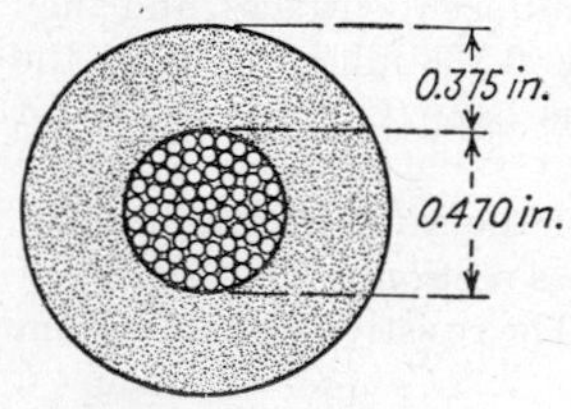

FIG. 22*A*.

22. In Fig. 22*A* is shown the cross section of a 000 AWG stranded copper cable. The surface of the cable may be considered smooth, and the diameter is 0.470 in. The wall of insulation is 0.375 in. thick, and the resistivity of the insulation is $5 \cdot 10^{15}$ ohm-cm. Determine the insulation resistance of (*a*) a 200-ft length; (*b*) a 850-ft length (see Sec. 9, p. 9).

23. In Fig. 23*A* is shown a metal bar, rectangular in cross section, the center portion of which is bent into semicircular form. The straight portions are each 5 cm long. The inner radius of the bent portion is 2 cm, the outer radius is 3 cm, and the thickness of the conductor is 1.5 cm. The resistivity is ρ ohm-cm. Current enters end surface *A* and leaves at *D*. Determine resistance between surfaces *A* and *D*. The resistance of the path between surfaces *B* and *C* should be determined by integration. NOTE. In order to perform the integration it is necessary first to find the *conductance* of path *BC*.

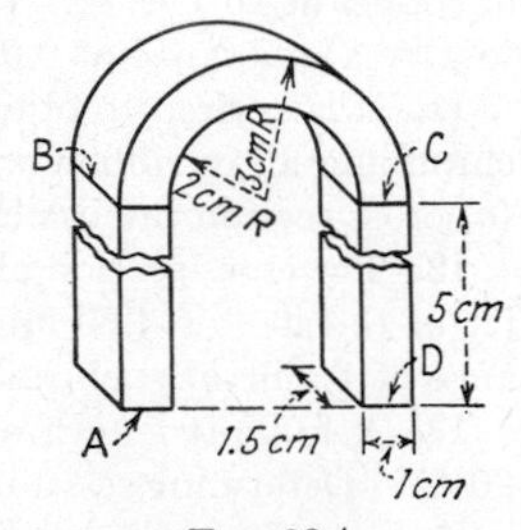

FIG. 23*A*.

24. The insulation resistance of a mile of rubber-insulated 000 solid copper wire is $3.45 \cdot 10^4$ megohms. The diameter of the conductor is 0.4096 in., and the thickness of the wall of insulation is 0.25 in. Determine resistivity of the rubber in (*a*) ohm-inches; (*b*) ohm-centimeters.

25. A sample of 000 AWG soft-drawn solid copper wire is measured at 20°C for resistivity, and the resistance between contact points 4 ft apart is found to be $2.52 \cdot 10^{-4}$ ohm. The weight of 1,000 ft of the 000 solid copper conductor is 508 lb. Determine for sample (*a*) resistance of 1 mile; (*b*) resistance of pound-mile; (*c*) resistance as per cent of ASTM and ASA Standard of 875.20 ohms (mile-pound) (Sec. 17, p. 16); (*d*) per cent conductivity in terms of standard in (*c*).

26. The resistance of a 500-ft coil of No. 6 AWG medium-soft-drawn solid copper wire is measured for resistivity at 25°C, and the resistance is found to be 0.2055 ohm. The weight of 1,000 ft of the No. 6 wire is 79.5 lb, and the temperature coefficient at 20°C is 0.00393. Determine: (*a*) resistance of coil at 20°C; (*b*) resistance of 1 mile; (*c*) resistance of pound-mile; (*d*) resistance as per cent of ASTM and ASA Standard of 905.44 ohms (mile-pound) (Sec. 17, p. 16); (*e*) per cent conductivity in terms of standard in (*d*).

27. A sample of 0000 AWG hard-drawn solid copper wire is measured at 26°C for resistivity, and the resistance between contact points 6 ft apart is found to be $3.04 \cdot 10^{-4}$ ohm. The weight of 1,000 ft of the 0000 solid copper wire is 641 lb, and the temperature coefficient of resistance of copper at 20°C is 0.00393. Determine for the sample (*a*) resistance at 20°C; (*b*) resistance of 1 mile; (*c*) resistance of pound-mile; (*d*) resistance as per cent of ASTM and ASA Standard of 900.77 ohms (mile-pound) (Sec. 17, p. 16); (*e*) per cent conductivity in terms of standard in (*d*).

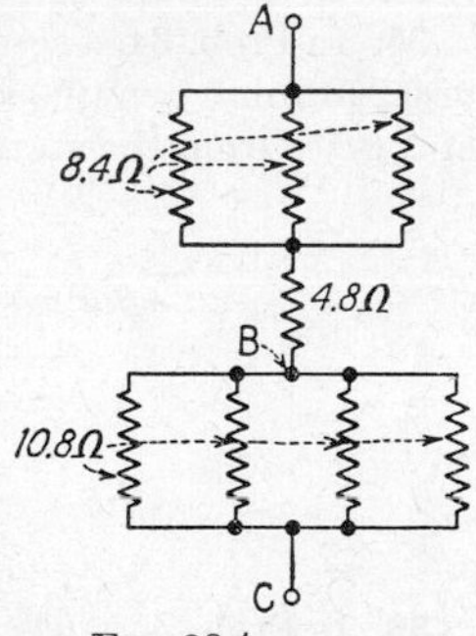

FIG. 28*A*.

28. Three resistors each 8.4 ohms are connected in parallel. This parallel combination is in series with a resistance of 4.8 ohms and another parallel group of four resistors, each equal to 10.8 ohms (see Fig. 28*A*). Determine resistance between terminals (*a*) *AB*; (*b*) *AC*.

29. A 300,000-cir-mil copper conductor, 400 ft long, is connected to carry a large current from a positive bus bar to a power load with ground return, the resistance of which is 0.6 ohm. The load increased until it became necessary to connect a 0000 copper conductor, 211,000 cir mils cross section, in parallel with the 300,000-cir-mil one. Also, in order to reduce the resistance of the ground return, a 400-ft length of the 0000 copper conductor was connected from the negative terminal of the apparatus to the negative bus bar. The resistance of a circular-mil-foot may be taken as 11 ohms. Determine: (*a*) combined initial resistance of conductor and ground return; (*b*) resistance of 0000 conductor; (*c*) total final resistance of positive conductor and negative return circuit.

30. In Fig. 30*A* is shown a series-parallel combination of seven resistors. Determine resistance between points (*a*) *AC*; (*b*) *CB*; (*c*) *AD*; (*d*) *AB*.

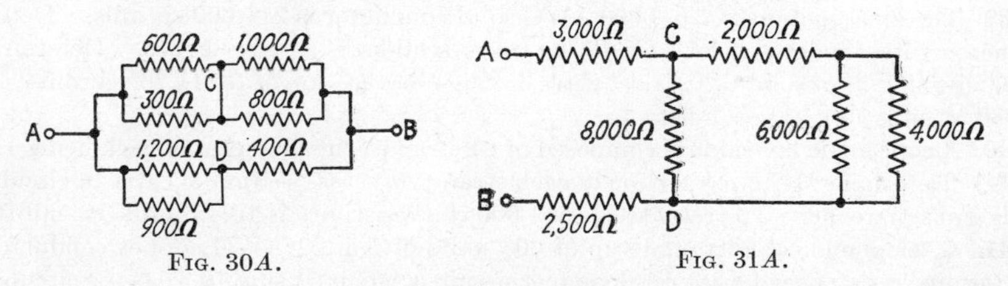

FIG. 30*A*. FIG. 31*A*.

31. In Fig. 31*A* is shown a series-parallel combination of resistors. Determine resistance as measured between terminals (*a*) *AB*; (*b*) *CD*, terminals *AB* being disconnected.

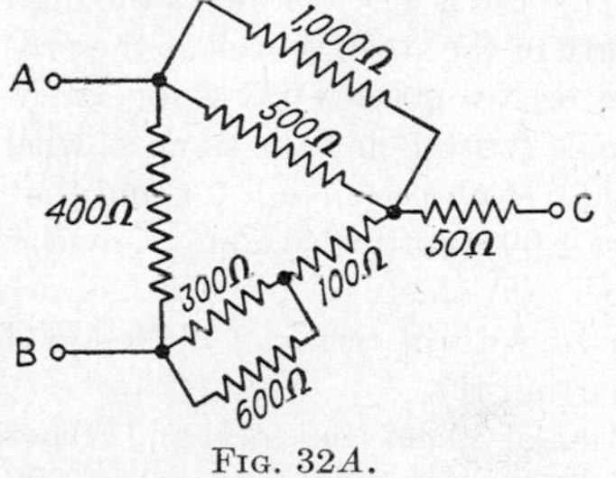

FIG. 32*A*.

32. In Fig. 32*A* is shown a resistor network with three terminals *A*, *B*, *C*. Determine resistance between terminals (*a*) *AB*; (*b*) *BC*; (*c*) *CA*.

33. In Fig. 32*A* determine resistance between (*a*) terminals *AB* connected together and *C*; (*b*) *BC* connected together and *A*; (*c*) *AC* connected together and *B*.

34. A 0000 trolley wire (hard-drawn) having a resistance of 0.0504 ohm per 1,000 ft extends 4.5 miles from the power station. It is paralleled for 3 miles by a 400,000-cir-mil cable, having a resistance of 0.0270 ohm per 1,000 ft, the feeder and the trolley being connected every half mile by taps (Fig. 34*A*). The resistance of *each* rail is

0.0154 ohm per 1,000 ft. Determine: (*a*) total resistance of the overhead circuit from powerhouse to end of trolley line; (*b*) total resistance from powerhouse to end of line and track return to powerhouse, assuming that return current is confined to the two rails.

35. In Prob. 34, a second feeder of 250,000 cir mils cross section, having a resistance of 0.0431 ohm per 1,000 ft, is connected in parallel with the trolley wire for a distance of 3 miles from the station (see Fig. 34*A*). Repeat (*a*), Prob. 34.

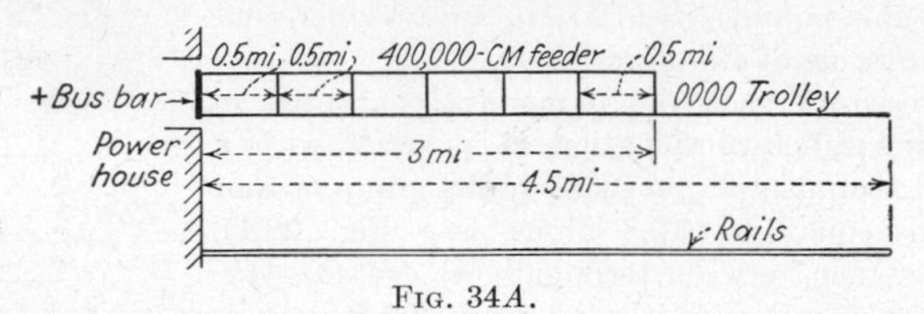

Fig. 34*A*.

36. In Prob. 34 a negative feeder consisting of a 300,000-cir-mil cable having a resistance of 0.0360 ohm per 1,000 ft is connected from the negative bus bar at the powerhouse to both rails 3 miles from the station, in addition to the trolley feeder, Prob. 35. Repeat (*b*), Prob. 34, assuming that return current is confined to two rails and negative feeder.

37. The diameter of a solid cylindrical rod is 0.375 in. Determine cross section in (*a*) square inches; (*b*) square mils; (*c*) circular mils. For a similar rod with a diameter of 0.625 in., determine cross section in (*d*) square inches; (*e*) square mils; (*f*) circular mils.

38. The diameter of No. 17 AWG solid conductor is 0.045 in. Determine its cross section in (*a*) square mils; (*b*) circular mils. The diameter of No. 00 AWG solid conductor is 0.365 in. Determine its cross section in (*c*) square mils; (*d*) circular mils.

39. The cross section of No. 0000 AWG solid conductor is 211,600 cir mils. Determine: (*a*) its diameter in inches; (*b*) its cross section in square inches. Determine diameter in mils of solid cylindrical wires having cross section of (*c*) 41,700 cir mils; (*d*) 5,180 cir mils; (*e*) 509 cir mils.

40. A concentric lay cable is composed of 61 strands, the diameter of each being 118 mils. Determine: (*a*) cross section of each strand; (*b*) cross section of cable in circular mils and square inches; (*c*) resistance per 1,000 ft if resistivity is 10.45 ohms (cir-mil-ft).

41. A telephone cable is made up of 303 pairs of No. 22 AWG copper conductor. Determine resistance of a 30-mile loop (consisting of a pair), using 10.37 as the circular-mil-foot resistivity of the copper. The diameter of No. 22 wire is 25.3 mils.

42. Copperweld consists of a steel wire over which an outer jacket of copper forms a weld, or a molecular union, with the inner core of steel. Such wire combines the high conductivity of the copper with the high tensile strength of the steel, as well as the protection of the steel against corrosion. The diameter of No. 0000 AWG Copperweld wire is 0.460 in., and the cross section is 211,600 cir mils (both being the same as with solid copper). The resistivity of the copper at 20°C is 10.5 ohms (cir-mil-ft), and that of the steel is 7.2 times this amount. The resistance of 1,000 ft of such a composite wire is 0.1250 ohm. Determine circular mils of (*a*) copper; (*b*) steel; (*c*) per cent copper and steel in cross section; (*d*) per cent conductivity of wire in terms of 0000 AWG copper wire, with resistivity of copper 10.35 ohms (cir-mil-ft).

43. Assume that a Copperweld wire has a cross section of 30 per cent steel and 70 per cent copper. Using data of Prob. 42, determine resistance of a 1,000-ft length of 000 wire, diam = 0.4096 in.

44. Steel-reinforced hard-drawn aluminum cable (ACSR) is used for high-voltage transmission-line conductors. A 0000 (0 copper equivalent) cable consists of six strands of aluminum and a solid steel core. The diameter of the individual strands of the aluminum and of the steel core is 0.1878 in. At 20°C aluminum has a resistivity of 17.02 ohms (cir-mil-ft) and the steel a resistivity of 76 ohms (cir-mil-ft). Determine resistance of a single 80-mile length of such conductor (*a*) neglecting conductance of steel core; (*b*) including conductance of steel core. The specific gravity of the aluminum is 2.70, and that of the steel is 7.9. (*c*) Determine weight per 1,000 ft of cable.

45. The temperature coefficient of resistance of copper at 0°C is 0.00427 (see p. 19). The resistance of a coil of copper wire is 8.820 ohms at 24°C. Determine its resistance (*a*) at 0°C; (*b*) at 42°C.

46. The resistance of a 4-mile length of hard-drawn 0000 trolley wire is 1.065 ohms at 20°C. Determine resistance at (*a*) 0°C; (*b*) minimum winter temperature of −10°C; (*c*) maximum summer temperature of 40°C.

47. In order to determine the operating temperature of an 800-ft length of 2-conductor 00 solid copper cable, the far ends are connected together, and the resistance is measured from the near end and found to be 0.1575 ohm. The resistance of the cable was similarly measured before installation at a temperature of 23°C and was found to be 0.1278 ohm. The connection between the far ends in each test has negligible resistance. Determine operating temperature of cable.

48. The resistance of the field coils of a 400-kw 230-volt shunt generator is measured after the machine has been standing for some time in a room the temperature of which is 21°C and is found to be 14.6 ohms. After the generator has been in operation for 3 hr, the resistance is again measured and found to be 16.2 ohms. Determine: (*a*) average temperature of field coils after 3 hr; (*b*) temperature rise.

49. The resistance at 25°C of 2,500 ft of 250,000-cir-mil (copper equivalent) hard-drawn aluminum cable is 0.1113 ohm. The temperature coefficient of resistance at 20°C for aluminum is 0.0403 (see p. 21). Determine the resistance at 0° and at 40°C.

50. The resistance of one of the conductors of a 2-mile 000 AWG 3-conductor solid copper cable was measured at a temperature of 23°C and found to be 0.684 ohm. After operating several hours under load the resistance of this same conductor was measured immediately after the power was disconnected and found to be 0.784 ohm. (*a*) Determine temperature at which the cable had been operating. (*b*) If the maximum safe operating temperature is 85°C, what would be the resistance of the foregoing conductor?

51. The resistance of the armature of a d-c generator, excluding brush and contact resistance, is 0.0846 ohm at a room temperature of 21°C. Determine its resistance (*a*) at 0°C; (*b*) at its allowable operating temperature, which is 40°C above room temperature.

52. The resistance of one of the circuits in the armature of an a-c generator is measured at a room temperature of 22°C and found to be 0.0642 ohm. After the generator has been in operation 6 hr, the resistance of the same circuit is again measured and found to be 0.0728 ohm. Determine rise in temperature at the end of the 6 hr.

53. Tungsten wire has a temperature coefficient of resistance of 0.0045 at 20°C. The hot resistance of a 100-watt 115-volt lamp is 132 ohms at its operating temperature of 2580°C. Determine its cold resistance at a room temperature of 25°C.

54. In Prob. 53 determine the temperature coefficient of resistance of tungsten at 0°C; at 40°C.

55. Determine temperature coefficient of resistance for copper at reference temperatures of 17°C; of 37°C; of 48°C.

56. The temperature coefficient of resistance at 20°C for aluminum is 0.0403. Determine: (*a*) "inferred zero resistance" (p. 21); (*b*) temperature coefficient at 0°C; (*c*) at 15°C; (*d*) at 43°C.

The following problems, 57 to 60, should be solved without consulting the wire tables.

57. Determine approximate resistance and cross section in circular mils of a 1,000-ft length (*a*) of No. 7 AWG solid copper wire; (*b*) of No. 16; (*c*) of No. 4. Determine approximate diameter of the wire (*d*) in (*a*); (*e*) in (*b*); (*f*) in (*c*).

58. Determine approximate cross section, diameter, resistance, and weight of (*a*) 1,600 ft of No. 000 AWG solid annealed-copper wire; (*b*) 1,200 ft of No. 1.

59. Determine approximate resistance, weight, cross section, and diameter of (*a*) 2,200 ft of No. 34 AWG solid copper wire; (*b*) 2,200 ft of No. 28 AWG solid copper wire.

60. Determine approximate resistance, weight, circular mils, and diameter of a 6-mile length of No. 0000 AWG trolley wire.

QUESTIONS ON CHAPTER II

Ohm's Law and the Electric Circuit

1. Upon what fundamental relation is the cgs electrostatic system of units based? Where is this system used?

2. Upon what fundamental relation is the cgs electromagnetic, or absolute, system of electrical units based? Where is this system generally used? How is the absolute unit of current defined?

3. What is the objection to the cgs electromagnetic system for ordinary use? Show how the practical system is derived from the cgs electromagnetic system.

4. State the difficulty which is encountered when attempt is made to base the practical system on dimensional units. Show how this difficulty is overcome in the mks system.

5. In the practical, or mks, system state why the absolute units have superseded the international units. What is the order of the differences between the two sets of units?

6. Define the international coulomb; the international ampere. How is the international ampere defined on an experimental basis?

7. Define the international ohm; the volt from the fundamental point of view and from the point of view of reproducing it readily. To what quantity in mechanics is the volt analogous?

8. Define the unit of power; of energy. State Joule's law.

9. State briefly the meaning of *absolute potential.* Why is it usually not important to know absolute potential?

10. What is the nature of voltage drop in a line? Compare it with pressure drop in a pipe. Show that it is impossible to supply power over a simple d-c power line with the voltage at the load equal to the voltage at the sending end of the line. Show that there must be a drop in potential in the return wire to the generator as well as in the outgoing wire. Can potential exist without current? Illustrate.

11. What is meant by *difference of potential?* Show that it is possible for two or more emfs to exist within a circuit without there being any difference of potential between the circuit terminals.

12. By means of a diagram show the correct method of connecting a voltmeter in a typical electric circuit. On the same diagram show the connections of an ammeter to measure the current to a load. Why should an ammeter never be connected across the power wires?

13. What fundamental relation does Ohm's law express? Give the three forms in which the law may be expressed. Name the conditions under which it is most convenient to use each of these expressions.

14. How are series-connected resistances combined to give a single equivalent resistance? Derive the expression by means of which a number of parallel-connected resistances may be replaced by a single equivalent resistance. In a two-branch parallel circuit, derive the relation between each current and the total current. In a parallel circuit of three branches, derive the relation between each current and the total current.

15. Express power in terms of volts, amperes, and ohms, taken two at a time. Differentiate carefully between power and energy. What is the practical unit of electrical energy and what is its relation to the unit of power? What is the unit of mechanical power? What is its relation to the watt and to the kilowatt?

16. How is energy related to power? Name and define the fundamental cgs unit of energy. Name the practical, or mks, unit of energy, and state its relation to the fundamental cgs unit. Discuss the various forms in which energy is stored or in which energy may appear. Describe the energy cycle involved in a steam-driven electrical power plant. In what forms does the energy appear ultimately? Approximately what is the over-all efficiency of a modern power system?

17. Define the British thermal unit; the gram-calorie. What is the relation between the gram-calorie and the watt-second?

18. What simple relation exists between the voltages at the sending and receiving ends of a power feeder, having a single concentrated load at its far end, and the efficiency of transmission?

19. Under what conditions is the voltage drop in each foot of wire independent of the total current? How is this principle utilized in solving electrical problems? Show how this method may be expanded to obtain the power loss.

PROBLEMS ON CHAPTER II

Ohm's Law and the Electric Circuit

61. A wire is in the form of a circle, the diameter of which is 2 cm, and connection to a source of current is made by carrying the two connecting wires away radially and adjacent to each other. The diameter of the wire is small compared with the radius of the circle. The current in the wire exerts a force of 42 dynes on a small magnetic pole placed at the center of the circle and having a strength of 4 cgs unit poles. Determine the current in the wire both in cgs absolute amperes and in practical amperes.

62. A coil of wire of eight turns is in the form of a circle with a diameter of 6 cm, and the connection to a source of current is made by carrying the two connecting wires away radially and adjacent to each other. The cross-sectional diameter of the coil is small compared with the radius of the coil. A current in the wire exerts a force of 128 dynes on a small pole of 6 cgs units strength placed at the center of the coil. Determine the current in both cgs (absolute) and practical amperes.

63. The exciting current of an electromagnet is rated at 12 amp. When connected across a 122-volt source the current is 14 amp. Determine the ohms in a resistor which must be connected in series to limit the current to (*a*) rated value; (*b*) 9.0 amp.

64. The cold resistance of a 100-watt gas-filled tungsten lamp is 16.8 ohms, and the hot resistance at its operating voltage of 118 volts is 139 ohms. Determine the current at the instant that the lamp is connected across the voltage and the current after it has reached the steady operating condition.

65. In Fig. 65*A* is shown a diagram of a 230-volt shunt motor with its field and rheostat. The voltage across the motor terminals is 230 volts. The resistance of the field coils is 180 ohms. It is desired that the field current shall not exceed 1.1 amp and that it be possible to reduce the field current to 20 per cent of the maximum value of 1.1 amp. Determine: (*a*) minimum and maximum values of the rheostat resistance; (*b*) minimum and maximum values of voltage across the field rheostat, the terminal voltage remaining constant at 230 volts.

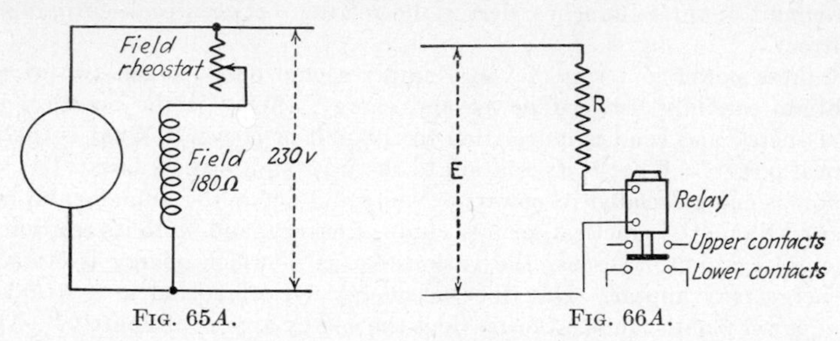

Fig. 65*A*. Fig. 66*A*.

66. In Fig. 66*A* is shown a relay in series with a resistor *R*. The relay operates to raise the plunger when the current is 0.36 amp, and the plunger drops when the current reaches 0.25 amp. The resistance of the relay is 130 ohms. Determine: (*a*) ohms of resistor *R* if it is desired that the relay operate to close the upper contacts when the voltage *E* is 120 volts; (*b*) value of voltage *E* when the plunger drops to close the lower contacts.

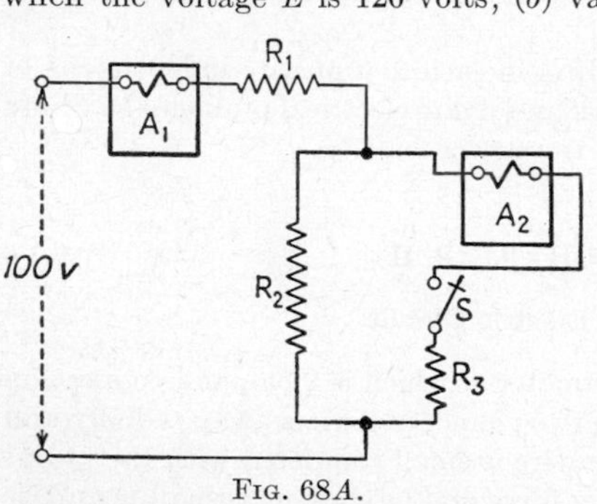

Fig. 68*A*.

67. A telegraph relay which has a resistance of 250 ohms and operates with 42 ma (1 ma = 0.001 amp) is connected at the far end of a 250-mile telegraph line. The line consists of No. 12 AWG hard-drawn copper wire having a loop resistance (*i.e.*, of both wires) of 20 ohms per mile. Determine: (*a*) voltage at sending end of line necessary to operate relay; (*b*) voltage drop in line; (*c*) voltage across relay.

68. In Fig. 68*A* is shown a circuit consisting of a resistor R_1 in series with two resistors R_2, R_3 in parallel. The circuit is connected across a constant 100-volt supply. When the switch *S* is open, the ammeter A_1 reads 8.0 amp. When the switch *S* is closed, the ammeter A_1 reads 10 amp and the ammeter A_2 reads 4 amp. Determine: (*a*) ohms of resistors R_1, R_2, R_3; (*b*) voltage across R_1, R_2 when *S* is open; (*c*) voltage across R_1, R_2 when *S* is closed.

69. Three wires *A*, *B*, *C*, Fig. 69*A*, of an alarm system are short-circuited at their far ends *O* by jumpers. When a voltage of 8.2 volts is impressed across the two home-end terminals *a* and *b*, the current is 1.125 amp; when 10.5 volts is impressed across the two home-end terminals *b* and *c*, the current is 1.33 amp; when 9.8 volts is impressed across the home-end terminals *c* and *a*, the current is 1.44 amp. Determine resistance of wires *A*, *B*, *C*.

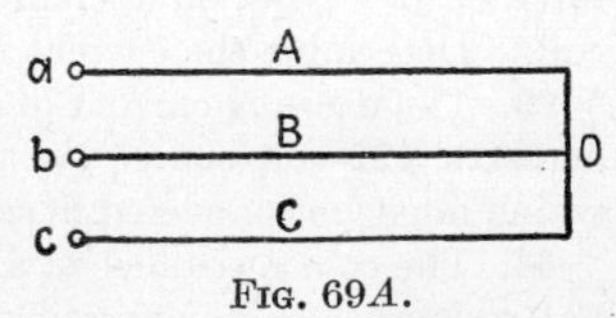

Fig. 69*A*.

70. The resistance of the shunt-field winding of a 230-volt generator is 130 ohms (circuit same as in Fig. 65*A*). When the field current is adjusted to 1.42 amp, the generator terminal voltage is 230 volts. Determine: (*a*) setting in ohms of field rheostat; (*b*) voltage across winding; (*c*) voltage across rheostat.

71. Four resistors of 12.4, 8.6, 14.7, 16.2 ohms are connected in series across a 115-volt d-c source. Determine: (*a*) equivalent resistance of system; (*b*) current; (*c*) voltage across each resistor.

72. A current of 35 amp is necessary to operate a large electromagnet. There are four series-connected spools on the magnet the resistances of which are 1.6, 1.6, 1.2, 1.2 ohms. A rheostat, the resistance of which is 0.56 ohm, is in series with the magnet, and the resistance of the connecting wires is 0.12 ohm. Determine: (*a*) voltage which must be applied to system; (*b*) voltage across each coil; (*c*) voltage across rheostat; (*d*) voltage drop in the connecting wires.

73. A series lighting system consists of 82 tungsten-filament incandescent lamps, each having a resistance of 4.83 ohms and requiring 6.6 amp. The total series line resistance is 32 ohms. Determine voltage of supply system.

74. In order to measure the resistance of a d-c armature with 115 volts as the source of supply, a resistor in series with the armature is necessary to limit the current (see Fig. 415, p. 524). In such a measurement the current is adjusted to 48.2 amp, and the voltage drop across the armature, including brushes, is 8.6 volts. Determine resistance of: (*a*) armature inclusive of brushes; (*b*) series resistor.

75. A copper bus bar, 6 by ¼ in. cross section, is measured for its resistance. With a current of 640 amp the voltage drop between points 8 ft apart is found to be 27.6 mv. The temperature is 24°C. Determine: (*a*) resistance per foot at 20°C; (*b*) resistivity in ohm-inches at 20°C; (*c*) per cent conductivity in terms of soft drawn copper (p.15); (*d*) voltage drop in 40 ft at 30°C when four such bus bars are connected in parallel and the current is 4,900 amp.

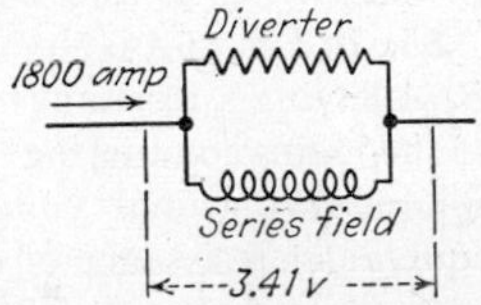

76. The resistance of the series field, alone, of a compound generator is measured by measuring the voltage drop when the line current is 1,800 amp. The voltage drop is found to be 4.32 volts. The series field is then shunted by its diverter, Fig. 76*A* (also see p. 454). When the line current is 1,800 amp, the voltage drop across the field and diverter in parallel is 3.41 volts. Determine resistance (*a*) of series field; (*b*) of diverter.

Diverter
1800 amp
Series field
3.41 v

Fig. 76*A*.

77. A diverter is shunted across the series field of a compound generator as in Fig. 76*A*. When the line current is 1,200 amp, the voltage drop across the series field and diverter in parallel is 3.73 volts. The resistance of the diverter is then shunted so that its value is halved. The voltage drop across the field and diverter in parallel is now 2.37 volts. Determine resistance of: (*a*) series field; (*b*) diverter.

78. The resistance of a voltage divider *ac*, Fig. 78*A*, is 30,000 ohms, the center tap *b* being at the mid-point. A resistor *b′c′* of 20,000 ohms is connected across *bc*. The voltage divider is connected across a 300-volt supply. Determine: (*a*) equivalent resistance between points *b* and *c*; (*b*) resistance between points *a* and *c*; (*c*) currents in *ab*, *bc*, *b′c′*; (*d*) voltage across *bc*.

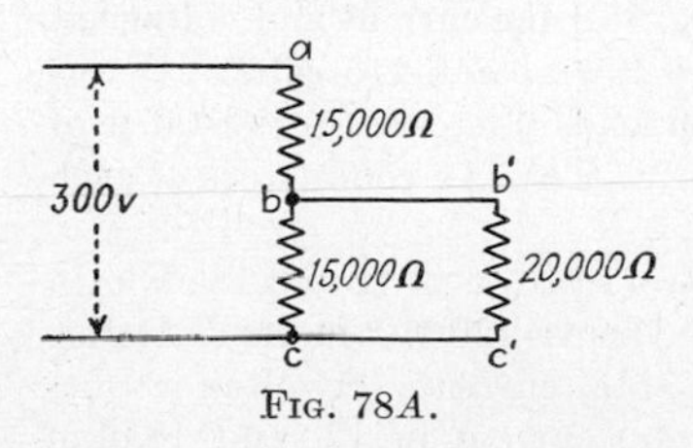

Fig. 78*A*.

79. Repeat Prob. 78 with the resistance *b′c′* changed to 25,000 ohms. (Problems 78 and 79 illustrate the fact that a voltage divider divides the voltages in proportion to the resistances between the terminals and the tap only when the current taken from or delivered to the tap is zero. See volt box, p. 186.)

80. Three resistors of 50, 40, 73.4 ohms are connected in parallel. (*a*) Determine equivalent resistance of combination. The current in the 73.4-ohm resistor is 3.27 amp. Determine: (*b*) voltage across system; (*c*) current in each resistor.

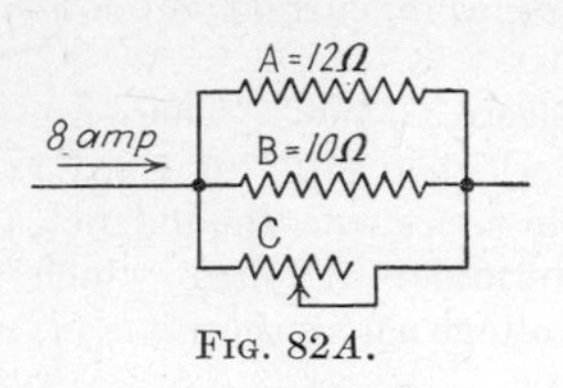

FIG. 82*A*.

81. Three resistors of 100, 120, 150 ohms are connected in parallel. Determine value of current to parallel system which will make current in 120-ohm resistor equal to 1.0 amp.

82. Three resistors, *A*, *B*, *C* are connected in parallel, Fig. 82*A*. The resistance of *A* is 12 ohms and that of *B* 10 ohms. *C* is adjustable. The current to the circuit is 8 amp. To what value should the resistance of *C* be adjusted in order that it may take 2.5 amp?

83. Four resistors *A*, *B*, *C*, *D* are connected in parallel, Fig. 83*A*. The resistors *A*, *B*, *D* are 56, 50, 40 ohms. The current in resistor *D* is 2.5 amp, and the current to the system is 9.0 amp. Determine: (*a*) resistance of *C*; (*b*) equivalent resistance of combination; (*c*) current in resistors *A*, *B*, *C*.

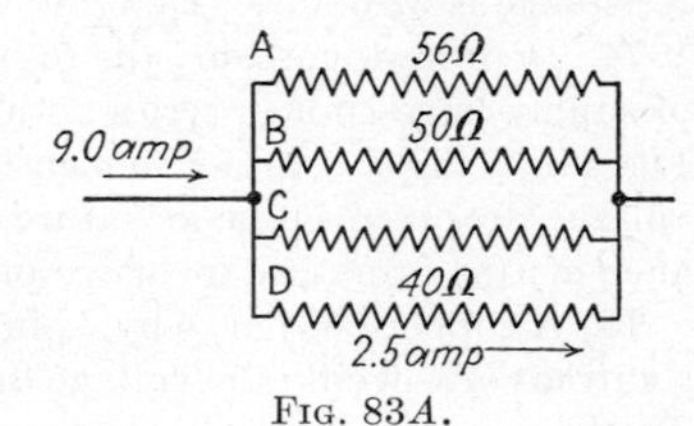

FIG. 83*A*.

84. In a system similar to that shown in Fig. 83*A* the resistors *A*, *B*, *C* have resistances of 24, 36, 48 ohms. Determine (*a*) equivalent resistance of *A*, *B*, *C* in parallel. The current to the parallel system is 12 amp. Determine: (*b*) resistance of *D* which will make current in *D* equal to sum of currents in *B* and *C*; (*c*) currents in *A*, *B*, *C*, *D*.

85. In Fig. 85*A* is shown a shunt generator supplying power to two lamp loads *A* and *B*, *A* having a resistance of 3.0 ohms and *B* a resistance of 5.0 ohms. The resistances of the mains conducting the power to the lamps are 0.08 and 0.12 ohm as shown. The generator terminal voltage is maintained constant at 120 volts. Determine: (*a*) equivalent resistance of entire circuit; (*b*) total current; (*c*) current to 3.0-ohm lamp bank; (*d*) current to 5.0-ohm lamp bank.

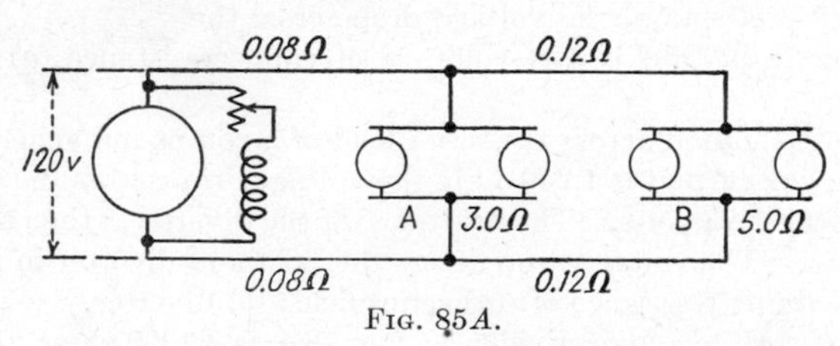

FIG. 85*A*.

86. In a lighting system similar to that shown in Fig. 85*A* the current and voltage at lamp bank *B* are 25 amp and 108 volts; those at *A* are 40 amp and 115 volts. Determine: (*a*) resistance of each conductor of main between loads *A* and *B*; (*b*) resistance of each conductor of main between generator and load *A*. The two conductors of each main have the same resistance.

87. A resistor of 8 ohms is connected in series with two resistors of 12 and 18 ohms in parallel. This entire series-parallel circuit is connected across 120-volt mains. Determine: (*a*) equivalent resistance of entire circuit; (*b*) total current; (*c*) voltage across 8-ohm resistor; (*d*) voltage across parallel circuit; (*e*) current in 12- and 18-ohm resistors.

88. A resistor of 40 ohms is in series with two resistors *A* and *B* in parallel. The resistance of *A* is 100 ohms. The entire series-parallel circuit is connected across a

120-volt supply. Determine: (*a*) ohms to which resistor *B* must be adjusted in order that current to entire circuit be 1.2 amp; (*b*) current in resistors *A* and *B*; (*c*) voltage across resistors *A* and *B*.

89. A series-parallel circuit shown in Fig. 89*A* is connected across a 120-volt supply. Determine: (*a*) equivalent resistance of parallel circuits *ab* and *bc*; (*b*) total resistance; (*c*) total current; (*d*) voltage between points *ab* and *bc*; (*e*) current in each resistor.

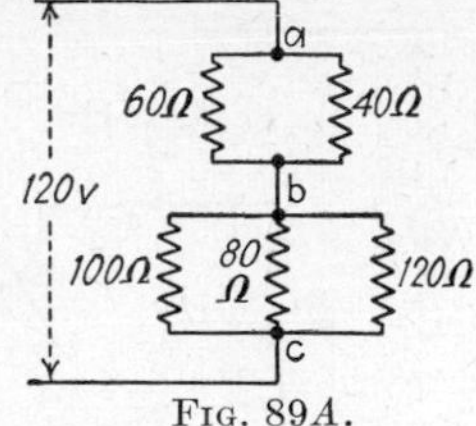

FIG. 89*A*.

90. In Fig. 89*A* the 60-ohm resistor is made variable. (*a*) To what value should it be adjusted in order that the total current shall be 2.4 amp? Under these conditions determine: (*b*) voltage between points *ab* and *bc*; (*c*) current in each resistor.

91. In Fig. 91*A* is shown a series-parallel combination of resistors connected across a 100-volt source. Determine: (*a*) equivalent resistance of parallel circuit *e'e*; (*b*) equivalent resistance of parallel circuit *fb'-ge*; (*c*) resistance of entire system; (*d*) voltage across resistors *ab*, *b'e'*, *cc'*, *fg*; (*e*) current in each resistor, *ab*, *b'e'*, *cc'*, *dd'*, *fg*.

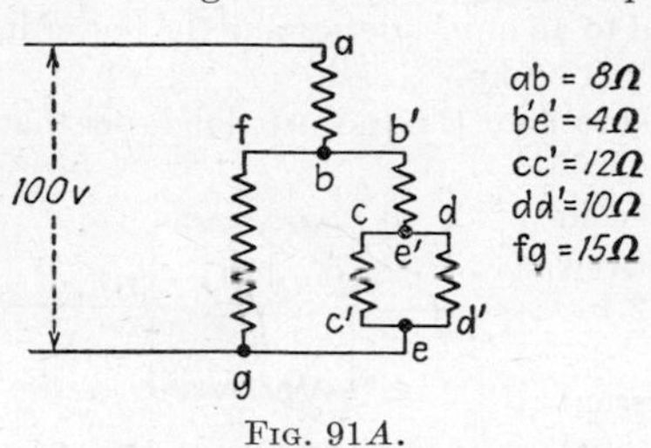

FIG. 91*A*.

92. Repeat Prob. 91 with resistances of resistors *ab* and *fg* changed to 4 and 6 ohms.

93. A d-c compound generator is rated at 500 kw and 250 volts, and its efficiency at rated load is 0.93. Determine: (*a*) current rating; (*b*) kilowatts and horsepower input.

94. The efficiency of a 50-hp 230-volt motor at its rated load is 0.885. Determine: (*a*) horsepower input; (*b*) kilowatts input; (*c*) rated current.

95. In Fig. 95*A* is shown a series-parallel circuit. The applied voltage *E* is equal to 250 volts. Determine: (*a*) equivalent resistance of resistors, *aa'* and *bb'* in parallel, and *cc'*, *dd'* and *ee'* in parallel; (*b*) total current; (*c*) current in each resistor; (*d*) power to each resistor; (*e*) total power.

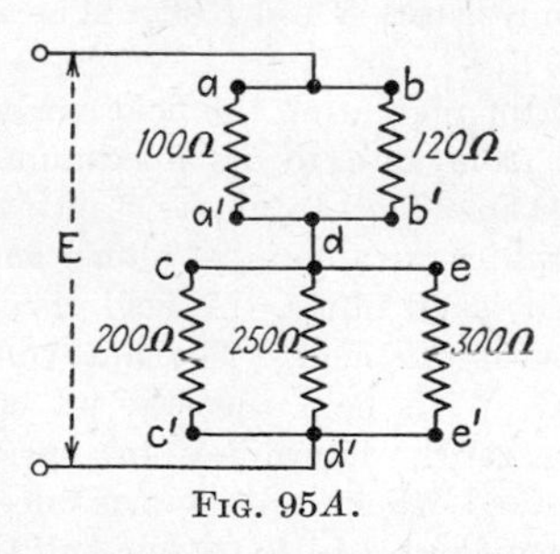

FIG. 95*A*.

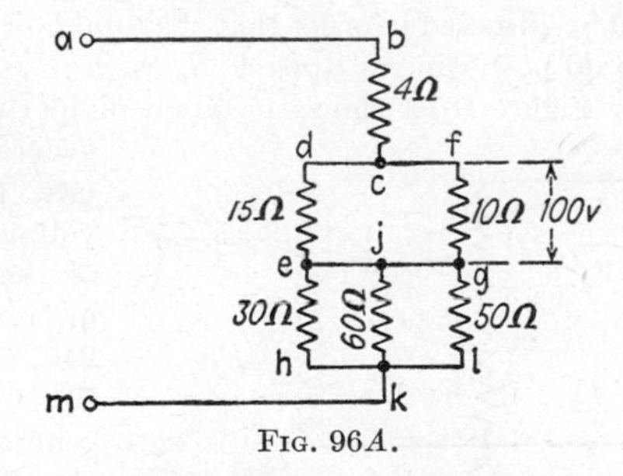

FIG. 96*A*.

96. In Fig. 96*A* is shown a series-parallel circuit in which a resistor *bc* of 4 ohms is in series with two parallel combinations of resistors, one of which consists of *de* and *fg*, of 15 and 10 ohms. The voltage across this parallel combination is 100 volts. The second parallel combination consists of three resistors *eh*, *jk*, *gl*, their resistances being 30, 60, 50 ohms. Determine: (*a*) voltage across resistor *bc*; (*b*) voltage across resistor *jk*; voltage across *am*, the entire circuit; (*c*) power in each of six resistors; (*d*) total power to circuit.

97. In Fig. 97*A* is shown a 6-ohm resistor in series with a 30-ohm resistor and a variable resistor *R* in parallel with each other. The entire circuit is connected across a

120-volt supply. Determine: (*a*) value to which R should be adjusted so that the power to the entire circuit is 988.3 watts; (*b*) power in 6- and 30-ohm resistors.

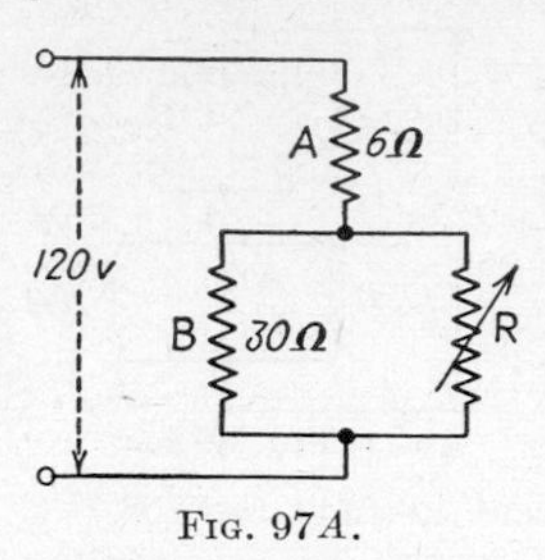

Fig. 97A.

98. In the circuit, Fig. 97A, determine the two values to which R should be adjusted in order to make the power in R equal to that in the 6-ohm resistor.

99. When the power in resistor dd', Fig. 95A, is equal to 100 watts, determine: (*a*) current in resistor dd', cc', ee'; (*b*) voltage between points dd'; (*c*) voltage across parallel circuit ab, $a'b'$; (*d*) voltage E; (*e*) current in resistors aa', bb'; (*f*) power in resistors aa', bb', cc', ee'; (*g*) total power.

100. In Fig. 76A, determine: (*a*) power loss in diverter; (*b*) power loss in series field; (*c*) total power.

101. In Fig. 83A, with the resistance of C equal to 45 ohms, determine the power in each of the four resistors when the total current is 12 amp.

102. In Fig. 102A, to what value in ohms should resistor R be adjusted in order that the power in resistor ab shall be 441 watts?

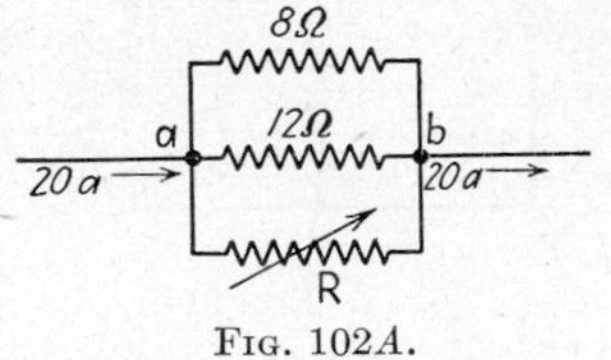

Fig. 102A.

103. Two heating units A and B are connected in parallel across a 120-volt supply. Unit B takes twice as much power as A, and the total power is 2,160 watts. Determine resistance of A and B.

104. Four 100-watt and ten 60-watt incandescent lamps operating at their watt ratings are connected in parallel across a 115-volt supply. Determine: (*a*) current to each 100-watt lamp; (*b*) current to each 60-watt lamp; (*c*) total current.

105. A variable resistor R in series with a fixed resistor of 22 ohms is connected across a 110-volt supply. Determine: (*a*) resistance to which R should be adjusted in order that its power may be a maximum; (*b*) current; (*c*) value of R which will make power in R twice that in the 22-ohm resistor; (*d*) value of current.

106. In the circuit shown in Fig. 97A, determine: (*a*) resistance to which resistor R should be adjusted in order that the total power in resistors R and B should be a maximum; (*b*) power in resistors A, B, R.

107. Figure 107A shows a voltage divider used for regulating the field current of a generator from zero to its maximum value (see p. 411). The total resistance of the voltage divider wire ab is 24 ohms, and that of the field is 60 ohms. A field rheostat is in series with the field. The line voltage is 240 volts. With field rheostat all cut out (resistance zero), determine: (*a*) current to generator field when contact x is one-fourth the distance from a to b; (*b*) one-half the distance; (*c*) three-fourths the distance; (*d*) in (*a*), (*b*), (*c*) percentage of total power which goes to field.

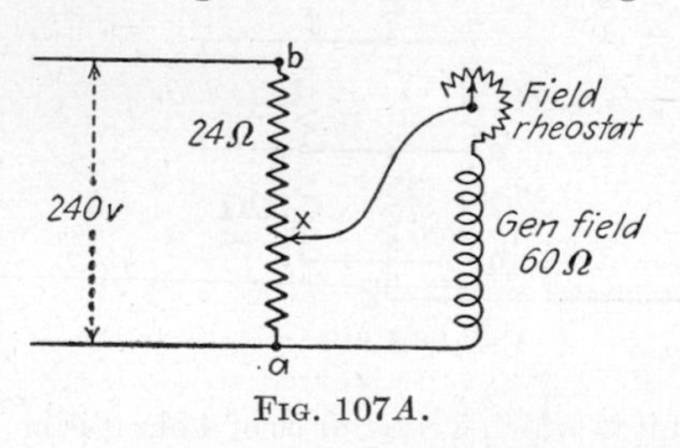

Fig. 107A.

108. In Prob. 107 repeat (*a*), (*b*), (*c*), (*d*) with field rheostat set at 15 ohms. (*e*) Determine power lost in rheostat in (*a*), (*b*), (*c*).

109. The energy to an electric oven which is operating under steady load is registered by a watthour meter which shows 3,240 kwhr over a period of 102 hr. Determine: (*a*) average power to oven; (*b*) average current if voltage is 220 volts; (*c*) total cost of energy if first 60 kwhr is sold at 5 cents per kwhr and the remainder at 3½ cents per kwhr.

110. The output of a 230-volt 15-hp blower motor is equal to 12.4 hp at an efficiency of 86.7 per cent. At 3.2 cents per kwhr, determine monthly cost of energy if the motor operated steadily 24 hr per day for 30 days.

111. At 5 cents per kwhr, determine: (*a*) cost of raising temperature of 2.5 qt of water in an electric kettle from 20 to 100°C; neglect losses; 1 qt = 0.946 l; (*b*) cost for a month of 30 days if kettle is operated twice each day.

112. At an energy cost of 5 cents per kwhr determine cost of heating 3 gal of water at room temperature of 22°C to the boiling point (100°C). Assume that the efficiency of the heater is 80 per cent (water weighs 8.345 lb per gal).

113. A water-barrel rheostat contains 52 gal of water. Determine time which 85 amp at 230 volts must flow through rheostat before the temperature of the water is raised to 200°F from a room temperature of 70°F. (One gallon of water weighs 8.345 lb.) Neglect losses.

114. Electric boilers are frequently used, particularly in Canada, where there is an excess of electrical energy. In a common type, heating is accomplished by current at high voltage passing from an electrode through the water to be heated. Determine: (*a*) kilowatthours necessary to heat 20 tons of water per hour from an initial temperature of 20°C to boiling point of 100°C; (*b*) cost at 0.62 cent per kilowatthour. The boiler efficiency is 97 per cent.

115. The current to a water-immersed resistor of 2.9 ohms within an electric boiler is 50 amp. There are 190 l of water in the boiler, and the efficiency of the boiler is 95 per cent. Determine temperature which water will reach at end of 2 hr. The room temperature is 20°C.

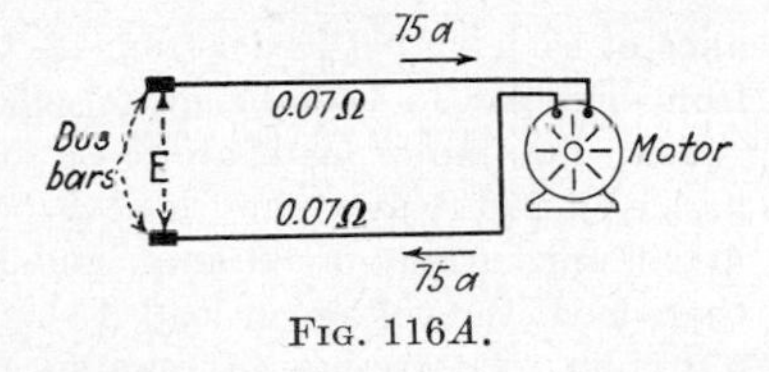

Fig. 116*A*.

116. In Fig. 116*A* is shown a 20-hp motor which takes 75 amp over a feeder, each conductor of which has a resistance of 0.07 ohm. The bus-bar voltage E is 240 volts. Determine: (*a*) voltage at motor; (*b*) efficiency of power transmission.

117. The motor, Fig. 116*A*, delivers 15 hp at an efficiency of 0.86, and the voltage at the terminals of the motor is 230 volts. Determine: (*a*) bus-bar voltage E; (*b*) efficiency of transmission; (*c*) over-all efficiency from motor shaft to bus bars.

118. Power is delivered over a feeder to a combined power-and-lighting load with 240 volts at the sending-end bus bars. The resistance of each of the two wires of the feeder to the load is 0.04 ohm. Determine voltage at load and efficiency of transmission when current to the load is (*a*) 150 amp; (*b*) 120 amp.

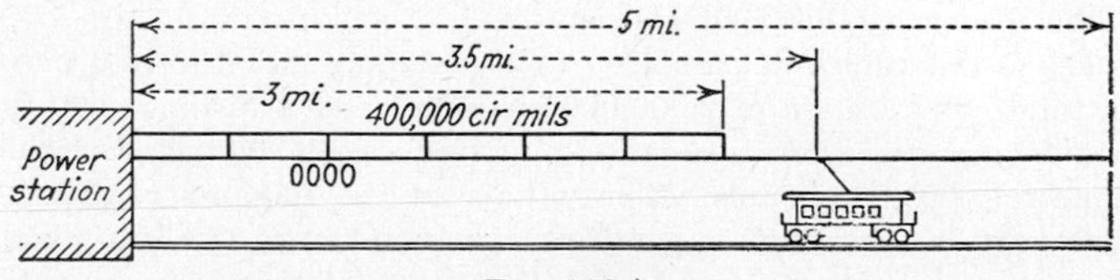

Fig. 119*A*.

119. An electric railway is fed by a 5-mile trolley wire of No. 0000 AWG hard-drawn copper. A 400,000-cir-mil feeder parallels the trolley wire for 3 miles, being tapped in every half mile (Fig. 119*A*). The resistance of the trolley is 0.269 ohm per mile and that of the feeder 0.143 ohm per mile. The resistance of the ground return may be considered as 0.02 ohm per mile. The power station voltage is 600 volts. When the car is $3\frac{1}{2}$ miles from the station and is taking 140 amp, determine: (*a*) voltage at car; (*b*) voltage at end of line; (*c*) efficiency of transmission.

120. In Prob. 119 the car is at the end of the line and is just starting, the starting current being 150 amp. Determine: (*a*) voltage at car; (*b*) efficiency of transmission.

121. A 120-kw load is situated 2,000 ft from the bus bars of a d-c power station at which the voltage is 238.9 volts. It is desired that the voltage at the load be 220 volts when the load is 120 kw. Determine: (*a*) current; (*b*) resistance of each conductor of feeder; (*c*) size, in circular mils, of feeder, taking 10.8 ohms as the resistance of a circular-mil-foot of copper; (*d*) efficiency of transmission; (*e*) weight in pounds of copper.

122. In Prob. 121 determine voltage along the feeder at distances of 500, 1000, and 1,500 ft from the station bus bars. Plot voltage as function of distance along feeder.

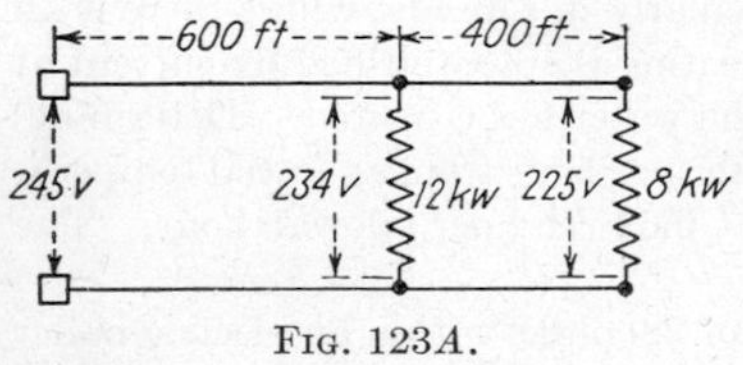

FIG. 123*A*.

123. It is desired to supply a load of 12 kw at a distance of 600 ft from the station bus bars and a second load of 8 kw at a further distance of 400 ft, Fig. 123*A*. The voltage at the bus bars is 245 volts; that at the 12-kw load must be 234 volts, and that at the 8-kw load must be 225 volts. Determine: (*a*) resistance of each wire of feeder from 12- to 8-kw load; (*b*) resistance of each wire of feeder from bus bars to 12-kw load; (*c*) efficiency of transmission.

124. Two motor loads are to be supplied from 600-volt bus bars, the load *A* being located 1,200 ft away and load *B* being located 800 ft farther. Load *A* requires a maximum current of 80 amp, and load *B* a maximum current of 60 amp. With these loads the voltage at load *A* should be 562 volts and that at load *B* not less than 531 volts. Determine: (*a*) resistance per conductor of feeder between loads *B* and *A*; (*b*) resistance per conductor between load *A* and bus bars; (*c*) kilowatts of loads *A* and *B* and kilowatts supplied from bus bars; (*d*) copper loss in each feeder; (*e*) efficiency of transmission; (*f*) size wire, AWG, which should be used for the conductor in (*a*); size wire, AWG, which should be used for the conductor in (*b*).

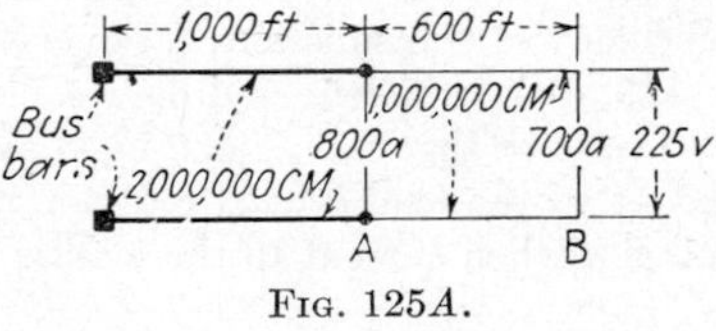

FIG. 125*A*.

125. A feeder from the bus bars of d-c substation supplies two concentrated loads as in Fig. 125*A*. A load of 800 amp is located at *A*, 1,000 ft, in terms of length of feeder, from the bus bars, and each conductor of the feeder to this load consists of two 1,000,000-cir-mil cables in parallel. (The outgoing and the return conductor each has a total cross section of 2,000,000 cir mils.) At a distance 600 ft beyond *A* at *B* is a 700-amp load which is supplied by a feeder each conductor of which has a cross section of 1,000,000 cir mils. The voltage at the 700-amp load is 225 volts. The resistivity at the operating temperature may be taken as 11 ohms per cir-mil-ft. Determine: (*a*) voltage at 800-amp load; (*b*) voltage at bus bars; (*c*) total power transmitted; (*d*) total power loss; (*e*) efficiency of transmission; (*f*) voltage at distances of 500 and 1,300 ft from bus bars.

126. In Prob. 125 assume that the voltage at the bus bars is 240 volts and that the loads have decreased so that the load at *A* is now 600 amp and that at *B* is now 400 amp. Determine: (*a*) voltage at 600-amp load; (*b*) voltage at 400-amp load; (*c*) total power transmitted; (*d*) total power loss; (*e*) efficiency of transmission.

In the following problems, 127 to 132, assume that the resistance of a circular-mil-foot of copper is 10 ohms. The *normal current density* is 0.001 amp per cir mil.

127. An 800-ft feeder consisting of two (one positive and one negative) 300,000-cir-mil copper conductors is supplying a single load at its far end, and the sending-end voltage is 240 volts. Determine: (*a*) total voltage drop in feeder if it is operating at *normal* density of 0.001 amp per cir mil; (*b*) efficiency of transmission under these conditions; (*c*) load current; (*d*) power input to feeder.

128. If the voltage drop, Prob. 127, is limited to 10 volts, determine: (*a*) cross section in circular mils of feeder which is necessary; (*b*) efficiency of transmission; (*c*) power at load; (*d*) power input to feeder; (*e*) current density, amperes per circular mil.

129. A load of 600 amp is located 1,500 ft from 240-volt bus bars, and it is desired that the voltage at this load be not less than 230 volts. With the feeder operating at the *normal* density, determine: (*a*) circular mils of feeder; (*b*) total voltage drop; (*c*) loss in feeder; (*d*) efficiency of transmission; (*e*) size feeder necessary to give 230 volts at load; (*f*) loss in this feeder; (*g*) efficiency of transmission.

130. It is desired to supply power to a 100-hp 550-volt motor, located 2,500 ft from 600-volt bus bars, the minimum permissible voltage at the motor being 550 volts. The motor efficiency at rated load is 0.90. Determine: (*a*) circular mils of copper conductor if copper operates at *normal* current density; (*b*) circular mils of copper conductor necessary to give 550 volts at load; (*c*) power at load; (*d*) total power loss in (*b*); (*e*) efficiency of transmission; (*f*) current density, amperes per circular mil.

131. A 75-amp load is located 1.34 miles from 600-volt bus bars. Determine: (*a*) circular mils of wire which should be used if feeder is to operate at *normal* density; (*b*) voltage at load; (*c*) line loss; (*d*) efficiency of transmission; (*e*) size wire, AWG, which must be used if voltage at load is to be not less than 550 volts; (*f*) circular mils of this wire; (*g*) loss in this feeder; (*h*) efficiency of transmission. (NOTE. Number 10 wire may be assumed as having a cross section of 10,000 cir mils; No. 0, 100,000 cir mils, etc.)

132. A No. 0000 AWG hard-drawn trolley wire operating at 600 volts above ground potential is paralleled for 6 miles by a 500,000-cir-mil feeder. The circular mils of the trolley wire is 211,000. When this parallel system is operated at the *normal* current density, determine: (*a*) total voltage drop in feeder and trolley; (*b*) power loss in feeder and trolley. The voltage drop in the overhead system is to be held to 50 volts. Determine: (*c*) maximum current density at which system may operate; (*d*) total power loss in overhead system; (*e*) current at load; (*f*) power at load; (*g*) power input to system; (*h*) efficiency.

QUESTIONS ON CHAPTER III

Battery Electromotive Forces—Kirchhoff's Laws

1. What is the effect on the terminal voltage of a battery of applying a load to the terminals? Explain. Why does the emf of a battery differ from the terminal voltage? Under what conditions are they the same?

2. Discuss the possibility of making a *direct* measurement of the internal voltage of a battery when it is delivering current. How may this internal voltage be calculated if the battery resistance be known?

3. To what factors is the internal resistance of a battery due? Is this resistance a constant quantity?

4. Show the method of calculating the current delivered to an external resistor if the emf and the resistance of a battery be known. If the battery becomes short-circuited, what value of current does it deliver? Account for the energy that the cell develops under these conditions.

5. When a battery has constant emf and constant internal resistance, for what value of external resistance is the power delivered a maximum? What is the battery efficiency under these conditions? Discuss the advisability of operating a battery so that it delivers maximum power. Explain.

6. Under what conditions may a battery be made to receive electrical energy? What relation does the direction of current have to its direction when the battery delivers energy? The emf of a generator is equal to that of a battery. Discuss any effects which may be noted when the generator is connected to the battery, terminals of like polarity being connected together. What effect is noted when the generator voltage is raised above this value? Explain what is meant by the battery "floating."

7. Before current can be made to enter the positive terminal of a battery, what voltage must be applied? Explain why any voltage in excess of the battery emf is effective in producing current. Give a very common illustration of a battery's receiving energy.

8. If several cells are connected in series, what is the resultant emf of the combination? What is the resultant resistance of the combination? Give the method of computing the current if the external resistance be known.

9. Under what conditions do batteries operate most satisfactorily in parallel? What is the emf of the combination under these conditions? What is the relation between the external current and the current in the individual batteries? What is the relation between the total battery resistance and the resistances of the individual batteries?

10. With batteries in parallel having equal emfs but unequal internal resistances, explain how the resistance of the entire battery may be found. What relation does the current delivered by each battery have to the resistance of that battery? What relation exists among the terminal voltages of individual batteries when connected in parallel?

11. Show a series-parallel grouping of similar cells. How is the voltage of the entire battery determined? How may the resistance of the battery be found if the resistance of the individual cells be known? Derive the equation which gives the current in an external circuit if the external resistance, the emfs, and resistances of the individual cells and their arrangement be known.

12. In general, how should cells be grouped to obtain the best economy? How should cells be grouped to obtain the maximum power output?

13. Derive the equation which gives the equivalent emf and the equivalent internal resistance of a battery, consisting of a number of cells in parallel, having different emfs and resistances.

14. Discuss the principle on which are based the *"floating"-battery* method and the *circulatory-current* method for determining the division of current among unequal batteries in parallel.

15. Analyze the *"floating"-battery* method, showing how to determine the total current in each battery.

16. Repeat Question 15 for the *circulatory-current* method.

17. State the two fundamental principles which are enunciated in Kirchhoff's two laws. If several currents meet at a junction, how should their directions be taken into account?

18. How should a rise in potential be represented? A drop in potential? When going from a negative to a positive terminal of a battery, what should be the sign of the potential change and why? When passing from positive to negative? When going through a resistance in the direction of the current, does a rise or a drop in potential occur? What, then, should be the proper sign to use? When going through the resistance in opposition to the current, what sign should be used? Explain.

19. If the assumed direction of a current in a network is in error, how is this fact indicated in the result?

20. In applying Kirchhoff's first law to a network, what rule regarding every current must be followed? In applying Kirchhoff's second law to a network, what rule regarding each path through the network must be followed?

21. Outline the procedure by which Kirchhoff's two laws may be systematically applied to a network.

22. Discuss the method by which the number of equations for any network may be reduced.

23. Discuss the limitations in the application of Kirchhoff's laws to railway and other power systems. In what manner do these circuits differ from the usual battery circuits in which the emfs and resistances only are given?

24. Show how a network may be divided into meshes and Maxwell's mesh equations applied. What general system of current direction gives a systematic arrangement of the terms of the equations?

25. Define: *circuit; linear circuit; nonlinear circuit; bilateral circuit; unilateral circuit.*

26. Define: *electric network; active electric network; passive electric network; L network; T network; π network.*

27. Define: the *superposition theorem*, explaining in simple terms its significance.

28. Define *Thévenin's theorem*, describing its method of application.

29. Define the *reciprocity theorem*, explaining how it is applied. Define "transfer impedance."

30. Show how an electric network may be simplified, and its solution rendered comparatively easy by: (*a*) substituting star systems for delta meshes; (*b*) substituting delta meshes for star systems.

31. (*a*) Define a 4-*terminal network*. (*b*) What is the number of measurable quantities by which it is possible to define a passive 4-terminal network? How many such quantities are necessary?

32. Draw the diagram of a π network. Of how many independent elements does it consist? Express the open- and short-circuit resistances measured at the two pairs of terminals in terms of the network elements.

33. Draw the diagram of a T network. Repeat (*b*) of Question 31.

PROBLEMS ON CHAPTER III

Battery Electromotive Forces—Kirchhoff's Laws

133. The open-circuit emf of a dry cell is 1.35 volts. When the cell delivers a current of 1.5 amp, its terminal voltage drops to 1.30 volts. (*a*) Determine its apparent internal resistance. A resistance of 10 ohms is connected across the terminals of the cell. (*b*) Determine current, and voltage across terminals.

134. The internal emf of a gravity cell is 1.07 volts and the terminal voltage is 0.98 volt when it delivers a current of 2.1 amp. Determine: (*a*) internal resistance; (*b*) power lost within cell; (*c*) power generated within cell; (*d*) ratio of output to power generated.

135. A starting battery consists of three lead cells connected in series. On open circuit, the emf of the battery is 6.30 volts. When it delivers a current of 80 amp, its terminal voltage drops to 5.10 volts. Determine: (*a*) its internal resistance; (*b*) terminal voltage when battery delivers 40 amp; (*c*) power lost in battery in (*b*); (*d*) load resistance in (*b*).

136. A battery of six dry cells in series has an open-circuit emf of 8.1 volts and a total internal resistance of 0.42 ohm. When an external load is applied, the terminal voltage drops to 6.15 volts. Determine: (*a*) load current; (*b*) load resistance; (*c*) total power generated; (*d*) per cent of power in (*c*) delivered to load.

137. The open-circuit emf of a 60-cell storage battery is 127.2 volts, and the total internal resistance is 0.06 ohm. Determine: (*a*) maximum current which battery can deliver without its terminal voltage dropping below 123 volts; (*b*) current which will give a terminal voltage of 120.6 volts; (*c*) total power developed in (*b*); (*d*) power lost in battery in (*b*); (*e*) ratio of power delivered to internal power in (*c*).

138. When the external resistance in Prob. 137 is 0.8 ohm, determine: (*a*) current; (*b*) total power developed by battery; (*c*) power lost in battery heating; (*d*) power to external circuit; (*e*) ratio of (*d*) to (*b*).

139. The emf of a dry cell is 1.40 volts, and the internal resistance is 0.06 ohm. Determine: (*a*) value of external resistance which will give maximum delivered power; (*b*) maximum delivered power; (*c*) power lost within cell; (*d*) total power developed.

140. The emf of a starting battery is 6.03 volts, and each of the three series-connected cells has an internal resistance of 0.006 ohm. Determine: (*a*) maximum power which battery can deliver to starting motor, including the resistance of leads; (*b*) value of current under these conditions; (*c*) terminal voltage of battery; (*d*) power lost as heat in battery.

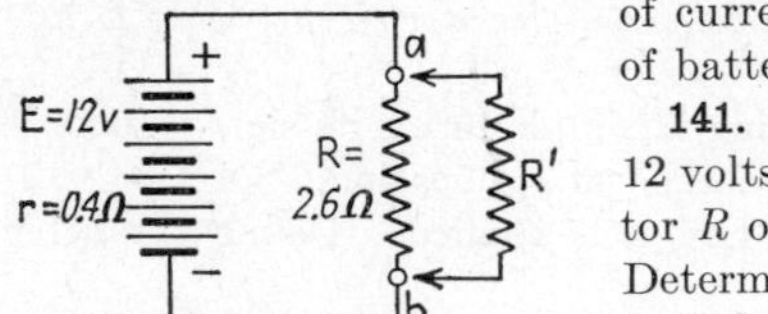

Fig. 141*A*.

141. In Fig. 141*A* is shown a battery having an emf of 12 volts and an internal resistance of 0.4 ohm. A resistor *R* of 2.6 ohms is connected across its terminals *ab*. Determine: (*a*) resistance of resistor *R'* which, when connected across terminals *ab* in parallel with *R*, will make power delivered by battery a maximum; (*b*) current in *R* and *R'*; (*c*) terminal voltage of battery; (*d*) power in *R*, *R'*; (*e*) power lost in battery.

142. The battery, Prob. 135, is being charged at a 10-amp rate. Determine: (*a*) terminal voltage; (*b*) power delivered to battery; (*c*) power lost in heating battery.

143. The battery, Prob. 137, is being charged at an 80-amp rate. Determine: (*a*) terminal voltage; (*b*) total power delivered to battery; (*c*) power loss in battery.

144. A storage battery consists of 120 cells, connected in series. Each cell has an emf of 2.10 volts and an internal resistance of 0.0015 ohm. Determine: (*a*) voltage necessary to charge battery at 60-amp rate; (*b*) total power delivered to battery and power lost in battery; (*c*) terminal voltage when battery is disconnected from charging source and a resistor of 2.5 ohms is connected across terminals.

145. A storage battery consisting of 60 cells, each of which has an emf of 2.08 volts and an internal resistance of 0.0008 ohm, is charged at a 100-amp rate from 150-volt bus bars. Determine: (*a*) terminal voltage of battery; (*b*) resistance of resistor which must be connected in series with battery; (*c*) power to battery; (*d*) power lost in resistor.

146. Repeat Prob. 145 with battery being charged from 240-volt bus bars.

147. Four dry cells with emfs of 1.35, 1.38, 1.32, 1.28 volts are connected in series aiding and in series with an external resistor of 30 ohms. The internal resistances of the cells are 0.08, 0.06, 0.09, 0.12 ohm. Determine: (*a*) current; (*b*) terminal voltage of each cell; (*c*) internal power developed by each cell; (*d*) internal power lost in each cell; (*e*) power delivered to the 30-ohm resistor.

148. In Prob. 147, the third cell, with emf of 1.32 volts and resistance of 0.09 ohm, is reversed. Repeat (*a*) to (*e*).

149. In Prob. 148, the 30-ohm resistor is short-circuited. Repeat (*a*) to (*d*).

150. The emfs of four storage cells, connected in series aiding, are 2.11, 2.02, 2.06, 2.08 volts. The resistances are 0.0006, 0.0008, 0.0012, 0.001 ohm. When the battery delivers a current of 45 amp, determine: (*a*) terminal voltage of battery; (*b*) terminal voltage of each cell; (*c*) internal power developed by each cell; (*d*) power loss in each cell; (*e*) resistance of external resistor; (*f*) power to external resistor.

151. The four cells, Prob. 150, are all charged in series at a 30-amp rate. Determine: (*a*) terminal voltage of battery; (*b*) terminal voltage of each cell; (*c*) total power to cells; (*d*) power lost in each cell.

152. In Fig. 152*A* a resistor R is connected in series with four batteries, all in series aiding. The emfs and internal resistances are given. With resistor R equal to 5.0 ohms determine: (*a*) current; (*b*) power p_1, p_2, p_3, p_4 developed in each battery; (*c*) power P_1, P_2, P_3, P_4 delivered by each battery; (*d*) power lost in each battery; (*e*) voltage v_1, v_2, v_3, v_4 across each battery; (*f*) voltage V across resistor.

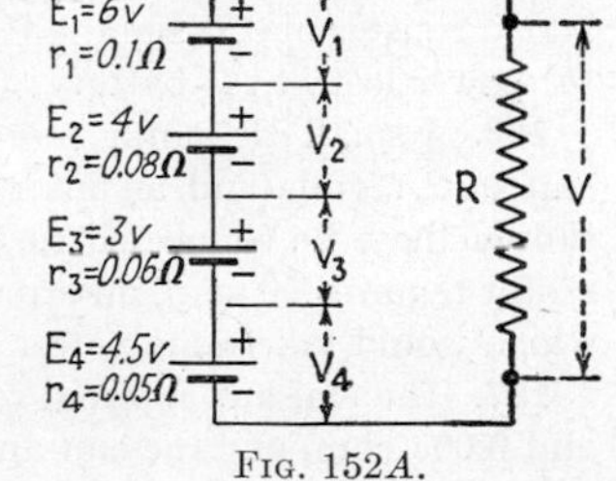

Fig. 152*A*.

153. Repeat Prob. 152 with the battery whose emf is 3 volts reversed. (If a battery is absorbing energy, the power developed is negative.)

154. In Prob. 152 determine: (*a*) value of R for maximum power delivered; (*b*) current; (*c*) power delivered by each battery; (*d*) terminal voltage of each battery.

155. Five dry cells have the following emfs and internal resistances: 1.40, 1.37, 1.32, 1.30, 1.23 volts; 0.06, 0.08, 0.06, 0.10, 0.10 ohm. All are connected in series aiding and in series with an external resistor of 20.7 ohms. Determine: (*a*) current; (*b*) power lost in each cell; (*c*) terminal voltage of each cell; (*d*) voltage across external resistor.

156. Repeat Prob. 155, reversing the fourth cell, that is, the cell whose emf is 1.30 volts and internal resistance is 0.10 ohm.

157. Four dry cells, each of which has an emf of 1.40 volts and an internal resistance of 0.06 ohm, are connected in parallel, with terminals of like polarity together. Determine: (*a*) current to an external resistor of 3.985 ohms; (*b*) terminal voltage of battery; (*c*) internal loss in each cell; (*d*) power to external circuit.

158. In Prob. 157 determine: (*a*) maximum power which battery can deliver; (*b*) terminal voltage of battery under these conditions; (*c*) resistance of external resistor.

159. Six batteries, each of which has an emf of 20 volts and an internal resistance of 0.75 ohm, are connected in parallel, with terminals of like polarity together. An external resistor of 7.85 ohms is connected across the terminals. Determine: (*a*) current to external circuit; (*b*) terminal voltage of battery; (*c*) power lost in each battery.

160. Each of four dry cells has an emf of 1.36 volts, but their internal resistances are 0.08, 0.06, 0.08, 0.09 ohm. These cells are connected in parallel, with terminals of like polarity together. Determine: (*a*) emf and internal resistance of a single cell that would replace battery; (*b*) current which battery delivers to an external resistor of 0.8 ohm; (*c*) terminal voltage; (*d*) current delivered by each cell; (*e*) maximum power which battery can deliver; (*f*) resistance of external resistor to give (*e*).

161. Each of two batteries has an emf of 20 volts, but the internal resistance of one is 0.04 ohm and that of the other is 0.05 ohm. These batteries are connected in parallel, with terminals of like polarity together. When the external current is 80 amp, determine: (*a*) current delivered by each battery; (*b*) terminal voltage of battery; (*c*) value of external resistance; (*d*) emf and internal resistance of a single battery which would replace these two in parallel.

162. A battery consists of four storage cells connected in parallel, each having an emf of 2.10 volts. The internal resistances of these cells are 0.004, 0.005, 0.003, 0.0025 ohm. Determine: (*a*) emf and internal resistance of single equivalent cell; (*b*) current when terminal voltage is 1.95 volts; (*c*) current in each cell.

163. Twenty-four dry cells are arranged in rows of six in series and the four rows in parallel. The emf of each cell is 1.40 volts, and the internal resistance of each is 0.08 ohm. Determine: (*a*) total battery emf; (*b*) total equivalent battery resistance; (*c*) current to an external resistor of 3.2 ohms; (*d*) terminal voltage; (*e*) resistance of external resistor to give maximum power; (*f*) maximum power.

164. Repeat Prob. 163 with the cells arranged in rows of four in series and six rows in parallel.

165. Arrange the cells of Prob. 163 so that the maximum power may be supplied to a load resistor of 0.48 ohm. Under these conditions, determine: (*a*) power to resistor; (*b*) power lost in the battery; (*c*) power to a load resistor of 8 ohms.

166. A small d-c motor is rated at 6.0 volts. Twelve storage cells, each having an emf of 2.1 volts and an internal resistance of 0.004 ohm, are available. (*a*) How should these be connected so that the maximum efficiency is obtained? When the motor requires 50 amp, determine: (*b*) battery terminal voltage; (*c*) ohms of a resistor which would take same power as motor; (*d*) battery efficiency.

167. The emf and internal resistance of one of two starting batteries are 6.33 volts and 0.006 ohm, and the emf and resistance of the other are 6.15 volts and 0.004 ohm. These batteries are connected in parallel, with terminals of like polarity together. Determine: (*a*) emf and internal resistance of a single equivalent battery; (*b*) current to an external-load resistance of 0.30 ohm; (*c*) current in each battery; (*d*) terminal voltage.

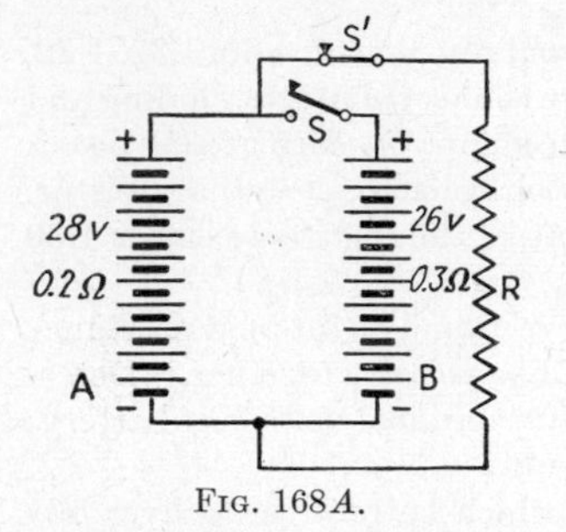

Fig. 168*A*.

168. The emf and internal resistance of two batteries *A* and *B* are 28 volts and 0.2 ohm and 26 volts and 0.3 ohm. These batteries are connected in parallel, with terminals of like polarity together (see Fig. 168*A*). Determine: (*a*) emf and internal resistance of a single equivalent battery; (*b*) current delivered by each battery when external current is 6 amp; (*c*) terminal voltage; (*d*) resistance of load resistor; (*e*) resistance of load resistor for maximum power delivered; (*f*) current delivered by each battery in (*e*).

169. The emfs and internal resistances of two storage batteries in parallel, with like terminals connected together, are 120 volts and 0.02 ohm and 118 volts and 0.03 ohm. Determine: (*a*) emf and internal resistance of a single equivalent battery; (*b*) current when resistance of load is 1.2 ohm; (*c*) terminal voltage; (*d*) current delivered by battery; (*e*) power developed by each battery; (*f*) power delivered by each battery; (*g*) current in each battery when resistance of load is infinite.

170. In Fig. 168*A* are shown the two batteries of Prob. 168, with a switch *S* in series with *B*. The division of the load current of 6 amp to the external circuit *R* is to be determined by means of the *floating-battery* method (p. 67). (*a*) With the switch *S* open (and *S'* closed), determine current which battery *A* must deliver in order that battery *B* may just "*float*" when switch *S* is closed. Determine: (*b*) division of remaining load current between two batteries; (*c*) total current delivered by each battery; (*d*) terminal voltage in (*c*). (Compare results with those obtained in Prob. 168.)

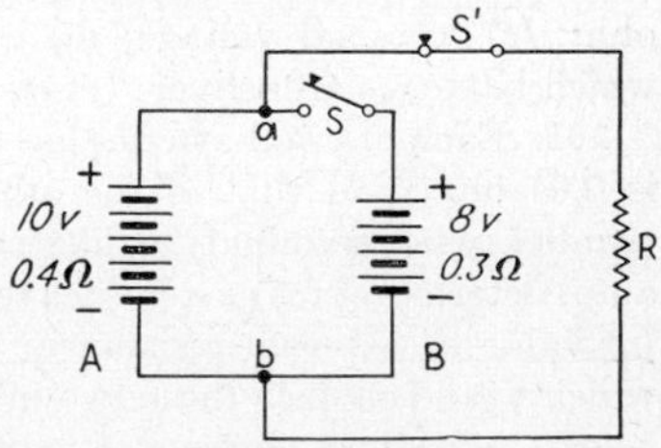

Fig. 171*A*.

171. In Fig. 171*A* are shown two batteries *A* and *B*, having emfs and internal resistances of 10 volts and 0.4 ohm and 8 volts and 0.3 ohm. A switch *S* is in series with battery *B*. The external-load resistor *R* takes 6 amp. It is desired to determine the division of this current between the two batteries by means of the floating-battery method (see p. 67). (*a*) With switch *S* open (and *S′* closed), determine current which must be delivered by *A* in order that *B* may float when switch *S* is closed. Determine: (*b*) division of remainder of load current between two batteries; (*c*) total current delivered by each battery; (*d*) resistance of load resistor *R*.

172. In Prob. 167, determine by means of the floating-battery method, when a load resistor takes 100 amp, (*a*) current in each battery; (*b*) terminal voltage; (*c*) resistance of load resistor.

173. Two batteries *A* and *B*, Fig. 173*A*, having emfs of 50 and 48 volts and internal resistances of 0.06 and 0.04 ohm, are connected in parallel, with terminals of like polarity together. The current taken by load resistor *R* when the switch *S* is closed is 48 amp. The division of current between the batteries is to be determined by the circulatory-current method (p. 68). Determine: (*a*) circulatory current with switch *S* open; (*b*) currents, with proper sign, delivered by *A* and *B*; (*c*) additional current delivered by *A* and *B* when switch *S* is closed; (*d*) total current delivered by *A*; (*e*) total current delivered by *B*; (*f*) terminal voltage across *ab*; (*g*) resistance of *R*.

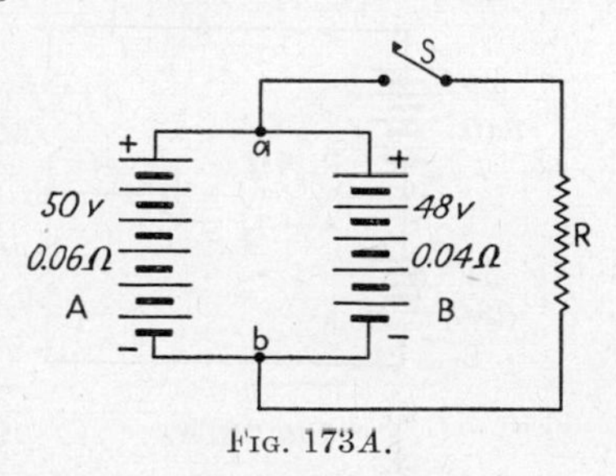

FIG. 173*A*.

174. Problem 170 is to be solved by the circulatory-current method (p. 68). With switch *S* closed and *S′* open, Fig. 168*A*, determine (*a*) circulatory current with its correct sign in batteries *A* and *B*. With switch *S′* closed so that the load resistor *R* takes 6 amp, determine: (*b*) division of this current between batteries *A* and *B*; (*c*) total current delivered by *A* and by *B*; (*d*) terminal voltage; (*e*) resistance of *R*. (Compare results with those obtained in Prob. 170.)

175. Solve the circuit shown in Fig. 171*A* by the circulatory-current method, that is, with switch *S* closed and switch *S′* open at first. The load current is now 6 amp. Determine: (*a*) current delivered by each battery; (*b*) terminal voltage; (*c*) power developed by each battery; (*d*) power lost in each battery. [Compare (*a*) with (*c*) in Prob. 171.]

176. Repeat Prob. 175 with the load current equal to 10 amp.

177. Solve Prob. 173 by the circulatory-current method with the emf of battery *A* still equal to 50 volts and that of battery *B* changed to 53 volts. The external-load current is still 48 amp, and the resistance of each battery remains unchanged. Determine: (*a*) current delivered by each battery; (*b*) terminal voltage; (*c*) power loss in each battery; (*d*) resistance of *R*.

Kirchhoff's Laws

178. Two batteries *A* and *B*, Fig. 178*A*, having emfs of 6.0 and 5.0 volts and resistances of 0.8 and 0.6 ohm, are connected in parallel, positive terminal to positive terminal. A resistor *R* of 2.5 ohms is connected across the common terminals. Determine: (*a*) current *I* in resistor *R*; (*b*) current I_1 in *A* battery and current I_2 in *B* battery; (*c*) voltage between terminals *ab* of the combination.

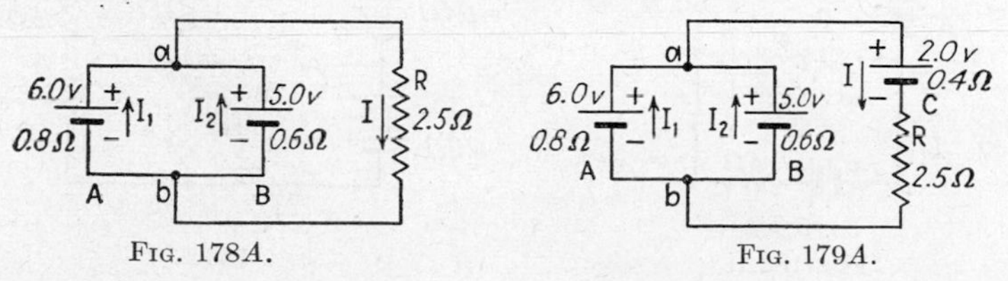

FIG. 178*A*. FIG. 179*A*.

179. In Fig. 179A is shown the circuit of Fig. 178A, with the addition of a third battery C, emf 2.0 volts and resistance 0.4 ohm, in series with the 2.5-ohm resistor R. Determine: (a) current I to battery C; (b) currents I_1, I_2 in batteries A, B; (c) voltage between terminals ab of batteries A and B; (d) terminal voltage of battery C.

180. Repeat Prob. 179 with battery C reversed.

181. In Fig. 181A is shown an electric network consisting of three batteries A, B, C and three resistors R_1, R_2, R_3. Determine: (a) currents I_1, I_2, I_3 with their proper signs; (b) terminal voltages of batteries A, B, C; (c) voltage between terminals ab.

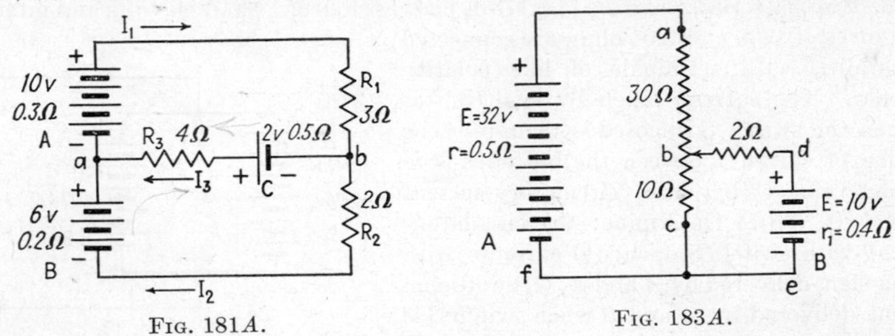

Fig. 181A. Fig. 183A.

182. Repeat Prob. 181 with battery C reversed.

183. In the battery system in Fig. 183A, the emf of battery A is 32 volts, and its internal resistance r is 0.5 ohm. A resistor abc of 40 ohms is connected across the battery terminals, the end a being connected to the positive terminal. The emf of battery B is 10 volts, and its internal resistance r_1 is 0.4 ohm. Its negative terminal e is connected to the negative terminal f of battery A and to the end c of the resistor. Its positive terminal d is connected through a 2-ohm resistor to the point b in the resistor abc, where resistance bc = 10 ohms. Determine: (a) currents in batteries A and B; (b) point to which b should be moved (in terms of ohms from b to c) in order that the current in battery B may be zero. The total resistance ac remains unchanged.

184. Repeat Prob. 183 with the resistance between points bc equal to 6 ohms, the total resistance between a and c remaining unchanged.

185. In Prob. 181 and Fig. 181A, determine the value of R_1 which will make the current I_3 equal to zero.

186. In Fig. 186A is shown a network in which the directions of the three currents I_1, I_2, I_3 are all toward the common junction a. Determine I_1, I_2, I_3, stating actual directions.

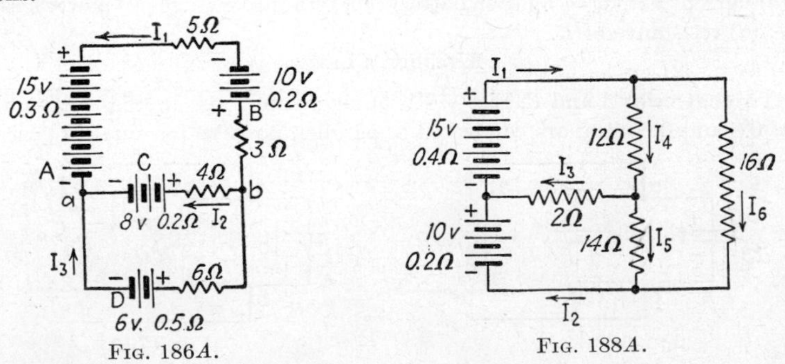

Fig. 186A. Fig. 188A.

187. Repeat Prob. 186 with the polarity of battery D reversed.

188. In Fig. 188A is shown an electrical network. Determine the six network currents (a) I_1; (b) I_2; (c) I_3; (d) I_4; (e) I_5; (f) I_6.

189. In Fig. 189*A* is shown an electric network in which there are three batteries *A*, *B*, *C*, having emfs of 12, 20, 30 volts, and negligible internal resistances. Determine six network currents I_1 to I_6, and show their values and actual directions on diagram.

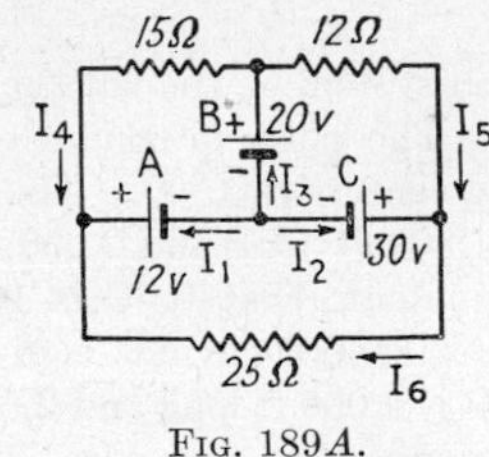

Fig. 189*A*.

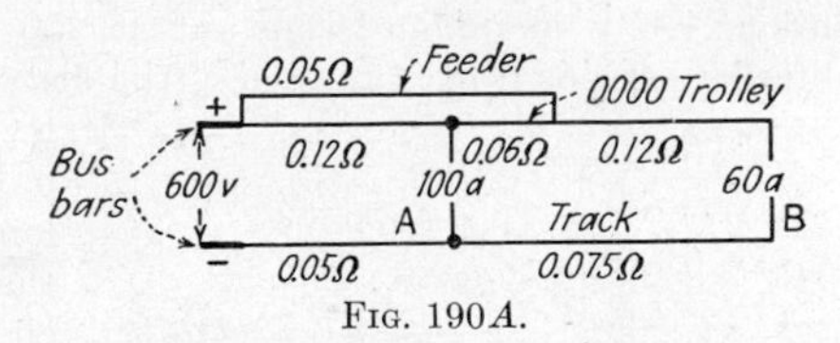

Fig. 190*A*.

190. In Fig. 190*A* is shown a railway system with two cars at *A* and *B* taking 100 and 60 amp. For a portion of the length of the trolley there is a feeder in parallel with the trolley. The voltage at the station bus bars is 600 volts. The resistances of each part of the overhead and track systems are given. Determine voltage at (*a*) car at *A*; (*b*) car at *B*.

191. Repeat Prob. 190 with car *A* at the junction of the feeder and the trolley. The track resistance from station to junction is 0.05 ohm and from junction to end of line is 0.075 ohm.

192. In Fig. 192*A* is shown the wiring diagram of a loop trolley system with a single 300,000-cir-mil feeder *ac*. A potential difference of 600 volts is maintained between trolley and rail at the bus bars *ab*. The No. 0000 trolley wire has a resistance of 0.265 ohm per mile, and the 300,000-cir-mil feeder has a resistance of 0.187 ohm per mile and is connected from *a* to *c*, a distance of 3.0 miles. A car at *A*, 2 miles from the station, takes 100 amp, and a car at *B*, 3 miles from the station on the other side of the loop, takes 80 amp. The resistance of the rail is 0.04 ohm per mile. Determine: (*a*) voltage at car at *A*; (*b*) voltage at car at *B*.

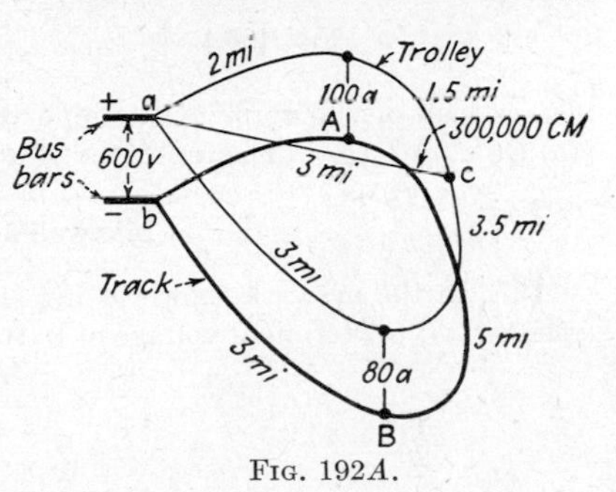

Fig. 192*A*.

193. Repeat Prob. 192 when the car at *B* has reached *c*. The currents to the cars remain unchanged.

194. Repeat Prob. 192 when the car at *A* has reached *c* and the car at *B* is again in the position shown in Fig. 192*A*. The current to the cars remains unchanged.

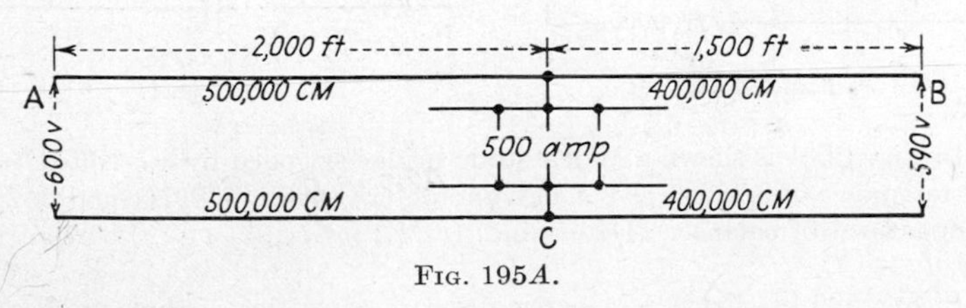

Fig. 195*A*.

195. Two substations *A* and *B* feed into the same distributing center *C*, Fig. 195*A*. The voltage at the bus bars of station *A* is maintained constant at 600 volts, and that at station *B* is maintained at 590 volts. Station *A* feeds a distance of 2,000 ft through

500,000-cir-mil cable and station B a distance of 1,500 ft through 400,000-cir-mil cable to distributing center C. The load at the distributing center is 500 amp. Determine: (a) current supplied by each station; (b) power supplied by each station; (c) voltage at C; (d) power delivered at distributing center C. The resistance of a circular-mil-foot may be taken as 10 ohms.

196. Figure 196A shows a 250-volt power-distribution system. The voltage at the substation AA' is maintained constant at 250 volts. The positive conductor of a radial feeder extends from A to each of the distributing centers B, C, D. The feeder to B is 1,500 ft long and 2,000,000 cir mils equivalent; that to C is 1,600 ft long and 2,000,000 cir mils equivalent; that to D is 2,000 ft long and 2,500,000 cir mils equivalent (per wire in every case). A tie line, 750 ft long and of 400,000 cir mil cross section, connects B and C, and another similar line connects C and D. The negative side of the system, which is in every way identical with the positive side, is shown by dashes in the figure. Across BB' there is connected a load of 1,000 amp, across CC' a load of 600 amp, and across DD' a load of 900 amp. Determine voltage at each of distributing centers (a) BB'; (b) CC'; (c) DD'. (The resistance of a circular-mil-foot may be taken as 10 ohms.)

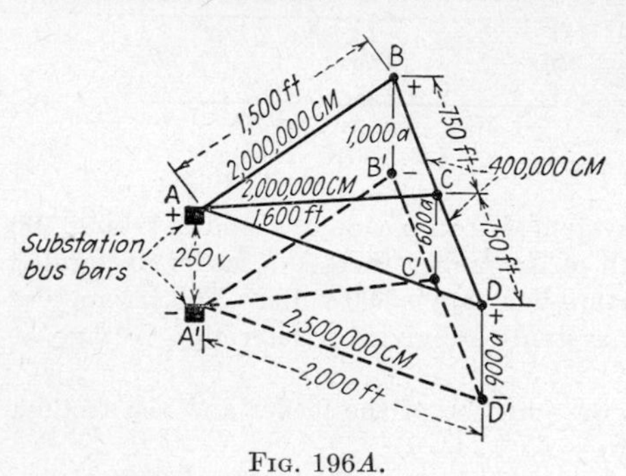

Fig. 196A.

Maxwell's Mesh Equations

197. In the network shown in Fig. 197A, determine: (a) I_1; (b) I_2; (c) current in resistor ab; (d) terminal voltage of batteries A, B, C.

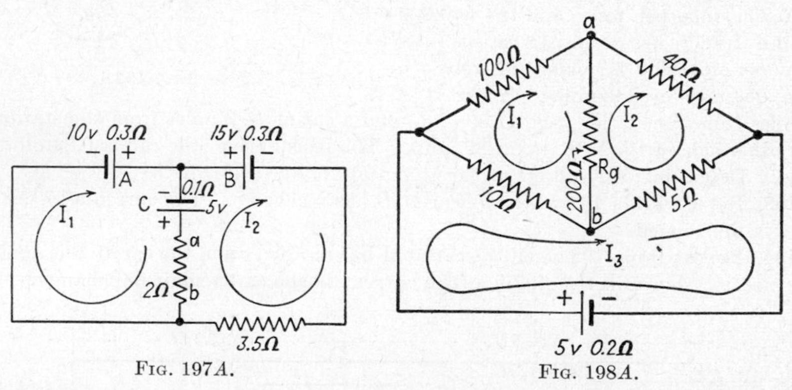

Fig. 197A.

Fig. 198A.

198. In Fig. 198A is shown a Wheatstone bridge supplied by a 5-volt battery with internal resistance of 0.2 ohm. The galvanometer resistance R_g is equal to 200 ohms. The bridge is out of balance. Determine: (a) I_1; (b) I_2; (c) I_3; (d) current in galvanometer, I_{ab}.

199. In Fig. 199A is shown an electric network consisting of three meshes in which the currents I_1, I_2, I_3 circulate. Determine by the Maxwell mesh equations (a) I_1, I_2, I_3; (b) currents in elements ab, cb, bd; (c) terminal voltages of batteries A, B, C.

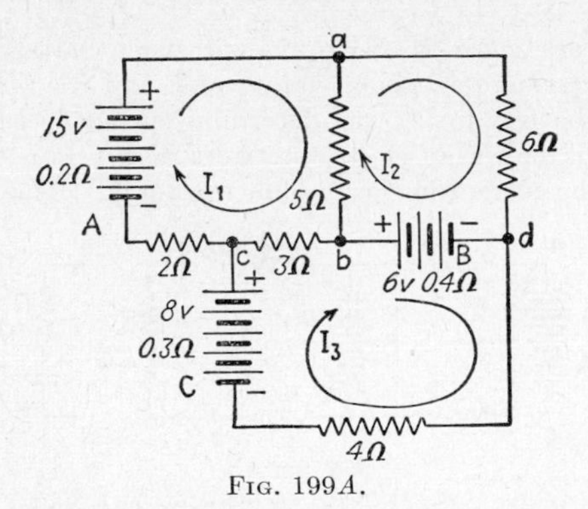

FIG. 199A.

NOTE. The preceding problems, Nos. 178 to 196, in which the solution by Kirchhoff's two laws is indicated, also may be solved by the Maxwell mesh equations.

Superposition Theorem

200. Solve Prob. 178 by the superposition theorem. Let I_1' be the current in battery A and I_2' the current in the resistance of battery B when the emf of battery B is removed. Let I_1'' be the current in the resistance of battery A and I_2'' be the current in battery B when the emf of battery A is removed. Let I' and I'' be the currents in R under the foregoing conditions. Determine: (*a*) I_1', I_2', I'; (*b*) I_1'', I_2'', I''; (*c*) by superposition the total currents I_1, I_2, I.

201. Solve the network, Fig. 201A, by the superposition theorem. First compute the current in each element of the network with the emf of battery B removed, and then repeat with the emf of battery A removed. Required: (*a*) two component currents, and total current I_1 in battery A; (*b*) two component currents, and total current I_2 in battery B; (*c*) by superposition, total current in each element *ab*, *bc*, *cd*, *be*.

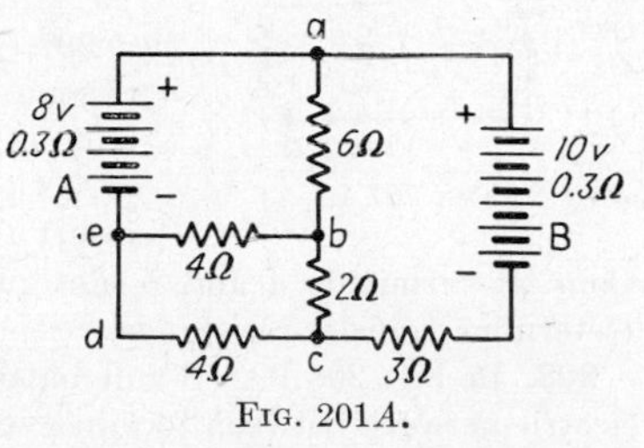

FIG. 201A.

202. Solve Prob. 183 by the superposition theorem. Determine: (*a*) current I_1', in battery A, I_2' in the resistance of battery B, I' in resistor *bc* when emf of battery B is removed; (*b*) current I_1'' in resistance of battery A, I_2'' in battery B, and I'' the current in resistor *bc* with emf of battery A removed; (*c*) by superposition, total current I_1 in battery A, I_2 in battery B, I in resistor *bc*.

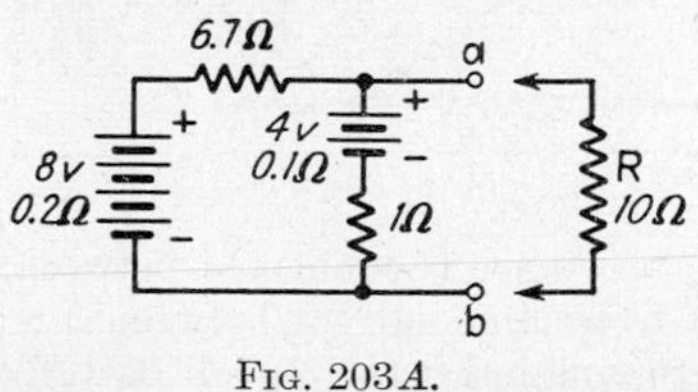

FIG. 203A.

Thévenin's Theorem

203. In Fig. 203A is shown an electric network with terminals *ab*. It is desired to determine by Thévenin's theorem the current in resistor R of 10 ohms. Determine: (*a*) voltage across terminals *ab* before connecting resistor R across these terminals; (*b*) resistance R_0 of the network as measured between terminals *ab*; (*c*) current in R when connected across terminals *ab*.

204. It is desired to determine by Thévenin's theorem the current in branch *bde* of Fig. 183A. With the contact at b removed, determine: (*a*) voltage between points *bc*; (*b*) resistance between points *bc*; (*c*) potential difference between points *bd*.

(*d*) Reduce the network *abcfa* to an equivalent single battery with terminals *ab*, emf *E*, and internal resistance *r*, giving values of *E* and *r*. (*e*) Connect the circuit *bde* to the equivalent battery in (*d*), and determine current in *bde*.

205. In Fig. 205*A* is shown an electric network *abcd*. It is desired to obtain by Thévenin's theorem the current in the 12-ohm resistor *R*. The emfs and resistances

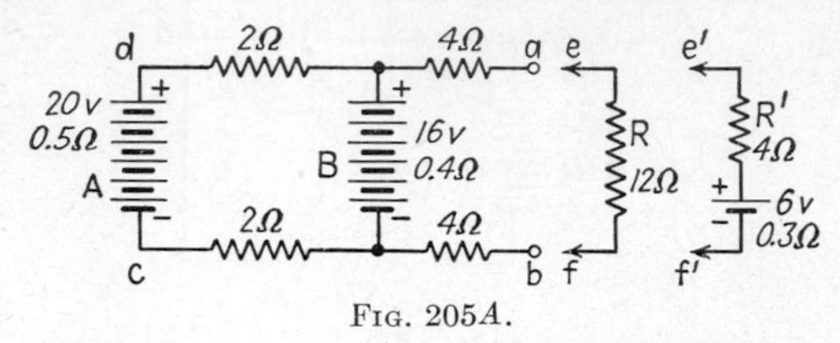

Fig. 205*A*.

of batteries *A* and *B*, as well as the resistances of the other circuit elements are all given. Under the conditions shown in the figure, determine: (*a*) voltage across terminals *ab*; (*b*) resistance as measured between terminals *ab*. (*c*) Reduce the network to an equivalent single battery with terminals *ab*, emf *E*, and internal resistance *r*. (*d*) Determine current in circuit *ef* when terminal *e* is connected to *a* and *f* to *b*.

206. Repeat Prob. 205 (*d*) with circuit *e'f'* replacing *ef*, other conditions remaining unchanged.

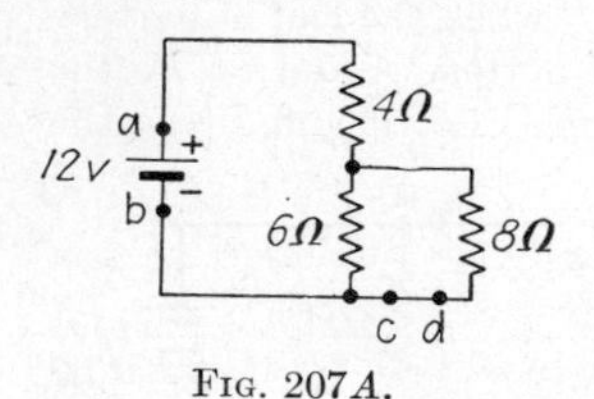

Fig. 207*A*.

Reciprocity Theorem

207. In Fig. 207*A* a 12-volt battery with negligible resistance is connected between terminals *ab* in the electric network. (*a*) Determine current between terminals *cd*. Open the connection between terminals *cd*, and insert the battery with the positive terminal at *c*. (*b*) Connect terminals *a* and *b*, determine current in *ab*, and compare with (*a*). (*c*) Determine transfer resistance.

208. In Fig. 208*A* an 8-volt battery with negligible resistance is connected to the electric network between terminals *ab* as shown. (*a*) Determine current between terminals *cd*. (*b*) Open the connection between terminals *cd*, and insert the 8-volt battery with the positive terminal at *c*. Then connect terminals *a* and *b*, determine current in *ab*, and compare with (*a*). (*c*) Determine transfer resistance.

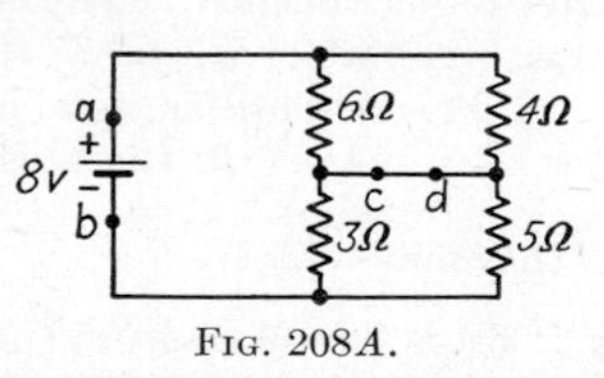

Fig. 208*A*.

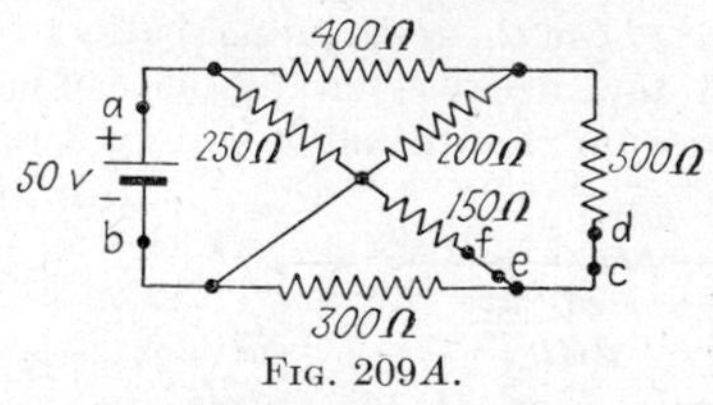

Fig. 209*A*.

209. In Fig. 209*A* a 50-volt battery of negligible resistance is connected between terminals *ab* of the electric network as shown. (*a*) Determine current between terminals *cd*. Open the connection between terminals *cd*, and insert the 50-volt battery with the positive terminal at *c*. (*b*) Connect terminals *a* and *b*, determine current in *ab*, and compare with (*a*). (*c*) Determine transfer resistance.

210. In Fig. 209*A* determine (*a*) current between terminals *ef*. Open terminals *ef*; transfer battery so that its positive terminal is at *e* and its negative at *f*. (*b*) Close terminals *a* and *b*, determine current in *ab*, and compare with (*a*). (*c*) Determine transfer resistance.

Equivalent Delta-Y Transformations

211. In Fig. 211*A* is shown a delta system of resistors in which $AB = 20$ ohms, $BC = 25$ ohms, $CA = 16$ ohms. Determine and construct an equivalent Y system having terminals *ABC*. Verify the correctness of the Y system by computing resistances between different terminals and comparing them with the corresponding values of resistance in the delta system.

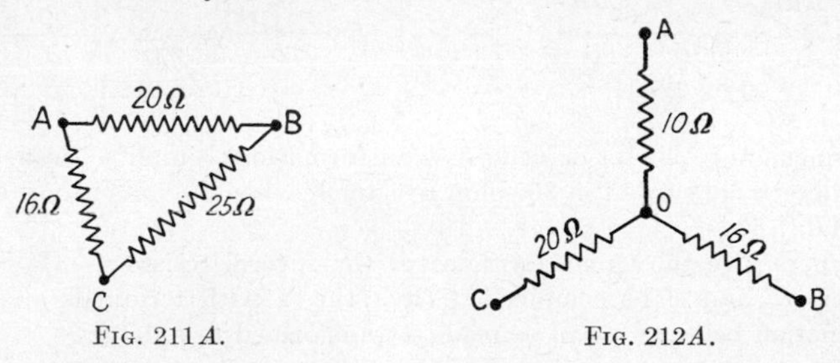

Fig. 211*A*. Fig. 212*A*.

212. In Fig. 212*A* is shown a Y system of resistors in which $AO = 10$ ohms; $BO = 16$ ohms; $CO = 20$ ohms. Determine and construct an equivalent delta system having terminals *ABC*. Verify the correctness of the delta system by computing resistance between different terminals and comparing them with corresponding values of resistance in the Y system.

213. In Fig. 213*A* is shown an electric network. The numbers designate the ohms resistance of each member. There is no connection at the center between elements *ab* and *cd*. (*a*) Convert the Y system, *ac*, *dc*, *bc*, into an equivalent delta. (*b*) Combine (*a*) with the remainder of the network to determine the resistance between terminals *AB*. (*c*) With 50 volts across terminals *AB* compute the current in members *ab*, *bc*, *ca*, *cd*, *bd*, *da*.

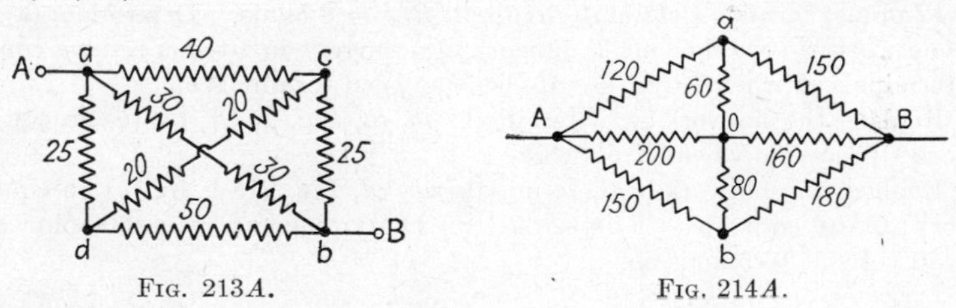

Fig. 213*A*. Fig. 214*A*.

214. In Fig. 214*A* is shown an electric network between the terminals *AB*. The numbers in the figure designate the ohms resistance of each member. Simplify the network by converting the Y sections *Ab*, *ob*, *Bb* and *Aa*, *oa*, *Ba* into equivalent deltas. (*a*) Determine resistance between terminals *AB*. (*b*) With 100 volts impressed across *AB*, determine current in members *AO* and *OB*.

215. In the network in Fig. 215*A*, 25 volts is applied to terminals *AB*. Determine: (*a*) resistance between terminals *AB*; (*b*) current in each member *a′b′*, *ao*, *ob*, *oc*, *dd′*. (A simple solution is to convert the Y system *ao*, *bo*, *co* into an equivalent delta.)

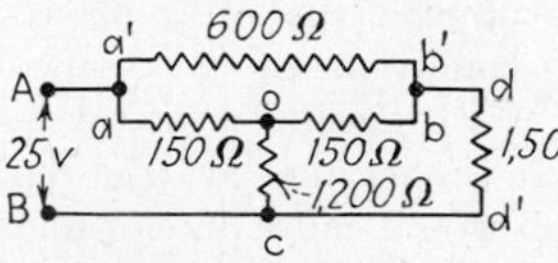

Fig. 215*A*.

216. In Fig. 56(*a*) (p. 90) determine current in the 10-ohm member when voltage across terminals *AB* is 20 volts.

217. By means of Y-delta or delta-Y transformations simplify the network, Fig. 217*A*, and determine current in the 600-ohm resistor when 20 volts is impressed across terminals *AB*.

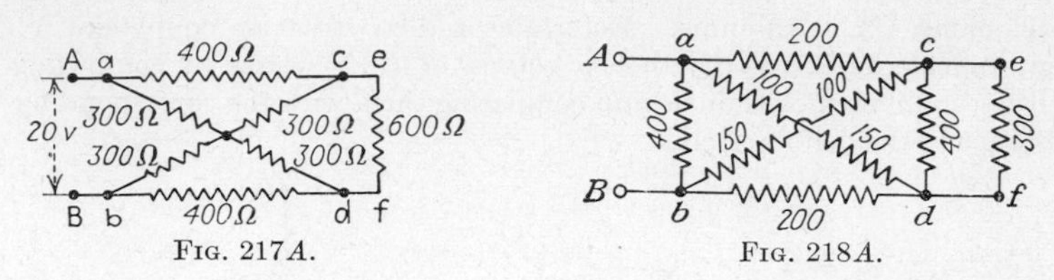

Fig. 217*A*. Fig. 218*A*.

218. By means of Y-delta or delta-Y transformations simplify the network, Fig. 218*A*, and determine current in 300-ohm resistor *ef* when 30 volts is impressed across terminals *AB*.

The numbers give the ohms resistance in the several resistors. (It is suggested that resistors *cd* and *ef* be combined. Then the Y with terminals at *a*, *b*, *d*, the common junction being at *c*, can be readily transformed to a delta.)

Four-terminal Networks

219. In Fig. 219*A* is shown a 4-terminal network with terminals *ab* and *cd*. The following resistance measurements are made: *cd* open, $R_{ab} = 42$ ohms; *cd* short-circuited, $R_{ab}' = 22$ ohms; *ab* open, $R_{cd} = 34$ ohms. Determine: (*a*) equivalent π network; (*b*) equivalent T network. (*c*) With 20 volts applied across terminals *ab*, determine current in a 50-ohm resistor connected across *cd*.

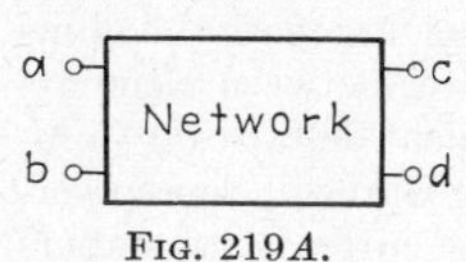

Fig. 219*A*.

220. In a network similar to that shown in Fig. 219*A* resistance measurements are made as follows: terminals *cd* open, $R_{ab} = 18$ ohms; terminals *cd* short-circuited, $R_{ab}' = 12$ ohms; terminals *ab* short-circuited, $R_{cd}' = 8$ ohms. Determine: (*a*) equivalent π network; (*b*) equivalent T network; (*c*) current in 10-ohm resistor connected across terminals *cd* when 15 volts is applied between terminals *ab*.

221. Replace the network with terminals *ab*, *cd*, Fig. 217*A*, by (*a*) an equivalent π network; (*b*) an equivalent T network.

222. Replace the network with terminals *ab*, *cd*, Fig. 218*A*, by (*a*) an equivalent π network; (*b*) an equivalent T network. (*c*) Determine current in 300-ohm resistor *ef* with 30 volts at terminals *ab*.

QUESTIONS ON CHAPTER IV

Primary and Secondary Batteries

1. State the reactions which occur when two copper strips are immersed in a dilute sulfuric acid solution and a voltmeter is connected between them. Repeat when the two copper strips are replaced by two zinc strips; by two lead strips. In general, what conditions are necessary in order that there may be an emf between the strips?

2. With dissimilar metals as electrodes, discuss the possibilities of obtaining an emf if the sulfuric acid be replaced by some other solution. Name three solutions which would cause an emf under these conditions.

3. What is meant by one metal being electrochemically positive to another? If metal *A* is electrochemically positive to metal *B*, what will be the direction of the current between them within the cell? What will be the direction of the current between them through the external circuit?

4. Define: electrolyte, electrolytic cell, electrode, anode, cathode, primary cell, storage cell.

5. In what form is the energy stored within the cell? What changes take place in the electrodes when the cell delivers current? Distinguish between a primary cell and a secondary cell.

6. Name four requirements for a satisfactory primary cell.

7. Discuss the nature of the internal resistance of a cell. In what manner may this resistance be reduced? In what way does increasing the size of the elements of a cell affect its current capacity? Its emf?

8. What voltage does a voltmeter indicate when it is connected to the terminals of a cell which is open-circuited? If the circuit is suddenly closed, to what is the initial voltage drop due? To what is the excess drop over this initial drop due? Explain the part that hydrogen plays in polarization. Describe two general methods of reducing polarization.

9. Discuss the change with time of the terminal voltage of a cell under constant-resistance load. Discuss the recovery of the cell when the load is removed.

10. Describe the construction of the Daniell cell, stating the materials of the electrodes and the electrolytes. For what type of work is it best adapted? What is the emf of this cell?

11. In what way does the gravity cell differ from the Daniell cell? Which electrode requires replacing? What changes occur in the other electrode? What is the cell emf, and for what type of work is the gravity cell best adapted?

12. What materials are used for positive and negative electrodes in the Leclanché cell, and what is used for the electrolyte? What is the approximate value of the emf? When planning to use the cell commercially, about what voltage per cell should be allowed? What materials are introduced in the cell to reduce polarization? How is the cell renewed? For what type of work is this cell best adapted?

13. In what way does a dry cell resemble a common type of wet cell? Is a "dry" cell really dry? Of what material is the positive electrode composed? The negative? What is the electrolyte, and how is it placed in the cell? What materials are placed between the carbon and the zinc, and what are their functions?

14. What is the emf of a Leclanché type dry cell when new? After it has stood idle for some time? What is the magnitude of the internal resistance when new? Discuss the effect of time on the internal resistance. How does the polarization effect compare with the internal-resistance effect? About what current should a good cell deliver on short circuit? What is the approximate value of the terminal voltage when the cell delivers a moderate current?

15. What is the principal cause of the cell becoming exhausted? Name some of the commercial applications of dry cells.

16. Name the materials used for the anode, the cathode, and the electrolyte of the Ruben cell. In what two forms is the cell made? Describe each.

17. Give the emf of the Ruben cell. State its advantages over the Leclanché type.

18. Name the materials used for the cathode, the anode and the electrolyte of the silver chloride–magnesium cell. What is its emf? For what type of work is this cell designed?

19. What is the function of a Weston standard cell in contrast to the uses made of other types of cells? In practice, what two common electrical quantities are most easily reproduced and maintained as standards? What must be the characteristics of a standard cell? Describe the construction of the Weston cell and its elements. How is its permanency ensured? In what respect does the saturated cell differ from the normal cell? Why cannot the emf of the Weston cell be measured with an ordinary voltmeter?

20. In what way is a storage cell renewed when it becomes discharged? What condition concerning the materials of the cell is necessary for proper functioning of the cell? What three general types of storage cells are in commercial use?

21. Describe an elementary experiment which illustrates the underlying principle of the lead cell. State the change that occurs in each of the lead strips. What voltage is observed to exist at different times in the experiment? What gases are evolved, and at which plate is each gas given off?

22. Even though both of its plates are of lead, show that the existence of an emf in a lead storage cell does not in any way violate the principle governing the emf of electric cells in general. When the cell is approaching complete discharge, what changes in the materials would account for the approach of the voltage to zero? Account for the 2.5 volts per cell utilized in the process of charging.

23. What change in the electrolyte during charge and discharge of a cell is shown by the chemical equation, (p. 109)? Why is a cell composed of plain lead plates not useful in practice? Give two reasons. Describe briefly the Planté process, and describe two commercial plates that are formed by this process.

24. Describe the Faure, or pasted, process for making battery plates. What are the advantages and disadvantages of pasted plates over Planté plates? What commercial conditions demand a pasted plate and why? How may erosion of the positive plate be retarded and the life of the battery increased? How does the life of a pasted plate compare with that of a Planté plate?

25. Describe briefly the construction of the Exide-Ironclad cell and its principal use in practice.

26. What are the two general classes into which lead storage batteries may be divided? What types of plate are best suited for regulating duty and for emergency duty in stationary batteries? Why? What material is now used for the tanks of stationary lead-type batteries?

27. Name at least three functions of separators. Name at least four materials which are used for separators. Indicate the type of service for which each is best adapted, including combinations of materials.

28. In lead-type batteries, why is a low specific gravity of the electrolyte desirable, and why is a high specific gravity desirable? Name the upper limit of specific gravity when the battery is fully charged and the lower limit when it is at the end of discharge.

29. What precaution should be taken in diluting sulfuric acid for storage-battery use? What simple device is used for determining specific gravity? How is this device adapted for use with vehicle and portable batteries?

30. What change takes place in the electrolyte during the charging period? What is the effect of gassing on the specific gravity? What change takes place in the specific gravity after the charging has ceased? Explain. How does the specific gravity of the electrolyte change during discharge? What practical use is made of these changes of specific gravity?

31. State the effect of temperature on the capacity of a lead battery. Of what order of magnitude is the change per degree Fahrenheit?

32. What changes occur in the active material of a cell if the cell is allowed to stand idle over long periods? In what way may injury to the battery from this cause be avoided? If it is desired to withdraw a battery from service for an indefinite period, what procedure should be followed?

33. What are the requirements of a portable battery that make its design different from that of a stationary battery? What changes are made in the plates? Separators? Specific gravity of the electrolyte? How is a battery assembled for a particular type of service? What special attention should be paid to the electrolyte?

34. In what way is the rating of a storage battery expressed? What is meant by the 8-hr rate? Can as many ampere-hours be withdrawn from a cell at the 3-hr rate as at the 8-hr rate? To what is any difference due? If a cell is apparently exhausted after discharging at the 3-hr rate, would it be possible later to obtain any further ampere-hours from it? What can be said of the overload capacity of a storage battery?

35. What general principle governs the charging rate of a battery? When does it become necessary to reduce this current? What are the objections to pronounced gassing in a cell? What is the *finishing rate?*

36. Name a common example of constant-current method of charging. What type of apparatus is necessary for charging a battery from an a-c source?

What care should be taken in the connecting up of the battery? Describe a simple test by which the correct terminal polarity may be ascertained.

37. What is the one advantage of the constant-potential method of charging? About what voltage per cell is necessary in this method? Why is the use of some resistance desirable?

38. When a battery is just floating on a bus bar and it is desired to charge it, in what manner may the necessary excess potential for charging be obtained? What proportion of the entire energy necessary for charging is supplied by the booster?

39. What change occurs in the emf of a cell during the charging period? What corresponding change occurs in the terminal voltage? To what is the difference between the cell emf and the terminal voltage due?

40. What is the active positive material of the Edison alkali cell? Describe the construction of the positive plate and the manner of applying the active positive material.

41. What is the active negative material? Describe the construction of the negative plate and the manner of applying the active material.

42. What is used for the electrolyte of the Edison cell? In the chemical reaction that takes place on both charge and discharge, what part does the electrolyte play?

43. On complete charge, what is the material of the positive electrode? Of the negative electrode? To what do these materials change on discharge? Discuss the changes, if any, which occur in the electrolyte on charge and on discharge, and compare with the changes which occur in the electrolyte of the lead cell.

44. Describe briefly the mechanical construction and assembly of the Edison cell, stating the method of holding the plates and connecting them with the binding posts. What kind of tank is used for this cell? What is the advantage of this type of construction? For what purpose is the valve necessary and what care does the valve require? How is the battery mounted?

45. In what way does the normal rating of an Edison cell differ from that of a lead cell? What is the voltage per cell? Is it possible to tell accurately the condition of charge by readings of either voltage or specific gravity? How can the condition of complete charge be determined?

46. Why does the level of the electrolyte gradually decrease with service? Discuss the replacement of the electrolyte.

47. State the advantages of the Edison battery and some of its commercial applications. What factors limit its applications?

48. Describe the construction of the positive and negative plates of the nickel-cadmium-alkali (Nicad) cell. What is the active material of each plate? Compare these materials with those of the Edison cell.

49. What are the materials used for the separators? Describe the construction of the container.

50. What is used for the electrolyte, and what part does it play in the operation of the cell? What is its normal specific gravity?

51. What is the normal voltage of the cell? On charge, at what voltage does it begin to gas?

52. State the advantages of the Nicad battery and some of its commercial applications.

53. In what terms may the efficiency of a storage battery be expressed? Discuss the ampere-hours efficiency as a true criterion of efficiency.

54. State the reason why the ratio of the kilowatthours of discharge at the 3-hr rate to those of charge at the 8-hr rate in a lead battery does not give the true efficiency. Give some of the factors which determine the efficiency of a battery.

55. What is the order of magnitude of the kilowatthours efficiency of a lead storage battery? The ampere-hours efficiency? Why do the two differ? In what manner does the cycle of operation of a storage battery affect the efficiency?

56. State some of the factors which govern the selection of a storage battery for a particular purpose.

57. In what manner may water be made a good conductor? Define *electrolysis* and *electrolyte*. What are the products of the electrolysis of water and where is each released?

58. Define: *electrolytic dissociation, ion, positive ions* or *cations, negative ions* or *anions*. Relate the movement of the ions to the electric current.

59. Analyze the electrolysis of copper sulfate, showing that sulphuric acid is formed. Give examples of industrial applications of electrolysis.

60. State briefly Faraday's two laws of electrolysis. In simple language, explain their meaning.

61. State a simple method of producing copper plating upon a carbon brush such as is used with generators. Which electrode is connected to the positive terminal of the supply, and which is connected to the negative terminal? When copper is used in connection with a copper sulfate solution, is there any marked change in the electrolyte? Explain.

62. Can copper be plated from a solution in which neither electrode is copper? What voltages in the plating bath must the supply voltage overcome? How are these voltages reduced to a minimum? Is electroplating a high-voltage or a low-voltage process? In what way are plating baths connected, when possible?

63. Show how the gravity cell is an electroplating bath which supplies its own electroplating current.

64. Describe briefly the process of electrotyping.

PROBLEMS ON CHAPTER IV

Primary and Secondary Batteries

223. The emf of a Daniell cell is 1.1 volts, and the internal resistance is 0.20 ohm. Determine: (*a*) maximum current which cell can deliver. The size of the cell is increased in such a manner that the plate area is doubled. Determine: (*b*) the new emf; (*c*) approximate maximum current which latter cell can deliver; (*d*) maximum power which latter cell can deliver.

224. Two gravity cells have electrodes of the same materials and the same solutions, concentration, etc., but in one cell each linear dimension is twice that of the other, making its volume eight times as great. The two cells are connected with terminals of like polarity together. The emf of the smaller cell is 1.07 volts, and its internal resistance is 0.3 ohm; the internal resistance of the larger cell is 0.1 ohm. Determine: (*a*) current between two cells; (*b*) short-circuit current of larger cell; (*c*) short-circuit current of smaller cell; (*d*) short-circuit current of two cells in series aiding; (*e*) maximum power which two cells in series aiding can deliver to a resistor; (*f*) maximum power which two cells in parallel can deliver to a resistor.

225. The emf of a Leclanché cell is 1.48 volts. A load of 2.5 amp is applied, and the terminal voltage drops to 1.25 volts almost instantly. After a lapse of some time it drops to 1.06 volts, the current remaining at 2.5 amp. Determine: (*a*) actual internal resistance of cell; (*b*) emf of polarization; (*c*) total apparent cell resistance.

226. The ignition system of a gasoline engine requires for its operation a voltage somewhat in excess of 6 volts. Six Leclanché type dry cells connected in series, aiding, each having an emf of 1.30 volts, are used. Determine: (*a*) current which battery can deliver without its terminal voltage falling below 6 volts; (*b*) resistance of ignition coil if it is to operate at this value of current and at 6 volts.

227. The open-circuit emf of a dry cell is 1.36 volts, and the short-circuit current is found to be 16.0 amp. Determine: (*a*) its internal resistance; (*b*) maximum power which it can deliver; (*c*) terminal voltage when external resistance is 2.0 ohms.

228. Each of five dry cells of a 6-cell ignition battery has an emf of 1.45 volts and an internal resistance of 0.09 ohm. The cells are connected in series aiding. One cell, which has become exhausted, has an emf of 0.8 volt and an internal resistance of 0.6 ohm. Determine: (*a*) voltage across exhausted cell when battery delivers 200 ma; (*b*) terminal voltage of battery; (*c*) short-circuit current of battery; (*d*) voltage across exhausted cell under conditions of (*c*).

229. A Weston cell having an emf of 1.0187 volts is connected to a potentiometer wire as shown in Fig. 229*A*, in order to calibrate the wire *AC*. Between *A* and *B* is a

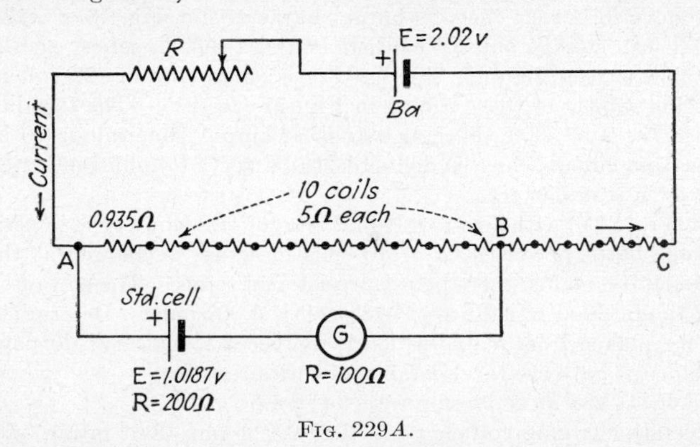

Fig. 229*A*.

resistance of 0.935 ohm and 10 coils having a resistance of 5 ohms each. The internal resistance of the cell is 200 ohms, and the resistance of the galvanometer is 100 ohms. Determine: (*a*) current in galvanometer and its direction when current in *AB* is 0.021 amp. (*b*) Repeat (*a*) with current equal to 0.0195 amp. Determine: (*c*) current in wire *AC* when current in standard cell and galvanometer is zero; (*d*) voltage across each of 5-ohm coils in (*c*); (*e*) resistance of resistor *R*, Fig. 229*A*, under conditions of (*d*) when emf of battery *Ba* is 2.02 volts, its resistance being negligible. [This problem illustrates the principles of the potentiometer (see Sec. 137, p. 179, and Fig. 132, p. 181).]

230. In Prob. 229 determine (*a*) current in galvanometer when current in wire *AB* is 0.0205 amp. In the process of adjustment this current is increased 2 per cent. Determine (*b*) corresponding percentage change in galvanometer current. (Note that this arrangement gives a sensitive method of adjustment.)

231. A voltmeter, the resistance of which is 1,000 ohms, is used in an attempt to measure the emf of the Weston cell, Prob. 229. Determine (*a*) voltmeter reading. (*b*) Discuss the practicality of this method of using the Weston cell as a standard.

232. It is desired to dilute a liter of concentrated sulfuric acid (sp gr = 1.84) to make acid having a specific gravity of 1.210. Determine: (*a*) liters of water which it is necessary to add; (*b*) total volume of acid when the solution is mixed; (*c*) total weight in kilograms of final solution. [The table (p. 116) must be used. Solving the problem algebraically does not give the correct result, owing to the interdiffusion of the molecules of water and acid.]

233. A carboy contains 12 l of concentrated sulfuric acid (sp gr = 1.84). Determine: (*a*) weight of acid in kilograms; (*b*) liters of dilute sulfuric acid (sp gr = 1.200) which can be made from it; (*c*) gallons to which this is equivalent; (*d*) weight in kilograms of the final solution (see Appendix A, p. 579).

234. The specific gravity of the electrolyte in the pilot cell of a 640-amp-hr storage battery is found to be 1.110 when the battery is in the (not totally) discharged condition. The specific gravity varies in accordance with the charge characteristics (Fig. 76, p. 117). The battery is then charged at the normal 8-hr rate of 80 amp until the specific gravity reaches 1.190 (after the charge is stopped sufficiently long to permit the specific gravity to become constant). Determine: (*a*) ampere-hours delivered to battery; (*b*) ampere-hours necessary to charge battery completely to its rating.

235. After the battery (Prob. 234) has been completely charged, it is discharged until its specific gravity becomes 1.190. Determine theoretically available ampere-hours which remain in battery (see discharge characteristic, Fig. 76, p. 117).

236. A 6-volt lead storage battery consists of three cells in series, each having an internal resistance of 0.0075 ohm. The battery is charged from 120-volt mains, the connections being similar to those shown in Fig. 77 (p. 121). The terminal voltage of each cell is 2.45 volts The charging rate is 14 amp. Determine: (*a*) percentage of total power from circuit which is delivered to battery; (*b*) ohms of series resistor; (*c*) power lost as heat in battery.

237. Repeat Prob. 236 with two 6-volt batteries of this same type in series aiding.

238. A storage battery, consisting of 20 cells in series, is charged at the 50-amp rate from 120-volt d-c mains, there being a resistor in series. The emf of each cell is 2.2 volts, and the internal resistance of each cell is 0.007 ohm. Determine: (*a*) percentage of energy taken from mains which is delivered to battery; (*b*) power lost in internal resistance of battery; (*c*) resistance of series resistor.

239. Repeat Prob. 238 for a 40-amp rate.

240. The average charging voltage per cell of a 120-amp (8-hr rating) storage battery consisting of 120 cells in series is 2.3 volts. It is desired to charge the battery from constant-voltage bus bars. In order to stabilize the system, a 0.2-ohm resistor is connected between the bus bars and the battery. Determine: (*a*) voltage of bus bars; (*b*) cost at 1½ cents per kwhr of energy for charging battery for 8 hr at this normal rate; (*c*) internal resistance of battery if the emf per cell is 2.12 volts.

241. A booster set (see Fig. 78, p. 123) is used to charge a 124-cell storage battery from 230-volt bus bars. The battery requires a maximum charging current of 80 amp, and, when charging at this rate, the terminal voltage per cell is 2.45 volts. Determine: (*a*) voltage and current rating of booster; (*b*) power taken by booster set from bus bars if the motor efficiency is 0.84 and the generator efficiency is 0.82; (*c*) percentage of power to battery supplied by booster.

242. A booster set is used to charge a 120-cell 800-amp-hr lead storage battery from 240-volt bus bars. The emf of each cell is 2.05 volts, and the internal resistance is 0.002 ohm. The battery is being charged at the normal 100-amp rate. Determine: (*a*) terminal voltage per cell; (*b*) rating of booster generator; (*c*) power taken by booster set if generator has efficiency of 0.83 and motor of 0.85; (*d*) percentage of power to battery supplied by booster; (*e*) cost of charging battery for 8 hr at normal rate if energy costs 1.8 cents per kwhr. Assume that emf and resistance of battery remain constant during charging period.

243. A 20-amp 100-amp-hr Edison cell is charged at the normal rate for 5 hr and then discharged at the same rate for the same period. From the curves of Fig. 83 (p. 127) determine the watthours efficiency. (In solving, average the ordinates of the two curves.)

244. A Nicad battery is charged at 15-amp rate for 10 hr in accordance with the "charge" curve, Fig. 86 (p. 131), and is discharged at a 12.5-amp rate in accordance with the curve which shows the "end voltage," at the end of 10 hr. Determine: (*a*) ampere-hours efficiency; (*b*) watthours efficiency. (In solving, average the ordinates of the curves.)

245. Nickel is being plated in a nickel-sulfate bath with a current of 20 amp. Determine weight of nickel in grams which is plated on cathode each hour (see Sec. 110, p. 134.)

246. Repeat Prob. 245 except that copper is plated and the electrolyte is copper sulfate.

247. From the table of electrochemical equivalents (p. 135), determine (*a*) grams of copper which will be plated from a copper sulfate bath for each ampere-hour. (*b*) In an electrolytic refining process how many kilograms of copper will be refined in 12 hr by a current of 250 amp? (*c*) Determine kilowatthours if voltage across the bath is 15 volts.

QUESTIONS ON CHAPTER V

Electrical Instruments and Electrical Measurements

1. If a coil carrying a current be placed in a magnetic field, what effect is noticed? Explain this effect in two ways, showing that it is based on fundamental laws of the magnetic field. Of what importance is this principle?

2. How is the principle of the moving coil adapted to measuring small currents in the D'Arsonval galvanometer? How is the coil suspended? How is the current led in and out of the coil? Why is a soft-iron core usually placed between the poles?

3. What two common methods are used to read the galvanometer deflection? What is meant by the *damping* of a galvanometer? How may this damping be accomplished?

4. How may a galvanometer be protected from excessive currents? Sketch the connections of two types of shunt. What are the advantages of the Ayrton shunt? Define the multiplying power of the Ayrton shunt.

5. Show that the movement of a Weston d-c instrument is an evolution of the D'Arsonval galvanometer. How is the moving coil pivoted? How is the current led to the coil? What means are used to oppose the motion of the coil? Discuss the damping of the coil. What is meant by a *radial field*, and what effect does it have on the calibration of the instrument scale? Why are the top and the bottom springs coiled in opposite directions? Discuss the application of the movement of a Weston instrument to a galvanometer.

6. Of what order of magnitude is the current that will give full-scale deflection in a Weston instrument? Describe the method by which the instrument may be used for measuring current in excess of this value.

7. Describe briefly the construction of a shunt. Why are four posts, or terminals, necessary? Show that when a Weston instrument is used in connection with a shunt, it also acts as a voltmeter.

8. What law does the current follow in dividing between the shunt and the instrument? Why should the resistance of the shunt and the resistance of the instrument remain constant? What errors may be caused by the heating of the shunt or of the instrument?

9. In what way may an ammeter be made to have several scales? In general, when is an internal shunt used? An external shunt?

10. Compare the movement of the voltmeter with that of the ammeter. In what important respect does the voltmeter differ from the ammeter? How is the current in the coil of a voltmeter limited when the voltmeter is connected across the line?

11. Show that it is possible for a voltmeter to have more than one scale. Explain. What is meant by a multiplier or extension coil?

12. What property of Alnico makes possible the use of magnets whose length is small as compared with their cross-sectional dimensions? Sketch the design of a concentric-magnet type instrument using Alnico for the magnets.

13. Sketch the design of a concentric-scale instrument showing how a single Alnico magnet is used to produce the magnetic field. Describe the method by which torque is produced, and compare with that of the Weston movement. What is the principal advantage of this type of instrument?

14. In what manner may the heating effect of an electric current be utilized to measure the value of the current? Describe the construction and the method of operation of the vacuum thermocouple. To what type of measurements are such thermal instruments adapted?

15. On what fundamental principle do photocells operate? Describe the construction of the General Electric photocell. Sketch graphs showing the variation of current with foot-candles for different values of resistance.

16. Show the connections that are used in measuring resistance with a voltmeter and an ammeter. What precaution should be taken in connecting the voltmeter? What special type of voltmeter contact should be used in measuring very low resistances?

17. Show the connections whereby resistance may be measured by means of a voltmeter alone. What is the order of magnitude of resistances that can be measured by this method? What special type of voltmeter is often desirable for this work and why? To what type of resistances is this method especially applicable?

18. Show the relation of the ohmmeter principle to the voltmeter-ammeter method of Question 16. What are the relations among the "infinite-resistance," "zero-current," "zero-resistance," and "maximum-current" points on the scale? Sketch the internal connections of an ohmmeter, and show how several ranges may be obtained.

19. Give the uses of the *megger insulation tester*, and describe briefly the construction of its magnetic circuit. Compare the instrument movement with that of the Weston instrument, stating the functions of the two principal coils and showing their connections. Describe the operation of the instrument, showing how it gives correct indications without any spring control.

20. What is the function of the compensating coil? Show the connection of the guard wire, and state its purpose. Why is a slipping clutch frequently used?

21. Sketch an arrangement of four resistances, three of which are known, a galvanometer, and a battery, whereby the fourth resistance may be measured. Prove the law of proportionality that exists when the condition of balance has been reached.

22. State the differences between the portable type and the desk type of Wheatstone bridge. In bridge measurements why should a balance with the battery reversed be made? To what bridge points should the galvanometer be connected in order to obtain maximum sensitivity?

23. Compare the plug bridge with the dial bridge from the standpoint of ease of manipulation; plug-contact resistance; convenience.

24. Describe briefly a systematic procedure which should be followed in obtaining a balance with a Wheatstone bridge.

25. In what way does the slide-wire bridge resemble the Wheatstone bridge? Compare it with the Wheatstone bridge from the standpoint of simplicity and accuracy.

26. Describe the type of measurement which makes necessary a bridge involving the principle of the Kelvin type. Make a sketch showing the connections of the Kelvin bridge. Indicate the auxiliary arms, and show the relation which their resistances must have with those of the other bridge arms in order that the Wheatstone-bridge equation may be applied. Derive the equation which gives the necessary relations which must exist among the several bridge arms.

27. Define an "open," a "cross," and a "ground" in an insulated conductor, and describe the tests that can be used to determine which of these types of fault may exist.

28. Draw the connections for the Murray loop test which includes bridge arms, when the test is made for a ground. Derive the equations which give the relations among the resistances of the bridge arms and the resistance and distance to the fault.

29. Repeat Question 28 except that a slide wire is used. Explain why the galvanometer and the battery do not occupy the same positions in Figs. 124 and 125 (pp. 173 and 174) as they do in Fig. 119 (p. 168).

30. Repeat Question 28 when a slide wire is used and the test is made for a cross.

31. Draw the connections for the Varley loop test when the test is made for a ground. Derive the equations which give the relations among the resistances of the bridge arms and the resistance and distance to the fault.

32. Repeat Question 31 except that the test is made for a cross.

33. Why is it desirable in practice to know the insulation resistance of cables? Why is the voltmeter method not always practicable? What is the general principle of the method described in Sec. 135 (p. 175)?

34. What method is used to obtain readable deflections of the galvanometer under all conditions of circuit resistance? Why is it desirable to keep the 0.1 megohm in circuit continuously? Discuss any error which it may introduce. Derive the equation which gives the value of the insulation resistance in terms of the galvanometer deflections and the multiplying powers of the Ayrton shunt.

35. What factor other than the resistance of the insulation affects the value of the current? What time of electrification has been adopted as standard in commercial measurements of insulation resistance? What precautions should be observed in the installation of cable-testing apparatus?

36. Why is a guard wire sometimes necessary in insulation measurements? Explain the principle of the guard wire, showing the path of the end-leakage current.

37. Why can the potentiometer be used to make accurate measurements of emf which are not possible with the usual types of voltmeter? Compare the precision obtainable with the potentiometer with that obtainable with a voltmeter.

38. Upon what standard are potentiometer measurements primarily based? Make a simple diagram of connections, and show how the emf of a standard cell may be utilized without its delivering any appreciable current. Why is a null method necessary in such measurements? What care as regards polarity must be observed if a balance is to be obtained?

39. Show how a potentiometer resistor may be calibrated and marked in volts, after the standard-cell balance has been obtained. Describe and illustrate the method by which unknown emfs may be measured by means of the standardized resistor.

40. Compare the Leeds and Northrup potentiometer, the connections of which are shown in Fig. 133 (p. 182), with the simple potentiometer diagram shown in Fig. 132 (p. 181). Indicate any minor differences, giving the reasons. Where are the 0.1-volt divisions located, and how are they utilized when obtaining a balance? How are the smaller decimal divisions obtained? What is the resistance of the 0.1-volt units? What is the working current of this potentiometer?

41. Describe the device in the Leeds and Northrup potentiometer by means of which compensation for variations in the emfs of standard cells may be secured. In what manner is protection provided for the galvanometer?

42. What is the disadvantage of a potentiometer in which there are no sliding contacts in the circuit of the working current? Make a diagram showing how the number of dials may be increased by the Thomson-Varley method. Indicate how the total resistance of the potentiometer remains unchanged, irrespective of the positions of the dial contacts.

43. Make a diagram of connections of the Wolff potentiometer showing how the several decimal values of emf are obtained without the resistance of the potentiometer changing with the different positions of the dial contacts.

44. What is the maximum voltage ordinarily measurable with a potentiometer alone? Make a wiring diagram of the device by means of which the voltage range of the potentiometer may be increased indefinitely. Also make a diagram of a *voltage divider*, and explain how it may be used to vary the voltage when the supply is at constant voltage.

45. Show that the potentiometer, which is fundamentally a voltage-measuring device, is adapted to measuring currents. On what fundamental law is the measurement of current based? What is meant by a standard resistance, and why are four terminals employed? In what units of resistance are standard resistances generally manufactured? Why is it desirable that their temperature remain normal, and what means are adopted to accomplish this?

46. What instruments are generally used in measuring the power in a d-c circuit? Show that these instruments themselves take power. What should be the relative positions of the voltmeter and the ammeter when the power delivered to a high resistance is being measured? When that delivered to a low resistance is being measured? Show the methods by means of which correction for power taken by the instruments may be made.

47. Describe the construction of a wattmeter, and show the principle of its operation. In what way do the fixed and moving coils differ in construction? In their manner of connection to the circuit? Why are the instrument deflections a function of the power? What care is necessary in using this type of instrument with direct current?

48. What quantity does a watthour meter measure? Upon what familiar electrical device is it based? Show the connections of the field coils, and state the factor which determines the current in them. What source supplies the armature current, and to what is the armature current proportional? To what quantity is the torque developed by the armature proportional?

49. Why is a retarding device necessary, and what must be the law of retardation? Upon what principle does this device operate?

50. At what values of meter load does friction produce the greatest error? Explain. How is this friction error practically eliminated?

51. What methods are used to reduce friction in a watthour meter? What are some of the causes of a meter's running slow? How is the recording dial of a meter actuated?

52. Why is it usually important that a watthour meter register accurately? What load and measuring devices are necessary in testing a meter?

53. Give the fundamental relation which exists in some meters between the revolutions of the disk and the energy. What measurements are made in checking the meter?

54. What two adjustments are made to change the meter speed? What is the effect of moving the magnets nearer the center of the disk? Nearer the periphery? At what loads is this adjustment made?

55. What adjustment is made to correct the meter registration at light loads? Why is this adjustment made at light rather than at heavy loads?

56. Show the connections of a 3-wire watthour meter, and compare them with those of the 2-wire watthour meter. Explain the reason why the connection of the 3-wire meter is different from that of the 2-wire meter.

57. Describe in a general way the construction of a watthour meter which makes the meter practically astatic and therefore enables it to be used near bus bars carrying heavy currents. What two elements in a meter are most likely to be affected by stray fields? How are these elements safeguarded from these effects?

PROBLEMS ON CHAPTER V

Electrical Measurements and Electrical Instruments

248. The resistance of a galvanometer is 480 ohms. (*a*) Compute resistances of three resistors of a shunt for use with galvanometer so that one-tenth, one-hundredth, and one-thousandth the total line current will go to galvanometer [see Fig. 95(*a*), p. 141]. (*b*) Determine resistance introduced into system by galvanometer alone and by galvanometer and shunt together for each value of shunt resistance.

249. Repeat Prob. 248 for a galvanometer of resistance 820 ohms. (*c*) With a galvanometer current of $2.4 \cdot 10^{-9}$ amp, determine, by Ohm's law, line current with each shunt resistor in circuit. By means of these line currents and the specified ratios, verify computed values of shunt resistance.

250. The resistance from *A* to *B* of an Ayrton shunt, Fig. 250*A*, is 10,000 ohms. The shunt is used in connection with a galvanometer, the resistance of which is 1,500 ohms. (*a*) When shunt is set at the 0.001 point (*C*) (resistance between *A* and *C* = 10 ohms), determine current to galvanometer when line current is $2.3 \cdot 10^{-7}$ amp. (*b*) Repeat (*a*) with line current equal to $2.3 \cdot 10^{-8}$ amp with shunt set at 0.01 point (*D*), resistance of *AD* being 100 ohms. (*c*) Compare galvanometer currents in (*a*) and (*b*), together with their theoretical values as determined by Eq. (83) (p. 143).

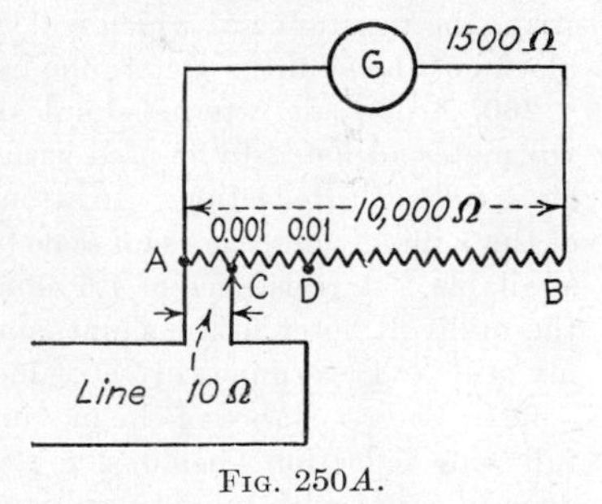

Fig. 250*A*.

251. In Prob. 250 a galvanometer current $2.5 \cdot 10^{-10}$ amp produces full-scale deflection. (*a*) With galvanometer current equal to this value, determine line current when shunt is set at 0.001, 0.01, and 0.1 (*b*) By what ratio is maximum sensitivity of galvanometer reduced by presence of shunt?

252. The total resistance of an Ayrton shunt is 30,000 ohms. (*a*) Determine largest resistance which a galvanometer used in conjunction with shunt may have without maximum sensitivity of galvanometer being reduced to less than 0.9 its normal value. A galvanometer current of $1.5 \cdot 10^{-10}$ amp will produce a deflection of 5 cm. (*b*) Determine line current when shunt is set at 0.0001. (*c*) With shunt in circuit, determine minimum line current which will produce 1 cm deflection in galvanometer. (*d*) With shunt set at 0.0001 determine ratio of line to galvanometer current in (*b*).

253. The resistance of a 0-to-50-scale millivoltmeter is 10 ohms. Determine: (*a*) resistance of shunt which, when used in conjunction with instrument, will produce full-scale deflection with 75 amp; (*b*) resistance of shunt for 150 amp; (*c*) ratio of millivoltmeter current to shunt current in (*a*) and (*b*).

254. The resistance of a 50-scale millivoltmeter is 7.2 ohms. It is desired that it measure a current of 100 amp with full-scale deflection. Determine: (*a*) resistance of shunt; (*b*) current in instrument; (*c*) ratio of instrument to shunt current and whether or not instrument current may be neglected as compared with shunt current; (*d*) maximum resistance which leads may have and not introduce an error of over 0.2 per cent.

255. With millivoltmeter of Prob. 254, determine resistances of shunts for measuring currents of 150 and 600 amp, giving full-scale deflection. In each case compute power loss in shunt.

256. The resistance of a millivoltmeter is 4.5 ohms. It is used to measure a current of 40 amp. Resistance of shunt is 0.0012 ohm. Determine: (*a*) current in instrument; (*b*) current in shunt. When current in shunt is 75 amp, instrument needle deflects full scale. (*c*) Determine rating of instrument in millivolts.

257. The resistance of a 0-to-30-scale millivoltmeter is 2.8 ohms. In order to measure current, this instrument is to be adapted to a 0.008-ohm shunt, the rating of which is 5.0 amp. Determine: (*a*) additional resistance which must be connected in series with millivoltmeter; (*b*) resistance of 30-amp shunt; (*c*) resistance of 75-amp shunt.

258. The resistance of a 15-scale ammeter with its shunt is 0.003 ohm. In order to increase its range, another shunt, the resistance of which is 0.0010 ohm, is connected in parallel with the complete instrument. Determine current in external circuit when instrument reads (*a*) 8 amp; (*b*) 15 amp.

259. The resistance of the shunt of a 30-scale ammeter is 0.0015 ohm. A manganin strip, the resistance of which is 0.00225 ohm, is brazed between the copper terminal blocks of the shunt. Determine new range of instrument.

260. A 50-scale external-shunt ammeter consists of the shunt and a 50-scale millivoltmeter adjusted to be used with it. A current of 0.025 amp in the millivoltmeter gives full-scale deflection. In attempting to measure an unknown current, the pointer of the millivoltmeter goes off scale by a few divisions, and no larger scale instrument is available. A resistance of 1.5 ohms is connected in series with the leads connecting the millivoltmeter to the shunt, and the millivoltmeter now indicates 45.0 on the 50-mv scale. Determine correct value of unknown current.

261. The resistance of the moving coil of a d-c voltmeter is 62.1 ohms, and it gives full-scale deflection when 0.54 volt is impressed across the coil alone. (*a*) What resistance in series with moving coil is necessary if instrument is to have a 5-volt range? (*b*) 150-volt range? (*c*) What are ohms per volt in this instrument?

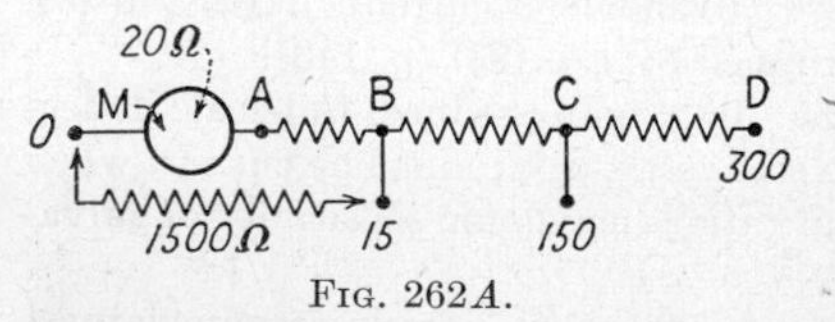

Fig. 262*A*.

262. In Fig. 262*A* is shown the moving coil *M* of a voltmeter in series with the resistors *AB*, *BC*, *CD*. The resistance of *M* is 20 ohms, and the instrument gives full-scale deflection with 0.01 amp in *M*. Three scales, 15-, 150-, 300-volt, are desired, and *B*, *C*, *D* are the respective three terminals. (*a*) Determine resistance between *AB*, *BC*, *CD*. A 1,500-ohm resistor is connected between terminals *OB*, and terminals *OD* are connected to an unknown voltage. The 300-volt instrument scale reads 280 volts. (*b*) Determine unknown voltage.

263. It is desired to determine resistance of coil M of a 0-to-15-to-150-scale voltmeter which is connected as shown in Fig. 263A [also see Fig. 102(b), p. 151]. Values of resistance measured with a Wheatstone bridge between terminals O, A, B, are as follows: O to A = 17,500 ohms; O to B = 1,750 ohms; A to B = 19,130 ohms. Determine (a) resistance of coil system. (b) Show that with the foregoing values of resistance the voltmeter must be connected as shown in Fig. 263A or 102(b) and not in the manner shown in Fig. 102(a) (p. 151). (c) What measured value of resistance between terminals A and B would have shown that voltmeter is connected in the manner shown in Fig. 102(a)?

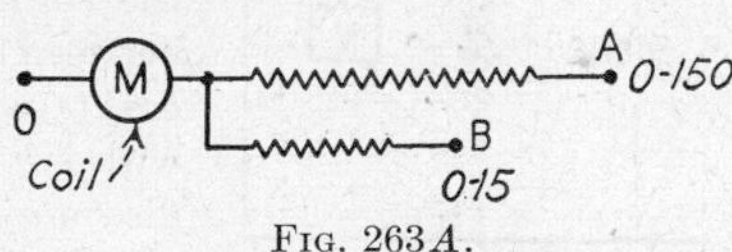

FIG. 263A.

264. In measuring an unknown voltage the voltmeter of Prob. 263 deflects slightly beyond the 150-volt range. The 15-volt terminal B is then connected to the O terminal, and the voltmeter indicates 148 volts. Determine unknown voltage.

265. It is desired to measure the voltage between trolley and rail of a 1,200-volt railway system. A 300-scale d-c voltmeter, the resistance of which is 32,000 ohms, is available. (a) Determine resistance of additional series resistor which is necessary in order that scale may have multiplying factor of 5. (b) Should this resistor be connected between the instrument and trolley or between instrument and ground? Explain.

266. The voltmeter, Prob. 265, is used to measure the voltage of a generator, which supplies the plate circuit of an electron tube. The voltmeter pointer deflects somewhat off scale. The voltmeter itself is shunted with a 75,000-ohm resistor, and the reading is 268 volts. Determine unknown voltage.

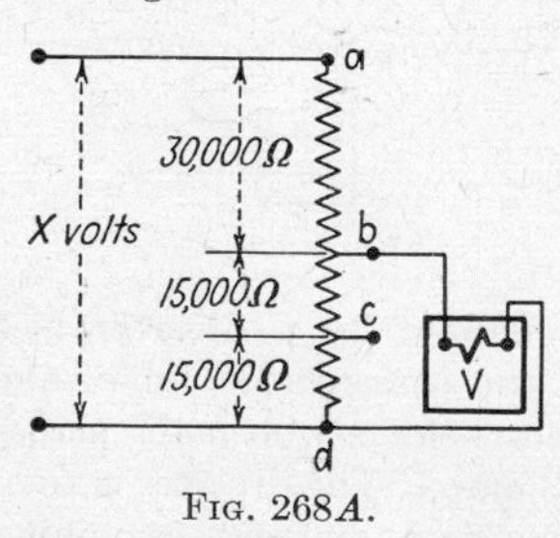

FIG. 268A.

267. The resistance of a 150-scale voltmeter is 15,000 ohms. The instrument is slightly off scale when connected across a voltage somewhat in excess of 150 volts. When a 2,000-ohm resistor is connected in series with it, the instrument reads 145 volts. Determine unknown voltage.

268. It is desired to measure an unknown voltage in the neighborhood of 600 volts (X volts, Fig. 268A). A 60,000-ohm resistor, $abcd$, is connected across the unknown voltage; the voltmeter, which has a resistance of 30,000 ohms, is connected between the mid-point b of the resistor and d. The scale reading is 242 volts. Determine: (a) unknown voltage; (b) voltmeter reading, unknown voltage remaining unchanged, if the resistor $abcd$ were connected in series with the voltmeter.

269. In Fig. 268A the voltmeter is connected between tap c and the end d of resistor in order to measure a voltage in the neighborhood of 1,500 volts. The voltmeter reads 269 volts. Determine: (a) unknown voltage; (b) voltmeter reading, unknown voltage remaining unchanged, if resistor $abcd$ were connected in series with voltmeter.

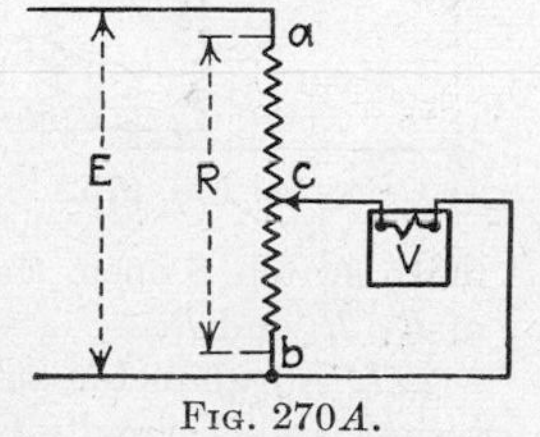

FIG. 270A.

270. A resistor R, Fig. 270A, is connected across a voltage supply E. A 300-scale voltmeter V, the resistance of which is 15,000 ohms, is first connected between terminals ab and reads 240 volts. It is then connected between the center tap c of the resistor and terminal b and indicates 65.6 volts. Determine resistance of resistor R.

271. It is desired to measure the potential between point c on a resistor ab, Fig. 271A, connected across a 300-volt power source, and point b, when no connection is made at c. A 300-scale voltmeter, the resistance of which is 32,000 ohms, is first connected across ab and indicates 300 volts. It is then connected between b and c and indicates 175.5 volts. The resistor is then disconnected from the lower line at b, and the voltmeter reads 234 volts. Determine: (a) resistance between terminals ac; (b) resistance between terminals bc; (c) potential difference between points b and c with b connected to lower line and voltmeter disconnected.

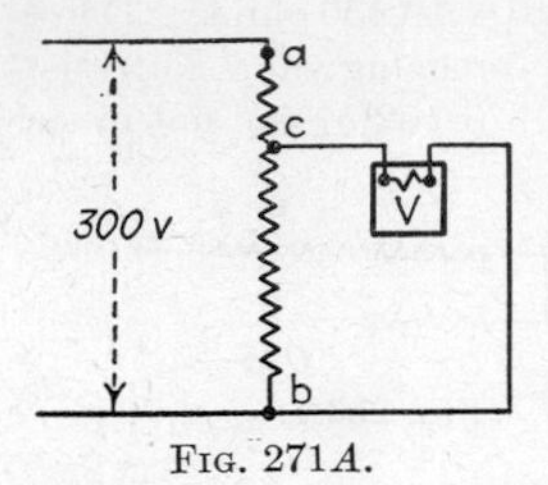

Fig. 271A.

272. A 150-scale voltmeter, the resistance of which is 16,000 ohms, and a 300-scale voltmeter, the resistance of which is 30,000 ohms, are connected in series across a potential difference of 410 volts. Determine reading of each voltmeter.

273. A 100-scale ammeter reads 84.6 amp; a millivoltmeter connected across its terminals reads 38.5 mv. (a) Determine resistance of ammeter, neglecting current taken by millivoltmeter. When the instrument coil of the ammeter deflects full scale, the coil current is 0.018 amp. (b) Determine resistance of instrument itself, exclusive of shunt.

274. It is desired to measure the resistance of the three series resistor units ab, bc, cd of a motor starter, Fig. 274A. The power supply is 115 volts d-c. A resistor R is connected in series to limit the current (see Fig. 108, p. 155). When the ammeter indicates 32.6 amp, the voltmeter reading across each of the three resistors ab, bc, cd is 5.6, 8.2, 11.4 volts. Determine: (a) resistance of each of three resistors; (b) resistance of R. (c) Determine voltage across resistors ab, bc, R when resistor cd is short-circuited.

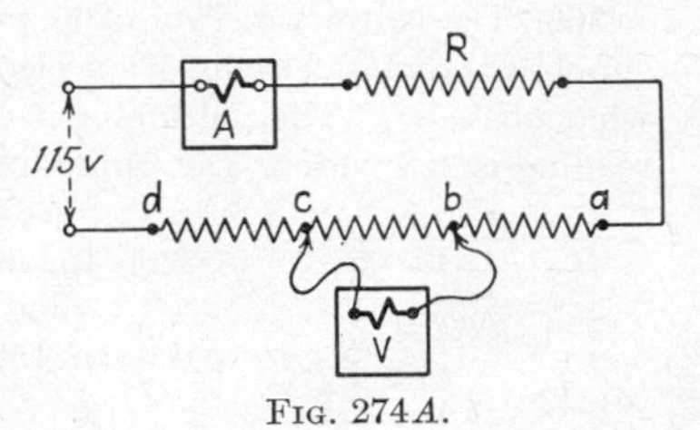

Fig. 274A.

275. The series field of a compound generator is shunted by a diverter (see p. 453). It is desired to measure the resistance of the series field and of the diverter. With the diverter connected across the series field, a voltmeter across the two reads 3.38 volts when the total current is 108 amp. The diverter is then disconnected, and the voltmeter reads 5.18 volts, the total current remaining unchanged. Determine resistance of diverter and of series field.

276. It is desired to measure the resistance of each of the two resistors R_1, R_2, Fig. 276A, connected in parallel. A resistor R is connected in series to limit the current. With the switch S closed, the voltage measured across the parallel circuit is 78.4 volts, that across R is 36.6 volts, and the ammeter indicates 9.8 amp. With switch S open, the voltmeter across R_1 reads 97.4 volts. Determine resistance of R_1, R_2 and R.

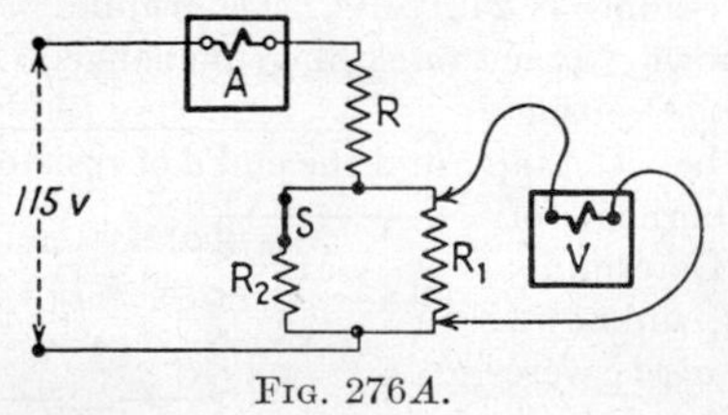

Fig. 276A.

277. An ammeter and voltmeter are connected to measure the resistances in a series-parallel circuit, Fig. 277A, consisting of a resistor R in series with resistors R_1 and R_2 in parallel. The supply voltage is 120 volts. With the switch in series with R_2 closed, the ammeter reads 5.77 amp, and the voltmeter across R reads 92.3

volts. With the switch in series with R_2 open, the voltmeter across R indicates 68.6 volts. Determine resistances of resistors R, R_1, and R_2.

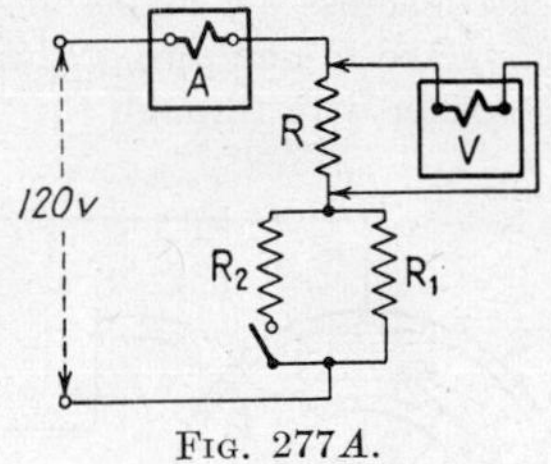

Fig. 277*A*.

278. The resistance of a sample of copper bus bars is measured at 20°C by the method shown in Fig. 109 (p. 156). When the ammeter reads 200 amp, the millivoltmeter reads 4.38 mv. The bus bar is 0.5 by 3 in. in cross section, and the distance between voltmeter contacts is 4.0 ft. Determine: (*a*) resistance of sample; (*b*) resistivity, ohm-centimeters. (*c*) Compare resistivity with the commercial standard (see Sec. 15, p. 14). Resistance of standard copper is 1.756 microhm-cm at 20°C.

279. In order to measure the resistance of a 110-lb rail, it is connected in series with a standard 0.0001-ohm resistor, Fig. 279*A*. Contact points *a* and *b* are then set in the rail 12.4 ft apart. A millivoltmeter is first connected across the standard resistor and indicates 642 mv; the millivoltmeter connection is then transferred to the

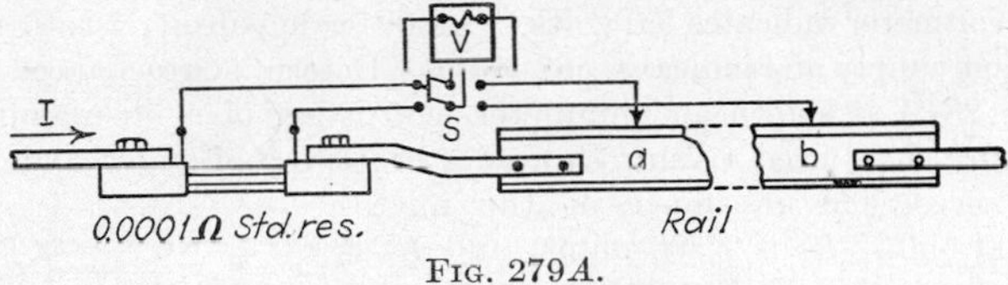

Fig. 279*A*.

contact points *a* and *b* on the rail by means of the D-P D-T switch *S*, and the reading now is 41.3 mv. Determine resistance per foot of rail.

280. In order to measure the resistance of a short length of installed rail including a joint and bond, the circuit of Fig. 280*A* was used. It was known that there was current *I* of unknown value in the rail. Hence two contacts were clamped to the rail at

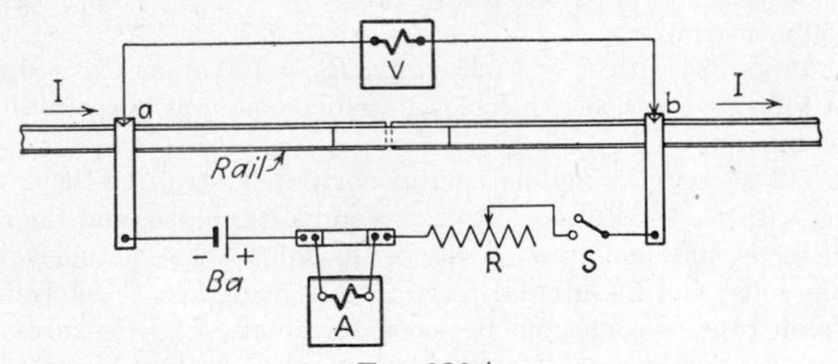

Fig. 280*A*.

a and *b*, and a battery *Ba*, ammeter *A* (with shunt), adjustable resistor *R*, and switch *S* were connected in series between the clamps *a* and *b*. A millivoltmeter *V* was connected between two point contacts on the rail at *a* and *b*. With switch *S* open the millivoltmeter *V* read 16.6 mv. The switch *S* was then closed and the resistor adjusted until the millivoltmeter read zero. The ammeter *A* then read 320 amp. Determine the resistance of the rail and joint between points *ab*.

281. A 300-scale voltmeter, the resistance of which is 32,000 ohms, is connected across d-c mains and indicates 240 volts. It is then connected in series across these same mains with a multiplier whose resistance is unknown. The voltmeter now indicates 48 volts. Determine resistance of multiplier.

282. The resistance of a special 150-scale voltmeter is 100,000 ohms. When connected across d-c mains, it indicates 125 volts. The iron frame of a generator is connected to one wire of these mains, and the copper of the field coil is connected to the other wire through the voltmeter, Fig. 282A. Under these conditions the voltmeter reads 3.5 volts. (*a*) Determine resistance in megohms of insulation of field circuit to frame of machine. When the voltmeter is similarly connected in series with the commutator, it indicates 5.4 volts. (*b*) Determine insulation resistance in megohms between armature and frame.

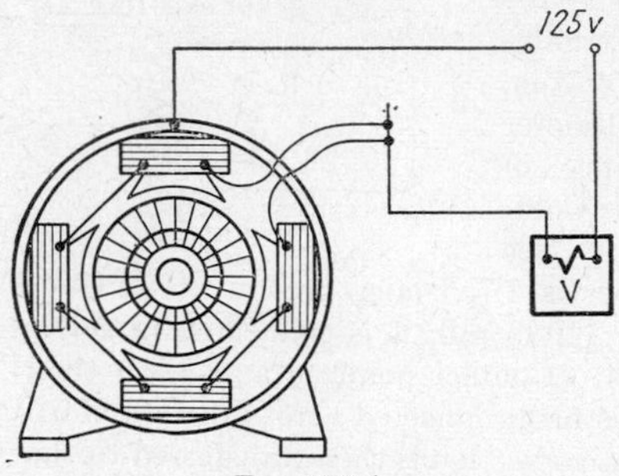

Fig. 282A.

283. In order to obtain increased precision in the measurement of the resistance of some high-voltage insulation, the insulation is connected in series with the special 100,000-ohm voltmeter of Prob. 282 across a voltage supply of approximately 600 volts, and the voltmeter indicates 5.6 volts. A 600-scale voltmeter is then connected across the voltage supply and indicates 588 volts. Determine resistance of insulation.

284. In Fig. 284A is shown an ohmmeter, consisting of a microammeter A, an adjustable resistor R_v, a fixed resistor R_1, and a battery B of emf E and of negligible internal resistance. The resistance of the microammeter is 400 ohms, R_1 is 1,500 ohms, and R_v is adjusted to 100 ohms. The emf E is 30.5 volts. When the pointer is at the center of the scale of the microammeter, the current is 250 microamp. Determine: (*a*) unknown resistance connected across terminals XX to give 250 microamp in A; (*b*) current in A should terminal XX become short-circuited; (*c*) unknown resistance to give one-tenth full-scale deflection, or 50 microamp.

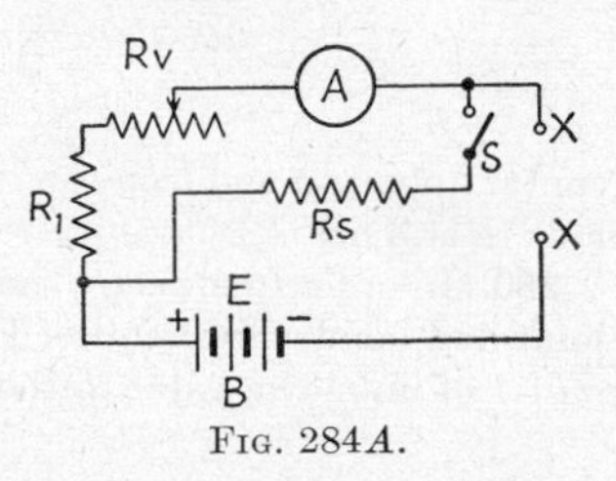

Fig. 284A.

285. Repeat Prob. 284 with $E = 1.625$ volts, $R_1 = 100$ ohms, $R_v = 0$.

286. Repeat Prob. 284 with switch S closed, which connects the shunting resistance R_s of 222 ohms in circuit.

287. In Fig. 112 (p. 159) the switch is set at position 3, shunting the microammeter and R_1 and R_2 with $R_8 = 54$ ohms. R_1 is given as 500 ohms, and the resistance of the microammeter is 400 ohms. R_2 is set at 90 ohms. The actual voltage of the battery is 31.09 volts, and its internal resistance is negligible. Determine: (*a*) current to 4,000-ohm resistor connected between terminals XX; (*b*) current in microammeter; (*c*) current in microammeter with terminals XX short-circuited; (*d*) resistance of a resistor connected between terminals XX which will give full-scale deflection of 500 microamp; (*e*) resistance of a resistor connected between terminals XX which will give one-tenth full-scale deflection, or 50 microamp.

288. In a Wheatstone-bridge measurement, the unknown resistor is connected at X between one end of the arm A and the arm P (see Fig. 116, p. 164). When a balance is obtained, $A = 100$ ohms; $B = 1{,}000$ ohms; $P = 1{,}389$ ohms. (*a*) Determine resistance of unknown resistor. A resistor of 105 ohms is connected in parallel with the unknown resistor in (*a*). It is desired to measure the combined resistance to four significant figures. Determine: (*b*) values of ratio arms A and B; (*c*) value of balance arm P when bridge is balanced.

289. It is desired to measure the resistance of a resistor which is known to lie between 6 and 7 ohms. (*a*) Determine ratio of A to B arm in order that unknown resistor may be measured to four significant figures (see Fig. 116, p. 164). (*b*) Repeat (*a*) for a resistor having a resistance between 36 and 44 ohms; (*c*) 580 and 800 ohms; (*d*) 12,000 and 14,000 ohms.

290. Choose proper values of A and B (Fig. 116, p. 164) to give four significant figures in value of X when X = (*a*) 12,320 ohms; (*b*) 2.876 ohms; (*c*) 57.21 ohms; (*d*) 3,284 ohms. Give value of P for each balance.

291. A Wheatstone bridge, similar to that shown in Figs. 116 and 118 (pp. 164 and 167) is used to measure the resistance of an unknown resistor X. With A = 1,000, B = 1,000, an approximate balance is obtained when P = 46 ohms, the galvanometer deflecting decidedly to the right when P = 45 ohms and deflecting to the right to a considerably less degree when P = 46 ohms. The galvanometer reverses, deflecting to the left when P = 47 ohms. Determine: (*a*) values of resistance in arms A and B to give four significant figures; (*b*) unknown resistance when P = 4,618 ohms.

292. In Fig. 292*A* is shown a Wheatstone bridge in balance. Determine: (*a*) resistance between points *o* and *c*; (*b*) current in arms A, B, P, and X. The emf of the battery is 2.2 volts, and its internal resistance is negligible.

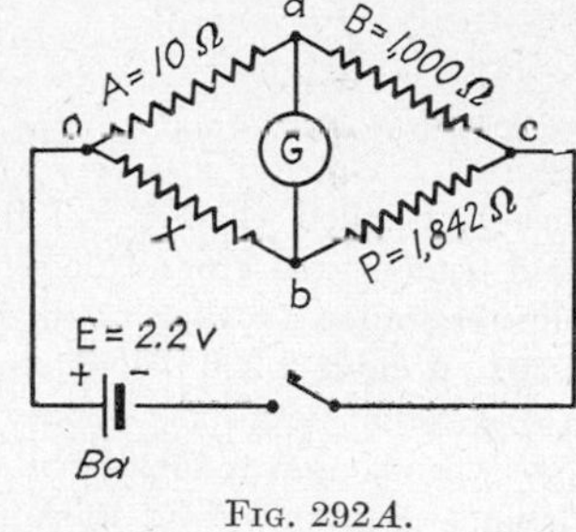

Fig. 292*A*.

293. In Fig. 292*A* with the bridge out of balance, the arm P being equal to 1,500 ohms, determine: (*a*) resistance between points *o* and *c*; (*b*) current in arms A, B, P, X and in galvanometer. The internal resistance of the battery is negligible (see Sec. 127, p. 165).

294. In Fig. 292*A* with arm P = 1,500 ohms, determine: (*a*) resistance of bridge between points *a* and *b*, the galvanometer and the battery being interchanged; (*b*) current in four bridge arms A, B, P, X. The internal resistance of the battery is negligible.

295. An unknown resistor X is measured by means of a slide-wire bridge, similar to that shown in Fig. 119 (p. 168). With R = 100 ohms, a balance is obtained when the slider reads 22.6 cm. Determine: (*a*) value of X; (*b*) reading of slider when bridge is balanced with a 10-ohm resistor at R.

296. An unknown resistor is measured by means of a 100-cm slide-wire bridge. A known resistor of 100 ohms is inserted in the position of X, Fig. 119 (p. 168). A balance is obtained when the slider reads 66.5 cm. Determine: (*a*) resistance of unknown resistor; (*b*) reading on slide wire for balance when a 200-ohm resistor is inserted at X.

297. A Kelvin bridge, similar to that in Fig. 121 (p. 170), is used to measure the resistance of a sample of No. 0000 AWG solid copper wire. The distance between the contact points p and p' is 32 in. The temperature is 20°C. With $A = a = 100$ ohms, $B = b = 1{,}000$ ohms, a balance is obtained when R = 0.001343 ohm. Determine: (*a*) resistance of copper sample; (*b*) ohm-centimeters of sample. The diameter of the wire is 0.460 in.

298. A No. 00 stranded wire is measured for its resistance in the Kelvin bridge, Fig. 121 (p. 170), as was done in Prob. 297. The distance between contacts p and p' is 27.6 in. The bridge balances when R = 0.006164 ohm, with the ratio arms $A = a$ = 300 ohms and $B = b$ = 10,000 ohms. Determine: (*a*) resistivity, ohm-centimeters of copper sample; (*b*) resistivity, ohm-circular-mil-feet. The wire is made up of 19 strands, the diameter of each of which is 0.0837 in.

299. A 0 AWG cable, 1,800 ft long, is known to be grounded. A similar cable, but with no fault, is looped to the faulty cable at the far end, and the Murray loop test, using bridge arms, Fig. 123 (p. 172), is applied to locate the fault. When the system is in balance, $A = 1{,}000$ ohms, $P = 524$ ohms. In a loop-resistance measurement r is found to be 0.364 ohm. Determine: (a) resistance to ground fault; (b) distance to ground fault.

300. A ground is known to exist in conductor B of a lead-covered No. 6 AWG twin pair. The entire cable is 3,600 ft long. To locate the fault, the far end of the pair is looped, Fig. 300A, and the Murray loop test, using bridge arms, is applied. A balance is obtained when $A = 100$ ohms and $P = 284$ ohms. Determine: (a) resistance from near end to ground in B; (b) distance in feet to fault. A measurement of the loop resistance r is then made, and the value is found to be 2.92 ohms.

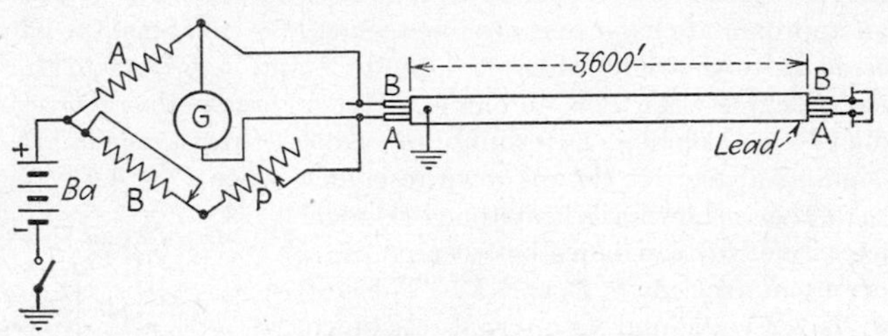

FIG. 300A.

301. A cable 2,200 ft long consists of two conductors. One conductor is grounded at some point between stations. A Murray loop test, Fig. 124 (p. 173), with a 100-cm slide wire, is used to locate the fault. A balance is obtained at 82.4 cm. Determine distance of ground from station end.

302. An installed two-conductor cable of No. 00 AWG copper wire is 2,600 ft long. Owing to a burnout, both conductors are short-circuited and grounded at the same point. To locate the fault, a single No. 000 AWG conductor of another cable, which parallels the faulty one, is looped to one conductor of the faulty cable at the far end, as in Fig. 302A. The perfect conductor is connected to the 0 end of the slide wire and one of the faulty conductors to the 100-cm end. A balance is obtained at 77.4 cm. The resistance of the 00 conductor is 0.0795 ohm per 1,000 ft, and the resistance of the 000 conductor is 0.0630 ohm per 1,000 ft. How far out on the faulty conductor is burnout?

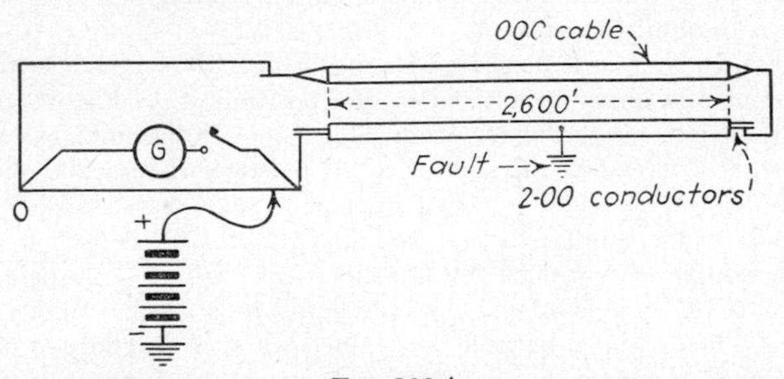

FIG. 302A.

303. A cross occurs between two conductors b and c of a 2,800-ft 3-conductor No. 0 AWG power cable, Fig. 303A. The two conductors a and b are looped at the far end, the near ends are connected to the ends of a 100-cm slide wire, and the Murray loop test is made. A balance occurs when the slide-wire contact is made at 64.5 cm. The loop resistance of conductors a and b is measured and found to be 0.57 ohm. Determine: (a) resistance to "cross"; (b) distance to "cross."

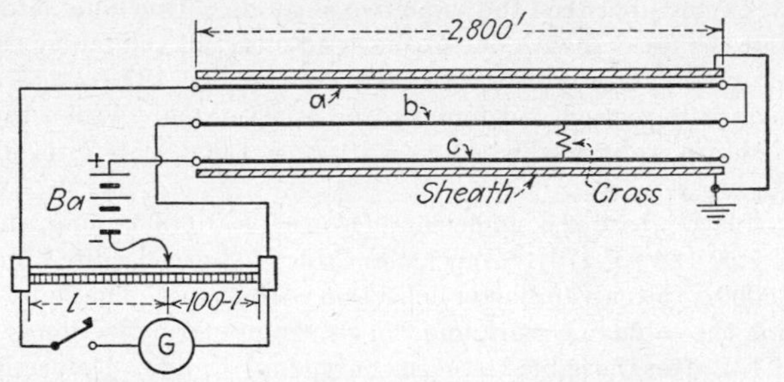

FIG. 303A.

304. A 2,600-ft length of twin-conductor No. 14 AWG underground lead-covered cable develops a ground fault in one conductor. The far ends of the two conductors are looped and tested for the fault by means of the Varley loop test, the connections of which are shown in Fig. 126 (p. 174). With the switch S at b, so that the loop resistance of the cable is measured, the bridge balances under the following conditions. $A = 10$, $B = 1{,}000$, $P = 1{,}358$ ohms. With the switch S at a, in order to locate the fault, the bridge balances under the following conditions: $A = 10$, $B = 1{,}000$, $P = 1{,}036$ ohms. Determine: (a) resistance to fault; (b) distance from home end to fault.

305. The underground cable of a series open-loop arc-lighting system (see Fig. 454, p. 577) is grounded at one point. The cable is solid No. 6 AWG copper, and the loop circuit is 32,000 ft in length. To locate the fault, a Varley loop test is made, the connections being shown in Fig. 305A. With the switch S at b, so that the bridge is con-

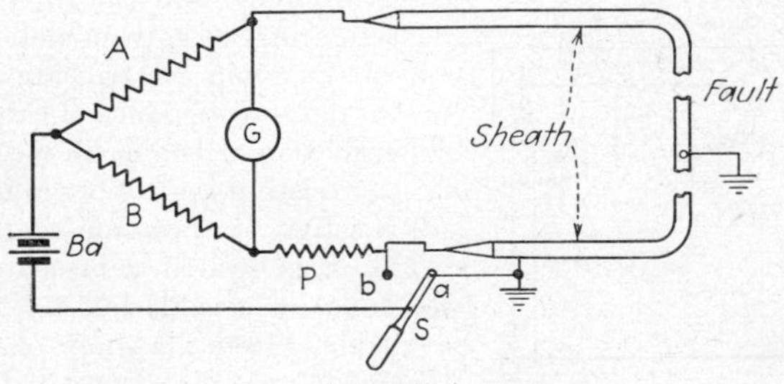

FIG. 305A.

nected to measure the loop resistance of the cable, the bridge balances when, with $A = 10$ and $B = 1{,}000$, the arm P is made equal to 1,304 ohms. The switch S is then moved to position a in order to determine the location of the fault. The bridge balances under the following conditions: $A = 10$, $B = 1{,}000$, $P = 540$ ohms. Determine distance from point b to fault.

306. One conductor in a cable containing two No. 12 wires a and b, each 5,000 ft long, is known to be grounded. The two are looped at the far end, and the Varley loop test is made. P is connected in series with conductor a. The two arms A and B, Fig. 126 (p. 174), are each set at 100 ohms. A balance cannot be obtained with P as the galvanometer is found to deflect the same way with $P = 0$ and $P = \infty$. P is then shifted over in series with b, the other conductor, and a balance obtained when $P = 4.6$ ohms. The resistance of the conductors is known to be 1.62 ohms per 1,000 ft. Determine: (a) faulty conductor; (b) distance of fault from home end.

307. A cross occurs between the two conductors of a No. 12 AWG twisted-pair signal cable. The cable is 5,200 ft long. A similar cable to the foregoing one, but having no fault, extends between the same two stations. One conductor of the latter cable is looped at the far end with one of the conductors of the faulty cable to form a Varley-loop-test circuit for a cross such as is shown in Fig. 127 (p. 175). The resistance r of the loop is measured and found to be 16.94 ohms. When the Varley loop test is made, a balance is obtained when $A = 10$, $B = 1{,}000$, $P = 1{,}167$ ohms. Determine distance to cross.

308. In an insulation test of a single-conductor cable 1,600 ft long, the connections are made as in Fig. 128 (p. 176). When the cable is short-circuited and the Ayrton shunt is set at 0.0001, the galvanometer deflection is 18.4 cm. The short circuit is then removed, putting the cable in circuit, and the galvanometer deflection is 12.4 cm, with the shunt set at 1.0, after the cable has been charged for 1 min. Determine: (*a*) insulation resistance of cable; (*b*) insulation resistance of cable in megohms for 1,000 ft; (*c*) megohms for a mile.

309. In Prob. 308, the resistance of the Ayrton shunt is 12,000 ohms, and the resistance of the galvanometer is 1,000 ohms. The emf of the battery is 350 volts, and its internal resistance is negligible. Determine: (*a*) battery current when cable is short-circuited; (*b*) galvanometer current when cable is short-circuited; (*c*) galvanometer current with 0.1 megohm and cable in circuit; (*d*) battery current under conditions of (*c*). (*e*) By means of (*a*), (*b*), (*c*), (*d*), and Eq. (111) (p. 176), verify insulation resistance of cable.

310. The insulation resistance of a 9,500-ft length of No. 6 AWG solid single-conductor underground cable is measured between conductor and lead sheath, the connections in Fig. 128 (p. 176) being used. The diameter of the conductor is 0.162 in., and the wall of rubber insulation is ⅛ in. With the cable short-circuited, and the Ayrton shunt set at 0.0001, the deflection of the galvanometer is 6.8 cm. With the cable in circuit and the shunt set at 0.1, the deflection of the galvanometer becomes 18.4 cm after 1 min electrification. Determine: (*a*) insulation resistance of cable in megohms; (*b*) insulation resistance in megohms for 1,000 ft; (*c*) resistivity of rubber in megohm-inches; (*d*) resistivity in megohm-centimeters.

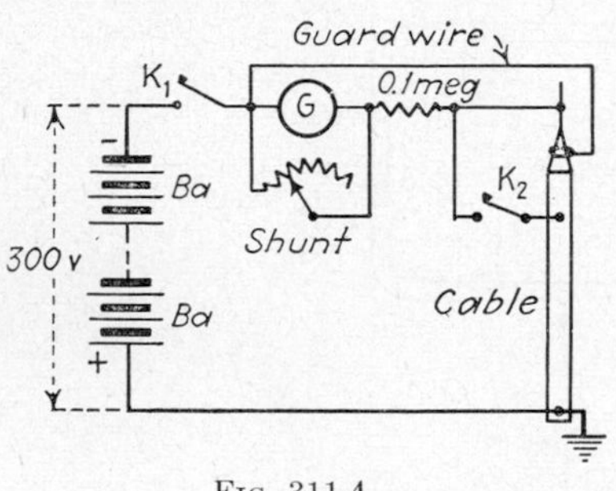

Fig. 311*A*.

311. It is desired to measure the insulation resistance of a cable but no Ayrton shunt is available. Hence, a shunt of the type shown in Fig. 95 (p. 141) is used, the connections being shown in Fig. 311*A*. The galvanometer, 0.1-megohm resistor, cable insulation, and battery are all in series. The emf of the battery is 300 volts, and its resistance is negligible. The resistance of the galvanometer is 840 ohms. With the cable short-circuited by closing key K_2 and the galvanometer shunt in the short-circuit position, the key K_1 is closed. The resistance of the galvanometer shunt is then gradually increased until it is equal to 12 ohms. The galvanometer deflection is then 22.8 cm.

The short circuit of the cable is then removed by opening K_2, and the galvanometer deflection becomes very small. The resistance of the galvanometer shunt is now gradually increased until it becomes infinite. The deflection of the galvanometer then becomes 1.2 cm after 1 min electrification. Determine: (*a*) galvanometer current with cable short-circuited; (*b*) line current in (*a*); (*c*) galvanometer current with cable in circuit; (*d*) insulation resistance of cable.

312. Figure 312*A* shows a 100-cm slide wire *ab*, the total resistance of which is 2.0 ohms, connected in series with the adjustable resistor *R* to the terminals of the storage cell *Ba*, the end *a* being connected directly to the negative terminal of *Ba*. The emf of the storage cell is 2.10 volts, and the internal resistance is 0.04 ohm. *A* is a dry cell, the emf of which is 1.40 volts. Its negative terminal is also connected to *a*, and its positive terminal is connected through a galvanometer *G* to a slider *c* on *ab*. With the resistor *R* adjusted to 0.585 ohm, determine position of *c*, in centimeters from *a*, which will make galvanometer deflection zero.

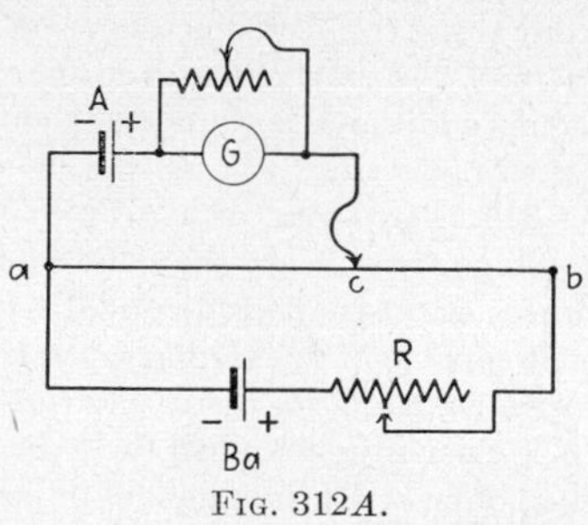

FIG. 312*A*.

Explain the effect on the current delivered by the battery *Ba* of connecting the battery *A* to the system under the conditions that make the galvanometer current equal to zero.

313. A resistor *bd*, whose resistance is 20 ohms, is divided into 10 equal resistors and is connected in series with a 100-cm slide wire *ab*, the resistance of which is 2.0 ohms, Fig. 313*A*. A battery *Ba*, whose emf is 2.15 volts and whose internal resistance is 0.05 ohm, supplies current to the system through the resistor *R*. It is desired that this system operate as a potentiometer, the slide wire *ab* corresponding to 0.1 volt, and each division, 0 to 0.1, 0.1 to 0.2, etc., of *bd* corresponding to 0.1 volt. Determine: (*a*) value to which current must be adjusted; (*b*) value of resistance to which *R* must be adjusted. A Weston cell, the emf of which is 1.0190 volts, is connected to the two contacts *cc'* through the galvanometer by throwing switch *Sw* to the left. (*c*) Determine position of contacts *c* and *c'*, position of contact *c* being given in centimeters from *b*, which will make galvanometer current equal to zero when value of potentiometer current is equal to that determined in (*a*). (*d*) An unknown emf is connected to the contacts *cc'* through the galvanometer by throwing switch *Sw* to the right. The galvanometer deflection is zero when the contact *c'* is 0.6, and the contact *c* is 32 cm from *b*. Determine value of unknown emf.

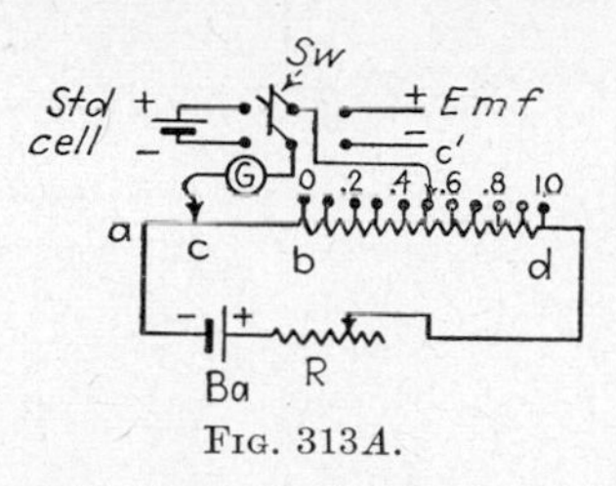

FIG. 313*A*.

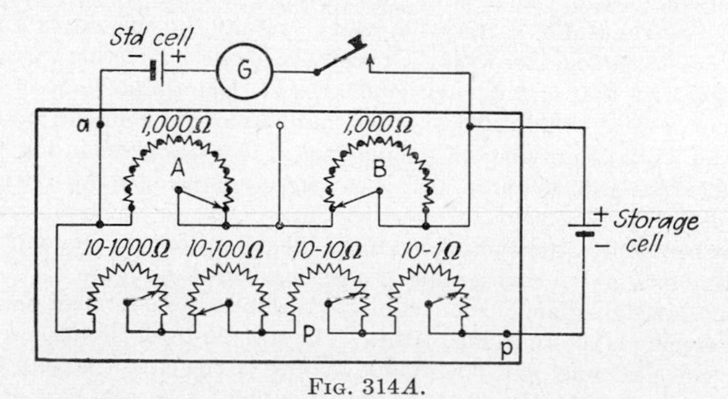

FIG. 314*A*.

314. It is desired to measure the terminal voltage of a storage cell by means of a standard cell. The ratio arms *A* and *B* and the rheostat arm *P* of a dial-type Wheatstone bridge, Fig. 314*A*, are connected in series across the terminals of the storage cell, and a standard cell having an emf of 1.0188 volts in series with a galvanometer and key is connected across arms A and B. Arm A is set at 1,000 ohms and arm B at zero. The galvanometer in the standard-cell circuit gives zero deflection when 1,078 ohms additional is connected in circuit by the dials in P. Determine terminal voltage of storage cell.

315. The storage cell of Prob. 314 is of such large capacity that its emf and terminal voltage are sensibly the same when delivering the small current required by the resistances of the magnitude of 2,078 ohms. To measure the emf of another cell, which is not capable of delivering appreciable current, its negative terminal is connected to the terminal p and its positive terminal to the terminal a through a key and galvanometer. P is then adjusted until the galvanometer reads zero. P is now read and found to be 946 ohms. Determine emf of cell.

316. Figure 316A shows a portion of a high-resistance potentiometer arranged on the Thomson-Varley-slide principle. Between a and b are sixteen 50-ohm resistors, each corresponding to 0.1 volt. $a'b'$ consists of eleven 10-ohm resistors. $a''b''$ is a 20-ohm resistor divided into ten 2-ohm resistors. (a) Determine working current of potentiometer. With the contacts in the positions shown, determine: (b) potential drop from a to c; (c) current in resistor $a'b'$; (d) potential drop from a' to c'; (e) current in $a''b''$; (f) potential drop between a'' and c''; (g) total potential drop from a to c'', or emf across ef. (Compare this potential drop with the readings of the potentiometer.)

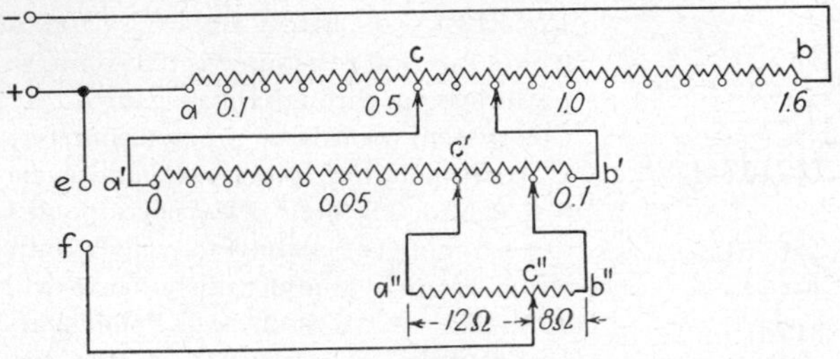

Fig. 316A.

317. In the Thomson-Varley potentiometer, the diagram of which is shown in Fig. 135 (p. 184), the current to the potentiometer is adjusted to the value which gives the correct values of voltage. Determine current in: (a) resistor BC; (b) resistor $B'C'$; (c) resistor $B''C''$. The emf of battery Ba, which supplies the current, is 2.10 volts, and its internal resistance together with the resistance of the connecting wires is negligible in comparison with that of the potentiometer. (d) Determine value of resistance to which resistor R must be adjusted in order that correct value of current be obtained.

318. In the Wolff potentiometer, the diagram of which is given in Fig. 136 (p. 186), the working current is 0.0001 amp. This current is supplied by two dry cells in series, the emf of each being 1.3 volts. Determine: (a) resistance which must be connected between dry cells and battery terminals Ba of the potentiometer; (b) emf between two moving contactors in dial b with dials in positions shown in figure.

319. A simplified diagram of connections of the potentiometer manufactured by the Rubicon Company is shown in Fig. 319A. The standard-cell circuit and other auxiliary connections are omitted. The unique feature of the circuit is that a second step dial II giving hundredths of volts is in circuit without a current-carrying contact to introduce resistance. The contactor of dial II′ moves simultaneously with that of II to maintain constant resistance in circuit acb. The slide wire III, tapped to contactors a and b, operates with one-tenth the normal potentiometer current, so that any effect of the two contactor resistances is reduced to one-tenth the value that would exist with the normal current. Dial I consists of fifteen 10-ohm resistors and has a range of 1.5 volts; dials II and II′ each consists of nine 1-ohm resistors. Determine: (*a*) normal potentiometer current; (*b*) current in slide wire III; (*c*) resistance of slide wire III; (*d*) voltage range of slide wire III. (*e*) With contactor *e* set at 0.7 the distance from 0 to *d*, and the dials II and II′ set as shown, compute voltage drop in dial I between the

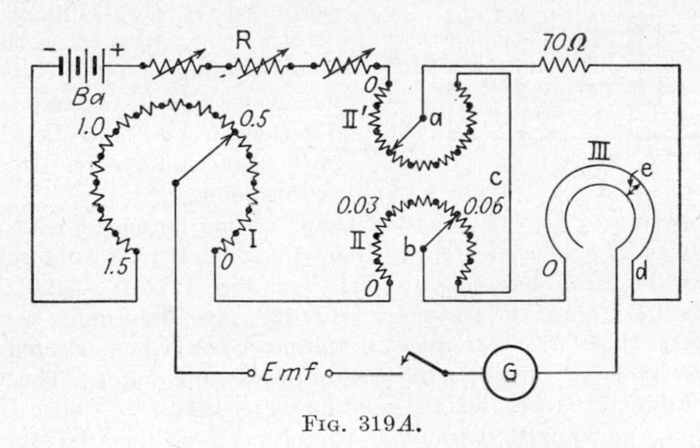

FIG. 319*A*.

contactor and 0, in dial II from 0 to the contactor, and from 0 to *e* in dial III, and add to obtain the total emf.

320. It is desired to calibrate a 15-scale voltmeter near the upper end of its scale. The positive terminal of the voltmeter is connected to the contact *C′* of a voltage divider, and the divider is connected across a battery, as shown in Fig. 320*A*. A resistor *abc* is connected in parallel with the voltmeter. Between point *b* and the negative terminal of the battery a standard cell *S*, whose emf is 1.0189 volts, is connected in series with a key *K* and galvanometer *G*, the negative terminal of the standard cell being connected to the negative side of the battery at *c*. The resistance between *b* and *c* is made equal to 100 ohms. When the resistance between *a* and *b* is adjusted to 1,325 ohms, the galvanometer does not deflect when the key *K* is depressed. At this instant the voltmeter reads 14.38 volts. Determine correction to voltmeter scale for this reading.

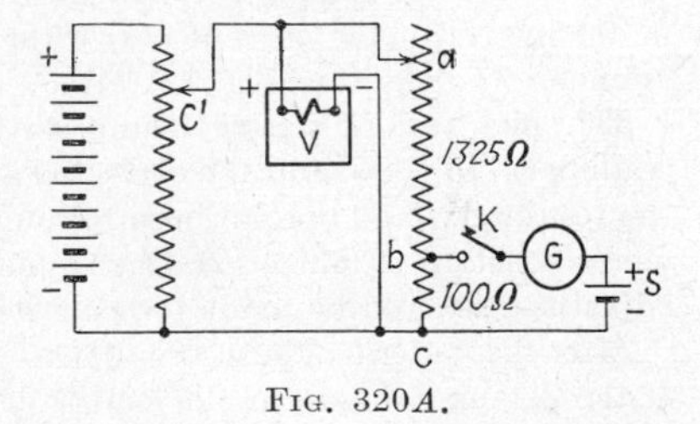

FIG. 320*A*.

321. In Prob. 320, determine value to which the resistance *ab* must be adjusted in order that the corrected reading of the voltmeter shall be 15 volts, the voltage-divider contact *C′* being changed accordingly.

322. In Fig. 320*A* the voltage-divider contact *C′* is adjusted so that the voltmeter indicates 10.00 volts. The galvanometer deflection with the key *K* depressed becomes zero when the resistance between *a* and *b* is 876 ohms. Determine correction to voltmeter scale for this reading.

323. It is desired to calibrate a voltmeter at the 125-volt point. No potentiometer is available. The voltmeter, whose voltage is adjusted by means of a voltage divider, is connected in parallel with the arms of a bridge box, Fig. 323*A*, and the divider is adjusted until the voltmeter reads just 125.0 volts. A standard cell *S*, which is known to have an emf of 1.0190 volts, is connected across the two ratio arms *A* and *B* in series with a key and galvanometer, the proper polarity being observed. Then a total resistance of 100 ohms is unplugged in these two arms. The galvanometer reads zero with the key depressed when 12,120 ohms is unplugged in P. Determine correction to voltmeter at this reading.

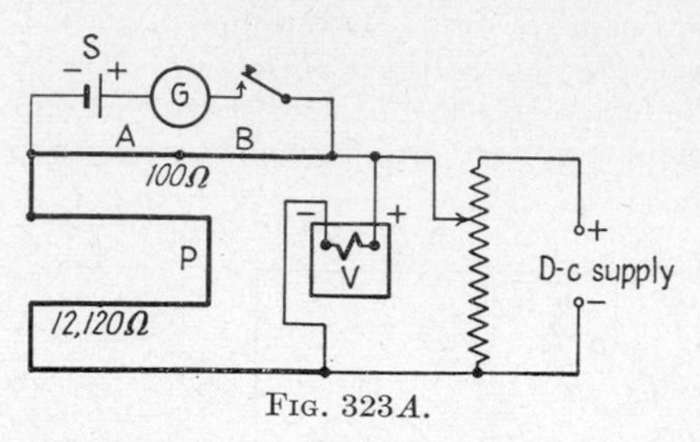

FIG. 323A.

324. In Prob. 323 the voltmeter is calibrated at the 110-volt point, the divider being adjusted so that the voltmeter reading is 110.0 volts. The galvanometer now reads zero with the key depressed, when 11,060 ohms is unplugged in P. Determine correction to voltmeter at this point.

325. The power to a 25-watt tungsten lamp is being measured with a voltmeter and an ammeter. The voltmeter, the resistance of which is 15,000 ohms, is connected directly across the lamp terminals [broken line, Fig. 141(*a*), p. 190]. When the ammeter reads 0.217 amp, the voltmeter reads 120 volts; determine: (*a*) true power to lamp; (*b*) percentage error introduced if voltmeter power be neglected.

326. The resistance of the ammeter of Prob. 325 is 0.05 ohm. The voltmeter is now connected directly across the line [solid line, Fig. 141(*a*), p. 190]. With the line voltage remaining unchanged, determine: (*a*) voltmeter reading; (*b*) true power now taken by lamp; (*c*) power given by product of voltmeter and ammeter readings; (*d*) percentage error if product in (*c*) is used.

327. In measuring the power taken by a low-resistance rheostat, an ammeter, the resistance of which is 0.0005 ohm, and a voltmeter, the resistance of which is 300 ohms, are used. When the ammeter reads 90 amp, the voltmeter, which is connected directly across the rheostat [solid lines, Fig. 141(*b*), p. 190], reads 2.16 volts. Determine: (*a*) true value of resistance; (*b*) true value of power; (*c*) percentage error introduced in (*b*) by voltmeter current; (*d*) error introduced by connecting voltmeter outside ammeter [broken line, Fig. 141(*b*)].

328. In a test of a d-c 15-amp watthour meter the corrected average voltmeter reading is 115 volts, and the corrected average ammeter reading is 14.8 amp. During the test interval 50 revolutions are counted, and the time is found to be 63 sec. The meter constant is 0.6. (*a*) Determine accuracy of meter at this load. (*b*) What adjustment should be made to bring it nearer correct registration?

After the meter has been brought to within 0.5 per cent accuracy by the movement of the damping magnets, the load is dropped to 1.5 amp but the voltage remains at 115 volts. It takes 49.7 sec for the disk to make 4 revolutions. (*c*) Determine accuracy of meter at this load. (*d*) What adjustment should be made in order to bring it nearer correct registration?

329. A 50-amp 230-volt watthour meter is tested for its accuracy near rated load and at light load. Near rated load the corrected average voltmeter reading is 230.5 volts, and the corrected average ammeter reading is 49.85 amp. The time required for the disk to make 40 revolutions is measured by means of a stop watch and is found to be 63.2 sec. The watthour meter constant is 5. (*a*) Determine accuracy at this load, and state the adjustment which should be made. The load is reduced, the corrected average voltage is 231.2 volts, and the corrected average current is 5.2 amp. The time required for the disk to make 3 revolutions is measured with a stop watch and found to be 44.8 sec. (*b*) Determine percentage accuracy. The meter is not adjusted between (*a*) and (*b*). From an analysis of the percentage accuracy in the two cases, discuss any adjustments of the light-load coil which should be made.

330. In order to make a laboratory test of a 2,000-amp 230-volt astatic watthour meter, Fig. 330*A*, its current coils are supplied with current from a 4-volt storage battery, and its armature circuit, which has a resistance of 2,000 ohms, is connected across a 240-volt supply. A calibrated voltmeter is connected in parallel with the armature circuit, and an external-shunt ammeter is connected in series with the current terminals of the meter. The meter constant is 150. The corrected voltmeter reading is 238.6 volts, and the corrected ammeter reading is 2,060 amp. The meter

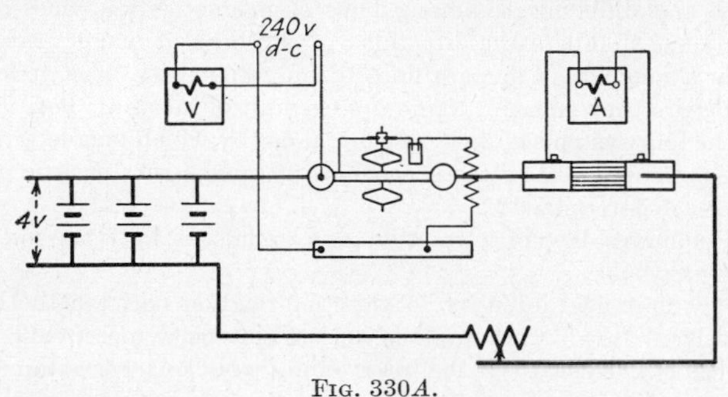

Fig. 330*A*.

makes 40 revolutions in 45.2 sec. Determine: (*a*) accuracy of meter at this load; (*b*) power required for test; (*c*) power which would be required if meter current were supplied at 238.6 volts.

QUESTIONS ON CHAPTER VI

Magnetism and Permanent Magnets

1. Into what two general classes may magnets be divided? Discuss the principal differences between permanent magnets and electromagnets. Describe natural magnets.

2. Name the principal magnetic materials and two other materials which have weaker magnetic properties. Compare ferromagnetic, paramagnetic, and diamagnetic materials.

3. Describe the general construction of the Bohr atom. Sketch an isolated iron atom showing the uncompensated electron spin within the inner orbits. Describe the relation among neighboring atoms which is necessary for ferromagnetic properties to exist. Why are ferromagnetic materials so few?

4. What is a "domain"? State the approximate number of atoms in a domain and its volume in centimeters.

5. Explain briefly why ferromagnetic properties are lost if the temperature exceeds a critical value. What is meant by the "Curie point"?

6. Into what aggregations do the domains combine? From this relation explain the changes in the orientation of the domains, Fig. 148 (p. 201), which produce weak magnetism; the condition when the magnetism increases almost proportionately to the magnetizing force; magnetic saturation. Show on the normal saturation curve where these three conditions occur.

7. Sketch the flux-density curve when the magnetizing force is decreased from a positive value to zero, showing the relation between the curve and the changes in orientation of the domains. Continue until the flux density becomes zero. What is remanence? Coercive force?

8. Describe the Barkhausen effect and what it proves. How is this effect detected?

9. Describe the Weber and Ewing theory, and compare with the spinning-electron domain theory.

10. Define the general property which permanent-magnet materials should have

What properties of the domains give permanent magnets this property? Define magnetic pole; N pole; S pole. What is the relation among the magnitudes of the N poles and the S poles of any single magnet?

11. Explain why equal N and S poles always appear on a fragment when a magnet is broken. Define consequent poles. What are magnetic figures?

12. Describe the compass needle. In what direction does the compass needle become oriented when placed in a magnetic field?

13. Describe and differentiate among lines of magnetization, lines of force, and lines of induction. Compare the directions of the lines of magnetization and lines of force within a magnet. Compare lines of induction with lines of force. Under what conditions are they equal? Name the cgs unit of magnetic flux.

14. Name the four systems of units in general use by which magnetic and electrical quantities are measured. How are the effects of magnetism, electric currents, and potential difference determined?

15. State Coulomb's law of attraction and repulsion between magnetic poles. Define the cgs unit pole.

16. Define cgs unit field intensity. State the relation between the lines of force and field intensity. In what two units is cgs field intensity measured?

17. Define cgs flux density. If the force on one unit pole 1 cm from another unit pole in vacuum is 1 dyne, what is the flux density on the surface of a sphere, 1 cm radius, with either pole as a center?

18. In Question 17 how many maxwells are intercepted by the surface of the sphere? How many maxwells leave or enter each unit cgs pole?

19. If the area of an N pole at the end of a bar magnet is A sq cm and the cgs poles per unit area are σ, how many maxwells leave the pole? How many maxwells go through the magnet at its center zone? Show that the flux density at the center zone $B = 4\pi\sigma$ gauss.

20. From Questions 17 and 18, explain Coulomb's law in which the force between two point magnetic poles varies inversely as the square of the distance between them.

21. Describe the production of magnetic poles by magnetic induction. What is the relation between the inducing and the induced pole? How does magnetic induction explain the attraction of soft iron to magnetic poles? How may a compass needle become reversed?

22. State the general law of the magnetic field, and show how it is illustrated when a horseshoe magnet attracts an armature to its poles.

23. Show that the force on a unit cgs pole, and hence the field intensity, on the axis extended of a cylindrical magnet is $2\pi\sigma\ (1 - \cos\beta)$ dynes. Show that very close to the magnetized surface or when the area of the pole face is infinite the force becomes $2\pi\sigma$ dynes.

24. From the relation given in Question 23, show that the force between magnetized parallel surfaces between which the field is substantially uniform is $2\pi\sigma^2 A = B^2 A/8\pi$ dynes.

25. Name the advantages of the mks system in so far as the magnitudes of the electrical and physical units are concerned. Compare the unrationalized and the rationalized systems. What must be the value of the permeability of free space in the unrationalized system? In the rationalized system what two values of space permeability must be used?

26. What unit of force is used with the two mks systems, and what is its value in dynes?

27. What property of the domains in magnetic materials makes them valuable for permanent magnets? What portion of the hysteresis loop is associated with permanent magnets?

28. Show how remanence, coercive force, and area under the demagnetization curve determine the properties of permanent magnets.

29. Show how permanent magnets may be used for magnetic chucks.

30. Describe the principle of shielding sensitive instruments from stray magnetic fields. Show that complete shielding is impossible.

PROBLEMS ON CHAPTER VI

Magnetism and Permanent Magnets

331. An N pole m of 1,000 cgs unit poles and an S pole m' of 1,200 cgs unit poles are spaced 8 cm apart in air. Determine: (a) force in dynes acting between the poles; (b) force in dynes exerted by N pole on a 10 cgs unit pole midway between the poles; (c) force in dynes exerted by S pole on a 12 cgs unit pole midway between the poles; (d) total force and its direction acting on a 5 cgs unit pole midway between the poles; (e) field intensity at point midway between the poles.

m=1,200 m=200 m'=1,500
a N c c' S b
6cm 10 cm 6cm
16 cm

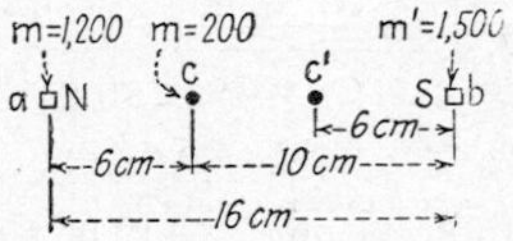

FIG. 332A.

332. In Fig. 332A are shown at a an N pole of 1,200 cgs unit pole strength and at b an S pole of 1,500 cgs unit pole strength. An N pole of 200 cgs unit pole strength is located at c, 6 cm from a. Determine: (a) total force acting on pole located at c; (b) field intensity in oersteds. If the 200 cgs N pole is located at c', 6 cm from b in the direction of a, determine: (c) total force acting on it and direction; (d) field intensity at c'. (The poles are in air.)

333. In Fig. 333A are shown three N poles a, b, c, in air, each 600 cgs unit poles, arranged at the three apexes of an isosceles right triangle. Determine resultant force and its direction acting on pole (a) at a; (b) at b; (c) at c.

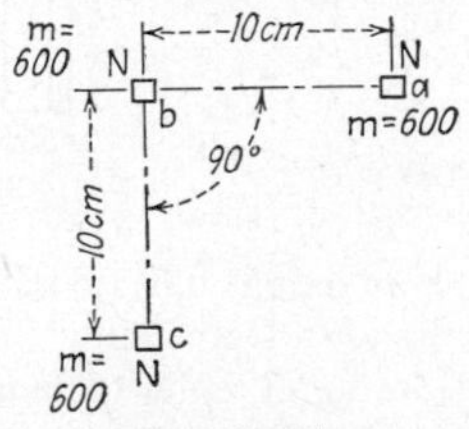

FIG. 333A.

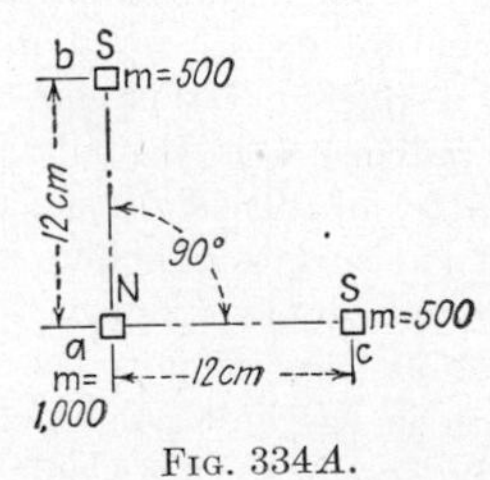

FIG. 334A.

334. In Fig. 334A are shown an N pole a of 1,000 cgs units strength and two S poles b, c, each 500 cgs units strength. Determine resultant force and its direction acting on pole (a) at a; (b) at b; (c) at c.

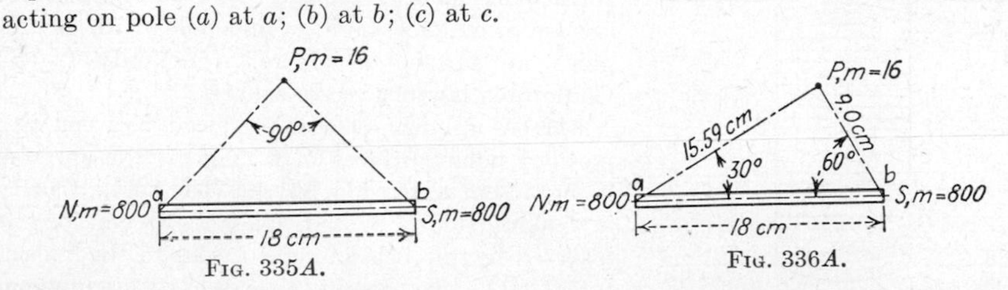

FIG. 335A. FIG. 336A.

335. A bar magnet, Fig. 335A, is 18 cm long, and the N and S poles at the ends of the magnet are each of strength $m = 800$ cgs unit poles. At point P, where angle aPb is 90° and P is equidistant from the N and the S pole, an N pole of 16 cgs units is located. Determine: (a) magnitude and direction of force which N pole of magnet at a exerts on N pole at P; (b) magnitude and direction of force which S pole of magnet at b exerts on N pole at P; (c) magnitude and direction of resultant force acting on N pole at P; (d) field intensity in oersteds and direction of magnetic field at P.

336. In Fig. 336A is shown a bar magnet similar to that of Prob. 335. The point P is located a distance of 15.59 cm from the N pole and 9.0 cm from the S pole, the angle aPb being 90°. An N pole of 16 cgs unit pole strength is located at P. Determine: (a) direction and magnitude of force exerted by N pole of magnet at a on pole at P; (b) direction and magnitude of force exerted by S pole of magnet at b on pole at P; (c) magnitude and direction of resultant force at P; (d) field intensity in oersteds at P

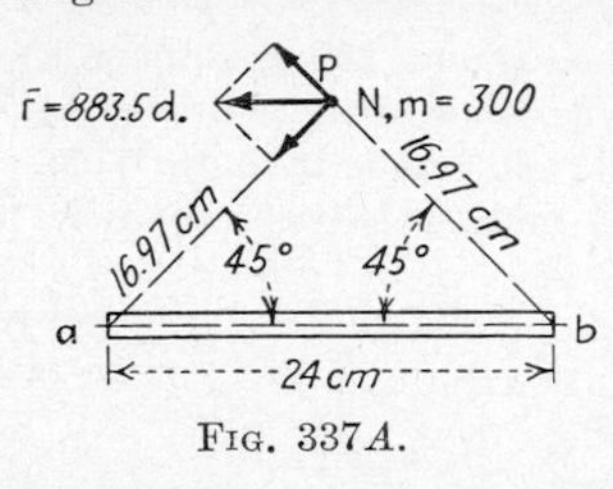

Fig. 337A.

337. An N pole of 300 cgs unit pole strength is located at P, Fig. 337A, 16.97 cm from each of the two ends a and b of a bar magnet 24 cm long. The triangle aPb is a right isosceles triangle. There is an N pole at one end of the bar magnet, and an equal S pole at the other end. The resultant force **f** exerted on the N pole at P is 883.5 dynes acting to the left and parallel to the direction of the magnet, as indicated. Determine magnitude of N and S poles. Indicate north end and south end of magnet.

338. Two similar bar magnets each 20 cm long are pivoted together at their centers, Fig. 338A. The pole strength of each of the N and S poles is 600 cgs unit poles. One of the bar magnets is held rigidly. Determine turning moment in centimeter-dynes acting on other bar.

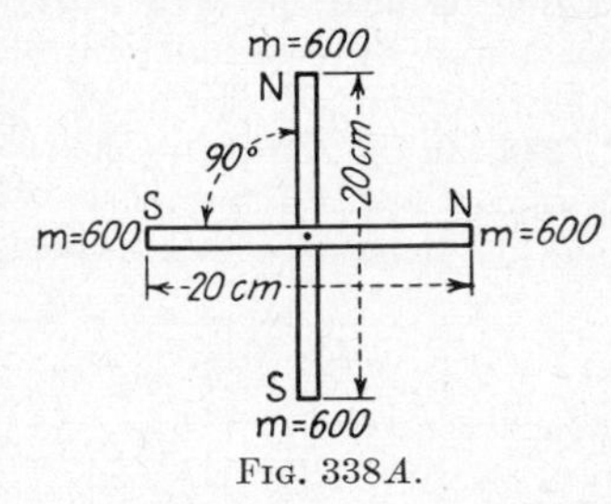

Fig. 338A.

339. The cross section of a bar magnet 20 cm long is 0.5 sq cm, and the flux density at the center section is 3,000 gauss. Determine: (a) intensity of magnetization at each end of magnet in cgs poles per square centimeter; (b) number of maxwells intercepted by a sphere at either end, having a pole as center and a radius of 4 cm, the poles being considered point sources; (c) flux density at surface of sphere; (d) field intensity at surface of sphere in oersteds.

340. The diameter of a cylindrical bar magnet 24 cm long is 0.5 cm, and the N and S poles at the ends have magnitudes of 50 cgs unit poles. Determine: (a) intensity of magnetization in cgs unit poles per square centimeter at ends of magnet; (b) flux intercepted by sphere having a pole at either end as center and a radius of 3 cm, the poles being considered point sources; (c) flux density in gauss, and field intensity in oersteds at surface of sphere; (d) total flux crossing center section of magnet; (e) force on a pole of 15 cgs unit poles at surface of sphere. (f) Verify (e) by Coulomb's law of inverse squares.

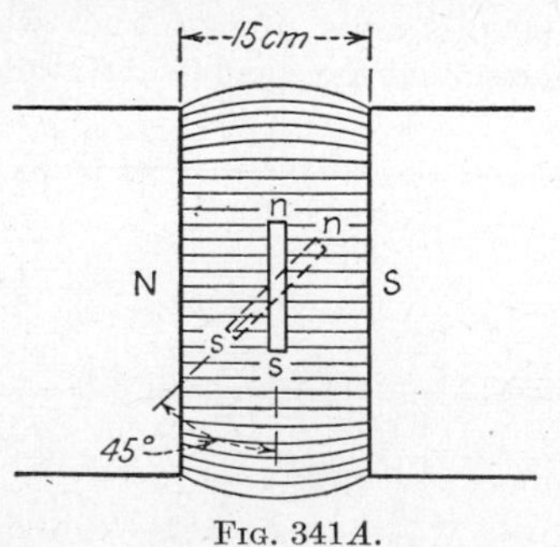

Fig. 341A.

341. A uniform field is produced between two parallel polar surfaces of a magnet, the surfaces being 15 cm apart, Fig. 341A. The field intensity is 500 oersteds. A bar magnet 10 cm long is inserted in this field at right angles to the lines of force. The two poles at the ends of the bar magnet are each 60 unit poles. Determine: (a) magnitude and direction of force acting on each pole of bar magnet; (b) turning moment acting on magnet in centimeter-dynes. (c) When magnet is turned 45° to direction of field, determine turning moment.

342. A thin bar magnet 12 cm long is located in a uniform magnetic field and perpendicular to the direction of the field. The N and S poles of the magnet are each 80 cgs unit pole strength. The turning moment of the bar magnet is $1.152 \cdot 10^6$ cm-dynes. Determine (*a*) field intenisty. (*b*) Make a sketch indicating general appearance of resulting magnetic field. (*c*) Determine turning moment acting on bar magnet when direction of magnet is 60° with direction of uniform field.

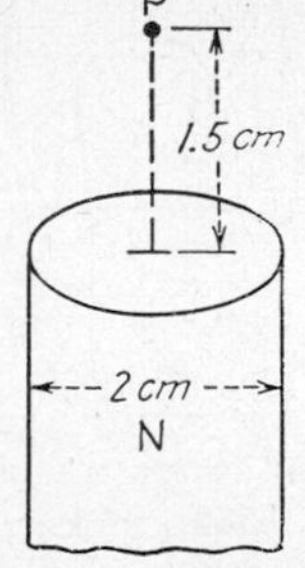

FIG. 343*A*.

343. In Fig. 343*A* is shown the end of a long cylindrical magnet, 2 cm diameter. The flux density at the center section of the magnet is 600 gauss. Determine: (*a*) intensity of magnetization at end of magnet; (*b*) pole strength in cgs unit poles; (*c*) field intensity in oersteds at point P on axis of magnet extended, 1.5 cm from end of magnet; (*d*) field intensity in oersteds when P is an infinitesimal distance from end of magnet at its center.

344. With a magnet similar to that of Fig. 343*A* except that the diameter is 2.5 cm, the pole at P consists of 12 cgs unit N poles, and P is 2 cm from the center of the end surface of the magnet. The force on the pole at P is 573.5 dynes. Determine: (*a*) intensity of magnetization σ on end of magnet; (*b*) total flux in maxwells at center section of magnet.

345. In Fig. 345*A* is shown an air-gap between two parallel circular pole faces, spaced 2 cm from each other. One pole is N, and the other is S. The diameters of the pole faces are 3 cm, and the intensity of magnetization is 60 cgs unit poles per square centimeter. Determine field intensity in oersteds at point P on a perpendicular to each pole surface at its center, point P being 0.8 cm from the N pole and 1.2 cm from the S pole.

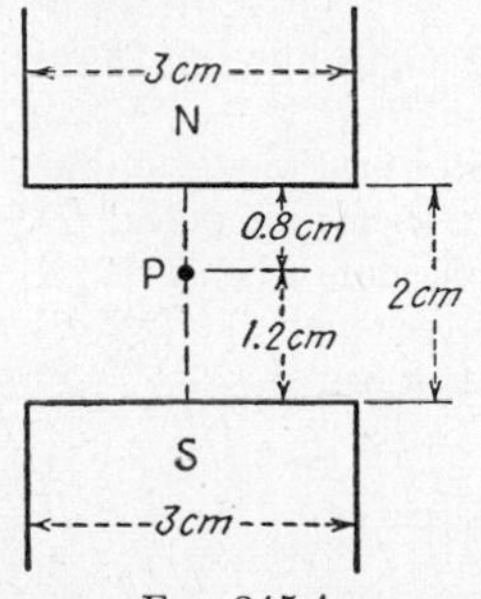

FIG. 345*A*.

346. A long cylindrical bar magnet has a diameter of 3 cm, and there are 420 cgs unit poles at each end. A small transverse saw cut is made at the center section of the magnet. Determine: (*a*) cgs unit poles per square centimeter on each of pole surfaces created by saw cut; (*b*) field intensity within short air-gap; (*c*) force exerted by one of pole faces on a unit cgs pole at surface of other; (*d*) total pull in dynes and in kilograms between two pole faces.

347. The diameter of a long cylindrical magnet is 3.6 cm, and the magnetic pull between two surfaces formed by a transverse saw cut at its center is 1,651 g. Determine: (*a*) maxwells per square centimeter on each of pole-face surfaces at saw cut; (*b*) pole strength at ends of magnet.

348. It is desired to make an electromagnet of the type shown in Fig. 348*A*, capable of holding a symmetrical armature load of 1,500 lb. The cores of the magnet are

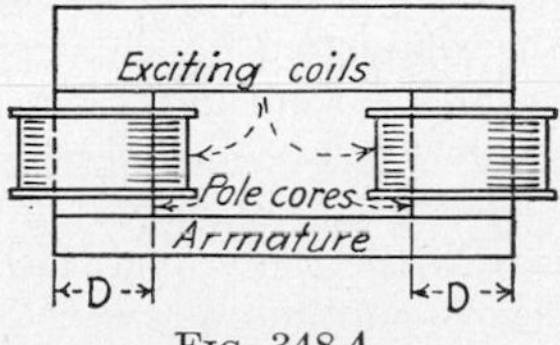

FIG. 348*A*.

circular in cross section. The pole faces are flat and make contact with the armature over their entire area. The flux density at the area of contact of poles and armature is to be 30,000 maxwells per sq in. Determine diameter D of pole cores.

349. In Fig. 349*A* is shown an Alnico horseshoe magnet with a soft-iron armature across the poles. The poles are 0.48 by 0.64 cm each, and the flux density at the pole pieces in contact with the armature is 7,500 gauss. Determine force in kilograms necessary to remove armature.

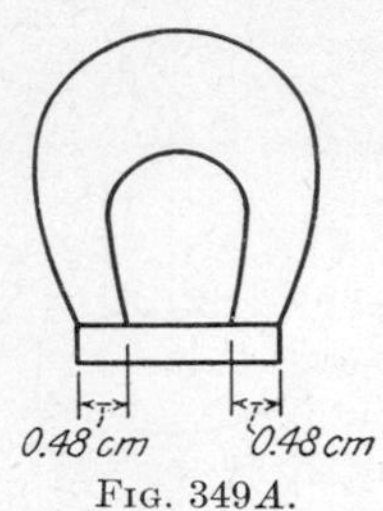

FIG. 349*A*.

MKS System

350. Two point poles, an N and an S pole, of $2 \cdot 10^{-4}$ unrationalized mks unit pole strength are spaced 10 cm apart in air. Determine force of attraction in: (*a*) newtons; (*b*) kilograms.

351. Determine the strength of two poles in terms of rationalized mks unit poles which will exert the same force of attraction as that between the poles in Prob. 350, the spacing of 10 cm remaining unchanged.

352. In Fig. 333*A* assume that the three N poles at a, b, c have magnitudes of $8 \cdot 10^{-6}$ unrationalized unit pole. Determine in newtons and kilograms the resultant force and its direction acting on pole (*a*) at a; (*b*) at b; (*c*) at c.

353. Repeat Prob. 352, assuming that the three N poles have magnitudes of $9.6 \cdot 10^{-5}$ rationalized unit pole, the spacings remaining unchanged.

354. In Fig. 336*A* the strength of the poles at a and b in unrationalized mks unit poles a, b is $8.00 \cdot 10^{-6}$ and at P, $m = 2.0 \cdot 10^{-8}$. Determine force in newtons on one unrationalized mks pole at P.

355. Repeat Prob. 354 with pole strengths in rationalized mks units. a, b = $7 \cdot 10^{-5}$; and at P, $m = 2.5 \cdot 10^{-7}$.

356. In Prob. 343 determine: (*a*) intensity of magnetization in unrationalized mks unit poles per square meter; (*b*) pole strength in mks unrationalized unit poles; (*c*) force on a unit mks pole at P in newtons; (*d*) force on a unit mks pole when P is an infinitesimal distance from the end of the magnet pole at its center.

357. Repeat Prob. 356, using rationalized mks poles and quantities.

QUESTIONS ON CHAPTER VII

Electromagnetism

1. What are the nature and general shape of the magnetic field about a cylindrical conductor carrying an electric current? What relation exists between the direction of the current and the direction of the field produced about the conductor?

2. How may the above relations be shown experimentally? What two simple rules enable one to remember the relation which exists between the current direction and the direction of the magnetic field?

3. The direction of the current in a conductor is from left to right. In what direction will the north end of a compass needle point if the compass needle is held over the conductor? If held beneath the conductor?

4. If two parallel conductors carry current in the same direction, state whether or not these conductors tend to separate or to come together. Give two reasons for the answer. Repeat for two conductors carrying current in opposite directions.

5. By means of a sketch illustrate the Biot-Savart law, which gives a quantitative relation between the magnitude of a current and the field intensity which it produces.

6. Show that if an element Δx of a conductor carries a current, only that component of Δx which is perpendicular to a line connecting Δx with a unit pole at P contributes to the force at P.

7. Derive, in cgs units, the equation from which the field intensity due to a current in a straight conductor of finite length can be calculated.

8. In Question 7 derive, in cgs units, the value of field intensity when the length of conductor becomes infinite. Approximately, for what ratio of length of conductor to the distance of the point from the conductor does the value of field intensity equal essentially that for an infinitely long conductor?

9. From the result in Question 7 derive in cgs units an expression which gives the work done in carrying a small magnetic pole once around a conductor carrying a current. Of what quantity is the work independent?

10. A single loop of wire lying in the plane of the paper carries a current in a clockwise direction. What effect will be noticed if a compass is placed within this loop? Compare the magnetic properties of this loop with those of a bar magnet.

11. Derive the equation which gives quantitatively the field intensity at the center of a circular loop of wire in which there is a current. Compare this relation with the fundamental definition of an electric current.

12. Derive the equation which gives quantitatively the field intensity at any point on a perpendicular at the center of the plane of a circular loop of wire in which there is current.

13. Show how loops similar to the one of Question 10 may be combined to form a solenoid.

14. State three methods whereby the polarity of the poles at the ends of a solenoid may be determined, provided that the direction of the current through the solenoid turns be known.

15. Derive, in cgs units, the equation which gives the field intensity at the center of an infinitely long, straight solenoid. Compare the result obtained when the ratio of the length to the radius of the solenoid is moderately large, with that obtained with the solenoid of infinite length.

16. Convert Eq. (138) (p. 231), which gives the Biot-Savart law in cgs units, into an equation employing rationalized mks units.

17. Derive the field intensities required in Questions 7 and 8 in terms of rationalized mks units.

18. Express the work required in Question 9 in terms of rationalized mks units. In what unit is the work expressed?

19. Derive the field intensities required in Questions 11 and 12 in terms of rationalized mks units.

20. Derive the field intensity required in Question 15 in terms of rationalized mks units.

21. Make a sketch showing the construction of (*a*) a simple solenoid with plunger; (*b*) an ironclad solenoid with plunger; (*c*) of (*b*) with stop. By means of a graph show the relation between the pull of the plunger and its position within the solenoid. Point out the effect of the ironclad feature and of the stop on the tractive pull of the plunger as it is drawn into the solenoid.

22. Explain by the fundamental laws of magnetism why the plunger is drawn into a solenoid when there is current in the solenoid winding. State several uses of commercial solenoids.

23. Describe the construction of a magnetic brake, stating any precautions which are taken in case of failure in the power supply.

24. Describe the construction and operation of a typical magnetic separator.

25. Sketch the cross section of a lifting magnet, showing the path of the magnetic flux. Where are such magnets used commercially, and in what way are they more economical than the older methods of handling material? Does the magnet itself do appreciable work when it is being used to handle iron and steel?

26. What basic principle should be followed in the location of the exciting coils in dynamos? Sketch the cross section of the magnetic circuits in a multipolar dynamo, and show the paths of the magnetic flux, including leakage. What are the disadvantages of magnetic leakage? Does it represent a loss of power?

PROBLEMS ON CHAPTER VII

Electromagnetism

(Most problems may be solved with either cgs or mks units.)

358. In Fig. 358*A* is shown a long straight conductor carrying a current of 300 amp. At *P*, a perpendicular distance of 12 cm from the axis of the conductor at 0, there is a point pole consisting of 10 cgs unit poles. Considering the effect only of the section

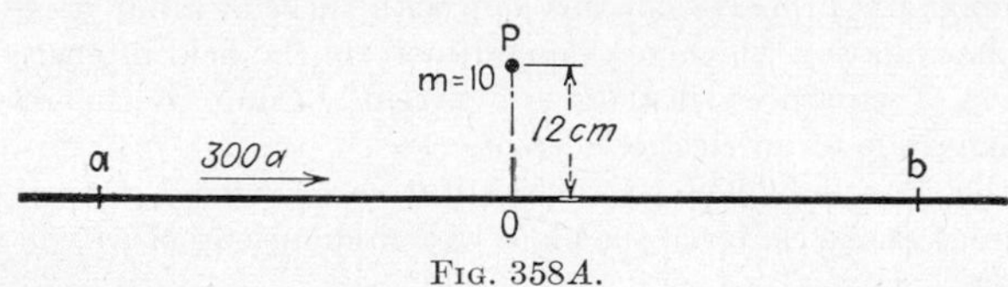

FIG. 358*A*.

of the wire *ao* and *ob*, each equal to 100 cm, determine: (*a*) field intensity at *P* in oersteds; (*b*) work in ergs performed in carrying *P* once about conductor in circular path, 12 cm radius, and in opposition to force acting; (*c*) mmf represented by (*b*); (*d*) direction of force at *P*.

359. Repeat (*a*), (*b*), (*c*), Prob. 358, with $a0 = 20$ cm and $0b = 50$ cm.

360. Repeat (*a*), (*b*), (*c*), Prob. 358, with $a0 = 0b =$ infinity.

361. In Fig. 361*A* is shown a straight conductor carrying a current of 200 amp. Parallel to the conductor and 8 cm from its axis is a thin bar magnet $n's'$, 20 cm long.

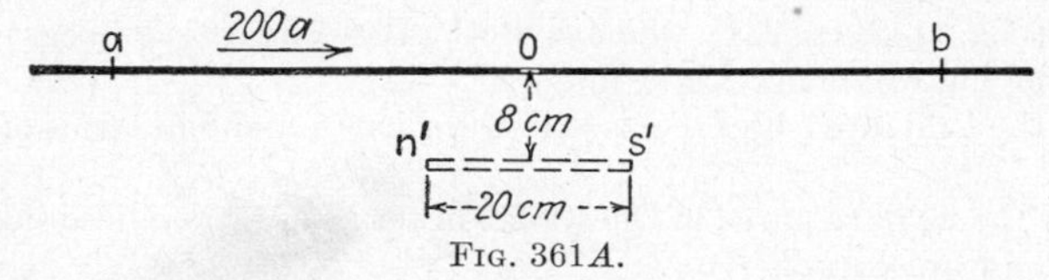

FIG. 361*A*.

A line from 0 perpendicular to the conductor intersects the center of the magnet. The strength of the poles of the magnet is 10 cgs unit poles. Considering the effect only of the section of the wire *ab*, where $a0 = 0b = 40$ cm, determine (*a*) turning moment acting on magnet in centimeter-dynes. (*b*) Repeat (*a*) with $a0 = 20$ cm; $0b = 40$ cm. (*c*) Repeat (*a*) with $a0 = 0b =$ infinity.

362. Repeat Prob. 361 with the n' pole of the magnet 8 cm from the axis of the conductor and the position of the magnet radial to the conductor, the s' pole being the more remote.

363. In Fig. 363*A* are shown two parallel wires *A* and *B* on crossarms, the wires being spaced 72 cm between centers, and each wire carrying a current of 500 amp in opposite directions, as indicated by the arrows.

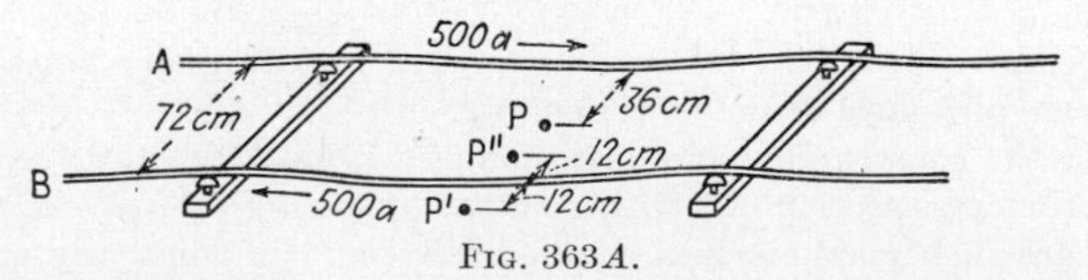

FIG. 363*A*.

Assuming that the conductors are infinite in length, determine: (*a*) field intensity in oersteds and its direction at point *P* midway between conductors; (*b*) field intensity at point *P'* 12 cm from conductor *B* and lying in plane of two conductors; (*c*) field intensity at point P'' 12 cm from conductor B in direction of conductor A and lying in plane of two conductors.

364. A current of 350 amp flows around the 90° arc ab, Fig. 364A, being led in and out by the two wires $a'a$ and $b'b$, the directions of which are radial. The radius of the arc is 15 cm, and a small S pole S of 50 cgs unit poles is located at the center of the arc ab. Determine direction and magnitude in grams of force acting on pole S. (See p. 27 for the definition of an abampere.)

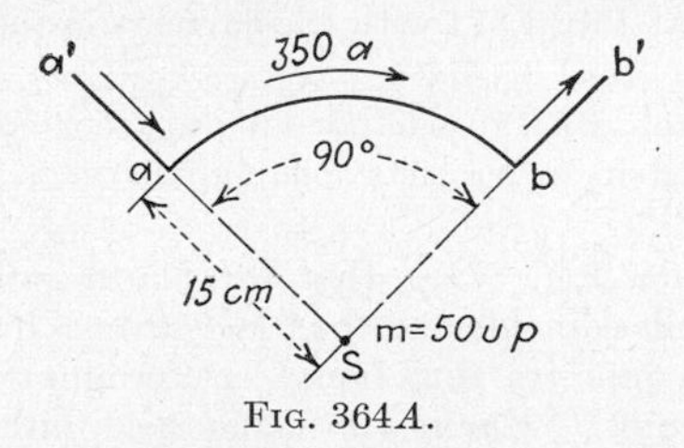

FIG. 364A.

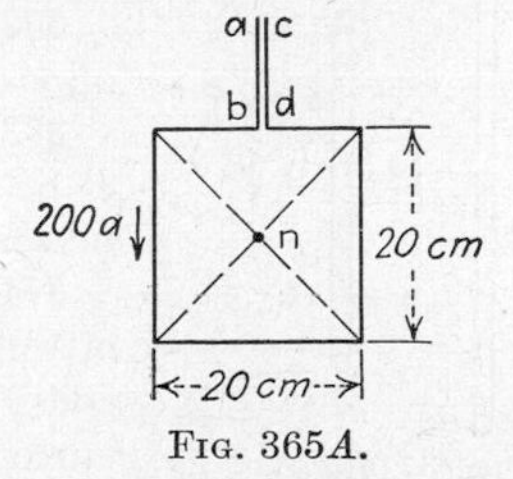

FIG. 365A.

365. A wire, Fig. 365A, is bent into the form of a square 20 cm on a side. There is a current of 200 amp in the wire, being conducted by the two leads ab and cd which are very close together. Determine magnitude in grams and direction of force on an N pole n at center of square, n having a pole strength of 50 cgs unit poles.

366. A wire, in Fig. 366A, is bent into the form of a rectangle 18 by 12 cm. There is a current of 300 amp in the wire being conducted by the two leads ab and cd, which are very close together. Determine: (a) field intensity at center n of rectangle; (b) force on a point N pole at n having a pole strength of 40 cgs unit poles.

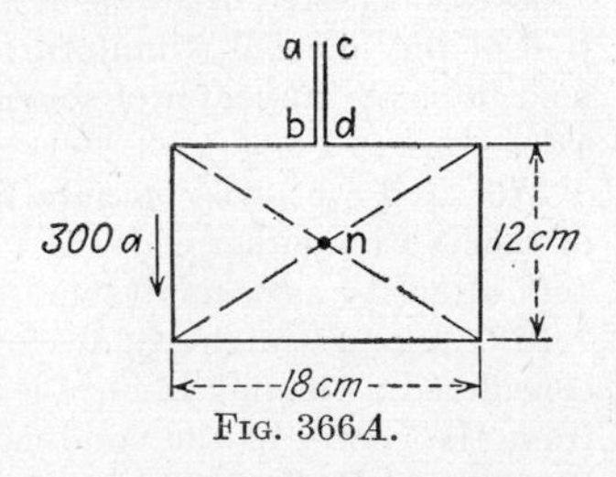

FIG. 366A.

367. The arc ab, Fig. 364A, is extended to complete a circle. With a current of 300 amp determine: (a) field intensity at its center; (b) force in dynes on a point S pole at the center, S having a pole strength of 25 cgs unit poles.

368. A flat coil of wire 18 cm diameter consists of 12 turns of small wire bound closely together. There is a current of 15 amp in the coil, the leads carrying the current to and from the coil being very close together. Determine: (a) field intensity in oersteds at center of coil; (b) field intensity at a point on a perpendicular to plane of coil at its center and 12 cm above plane of coil; (c) force acting on a small pole of 18 cgs unit pole strength, placed on perpendicular 6 cm above plane of coil.

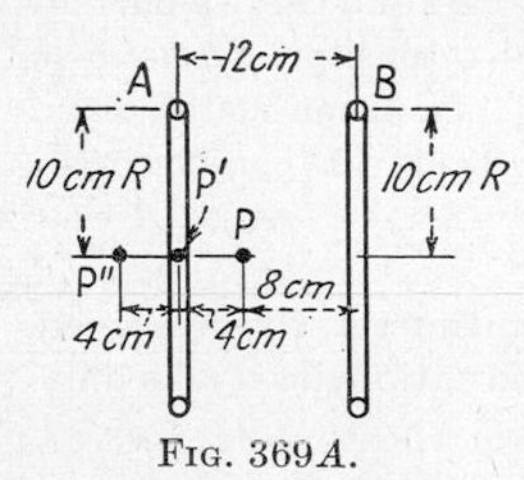

FIG. 369A.

369. In Fig. 369A are shown two circular coaxial coils A, B, each consisting of 12 turns and having small cross sections. The radius of each coil is 10 cm, and the planes of the coils are parallel and are spaced 12 cm. There is a current of 5 amp in each turn of the two coils. With the currents in the two coils having the same direction, determine: (a) field intensity in oersteds at point P on common axis of the coils and 4 cm from plane of coil A toward coil B; (b) field intensity at point P' at center of coil A; (c) field intensity at point P'' on common axis of coils 4 cm from plane of coil A in direction away from coil B.

370. Repeat Prob. 369 with the currents in the two coils in opposite directions.

371. In Fig. 371A are shown two circular coaxial coils A, B, each consisting of 15 turns and having small cross sections. The radius of coil A is 8 cm and that of coil B

is 6 cm, and the planes of the coils are parallel and are spaced 10 cm. There is a current of 75 amp in each turn of the two coils. With the currents in the two coils having the same direction, determine field intensity in oersteds at (*a*) point P_1, at center of coil *A*; (*b*) P_2, midway between planes of coils and on their common axis; (*c*) P_3, 4 cm from plane of coil *A* away from coil *B* and on common axis; (*d*) P_4, 3 cm from plane of coil *B* in a direction away from coil *A* and on the common axis.

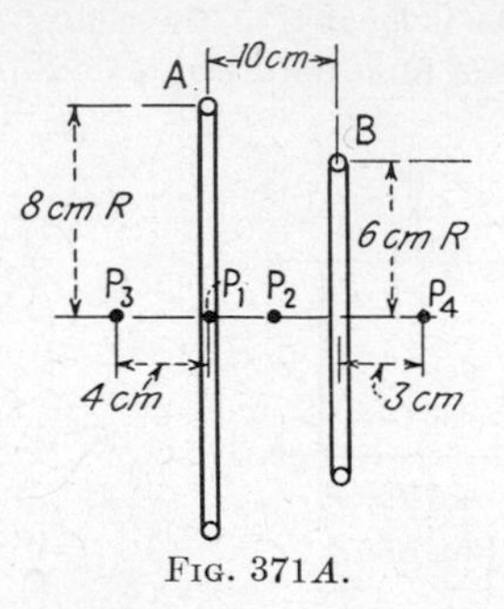

FIG. 371*A*.

372. Repeat Prob. 371 with the currents in the coils in opposite directions.

373. In Prob. 372, to what value must current in coil *B* be adjusted in order that field intensity at point P_2 be zero?

374. Assume, Fig. 371*A*, that the planes and centers of the two coils coincide and that the currents in the two coils are in opposite directions. Determine value of current in coil *B* which will make field intensity at point *P*, at center of coils, equal to zero.

375. The diameter of a cylindrical solenoid is 6.4 cm, and the length is 120 cm. There are 11 turns of No. 20 AWG enamel wire per centimeter length. There is a current of 4 amp in the winding. Determine: (*a*) field intensity in oersteds at the center of solenoid, assuming solenoid to be infinite in length; (*b*) flux density in maxwells per square centimeter, or gauss, at center of solenoid (the flux density over the center section of the solenoid is uniform); (*c*) flux in maxwells across center section; (*d*) exact field intensity at center of solenoid; (*e*) field intensity at either end of solenoid on its axis.

376. In Prob. 375 compute field intensity along axis of solenoid at the following distances from either end: (*a*) 1 cm; (*b*) 2 cm; (*c*) 3 cm; (*d*) 4 cm. Plot a curve with field intensity as ordinates and distance along solenoid as abscissas.

377. A long straight conductor similar to that shown in Fig. 358*A*, but which may be considered as having infinite length, carries a current of 250 amp. Point *P* is 8 cm from the center of the conductor. Determine (*a*) in ampere-turns per meter field intensity at *P*; (*b*) work in joules in carrying a rationalized unit mks pole in a circular path of 8 cm radius once about conductor.

378. In Prob. 377, determine field intensity at *P* in ampere-turns per meter due to effect of section ao = 40 cm and ob = 20 cm.

379. Two parallel conductors similar to those of Fig. 363*A*, but which may be considered as being infinite in length, are spaced 60 cm between centers and carry a current of 600 amp. Determine in ampere-turns per meter the field intensity at a point in plane of conductors: (*a*) midway between conductors; (*b*) 20 cm from conductor *B* and 40 cm from conductor *A*; (*c*) 70 cm from conductor *A* and 10 cm from conductor *B*.

380. Solve Prob. 368, using rationalized mks units.

381. Solve Prob. 368, using unrationalized mks units.

382. A long straight solenoid is wound with 10 turns per centimeter, the cross sectional area is 12 sq cm, and the current is 5 amp. Determine in rationalized mks units (*a*) field intensity at center; (*b*) field intensity at end.

383. Repeat Prob. 382, using unrationalized mks units.

384. In a simple solenoid and plunger, similar to that shown in Fig. 185 (p. 240), the field intensity is 2,500 oersteds just at the end of the plunger, and the approximate pole strength at the end of the plunger is 2,820 cgs unit poles. The plunger is cylindrical, and the diameter of the plunger is 3 cm. Determine force on plunger in grams, the other end of plunger being well outside of magnetic field.

385. Repeat Prob. 384 with the exciting current in solenoid reduced 20 per cent, field intensity and pole strength being proportionately reduced.

386. A solenoid similar to that of Prob. 384 is ironclad, and a stop of the same diameter as the plunger is added. When the end surface of the plunger is nearly in contact with the surface of the stop, the flux density between them is 3,000 gauss. Determine pull in kilograms between plunger and stop. (The pull may be considered as due entirely to magnetized surfaces.)

387. Repeat Prob. 386 with the exciting current in solenoid reduced 20 per cent. The iron may be assumed not saturated so that the flux density decreases proportionately.

If the magnetic members of a solenoid are not saturated, how does the pull on the plunger vary with the exciting current?

388. The flat circular pole pieces of an electromagnet, each 4 in. diameter, are in contact with each other, and a total flux of 400,000 maxwells passes from one to the other. Determine force in pounds necessary to separate these pole pieces. Assume that flux is distributed uniformly over pole faces.

389. In Fig. 389*A* is shown the cross section of a circular lifting magnet with its load, having an outside diameter of 36 in. The radial thickness of the annular pole piece is 3.51 in., and the diameter of the center pole is 15.5 in. With a maximum flux density of 30,000 maxwells per sq in. at surface of contact when a flat iron load is being lifted, determine holding force of magnet in pounds.

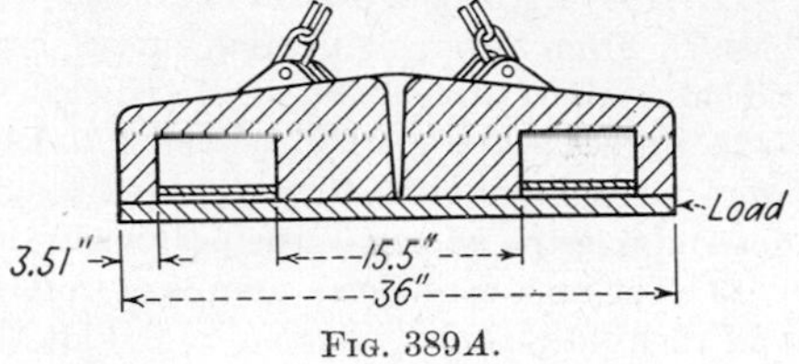

Fig. 389*A*.

390. In a lifting magnet constructed similar to that shown in Fig. 389*A*, the outside diameter of the annular pole shoe is 32 in., and the inner diameter is 28.87 in. The diameter of the center shoe is 13.8 in. Determine flux density in maxwells per square inch at surfaces of pole shoes when magnet is holding a flat iron piece with a force of 4,000 lb. Assume uniform flux distribution over pole surfaces.

QUESTIONS ON CHAPTER VIII

The Magnetic Circuit

1. In what way does the magnetic circuit resemble the electric circuit? In what three respects do they differ from each other? Why cannot magnetic flux be confined to definite paths? In a general way, how does the accuracy obtainable in magnetic calculations compare with that obtainable in electrical calculations?

2. Define ampere-turns. What is the numerical relation between mmf in gilberts and ampere-turns? Which is the larger unit, the gilbert or the ampere-turn? To what quantity in the electric circuit does mmf correspond?

3. Define reluctance. To what quantity in the electric circuit does it correspond? What is the fundamental unit of reluctance? How is permeance related to reluctance and to conductance? How should permeances in parallel be added?

4. Define permeability. To what quantity in the electric circuit does magnetic flux correspond? Name the cgs unit of flux; the mks unit. Define induction or flux density. Name the cgs unit of flux density.

5. How is the reluctance of a magnetic path related to its length? To its cross section? Its permeability? Write the equation for reluctance. How are reluctances in series combined? in parallel? How are permeances in parallel combined?

6. In iron and steel, why is it usually necessary to represent the relation between magnetizing force and flux by a curve? What is the general shape of the lower part of such curves? the upper part? What is meant by saturation? How may a permeability curve be obtained from a *B-H* curve? How does the variation of permeability compare with the usual variation of electrical resistance in conductors due to heating?

7. State the simple law governing the relation which exists among flux, mmf, and reluctance. Repeat, when there is a number of different reluctances in series. To what law in the electric circuit does this law correspond?

8. Show that in air the mmf per centimeter is equal *numerically* to the field intensity H in oersteds and that when $\mu_r = 1$, $B = H$ numerically.

9. Why is a method of trial and error sometimes necessary in solving magnetic problems? Show that when the flux or flux density is given and it is required to determine the ampere-turns, the method of trial and error is no longer necessary.

10. On what three factors is the mmf acting on a magnetic circuit dependent? Give the numerical equation for ampere-turns in centimeter units; in inch units.

11. How are magnetization curves plotted to reduce computations to the simplest basis? From the magnetization curves, compare the magnetic properties of cast iron, silicon steel, dynamo sheet steel, and cast steel.

12. Indicate the method of using the magnetization curves for determining the ampere-turns for different parts of a magnetic circuit. Indicate the procedure for determining the ampere-turns per pole in a multipolar dynamo.

13. The mmf acting on a sample of iron is increased from zero to some definite value and then decreased again to zero. Plot the relation between the mmf and the flux density. Compare the part of the curve for increasing values of mmf with that for decreasing values.

14. In Question 13 what value does the magnetic flux density reach when the excitation is decreased to zero? How may the flux density be brought back to zero? Define: cycle; hysteresis loop; remanence; coercive force.

15. Account for hysteresis loss by the domain theory. Show that hysteresis loss is equal to the area of the hysteresis loop multiplied by a constant. How does hysteresis loss per cycle vary with the maximum flux density? What is the relation of hysteresis loss to frequency?

16. What method is used to reduce eddy-current loss in iron? How does eddy-current loss vary with thickness of laminations? With frequency? With flux density? With the resistivity of the material?

17. Discuss the effect on hysteresis and eddy-current losses of the silicon content in magnetic steel. Why is the silicon content greater in transformer steel than in dynamo steel? On what general basis are core losses compared?

18. What relation between hysteresis and eddy-current losses makes it possible to separate the two? Of what two quantities are core losses a function? Show that by making measurements at two different values of these quantities, the losses may be separated.

19. Write the equation which gives the flux in unrationalized mks units. Write the equation which gives hysteresis loss as a function of the area of the hysteresis loop, in unrationalized mks units.

20. Repeat Question 19 for rationalized mks units.

21. What type of ferromagnetic alloy shows unusual magnetic properties, particularly at the lower flux densities? What is the general composition of Permalloy? What remarkable magnetic characteristics has it? Compare its magnetic properties with those of a pure iron, at both low and high flux densities. To what uses is it limited?

22. Describe Perminvar, and state its particular magnetic property.

23. Give the composition of Hipernik. What precautions are necessary in its manufacture? What particularly valuable properties has it, and what is its principal use? State the nature of Coupernik.

24. Beginning with carbon tool steel, discuss the alloys which were used for permanent magnets, including their properties, up to the development of the Alnico alloys.

25. What metals are used in the Alnico alloys, and what are the approximate percentages of each? How are the alloys improved by the development of a "grain"?

26. Compare the Alnico alloys with the earlier magnetic ones in the matter of remanence, coercive force, stored magnetic energy, and "energy product."

27. Derive the equations by means of which the values of H_m and B_m for any particular design may be determined. What is meant by a "shearing line," and how is its slope determined?

28. Show the paths of operation with changes in the air-gap, for different points on the demagnetization curve. Show that with improper operation demagnetization can readily occur. Sketch the types of demagnetization curve best adapted to short fixed air-gaps, for longer air-gaps which may be variable, and for devices which may be disassembled.

29. Describe two methods of magnetizing permanent magnets. Why do magnets lose with time some of the initial magnetization? Describe two methods of stabilization.

30. Describe the method by which flux may be measured by means of a ballistic galvanometer. Upon what three factors does the ballistic throw depend? Describe the means by which known values of flux are obtained.

31. Derive the equation which gives the flux in a ring-type solenoid having a cross-sectional area A sq cm, a mean circumferential length l cm, and wound with n turns per centimeter (circumferential). Under what conditions does this equation give the flux within a long straight solenoid near its center?

32. Describe the method of calibrating the ballistic galvanometer by means of a standard solenoid. Derive Eq. (203), (p. 288), which gives the quantity Q_1 discharged through the galvanometer when the flux in the standard solenoid is caused to change. In a similar manner derive Eq. (204) (p. 288), which gives the quantity Q_2 discharged through the galvanometer when the flux in the test specimen is changed from ϕ_1 to ϕ_2. By means of these two equations derive the galvanometer constant, [Eq. (206), p. 289].

33. Describe the yoke method of magnetic testing. What are its advantages? Name two important sources of error.

34. Describe the ring method of magnetic testing, comparing the procedure with that of the yoke method. State its advantages and disadvantages.

35. Upon what well-known principle does the Koepsel permeameter operate? What is the form of the test specimen, and where is it placed? Describe the exciting coil, and give the function of the compensating coils. What is the advantage of this instrument as a method of testing? What errors may exist in the instrument?

36. Make a diagram of connections used for obtaining hysteresis loops by means of a cathode-ray oscilloscope. Derive the equation which gives the functioning of the integrating circuit. What practical use is made of this method?

PROBLEMS ON CHAPTER VIII

The Magnetic Circuit

(Several problems other than those specified may be solved by either mks system.)

391. In Fig. 391*A* is shown a closed-ring type of solenoid, the core being of non-magnetic material. The average diameter of the ring is 8.0 cm, and the cross-sectional diameter of the ring is 0.8 cm. The winding on the ring is uniform, and there is a total of 1,170 turns. A current of 0.4 amp flows in the winding in the direction shown. Determine: (*a*) ampere-turns per centimeter of average circumference; (*b*) gilberts per centimeter in (*a*); (*c*) from (*a*) and (*b*) determine ratio of ampere-turn to gilbert, stating which unit is larger. Determine: (*d*) flux density in gauss; (*e*) flux in maxwells; (*f*) flux if nonmagnetic material is replaced by steel having permeability of 1,080.

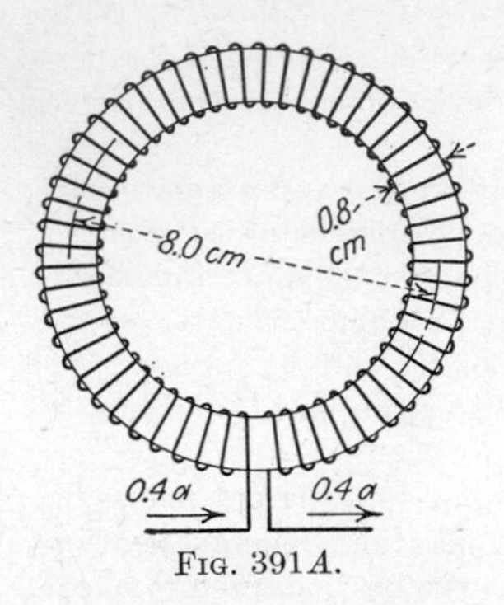

FIG. 391*A*.

392. An air-gap 0.1 cm long is made in the steel ring, Prob. 391(*f*), by transverse saw cut. Determine: (*a*) total mmf in gilberts; (*b*) reluctance of steel ring; (*c*) reluctance of air-gap; (*d*) flux in maxwells; (*e*) flux density in gauss. Neglect fringing and leakage.

393. In Fig. 393*A* is shown an electromagnet on which there are four equal exciting coils *A*, *B*, *C*, *D*, with 6,900 turns each, the resistance of each coil being 33.0 ohms. At first, coils *A* and *B* are connected in series across 120-volt mains, the connection being such that the coils are acting in conjunction on the magnetic circuit. (*a*) Determine total ampere-turns acting on magnetic circuit. (*b*) Coils *C* and *D* are connected in series with *A* and *B* in such a way that their ampere-turns are acting in conjunction with those of *A* and *B*. The four coils in series are then connected across the 120-volt mains. Determine total ampere-turns now acting on magnetic circuit. (*c*) Determine total power lost in exciting coils in (*a*) and (*b*), and find ratio of power loss in (*b*) to that in (*a*). This illustrates the principle that by increasing the amount of copper and likewise the amount of iron the excitation loss may be reduced to almost any desired value without changing the ampere-turns. (*d*) Determine total mmf in gilberts. (*e*) Determine ampere-turns and the excitation loss when coils *AB* in series are connected in parallel with coils *CD* in series, across 120 volts.

FIG. 393*A*.

394. (*a*) In Prob. 393(*b*) determine total ampere-turns when current in both pairs of coils, *AB* and *CD*, in series, is adjusted until heating in each coil is same as in (*a*). (*b*) Determine total ampere-turns when current is adjusted until total heating in Prob. 393(*b*) is same as total heating in Prob. 393(*e*).

395. An exciting coil, with 12,000 turns of No. 30 AWG enamel wire, is designed for a 120-volt circuit, the resistance being 126 ohms. (*a*) Determine number of turns and resistance of another exciting coil of same size and having same winding space factor (ratio of net copper section to total coil section), which is wound with No. 27 wire having twice the cross section of No. 30. (*b*) With same voltage, what is ratio of ampere-turns in two cases? (*c*) Determine heating in two cases. (*d*) What voltage should be impressed across second coil in order that ampere-turns in two cases may be same? (*e*) In order that heating may be same?

396. Two coils *A* and *B* have 8,400 and 5,600 turns and 72 and 48 ohms resistance. Both coils are designed to operate at 240 volts without overheating. Both are placed on the same magnetic circuit. Determine ampere-turns acting on circuit with (*a*) coil *A* alone; (*b*) coil *B* alone; (*c*) coils *A* and *B* in series; (*d*) coils *A* and *B* in parallel. The voltage is 240 volts in each case, and in (*c*) and (*d*) the coils act in conjunction on the magnetic circuit.

397. In Prob. 393 the average length of the steel circuit is 33 in., and the cross section is 7.1 sq in. The permeability of the steel is 950. Each of the two pole faces has an area of 36 sq in., and the air-gap, which is uniform, has a length of 1.0 in. The pole pieces are 1 in. thick, and their reluctance can be neglected. The four coils are connected in series across a 120-volt supply. Determine in centimeters and cgs units (*a*) length and cross section of steel circuit; (*b*) reluctance of steel circuit; (*c*) reluctance of air-gap; (*d*) flux in maxwells; (*e*) field intensity in air-gap in oersteds. Neglect fringing and leakage.

398. In Prob. 393 determine current in four coils in series which will produce a flux of 504,000 maxwells in the air-gap, the permeability of steel now being 700. As in Prob. 397 the four coils *A*, *B*, *C*, *D* are connected in series aiding across a 120-volt supply, the reluctance of the pole pieces, fringing, and leakage being neglected.

399. In Fig. 399*A* is shown a magnetic circuit with a steel core and an air-gap. The numbers give the dimensions in cms, and the thickness of the core into the paper is 7.5 cm. The air-gap may be considered as having the same cross-sectional area as the steel. The permeability of the steel is 1,000. There are 3,000 turns in each of the exciting coils, and the current is 1.0 amp. Determine: (*a*) reluctance of steel core, using average length; (*b*) reluctance of air-gap; (*c*) flux in maxwells; (*d*) flux density in iron and air-gap in gauss.

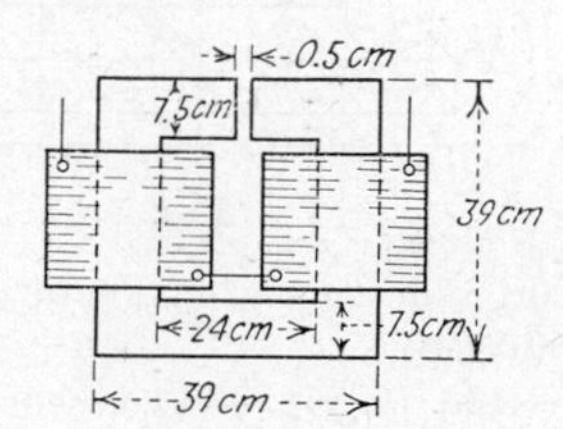

Fig. 399*A*.

400. In Prob. 399 the permeability of the steel is 800 when the flux density is 13,000 gauss. Determine: (*a*) ampere-turns for steel core; (*b*) ampere-turns for air-gap; (*c*) current in exciting coils.

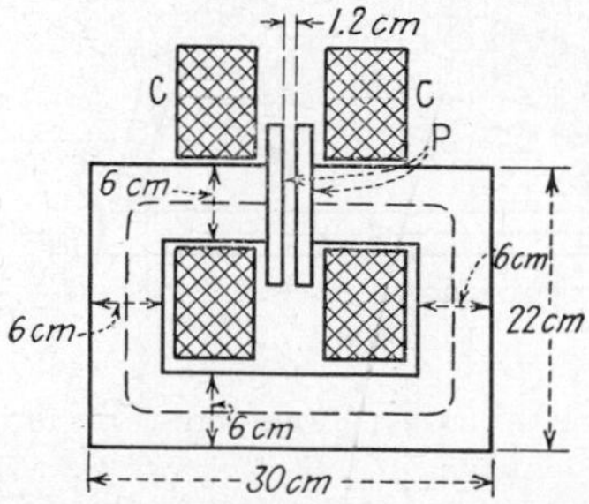

Fig. 401*A*.

401. In Fig. 401*A* is shown a magnet the core of which is soft steel. The core is 6 cm square, the pole pieces *P* are 12 cm square, and the length of the air-gap is 1.2 cm. There are two exciting coils *C*, *C*, each having 2,500 turns. The reluctances of the pole pieces are negligible. The mean path of the flux is shown by the dotted line. The core is operated at a flux density of 14,000 gauss, at which density the permeability is 650. Determine: (*a*) ampere-turns for steel core; (*b*) ampere-turns for air-gap; (*c*) exciting current; (*d*) field intensity in air-gap in gauss. Neglect fringing and leakage.

402. At a flux density of 15,000 gauss (Prob. 401) the permeability of the steel is 450. Repeat (*a*), (*b*), (*c*), (*d*).

403. In the magnetic circuit in Fig. 403*A*, the cross section of the iron core *A*, *B*, *C* is square, 4 cm on a side, and that of the iron armature *D* is 3 by 4 cm. The length of each air-gap is 1.5 mm. The permeability of the parts *A*, *B*, *C* is to be taken as 1,000 and that of the armature *D* as 800. Each of the two exciting coils has 1,500 turns, and the exciting current is 0.9 amp. Determine: (*a*) combined reluctance of the members *A*, *B*, *C*; (*b*) reluctance of armature *D*; (*c*) reluctance of two air-gaps; (*d*) total mmf in gilberts acting on circuit; (*e*) total flux; (*f*) flux density in air-gap in gauss. Neglect fringing and leakage.

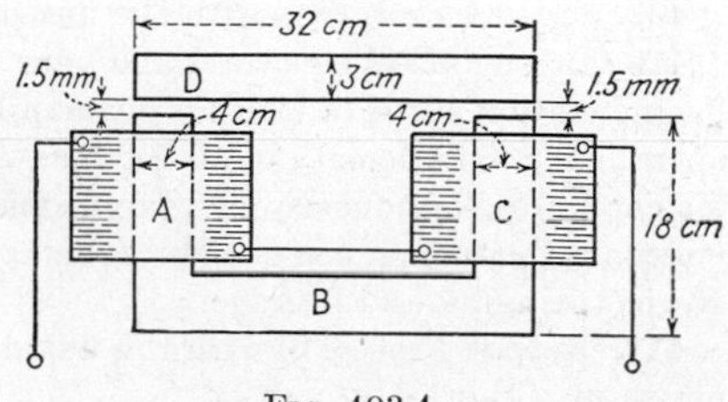

Fig. 403*A*.

404. In Prob. 403 it is desired to obtain a total flux of 150,000 maxwells in each air-gap. The increased flux density reduces the permeability of the core A, B, C to 900 and that of the armature D to 750. Determine: (*a*) flux density in core A, B, C and in air-gaps; (*b*) flux density in armature D; (*c*) mmf in gilberts necessary for core A, B, C; (*d*) mmf in gilberts necessary for two air-gaps; (*e*) mmf in gilberts necessary for armature D; (*f*) total ampere-turns; (*g*) exciting current.

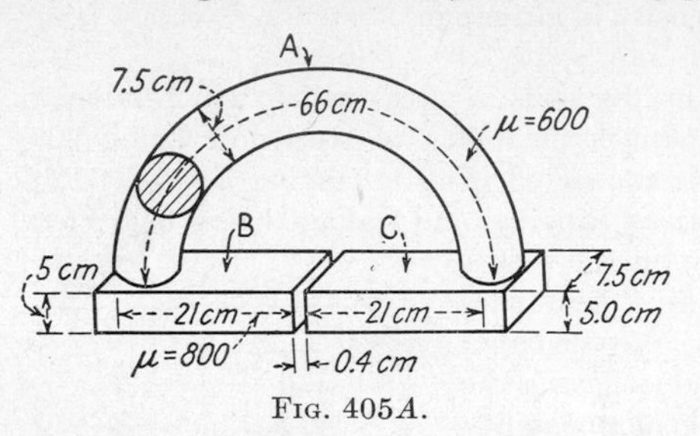

FIG. 405*A*.

405. In Fig. 405*A* is shown the core of an electromagnet composed of a semicircular portion A, and two cores, and pole pieces B and C in the form of rectangular prisms. The dimensions and permeability of each portion are given. An exciting winding of 8,000 turns is wound over the core, and the exciting current is 1.2 amp. Determine: (*a*) reluctance of magnetic circuit; (*b*) flux and flux density in core; (*c*) flux density in air-gap.

406. In Fig. 406*A* is shown an electromagnet composed of a yoke A 56 cm long and having a cross section of 4 by 10 cm and two cores B, each consisting of quarter rings having inner and outer radii of 16.5 and 24 cm. The cross sections of the cores are circular, 7.5 cm diameter. The two pole pieces are 15 cm square, and the air-gap is 3 cm in length. Six exciting coils are shown. The permeability of the yoke is 900, and that of the cores is 800. The reluctance of the pole pieces is negligible. It is desired to produce a flux of 360,000 maxwells in the air-gap. Determine: (*a*) flux density in air-gap; (*b*) flux density in cores; (*c*) flux density in yoke; (*d*) ampere-turns for air-gap; (*e*) ampere-turns for cores; (*f*) ampere-turns for yoke; (*g*) total ampere-turns. Neglect fringing and leakage.

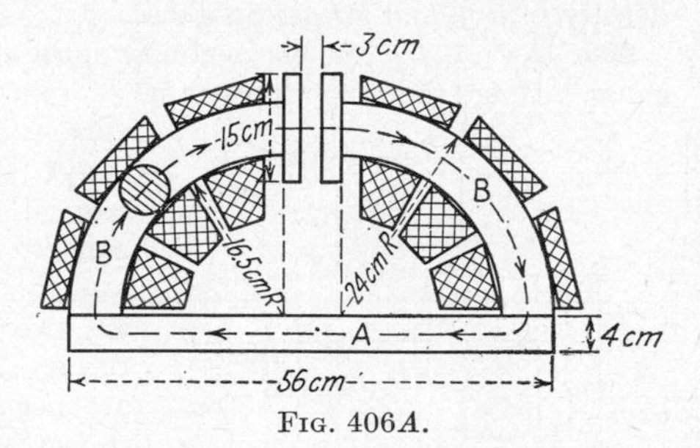

FIG. 406*A*.

407. Repeat Prob. 406 for a flux of 400,000 maxwells in the air-gap. The greater flux density decreases the permeability of the yoke to 800 and of the core to 720.

408. In Fig. 403*A* assume that the core is made of cast steel, the magnetic characteristics of which are given in Fig. 198 (p. 253), and that the core operates at a flux density of 10,000 gauss. Determine: (*a*) ampere-turns for core; (*b*) flux density in armature; (*c*) ampere-turns for armature; (*d*) total ampere-turns. Neglect fringing and leakage.

409. Repeat Prob. 408 with the flux density in the core equal to 12,000 gauss.

410. In Fig. 406*A*, the cores and yoke may be assumed to be made of cast steel, the magnetization curve of which is given in Fig. 202 (p. 258). Assume also that the cores operate at a flux density of 80,000 maxwells per sq in. Determine: (*a*) ampere-turns for cores; (*b*) flux density in yoke in maxwells per square inch; (*c*) ampere-turns for yoke; (*d*) flux density in air-gap; (*e*) ampere-turns for air-gap; (*f*) total ampere-turns. Neglect fringing and leakage.

411. Repeat Prob. 410 with the flux density in the cores raised to 90,000 maxwells per sq in.

412. Figure 412*A* shows a magnetic circuit composed of two branches, which are similar and in parallel. The permeability of the iron is 700 throughout. The mean length of path in the iron core may be taken as the distance l shown on the left-hand branch of the circuit. (*a*) Compute reluctance of each branch and total reluctance of circuit. A coil of 3,600 turns is placed on center core. When the exciting current is 1.6 amp, determine: (*b*) flux in each air-gap; (*c*) flux in center core. Neglect fringing and leakage.

413. In Fig. 412*A*, assume that the core is cast steel, the magnetic characteristics of which are given in Fig. 198 (p. 253). The steel is operated at a flux density of 12,000 gauss. For the left-hand circuit, determine: (*a*) ampere-turns for air-gap; (*b*) ampere-turns for core, using Fig. 198; (*c*) total ampere-turns for left-hand core; (*d*) total ampere-turns of coil wound on adjacent legs of the two magnetic circuits which will produce flux density of 12,000 gauss in both cores.

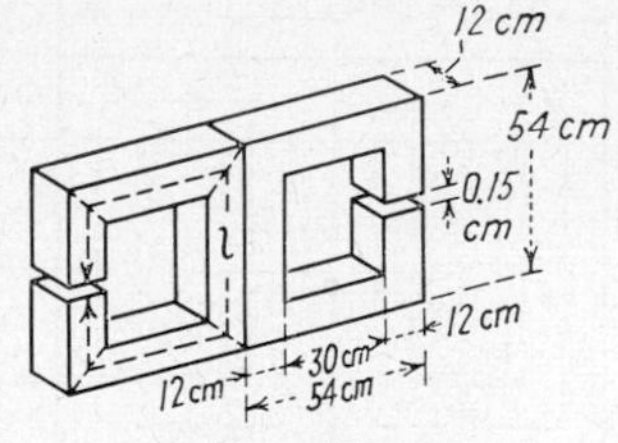

FIG. 412*A*.

414. In an ironclad solenoid, Fig. 414*A*, the reluctance of the yoke is negligible compared with that of the cylindrical cast-steel plunger. The diameter of the plunger is 1.5 cm, and the net length inside the yoke is 20 cm. The magnetic characteristics of the plunger are given in Figs. 198 and 199 (pp. 253 and 254). In the exciting coil are 500 turns, and the exciting current is 0.5 amp. By the method of trial and error (Sec. 188, p. 257), determine flux and flux density in plunger.

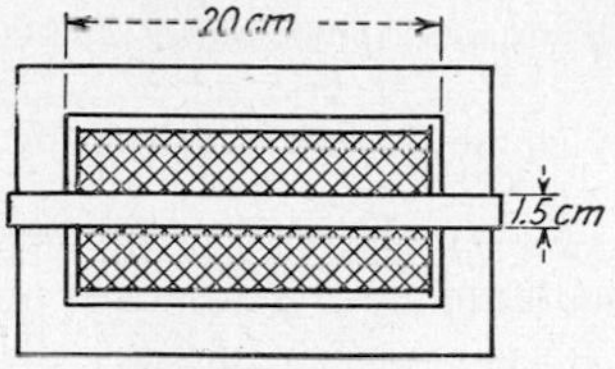

FIG. 414*A*.

415. Repeat Prob. 414 with the exciting current equal to 0.8 amp.

416. It is desired to produce a total flux of 18,500 maxwells in the plunger, Fig. 414*A*. Using the magnetization curve, Fig. 198 (p. 253), determine exciting current.

417. Repeat Prob. 416 for a flux of 23,000 maxwells.

418. In Fig. 418*A* is shown a ring specimen made of dynamo sheet steel, 0.014 in. thick, the characteristics of which are given in Fig. 202 (p. 258). The outside diameter of the ring is 6 in., the inside diameter is 5 in., and the gross cross section is ½ by 1 in. Because of the oxide on the laminations the net area of steel is 0.9 the gross, or measured cross section. There are 1,000 turns in the exciting winding. Using the curve, Fig. 202, determine ampere-turns necessary to produce a flux density (in the net cross section of steel) of (*a*) 80 kilomaxwells per sq in.; (*b*) 90 kilomaxwells per sq in.; (*c*) 100 kilomaxwells per sq in.; (*d*) exciting current in (*c*).

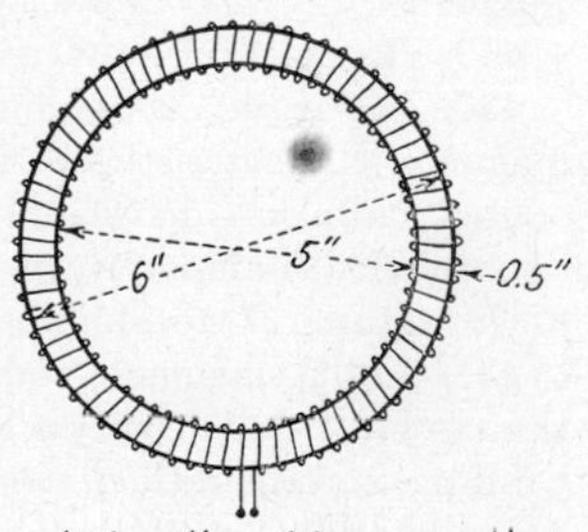

FIG. 418*A*.

419. When the current in the winding, Prob. 418, is 1.9 amp, determine: (*a*) flux in maxwells; (*b*) flux density in gauss. (Use curve, Fig. 202, and method of trial and error, p. 258.)

420. If, in Fig. 418*A*, a transverse saw cut 0.06 in. long is made in the iron core and the flux density is 92 kilomaxwells per sq in. in air-gap, determine: (*a*) ampere-turns for air-gap; (*b*) ampere-turns for steel core; (*c*) exciting current. Use Fig. 202 (p. 258). Neglect fringing and leakage.

421. If, in Fig. 418*A*, with air-gap of Prob. 420 the exciting current is 2.7 amp, determine: (*a*) flux in maxwells; (*b*) flux density in gauss. (Use curve, Fig. 202, p. 258, and method of trial and error, p. 257.)

422. Figure 422*A* shows an electromagnet consisting of the two similar cast-steel cores *A* and *B* forming a single air-gap. The different dimensions are given. The cores are 4 in. square, and the pole faces are 10 by 6 in. The air-gap is 1 in. long. The mmf for the pole pieces can be neglected. Determine ampere-turns necessary to produce a flux density of 50,000 maxwells per sq in. in air-gap. Use magnetization curve, Fig. 202 (p. 258). Neglect fringing and leakage.

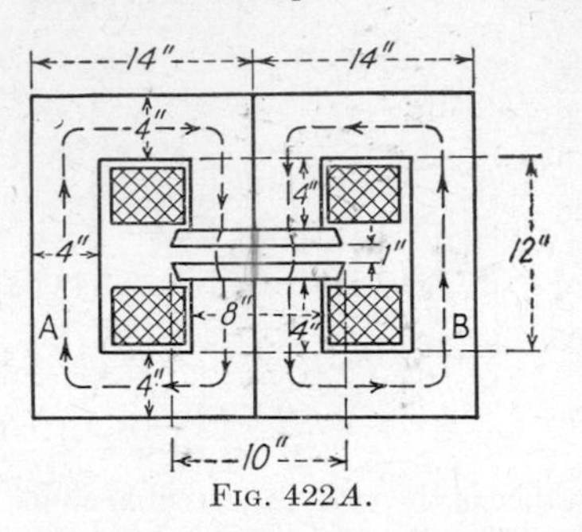

FIG. 422*A*.

423. Assume in Prob. 422 that the half *A* is isolated and that the air-gap dimensions are 6 by 6 in. The exciting coils are located in the same position as shown in Fig. 422*A*. The coils will of course be smaller in size since they must be wound about a core only 4 in. square. Using the magnetization curve for cast steel, Fig. 202 (p. 258), determine ampere-turns necessary to produce a flux density of 33,500 maxwells per sq in. in air-gap. Neglect fringing and leakage.

424. Repeat Prob. 422 with the flux density in the gap equal to 45,000 maxwells per sq in.

425. Repeat Prob. 422 with the flux density in the gap equal to 45,000 maxwells per sq in. and the air-gap 1.2 in. long.

426. In Fig. 391*A*, with nonmagnetic material, there are 1,170 turns, and the current is 0.4 amp. Determine in unrationalized mks units (*a*) mmf; (*b*) reluctance; (*c*) flux in webers; (*d*) mmf per meter; (*e*) flux density in webers per square meter.

427. Repeat Prob. 426 using rationalized mks units.

428. In Fig. 391*A* the non-magnetic material is replaced by steel having a relative permeability of 1,080. There are 1,170 turns and the current is 0.4 amp. Determine in unrationalized mks units (*a*) mmf; (*b*) reluctance of steel; (*c*) flux in webers; (*d*) flux density in webers per sq m.

429. Repeat Prob. 428, using rationalized mks units.

430. In Fig. 403*A*, assume that the core and armature are made of cast steel, the magnetic characteristics of which are given in Fig. 198 (p. 253), and that this core operates at a flux density of 1 weber per sq m. Using the rationalized mks system, determine: (*a*) ampere-turns for core; (*b*) flux density in armature; (*c*) ampere-turns for armature; (*d*) total ampere-turns. Neglect fringing and leakage.

431. In the ring made of dynamo sheet steel, Fig. 418*A*, the relative permeability of the steel at a flux density of 1.4 webers per sq m is 800. There are 1,000 turns in the winding, and the ratio of net steel to gross cross section is 0.9. In unrationalized mks units determine exciting current at flux density of 1.4 webers per sq m.

432. If in Fig. 418*A* a transverse saw cut 0.15 cm long is made at the flux density of 1.4 webers per meter, determine in unrationalized mks units (*a*) amp turns for core; (*b*) amp turns for gap; (*c*) total amp turns.

433. Repeat Prob. 431, using mks rationalized units.

434. Repeat Prob. 432, using mks rationalized units.

435. In Fig. 435*A* is shown the magnetic circuit of a 2-pole dynamo. The field cores are of cast steel and are 5.0 by 5.0 in. The armature is of dynamo sheet steel and has a net axial length of 5.2 in. over the iron; the yoke is of cast steel, the cross section being 1.75 by 6 in. The other necessary dimensions are given on the figure. Using the magnetization curves of Fig. 202 (p. 258), determine field ampere-turns per pole necessary to produce an average flux density of 40,000 maxwells per sq in. in air-gap. The coefficient of leakage is 1.2, that is, the flux in the pole cores and yoke is 1.2 that in the gap. The ampere-turns for the pole pieces may be neglected.

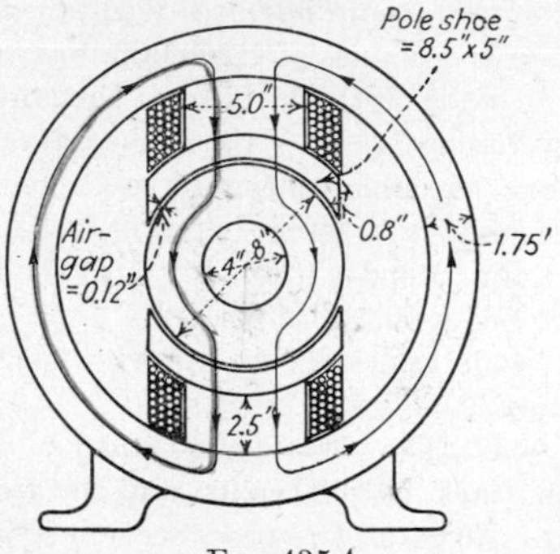

FIG. 435A.

436. Repeat Prob. 435 with an average air-gap density of 45,000 maxwells per sq in.

437. Repeat Prob. 435 with an air-gap length of 0.1 in.

438. Repeat Prob. 436 with an air-gap length of 0.1 in.

439. In Fig. 439A is shown a portion of a 6-pole 500-kw 250-volt d-c generator. Two complete magnetic circuits are shown, as well as portions of two others. The outside diameter of the armature is 30 in., the radial thickness of the armature iron including the teeth is 4.5 in., and the gross axial length of the armature is 14 in. The slots are 1.5 in. deep. The pole cores are 7 by 13.5 in., and the pole faces are 10 by 13.5 in. The radial thickness of the yoke is 3 in., and the axial length is 16 in. The pole cores and the armature are made of dynamo sheet-steel laminations, the magnetization curve for which is given in Fig. 202 (p. 258). The ratio of net to gross iron in the armature and the field cores is 0.92. The yoke is of rolled steel, the magnetization curve of which is essentially that for cast steel in Fig. 202.

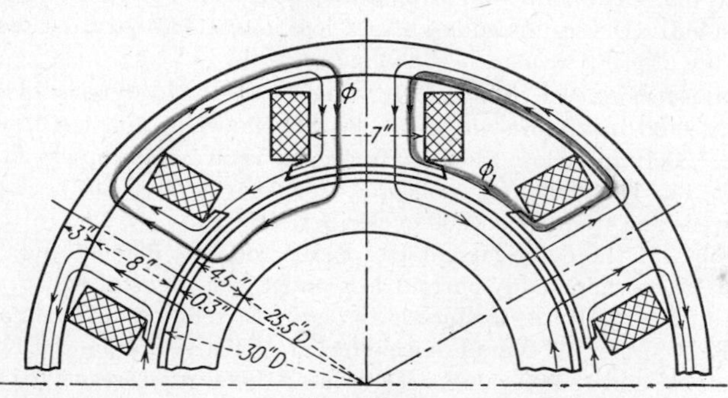

FIG. 439A.

The general path of the useful flux ϕ and the leakage flux ϕ_1 is indicated. The leakage factor, the ratio $(\phi + \phi_1)/\phi$, is 1.20. In computing the ampere-turns for the pole cores, the ampere-turns for the pole pieces may be neglected, a length of 7 in. being used. The air-gap has an equivalent length of 0.3 in. When the air-gap flux is $5.6 \cdot 10^6$ maxwells, determine: (*a*) average flux density in air-gap; (*b*) flux density in armature laminations; (*c*) pole cores; (*d*) yoke; (*e*) ampere-turns for air-gap. Using the magnetization curves, Fig. 202, determine: (*f*) ampere-turns for each pole core; (*g*) ampere-turns for yoke; (*h*) total ampere-turns per pole.

440. Repeat Prob. 439 with an air-gap flux of $6.0 \cdot 10^6$ maxwells.

441. Repeat Prob. 439 with an air-gap flux of $6.8 \cdot 10^6$ maxwells.

442. Repeat Prob. 440 with an effective length of air-gap of 0.26 in.

443. Repeat Prob. 441 with an effective length of air-gap of 0.26 in.

444. A transformer core built up of silicon-steel laminations 0.0356 cm (0.014 in.) thick and 12 cm wide has a cross-sectional area of 144 sq cm and a volume of 12,000 cu cm. The core operates with an alternating flux which varies between positive and negative values of 1,293,000 maxwells at a frequency of 60 cycles per sec. Owing to the oxide on the surfaces of the laminations, the ratio of the net steel to the gross cross section is 9 to 10. Using the data of Sec. 194 (p. 267) ($\eta = 0.001$), determine: (*a*) ergs loss per cubic centimeter per cycle; (*b*) total loss in ergs per cycle; (*c*) ergs loss per second; (*d*) hysteresis power loss in watts (1 watt = 10^7 ergs per sec).

445. Repeat Prob. 444 with the flux equal to 1,350,000 maxwells and the frequency equal to 50 cycles per sec.

446. Repeat Prob. 444 with the flux equal to 1,400,000 maxwells and the frequency equal to 25 cycles per sec.

447. The volume of a transformer core, made of silicon-sheet-steel laminations 0.014 in. thick, is 1,000 cu in., and the gross cross-sectional area is 16 sq in. The ratio of net iron to total core cross section is 9 to 10. Determine: (*a*) hysteresis loss in ergs per cubic inch per cycle if maximum flux density is 70,000 maxwells per sq in.; (*b*) hysteresis loss in watts at a frequency of 60 cycles per sec.

448. In Prob. 444 determine eddy-current loss in watts. The resistivity of the laminations is 60 microhm-cm.

449. In Probs. 447 and 448 determine eddy-current loss in watts when frequency is 25 cycles per sec.

450. A transformer core consists of transformer-steel laminations 0.014 in. thick, 4 in. wide, and stacked to make a gross cross section of steel of 16 sq in. The ratio of net to gross steel is 0.9. The total volume of steel is 960 cu in. The resistivity of the steel is 60 microhm-cm. Determine eddy-current loss in watts at frequencies of 60 and of 50 cycles per sec at a flux density of 9,000 gauss.

451. In a transformer core of laminated silicon steel the hysteresis loss is 240 watts when the total flux (maximum value) is 320,000 maxwells, and the frequency is 50 cycles per sec. Determine loss when (*a*) frequency is 60 cycles per sec, flux remaining unchanged; (*b*) flux is 300,000 maxwells and frequency is 50 cycles per sec; (*c*) flux is 280,000 maxwells and frequency is 60 cycles per sec.

452. In Prob. 451 the eddy-current loss is 104 watts at 320,000 maxwells and 50 cycles per sec. Determine eddy-current loss under conditions of (*a*), (*b*), (*c*).

453. In Table I (p. 269), the hysteresis and eddy-current loss in watts per pound for Allegheny "Transformer 'C'"-grade sheet steel are given as 0.658 and 0.114 watt per lb at 60 cycles per sec and 10,000 gauss. Determine these two losses at (*a*) 60 cycles per sec, 9,000 gauss; (*b*) 50 cycles per sec, 12,000 gauss; (*c*) 25 cycles per sec, 13,000 gauss.

454. Repeat Prob. 453 for Allegheny "Dynamo-Special"-grade sheet steel, in which the hysteresis and eddy-current losses are 0.733 and 0.128 watt per lb.

455. In a transformer core the core losses are measured at frequencies of 60 and 25 cycles per sec and at a flux density of 10,000 gauss and are found to be 67.5 watts and 23.2 watts. Separate the losses, and determine at foregoing flux density: (*a*) hysteresis and eddy-current loss at 60 cycles; (*b*) at 25 cycles.

456. In a transformer core the core losses at a constant flux density of 10,000 gauss are measured at frequencies of 60 and 25 cycles per sec and are found to be 309.5 and 105.5 watts. Determine: (*a*) hysteresis loss and eddy-current loss at 60 cycles per sec; (*b*) hysteresis loss and eddy-current loss at 25 cycles per sec.

457. A straight air-core solenoid, 150 cm long, consists of a single-layer primary winding of magnet wire, with 12 turns to the centimeter, and a secondary of 1,200 turns is wound over the primary winding near the center. The inside diameter of the solenoid is 5.0 cm. When the primary current is 0.60 amp, determine: (*a*) flux density in gauss at center of solenoid; (*b*) total flux in maxwells; (*c*) cgs flux linkages with secondary.

458. In Prob. 457, using unrationalized mks units, determine: (*a*) flux density in webers per square meter at center of solenoid; (*b*) total flux in webers; (*c*) mks flux linkages with secondary.

459. Repeat Prob. 458, using rationalized mks units.

460. A secondary coil having 24 turns, and used with the yoke method and a ballistic galvanometer, is connected in series with the secondary of the solenoid of Prob. 457. When the current of 0.60 amp in the primary of the standard solenoid is suddenly reduced to zero by opening the switch, the ballistic deflection of the galvanometer is 8.5 cm. (*a*) Determine galvanometer constant [see Eq. (206), p. 289]. (*b*) The current in the primary of the yoke specimen is increased from zero to 0.4 amp, and one section of the test specimen is withdrawn, thus reducing the flux suddenly to zero, practically. The corresponding galvanometer deflection is 8.8 cm. Determine value of flux in specimen. (*c*) If the diameter of the yoke specimen is 1 cm, determine flux density.

461. In Prob. 460, the current in the yoke specimen is increased to 1.5 amp, decreased to zero, and then increased to 0.9 amp in the reverse direction. At this point, half of the specimen is again withdrawn, and the corresponding galvanometer deflection is 12.3 cm (reversed). Determine flux density corresponding to this value of current. Make a sketch of hysteresis loop indicating this point and similar one given in Prob. 460.

462. The normal saturation curve of a ring specimen is being determined by the ring method. The cross section of the ring is 1 cm square, and the average diameter of the ring is 10 cm. The galvanometer of Prob. 460 is used in the measurement, the calibration remaining unchanged. There are 20 turns on the secondary of the ring. With a complete *reversal* of the current in the primary of the ring, the deflection of the galvanometer is 14 cm. Determine flux in ring for this value of current.

QUESTIONS ON CHAPTER IX

Self- and Mutual Inductance

1. Describe the method of inducing an emf in a coil by thrusting a bar magnet into its center. Analyze the reaction which develops between the induced current and the inducing agent.

2. Describe the reactions which develop when the bar magnet is withdrawn from the coil. Compare the direction of the induced emf with that in Question 1. Show that the reaction on the bar magnet is the same, whether the bar magnet is thrust into the coil or is withdrawn.

3. Give the equation for induced emf when the flux is changed by $\Delta\phi$ maxwells in Δt sec. Repeat for instantaneous rate of change of flux with time.

4. How is the geometrical position of the lines of induction related to the current in a circuit? Compare this relation with the term *linkages*. How may these linkages be calculated? With constant permeability, what is the relation of inductance to the flux linkages? Define inductance under these conditions, stating the unit.

5. How does inductance vary with the turns, the permeability remaining constant?

6. If the flux linking a coil be made to change by altering the value of the current in the coil itself, show that an emf must be induced. What is the relation between the direction of this emf and the direction of the current in the coil? How does the induced emf affect the rapidity with which the current builds up to its Ohm's law value?

7. Give the equation for induced emf when the current changes Δi amp in Δt sec. Repeat for instantaneous rate of change of current with time.

8. In Questions 3 and 7 why are the equations for induced emf preceded by a minus sign? State Lenz's law, showing that it is in accordance with the law of the conservation of energy.

9. Define inductance under the conditions of variable permeability. Describe a method for obtaining the value of the inductance under these conditions.

10. Derive the equation which gives the rise of current as a function of time, in a circuit having both resistance and inductance in series. Sketch the graph which shows this relation.

11. What is meant by the *time constant* of a circuit, and by what two quantities is it expressed? In a general way, what does it indicate as regards the circuit? What is the practical importance of the time lag of current due to self-inductance?

12. Explain why current continues in an inductive circuit after this latter is short-circuited. Derive the equation which gives the relation of current to time. Indicate the value of current at the value of time given by the time constant of the circuit.

13. Comment on the following two statements: It requires power over an interval of time to store energy in a magnetic field. It requires no power to maintain a steady magnetic field.

14. Compare the energy stored in the magnetic field with a mechanical analogue. Discuss the relation of the energy stored in the magnetic field with any expenditure of energy that may be necessary to maintain it. Account for the energy supplied to the exciting coils of electromagnets after the current reaches a steady value. How does stored magnetic energy vary with the current? Give the equation for stored energy in terms of inductance and current.

15. In what way does the energy of the magnetic field manifest itself when the current maintaining the field is interrupted? How can it be shown that this condition is not produced by the mere interruption of the current itself? Analyze the arcing at switch contacts which occurs when an inductive circuit is opened. Under what conditions in practice may such arcing become a menace? How may this menace be partially or wholly eliminated?

16. Describe, and draw the connections of, a field-discharge switch. Derive the equation by means of which the emf across the field circuit can be computed in terms of the exciter-bus voltage and the shunting resistance.

What personal dangers may result from opening inductive circuits? Make a wiring diagram showing the correct position of the voltmeter connected across an inductive circuit.

17. Show, with a wiring diagram, the method of utilizing stored magnetic energy for ignition in automobile engines.

18. Show that it is possible for a change of current in one coil to induce an emf in a second coil which is completely insulated from the first coil. Show that this is analogous to the production of emf by the insertion of a bar magnet into the second coil. What is the relation between the direction of the induced emf in the secondary when the primary circuit is closed and its direction when the primary circuit is opened? Compare the direction of the induced current to that of the inducing current. Upon what fundamental law is this relation based?

19. State the equation which gives the emf induced in one coil by a change of current Δi in the other coil. Repeat for an instantaneous rate of change of current with respect to time.

20. Discuss the possibility of all the flux produced by one coil, linking all the turns of a second coil. Define *coefficient of coupling*.

21. With unit current in one coil, to what factors is mutual inductance proportional? Define mutual inductance in terms of rate of change of current in one of the circuits.

22. Discuss methods of increasing mutual inductance between circuits. Show that if two electric circuits are linked with the same magnetic circuit, the mutual inductance $L_m = k\sqrt{L_1L_2}$, where k is the coefficient of coupling and L_1 and L_2 are the self-inductances of the two circuits.

23. If the two coils in Question 22 are connected in series, show that the total inductance $L = L_1 + L_2 \pm 2L_m$.

24. Write the equation which gives the total energy stored in a magnetically coupled circuit.

25. Describe methods of measuring mutual inductance by means of an a-c bridge.

26. State the general effect of self-inductance on changes in the current. To what mechanical property is it analogous? Give mechanical analogues of inductance.

27. Describe the operation of the induction coil showing that it depends on mutual inductance. By what method is the primary current interrupted, and why is it necessary that this current be interrupted? What is the character of the emf induced in the secondary?

PROBLEMS ON CHAPTER IX

Self- and Mutual Inductance

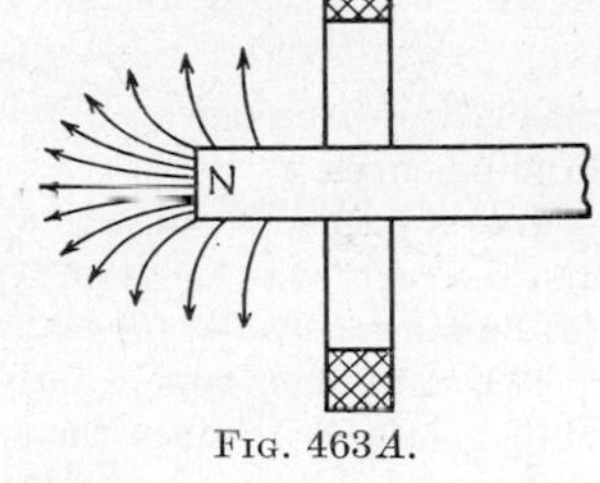

FIG. 463A.

463. In Fig. 463A an N pole of a bar magnet, having a pole strength of 120 cgs unit poles, is suddenly thrust through the center of a coil having 400 turns. The total time required for the pole to pass through the coil is 0.1 sec. Determine: (a) direction of induced emf (in or out top section of coil); (b) average induced emf. The pole is withdrawn in 0.08 sec. Determine: (c) direction of induced emf [see (a)]; (d) average induced emf.

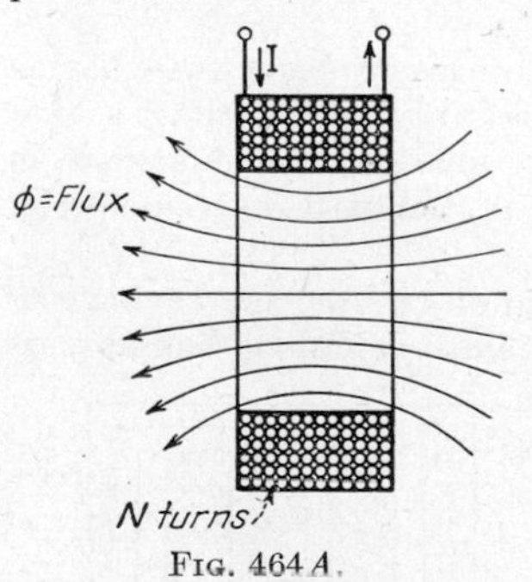

FIG. 464A.

464. A coil, Fig. 464A, is wound with 600 turns, and when the current to the coil is 4 amp, a flux ϕ = 8,000 maxwells links the turns. Determine: (a) flux linkages in maxwell-turns; (b) maxwell-turn flux linkages per ampere divided by 10^8; (c) self-inductance of coil in henrys.

465. A coil of the same dimensions as that in Fig. 464A is wound with twice the number of turns, but the wire is one-half the cross section so that the geometry of the coil remains unchanged. The current is still 4 amp. Determine (a), (b), (c) of Prob. 464. (d) Compare these results with those of Prob. 464, and state the relation of inductance to turns if the magnetic reluctance is constant.

466. In Fig. 466A is shown a small relay magnet energized by two coils in series aiding, each with 400 turns. The cross section of the iron is 1.8 sq cm, and there is an air-gap 1.5 mm long. The reluctance of the iron is negligible compared with that of the air gap. Neglect any fringing. When the current to the coils is 2.0 amp, determine: (a) reluctance of air-gap; (b) flux in maxwells; (c) maxwell-turn linkages; (d) inductance in henrys.

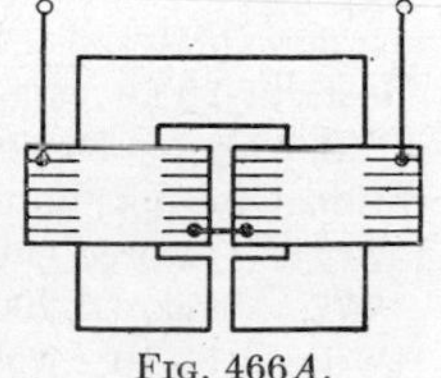
FIG. 466A.

467. In Prob. 466 the coils are connected in parallel aiding, and the total current to the two coils is 5.0 amp, which divides equally between them. Determine: (a) flux in maxwells; (b) maxwell-turn linkages of each coil; (c) inductance in henrys of *circuit*.

468. In Prob. 466 it is desired that the inductance be 0.16 henry. Determine number of turns for which each coil should now be wound.

469. In a ring solenoid, Fig. 469*A*, the equivalent length of the nonmagnetic core is 21 cm, and the cross section is 1.8 sq cm. The ring is wound with 600 turns. When the current is 0.8 amp, determine: (*a*) flux in maxwells; (*b*) maxwell-turn linkages; (*c*) the maxwell-turn linkages per ampere; (*d*) inductance of ring in henrys and millihenrys (1 mh = 0.001 henry).

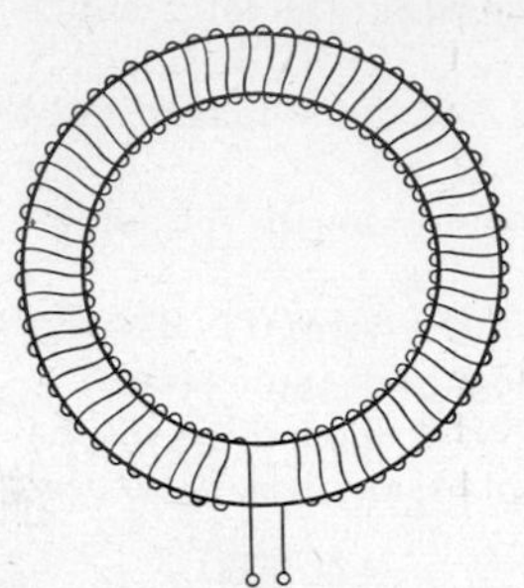

Fig. 469*A*.

470. Repeat Prob. 469 with the ring wound with 800 turns, other quantities remaining unchanged.

471. A ring solenoid of the same dimensions as that of Fig. 469*A* has a steel core whose permeability can be assumed constant at 800, and the winding has 600 turns. There is a transverse saw cut 0.04 cm long. The current is 0.05 amp. Determine: (*a*) flux in maxwells; (*b*) maxwell-turn linkages; (*c*) reluctance of iron; (*d*) reluctance of air-gap; (*e*) inductance in millihenrys.

472. A ring solenoid with a core similar to that of Prob. 471 is wound with 400 turns and the current is 1.5 amp. The permeability remains constant at 800. Determine: (*a*) flux in maxwells; (*b*) maxwell-turn linkages; (*c*) inductance in millihenrys.

473. A plunger-type tractive solenoid, Fig. 186 (p. 240), is wound with 2,500 turns of magnet wire. When the current is 4.0 amp, the net flux linking the turns is 60,000 maxwells. Assuming constant permeability, determine: (*a*) maxwell-turn linkages; (*b*) cgs linkages per ampere divided by 10^8; (*c*) inductance of solenoid in henrys. (*d*) Would inductance of such a solenoid, when in operation, be constant even if permeability of iron remained constant? Explain.

474. The solenoid of Prob. 473 is rewound with 5,000 turns of magnet wire having half the cross section of that of Prob. 473. It now operates at twice the voltage so that the current is 2.0 amp. Determine: (*a*) maxwell-turn linkages; (*b*) inductance in henrys; (*c*) relation of inductance to that of Prob. 473. (Compare with number of turns.)

475. The inductance of a coil having 800 turns wound on an iron core having constant permeability is 0.24 henry. When current is 10 amp, determine flux in maxwells, assuming that all the flux links all the turns.

476. In Fig. 476*A* is shown a magnetic circuit with two similar branches with an exciting coil having 1,600 turns on the center leg. The dimension into the paper is 2 cm. There is a transverse air-gap in each branch. The relative permeability of the magnetic material is 800 and may be assumed constant. The current to the exciting coil is 1.25 amp. Determine: (*a*) reluctance of each branch of magnetic circuit in rationalized mks units; (*b*) total reluctance; (*c*) webers linking coil; (*d*) inductance in henrys; (*e*) stored energy in joules.

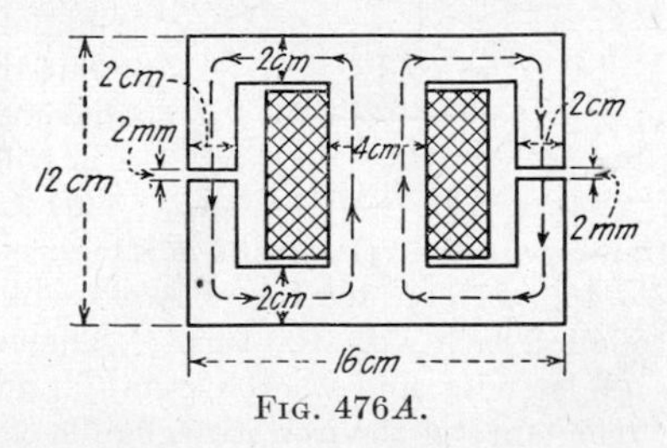

Fig. 476*A*.

477. A coil of 1,200 turns links a magnetic circuit, and when the current is 4.0 amp the flux is $5 \cdot 10^{-3}$ weber. Determine: (*a*) inductance; (*b*) number of turns which it is necessary to add to make inductance 2.0 henrys.

478. The two exciting coils of a bipolar dynamo are wound with 2,000 turns each. When the exciting current is 0.75 amp, the flux crossing each air-gap is 0.03 weber.

The coefficient of leakage is 1.25 (see p. 262). Assuming constant permeability for the iron, determine: (*a*) inductance of field circuit; (*b*) energy in joules stored in field; (*c*) average emf induced by change in flux linkages when circuit is opened in 0.08 sec.

479. In a 4-pole generator there are 3,600 turns per pole, and when the exciting current is 0.5 amp, the air-gap flux is 0.0135 weber. The coefficient of leakage is 1.25 (p. 262). Determine: (*a*) webers linking each field coil; (*b*) weber-turn linkages per pole; (*c*) total weber-turn linkages; (*d*) self-inductance of field circuit, neglecting any change in reluctance; (*e*) stored energy in joules; (*f*) average emf induced in field circuit by change of flux linkages if field is opened in 0.1 sec.

480. A solenoid is wound with 500 turns. The relation of the flux linking these turns to the current is given by Fig. 229(*b*) (p. 305). Determine self-inductance of solenoid when exciting current is (*a*) 1.5 amp.; (*b*) 2.5 amp (see Sec. 218, p. 304). (*c*) Determine induced emf in (*a*), if current is increasing at rate of 120 amp per sec; (*d*) in (*b*) if current is increasing at rate of 30 amp per sec. (The value of $d\phi/di$ at 1.5 amp is $0.86 \cdot 10^5$ and at 2.5 amp is $4.8 \cdot 10^4$ maxwells per amp.)

481. The accompanying data give the relation of flux to exciting current in a solenoid circuit in which there are 1,000 turns in the exciting winding. Determine inductance when current (*a*) varies from 0 to 0.5 amp (straight part of curve); (*b*) equals 1.0 amp; (*c*) equals 1.6 amp; (*d*) equals 2.2 amp. When current is increasing at rate of 120 amp per sec, determine induced emf (*e*) in (*a*); (*f*) in (*b*); (*g*) in (*c*). (*h*) Determine induced emf in (*d*) when current is increasing at rate of 150 amp per sec. (*i*) In (*a*) and (*b*) determine rate at which flux is changing with respect to current.

Amp.	0	0.4	0.6	0.8	1.1	1.4	1.7	2.0	2.2	2.4	2.6
Kilomaxwells	0	23.0	33.2	42.5	54.0	64.0	71.0	76.8	79.8	82.0	83.5

482. A circuit consisting of a resistor of 15 ohms in series with 0.60-henry inductance is connected suddenly across a constant 120-volt source. Determine: (*a*) equation giving current as a function of time, and plot: (*b*) time constant of circuit; (*c*) current at time (*b*); (*d*) current when time is 0.08 sec; (*e*) rate at which current is increasing at time (*b*); (*f*) rate at which current is increasing at time (*d*).

483. In Prob. 482, determine energy stored in magnetic field when current is (*a*) 3 amp; (*b*) 6 amp; (*c*) when current reaches its steady-state value. (*d*) Determine rate of increase of current at instant of closing circuit.

484. The resistance of a telephone relay, which operates at 24 volts, is 750 ohms, and its inductance is 8.6 henrys. Determine: (*a*) equation giving current (in milliamperes) as a function of time, and plot; (*b*) time constant of circuit; (*c*) rate at which current increases at instant of closing circuit; (*d*) rate of increase of current at 0.04 sec. (*f*) If it requires 28 ma to start moving the relay armature, determine time delay after circuit is closed.

485. The armature of a relay in a 240-volt circuit is not actuated until the current reaches 0.360 amp. It is desired that the relay close 0.005 sec after the relay circuit is closed. The resistance of the relay is 400 ohms, and its inductance is 2.0 henrys. Determine resistance of resistor which must be inserted in series with relay.

486. The inductance of the field of a synchronous generator is 6 henrys, and the total field resistance is 30 ohms. When field is connected across a constant 240-volt source, determine: (*a*) equation of current, and plot; (*b*) energy stored in magnetic field at value of time corresponding to time constant of circuit; (*c*) power loss in resistance in (*b*); (*d*) rate of increase of current at instant of closing circuit; (*e*) rate of increase of current when time is equal to time constant.

487. The circuit of Prob. 482 is suddenly short-circuited after the current has attained its steady-state value. Determine: (*a*) equation of current as a function of time; (*b*) rate at which the current begins to decrease; (*c*) current at instant corresponding to time constant of circuit; (*d*) energy stored in magnetic field in (*c*); (*e*) current when time $t = 0.06$ sec; (*f*) power lost in resistance and supplied by magnetic field in (*e*).

488. With the field current equal to the steady-state value, the field of the synchronous generator, Prob. 486, is disconnected from the power source and is simultaneously connected in series with a field-discharge resistor of 30 ohms (see Fig. 233, p. 312). Determine: (*a*) initial value of field and resistor current; (*b*) initial value of voltage across field winding, and resistor; (*c*) equation of current; (*d*) rate at which current is diminishing at 0.06 sec; (*e*) energy in magnetic field at time in (*d*).

489. In Prob. 486, it is desired that the emf across the field shall not exceed 600 volts. Determine: (*a*) resistance of field-discharge resistor; (*b*) initial field current at instant of opening field switch; (*c*) magnetic energy in field in (*b*); (*d*) equation of field current as function of time; (*e*) magnetic energy stored in field when time equals time constant; (*f*) power lost in field circuit at time in (*e*).

490. A series circuit, in which the resistance is 25 ohms and the inductance is 1 henry, is connected momentarily across a 120-volt supply. At the end of 0.05 sec, the circuit becomes short-circuited. Determine: (*a*) value of current at instant of short circuit; (*b*) energy stored in magnetic field at this instant; (*c*) equation of current as function of time. (*d*) From (*c*), plot current as a function of time until current has nearly reached its zero value. At instant of short circuit determine rate in amperes per second at which current (*e*) is increasing; (*f*) begins to decrease.

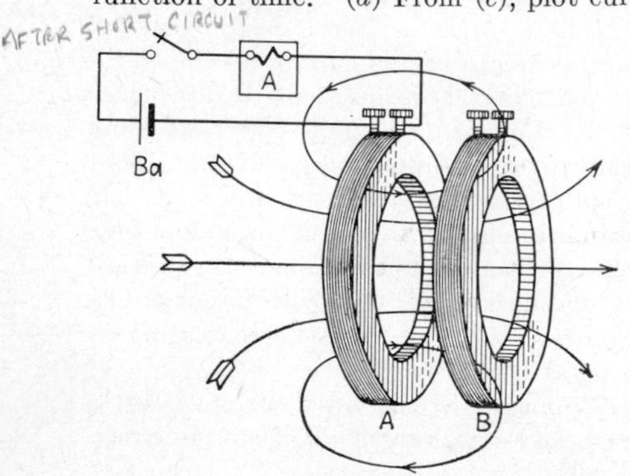

Fig. 491*A*.

491. Two coils *A* and *B*, in air, Fig. 491*A*, are insulated electrically but are so placed that 70 per cent of the flux produced by one of the coils links the other. In coil *A* there are 300 turns, and in coil *B* there are 250 turns. When the current in coil *A* is 1.5 amp, 100,000 maxwells link the coil. Determine: (*a*) coefficient of coupling of two circuits; (*b*) maxwells which link coil *B*. When circuit to coil *A* is opened in 0.05 sec, determine: (*c*) emf induced in coil *A*; (*d*) emf induced in coil *B*.

492. In Prob. 491, when the current in coil *B* is 1.8 amp, the same flux which was caused to link coil *A* by 1.5 amp now links coil *B*. When the circuit to *B* is opened in 0.08 sec, determine emf induced in (*a*) coil *B*; (*b*) coil *A*.

493. In Probs. 491, 492, determine self-inductance in henrys of (*a*) coil *A*; (*b*) coil *B*. (*c*) Determine mutual inductance in henrys of coils *A* and *B*, based on the definition *emf induced in one circuit per unit rate of variation of the current in the other* (see p. 316). (*d*) Verify (*c*) by Eq. 238 (p. 316).

494. Repeat Prob. 493 with coils *A* and *B* moved farther apart, so that the coefficient of coupling is now 0.60.

495. In Prob. 491 with 1.5 amp in coil *A* and 1.8 amp in coil *B* and the coils connected so that they produce flux in the same direction, determine magnetic energy (*a*) in coil *A* alone; (*b*) in coil *B* alone; (*c*) due to coupling; (*d*) of total coupled system.

496. Repeat Prob. 495 for the conditions of Prob. 494.

497. Coils *A* and *B* of Prob. 491 are now linked magnetically by an iron core, Fig.

497*A*, so that practically all the flux of one links with the other. One-tenth ampere in *A* now produces 100,000 maxwells in the joint magnetic circuit. Determine: (*a*) amperes in coil *B* which will produce this same flux; (*b*) self-inductance of coil *A*; (*c*) self-inductance of coil *B*; (*d*) mutual inductance; (*e*) total magnetic energy of coupled system with coils aiding when current is 1.0 amp in coil *A* and 2.0 amp in coil *B*; (*f*) (*e*) with coils opposing. Assume that permeability of magnetic core is constant.

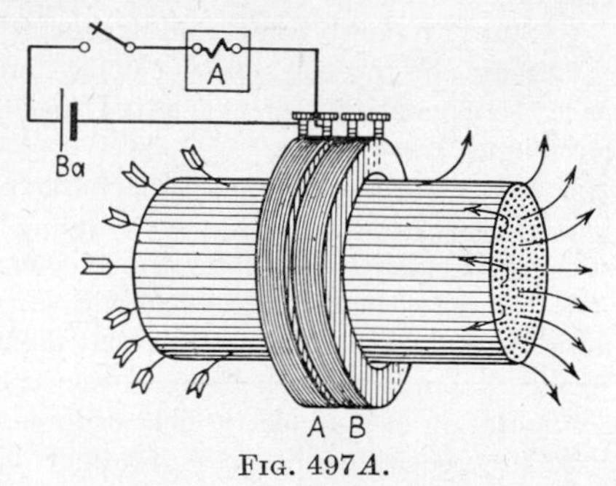

Fig. 497*A*.

498. In Prob. 497, if current of 0.1 amp in coil *A* is interrupted in 0.04 sec, determine (*a*) average emf induced in coil *B*. If a current of 0.2 amp in coil *B* is interrupted in 0.02 sec, determine (*b*) emf induced in coil *A*. Determine total stored energy of coupled system with the foregoing values of current with coils (*c*) aiding; (*d*) opposing.

499. In Prob. 498 determine: (*a*) time in which current in coil *A* must be interrupted in order to induce 10 volts in coil *B*; (*b*) time in which current of 0.2 amp in coil *B* must be interrupted in order to induce 15 volts in coil *A*.

500. In Fig. 497*A* the coils *A* and *B* are connected in series aiding. Determine: (*a*) self-inductance of entire circuit; (*b*) stored energy in magnetic field when current is 0.2 amp, using both Eq. (232) (p. 311) and Eq. (249) (p. 319).

501. Repeat Prob. 500 with the two coils connected in series opposition.

502. Two coils *A* and *B* are on the same magnetic circuit. There are 600 turns in coil *A* and 400 turns in coil B. A current of 1 amp in coil *A* produces 120,000 maxwells in coil *A*. The coefficient of coupling of the two coils is 0.80. Determine: (*a*) flux produced in coil *B* by 1 amp in coil *A*; (*b*) self-inductance of *A* and of *B*; (*c*) mutual inductance of *A* and *B*; (*d*) total self-inductance with two coils connected in series aiding. The reluctance of the magnetic circuit remains constant.

503. In Prob. 502, compute: (*a*) self-inductance of two coils in series opposing; (*b*) stored energy in (*a*) with current equal to 1.5 amp; (*c*) stored energy with coils in series aiding, current equal to 1.5 amp.

504. Two coils *A* and *B* are on the same magnetic circuit. The inductance of coil *A* alone is measured and is found to be 0.6 henry; the inductance of coil *B* is likewise found to be 0.320 henry. The inductance of the two coils in series aiding is then measured and is found to be 1.314 henrys. Determine: (*a*) mutual inductance of coils; (*b*) coefficient of coupling.

505. Two coils *C* and *D* are on the same magnetic circuit. The inductance of the two in series aiding is first measured and found to be 0.7764 henry; the inductance of the two in series opposing is found to be 0.0236 henry. Determine: (*a*) mutual inductance; (*b*) self-inductance of coil *C* if that of *D* is 0.16 henry; (*c*) coefficient of coupling.

QUESTIONS ON CHAPTER X

Electrostatics: Capacitance

1. According to modern electron theory, under what conditions is an atom electrically neutral? When does the atom become positively charged? When does matter become negatively charged?

2. Compare the dynamic electric circuit and associated electron phenomena with the static condition of electricity. Also compare dynamic electricity with static electricity, stating why the two sometimes appear to be different in their nature.

3. If two insulated conducting bodies near each other are connected to the terminals of an influence machine, upon what portions of the bodies will the density of charge be greatest?

4. State Coulomb's law, and express it by an equation. Define a unit cgs charge.

5. State the three systems of units that are in general use in electrostatics. Compare the capacitivity of evacuated space in the three systems. What is the unit of force in each system?

6. What effect does an electric charge produce in the surrounding medium? Compare this condition with that surrounding a magnet. Define an electrostatic field, and state any evidence that shows its existence. Define a "tube of force."

7. Compare the dielectric field with current; with magnetic lines of force; with magnetic lines of induction. Show that dielectric lines must be normal to a conducting surface where they enter or leave such a surface. State three laws which govern the configuration of a dielectric field of force.

8. If a positive charge is brought into the neighborhood of an insulated and uncharged conducting body, what phenomenon occurs? What is the relation of the induced charge to the inducing charge? State the laws relating to induced charges. Distinguish between free and bound charges. How may it be shown experimentally that free and bound charges behave differently?

9. Why must a positive charge on an isolated sphere reside on the surface and be uniformly distributed over it? Prove by two methods that a charge distributed uniformly over the surface of a sphere behaves, so far as its external effects are concerned, as if the charge were concentrated at the center of the sphere.

10. Define electrostatic field intensity. To what magnetic quantity does it correspond? In the cgs system what is the relation between field intensity and flux density? Show that 4π lines of force leave or enter each unit charge.

11. State Gauss' theorem, and derive the proof.

12. Define potential difference in terms of field intensity and unit charge. What is meant by the "integral of field intensity"?

13. Distinguish between the dielectric properties and the insulating properties of a medium. In what one important respect do dielectric lines differ from current and magnetic lines? Give examples of excellent insulators and of excellent dielectrics. In what terms is dielectric strength measured? Discuss the probable mechanism of dielectric rupture according to modern electron theory.

14. What is the usual effect of inserting a dielectric other than air between the electrodes of a capacitor? What is *capacitivity*, and to what magnetic property is it analogous? What is the capacitivity of glass? Of mica? Of rubber? For a given number of dielectric lines, how does the field intensity in a dielectric vary with the capacitivity?

15. Define a capacitor. What is the effect of applying voltage to a capacitor? Define capacitance. What is the order of magnitude of the time required to charge a capacitor directly from a d-c source? Why does the current cease?

16. How can it be shown that electricity is actually stored in a capacitor? How does the quantity which can be stored in a capacitor vary with the voltage? What simple relation does this give among charge, capacitance, and voltage? State the equation, written in three different ways, which gives the relation among charge, capacitance, and voltage.

17. What is the practical unit of capacitance? Why is the microfarad commonly used as a unit? Under what conditions is the micromicrofarad also used as a unit? Define *elastance*, stating the unit.

18. Determine the equivalent capacitance of capacitors in parallel. To what relation among conductances in the electric circuit is this analogous?

19. Determine the equivalent capacitance of capacitors in series. What is the relation among the electric charges on a number of capacitors in series? To what equation in the electric circuit is the equation relating to the equivalent capacitance of capacitors in series similar?

20. Derive the relation among the voltages across a number of capacitors in series, if the individual capacitances are known. Are these voltage relations dependent on the insulating properties of the dielectrics? In the case of leaky capacitors, on what does the ultimate voltage distribution depend?

21. Show that the field intensity between charged parallel electrodes is $4\pi\sigma$ dynes per unit charge provided that the distance between the electrodes is small compared with their dimensions. σ is the density of charge on the electrodes in esu per square centimeter. How many dielectric lines leave each square centimeter of each electrode? In a dielectric whose capacitivity is unity, what is the relation of field intensity **E** and flux density D?

22. Show that the force of attraction between charged parallel electrodes close together is $2\pi\sigma^2 A$ dynes.

23. How may it be shown that energy is stored in a capacitor? Outline the procedure by which it may be proved that the stored energy in a parallel-electrode capacitor is $q^2/2C$ ergs, where q is the charge in statcoulombs or esu and C is the capacitance in statfarads. Prove that the same equation holds when an additional charge is given to the capacitor.

24. How does stored energy vary with the voltage of a capacitor? Express the stored energy in terms of voltage and charge. Derive the expression which gives the stored energy per cubic centimeter as a function of the field intensity and the capacitivity of the dielectric.

25. Outline the procedure which is used in calculating the capacitance of a capacitor. Show that an electrostatic field cannot exist within a region totally enclosed by a conducting body provided that there is no charge within the region.

26. Derive the equation which gives the capacitance of a parallel-electrode capacitor. Upon what factors does the capacitance depend? What is the effect on the capacitance of changing the area of the electrodes? Of decreasing the distance between them? Of substituting hard rubber or glass for air? Show that the expression differs from the correct value when two simple electrodes alone are used.

27. Prove that the force exerted by a straight, infinitely long charged filament on a unit charge, h cm from the filament, is $2q/h$ dynes, where q is the esu per centimeter length.

28. From the relation in Question 27, derive the expression which gives the capacitance of cylindrical capacitors. How does the capacitance vary with the length of cylinder? The radius of the outer cylinder? The radius of the inner cylinder? State a common use of this type of capacitor.

29. Derive the equation for the capacitance of concentric spherical capacitors. Show that the capacitance of an isolated sphere in statfarads is equal to its radius in centimeters. What is the approximate capacitance in microfarads of the earth as an isolated sphere?

30. From the relation in Question 27 prove that the capacitance of two parallel cylinders is $1 \Big/ \left(4 \log_\epsilon \dfrac{D - r}{r}\right)$ statfarads per cm.

Unrationalized MKS System

31. Given that μ_v, the permeability of evacuated space, is equal to 10^{-7}, show that in the *unrationalized mks system* the capacitivity ϵ_v of evacuated space is $1.113 \cdot 10^{-10}$. Give Coulomb's law in the unrationalized system.

32. Show that 4π electrostatic lines leave each unit positive charge. Also show that the flux density $D = \epsilon_r\epsilon_v\mathbf{E}$, where ϵ_r is the relative capacitivity and $\mathbf{E}$ is the field intensity.

Derive the equations for the following:

33. Capacitance in farads of a parallel-electrode capacitor.
34. Field intensity due to a long straight filament with a charge of q coulombs per m.
35. Capacitance in farads per meter of a coaxial cylindrical capacitor.
36. Capacitance in farads of a concentric spherical capacitor.
37. Capacitance in farads per meter of a parallel-cylinder capacitor.

Rationalized MKS System

38. Given that μ_v', the permeability of evacuated space, is equal to $4\pi \cdot 10^{-7}$, show that in the rationalized mks system the capacitivity ϵ_v' of evacuated space is $8.854 \cdot 10^{-12}$.

39. Derive Coulomb's law, and show that the field intensity $\mathbf{E} = D/(\epsilon_r\epsilon_v')$, where D is the displacement.

Derive the equations for the following:

40. Capacitance in farads of a parallel-electrode capacitor.
41. Field intensity due to a long straight filament with a charge of q coulombs per m.
42. Capacitance in farads per meter of a coaxial cylindrical capacitor.
43. Capacitance in farads of a concentric spherical capacitor.
44. Capacitance in farads per meter of a parallel-cylinder capacitor.

45. A capacitor C is suddenly connected across a source of constant voltage E. What is the theoretical instantaneous value of current? Explain. If a resistor of resistance R is connected in series with the capacitor, what is the current I_0 at the instant of closing the circuit? Explain.

46. Derive the equation which gives the current i to a capacitor of capacitance C in series with a resistor of resistance R as a function of time t. Sketch and discuss this current function.

47. In Question 46 derive the equation for the quantity q in the capacitor. Sketch and discuss the function.

48. In Questions 46 and 47 determine the time constant. Discuss its significance with respect to current and to quantity during the time of charge.

49. A charged capacitor of C farads at emf E_0 is discharged through a resistor of resistance R. Derive the equation of current as a function of time. Sketch and discuss the function.

50. Describe the constitution of a simple type of gaseous atom according to modern electron theory. Describe the mechanism by which ions are produced by collision. What is meant by ionization? State the properties of ionized air. What is meant by corona? Sketch an arrangement of electrodes which will permit a high degree of ionization in the surrounding air at one electrode without producing a complete rupture of the air.

51. What two methods are commonly employed in the measurement of capacitance? On what fact does the ballistic galvanometer method depend? What relation exists between the quantity passing through the galvanometer and its maximum ballistic throw?

Should the measurement be made on *charge* or on *discharge?* Explain. How is the galvanometer calibrated?

52. Describe the bridge method of capacitance measurement. Compare it with the Wheatstone-bridge method of resistance measurement. How does the bridge formula for capacitance differ from the formula employed when resistance is measured? What is the source of power and what simple detector is used in the capacitance bridge?

53. How may a disconnection in a cable be located? On what principle does this method of measurement depend? Is this method applicable if the fault is grounded?

PROBLEMS ON CHAPTER X

Electrostatics: Capacitance

506. Each of two small spheres, spaced 15 cm between centers in air, has a charge of 5 esu (statcoulombs), one charge being positive and the other negative. Determine: (*a*) force in dynes acting between two spheres; (*b*) force acting between the spheres when they are immersed in oil, having a relative capacitivity of 2.5; (*c*) direction of force in (*a*) and (*b*). The distance between spheres and the charges remain unaltered.

In this problem, as well as in those which follow, the charges may be assumed to act as if concentrated at the centers of the spheres.

507. The charges on two small spheres, *A* and *B*, each having a radius of 1 cm, spaced 12 cm between centers in air, are 4 and 6 positive esu. Determine: (*a*) force in dynes between the spheres; (*b*) force in dynes on these spheres when immersed in oil, the relative capacitivity of which is 3.0; (*c*) direction of force in (*a*) and (*b*); (*d*) total electric flux leaving each sphere when in air and when in oil.

508. In Prob. 507, determine field intensity on a line connecting the centers of the two spheres at (*a*) surface of sphere *A*; (*b*) surface of sphere *B*.

509. Two spheres, each 1 cm radius, are spaced 12 cm between centers in air, Fig. 509*A*. One is given a positive charge, the other a negative charge of 8 statcoulombs. Determine: (*a*) force in dynes between spheres; (*b*) dielectric flux leaving or entering each; field intensity (*c*) at point *a*; (*d*) at point *b*; (*e*) field intensity at point 0 midway between centers of spheres; (*f*) field intensity at point *c* on the line joining the centers of the spheres, 4 cm from the center of left-hand sphere; (*g*) field intensity at point *P*.

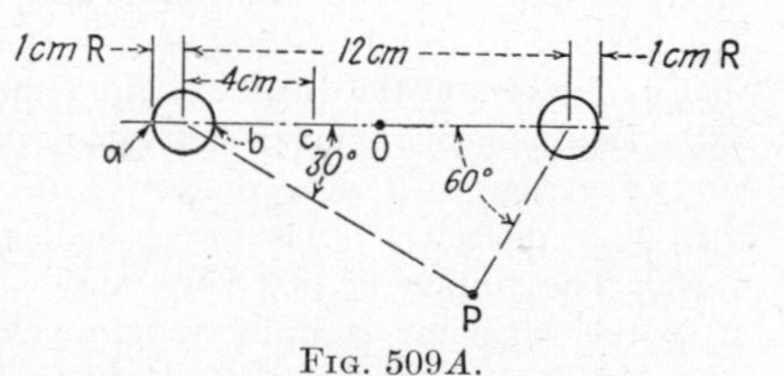

FIG. 509*A*.

510. Two small spheres in air are spaced 16 cm between centers. There is a charge of +12 esu on one sphere, and the force of attraction between the spheres is 1.5 dynes. Determine: (*a*) magnitude and sign of charge on second sphere; (*b*) force in dynes on a unit charge placed on line joining their centers and midway between them.

511. Two small spheres *A* and *B* in air, each of radius 0.5 cm, are charged with +8 and −12 esu. The force between them is 0.375 dyne. Determine: (*a*) distance in centimeters between centers of spheres; (*b*) number of electric lines leaving sphere *A*; (*c*) entering sphere *B*; (*d*) field intensity at surface of sphere *A*, on line joining centers of two spheres; (*e*) of sphere *B*; (*f*) force on a unit positive charge at mid-point of line joining centers of two spheres.

512. Repeat Prob. 511 with the spheres immersed in oil, the relative capacitivity of which is 2.5. The charges on the spheres remain unchanged.

513. In a concentric spherical capacitor similar to that shown in Fig. 261 (p. 348) the radius of the inner sphere is 3 cm, and the inside radius of the outer spherical shell is 8 cm. There are 150.8 electric lines leaving the inner sphere *A* to the outer sphere B. The dielectric is air. Determine: (*a*) charge in esu on inner sphere; (*b*) number of lines per square centimeter at surface of inner sphere A; (*c*) field intensity at surface of inner sphere; (*d*) number of lines per square centimeter at inner surface of outer spherical shell B; (*e*) field intensity midway between spherical surfaces. (*f*) State law of variation of density of dielectric lines with respect to distance from center of inner sphere.

514. A capacitor, the capacitance of which is 50 μf, is connected across a 200-volt source. Determine: (*a*) charge in coulombs; (*b*) charge when 320 volts is impressed across capacitor; (*c*) current in each case when capacitor is charged for 0.2 sec at constant rate; (*d*) total energy in each case.

515. The capacitance of a capacitor is 36 μf. Determine: (*a*) its emf when its charge is 9,000 microcoulombs; (*b*) value to which charge must be increased to make emf equal to 400 volts; (*c*) stored energy in (*a*) and (*b*).

516. A capacitor of 50 μf capacitance is charged at a uniform rate by a current of 0.001 amp. Determine: (*a*) time this current must continue to raise emf of capacitor to 300 volts; (*b*) stored energy at time in (*a*).

517. A capacitor is charged by a steady current of 0.0012 amp for 25 sec, at which time its emf is 600 volts. Determine: (*a*) capacitance of capacitor; (*b*) stored energy.

518. The capacitors used with an impulse, or "lightning," generator are 0.2 μf each, and each capacitor is charged to 60,000 volts before discharging to give the lightning stroke. The charging current to each capacitor is essentially constant at 0.30 amp. Determine: (*a*) seconds required to charge each capacitor; (*b*) energy stored in each capacitor.

519. An air capacitor consists of three equidistant parallel electrodes, the two outer electrodes being connected together to form one electrode, and the center electrode forming the other electrode [see Fig. 258(*b*), p. 345]. The capacitance of the capacitor is 0.00036 μf. An emf of 600 volts is applied to its terminals. The source of emf is then removed and the capacitor immersed in transil oil, the capacitivity of which is 3.2. Determine: (*a*) charge with air as dielectric; (*b*) stored energy with air as dielectric; (*c*) charge with oil as dielectric; (*d*) emf with oil as dielectric; (*e*) stored energy with oil as dielectric. Assume no leakage of charge.

520. The voltage of 600 volts applied to the capacitor, Prob. 519, is unchanged after the capacitor is immersed in the transil oil. Determine: (*a*) charge when immersed in oil; (*b*) stored energy in (*a*). While the capacitor is in the oil, the voltage source is disconnected and the capacitor is removed from the oil. With air now as the dielectric, determine: (*c*) charge; (*d*) voltage; (*e*) stored energy. Assume no leakage of charge.

521. The charges taken by four capacitors when they are connected in parallel across 240 volts are 2,880, 2,400, 5,760, 4,320 microcoulombs. Determine: (*a*) equivalent capacitance of combination; (*b*) energy stored in each capacitor; (*c*) total stored energy.

522. A capacitor A of 20 μf capacitance is charged at 600 volts. The voltage supply is then disconnected, being replaced by a capacitor B of 16 μf capacitance. Determine: (*a*) resulting charge in each capacitor; (*b*) voltage of system; (*c*) initial energy in A; (*d*) ultimate energy with A and B in parallel; (*e*) account for the difference in energy between (*c*) and (*d*).

523. A capacitor A of 50 μf capacitance is connected across 600 volts. The voltage supply is removed, and the capacitor is then connected across three uncharged capacitors B, C, D in parallel. The charges are 4,000, 6,000, and 8,000 microcoulombs. Determine: (*a*) capacitance of B, C, D; (*b*) voltage across parallel combination; (*c*) energy initially stored in A; (*d*) energy stored in A, B, C, D in parallel; (*e*) account for the difference in energy between (*c*) and (*d*).

524. Three capacitors, of capacitances 16, 24, 30 μf, are charged to 200, 240, 400 volts. They are then connected in parallel with terminals of like polarity together. Determine: (*a*) voltage across parallel combination; (*b*) total initial energy stored in three capacitors; (*c*) energy when in parallel. (*d*) Account for the difference between (*b*) and (*c*).

525. The three capacitors, Prob. 524, are now separated and recharged to the initial potentials of 200, 240, 400 volts. They are then connected again in parallel with terminals of like polarity together but with a fourth uncharged capacitor connected in parallel with the system. The voltage of the system is now 232.9 volts. Determine: (*a*) capacitance of fourth capacitor; (*b*) total initial energy stored in three capacitors; (*c*) energy of parallel system. (*d*) Account for the difference between (*b*) and (*c*).

526. After the three capacitors of Prob. 524 are charged to their respective voltages, they are again connected in parallel with the polarity of the 16-μf capacitor the reverse of the other two. Determine: (*a*) voltage across parallel combination; (*b*) total initial energy stored in three capacitors; (*c*) energy when in parallel. (*d*) Account for the difference between (*b*) and (*c*).

527. Three capacitors, of capacitance 8, 10, 12 μf, are connected in series across a 120-volt source. Determine: (*a*) single capacitance which will replace the three; (*b*) voltage across each; (*c*) energy stored in each. The three capacitors, without loss of charge, are disconnected and then connected in parallel, with electrodes of like polarity together. Determine: (*d*) total charge of parallel combination; (*e*) charge on each capacitor; (*f*) voltage across parallel combination; (*g*) energy stored in (*f*).

528. Repeat (*d*), (*e*), (*f*), (*g*), Prob. 527, with the polarity of the 8-μf capacitor reversed.

529. Four capacitors, of capacitance 20, 24, 36, 40 μf, are connected in series, and 240 volts is impressed across the four. Determine: (*a*) charge on each; (*b*) voltage across each; (*c*) energy stored in system. The four capacitors while still charged are disconnected and connected in parallel. The last three are connected with terminals of like polarity together, and the 20-μf capacitor is connected in parallel with them, but with its positive terminal to their negative terminal. Determine: (*d*) net charge on entire parallel combination (*e*) charge on each capacitor; (*f*) voltage of parallel combination; (*g*) total stored energy. (*h*) Account for difference between (*c*) and (*g*).

530. When four capacitors are connected in series across a 240-volt source, their voltages are 30, 50, 60, 100 volts and the charge on each is 1,800 microcoulombs. Determine: (*a*) capacitance of each; (*b*) capacitance of series combination; (*c*) total stored energy. The four capacitors are disconnected in the charged condition and are then connected in parallel, the last three with terminals of like polarity together and the 30 μf with reversed polarity. Determine: (*d*) voltage of parallel combination; (*e*) charge on each capacitor; (*f*) stored energy.

531. A parallel-electrode capacitor consists of two flat circular electrodes 50 cm diameter and spaced 0.4 cm in air. The charge on each electrode is 750 esu. Determine: (*a*) total dielectric lines leaving or entering each electrode; (*b*) density in lines per square centimeter at each electrode; (*c*) field intensity between electrodes; (*d*) work in ergs done in carrying a unit charge from one electrode to other; (*e*) force of attraction in dynes acting between the electrodes; (*f*) stored energy in ergs per cubic centimeter. Neglect effect of leakage flux and fringing.

532. In a capacitor identical with that of Prob. 531, except that the electrodes are spaced 0.50 cm, the mutual force of attraction between the electrodes is 5.0 dynes. Determine: (*a*) density of charge on each electrode; (*b*) total charge on each electrode; (*c*) field intensity between electrodes; (*d*) work done if two electrodes are allowed to move 0.20 cm nearer each other; (*e*) stored energy in ergs per cubic centimeter. The electrodes are perfectly insulated.

533. Repeat Prob. 532, with the capacitor electrodes immersed in oil, the capacitivity of which is 2.8. The mutual force of attraction is now 2.0 dynes.

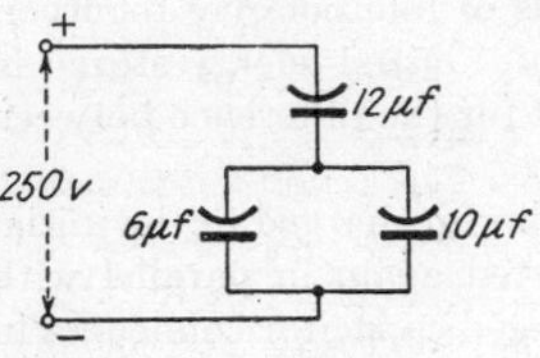

Fig. 534A.

534. A 6-μf and a 10-μf capacitor, connected in parallel, are in series with a 12-μf capacitor, Fig. 534A. The combination is then connected across a 250-volt source. Determine: (a) charge in each capacitor; (b) total energy; (c) energy in 6-μf capacitor; (d) energy in 10-μf capacitor; (e) energy in 12-μf capacitor.

535. Repeat Prob. 534 with the 10- and 12-μf capacitors interchanged in the circuit and the circuit voltage increased to 500 volts.

536. Three capacitors A, B, C, Fig. 536A, without initial charge, are connected in series parallel across a 240-volt source. The capacitance of capacitor A is 40 μf, and that of capacitor B is 12 μf. The charge on capacitor A is 3,200 microcoulombs. Determine: (a) voltage across parallel circuit; (b) charge on capacitor C; (c) capacitance of capacitor C; (d) energy stored in capacitors A, B, C.

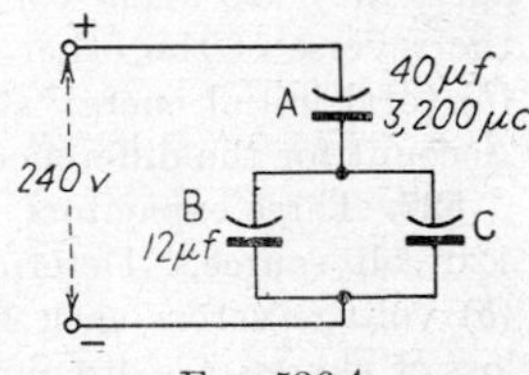

Fig. 536A.

537. An air capacitor consists of three electrodes. The two outer ones are connected together as one terminal, and the other terminal is connected to the intermediate plate between the two outers. The dimensions of each electrode are 36 by 36 cm, and the electrodes are spaced 0.15 cm apart. Determine: (a) capacitance; (b) stored energy if the voltage is 500 volts; (c) field intensity in dynes per unit charge. If the space between the electrodes is filled with paraffin, having a dielectric constant 2.4, determine: (d) capacitance; (e) stored energy at 300 volts; (f) flux density; (g) field intensity.

538. A high-voltage capacitor is to be made of alternate layers of glass and tin foil, the glass having a dielectric constant 6.4. The glass electrodes are $\frac{3}{64}$ in. thick and are 6 by 8 in. area; the tin foil is 2 mils thick, and its dimensions are 4 by 6 in. Determine: (a) number of glass electrodes and sheets of tin foil necessary to make a capacitor of 0.0662 μf; (b) size of completed capacitor.

539. It is desired to construct a 0.5-μf capacitor made up of alternate layers of tin foil 0.0025 cm thick and paraffined paper 0.004 cm thick and having a capacitivity of 2.51. Each tin-foil layer is a rectangle 10 by 15 cm. The two outer tin-foil layers are of the same polarity, Fig. 258(b) (p. 345). Determine number of tin-foil layers for each of the two systems of electrodes.

540. Determine (a) capacitance in micromicrofarads of the parallel-electrode capacitor in Prob. 531; (b) stored energy when it is connected across a 1,000-volt source. With the charged electrodes disconnected from the power source, they are moved to 0.6 cm. apart. Determine: (c) voltage; (d) stored energy. (e) From what source is the increased energy obtained?

541. A long straight wire of small diameter is charged with 10 esu per centimeter length. Determine: (a) force in dynes acting on a positive unit charge located 12 cm distant perpendicularly from center of wire; (b) work in ergs done in moving charge 10 cm farther away from wire.

542. An air capacitor consists of two coaxial cylinders, 2 m long. The outer diameter of the inner cylinder is 2 cm, and the inner diameter of the outer cylinder is 6 cm. Determine: (a) capacitance in micromicrofarads; (b) charge in coulombs when 2,000 volts is impressed between cylinders. Neglect end effect.

543. A single-conductor 4,000-volt cable consists of a solid No. 2 AWG copper conductor, the diameter of which is 257.6 mils, and a wall of rubber $\frac{12}{64}$ in. thick of capacitivity 4.5. (The rubber is surrounded by a 1/16-in. lead sheath.) Determine capacitance of 1-mile length of this cable.

544. In a 15,000-volt 350,000-cir-mil single-conductor impregnated paper cable, the diameter over the conductor is 0.710 in. The conductor is wrapped with a 13/32-in. wall of impregnated paper of dielectric constant 2.8. (The paper is surrounded by a 1/8-in. lead sheath.) Determine: (*a*) capacitance in microfarads of a 5-mile length of cable. The cable is tested with high-voltage direct current obtained from a Kenotron set. When 25,000 volts is impressed on the cable, determine: (*b*) charge in coulombs; (*c*) stored energy in joules.

545. The inside diameter of the outer sphere of a concentric spherical capacitor is 15 cm, and the outside diameter of the inside sphere is 5 cm. The dielectric is air. Determine: (*a*) capacitance of capacitor in statfarads; (*b*) charge when the potential difference between the spheres is 2 statvolts, the outer shell being positive (1 statvolt = 300 volts); (*c*) force on a cgs unit positive charge at surface of inside sphere; (*d*) flux density at inner surface of outer sphere; (*e*) work in ergs in carrying a unit positive charge radially from outer surface of inside sphere to inner surface of outside sphere.

546. In the spherical capacitor of Prob. 545, but with the potential difference between spheres equal to 2.5 statvolts, determine: (*a*) work in ergs in carrying unit charge (esu) from surface of inner sphere to inner surface of outer sphere; (*b*) field intensity at any point midway between electrode surfaces.

547. A single-phase 40-mile 33,000-volt transmission line consists of two 000 AWG solid copper conductors spaced 4 ft between centers. The diameter of the conductors is 0.410 in. Determine capacitance of line in microfarads.

548. A single-phase branch line extends 15 miles from a 132-kv transmission line. It consists of two 0000 AWG solid copper conductors having an outside diameter of 0.460 in. and spaced 12 ft between centers. Determine capacitance of line in microfarads.

Unrationalized MKS System

(Most of the foregoing problems may be assigned to be solved in either mks system.)

549. Two point charges of opposite sign and each equal to 24,000 esu are 16 cm apart in air. Determine: (*a*) force in newtons acting between charges; (*b*) electric lines between charges; (*c*) flux density at point midway between charges; (*d*) field intensity in volts per meter at point in (*c*).

550. Two spheres each of radius 0.005 m are spaced 0.25 m in air, and the charge on each is $6 \cdot 10^{-6}$ coulomb, the charges being of opposite sign. Determine: (*a*) electric lines from or to each sphere; (*b*) flux density at surface of each sphere due to its own charge; (*c*) total flux density at surface of each sphere on line connecting their centers; (*d*) field intensity in (*c*); (*e*) flux density 0.10 m from the center of either sphere on line joining centers of spheres; (*f*) field intensity in (*e*). Assume that charges act as if concentrated at centers of spheres.

551. A parallel-electrode air capacitor consists of two flat circular electrodes, each 0.60 m diameter and spaced 0.005 m. The charge on each electrode is $3.0 \cdot 10^{-7}$ coulomb. Determine: (*a*) capacitance; (*b*) voltage; (*c*) electric flux between electrodes; (*d*) flux density; (*e*) field intensity. (See Prob. 531.)

552. A long straight cylindrical conductor of small diameter is charged with $4 \cdot 10^{-7}$ coulomb per m. Determine: (*a*) force in newtons acting on a coulomb (field intensity) located 0.12 m perpendicularly from center of wire; (*b*) flux density at point in (*a*); (*c*) work done in moving coulomb 0.10 m farther from wire. (See Prob. 541.)

553. An air capacitor consists of two coaxial cylinders 2.5 m long. The radius of the inner cylinder is 0.0075 m, and the radius of the inner surface of the outer cylinder is 0.045 m. The voltage between the cylinders is 1,000 volts. Determine: (*a*) capacitance; (*b*) charge; (*c*) stored energy; (*d*) flux; (*e*) flux density at surface of inner cylinder; (*f*) flux density at inner surface of outer cylinder; (*g*) field intensity in (*e*); field intensity in (*f*).

554. Repeat Prob. 553 with a dielectric of capacitivity 4.0.

555. In a concentric spherical capacitor the inside diameter of the outer sphere is 0.15 m, and the outside diameter of the inner sphere is 0.05 m (see Prob. 545). The dielectric is air. The voltage between spheres is 600 volts. Determine: (*a*) capacitance in farads; (*b*) charge in coulombs; (*c*) stored energy; (*d*) total flux; (*e*) flux density at surface of inner sphere; (*f*) flux density at inner surface of outer sphere; (*g*) field intensity in (*e*); (*h*) field intensity in (*f*).

556. Repeat Prob. 555 with a dielectric of capacitivity 3.0.

Rationalized MKS System

557. Solve Prob. 549, using rationalized mks units.

558. Solve Prob. 550, using rationalized mks units.

559. Solve Prob. 551, using rationalized mks units.

560. Solve Prob. 552, using rationalized mks units.

561. Solve Prob. 553, using rationalized mks units.

562. Solve Prob. 554, using rationalized mks units.

563. A circuit consisting of a 50-μf capacitor in series with a 1,500-ohm resistor is connected suddenly across a 120-volt source. Determine: (*a*) initial value of current; (*b*) equation of current as function of time; (*c*) time constant; (*d*) value of current at instant in (*c*); (*e*) rate at which current begins to decrease. (*f*) Plot function in (*b*).

564. A 100-μf capacitor in series with a 150-scale voltmeter of 20,000 ohms resistance is connected suddenly across a 120-volt source. Determine: (*a*) equation of current as function of time; (*b*) reading of voltmeter when time $t = 1$ sec; (*c*) voltage across capacitor in (*b*); (*d*) value of current when voltmeter reads 20 volts; (*e*) time corresponding to (*d*). (*f*) Plot function in (*a*).

565. A 40-μf capacitor is charged to 600 volts and then is discharged through a resistor of 10,000 ohms. Determine: (*a*) initial value of current; (*b*) equation of current as function of time; (*c*) rate at which current begins to decrease.

566. (*a*) In Prob. 563 derive equation for quantity q. Determine: (*b*) rate at which quantity begins to increase; (*c*) quantity when time $t = 0.03$ sec; (*d*) time when charge in capacitor is 90 per cent ultimate value. (*e*) Plot function in (*a*).

567. (*a*) In Prob. 564, derive equation for quantity q. Determine: (*b*) rate at which quantity begins to increase; (*c*) quantity when time is equal to time constant; (*d*) voltage across capacitor at time in (*c*). (*e*) Plot function in (*a*).

568. In Prob. 564, the capacitor is charged to 240 volts and is then disconnected from the power source and connected across the voltmeter. Determine: (*a*) equation of current; (*b*) equation of quantity; (*c*) value of q when voltage across capacitor is 150 volts; (*d*) time t in (*c*); (*e*) value of current in (*c*).

569. In Prob. 564 the capacitor is charged to 300 volts and is then disconnected from the power source and connected across the voltmeter. Determine: (*a*) equation of quantity q; (*b*) charge in capacitor when voltmeter reads 150 volts; (*c*) rate at which current is decreasing in (*b*); (*d*) charge in capacitor when current has reached 10 per cent its initial value; (*e*) energy stored in capacitor when time t is equal to time constant of circuit.

570. In a ballistic measurement of capacitance (see Fig. 268, p. 363), the ballistic deflection of the galvanometer is 22.8 cm when the unknown capacitor C_1 is connected, the Ayrton shunt used with the galvanometer being set at 0.1. The galvanometer deflection is 7.6 cm with the Ayrton shunt set at 1.0 when the galvanometer is calibrated with a 0.05-μf standard capacitor. The same battery, whose emf is 45 volts, is used in each case. Determine: (*a*) galvanometer constant; (*b*) value of unknown capacitance.

571. In a bridge measurement of capacitance, the bridge is connected as in Fig. 269(*a*) (p. 364). When a balance is obtained, $R_1 = 100$ ohms, $R_2 = 1{,}250$ ohms, $C_2 = 0.8\ \mu$f. Determine value of C_x, the unknown capacitance.

572. In a test for a cable fault, the apparatus is connected as in Fig. 270 (p. 364). The length of each cable is 3,200 ft, and the two cables are looped at the far end as shown in the figure. In the capacitance measurement of the part x, the ballistic deflection of the galvanometer is 6.4 cm. In the measurement of the capacitance of the perfect cable plus the looped end of the faulty cable, the deflection is 18.6 cm. Determine distance of fault from the near end of cables.

QUESTIONS ON CHAPTER XI

The Generator

1. Define an electric generator. Which two principal elements of the generator are instrumental in the conversion of power? How is the emf induced? Discuss the relative motion of armature and field in d-c and a-c generators.

2. In what way is the flux linking any coil of a generator armature made to vary? Describe the manner in which this variation of flux causes an emf to be induced. How does this induced emf vary with the speed? The flux? The number of turns in the coil?

3. In the armatures of rotating machinery why is it usually more convenient to consider the emf as being due to the cutting of flux by the conductors, rather than to the change of flux linkages in the armature coils? If the induced emf is considered as being due to the cutting of flux by individual conductors, how does the emf vary with length of conductor? flux density? velocity of conductor?

4. Show, by means of an example, that the emf induced by the cutting of flux is equal to that induced by change of flux linkages. What is meant by a "transformer emf" and a "speed emf"?

5. What definite relation exists among direction of induced emf, direction in which conductor moves, and direction of flux? What simple rule enables one to determine the relation?

6. What are the relative values of the emf induced in a rotating coil, (*a*) when the coil is in the plane perpendicular to the flux? (*b*) When its plane lies parallel to the flux? Discuss any reversal of direction in the induced emf during the rotation of the coil.

7. Show how the alternating emf induced in the coil may be converted into d-c emf for the external circuit. What is the effect on the emf wave form of adding coils to the rotating member? To what are "ripples" in an emf wave due?

8. What functions does the commercial armature perform? Why is the core made of iron laminations? Why are the faces of the poles practically coaxial with the armature? Name two advantages of slotted construction. What factors must be considered when the winding is designed?

9. In what way is the open-coil type of armature different from the closed-coil type? Which type is the gramme-ring armature, Fig. 278 (p. 373)? Show that in the open-coil type of winding the contribution of the individual conductor to the total emf is different from that with the closed-coil winding.

10. Although obsolete, what characteristics of the gramme-ring armature make it useful in studying induced emfs and power generation within an armature?

11. In both a 2-pole and a 4-pole armature trace the paths in which the emfs induced in the individual coils all act in conjunction. Show the points in the windings between which the maximum difference of potential exists and the points at which the brushes should be placed.

12. Name three disadvantages of the gramme-ring winding.

13. Show that the three disadvantages of Question 12 are overcome by the use of the drum winding. State the advantages of the use of slots for holding the coils.

14. State four requirements which a drum winding should meet. Describe briefly the manner of adapting the preformed coils to a slotted armature.

15. Define *pole pitch.* What factor determines the spread of the coil on the armature?

Define *coil pitch* and its relation to pole pitch. What relative positions in the slots do the two sides of any coil occupy? Why? What is meant by a *winding element?* May it consist of more than one conductor? Explain.

16. What is the relation among number of winding elements, number of coils, and number of commutator segments? Define *front pitch, back pitch, average pitch.*

17. In a simplex lap winding, how many commutator segments does the winding advance each time that a coil is added? Define *commutator pitch.* What three fundamental conditions must be fulfilled by the winding? What is a winding table, and what is its practical value?

18. Why is it sometimes desirable to place more than two winding elements in a slot? In what type of generator is this necessary? Are the winding relations and the conductor numbering in any way affected? What one condition should be imposed on the multiple-coil type of winding, and why?

19. What is meant by "paths through the armature"? How is the current output of a machine affected by increasing the number of paths? How is the voltage affected? The power output? How many paths are there in all simplex lap windings?

20. What is meant by a duplex winding? Show that such a winding may be composed of two simplex windings each lying in alternate slots. How many closures may such a winding have, and what is its degree of reentrancy in each case?

21. If a duplex winding does not close after one passage around the armature, is the number of segments even or odd? When does such a winding close? How many times does it close, and what is its degree of reentrancy?

22. In a lap winding the multiplicity of which is m, how many winding elements does the winding advance each time that the winding is lapped back? How many parallel paths are there in a 6-pole generator having a simplex lap winding? A duplex lap winding? A triplex lap winding?

23. To what causes are unequal emfs in different paths of an armature winding due? Do equalizing connections do away with these inequalities? What is the purpose of equalizing connections? What care should be taken in regard to the number of slots per pole when equalizing connections are used? Why?

24. What is the fundamental difference between a lap winding and a wave winding? Does the direction of induced emf in opposite sides of a coil differ in the two types? Explain.

25. After a wave winding has passed under every pole in going around an armature, what relation should it have to its starting position if the winding is simplex? What would a closure after one passage around the armature mean?

26. Show that the definitions of *front pitch* and *back pitch* in a wave winding do not differ from the definitions in a lap winding. Can the front pitch be even? Odd? Can the back pitch be even? Odd? Can the front pitch and the back pitch be equal? Can the average pitch be even? Odd? When is a winding progressive? Retrogressive? Explain.

27. Is it always possible to fit a wave winding to an armature having a fixed number of slots if all the slots are to be utilized? Explain. What makeshift may be used to accomplish the desired result?

28. If the number of pairs of poles is even, is the number of commutator segments even or odd? Answer if the number of pairs of poles is odd?

29. Explain the meaning of *forced winding.* Under what conditions is it necessary to use such a winding? Compare the formed coil used for the wave winding with that used for the lap winding.

30. What is the minimum number of brush sets that can be used in a wave winding? What is the maximum number that it is possible to use? When would only two sets be used, and why? Why is the maximum possible number usually desirable?

31. How many paths are there in a simplex wave winding? In what way is the number of such paths affected by the number of poles? How many paths in a duplex wave winding? a triplex wave winding?

32. When is it desirable to use a wave winding, and why? A lap winding? Give specific reasons.

33. In addition to forming a part of the magnetic circuit, what other function does the yoke of a dynamo perform? Of what two materials is it made, and why? Describe a process whereby the yoke is made without casting.

34. Of what materials are the field cores made? The pole shoes? What is the advantage of using laminations?

35. What type of wire is used for field coils, and how is it treated? What is the advantage of using a spool? How is the series winding frequently formed?

36. Why is it necessary to construct the armature of laminations? By what two methods are the laminations and slots produced? How are the laminations held in position in the armature? Discuss ventilating ducts.

37. When the diameter of the armature exceeds 38 in. or so, of what do the laminations consist, and how are they assembled and held in place?

38. Sketch two general types of slot. Where is each used? What two methods are used to hold the armature conductors in the slots?

39. Of what is the commutator made? What insulation is used between segments? How are the segments clamped together? How are the coil connections made?

40. What is the purpose of the brushes? Of what material are brushes made usually? What pressure is used to hold the brush on the commutator? What is the purpose of the plating on the brush? What is the purpose of the pigtail?

PROBLEMS ON CHAPTER XI

The Generator

573. A coil 25 cm square, of 80 turns, has its plane perpendicular to a uniform magnetic field of density 900 gauss. The coil is made to revolve a quarter turn about its axis in 0.05 sec, so that it then lies parallel to the direction of the field. Determine: (*a*) maximum flux through coil; (*b*) average induced emf during period that coil is making quarter turn; (*c*) average induced emf when coil rotates at 5 rps, assuming rectified half waves, Fig. 276(*b*) (p. 370); (*d*) induced emf at instant that coil is perpendicular to field; (*e*) parallel to field.

574. A coil 20 cm square, of 50 turns, rotates at a speed of 600 rpm in a uniform magnetic field of density 800 gauss. Determine: (*a*) maximum flux through coil; (*b*) time in seconds for coil to make a quarter turn; (*c*) average emf induced in coil, assuming rectified half wave, Fig. 276(*b*) (p. 370). (*d*) If flux and speed are both doubled, what is average induced emf?

575. In Prob. 574, determine: (*a*) emf per conductor when coil is parallel to direction of field; (*b*) induced emf per coil side at this instant; (*c*) total emf induced in coil at this instant. (*d*) Show that ratio of maximum emf to average emf under these conditions is $\pi/2$.

576. In Prob. 574, the coil is stationary, and its plane is perpendicular to the field. The field circuit is interrupted so that the flux becomes zero in 0.04 sec. (*a*) Determine average induced emf during this period. The coil is turned so that its plane makes an angle of 45° with the direction of the field, and the coil remains stationary in this position. After the flux is brought to the density of 800 gauss, it is reduced to zero in 0.05 sec. (*b*) Determine average induced emf during this interval.

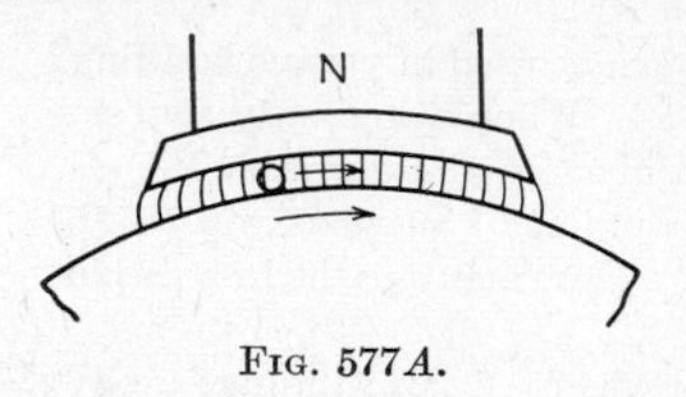

FIG. 577*A*.

577. Figure 577*A* shows a conductor 30 cm long on the surface of an armature of diameter 32 cm. The armature rotates at a speed of 25 rps. Determine: (*a*) emf induced in conductor when it is in the position shown, directly under pole, where the flux density is uniform at 7,500 gauss. (*b*) Determine speed in rps at which armature must rotate in order that emf induced in conductor be 6.79 volts.

578. In Fig. 578*A* are shown the two poles of an electromagnet with a uniform air-gap between the poles, the poles being rectangular, of dimensions 25 by 20 cm. A coil *C* of 80 turns, also 25 by 20 cm, lies in the gap as shown, so that all the flux across the gap links the coil. The density of the flux in the gap is 4,800 gauss. The coil slides out of the gap in 0.001 sec. Determine emf induced in coil computed from (*a*) change of flux linkages; (*b*) cutting of flux by individual conductors. [Solve (*b*) with the coil sliding in two directions, one parallel to the 20-cm side and one parallel to the 25-cm side.]

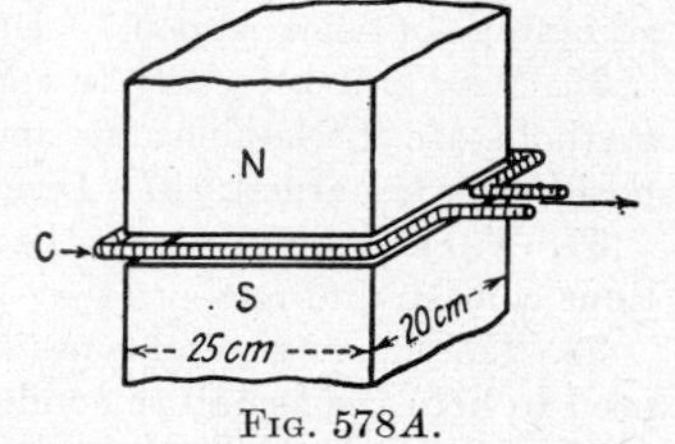

FIG. 578*A*.

579. There are 53 slots in the armature of a 4-pole generator in which single coils are used. (*a*) Determine number of winding elements. (*b*) Design a progressive simplex lap winding in which the back pitch is 27, and make a winding table.

580. Repeat Prob. 579 for a retrogressive winding with back pitch of 25.

581. Repeat Prob. 579 with back pitch 25 and front pitch 23.

582. There are 83 slots in the armature of a 6-pole generator, and there are 83 coils. Determine: (*a*) number of winding elements; (*b*) appropriate values of back pitch and front pitch for a progressive simplex lap winding. (*c*) Sketch a portion of winding. (*d*) Make a winding table.

583. In an armature for an 8-pole generator there are 120 slots, and the winding is to be a 2-layer simplex lap winding, with two coil sides per slot. Determine: (*a*) winding elements; (*b*) suitable values of back pitch and front pitch to give a progressive winding. (*c*) Sketch a portion of winding. (*d*) Make a winding table.

584. There are 120 slots in the armature of a 6-pole generator. It is desired to wind the armature with 360 coils, necessitating the employment of triple coils. The winding is to consist of a 2-layer simplex progressive lap winding. Determine: (*a*) number of winding elements; (*b*) suitable back pitch; (*c*) suitable front pitch; (*d*) number of commutator segments. (*e*) Make a sketch of a portion of winding. (*f*) Make a portion of winding table. NOTE. The back pitch should be less than the average pitch but as nearly equal to it as possible.

585. On the armature of an 8-pole generator there are 140 slots and 6 winding elements per slot. Determine (*a*) value of back and front pitch for a simplex lap winding. Choose the value of back pitch which is nearest the value of average pitch and yet fulfills the conditions which such a winding necessitates. (*b*) Sketch a few slots with their winding elements and connections. (*c*) How many commutator segments are necessary? (See Note, Prob. 584.)

586. A 300-kw 250-volt 6-pole generator has a simplex lap winding. Determine: (*a*) total amperes; (*b*) amperes per armature path; (*c*) volts per path.

587. A 500-kw 250-volt 8-pole generator has a duplex lap winding. Determine: (*a*) total amperes; (*b*) amperes per armature path; (*c*) volts per path.

588. There are 140 slots in the armature, Prob. 587, and double coils are used. The back pitch is less than the average pitch but as near its value as permissible. The winding is progressive. (*a*) Determine front and back pitch. (*b*) Sketch a portion of the winding with commutator connections. (*c*) Make a portion of the winding table.

589. Repeat Prob. 588 for a triple-coil winding, the conditions remaining the same.

590. In the armature of a 4-pole generator there are 72 slots and a double-coil duplex progressive lap winding is used. (*a*) With a back pitch of 73, sketch a portion of winding, including commutator connections. (*b*) Make a winding table. If the generator is rated at 20 kw, 250 volts, (*c*) determine current per path.

591. Repeat Prob. 590 except that armature has 71 slots.

592. In the armature of a 15-kw 250-volt 4-pole generator there are 63 slots. (*a*) Determine pitch which will give a simplex retrogressive wave winding with two elements per slot. (*b*) Sketch winding for two or three passages around armature. (*c*) Make portion of winding table. (*d*) Determine voltage and current per path.

593. Using the pitch of Prob. 592, determine number of slots which will make a progressive winding possible.

594. The armature of a 4-pole generator has 43 slots. (*a*) With two elements per slot, making $y_b = 23$ and $y_f = 21$, sketch a simplex wave winding showing at least three passages around armature. (*b*) Make a winding table. Check with Eq. (331) (p. 391) and Eq. (332) (p. 392). (*c*) Is this winding progressive or retrogressive?

595. Repeat Prob. 594, making $y_b = 21$ and $y_f = 21$. Again check with Eq. (331) (p. 391) and Eq. (332) (p. 392). Is this winding progressive or retrogressive?

596. In a 6-pole generator there are 89 slots on the armature with two elements per slot. (*a*) Sketch a portion of a wave winding, $y_b = 31$, $y_f = 29$, for at least three passages around armature. (*b*) Make a winding table. (*c*) Is this winding progressive or retrogressive?

597. (*a*) In Prob. 596 determine number of slots, nearest 89, which will make possible a retrogressive wave winding. (*b*) Determine back pitch and front pitch.

598. It is desired to wind a 6-pole armature with a progressive wave winding, two elements per slot, and the front and back pitch are both to be 33. (*a*) Determine number of slots. (*b*) Repeat (*a*) for a retrogressive winding.

599. In a 4-pole generator there are 68 slots, and it is desired that the armature be simplex wave-wound. (*a*) Attempt to design a winding which will fulfill the necessary conditions. (For example, try $y_b = 35$, $y_f = 33$.) (*b*) By use of a dummy coil again try (*a*). (*c*) Make a winding table.

600. In a 6-pole armature there are 81 slots, and there are to be two winding elements per slot. Attempt to place a simplex wave winding on this armature, making $y_b = y_f = 27$. Omit the connection of a single coil (dummy coil), and investigate as to whether or not the winding is possible. Use Eq. (331) (p. 391).

601. In Prob. 599, use an average pitch of 33, and, without employing a dummy coil, design a duplex retrogressive wave winding. (*a*) Make a winding table. (*b*) Sketch winding for three passages around the armature.

602. The armature of a 4-pole dynamo of approximately 10 kw rating has 33 slots and a triple-coil simplex wave winding is used, making six winding elements per slot. (*a*) Determine values of back pitch and front pitch which are nearest to full pitch and which fulfill conditions imposed by wave winding and triple coil. Make $y_b = y_f$. (*b*) Make winding table for three passages of winding around armature. (*c*) Sketch portion of winding for slots near beginning and end of winding.

603. The armature of an 8-pole 500-kw 250-volt generator has a simplex lap winding. Determine its rating in volts and amperes if rewound as follows: (*a*) duplex lap winding; (*b*) duplex wave winding. The kilowatts rating remains unchanged.

QUESTIONS ON CHAPTER XII

Generator Characteristics

1. What fundamental relation gives the emf induced in a single armature conductor while it is cutting flux?

2. Show that in a ring winding and in a simplex lap winding, the emf between brushes at any instant is equal to the sum of the emfs in all the conductors between any two consecutive commutating planes. Show from this that the emf between brushes is equal to the average emf induced in any single conductor during the time it is passing between the two commutating planes, multiplied by the number of conductors between commutating planes. Why is the curve of emf and time for any one conductor identical in shape with the curve of flux density along the air-gap?

3. Derive the equation which gives the emf induced in the armature of a generator in terms of flux per pole, speed, number of armature conductors, number of poles, and number of parallel paths in the armature.

4. A certain armature has a fixed number of conductors on its surface. What are the separate effects on the induced emf of (*a*) doubling the speed of the armature; (*b*) doubling the flux; (*c*) reconnecting the armature so that the number of parallel paths in the armature is doubled?

5. In a given generator, on what two factors does the induced emf depend? If the speed of the generator be maintained constant, on what one factor does the induced emf depend?

6. Show that a similarity should exist between two curves plotted as follows: (*a*) The field ampere-turns of a generator as abscissa and the flux leaving one of its N poles as ordinate. (*b*) The field current of the same generator as abscissa and the induced armature emf at constant speed as ordinate.

7. In the curve relating ampere-turns of the field and flux of one N pole, why does not the flux start at zero value? In the curve giving induced emf as a function of field current, why is the first part of the curve practically a straight line? At the higher values of field current, why does the induced emf increase less and less rapidly for any given increase in field current?

8. Discuss any difference that may exist between the saturation curve obtained with *increasing* values of field current and that obtained with *decreasing* values.

9. Sketch the connections used in determining a saturation curve (*a*) using a simple field rheostat; (*b*) using a voltage divider with the field. Give two reasons why the generator should be separately excited.

10. Show that Ohm's law can be expressed graphically. What two quantities are plotted when expressing Ohm's law in this manner?

11. Sketch the connections of a shunt generator. Is the field of comparatively low resistance or of high resistance? Explain.

12. Explain in detail how a shunt generator "builds up." What limits the voltage to which a generator can build up?

13. What is meant by critical field resistance? Give four causes, each of which may prevent the building up of a generator. What tests and remedies should be used for each cause?

14. What is the relation of the general direction of the flux produced by the current in the armature conductors to the brush axis? What effect does the armature mmf have on the resultant flux in a generator? How does it affect the position of the neutral plane? What effect does the change in position of the neutral plane have on the brush position?

15. When the brushes are moved forward in a generator, what is the resulting direction of the armature mmf? Into what two components can this mmf be resolved? What is the effect of each component on the resultant flux?

16. Which conductors on an armature produce a demagnetizing effect? Which produce a cross-magnetizing effect?

17. Indicate the mmf and its distribution produced by the current in a single armature coil. Show how the mmfs of the several armature coils combine to produce a stepped triangular mmf distribution. Compute the maximum value of the mmf curve in terms of the ampere-conductors per peripheral inch Δ and the pole pitch λ_p. What is the slope of the mmf curve?

18. Sketch the conductors on the armature, together with the field poles, for a loaded multipolar generator, indicating the current directions in the various conductors. Sketch a curve showing the values of armature mmf along the armature surface. Show the flux produced by this mmf when acting alone.

19. Show the effect of the flux due to the armature mmf on the distribution of the total flux along the armature surface. How is the neutral zone affected? What change must be made in the brush position? Designate the cross-magnetizing and the demagnetizing ampere-turns on a multipolar armature.

20. Show that, even with the brushes in the geometrical neutral so that there are no demagnetizing armature ampere-turns as such, demagnetizing action is produced by the saturation of the poles.

21. Name three methods by which armature reaction is either reduced or practically eliminated. State the principle of each method.

22. Sketch an *ideal* commutation curve, assuming uniform current distribution over the brush.

23. What is the effect of having emfs induced in a coil during the time that it is being short-circuited by the brush? What limits the current in such a coil? How does this current affect the distribution of current over the brush?

24. Sketch commutation curves for the following conditions: (*a*) brush too far forward; (*b*) brush too far back; (*c*) brush too wide.

25. Why does an armature coil have self-inductance? What is the effect of this self-inductance during the commutation period? What effect does the emf of self-induction have on the relation of the brush position to the neutral zone?

26. What is the order of magnitude of the emfs induced in a coil undergoing commutation? If such emfs are small, what makes them objectionable?

27. What is the advantage of copper over carbon brushes? Why are carbon brushes used almost universally?

28. What evidence points to the fact that the passage of current between the commutator and the brushes is not pure conduction? To what is "high mica" due? How may it be reduced or even eliminated? Name two methods.

29. In general, what is the effect of arcing on the commutator? Why should any appearance of arcing be a reason for eliminating the cause of the arcing as soon as possible? Why is it not desirable to use emery paper or emery cloth in grinding brushes or smoothing the commutator?

30. What changes occur in the flux at the geometrical neutral of a generator as load is applied? What is the effect of these changes on the brush position? Why may it be necessary to move the brushes ahead of the load neutral plane?

31. Show that rather than moving the brushes forward in order to obtain the proper commutating flux, the same result may be obtained by the use of commutating poles.

32. Why are the commutating poles connected in series with the armature? Why have they an unusually long air-gap?

33. What is the relation of the polarities of main poles and commutating poles to the direction of rotation, in a generator? In practice, how are the commutating poles adjusted to the proper strength?

34. Sketch the connections used in obtaining the shunt characteristic. Sketch the characteristic. Why does the generator finally "break down"? Why does the return curve from short circuit not follow the curve obtained with decreasing values of load resistance?

35. Give three reasons why the voltage of a shunt generator drops as load is applied. Why are the three reactions cumulative? What prevents a generator from "unbuilding" as soon as any load is applied?

36. What effect has running a shunt generator at higher than rated speed have on its characteristic, provided that the field current is adjusted so that the no-load volts remain unchanged?

37. Define "the regulation of a d-c generator" together with such specifications as "method of applying load," "speed," "excitation," "temperature."

38. What is meant by the *total characteristic* of a generator? What is its relation to the shunt characteristic? How may the total power developed within an armature be determined?

39. Determine graphically the shunt characteristic of a generator, given the saturation curve, field resistance, armature resistance, and armature reaction: (*a*) neglecting armature reaction; (*b*) taking the demagnetizing effect of armature reaction into consideration. Show the effects of speed and degree of saturation on the shunt characteristic.

40. How may the objectionable drooping characteristic of the shunt generator be improved? How are the additional turns connected, and in what way do they differ from the shunt-field turns?

41. Show the difference between *long-shunt* and *short-shunt* connection. What is the effect of the connection on the characteristic? Sketch the characteristics of an over-compounded, a flat-compounded, and an under-compounded generator. Where is each used, and why?

42. How is the degree of compounding in a generator adjusted? When do generators have two separate series fields?

43. Determine graphically the compound characteristic of a generator, given the saturation curve, shunt, series-field and armature resistances, demagnetizing armature-turns per pole, and shunt- and series-field turns per pole.

44. Show the effect of speed on the degree of compounding, if the no-load voltage is the same in each case. Compare this with the effect of speed on the shunt characteristic, and explain.

45. Show how the number of series turns for a desired degree of compounding may be determined experimentally. What is the armature characteristic and how may it be utilized?

46. Show how the commutating poles may have the effect on the characteristic of (*a*) cumulative compounding; (*b*) differential compounding.

47. In what way does the series generator differ fundamentally from the shunt generator in construction? In the type of load that it supplies?

48. Describe the external characteristic of the series generator, and show its relation to the saturation curve.

49. In what way does the series generator build up? What is meant by the critical external resistance? Why is it desirable to operate on the right-hand side of the external characteristic?

50. Describe briefly an early use of the series generator. What is the *Thury system* of power transmission, and where was it used?

51. How may the speed of a prime mover affect the generator characteristic? Is a drop in speed chargeable to the generator? How may it be taken into consideration?

52. State one essential difference between a unipolar generator and the ordinary type of generator. What design is necessary to prevent the armature being short-circuited on itself? What is the advantage of this type of generator over the ordinary type and for what type of work is it best adapted? What are its disadvantages?

53. What is the basic principle of the Tirrill regulator?

54. Describe the construction and operation of the type GDA direct-acting voltage regulator of the General Electric Company. What are the advantages of this type of regulator?

55. Make a diagram showing the connections of the third-brush generator. Analyze the reactions which cause the generator to deliver a substantially constant current. What is the effect of moving the third brush forward? backward? For what type of work is this generator used?

56. Make a sketch of the diverter-pole generator, showing the flux relations at no load. Analyze the changes which occur when load is applied. To what type of work are the characteristics of this generator particularly well adapted?

57. What three characteristics are necessary in a welding generator? Compare the transient with the steady-state characteristic. Why is the comparison particularly necessary with arc-welding generators?

58. Describe the construction of the General Electric arc-welding generator. What means are used to obtain the desired volt-ampere characteristics? Why does this generator do away with the use of an external inductance?

59. What is the primary function of the Amplidyne? Show that if the brushes of the conventional generator are short-circuited a small field current can produce a large armature-reaction flux. In the Amplidyne how is this flux utilized to supply a normal load current? Why are recesses in the main pole pieces necessary, and why must a compensating winding in series with the load be placed on the main poles?

60. Show with a diagram how an a-c motor-driven Amplidyne can be used to control the speed of a d-c motor.

61. In the Rototrol describe the function of the *pattern field*, the *pilot field*, the *self-energizing field*. Make a diagram of connections showing the application of the Rototrol to the voltage regulation of a d-c generator. By means of the saturation curve and voltage–ampere-turn line of the energizing-field circuit, analyze the reactions which occur in the Rototrol when the regulated voltage departs from its constant value. Draw the connections by which the Rototrol may be made to control the speed and torque of a motor.

PROBLEMS ON CHAPTER XII

Generator Characteristics

604. Figure 604*A* shows the flux leaving an *N* pole and entering the armature of a 4-pole generator. Directly under the pole the flux density is 7,200 gauss, as shown by the graph. The diameter of the armature is 36 cm, and the speed is 1,800 rpm. The axial length of active conductor is 18 cm. Determine: (*a*) peripheral velocity in centimeters per second of a conductor *a* on surface of armature; (*b*) emf induced in conductor when it is directly under pole where flux density is constant at 7,200 gauss.

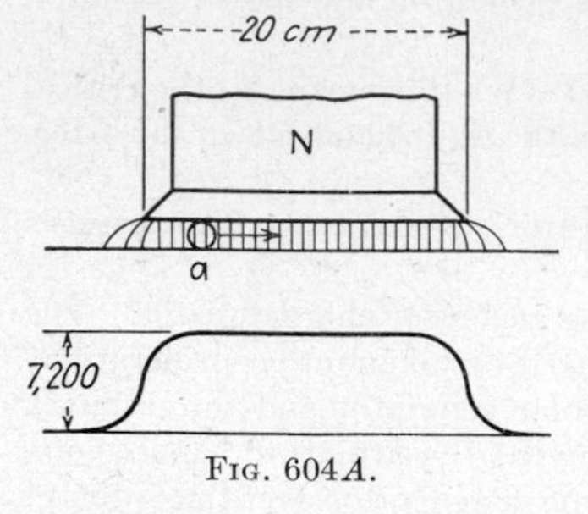

FIG. 604*A*.

605. In Prob. 604 the pole arc is 20 cm, Fig. 605*A*. The *average* value of the flux density directly under the pole and included in a distance equal to the pole arc is now 7,400 gauss. The average flux density over the entire *pole pitch* is 5,230 gauss. Determine: (*a*) average value of emf induced in a conductor during time that it is directly under pole; (*b*) average value of emf induced in a conductor during time that it is passing between two adjacent brush sets; (*c*) emf induced in any one path between brushes if there are 98 series-connected conductors in each path.

606. The axial length of the pole faces of a 4-pole 250-volt 12-kw generator is 4.5 in., and the pole arc is 6 in. The diameter of the armature is 11 in., and the speed is 1,200 rpm. The flux density directly under the pole faces is 45,000 maxwells per sq

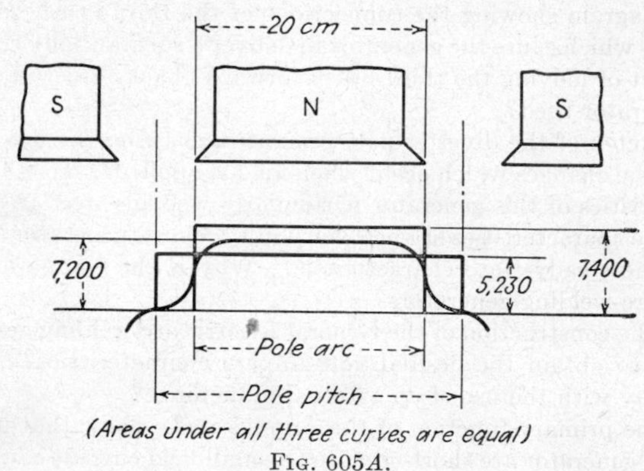

FIG. 605*A*.

in., and the flux-density curve may be considered a rectangle, the peripheral length of which is equal to the pole arc. Determine: (*a*) emf induced in a single conductor on surface of armature when it is directly under a pole face; (*b*) average emf induced in conductor during time that it is passing between any two adjacent brush sets; (*c*) induced emf between brushes. There are 55 slots on the armature and 12 conductors per slot. The armature is simplex lap-wound, giving the same number of parallel paths as there are poles.

607. The pole faces of a 4-pole shunt generator are 10 in. square, and the average flux density *under the poles* is 48,000 maxwells per sq in. The flux-density curve may be considered a rectangle with a peripheral length equal to the pole arc. There are 336 surface conductors on the armature. The armature is wave-wound, giving two parallel paths. Determine: (*a*) induced emf when armature speed is 1,200 rpm; (*b*) power generated if current per armature path is 150 amp.

608. Repeat Prob. 607 for a simplex lap winding; number of conductors, speed, flux, etc., remain the same.

609. In a 500-kw 6-pole 250-volt 900-rpm generator, the diameter of the armature is 28 in., the core length is 13 in., the pole faces are 12 in. square. The average flux density directly under the pole faces at no load is 48,300 maxwells per sq in., and the flux-density curve may be considered rectangular with a peripheral length equal to the pole arc. There are 20 slots per pole and two conductors per slot. The speed is 900 rpm. The armature is simplex lap-wound. Determine: (*a*) peripheral speed of armature in centimeters per second; (*b*) maximum induced emf per conductor; (*c*) average induced emf per conductor; (*d*) conductors in series between brush sets; (*e*) emf between brushes. Verify (*e*) by Eq. (334) (p. 407).

610. In a generator having the same kilowatt rating, speed, and dimensions as that of Prob. 609 the number of slots is 118, and a simplex wave winding is used. The flux density directly under the poles is now 39,300 maxwells per sq in. Determine: (*a*) maximum induced emf per conductor; (*b*) average induced emf per conductor; (*c*) conductors in series between brushes; (*d*) emf between brushes. Verify (*d*) by Eq. (334) (p. 407).

611. In a 6-pole 600-volt generator there are 18 slots per pole, there is a double coil in each slot, and there is a single turn per coil. The armature is simplex lap-wound. The total flux per pole is 6,940,000 maxwells. Determine: (*a*) speed in rpm necessary to give 600 volts; (*b*) current per armature path which will make the internal-power rating 200 kw.

612. The accompanying data are given for the saturation curve of an 80-kw 220-volt 1,200-rpm shunt generator, the data being taken at 1,200 rpm and for increasing

Field current..........	0	0.4	0.8	1.2	1.6	2.0	2.5	3.2	4.0	4.5	5.0	5.5
Induced emf..........	10	38	66	96	128	157	188	222	248	259	267	275

values of field current. (*a*) Plot saturation curve for speeds of 1,000 and 1,100 rpm. Determine critical field resistance at (*b*) 1,200 rpm; (*c*) 1,000 rpm. Draw field-resistance lines to give at no load (*d*) 260 volts at 1,200 rpm; (*e*) 250 volts at 1,000 rpm.

613. The generator of Prob. 612 has four poles and 1,000 shunt-field turns per pole. The armature is simplex lap-wound, and there are 72 slots and four conductors per slot. (*a*) Plot a curve with the field ampere-turns as abscissa and flux per pole as ordinate. (*b*) Determine flux per pole when generator operates at 1,200 rpm and generates 260 volts.

614. When the generator of Prob. 612 has been brought up to the speed of 1,200 rpm and the adjustment of the field resistance is such that the generator builds up to 260 volts, what initial current flows through the field due to the residual magnetism? What induced emf results from this field current? What field current results from this last emf? Trace the successive increments of field current and emf which follow each other until the induced emf reaches the condition of stability.

615. A shunt generator when operating at 800 rpm builds up to 250 volts. The speed and the field resistance are both doubled. To what voltage does it now build up?

616. There are 320 conductors on the surface of the armature of a bipolar generator. The generator delivers 50 amp, giving 25 amp in each conductor. The brushes are advanced 15°. Determine: (*a*) demagnetizing and cross-magnetizing ampere-conductors; (*b*) demagnetizing and cross-magnetizing ampere-turns.

617. The no-load flux per pole of a bipolar generator is 1,800,000 maxwells, there are 2,500 turns per field pole, and the field current is 1.2 amp. There are 240 armature conductors, and the current per conductor is 40 amp. The brushes are advanced 18° beyond the no-load neutral plane. Determine: (*a*) cross-magnetizing armature ampere-turns; (*b*) demagnetizing armature ampere-turns; (*c*) net ampere-turns acting on magnetic circuit if effect of (*a*) is neglected; (*d*) net flux entering armature from *N* pole, neglecting (*a*) and saturation.

618. There are 72 slots on the armature of a 4-pole generator, the armature is simplex lap-wound with double coils (four coil sides per slot), and there are two turns in each coil. The brushes are advanced 8°. The generator armature delivers 180 amp, the shunt-field current is 2.4 amp, and there are 1,200 shunt turns per pole. Determine: (*a*) cross-magnetizing ampere-turns per pole; (*b*) demagnetizing ampere-turns per pole; (*c*) net ampere-turns per pole, taking into consideration field ampere-turns and (*b*).

619. On the armature of an 8-pole 800-kw 250-volt 400-rpm generator there are 160 slots and two conductors per slot. The winding is simplex lap, and there are 160 commutator segments. The field current is 24 amp, and there are 250 shunt turns per pole. The brushes are moved ahead of the geometrical neutral by a distance of 1½ commutator bars. At rated load determine: (*a*) cross-magnetizing ampere-turns per pole; (*b*) demagnetizing ampere-turns per pole; (*c*) net field ampere-turns per pole, considering effect of (*b*) only.

620. On the armature of a 10-pole 800-kw 250-volt shunt generator are 200 slots, 200 commutator segments, 400 surface conductors, and the armature is simplex lap-wound. The diameter of the armature is 80 in., and the pole faces cover 65 per cent of the armature surface. The brushes are moved two commutator segments ahead of the no-load neutral plane. Determine: (*a*) rated current of generator; (*b*) current per armature path; (*c*) demagnetizing ampere-turns per pole; (*d*) cross-magnetizing ampere-turns per pole. (*e*) Make a sketch of the poles and armature surface over a distance equal to at least twice the pole pitch (see Fig. 331, p. 425). Show the demagnetizing and cross-magnetizing ampere-turns. (*f*) Plot separately the mmf of the demagnetizing and cross-magnetizing ampere-turns.

621. In Prob. 620 the field excitation at rated load is such that, if acting alone, 3,800 amp-turns per pole would be consumed in the air-gap and 1,400 amp-turns in the teeth. Draw the approximate resultant mmf distribution along the armature surface and the resulting flux distribution.

622. In Prob. 620 determine: (*a*) total armature ampere-conductors at rated current; (*b*) ampere-conductors per peripheral inch (Δ). (*c*) Draw armature mmf graph, Fig. 326 (p. 420), and determine maximum values in ampere-turns, assuming graph to be a smooth triangular one. (*d*) From the data in Prob. 621, include the graph of the pole mmfs, and determine net mmf at leading and trailing pole tips.

623. In a 4-pole 50-kw 250-volt 1,200-rpm generator the diameter of the armature is 30 cm, and there are 64 slots on the armature and 8 conductors per slot. The diameter of the commutator is 22 cm, there are 64 commutator segments, and the peripheral brush width is 1 cm. The armature is simplex lap-wound with two coil sides per slot (see Fig. 339, p. 433). When the generator delivers rated current, the equivalent of 30,000 maxwells links each armature coil. Determine: (*a*) peripheral velocity of armature in centimeters per second; (*b*) time of commutation; (*c*) total change in flux linking each coil each time coil goes through commutating zone; (*d*) average rate of change of flux in maxwells per second in each coil while it is going through commutating zone; (*e*) average induced emf per coil while it is going through commutating zone.

624. Repeat Prob. 623 with 24,000 maxwells linking each coil and the speed reduced to 1,000 rpm.

625. The armature of a 25-kw 1,600-rpm 240-volt compound generator is 11 in. diameter, the axial length is 6 in., and there are 35 slots in the armature. The winding is simplex lap with triple coils. There are three turns per coil, or three conductors per coil side, and in each slot there are 18 conductors. The commutator is 8 in. diameter, and there are 105 segments. Peripheral width of each brush is 0.4 in. When the generator is carrying its rated load at 1,600 rpm, 12,000 maxwells link each coil side (see Fig. 339, p. 433). Determine: (*a*) peripheral speed of commutator in inches per second; (*b*) time for current in any one coil to reverse from its full positive to its full negative value; (*c*) total flux linking each coil before commutation begins; (*d*) total change of coil flux during commutation period; (*e*) emf induced in a single coil during commutation period, assuming straight-line commutation. Neglect mutual induction between different armature coils.

626. Repeat Prob. 625 with the speed reduced to 1,200 rpm and the current reduced to 0.80 of its value in that problem.

627. The terminal voltage of a 200-kw shunt generator is 600 volts when it delivers rated load current. The resistance of the shunt-field circuit is 250 ohms, the armature resistance is 0.032 ohm, and the brush resistance is 0.014 ohm. (*a*) Determine induced emf at rated current. (*b*) The terminal voltage is 620 volts at half rated current. Determine induced emf.

628. In a 150-kw 250-volt shunt generator, 258 volts is induced in the armature when the generator delivers rated load at 250 volts. At the same time the shunt-field current is 5.8 amp. Determine (*a*) armature resistance including that of brushes. The no-load voltage of the generator is 264 volts. (*b*) Determine regulation. (*c*) Why is the induced emf at rated load not equal to that at no load?

629. The emf induced in the armature of a 400-kw 250-volt shunt generator is 258.8 volts when the terminal voltage and the load current are at rated values and the field current is 12.0 amp. The armature resistance including brushes and commutating-pole field is 0.0055 ohm. Determine: (*a*) terminal voltage; (*b*) power generated; (*c*) power output; (*d*) electrical efficiency of generator.

630. In the accompanying tabulation are the saturation-curve data for a 4-pole 100-kw 250-volt 1,200-rpm shunt generator, obtained with *decreasing* values of field current. The armature resistance including brushes and commutating field is 0.030 ohm, and there are 550 shunt-field turns per pole.

Field current..	6.50	5.82	5.50	5.00	4.5	4.0	3.50	3.0	2.5	2.0	1.0	0.5	0
Induced emf...	290	281	274	262	248	230	210	186	156	125	64	34	8

(*a*) Determine rated load current. Neglecting armature reaction, determine (*b*) field resistance which will give rated terminal voltage of 250 volts at rated current. [In (*b*),the armature-resistance drop requires a knowledge of the field current before the exact value of the field current can be determined. However, it is necessary to know only the approximate value of field current since it has small effect on the armature-resistance drop. In fact, a close estimate of the actual value of field current can be readily made.] Determine (*c*) no-load terminal voltage, neglecting voltage drop in armature due to field current. (*d*) Plot terminal voltage as function of *armature* current to practically short-circuit. (*e*) Plot terminal voltage as function of *load* current. Determine: (*f*) maximum value of load current (see Figs. 352, 353, pp. 446 and 447); (*g*) regulation.

(In Probs. 631, 632, 633 neglect any small hysteresis effects in the saturation curve occurring between the different no-load emfs.)

631. In Prob. 630 the field rheostat is adjusted to give 265 volts at no load. Neglecting armature-resistance drop due to field current, determine: (*a*) field resistance; (*b*) terminal voltage when generator *load* current is 400 amp. (*c*) Plot terminal voltage as function of *armature* current to practically short-circuit. (*d*) Plot terminal voltage as function of *load* current. Determine: (*e*) maximum value of load current; (*f*) regulation.

632. In the generator, Prob. 630, there is the equivalent of 110 demagnetizing ampere-turns per pole (see Sec. 296, p. 424) at rated-load current. (*a*) Determine at rated-*load* current the triangle corresponding to *bcd*, Fig. 354, p. 449, using corresponding *armature* current. (See brackets, Prob. 630.) Determine: (*b*) field resistance which will give rated voltage of 250 volts at rated load current; (*c*) no-load terminal voltage, neglecting voltage drop in armature due to field current. (*d*) Plot terminal voltage as function of armature current to practically short-circuit. (*e*) Plot terminal voltage as function of load current (see Figs. 352, 353). Determine: (*f*) maximum value of load current; (*g*) regulation.

633. The speed of the generator, Prob. 632, is reduced from 1,200 rpm to 1,160 rpm. Repeat Prob. 632.

634. The following are the constants of a 25-kw 250-volt 1,750-rpm compound generator: armature resistance 0.095 ohm; series-field resistance 0.04 ohm; series-field-diverter resistance 0.02 ohm; commutating-pole resistance 0.025 ohm; shunt-field resistance 240 ohms. The generator is connected short-shunt. With the generator delivering rated current at rated voltage, determine power loss in following: (*a*) armature; (*b*) series field; (*c*) diverter; (*d*) shunt field. Determine: (*e*) induced emf; (*f*) total power generated in armature; (*g*) electrical efficiency [output divided by (*f*)].

635. Repeat Prob. 634 with load current at one-half rated value, the terminal voltage remaining at 250 volts.

636. The following are the constants of a 500-kw 250-volt 900-rpm compound generator: armature resistance 0.00144 ohm; brush resistance 0.001 ohm; series-field resistance 0.00045 ohm; commutating-pole resistance 0.00054 ohm; shunt-field resistance 21 ohms. The generator is connected short-shunt. When it delivers rated load at rated terminal voltage, determine power loss in (*a*) armature; (*b*) brushes; (*c*) series field; (*d*) commutating poles; (*e*) shunt field. Determine: (*f*) total power loss; (*g*) total power generated; (*h*) electrical efficiency of generator [output divided by (*g*)].

637. Repeat Prob. 636 with the load current at three-fourths rated value and the terminal voltage 254 volts.

638. Repeat Prob. 636 with the generator delivering one-half rated current at 256 volts.

639. A 500-kw 550- to 650-volt compound railway generator is compounded so that it maintains the voltage constant at 550 volts at all loads for a point 2.5 miles distant. The overhead system consists of a No. 4/0 hard-drawn trolley wire, having a resistance of 0.28 ohm per mile, paralleled by three 500,000-cir-mil feeders in parallel, each feeder having a resistance of 0.114 ohm per mile. The resistance of the track return is 0.020 ohm per mile. Determine: (*a*) value of generator terminal voltage when load at 2.5-mile point is 800 amp; (*b*) efficiency of transmission.

640. The no-load voltage of a 400-kw compound generator is 250 volts. It supplies a 400-kw load, situated 1,000 ft distant, over a 1,000,000-cir-mil cable. It is desired to maintain the voltage at the load constant at 250 volts from no load to rated load of 400 kw. Determine no-load and rated-load voltage of generator. Assume that a circular-mil-foot of copper has a resistance of 11 ohms at the operating temperature of the cable.

641. Repeat Prob. 640 for the condition that the voltage at the load shall rise from 250 to 265 volts from no load to full load.

642. The generator of Prob. 640 is connected short-shunt. Armature resistance is 0.012 ohm, shunt-field resistance is 28 ohms, series-field resistance is 0.0035 ohm, diverter resistance is 0.009 ohm, and commutating-field resistance is 0.0020 ohm. Determine: (*a*) emf induced in armature with the 400-kw load of Prob. 640; (*b*) power loss in armature, in shunt field, in series field, in diverter, in commutating-pole circuit, and in cable; (c) percentage of power generated which reaches load.

643. Repeat Prob. 642 for the 400-kw load of Prob. 641. It is now necessary to remove the series-field diverter.

644. In the generator of Probs. 612 and 613, there are 3½ series turns per pole. The combined resistance of the armature, brushes, and commutating-pole field in series is 0.022 ohm, and the resistance of the series field is 0.010 ohm. The generator is connected long-shunt. Determine: (a) rated load current; (b) rated field current with flat compounding; (c) series-field ampere-turns to make generator flat-compounded, neglecting armature reaction; (d) series-field current in (c); (e) resistance of necessary diverter.

645. In the 100-kw 250-volt generator, Prob. 630, two series-field turns per pole are added, and the generator is connected long-shunt. The combined armature, brush, and commutating-pole resistance is 0.030 ohm, and the series-field resistance is 0.015 ohm. There are 550 shunt turns per pole. In the accompanying tabulation are the saturation-curve data taken with increasing values of field current.

Field current............	0	1.0	2.0	3.0	3.5	4.0	4.5	5.0	5.5	6.0	7.0	8.0
Induced emf............	6	62	122	180	205	226	244	258	271	281	289	294

It is desired that the generator be flat-compounded. As in Probs. 630 and 632, at rated load armature reaction produces 110 demagnetizing ampere-turns per pole. It will be necessary to use a diverter to obtain flat compounding. This will necessitate a trial-and-error method requiring first an assumed diverter resistance, the corresponding voltage drop in the series field, and the corresponding series-field current, etc. (The diverter resistance will be in the neighborhood of the series-field resistance.) With flat compounding the shunt-field current is known.

(a) Determine diverter resistance which at rated-load *armature* current will give in Fig. 361 (p. 456) correct values of b_1c_1 due to series ampere-turns, c_1d_1 due to armature reaction, and e_1d_1 produced by voltage drop in the armature, brushes, commutating-pole field, and equivalent resistance of series field and diverter in parallel, all in series. Note that for flat compounding points b_1 and a coincide. (b) By method shown in Fig. 361, determine terminal voltage at 150 per cent and at 50 per cent rated-load current. (c) Plot load characteristic.

646. In Prob. 645, the diverter is disconnected. Determine terminal voltage by the method of Fig. 361 at (a) 150 per cent rated load; (b) rated load; (c) 50 per cent rated load. (d) Plot load characteristic.

647. It is desired to add series turns to a 75-kw 250-volt shunt generator, so that its rated-load terminal voltage is the same as the no-load terminal voltage. There are 1,050 shunt turns per pole. When load is applied, it is found necessary to increase the shunt-field current from 4.20 to 5.63 amp in order to keep the rated-load terminal voltage equal to the no-load terminal voltage. The generator is connected long-shunt. The rated current is 300 amp. (a) Determine series turns per pole which it is necessary to add. (b) If 7½ turns per pole are added and the resistance of the series-field circuit is 0.008 ohm, determine resistance of diverter. The voltage drop in the series field may be neglected; that is, the voltage across the brushes at rated load and at no load are the same. (The small voltage drop in the series field can be compensated for by the diverter.) The armature current at rated load may be taken as 300 amp.

648. It is desired that the voltage of a 500-kw 600-volt compound generator, connected long-shunt, shall increase from 550 volts at no load to 600 volts at rated load. With the series field out of circuit and the shunt field excited from an external source, it is found that the desired increase of voltage, in addition to the combined series-field and diverter voltage drop, may be obtained by increasing the shunt-field current from its no-load value of 7.8 to 14.3 amp. There are 500 shunt turns per pole and 6½ series turns per pole. The series-field resistance is 0.008 ohm. Determine resistance of a diverter to be connected across series field.

649. Assume that a series generator is supplying a current of 6.6 amp to a series lighting system. The terminal voltage of the generator is 2,700 volts. The armature resistance is 22 ohms, and the series-field resistance is 18 ohms. The series field is shunted by a 35-ohm shunt. Determine: (*a*) induced emf in generator; (*b*) armature loss; (*c*) series-field loss; (*d*) shunt loss.

650. A 150-kw load is situated 2,200 ft distant from the 240-volt bus bars of a station. The load is supplied over a 750,000-cir-mil feeder. It is desired that when the load is 160 kw, the load voltage shall be not less than 230 volts. (*a*) Determine current and voltage rating of a series booster designed to maintain voltage at this value. Assume that a circular-mil-foot has a resistance of 11 ohms at the operating temperature of the feeder. The efficiency of the booster is 87 per cent. It is driven by a shunt motor connected across the bus bars, the motor efficiency being 88 per cent. (*b*) Determine over-all efficiency of feeder.

QUESTIONS ON CHAPTER XIII

The Motor

1. In what way does a motor differ from a generator in the function which it performs? In general construction?

2. What effect occurs when a straight conductor carrying a current is placed in a magnetic field perpendicular to the direction of the field? Explain this action by two elementary laws of magnetism. What is the effect of reversing the current in the conductor?

3. To what three factors is the force proportional? If the flux density alone is doubled, how is the force affected? If the current alone is doubled?

4. From the relation giving the field intensity at the center of a coil carrying current derive the equation which gives the force on a conductor carrying current in a magnetic field.

5. State a convenient rule by which the relation among the direction of the current, the direction of the field, and the direction of the force can be determined. What other simple method enables one to determine this relation?

6. Define torque. In what units is it expressed in the British system? In the metric system?

7. Show that a coil carrying current when placed in a magnetic field may develop a torque. In what position of the coil is the torque a maximum? When is it zero? If continuous rotation is desired, what change in the connection to the coil should be made when the torque reaches its zero value?

8. Why is a large number of conductors on the armature desirable? To what three factors is the torque of an armature proportional? In any given motor to what two factors is the torque proportional?

9. How can it be shown that resistance alone does not determine the current to a motor armature? Why must there be an emf induced in a motor armature when it is rotating? What is the relation of this emf to the direction of the current; to the direction of the applied voltage?

10. Is the counter emf greater or less than the applied voltage? Why? By what quantity do the two voltages differ?

11. Fundamentally, upon what two quantities does the speed of a motor depend? Derive the equation which gives the speed in terms of terminal voltage, armature-resistance drop, and flux per pole.

12. Show that the mechanical power developed by a motor armature is equal to the product of the current and the counter emf.

13. In what direction is the flux of a motor distorted by armature reaction? In what direction should the brushes be moved as the load is applied to a motor? What general effect on the field flux does this movement of the brushes have? What is the effect on the speed?

14. What is the relation among the main poles, the commutating poles, and the direction of rotation of a motor? How does this relation compare with the similar one for a generator?

15. When load is applied to a motor what is its first reaction? With the shunt motor, how does this reaction affect the counter emf? The current to the armature?

16. What two characteristics are important in considering the adaptability of a motor for commercial work?

17. When load is applied to a shunt motor, show the relation of internal torque to armature current. Derive the equation which gives the speed as a function of armature current. Discuss the effect of armature reaction on speed. Define *speed regulation* and its significance as regards a motor's performance.

18. To what general type of work is a shunt motor adapted, and why? Compare adjustable-speed operation with variable-speed operation of a motor. Discuss the starting of shunt motors under load.

19. How does the flux in a series motor vary with the load current? Show the relation of internal torque to load current, assuming no saturation in the magnetic circuit. Show the relation of speed to load current. What precautions should be taken when the series motor is being installed for industrial drives?

20. To what general types of load is a series motor adapted, and why? For what reasons is it especially adapted to railway work?

21. What quantities are plotted as the characteristics of a series railway motor? Why?

22. In what way do the windings of a compound motor differ from those of a shunt motor? A series motor? In what two ways, with respect to the shunt winding, may the series winding be connected?

23. Discuss the speed characteristic of the cumulative-compound motor; the torque characteristic. What is the one advantage of this motor over the series motor? For what general type of work is it best adapted?

24. What is the nature of the speed and torque characteristics of the differential-compound motor? Is this type of motor in general use? Explain. What precaution is necessary in starting this type of motor?

25. How may the direction of rotation of a motor be reversed? What is the effect of reversing the line terminals?

26. Why is a starting rheostat necessary for d-c motors? With the shunt motor, in what circuit is the starting resistor connected? Why should it not be connected in the line?

27. What two additions to the starting resistor of Fig. 396 (p. 501) are incorporated in a three-point starting box? Why? Sketch the connections of a three-point box. Show that the starting resistor, which is in series with the shunt field when the arm is in the running position, has little effect on the field current.

28. Under what conditions of motor operation is a three-point box undesirable? Why? Show that this objection is overcome by the use of a four-point box. Sketch the connections of a four-point box. What is the principal advantage of having the hold-up magnet in series with the shunt field?

29. Sketch the connections of a starting box containing the field rheostat. Why is it necessary to short-circuit this rheostat on starting? How is this accomplished?

30. How should a shunt motor be stopped? Give reasons. What is the effect of stopping the motor by throwing back the starting arm?

31. Sketch the connections of series-motor starters. What is the advantage of the no-load release over the no-voltage release?

32. When are controllers used, and why? What two functions may a controller perform outside actual starting duty?

33. What are two advantages of automatic starters in medium sizes of motors? In the larger sizes of motors? Describe the method of operation of the General Electric automatic starter shown in Fig. 402 (p. 507). Compare the operation of the temperature overload relay with that of a fuse.

34. What is the principle of the magnetic blowout? Under what conditions is it used?

35. What two factors only can be varied in obtaining speed control of a motor? In the armature-resistance-control method, which of these factors is varied? What are the advantages of this method of control? Name two serious disadvantages.

36. What is the principle of the multivoltage system? How are coarse adjustments of speed obtained? Fine adjustments? What is the objection to this system?

37. What factor in the speed equation is varied in the Ward Leonard system of speed control? How many machines are necessary in this system? What is the chief advantage of the system, and where is it used? Name two disadvantages.

38. What factor in the speed equation is varied in the field-control method? Name two distinct advantages of this method. What limits the range of speed obtainable? What type of motor is especially adapted to this type of speed control?

39. Upon what principle does the Lincoln motor operate? What are its advantages?

40. What is meant by *series-parallel* control of railway motors? Why is such control desirable? Sketch the half-speed and the maximum-speed connections in a two-motor car; in a four-motor car.

41. Give three reasons why it is objectionable to place the main controller on the platform in the larger sizes of electric cars. How are these objections overcome? Give two other reasons why automatic control is desirable.

42. What is the general principle underlying the multiple-unit control? What is the train line?

43. Name briefly the sequence of closing of the contactors in starting a train.

44. What is meant by *dynamic braking?* Where is it used? Can a motor armature be brought to a standstill by this method of braking? Explain. Show the sequence of operations by which a series motor is brought from operation as a motor to full dynamic braking.

45. What is regenerative braking, and where is it used? What special auxiliary equipment is necessary when regenerative braking is used with series motors?

46. Under what circumstances is it desirable to know the efficiency of a motor? What type of brake is often used for loading motors? Does this type lend itself readily to calculation of torque and power output of the motor? Explain. What is meant by the "tare reading" of the brake arm, and how can it be determined and correction be made? What is a common method of cooling prony brakes?

47. Derive the equation which gives the horsepower of a prony brake.

48. Describe the cradle dynamometer. To what several uses is it adapted?

49. In what way does a speed counter differ from a tachometer? Upon what principle is the magneto-voltmeter method of measuring speed based?

50. Define a dynamotor. What factors determine the voltage ratio between the two commutators? Discuss the effect on the voltage ratio of varying the field excitation.

PROBLEMS ON CHAPTER XIII

The Motor

651. The average flux density directly under an N pole of a motor, Fig. 651A, is 7,500 gauss. The active length of conductor is 24 cm, and the current per conductor is 25 amp. Determine force on each conductor in (a) dynes; (b) grams; (c) kilograms. There are eight slots under each pole face, there are four poles and 16 conductors per slot. Assuming that the flux density is constant directly under the pole shoe and zero between poles, determine (d) total peripheral force on surface of armature in kilograms, developed by armature conductors.

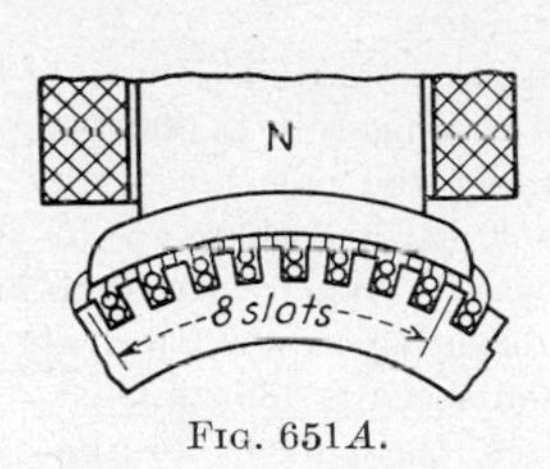

FIG. 651A.

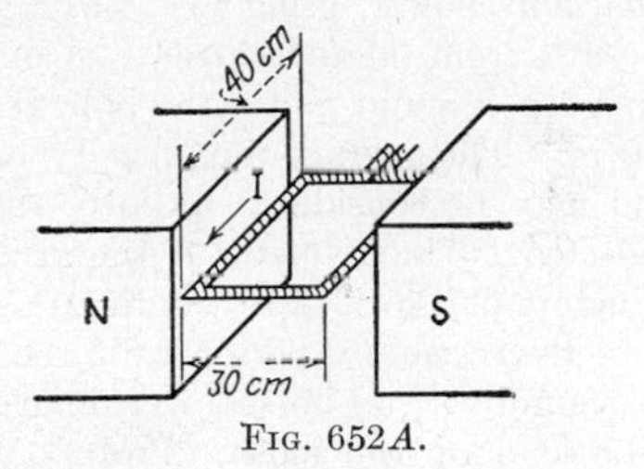

FIG. 652A.

652. A coil of 20 turns, Fig. 652A, of length 40 cm and width 30 cm, lies in a uniform magnetic field, the density of which is 1,800 gauss. The plane of the coil is parallel to the direction of the field; the direction of the flux is from left to right; and the direction of the current in the left-hand coil side is toward the observer. The current in each turn of the coil is 15 amp. Determine: (a) force developed by each horizontal coil side; (b) turning moment or torque in gram-centimeters. Determine torque in gram-centimeters when coil has turned in a clockwise direction (c) 45°; (d) 60°.

653. In Fig. 653A is shown a 4-coil air-core armature with 45° between successive coils and the common axis of the four coils perpendicular to a uniform magnetic field the flux density of which is 2,000 gauss. The coils are rectangular, and each coil is 30 cm parallel to the pole faces and 20 cm perpendicular to the axis. There are 24 turns in each coil, and the current per turn is 20 amp. When the armature is in such a position that the plane of a coil ab is parallel to the magnetic field, Fig. 653A, determine (a) torque in gram-centimeters developed by armature. (b) Repeat (a) when coil has turned through an angle of 22.5° in a clockwise direction.

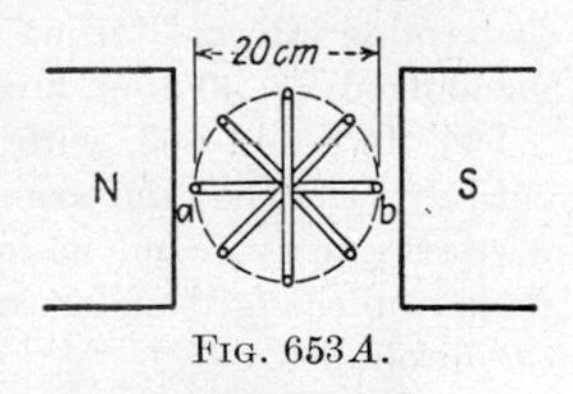

FIG. 653A.

654. The diameter of the armature, Fig. 651A, is 50 cm. Using the data of Prob. 651 determine torque in kilogram-meters when average flux density under the pole face is (a) 7,500 gauss and current is 30 amp; (b) 8,000 gauss and current is 24 amp.

655. The diameter of the armature of a 15-hp 230-volt 1,200-rpm 4-pole shunt motor is 10.5 in., and the axial length of the core is 4 in. The pole arc is 5.4 in., and the axial length of the pole face is 3.75 in. There are 39 slots on the armature and

18 conductors per slot. The winding is simplex wave. The current to the armature is 54 amp, the average flux density directly under the pole faces is 40,000 maxwells per sq in., and any fringing may be considered negligible. Determine: (*a*) force in dynes on single conductor; (*b*) number of armature conductors which at any instant lie under the four pole faces (multiply total armature conductors by ratio of pole arc to pole pitch); (*c*) peripheral force in dynes acting on armature; (*d*) peripheral force in grams; (*e*) peripheral force in kilograms and pounds (1 kg = 2.205 lb); (*f*) internal torque in pound-feet.

656. In Prob. 655, the average flux density becomes 42,000 maxwells per sq in. and the armature current 62 amp. Determine: (*a*) peripheral force in dynes acting on armature; (*b*) peripheral force in pounds; (*c*) internal torque in pound-feet.

657. In Prob. 655, at rated speed of 1,200 rpm, determine from torque and speed (*a*) internal horsepower, using Eq. (361) (p. 519). Determine: (*b*) counter emf; (*c*) internal power in watts from (*b*) and current. Compare (*c*) with (*a*).

658. In Prob. 656, at rated speed of 1,200 rpm, determine from torque and speed (*a*) internal horsepower, using Eq. (361). Determine: (*b*) counter emf; (*c*) internal power in watts from (*b*) and current. Compare with (*a*).

659. In a 4-pole shunt motor the pole arc is 10 in., and the axial length of the pole face is 10 in. The average flux density under the pole faces is 48,000 maxwells per sq in. and may be considered uniform directly under the pole faces, any fringing being neglected. The diameter of the armature is 20 in., and there are 57 slots and four conductors per slot. The winding is simplex wave. When current to armature is 280 amp, determine: (*a*) peripheral force in pounds acting on armature; (*b*) internal torque in pound-feet; (*c*) horsepower developed when speed is 658 rpm.

660. The load on the motor, Prob. 659, changes, the current to the armature becoming 200 amp. Owing to armature reaction the flux density under the leading pole tip becomes 54,000 maxwells per sq in. and that under the trailing pole tip 36,000 maxwells per sq in., and the flux density may be considered to vary uniformly along the pole arc. Determine internal torque in pound-feet.

661. In Prob. 659, determine: (*a*) speed in rpm necessary to induce a counter emf of 240 volts; (*b*) internal power in kilowatts.

662. In Prob. 660, determine: (*a*) speed in rpm necessary to induce a counter emf of 244 volts; (*b*) internal power in kilowatts.

663. When the flux per pole in the air-gap of a shunt motor is 800,000 maxwells and the armature current is 75 amp, the motor develops 90 lb-ft internal torque. Determine internal torque when armature current is (*a*) 45 amp; (*b*) 55 amp, flux unchanged; (*c*) 40 amp, flux equal to 900,000 maxwells.

664. In Prob. 663, with the flux equal to 800,000 maxwells and the shaft load entirely removed, the armature current is 7 amp. (*a*) Determine internal torque necessary to overcome no-load rotational losses. (*b*) Assuming that rotational losses remain unchanged under conditions of (*a*), Prob. 663, determine torque at pulley in (*a*), Prob. 663.

665. The flux per pole of a 35-hp 230-volt 1,200-rpm shunt motor is 2,400,000 maxwells, and the electromagnetic torque is 120 lb-ft when the armature current is 100 amp. Series turns are added to the field poles and are so connected that the motor is cumulative-compound, long-shunt. It is desired that the electromagnetic torque be 200 lb-ft when the armature current is 140 amp. Determine maxwells per pole by which the flux must be increased by series winding. Neglect effect of armature reaction.

666. The resistance of the armature of a 25-hp 240-volt shunt motor is 0.083 ohm. When connected to a 240-volt supply the armature develops a counter emf of 232.8 volts. Determine: (*a*) armature current; (*b*) armature current when connected across same power supply while stationary; (*c*) counter emf when armature current is 110 amp.

667. When the armature of the motor, Prob. 666, is taking 80 amp, determine: (*a*) counter emf; (*b*) internal power; (*c*) internal torque if speed is 1,500 rpm.

668. In Prob. 666 the speed is 1,500 rpm. Determine: (*a*) speed at which machine must operate as a generator in order that armature output may be 87 amp at 240 volts; (*b*) speed at which armature current is zero when terminal voltage is 240 volts.

669. There are 702 conductors on the armature of a 230-volt 4-pole 15-hp shunt motor, the winding is simplex wave, and its resistance is 0.252 ohm. The flux per pole is 765,000 maxwells, and the armature current is 60 amp. Determine speed of armature.

670. On the armature of a 4-pole shunt motor are 456 surface conductors, and the armature is simplex wave. The flux is $2.41 \cdot 10^6$ maxwells per pole. (*a*) Determine counter emf when speed is 1,500 rpm. The armature resistance is 0.2 ohm. (*b*) Determine terminal voltage when armature current is 60 amp if speed and flux remain constant.

671. In Prob. 670 determine current in armature when speed drops to 1,480 rpm, the terminal voltage and flux remaining constant.

672. In a 500-hp 6-pole 250-volt 800-rpm shunt motor the pole faces are 0.30 meter square, the average flux density directly under the poles is 0.77 weber per sq m, and fringing may be neglected. There are 270 armature conductors, and the winding is simplex lap. The armature resistance including that of the brushes is 0.004 ohm, and the resistance of the commutating pole circuit is 0.0012 ohm. With 250 volts terminal voltage determine speed when armature current is (*a*) 1,600 amp; (*b*) 800 amp.

673. The resistance of the armature of a 25-hp 250-volt shunt motor is 0.11 ohm. When running without load, the motor takes 6.32 amp at rated voltage, the field current is 0.92 amp, and the speed is 1,280 rpm. Neglecting armature reaction, determine: (*a*) speed when *motor* current is rated value of 84 amp, field current remaining unchanged; (*b*) speed regulation. Determine speed when motor current is (*c*) 60 amp; (*d*) 40 amp.

674. The resistance of the armature of a 230-volt 15-hp 1,800-rpm shunt motor is 0.252 ohm, and the resistance of the commutating-pole circuit is 0.033 ohm. The rated current is 55.3 amp. At no load the current to the motor is 3.85 amp, 0.95 amp of which is shunt-field current, and the speed is 1,810 rpm. Neglecting armature reaction, at rated voltage determine: (*a*) speed at rated-load current; (*b*) speed regulation; (*c*) internal power; (*d*) internal torque; (*e*) load torque.

675. In Prob. 674 determine: (*a*) speed at 0.75 rated-load current; (*b*) internal power; (*c*) internal torque.

676. A compound winding on the motor of Prob. 674 is connected long-shunt and aids the shunt field. Its resistance is 0.029 ohm. When the motor current is at its rated value of 55.3 amp at 230 volts, the compound winding increases the flux per pole 20 per cent. Assume that the increase in flux is proportional to the armature current, and neglect armature reaction. Determine speed when motor takes (*a*) 3.85 amp; (*b*) 55.3 amp, the shunt-field current remaining unchanged. (*c*) Compare internal torques at 55.3 amp with and without series field.

677. At no load the flux per pole to the armature in the motor of Prob. 674 is 1,050,000 maxwells. It is desired that the motor (Probs. 674 and 676) have the same speed as at no load when the line, or motor, current is 55.3 amp. Determine flux per pole.

678. Determine: (*a*) the mechanical power in kilowatts and horsepower developed in armature of Prob. 674 when motor current is 55.3 amp at 230 volts; (*b*) internal torque in (*a*).

679. A 60-hp 250-volt 1,200-rpm shunt motor takes 214 amp at 250 volts. The field current is 1.05 amp, and the combined armature, brush, and commutating-field resistance is 0.039 ohm. The motor speed when running light is 1,200 rpm, and the line current is 8.6 amp. Determine (*a*) internal power developed in kilowatts and horsepower. When line current is 214 amp, determine: (*b*) internal power in kilowatts and horsepower; (*c*) internal torque in pound-feet.

680. In a 100-hp 600-volt 1,200-rpm, shunt motor the field resistance is 500 ohms, and the combined armature, brush, and commutating-field resistance is 0.13 ohm. The efficiency of the motor at its rated load is 90 per cent. At rated output and speed determine: (*a*) line current; (*b*) field current; (*c*) counter emf; (*d*) internal power in kilowatts; (*e*) internal torque; (*f*) torque at pulley.

681. Repeat Prob. 680 for one-half rated horsepower output. The efficiency is now 87.5 per cent. Note that speed changes.

682. In Prob. 680 the armature is blocked so that it remains stationary, and an external resistor is connected in series with one of the *line* wires and is adjusted so that the current is at its rated value. Determine: (*a*) field current; (*b*) armature current. (*c*) Compare this division of field and armature current with that of Prob. 680, and explain.

683. The resistance of the armature of a 25-hp 250-volt series motor is 0.12 ohm, and the resistance of the series field is 0.10 ohm. When the motor takes 85 amp, the speed is 600 rpm. Determine speed when the current is (*a*) 100 amp; (*b*) 40 amp. Assume saturation curve is a straight line, and neglect armature reaction.

684. In Prob. 683, determine speed in (*a*) and (*b*) with series field shunted with 0.5-ohm resistor.

685. In a 60-hp 550-volt series motor, the combined armature, brush, and commutating-field resistance is 0.21 ohm, and the series-field resistance is 0.10 ohm. At rated current of 90 amp the speed is 420 rpm. Determine speed when current is (*a*) 100 amp; (*b*) 50 amp. (*c*) Determine current when speed becomes 1,200 rpm. Assume saturation curve is straight line, and neglect armature reaction.

686. The rated current of a 10-hp 230-volt 1,500-rpm shunt motor is 37.5 amp. The field current is 0.45 amp. The armature resistance is 0.25 ohm. At rated current and speed, the internal torque is 38.7 lb-ft. Determine internal torque when line current is (*a*) 18 amp; (*b*) 30 amp. (*c*) Determine speed in (*a*) and (*b*). Neglect armature reaction. Determine: (*d*) speed regulation at 37.5 amp if no-load line current is 2.55 amp; (*e*) torque at pulley at rated current. Neglect armature reaction.

687. The flux of the motor, Prob. 686, is reduced to 0.88 of the value in Prob. 686. The field current is now 0.37 amp. Determine: (*a*) internal torque and speed at rated current with this new value of field current; (*b*) internal torque and speed when motor current is 20 amp and field current is 0.37 amp. Neglect armature reaction.

688. A 7.5-hp 240-volt series motor develops 78 lb-ft internal torque when the current is 27 amp. Determine internal torque when current is (*a*) 36 amp; (*b*) 20 amp; (*c*) 10 amp. Neglect armature reaction, and assume straight-line saturation curve.

689. The armature resistance of the motor, Prob. 688, is 0.54 ohm, and the field resistance is 0.15 ohm. Determine speed when current at 240 volts is (*a*) 36 amp; (*b*) 20 amp; (*c*) 10 amp. Determine internal horsepower when current is (*d*) 36 amp; (*e*) 20 amp.

690. The resistance of the armature of a 60-hp 600-volt series railway motor is 0.215 ohm, the resistance of the commutating-field is 0.050 ohm and that of the series field is 0.080 ohm. At rated voltage, and rated current of 82.0 amp, the speed is 600 rpm. Determine speed and internal torque when current is (*a*) 95 amp; (*b*) 40 amp. Assume straight-line saturation curve, and neglect armature reaction.

691. In Prob. 690 repeat (*a*) and (*b*) when series field is shunted by a 0.5-ohm resistor.

692. When a railway car, operating with two series motors in parallel, takes 200 amp, the total tractive effort developed is 6,000 lb. Determine approximate tractive effort when car is starting with (*a*) two motors in series and car is taking 220 amp; (*b*) with motors in parallel and current to car 380 amp. Assume straight-line saturation curve for motors, and neglect armature reaction.

693. The railway car of Prob. 692 starts under conditions which require a tractive effort of 6,800 lb, the two motors being connected in series. When the car is running with the two motors connected in parallel, a tractive effort of 4,000 lb is required. Determine approximate current to car when (*a*) car is starting with motors in series; (*b*) car is running with motors in parallel.

694. The speed of a 25-hp 250-volt cumulative-compound motor, when running light, is 1,500 rpm, and the line current is 6.10 amp. The shunt-field resistance is 300 ohms, the series-field resistance is 0.04 ohm, the commutating-field resistance is 0.03 ohm, and the armature resistance is 0.10 ohm. The motor is connected long-shunt. The line current at rated load is 84.0 amp, and the corresponding speed is 960 rpm. Determine: (*a*) counter emf at no-load speed; (*b*) counter emf at rated-load speed; (*c*) ratio of rated- to no-load flux; (*d*) internal torque at rated load. Neglect armature reaction.

695. In Prob. 694, when line current is 42.0 amp determine: (*a*) counter emf; (*b*) ratio of flux to no-load flux; (*c*) speed; (*d*) internal torque. Assume that the increase in flux is proportional to the series-field current.

696. The rated current of a 50-hp 250-volt shunt motor is 168 amp. The no-load speed of the motor is 850 rpm, the combined armature and commutating-field resistance is 0.052 ohm, and the shunt-field resistance is 150 ohms. It is desired that the starting torque of the motor be equal to the rated-load torque. Determine: (*a*) total initial resistance of starting box; (*b*) armature current when speed becomes 25 per cent of no-load speed, with entire starting resistance still in circuit. Neglect armature-resistance drop at no load and armature reaction.

697. When the motor of Prob. 696 has reached 25 per cent no-load speed, as in (*b*), it is desired that the armature current again be made equal to its rated value by moving the starting arm to the next contact. Determine remaining resistance in starting box. Neglect armature-resistance drop at no load, and armature reaction.

698. The motor of Prob. 696 reaches one-half the no-load speed with the resistance determined in Prob. 697 still in circuit. (*a*) Determine armature current. (*b*) It is desired that the armature current again be made equal to its rated value by moving the starting arm to the next contact. (*c*) Determine remaining resistance in starting box. Neglect armature-resistance drop at no load, and armature reaction.

699. The resistances of the armature and field of a 60-hp 600-volt series motor are 0.24 and 0.08 ohm. The rated current is 82 amp. Determine resistance of first position of starting controller in order that motor may develop on starting (*a*) rated-load torque; (*b*) 200 per cent rated-load torque. Assume that saturation curve is a straight line, and neglect armature reaction.

700. The resistance of the armature of a 25-hp 230-volt shunt motor is 0.076 ohm. When the armature current is 4.55 amp, the speed is 1,200 rpm. It is desired that the speed be reduced to 750 rpm at rated armature current of 91 amp by inserting external resistance in the armature circuit (see Fig. 404, p. 509). (*a*) Determine necessary external series armature resistance. (*b*) With this external resistance in circuit determine speed when armature current is 45 amp. (*c*) In (*b*) determine per cent of rated-load torque. In (*a*) and (*b*) determine per cent of power to armature circuit that is converted to (*d*) mechanical power; (*e*) heat.

701. Repeat Prob. 700 for 500 rpm.

702. The resistance of the armature of a 15-hp 230-volt 1,500-rpm shunt motor is

0.252 ohm, and the resistance of the shunt-field circuit is 275 ohms. The rated motor current is 56.3 amp. The speed with 230 volts and at rated current is 1,500 rpm. A 0.75-ohm resistor is inserted in series with the armature. Determine: (*a*) speed; (*b*) speed when armature current is 28 amp. In (*a*) and (*b*) determine per cent of power to armature circuit that is converted to (*c*) mechanical power; (*d*) heat.

703. Repeat Prob. 702 with the 0.75-ohm resistor replaced by a 2-ohm resistor.

704. In a Ward Leonard system of speed control the efficiencies of the machines are as follows: M_1, Fig. 406 (p. 511), 91.0 per cent; G, 88.0 per cent; M_2, 86.8 per cent. The voltage across the mains is 250 volts. When M_2 delivers 45 hp, determine: (*a*) over-all efficiency of system; (*b*) current supplied by mains.

705. In Prob. 704, the load on the motor is 25 hp, and the corresponding efficiencies are M_1, 87.9 per cent; G, 86.0 per cent; M_2, 84.5 per cent. Repeat (*a*) and (*b*).

706. In a brake similar to that shown in Fig. 412 (p. 517), the length L is 2 ft, the balance reading is 19.8 lb, the tare weight of the arm is 1.6 lb, and the speed of the armature is 1,530 rpm. The terminal voltage is 250 volts, and the current is 36.4 amp. Determine: (*a*) horsepower output; (*b*) input in watts; (*c*) efficiency.

707. Repeat Prob. 706 for a balance reading of 10.3 lb and a speed of 1,540 rpm. The motor input is now 18.45 amp at 250 volts. The tare weight of the arm remains unchanged.

708. It is desired to conduct a brake test on a 20-hp 250-volt 1,500-rpm shunt motor. A brake with a 2-ft arm similar to that in Fig. 412 (p. 517) is available. The test is to be carried to 25 per cent overload. Determine rating in pounds of balance, allowing 3 lb for tare weight.

709. A prony-brake test is made on a 15-hp 240-volt 1,200-rpm shunt motor, a brake of the general type of that shown in Fig. 412 (p. 517) being used. The terminal voltage is maintained constant at 240 volts, and after the motor has reached its operating temperature, the shunt-field current is adjusted to give 1,200 rpm at 15 hp and then remains constant at 1.07 amp. The lever distance of the brake arm is 2 ft, and the tare weight is 0.8 lb. The experimental data are given in the accompanying tabulation. From the data, compute: (*a*) net balance reading; (*b*) torque in pound-

Motor current amp	71.1	66.07	59.1	51.9	45.3	39.6	33.3	26.8
Balance, lb	44.66	41.3	37.1	32.5	28.4	24.8	20.8	16.53
Rpm	1,176	1,189	1,193	1,204	1,213	1,219	1,226	1,235
Motor current, amp	21.5	16.7	11.9	9.1	6.1	4.6	3.5	
Balance, lb	13.1	9.98	6.83	5.02	3.02	1.93	*	
Rpm	1,243	1,250	1,257	1,261	1,265	1,267	1,270	

* Brake removed.

feet; (*c*) horsepower output; (*d*) watts output; (*e*) watts input; (*f*) efficiency. Plot as function of horsepower output (see Fig. 390, p. 494) (*g*) current; (*h*) torque; (*i*) rpm; (*j*) efficiency. It is suggested that the data and computations be tabulated in columns headed as follows: I; VI = input watts; Balance reading; Net pounds; Torque; Rpm; Hp output; Watts output; Efficiency.

QUESTIONS ON CHAPTER XIV

Losses; Efficiency; Operation

1. State the method of determining each of the following losses, which are scheduled by ASA Standard C50 "Rotating Electrical Machinery": (*a*) shunt-field loss; (*d*) friction and windage loss; (*e*) brush friction loss; (*g*) core loss; (*h*) armature I^2R loss;

(*i*) series-field windings I^2R loss; (*j*) brush-contact loss; (*k*) stray-load loss. State the nature of (*k*).

2. Draw the diagram of connections for measuring the resistance of the armature copper.

3. Show, with sketches, the nature of eddy-current losses in the iron of dynamos. What means are employed to reduce the losses to permissible values? Why is silicon steel seldom used for dynamo cores?

4. To what two quantities are eddy currents proportional? How does the eddy-current loss vary with each of these quantities?

5. Show, with a sketch, how hysteresis loss occurs in the armature core of a dynamo. How does hysteresis loss vary with the speed and the flux?

6. Show, with a sketch, the nature of pole-face losses. What means are taken to reduce such losses to small values?

7. Give three formulas for obtaining efficiency. Which of the three is used ordinarily for a generator? For a motor? Explain.

8. With electrical machines, why is it almost always more accurate to obtain the efficiency by measurement of the losses, rather than by direct measurements of output and input?

9. Which of the losses in the ASA schedule can be determined directly by electrical measurement?

10. Which of the losses in the ASA schedule can be combined and denoted as "stray power"? Of what quantities are these losses a function, and how are the losses supplied?

11. Why is it possible to duplicate under no-load conditions the stray power which exists when the machine is under load?

12. Give the equations by which the efficiency of a generator may be determined from the losses which include stray power. Repeat for a motor.

13. Show why stray power is a function of E/S and S. To what operating conditions is this relation applied?

14. Under what conditions is a machine operated in order to determine its stray power? Derive the equation which gives the stray power. Show a diagram of connections, and state the measurements from which stray power may be determined.

15. In the measurement of stray power, show how the correct value of flux (E/S) is obtained. Repeat for speed. Show that these adjustments can be made independently.

16. For what purpose is a set of stray-power curves desirable? Why cannot the stray power over the entire operating range of a dynamo be shown with a single curve?

17. In the opposition method what assumption is made as to the distribution of stray-power and stray-load losses between the two machines? Does this assumption introduce appreciable error? In this method how are the two machines started and adjusted? What instruments are used, and what measurements are necessary? State the disadvantages of this method.

18. In general, what factor determines the rating of a steam engine? A steam turbine? A gas engine? An electric machine? Give reasons in each case.

19. State the effects of excessive temperature on the insulation of electric machinery. Discuss the relation between electrical and mechanical strength of insulation.

20. Enumerate the insulating materials which are included in Class A and Class B. State their "hottest spot temperatures."

21. Discuss the general relations existing between allowable hottest spot temperatures and the "limiting observable temperature rise" in the different parts of electrical machinery.

22. Describe the thermometer method of measuring the temperatures of the different parts of electric machines. Repeat for the resistance method.

23. For what length of time should a temperature test be run? How may the temperature rise be accelerated? In what way may a machine's approach to constant temperature be determined? Why does the temperature of a machine rise more rapidly at the beginning of a test than at the end? What relation exists between the heat supplied and the heat dissipated when a constant temperature is reached?

24. Why must care be taken not to include the brush and contact resistance when measuring the armature resistance for temperature determination? Where must the voltmeter leads be held?

25. What difficulties arise when the resistance of a multipolar armature is measured for temperature determination? How may these difficulties be eliminated? What precautions should be taken when the field temperature is being determined by resistance measurements?

26. Give five reasons why it is either necessary or desirable to operate shunt generators in parallel. Why does the load characteristic of the shunt generator adapt this type of generator particularly well to parallel operation?

27. Analyze the reactions which follow when one generator begins to take more than its share of the load. What is meant by *stable equilibrium?*

28. State in detail the steps necessary to connect a generator in service. If the generator is connected in service with its voltage equal to that of the bus, why does it not take load? What must be done in order that it may take load?

29. Describe the steps necessary to remove a generator from service. Why is it undesirable to open the generator switch when the machine is supplying load? What is necessary as regards the generator characteristics in order that the machines may properly divide the load over their entire range of operation?

30. Show that overcompounded generators in parallel are in unstable equilibrium. What simple connection makes their operation stable?

31. What two conditions are necessary for two compound generators to divide the load properly over their entire range of operation?

32. Why does not a diverter change the division of load between two compound generators in parallel? What adjustment can be made to change the load division?

33. How many equalizers may be necessary in certain types of compound generators? How many poles must the switch have for such generators?

34. Explain why a compound generator when connected to the bus bars usually takes load, even although at the instant of switching its emf is equal to the bus-bar voltage. What change can be made in the manner of switching which will prevent the foregoing effect?

PROBLEMS ON CHAPTER XIV

Losses; Efficiency; Operation

710. The eddy-current loss in a 25-kw shunt generator is 320 watts when it is operating at 1,200 rpm with a flux of 1,200,000 maxwells per pole. Determine loss (*a*) when speed is 1,500 rpm, the flux remaining unchanged; (*b*) at 1,200 rpm with flux of 1,000,000 maxwells per pole; (*c*) with flux in (*b*) but with speed of 1,500 rpm.

711. The hysteresis loss in the generator of Prob. 710 is 460 watts when the speed is 1,200 rpm. Determine hysteresis loss under conditions of (*a*), (*b*), (*c*).

712. When the induced emf in a 100-kw 250-volt shunt generator is 265 volts and the speed is 1,200 rpm, the hysteresis loss is 1,420 watts. Determine hysteresis loss under following conditions: (*a*) induced emf 280 volts, speed 1,200 rpm; (*b*) induced emf 230 volts, speed 1,020 rpm; (*c*) induced emf 240 volts, speed 1,020 rpm.

713. In Prob. 712, when induced emf is 265 volts and speed is 1,200 rpm, the eddy-current loss is 680 watts. Determine eddy-current loss under conditions of (*a*), (*b*), (*c*).

714. It is desired to separate the eddy-current and hysteresis loss in a 200-kw d-c generator. The generator is operated at 1,000 rpm; the core loss is measured and found to be 3,500 watts. At 1,400 rpm the core loss is found to be 5,790 watts. At 1,000 rpm determine: (*a*) eddy-current loss; (*b*) hysteresis loss. [Use the methods of Sec. 196, p. 270. The use of Eq. (180) is suggested.] (*c*) and (*d*) Repeat (*a*) and (*b*) for 1,200 rpm.

715. A 400-kw 250-volt 1,500-rpm shunt generator delivers 1,500 amp at 245 volts and rated speed. The total losses are 34,100 watts. Determine: (*a*) power input in horsepower; (*b*) torque; (*c*) efficiency.

716. The input to a 50-hp 240-volt shunt motor is 176.5 amp at 240 volts, and the speed is 1,480 rpm. The total losses are 4,420 watts. Determine: (*a*) input; (*b*) output in horsepower; (*c*) efficiency; (*d*) torque.

717. The following data are given for a 50-kw 250-volt 1,500-rpm shunt generator. Resistances are corrected for 75°C. (See symbols for Tables II, III, p. 529.) $V = 250$ volts; $I = 200$ amp; $I_f = 1.18$ amp; $R_a = 0.0245$ ohm; $R_c = 0.0092$ ohm; $P_{SL} = 0.01$ output; $P_{CL} = 1{,}040$ watts; $P_{FW} = 1{,}060$ watts. Arrange data as is done in Table II, including the stray-load loss and brush-contact loss [see (*j*), p. 524, carbon brushes, shunts attached]. Determine: (*a*) total losses; (*b*) input; (*c*) efficiency; (*d*) torque.

718. In Prob. 717 the load is reduced to 100 amp, and the terminal voltage is maintained at 250 volts, other conditions remaining the same. The core loss may be considered to vary as the square of the flux, and hence as E^2, for the small difference in the two cases. Repeat (*a*), (*b*), (*c*), (*d*), Prob. 717.

719. The generator, Prob. 717, operates as a motor at 1,500 rpm. The input is 210 amp at 250 volts, and the shunt-field current is 1.04 amp. The core loss may be considered to vary as the square of the flux, and hence as E^2, as in Prob. 718. Arrange data as is done in Table III (p. 529), and determine: (*a*) total losses; (*b*) output; (*c*) efficiency; (*d*) torque. (The stray-load loss must be found by trial and error.)

720. The following data are given for a 200-kw 240-volt 1,200-rpm compound generator connected long-shunt. Resistances are corrected for 75°C. (See symbols for Tables II, III, p. 529.) $V = 240$ volts; $I = 800$ amp; $I_f = 8.6$ amp; $R_a = 0.0068$ ohm; $R_c = 0.0022$ ohm; $R_s = 0.0018$ ohm; $P_{SL} = 0.01$ output; $P_{CL} = 3{,}200$ watts; $P_{FW} = 3{,}800$ watts. Arrange data and obtain results in accordance with the requirements of Prob. 717.

721. The generator, Prob. 720, operates as a motor at 1,200 rpm, the line current being 750 amp. The field current is 7.8 amp, and as in Probs. 718 and 719 the core loss may be considered to vary as the square of the flux. Arrange data and obtain results in accordance with the requirements of Prob. 719.

722. In a 10-kw 230-volt 1,200-rpm shunt generator the resistance of the armature including brushes is 0.252 ohm, and that of the commutating-field is 0.032 ohm. The shunt-field resistance is 244 ohms. The stray power is 470 watts, the stray-load loss 0.01 the output. At rated load determine: (*a*) input; (*b*) efficiency [Eq. (366), p. 531].

723. In a 500-kw 600-volt 900-rpm compound generator connected short-shunt the resistance of the armature including brushes is 0.0148 ohm, that of the commutating field is 0.0032 ohm, and that of the series field is 0.0041 ohm. The shunt-field resistance is 72.0 ohms; the stray power at rated load and speed is 17.2 kw; the stray-load loss is 0.01 output. Determine at rated load and speed (*a*) total losses; (*b*) efficiency; (*c*) torque necessary to drive generator.

724. In a 220-volt 10-hp 1,800-rpm shunt motor the resistance of the armature including brushes is 0.262 ohm, and that of the commutating field is 0.081 ohm. The shunt-field resistance is 385 ohms. When the motor is operating at rated speed and the input is 39.0 amp at 220 volts, the stray power is 475 watts and the stray-load loss is 0.01 the output. Determine: (*a*) output in horsepower; (*b*) efficiency; (*c*) torque [see Eq. (367), p. 531].

725. In a 5-hp 230-volt 1,500-rpm shunt motor the resistance of the armature including brushes is 0.175 ohm, and that of the shunt field is 610 ohms. The stray power including stray-load losses, when the motor delivers rated load at rated voltage, is 305 watts. Determine: (*a*) input at rated load; (*b*) efficiency; (*c*) percentage error in efficiency caused by a 10 per cent error in determining stray power. (HINT: A simple quadratic equation involving the armature current I_a may be used to find I_a. A trial-and-error method is an alternative.)

726. A 10-kw 220-volt 1,400-rpm shunt generator is running light at rated speed as a motor, the connections being those of Fig. 420 (p. 533). The armature takes 1.95 amp, and the voltage V_1 is 233.0 volts. The armature resistance, including brushes, is 0.275 ohm. Determine stray-power loss of machine.

727. In Prob. 726 when the generator is delivering rated-load current at 1,400 rpm, its induced emf is 233.5 volts, and the field resistance is 424 ohms. Its stray-load loss is 71 watts. Determine: (*a*) input; (*b*) rated-load efficiency.

728. The generator of Prob. 726 is operating at 1,400 rpm as a shunt motor. The line current is 40 amp, the induced emf is 232.5 volts, and the field current is 0.52 amp. The stray-load losses remain unchanged. Using the data of Prob. 726, determine: (*a*) total losses; (*b*) output in horsepower; (*c*) efficiency; (*d*) torque at pulley.

729. The current to a 25-hp 250-volt 1,500-rpm shunt motor is 84.0 amp at 250 volts. The armature resistance including brushes is 0.084 ohm, and the commutating-field resistance is 0.032 ohm. The shunt-field current is 0.94 amp. Determine: (*a*) counter emf; (*b*) value of E/S, and of S at which motor should be operated at no load to give correct value of stray power; (*c*) value to which V_1, Fig. 420 (p. 533), should be adjusted if current to armature I_a is 4.96 amp; (*d*) stray power; (*e*) motor output if stray-load loss is 162 watts; (*f*) efficiency.

730. The stray-power curves in Fig. 421 (p. 535) were taken for a 20-kw 220-volt 920-rpm shunt generator; the resistance of the armature and brushes is 0.075 ohm and of the commutating field is 0.015 ohm. When the generator delivers its rated output at rated voltage and speed, the field current is 1.42 amp. Determine: (*a*) armature and brush loss; (*b*) field loss; (*c*) value of E/S which determines flux. If stray power from interpolation between the curves, Fig. 421, is 840 watts and the stray-load loss is 140 watts, determine: (*d*) input; (*e*) efficiency.

731. Two similar 15-kw 230-volt generators are connected for the Kapp opposition test, Fig. 422 (p. 537), for the purpose of measuring their losses. When the machine operating as generator is delivering its rated armature current of 66.5 amp at 230 volts, the line current I is 16.3 amp. The generator-field current is 1.4 amp, and the motor-field current is 1.08 amp. The resistance of each armature, including brushes, is 0.102 ohm, and the resistance of the commutating fields is 0.034 ohm. Determine: (*a*) power input to armature; (*b*) resistance losses in armature, including brushes, and in commutating fields of two machines; (*c*) induced emf in generator and motor; (*d*) stray-power loss of generator, including stray-load losses; (*e*) field loss in generator; (*f*) total losses in generator; (*g*) efficiency of generator. Assume combined stray-power and stray-load losses proportional to induced emfs.

732. In Prob. 731, determine efficiency of machine which is operating as a motor. (It operates at overload.)

733. When the current in the generator armature of Prob. 731 is 30.0 amp, the line current I is 10.9 amp. The generator-field current is now 1.24 amp, and the motor-field current is 1.2 amp. Determine (*a*) to (*g*), Prob. 731.

734. In Prob. 733 determine efficiency of machine operating as motor.

735. The armature and the field resistance of a 100-kw 600-volt shunt generator are measured after the machine has been standing idle for some time in a dynamo room, the temperature of which is 22°C. The voltage across the field winding, exclusive of the rheostat, is found to be 460 volts and the field current 2.92 amp. The armature resistance between two marked commutator segments is found to be 0.081 ohm. After the machine has been running under load for 6 hr, these same measurements are repeated. The armature resistance is now 0.088 ohm. The field voltage is 455 volts and the field current 2.54 amp. Determine rise in temperature above room, or ambient, temperature of (*a*) field coils; (*b*) armature winding. State whether or not these temperatures are within safe limits for class A insulation (see p. 542).

736. A 25-hp 230-volt 1,340-rpm shunt motor has been standing idle for some time in a room the temperature of which is 23°C. The armature resistance between marked segments is measured and found to be 0.062 ohm. The resistance of the field coils themselves is measured by the voltmeter-ammeter method. The ammeter reads 1.083 amp; the voltmeter, connected across the field coils, reads 210 volts. After the machine runs at rated load for 5 hr, these measurements are repeated. The armature resistance between the same two segments is found to be 0.0738 ohm. The field ammeter reads 0.948 amp and the voltmeter 213 volts. Determine measured temperature rise in (*a*) armature; (*b*) field.

737. Two 50-kw 240-volt shunt generators are operating in parallel. They are both adjusted to 240 volts at rated load of 208 amp and are then switched in parallel. When operating alone, the terminal voltage of generator 1 rises uniformly from 240 volts at rated load to 247 volts at no load; the terminal voltage of generator 2 rises uniformly from 240 volts at rated load to 249 volts at no load. (*a*) Plot characteristics. (*b*) When the load on the system is 360 amp, determine current supplied by each generator.

738. Repeat Prob. 737 when load on system is (*a*) 220 amp; (*b*) 410 amp.

739. The field rheostat of generator 1 of Prob. 737 is adjusted so that both generators supply equal currents when the load on the system is 240 amp. The adjustment raises the voltage of the characteristic by an equal number of volts at each point. (*a*) Plot characteristics. Determine: (*b*) no-load voltage of generator 1; (*c*) current supplied by each when load on system is 300 and 400 amp; (*d*) system voltages in (*c*).

740. In Prob. 737 the field rheostat of generator 1 is again adjusted so that its emf at no load is also 249 volts. The voltage is raised by 2 volts over the entire characteristic. (*a*) Plot characteristics. (*b*) Determine current delivered by each generator when system load is (*c*) 370 amp; (*d*) 400 amp. Determine bus-bar voltage (*e*) in (*c*); (*f*) in (*d*).

741. It is desired to operate a 200-kw 240-volt shunt generator and a 150-kw 240-volt shunt generator in parallel. The terminal voltage of generator 1 drops uniformly by 10 volts from a no-load voltage of 250 volts when its rated load is applied. Determine: (*a*) drop in terminal voltage of second generator 2 from no load to rated load in order that each generator may take its proper share of the load at all times. Assume that voltage-current characteristics are straight lines and the no-load voltage is 250 volts in each case. (*b*) Plot characteristics. Determine current output of each generator when system load is (*c*) 1,100 amp; (*d*) 1,400 amp. Determine bus-bar voltage (*e*) in (*c*); (*f*) in (*d*). Determine kilowatts output of each generator (*g*) in (*c*); (*h*) in *d*.

742. Two 250-volt compound generators are operating in parallel. Generator 1 is rated at 250 kw, and generator 2 is rated at 150 kw. The resistance of the series field

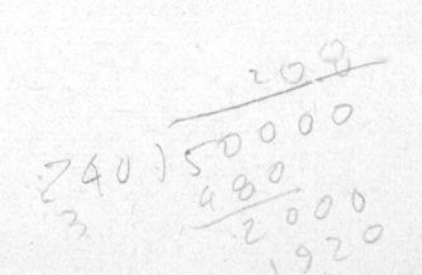

of generator 1 is 0.005 ohm. (*a*) Determine resistance of series field of generator 2 for proper division of load. The two generators are overcompounded so that the voltage of each rises in a straight line from a no-load voltage of 240 volts to 250 volts at rated load. Determine: (*b*) load of each generator when system load is 1,400 amp; (*c*) 800 amp.

QUESTIONS ON CHAPTER XV

Transmission and Distribution of Power

1. State two reasons why power for large d-c loads is usually generated initially as a-c power, transmitted, and then converted to d-c power. Why is it usually uneconomical to generate d-c power on a large scale from a primary source such as coal or water?

2. Where is large-scale d-c distribution now used? Give four reasons.

3. Make a wiring diagram showing three methods which are in general use for obtaining both 600 volts and 230/115 volts d-c from the 13,800-volt a-c bus bars.

4. How does the weight of conductor vary with the transmission voltage if the power transmitted, the distance, and the loss are all fixed? Demonstrate. If the transmission voltage be doubled, how is the weight of conductor affected, the other factors remaining unchanged?

5. How does the weight of conductor vary with the transmission distance if the power transmitted, the voltage, and the loss are all fixed? Demonstrate.

6. Enumerate the four conditions which in general determine the size of conductor. For what conditions does the question of heating particularly apply? In what way may the economics of the problem determine the size of conductor? State the disadvantage of having too large a conductor; too small a conductor.

7. Why is 100 to 120 volts most convenient for incandescent lighting? Why is a substantially higher voltage undesirable? What are the advantages and disadvantages of a lower voltage for this purpose?

8. What are the common trolley voltages? Why are these voltages so chosen?

9. What is meant by *distributed loads?* Where do such loads occur? Under what conditions are conductors of uniform cross section throughout most commonly used?

10. Theoretically, what type of conductor is most economical for uniformly distributed loads? What is the practical condition that most nearly approaches this theoretical condition?

11. Why is the *return-loop* system of distribution used? What is its disadvantage?

12. What system overcomes the disadvantage of the return-loop system? Make a sketch, and show how this system may be further modified to form a still more efficient system.

13. What advantage is gained by connecting 115-volt loads in series groups of two, and utilizing 230-volt supply? What are the disadvantages of so grouping the loads?

14. How are the objections to the series-parallel system overcome? What are the relations existing among the voltages of the Edison 3-wire system?

15. If the neutral wire be of the same size as the two outers, what are the relative weights of conductor in the 3-wire system with 230 volts across outers and the simple 115-volt system, other conditions being the same?

16. What is meant by *balanced loads?* Under this condition what is the value of the neutral current?

17. What is the direction of the neutral current if the positive load is the greater? The negative load? What is the relation of the neutral current to the current in the outer wires? What type of ammeter should be used in the neutral? What are the commercial limits of unbalancing?

18. State briefly the effect of opening the neutral with (*a*) balanced loads and (*b*) unbalanced loads. Why is the neutral usually grounded? Why are circuit breakers and fuses usually omitted in the neutral?

19. What in general is the effect of putting too heavy a load on one side of a 3-wire system on the voltage of that side of the system? On the voltage of the other side of the system?

20. Sketch a method of obtaining a neutral by means of two generators. What is the principal disadvantage of this method?

21. How may a storage battery be used for obtaining a neutral? In general, how does the current in the neutral wire divide when it reaches the center of the battery? State the objection to this method.

22. On what principle does the balancer set operate? What factor determines which machine shall operate as motor? As generator? What two methods are used to accentuate motor and generator actions and thus produce tendencies toward balanced voltages?

23. On what principle does the 3-wire generator operate? Where is the path of the alternating current? The direct current returning from or going to the neutral? Why can the direct current go so readily into or out from the armature?

24. How in general is power supplied to d-c loads in the more congested districts? What is the function of the feeders? The mains? The junction boxes? Where are the house services connected? How are the voltages at feeding points generally determined? Why do not the circuit breakers in the feeders trip on straight overload?

25. A concentrated load is supplied from constant-voltage bus bars over a line of constant resistance. Under what conditions is the power taken by the load a maximum? What is the efficiency of transmission under these conditions? When is the current a maximum? What is the efficiency of transmission when the current is a maximum?

26. What type of generator is most commonly used to supply power for railways? How are such generators connected to the system?

27. Under what conditions does a single trolley suffice for transmitting the power to the car? If a single trolley of the ordinary size is not of sufficient cross section, what means can be taken to assist it in supplying the required power? Why is the size of trolley not increased? Describe the ladder system.

28. Under what conditions are multiple feeders employed? What is the disadvantage of their use? How may this disadvantage be overcome?

29. Why does the return current from a trolley car leave the track? What determines the paths which it follows? What damage, if any, occurs at the point where the current enters a pipe? Where it leaves the pipe?

30. Name two methods by which electrolysis may be reduced. What measurements give a good idea of the magnitude of stray currents between pipes and track?

31. What is the object of "stand-by service" for station batteries? How are they connected to the bus bars? How is their discharge controlled, and how are they charged? What type of battery plate is used?

32. What is meant by "regulating duty" of a battery? Sketch a typical central-station load curve, explaining how it is influenced by the habits of the community. Define "load factor." Why are batteries not generally used in large installations for smoothing the load curve?

33. Under what conditions are batteries used for emergency light and power?

34. Describe the resistance method for controlling battery discharge, stating the disadvantages.

35. Upon what simple principle do counter-emf cells operate? What is the chief advantage of this method of control over the resistance method?

36. What is meant by end-cell control? In what manner is the connection changed from one cell to the next without opening the circuit or dead-short-circuiting the battery?

37. What is the essential difference between the series system and the parallel system of distribution? In the series system what is the effect of attempting to remove a load by opening the circuit? How is a load cut out in a series system?

38. What type of power apparatus now supplies constant current for street lighting? What are the advantages of the series system? Where does its field of application lie? Sketch the circuits of two different systems of series-lighting distribution. State the advantages of each.

PROBLEMS ON CHAPTER XV

Transmission and Distribution of Power

743. Power is being transmitted over a feeder to a distance of 800 ft from 250-vol. bus bars. The current at the load is 250 amp, and the voltage at the load is 239 volts. Determine: (*a*) resistance of feeder; (*b*) circular mils; (*c*) power loss; (*d*) efficiency of transmission; (*e*) power which could be transmitted over feeder from 125-volt bus bars, with efficiency remaining unchanged. Assume resistivity of circular-mil-foot of copper is 11 ohms.

744. In Prob. 743 a feeder of the same length but of four times the cross section is used. With 125 volts at the bus bars determine: (*a*) power which can be transmitted with load voltage equal to 119.5 volts; (*b*) power loss; (*c*) efficiency of transmission. Compare (*b*) and (*c*) with (*c*) and (*d*) of Prob. 743.

745. In Prob. 743 it is desired to transmit the same power with the same loss a distance of 1,600 ft. Determine: (*a*) resistance of feeder; (*b*) circular mils; (*c*) ratio of weight of feeder to that in Prob. 743.

746. A motor takes 300 amp at 225 volts over a 1,050-ft length of 300,000-cir-mil feeder (two wires, each 1,050 ft), having a resistance of 0.0360 ohm per 1,000 ft of single conductor. Determine: (*a*) kilowatts transmitted; (*b*) voltage at sending end of feeder; (*c*) power loss; (*d*) efficiency of transmission; (*e*) weight of copper. (A 1,000-ft length of No. 10 AWG wire, having a cross section of 10,400 cir mils, weighs 31.4 lb.)

747. In Prob. 746, assume that the same amount of power has been transmitted to the motor at 112.5 volts, and the power loss and efficiency remain the same. Determine: (*a*) current; (*b*) total resistance of feeder; (*c*) resistance per 1,000 ft; (*d*) circular mils of feeder; (*e*) weight of copper; (*f*) sending-end voltage. (*g*) Compare weight of copper with that in Prob. 746.

748. A 25-hp motor, which is located 900 ft from 250-volt bus bars, is operating at rated output and at an efficiency of 0.875. The motor is supplied by a 00 copper feeder which has a resistance of 0.0811 ohm per 1,000 ft of single conductor. Determine: (*a*) voltage at motor terminals; (*b*) efficiency. The motor is moved to a distance of 1,435 ft from the bus bars. It is desired that the voltage drop to the motor remain unchanged. (*c*) Determine size conductor which must be used.

749. A 12-hp motor is fed from a switchboard, the bus bars of which are maintained at 125 volts. The motor is located at a distance of 800 ft from the switchboard, and it is desired to have a potential difference of 115 volts at the motor terminals when the motor is carrying its full load of 12 hp. Determine (*a*) diameter in mils of copper conductor used to connect motor to the switchboard. The resistance of a circular-mil-foot of copper at the operating temperature is 11.0 ohms. The efficiency of motor at full load is 86.5 per cent. (*b*) Copper weighs 0.32 lb per cu in. Determine weight of conductor in (*a*). (*c*) Repeat (*a*) and (*b*) for a switchboard voltage of 250 volts and same per cent voltage drop to motor. (*d*) Repeat (*a*) and (*b*) for a switchboard voltage of 625 volts and the same per cent drop to motor.

750. A load located 1,200 ft from 240-volt bus bars takes 120 kw over a 1,000,000-cir-mil feeder the resistance of which is 0.0108 ohm per 1,000 ft of single conductor. Determine: (*a*) resistance of feeder; (*b*) current; (*c*) voltage at load; (*d*) efficiency.

751. Repeat Prob. 750 with load of 100 kw.

752. In a system similar to that of Prob. 750 the distance to the load is 1,440 ft, and in order that the efficiency of transmission remain unchanged a 1,200,000-cir-mil cable having a resistance of 0.00899 ohm per 1,000 ft of single conductor is used. Determine: (*a*) resistance of feeder; (*b*) current; (*c*) voltage at load; (*d*) weight of feeder in pounds; (*e*) ratio of (*d*) to weight of feeder in Prob. 750; (*f*) ratio of weights to distance in (*e*).

753. A street 1,400 ft long is illuminated by eight 485-watt multiple-connected lamps, placed 200 ft apart. Number 3 AWG conductors are used to supply this system (0.200 ohm per 1,000 ft of conductor). The supply voltage is 125 volts, and the distance from the supply to the first lamp is 200 ft. Determine: (*a*) voltage drops between adjacent lamps; (*b*) voltage at last lamp. Assume that each lamp takes 4.0 amp.

754. If the lamps of Prob. 753 are fed by the antiparallel system [see Fig. 433(*a*), p. 557], No. 3 AWG wire still being used, determine voltage at lamps at ends of street. Compare their absolute voltage and their difference of voltage with the results of Prob. 753.

755. In a system similar to that of Prob. 753 the lamps are fed at the center of the system, Fig. 755*A*, by two No. 3 AWG conductors (0.200 ohm per 1,000 ft of conduc-

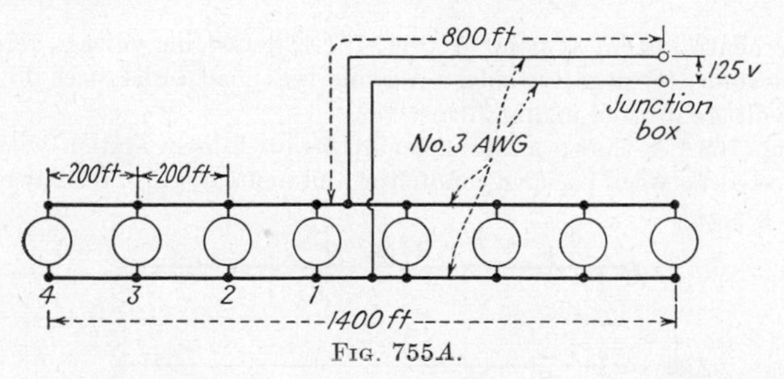

FIG. 755*A*.

tor) from a junction box 800 ft away, the bus bars of which are maintained at 125 volts. Determine: (*a*) voltage at lamps 1, 2, 3, 4; (*b*) transmission efficiency of system.

756. Power is to be transmitted from 250-volt bus bars to a motor 600 ft distant delivering 60 hp and to a motor 500 ft farther away delivering 25 hp. The efficiency at rated load of the 60-hp motor is 91.1 per cent and that of the 25-hp motor 87.5 per cent. With each motor operating at rated load the voltage at the 25-hp motor shall be not less than 230 volts and that at the 60-hp motor not less than 239 volts. Determine: (*a*) resistance of necessary feeders; (*b*) nearest size, AWG or circular mils; (*c*) weight of each feeder; (*d*) efficiency of transmission.

757. In Prob. 756 determine: (*a*) size of uniform feeder which will have same weight as two feeders; (*b*) voltage at each load with this feeder; (*c*) efficiency of transmission. Which system uses the copper more effectively? (Use values of resistance in Prob.

756, and compute size wire accordingly, even if it does not equal a standard-gage size.) Assume same load currents as in Prob. 756.

758. It is desired to operate a group of eighty 115-volt lamps located 600 ft from a 240-volt source of supply. The lamps are connected series-parallel, Fig. 434 (p. 557), and each takes 0.9 amp. Two No. 2 AWG copper conductors each having a resistance of 0.159 ohm per 1,000 ft are used to transmit the power. Determine: (*a*) voltage at lamps; (*b*) power loss in line; (*c*) efficiency of transmission. (*d*) If rubber-insulated wire is used, verify its carrying capacity (see Appendix G, p. 591).

759. In Prob. 758, assume that the lamps are all connected in parallel and are supplied from a 120-volt source. The distance and power loss remain unchanged. Determine: (*a*) size of conductor, circular mils; (*b*) ratio of weight of copper to that in Prob. 758. (Check carrying capacity, Appendix G, p. 591.) Use actual circular mils irrespective of standard gage sizes.

760. In Prob. 758 determine: (*a*) weight of conductors if a neutral equal in size to outer conductors is used; (*b*) if neutral is one-half size (No. 5 AWG); (*c*) ratio of weight of conductors in Prob. 759 to (*a*), (*b*).

761. In Fig. 761*A* is shown an Edison 3-wire system with several loads. Indicate current and its direction at each of the points *a* to *k*.

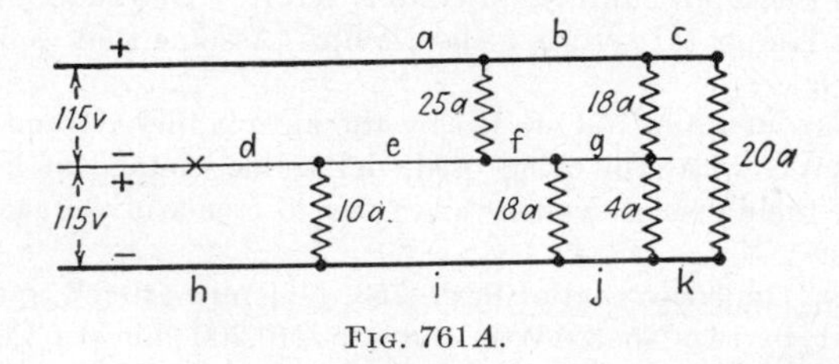

FIG. 761*A*.

762. If the neutral is cut at point *X*, Fig. 761*A*, determine voltage across (*a*) positive side of system; (*b*) negative side. Assume that load resistances do not change, and neglect voltage drop in mains themselves.

763. In Fig. 763*A* is shown a 230/115-volt 3-wire Edison system with a resistive load *A* connected between positive conductor and neutral and a resistive load *B* con-

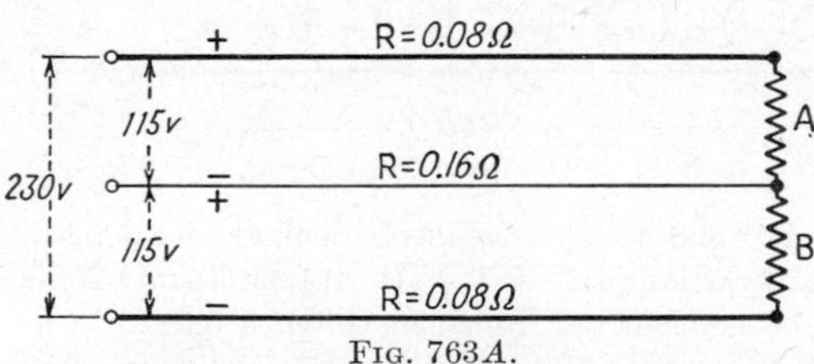

FIG. 763*A*.

nected between negative conductor and neutral. When the current to each load is 80 amp, determine voltage across (*a*) *A*; (*b*) *B*.

764. In Fig. 763*A* the current in load *A* remains at 80 amp, and the current in load *B* becomes 50 amp. Determine voltage across (*a*) *A*; (*b*) *B*.

765. In Fig. 763*A* the current in load *A* becomes 40 amp, and that in load *B* becomes 70 amp. Determine voltage across (*a*) *A*; (*b*) *B*.

766. If, in Prob. 765, the neutral becomes opened, determine voltage across load (*a*) *A*; (*b*) *B*.

767. In Fig. 767*A* is shown the diagram of a typical Edison 240/120-volt 3-wire system with lamp loads *AB* and *CB* connected to neutral and a motor across the outers. With the motor taking 100 amp, load $AB = 200$ amp, and load $CB = 150$ amp, determine voltages across *AB*, *CB* and at the motor. The resistance of a circular-mil-foot of copper may be taken as 11 ohms.

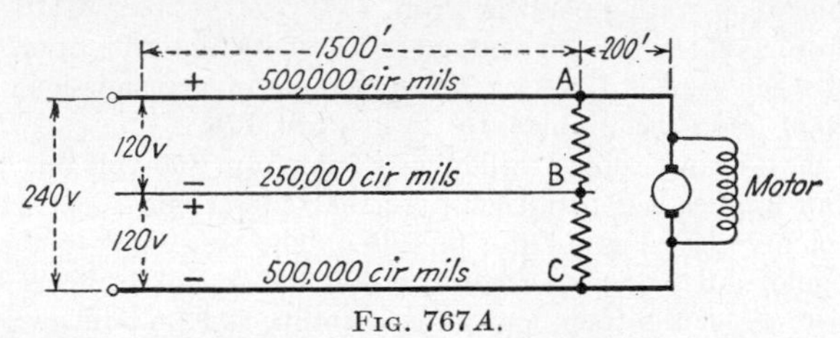

FIG. 767*A*.

768. Repeat Prob. 767 with the motor current 150 amp, the load $AB = 100$ amp, and the load $CB = 180$ amp.

769. Repeat Prob. 767 with the motor connected between the neutral and the negative conductor. Owing to the fact that the voltage is halved, the motor must now take 200 amp to develop its former power.

770. In Fig. 770*A* is shown a balancer set consisting of two dynamos, *A* connected between the positive conductor and neutral, and *B* between the negative conductor and neutral of a 3-wire system. The efficiency of each machine may be taken as 0.85. With the current $I_{ab} = 160$ amp and the current $I_{fe} = 120$ amp, determine current in (*a*) machine *A*; (*b*) machine *B*. (*c*) Designate which machine is motor and which is generator.

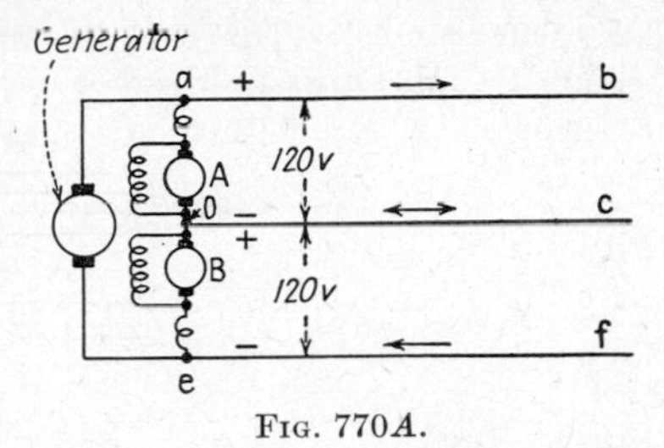

FIG. 770*A*.

771. Repeat Prob. 770 with $I_{ab} = 100$ amp and $I_{fe} = 180$ amp.

772. Repeat Prob. 770 with a load of 150 amp across the negative side of the system and with no load across the positive side.

773. A d-c load is located 800 ft from d-c bus bars and is supplied by a 2-conductor feeder. When the load current is 500 amp, the voltage at the load is 232.4 volts; when the load current is 300 amp, the voltage at the load is 237.1 volts. Determine: (*a*) voltage at bus bars; (*b*) resistance of feeder; (*c*) circular mils of feeder. The resistance of a circular-mil-foot may be taken as 10.8 ohms.

774. A load of 200 kw is connected at the end of a 2-conductor 1,000,000-cir-mil feeder, 1,400 ft long, and the bus-bar voltage at the sending end of the feeder is 240 volts. The resistance of a circular-mil-foot may be taken as 10.8 ohms. Determine: (*a*) resistance of feeder; (*b*) current; (*c*) voltage at load; (*d*) efficiency of transmission; (*e*) theoretical maximum power which the feeder could deliver to a load; (*f*) theoretical maximum current. Discuss the alternate solution of (*b*). (*g*) Plot curve of power as function of current (see Fig. 448, p. 568).

775. In Prob. 774, but with the load equal to 160 kw, determine: (*a*) current; (*b*) voltage at load; (*c*) efficiency of transmission.

776. In Prob. 775 with bus-bar voltage of 120 volts and load of 50 kw, determine: (*a*) current; (*b*) voltage at load; (*c*) efficiency of transmission; (*d*) maximum theoretical power; (*e*) ratio of (*d*) in this problem to (*e*) in Prob. 774.

777. An electric motor located 2.5 miles from 600-volt bus bars takes 75 kw. A 2-conductor 500,000-cir-mil feeder supplies the power. The resistance of a circular-mil-foot may be taken as 10.8 ohms. Determine: (*a*) resistance of feeder; (*b*) voltage at motor; (*c*) power loss in feeder; (*d*) efficiency of transmission.

778. (*a*) In Prob. 777 attempt to obtain 175 kw at the load. Determine: (*b*) maximum power load; (*c*) voltage at load; (*d*) efficiency of transmission; (*e*) maximum current at load end. (*f*) Plot curve of power as function of current (see Fig. 448, p. 568), and indicate operating point in Prob. 777.

779. If, in Prob. 778, the bus-bar voltage is 750 volts, determine: (*a*) two values of voltage at load when load is 175 kw; (*b*) efficiencies of transmission; (*c*) maximum power; (*d*) ratio of (*c*) in this problem to (*b*) in Prob. 778.

780. A 0000 hard-drawn copper trolley wire runs from 600-volt bus bars to a point 4 miles out. For 3 miles it is paralleled by a 300,000-cir-mil feeder which is tapped at every quarter mile [see Fig. 449(*b*), p. 570]. The resistance of the 0000 wire is 0.268 ohm per mile, and the resistance of the 300,000-cir-mil feeder is 0.190 ohm per mile. The resistance of the track and ground return is 0.05 ohm per mile. Determine: (*a*) voltage at a car 3 miles out and taking 90 amp; (*b*) voltage at end of line.

781. (*a*) Determine voltage at car in Prob. 780 when car is 3.5 miles from bus bars and taking 90 amp; (*b*) when car is 2.5 miles from the bus bars and taking 60 amp.

782. Figure 782*A* shows a 6-mile length of hard-drawn 0000 copper trolley wire (211,000 cir mils). This is fed by three 400,000-cir-mil multiple feeders, feeding at points 1½ miles apart. The resistance of the track return is 0.05 ohm per mile. The

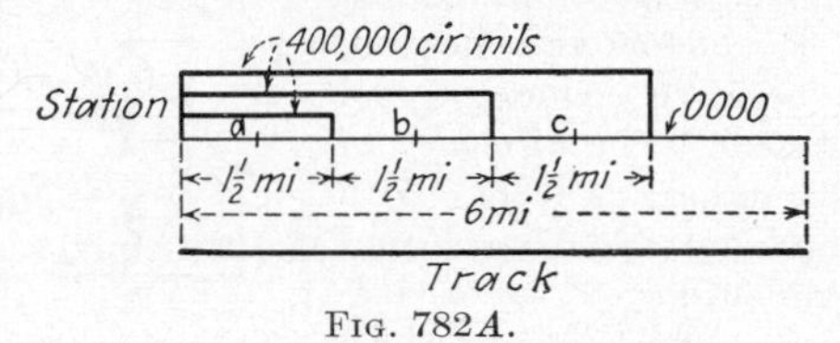

Fig. 782*A*.

resistance of a circular-mil-foot may be taken as 11 ohms. Determine: (*a*) equivalent resistance of trolley and feeders to end of line; (*b*) voltage at car 6 miles from station and taking 100 amp; (*c*) voltage at car 4.5 miles from station and taking 100 amp; (*d*) voltage at end of trolley wire in (*c*).

783. In Prob. 782 determine voltage at car 3.5 miles from station and taking 110 amp.

784. In Fig. 782*A*, the trolley is sectionalized at points *a*, *b*, *c* [see Fig. 449(*d*), p. 570]. Determine: (*a*) equivalent resistance of trolley and feeder to end of line; (*b*) voltage of car 6 miles from station and taking 100 amp. Compare (*b*) with (*b*) in Prob. 782.

785. In Fig. 782*A* (sectionalized) determine voltage at car 3.5 miles from station and taking 110 amp. Compare with Prob. 783, and state which system of feeding is the more economical of copper.

786. The peak load of a central station is 7,200 kw. The station output is 67,600 kwhr over a 24-hr period. Determine daily load factor.

787. A storage battery consists of 68 cells connected in series, the emf and resistance of each cell being 2.18 volts and 0.00227 ohm. It is desired that the battery discharge at the 50-amp rate into 125-volt bus bars. Determine: (*a*) necessary series resistor; (*b*) power developed within battery; (*c*) power lost in battery resistance; (*d*) power lost in series resistor.

788. In Prob. 787 the emf per cell drops to 2.05 volts. Determine: (*a*) discharge current; (*b*) resistance to which series resistor should be adjusted to produce 50 amp discharge.

789. Counter-emf cells, each having an emf of 2.218 volts, are used in Prob. 787. Determine number which is necessary. Neglect the internal resistance of the counter-emf cells.

790. Assume in Prob. 787 that end-cell control is used and that seven cells are cut off the end of the battery, Fig. 453 (p. 575). The bus-bar voltage remains at 125 volts. Determine: (*a*) current from battery; (*b*) power loss in battery.

791. A combination constant-current transformer and mercury-arc rectifier supplies 45 series-connected 510-watt 6.6-amp d-c arc lamps over a No. 6 AWG cable, the resistance of which is 0.403 ohm per 1,000 ft. The length of the arc circuit is 10.8 miles. Determine terminal voltage of generator and efficiency of transmission.

792. Repeat Prob. 791 for a 56-lamp circuit of which the length is 12.4 miles.

INDEX

C

D

P

Q

R